Supertraining

Mel Cunningham Siff   PhD   MSc

Supertraining Institute
Denver USA 2004

SUPERTRAINING

© *Copyright 2003* Mel C Siff   Sixth Edition

Enquiries should be addressed to the following e-mail address: mcsiff@aol.com

This book has been written solely for the purposes of education and information. It is not intended to be used as a practical manual by the unguided athlete or coach who may not be sufficiently aware of the efficient and safe ways of implementing the means and methods of training discussed in the text. While every effort has been made to stress the importance of safety and correctness of skill, there are many technical subtleties inherent in all of the methods which need to be learned with the assistance of a highly qualified coach. Before implementing any of the means, methods, exercises or techniques presented in this book, you are strongly advised to obtain medical clearance for strenuous strength training and to consult a specialist strength coach. Always be aware that any form of exercise inappropriately executed can lead to injury, for which the author and the publishers cannot be held responsible.

Typeset in Times New Roman for the main text and Bookman for headings.
Design and layout by M C Siff

Printed in Denver, USA

ISBN 1-874856-65-6

First Edition, 1993
Second Edition, 1996
Third Edition, 1998
Fourth Edition, 2000
Fifth Edition, 2000

CONTENTS

PREFACE

The great strides made in sport during the past few decades are a major tribute to the practical application of exercise science and systematic training. In keeping with the Olympic motto, the human being today is definitely stronger and faster. Plateaus of performance are regularly being transcended and the quest for exploring the limits of human potential continues unabated.

An Integrated Model of Sports Development

Without a doubt the greatest recent success in challenging these limits of performance was enjoyed by the former Soviet Union, whose extremely efficient system of sports development dominated international sport for about four decades. Its organisational and educational proficiency in integrating its research and experience with knowledge from other countries is clearly reflected by the number of medals and victories enjoyed over many decades by their athletes in numerous sports in World Championships and Olympic Games. Not many years after the USSR shared this model of sporting development and their coaches as part of an ongoing cultural exchange with 'Eastern bloc' countries such as East Germany, Poland, Romania, Hungary and Bulgaria, as well as Cuba, North Korea and China, the athletes of these nations began rivalling and defeating their Western counterparts. The introduction into China of the sports school system, methods of athlete selection, individualised periodisation schemes and formalised restoration regimes has already played a major role in producing the Chinese superstars who are beginning to dominate several sports today.

A vital aspect of the Russian model was the use of strength training to supplement the technical training of all sports. The few innovative concepts and methods of training, such as periodisation, sports modelling and plyometrics, which filtered across to the West were rapidly adopted and revolutionised training in many sports. Broad international familiarity with other specialised strength methods, however, has not yet developed. This book has been written to make many of these special strength conditioning techniques available to exercise scientists, coaches and sports medical professionals in countries which have not been exposed to the most important concepts and methods of Russian training. It has not confined itself to a purely Russian approach, because there is an equally valuable body of Western material which admirably complements and extends the Russian model. The resulting text, therefore, offers a synthesis of advanced Eastern and Western strength science.

Strength without Drugs

As competitors struggle near the asymptotes of their ability, they seek any means, scientific or mythical, in attempts to transcend their physical and mental limits. It is at this point that sport often degenerates into a form which invokes the use of magic potions, now classed euphemistically as ergogenic aids, those substances or devices which can enhance performance.

Among the best known of the illicit ergogenic drugs are the anabolic steroids, chemicals which are derived from male growth hormone to facilitate the growth of muscle bulk and strength. The epidemic proportions reached by the abuse of anabolic substances from pharmaceutical and so-called 'natural' sources is a consequence of commercial exploitation and predominantly male preoccation with size and strength. It is irrelevant to discuss any further aspects of this phenomenon here. Its existence is mentioned to emphasize the fact that the quest for strength is one of enormous importance to man and that he will resort to any means to achieve it. *The widespread use of steroids and other chemical supplement is frequently an admission that one has run out of training ideas to produce further progress naturally.* This is hardly surprising, because virtually the same repertoire of traditional bodybuilding exercises and techniques is usually applied in fashionable programmes devised by endless processions of bodybuilding heroes. The user often fails to appreciate the individuality of each programme and when progress ceases, he frequently resorts to anabolic supplementation. Even then, he invariably uses excessive doses of different anabolic-androgenic (AA) steroids, guided more by the experience of individual bodybuilders rather than by scientific knowledge of how to cycle clinically modest doses over a few weeks into a carefully periodised programme which includes different methods of restoration, autogenic mental training and shock training.

The urge to overdose on AA steroids is strengthened by the contention that it is impossible to become 'big' and strong without them. Despite prolific evidence that there have always been enormously powerful and large men throughout history, this belief persists. Admittedly, these substances can accelerate progress, but comparable and more enduring results are possible over a longer time period using more ethical means, though probably by many fewer competitors.

However desirable it is to test for and eliminate illicit drug use in sport, the medical quest to achieve this is probably doomed to failure because top competitors will always remain well versed in the use of drugs to enhance performance and avoid detection. Moreover, the huge sums paid to top teams and players because of public and media adulation will ensure that prominent drug users will rarely be severely penalised. After all, top athletes today, especially in media-prominent sports such as basketball, American football, soccer, tennis and golf are specialised entertainers and not just sports stars. *Drug assistance will cease in sport only when science produces an equally successful legitimate way of enhancing performance among all competitors,* not when drug tests become sensitive and affordable enough for routine application. The information in this book has been gathered from authoritative Western and Eastern sources to offer scientific and practical guidance in this direction.

The existence of an innovative concept which may be called *chrononutrition* emphasizes that scientifically cycled nutritional regimes can play an important role in enhancing the long-term adaptation and growth in performance of the athlete. Chrononutrition recognises that it is not only the content of food, but also the timing of ingestion and the interactive effects of nutritional components that determines the effectiveness of any dietary regime. In the West it is well known that certain drugs have more powerful effects when administered at a given time of the day and very different effects when prescribed with other drugs, yet this knowledge is not formally extended to the realm of general nutrition or sporting preparation.

The recent proliferation of English language articles on the ergogenic value of substances such as creatine and amino acids tends to create the impression that these findings are modern and original. Even cursory examination of Russian journals such as *Theoriya i Praktika Fizicheskoi Kultury*, *Legkaya Atletika* and the specialised publications in physiology, adaptation, nutrition and biochemistry reveals that these substances have been researched and used in Russia prior to 1970.

Clearly, the lack of familiarity of most English language exercise scientists with Russian and other foreign language research has often led to considerable duplication of work, a waste of financial resources and a delay in the progress of sports science. Besides research and training articles that appear in the Russian language, there is a considerable amount of original and often exciting material available in Japanese and other Oriental languages, as well as in German, Italian, French, Scandinavian and other European languages. This fact has also been a strong motivating factor behind the writing of this book, which attempts to integrate a great deal of information from different countries.

Objectives and Audience

It is one of the objectives of this book to show how a deeper understanding of the phenomenon of strength can enable one to consistently and safely develop all types of specific strength without resorting to drugs.

Although its title might imply that it is solely for the purpose of developing strength in sports competitors, this book presents information which is relevant to anyone who needs to enhance any of the strength-related qualities for effective participation in any form of physical exercise. This sports specific strength refers to the particular fitness quality comprising a series of strength-related factors which determine efficient motor performance and sporting excellence (see Ch 1).

Thus, this text is highly relevant not only to the athlete, coach, physical educator and personal trainer, but also to sports physiotherapists and doctors whose task it is to provide specific forms of musculoskeletal rehabilitation, all of which ultimately necessitate enhancing stability and mobility by some form of strength-based physical conditioning. For this reason, one of the chapters relates strength training to the physiotherapeutic system known as PNF (Proprioceptive Neuromuscular Facilitation).

One of the main aims of this book is to fill one of the gaps in the applied strength training field, i.e. the lack of a scientific methodology for systematically applying the different forms of strength training to improve sporting performance, particularly at the highest international level.

A major aim is also to extend the limited concepts of strength and fitness which have been perpetuated in many training books and exercise physiology texts in the West. These books have identified the most important fitness components as cardiovascular endurance, muscular endurance, strength and flexibility, but often have not recognised the existence of more specific components such as speed-strength, speed-endurance, flexibility-strength and speed-strength endurance. Consequently, sports training programmes which have been based on these simplistic fitness models often have been seriously deficient in key aspects of sports preparation.

The numerous books on strength training and bodybuilding have also had a profound impact on the use of strength training in sport. Some of them cover the general principles of non-specific weight training very adequately, while others offer much the same compendium of traditional physique or fitness conditioning exercises which have been used since the turn of this century. The proliferation of commercial fitness centres and popular physique magazines in the West has created the often-faulty impression that these centres, well-known bodybuilders and commercially-accredited instructors are ideally equipped to provide strength training for everyone, including elite athletes. Moreover, many of the more popular books on applied exercise science have been written by scientists with considerable knowledge of cardiovascular physiology, but less experience of specialised strength training in sport.

At the same time, some of the finest strength training experts and books are in Russia and Eastern European countries, so that the average physical educator, coach and sports scientist in the West has little or no access to them. Where English translations of these books exist, they are usually literal and do not adequately interpret their often-unfamiliar terminology and philosophy for Western readers. That the information they convey is definitely valuable is borne out by the dominance of most Olympic sports by athletes from these countries.

For the above reasons, the need for a more extensive book on applied strength conditioning became obvious, especially if it could synthesize scientific and practical findings from East and West. The new era of glasnost or 'openness' in the former Soviet Union also seemed to provide the opportune time for such a venture.

The Author

The first steps of this venture into the world of strength science commenced when the author at 9 years of age observed with increasing interest his medical father, Dr Isadore Siff, exercising religiously every morning with spring loaded Sandow dumbbells before he went off to work in the neurosurgical department at a major hospital in their home city, Johannesburg, South Africa. Typical childhood curiosity led to Mel being regaled with tales of the old time strongmen whose mighty performances fascinated his father as a youth. He heard about Eugene Sandow, Professor Attila, George Hackenschmidt, Louis Cyr and many other legends whose names were household words near the beginning of the 20th century.

His father also let him read well-worn training books on these strongmen and various coaches, including one published in 1926 (Renwick GR *Athletics For Boys*) that extolled the merits of logically constructed physical training programmes which included a progressive overload approach, skipping and jumping exercises, an emphasis on the central importance of technical style, an overlapping ('conjugation') of "style, speed and endurance training", and special attention being paid to keeping the muscles "supple, pliant and soft" before moving onto heavier loading.

In a 1958 athletics textbook he also read that high jump training in the former USSR sometimes involved using weighted vests and weight training. At that time, during the last two years of his schooling at Marist Brothers College, he had developed a passion for track and field, but was unable to try such strength training ideas out, because schools in South Africa had no weight training facilities.

However, soon after he started studying at the University of the Witwatersrand ("Wits") in 1960, Mel, eager to experiment with the little information which he had read in that publication, managed to locate the Weightlifting Club on campus which operated from a dilapidated post World War II prefabricated hut and immediately he began training there. Encouraged by the Club committee, he rapidly took up competitive weightlifting, a sport that was eventually to dominate over all of his other sports and lay the foundation for many years of competition and research in that field.

The South African Amateur Weightlifting Federation (SAAWLF) periodically held training workshops and invited various overseas lifters and coaches to address them. It was then that Mel began to appreciate that there was indeed a science behind the art of strength training, a point that was driven strongly home in the late 1960s when the renowned and approachable British athletics coach, Geoff Dyson, spoke at Wits on topics such as programme design and organisation of training. His 1946 textbook, *A New System of Training*, appeared to be one of the earliest English language books on what later came to be known as "periodisation" and this innovative material convinced Mel that careful objective and subjective organisation must be a vital part of sports training. Many years later, it surprised Mel that many Western coaches seemed to be enthralled with this 'new' training approach when it surfaced under its now popular name of "periodisation".

During the early 1970s, the SAAWLF invited the legendary strong man from Belgium, Serge Reding, the great rival of Alexeyev, to visit South Africa and, as fate would have it, he lived in the Siff family home in Johannesburg for much of his stay. This afforded Mel the unique opportunity of training with Serge and learning firsthand from this enormously powerful lifter training methods that he had never even heard of. He learned about many different forms of periodisation, jump or rebound training (this later became known as 'plyometrics'), sport specific electrical stimulation, formal restoration, complex training and innumerable lifting variations. No other single individual played such an extensive practical role in laying the foundations for all of the subsequent work that Mel carried out. His death just a few years later came as a sad blow to the entire Siff family who had become very close to this refined, genteel and helpful example of the Iron Game.

Photographs Two action photos taken of Serge Reding during training in the University of the Witwatersrand gymnasium, Johannesburg, showing the massive size and power of this legendary superheavy weightlifter, one of Alexeyev's greatest rivals

At about the same time, Mel, who was completing a Masters in applied mathematics began to see increasing applications for mathematical analysis in his own sport and he was fascinated to read about "force plates" to measure forces and torques involved in human movement. The only such devices were obtainable commercially from the USA at very high cost, but a fellow lifter and staff member in the Department of Civil Engineering, Andy Hofmeyr, stated that it would be relatively simple to construct a similar device using the expertise that he had acquired from making load cells for measuring forces and torques in bridges, buildings and other civil engineering projects. Not too long afterwards, Andy had constructed a successful force plate, which Mel eventually used for his PhD research.

A further going invaluable source of international research and coaching information came from the West German publication, *Lehrbeilage Gewichtheben*, which was very generously sent for many years to Mel by Lothar Spitz, prominent West German weightlifting coach whom he met at the 1979 World Weightlifting Championships in Thessaloniki, Greece. At the same event, the author met, filmed and observed during training some of the most renowned Russian lifters and coaches such as Vardanian, Rachmanov and Medvedev, an occasion that yielded insights that stimulated a great deal of his subsequent research.

During the early 1970s Mel made contact with Dr Michael Yessis, whose invaluable translations of Soviet training material in the "Yessis Review" and the "Soviet Sports Review" made available to him information that would never otherwise have reached the West. During 1983, he was able to invite Dr Yessis, then a professor in physical education at the University of California, Fullerton, to lecture widely throughout South Africa on strength training science and Soviet athletic training, ultimately leading to a friendship which paved the way to many later collaborative efforts.

This contact, augmented by his regular visits to Dr Yessis in the USA, furnished Mel with an extensive working familiarity with Soviet sports science and ultimately inspired him to visit Russia in July 1990 and November 1991. Dr Siff spent several weeks there with various Russian colleagues, in particular Dr Yuri Verkhoshansky, widely regarded as one of the world's most respected experts in special strength training and the programming of sports training. Possibly he is best known in the West for his concept of 'shock' training or plyometrics, as it is now popularly known..

They discussed their mutual research interests and met with other sports scientists at major Russian research institutes. A staff member and scientific interpreter at one of these institutes, Linna Moratcheva, served as an invaluable link between the author and his Russian colleagues, organising working meetings and willingly devoting much of her time to translating many of the difficult concepts.

Subsequently, Mel invited Dr Verkhoshansky to visit South Africa on a lecture tour in March 1992. During the month that he spent in Mel's home, he was able to discuss extensively with Mel the broad spectrum of Russian strength research and training, aided by Linna Moratcheva as their able interpreter.

The relaxing and unique atmosphere afforded by the African countryside, including its Game Parks and hospitable citizens, though entirely peripheral to the task of authorship, served to facilitate highly productive discussion between the two scientists which transcended the importance of purity of language translation and accuracy of content. These meetings led to their collaborative writing of the first edition of "Supertraining", upon which a great deal of this new edition has been based. At times, the African birthplace of the latest edition of this book suggested important analogies between the impressive physical performance of its wild animals and fitness qualities such as strength, speed, power, agility, reactive ability and plyometrics. This, in turn, indicated that many training secrets from 'darkest Africa' could be extracted by observant analysis of nature and applied with scientific guidance to advancing the sporting endeavours of humankind. That the land of the strongest land animal (the elephant), the fastest animal on earth (the cheetah), the most powerful ape (the gorilla) and many of the world's most effective jumping creatures (such as the graceful springbok) should have given birth to this 'strength-speed' book is coincidentally noteworthy.

Dr Mel Siff was Senior Lecturer in mechanical engineering at the University of the Witwatersrand in Johannesburg, South Africa for many years, where his major areas of research were biomechanics, ergonomics, strength conditioning and injury rehabilitation. His Masters degree (Applied Mathematics) was awarded summa cum laude in brain research and his PhD was in physiology, specialising in biomechanics. He has presented papers internationally at conferences in sports science, physiology, physiotherapy, sports medicine, psychology, engineering, ergonomics, physical education, linguistics and communication. He has published widely and lectured in several countries, including the USA, England, Israel, Australia and the Far East. A former weightlifter who received university, provincial and national awards for many years, he was chairman of the South African Universities Weightlifting Association for more than two decades and was manager-coach of the South African national weightlifting team in 1983 and 1984. He received two Meritorious Service awards for 'exceptional contribution to sport' and Weightlifting at his university, whose Sports Council passed a resolution (20/78) thanking him 'for doing more for Wits (University) sport than any other individual in the history of the university'. He now lives in Denver, USA with his American-born wife, Lisa Ericson.

The Book

Supertraining is a textbook which bore the preliminary title *The Biomechanics and Physiology of Sport Specific Strength Training* when the earliest draft of this book appeared, a title which still describes its content and aims accurately. The first editions (Siff & Verkhoshansky, "Supertraining") emerged from a combination of Dr Verkhoshansky's invaluable contributions from his earlier publications, his extensive research and a lifetime of lecturing and many years of analysis and review of Russian strength science and training, as well as from Mel's personal research, competitive and coaching experience, conference presentations and lecture notes given to undergraduate and postgraduate students in mechanical engineering, physiotherapy, physical education and ergonomics.

This latest edition no longer involves the direct contribution of Dr Verhoshansky, who has now requested not to be involved with this book, so that he can write a series of individual publications on strength science, which he ultimately intends to serve as his legacy to the world of sports training. Consequently, this edition includes a great deal of new research and practical information from a variety of Western scientists and elite coaches. This book is not intended to offer a prescriptive list of special exercises and training programmes for each specific sport, as this is a highly individualised task which depends on close contact between an experienced coach and each athlete. Instead, it has set out to provide the scientist, coach and serious competitor with the research background, a systematic approach and principles which can be applied to suit the needs of all athletes whose preparation involves special strength training in their quest for sporting excellence.

Supertraining also aims to provide the physiotherapist and sports doctor with a fuller understanding of the nuances of musculoskeletal conditioning so as to facilitate the prescription of effective injury rehabilitation regimes, with particular relevance to the fitness needs of competitive athletes.

In this book, the gender-independent term, 'athlete', does not refer to runners. It is synonymous with 'sportsperson' and refers to anyone who participates in sport or any other form of organised human movement, such as dance. Less familiar terms (such as heterochronicity and conjugate sequence) which are rarely encountered in similar books appear periodically and have deliberately not been oversimplified, because they are derived from Russian terminology with no entirely satisfactory English equivalent. Instead, they have been defined as new terms for use in the field of special sports training. In some places, traditional terms such as 'aerobic' and 'anaerobic' have been retained instead of their more pedantic equivalents, namely 'oxygen-dependent' and 'oxygen-independent', simply because the average reader will be more familiar with the more popular words.

This text not only reviews current research into the phenomenon of strength and physical conditioning, but also includes extensive original work. The author is most grateful to Dr Yessis, Andrew Charniga (a former USA champion weightlifter) and Linna Moratcheva, whose indispensable English translations of Russian work made their task considerably lighter. Where a more extensive interpretation of Russian biomechanical terminology was needed, the late Professor S Smoleniec, of the School of Mechanical Engineering at the University of the Witwatersrand, gave freely of his time and expertise.

An invaluable background to the Russian methods and philosophy of strength training covered in this text may be obtained from the vast compendium of Soviet scientific articles translated between 1966 and 1991 in the *Soviet Sports Review* (formely the Yessis Review of Soviet Physical Education and Sports) by Dr Yessis, and in the *Fitness and Sports Review International* (1992-1995), as well as in Dr Yessis' book: *Secrets of Soviet Sports Fitness and Training*. All of this material was used extensively to assist in interpreting many of the unique Soviet concepts in sports training and to facilitate cooperation between the two authors of this text. Had this source of information not been available, the numerous rewritings of this book no doubt would have been increased and publication would have been delayed for a considerable time.

The author hopes that the final product will enable the reader to share some of the excitement, pleasure and awe that he has experienced in attempting to understand the complexities and wonders of human strength and athletic performance. For those who wish to continue with the analysis, application and updating of any of the topics addressed in this book, Mel has initiated a free Internet *Supertraining discussion group*, which anyone may join at the following website:

http://groups.yahoo.com/group/Supertraining/

STRENGTH AND THE MUSCULAR SYSTEM

Objective

It is the objective of this book to explore the phenomenon of strength and to apply to physical conditioning the discoveries arising from this quest, with a particular emphasis on the development of *special fitness and preparedness for sporting performance* at the highest level. In meeting this objective, the concepts of work capacity, fitness and preparedness, as well as the different types of strength are examined in detail to provide the necessary framework for research and practical application of all findings.

It analyses the different types of strength, their roles in human movement and how they may be developed efficiently. In illustrating how scientific research may be applied in training or rehabilitation, it discusses the various means and methods of strength training, ranging from resistance training with weights to impulsive ('plyometric') loading without weights. It identifies which specific types of strength fitness are required by the athlete, the forms in which strength is produced over the range of a given sporting movement and the most appropriate sequences for developing the different types of strength fitness over a prolonged training period.

Since considerable research reveals that strength is not a single fundamental fitness factor like cardiovascular endurance, as is often implied, this textbook introduces the reader to the exquisite complexity of strength via an understanding of the biomechanics, functional anatomy and physiology of the human movement system. This is not done simply as an intellectual exercise, but to prevent the reader from devising sport specific training programmes based on deficient traditional schedules which may have ignored the nuances of the different types of strength and the specificity of training for a given sport and individual.

This text, although aimed primarily at the exercise scientist, specialist high level coach and physical educator, also has direct relevance to the sports medical practitioner or therapist who may be involved with rehabilitating athletes whose return to top level competition depends on restoration of the necessary type of strength fitness.

What is Strength ?

Strength is an essential component of all human performance and its formal development can no longer be neglected in the preparation of any athlete. Successful strength conditioning depends on a thorough understanding of all processes underlying the production of strength by the body. Therefore, it is appropriate that this text commences with an outline of the structure and function of the more important systems involved in producing all types of strength.

Strength is the product of muscular action initiated and orchestrated by electrical processes in the nervous system of the body. Classically, *strength is defined as the ability of a given muscle or group of muscles to generate muscular force under specific conditions.* Thus, *maximal strength* is the ability of a particular group of muscles to produce a maximal voluntary contraction in response to optimal motivation against an external load. This strength is usually produced in competition and may also be referred to as the *competitive maximum strength*, CFmax. It is not the same as *absolute strength*, which Zatsiorsky (1995) calls Fmm, the maximum of all maxima, and which usually is associated with the greatest force which can be produced by a given muscle group under involuntary muscle stimulation by, for example, electrical stimulation of the nerves supplying the muscles or recruitment of a powerful stretch reflex by sudden loading.

For certain practical purposes, absolute strength may be regarded as roughly equivalent to maximal eccentric strength, which is difficult or impractical to measure, because a maximum by definition refers to the limit point preceding structural and functional failure of the system. Thus, it is apparent that specific neural feedback mechanisms, like governors in a mechanical engine, exist to prevent a muscle from continuing to produce force to the point of mechanical failure. This is why it probably would be more practical to use the maximum explosive isometric strength (produced under so-called maximum plyometric conditions or explosive thrust against a dynamometer, as discussed in Ch 5) as a working approximation to absolute strength (or Fmm). To prevent confusion, it also should be noted that the term 'absolute strength' sometimes is used to define the maximum strength which can be produced by an athlete irrespective of bodymass.

It is vital to recognise a *training maximum* TFmax or training 1RM (single repetition maximum), which is always less than the competition maximum CFmax in experienced athletes, because optimal motivation invariably occurs under competitive conditions (Fig 1.1). Zatsiorsky states that *the training maximum is the heaviest load which one can lift without substantial emotional excitement*, as indicated by a very significant rise in heart rate before the lift (Medvedev, 1986). It is noteworthy that, in the untrained person, involuntary or hypnotic conditions can increase strength output by up to 35%, but by less than 10% in the trained athlete. The mean difference between TFmax and CFmax is approximately 12.5 ± 2.5% in experienced weightlifters, with a larger difference being exhibited by lifters in heavier weight classes (Zatsiorsky, 1995).

The merit of identifying the different types of strength or performance maximum lies in enabling one to prescribe training intensity more efficiently. Intensity is usually defined as a certain percentage of one's maximum and it is most practical to choose this on the basis of the competitive maximum, which remains approximately constant for a fairly prolonged period. *The training maximum can vary daily*, so, while it may be of value in prescribing training for less qualified athletes, it is of limited value for the elite competitor.

It is relevant to note that competitions involve very few attempts to reach a maximum, yet they are far more exhausting than strenuous workouts with many repetitions, since they involve extremely high levels of psychological and nervous stress. The high levels of nervous and emotional stress incurred by attempting a competitive maximum require many days or even weeks to reach full recovery, even though physical recuperation would appear to be complete, so that this type of loading is not recommended as a regular form of training.

In other words, any attempt to exceed limit weights requires an increase in nervous excitation and interferes with the athlete's ability to adapt, if this type of training is used frequently. In attempting to understand the intensity of loading prescribed by the apparently extreme Bulgarian coaches who are reputed to stipulate frequent or daily use of maximum loads in training, one has to appreciate that training with *training maxima* (which do not maximally stress the nervous system) is very different from training with *competitive maxima* (which place great stress on nervous processes).

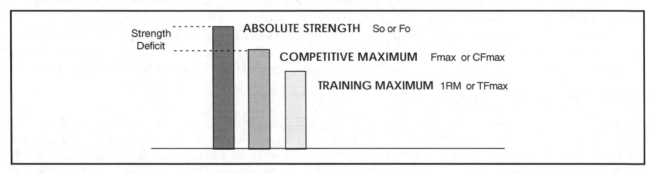

Figure 1.1 Different types of maximal strength. Absolute strength (or Fmm, maximum of maximum forces) is produced under involuntary conditions, whereas the other two maxima are the result of voluntary action. The strength deficit, the difference between absolute strength and maximal strength, is discussed later in this section.

Strength is a relative phenomenon depending on numerous factors, so it is essential that these conditions are accurately described when strength is being assessed. For instance, muscular strength varies with joint angle, joint orientation, speed of movement, muscle group and type of movement, so it is largely meaningless to speak of absolute strength without specifying the conditions under which it is generated. Sometimes, the term relative strength is introduced to compare the strength of subjects of different bodymass. In this context, *relative strength* is defined as the strength per unit bodymass produced by a given individual under specific conditions (e.g. executing a well-defined lift or combination of lifts, such as the squat, snatch or the weightlifting Total).

It is also useful to recognise that one may define isometric, concentric and eccentric strength maxima, since every sport requires distinct levels of each one of these types of maximum. The importance of these maxima is discussed later in the subsection entitled 'Strength Deficit'. As a matter of interest, these maxima given in order of magnitude are: eccentric, isometric, concentric.

Later, several other important strength-related terms such as explosive strength, starting-strength, acceleration-strength and speed-strength are analysed in detail. In particular, this text discusses strength and musculoskeletal conditioning in terms of the following fundamentals:

• The physiology of muscle action

- The biomechanics of strength production
- Neuromuscular stimulation and control
- Adaptation to physical loading
- The various types of strength fitness
- The specificity of muscular and neuromuscular training

The Origins of Strength Training Science

Strength training has always been synonymous with the so-called 'Iron Game', a broad generic term for the competitive lifting of heavy objects by strong men during the last century or so. Feats of lifting strength, however, have appeared throughout the history of most nations, but it has only been in very recent times that training to produce strength has become a scientific discipline. This science did not arise overnight: it is the culminating point of thousands of years of trial-and-error methods of training.

The earliest reference to formal strength training occurs in Chinese texts dating to as far back as 3600BC, when emperors made their subjects exercise daily (Webster, 1976). During the Chou dynasty (1122-249BC), potential soldiers had to pass weight-lifting tests before being allowed to enter the armed forces. There is abundant evidence of weight-training used in ancient Egypt and India, while the Greeks left numerous sculptures and illustrations of their athletes training with stone weights. In fact, the 6th century BC was known as the 'Age of Strength' and weight-lifting competitions involved the lifting of huge stones. The renowned ancient physician, Galen, referred frequently to exercising with weights (halteres), with his treatise *Preservation of Health* even classifying exercises into 'quick' exercises without weights and 'violent' exercises which are performed with weights. The Roman poet Martial (40-104AD) pondered: "Why do the strong men labour with their stupid dumbbells? A far better task for men is digging a vine trench". Weight training was not confined to men: a wall mosaic from a Roman villa in Piazza Almeria in Sicily depicted a girl exercising with weights.

It should not be surprising, then, that the quest for superior strength led to numerous systems of strength training, thereby laying a solid experiential foundation for the far more refined methods of today. During the 16th century in Europe, books on weight-training began to emerge, with Sir Thomas Elyot's text on the topic being published in England in 1531. Several universities in France and Germany offered weight training and in 1544, Joachim Camerius, a lecturer at Leipzig University, wrote several books recommending weight training as an essential activity for the model school. In 1728, John Paugh published *A Physiological, Theoretic and Practical Treatise on the Utility of Muscular Exercise for Restoring the Power to the Limbs*, revealing that even then it was recognised that weight training offered therapeutic benefits. In the 1860s, the Scot, Archibald MacLaren, compiled the first system of physical training with dumbbells and barbells for the British Army and formalised a crude form of progressive overloading. Some of his ideas appeared in McMillan's Magazine (1863) in his article, "National Systems of Bodily Exercise", which compared various systems of physical training used at that time.

Pioneers of Strength Training

The path to strength training science is synonymous with the history of many of the legendary heroes of yesteryear, ranging from the biblical Samson and the bull-lifting Milo of Italy to the Russian superheavy weightlifter, Alexeyev. The showmen and strong man entertainers of 19th century Europe in particular, laid the most solid foundations for the systematic development of formal strength and physique training methods and the eventual acceptance of the use of these methods in the general fitness and sports specific strength training revolution of today. Space permits the mention of only a few of these pioneering strong men of the past, so the history-minded reader is well advised to read David Webster's fascinating and thorough book, "The Iron Game", which presents the feats of these men from the distant past to 1975, upon which this brief summary is based.

On the basis of many years of research, Webster isolates the Italian circus and fairground performer, Felice Napoli, as the initiator of the strong man boom on an international scale. Born in 1820, some of his most illustrious disciples included Professor Attila (Louis Durlacher) and Eugen Sandow (Frederick Muller). The German-born Attila, in turn, became so well-known that he attracted as his pupils some of the world's most famous physical culturalists and many rulers of Europe. Royalty whom he taught included King George of Greece, King Edward of England (while he was Prince of Wales), Crown Prince Frederick who became King Haakon of Norway, the six children of King Christian of Denmark, the Queen Mother Alexandra of England, Princess Dagmar (who became Empress of Russia and mother of Tsar Nicholas), and the Duchess of Cumberland.

At the time, the training of royalty, the wealthy and the famous with weights and specialised exercises was a well-established and desirable profession, predating the current generation of so-called personal trainers by about 150 years. The fame and fortune of the strongmen of those days were a result of their regular and well-publicised one-on-one stage challenges and entertainment hall competitions using some highly individual and unusual one and two arm lifts, swings, supports and manoeuvres against loads of vehicles, humans and specially contrived barbells and dumbbells. These events, much like the music hall performances of famous composers and musicians, were often attended by royalty and the wealthy, and served to publicise these men, not only as entertainers, but also as teachers or mentors of 'physical culture'.

The great Sandow, born in Koningsberg in East Russia in 1867, was sought out by presidents and rulers from all around the world, with his book, *Life is Movement* being received enthusiastically by nine kings and queens and many princes of Europe, as well as US Presidents William Taft and Woodrow Wilson. Besides defeating many strongmen of his time, he was a generous sponsor of many charitable causes and an early champion of more hygienic conditions of working and living for all, including the central role of formal fitness and health management. As part of his vision, he pressed for the introduction of physical education and sport as compulsory school subjects, and the regular examination of pupils by school doctors and dentists. At the same time, he toured the world lecturing to promote physical culture as a means of improving quality of life, with his contributions being described as follows by the *Mirror of Life and Sport* (8 April 1911):

> *His Majesty King George has conferred an unique honour upon Mr. Eugen Sandow, the world-renowned exponent and founder of scientific physical culture. Mr. Sandow just having had the honour of being appointed Professor of Scientific Physical Culture to his Majesty.*
>
> *The keen interest which the King has always taken in the physical welfare of his people is well-known, and there is no desire more dear to his Majesty's heart than to improve the conditions of life for the masses.*
>
> *Mr. Sandow's appointment must be regarded as a striking recognition of the undoubted benefits of scientific physical culture, and there is no doubt that the interest shown by his Majesty in the subject will considerably increase the popularity of the science of which Mr. Sandow is the principal authority.*
>
> *Mr. Sandow is a man who has risen by his own unaided effort to a position in which he is not only a national but a world factor in the science of improvement of the human body and the combating of that physical degeneracy which in former eras has always accompanied the advances of civilisation.*

In many respects, therefore, Sandow was one of the most important founding fathers of the fitness revolution, with the history of his efforts revealing that the modern phenomenon of science-based physical training is by no means novel or innovative. Interestingly, Sandow's methods focused largely on the development of strength and skill as the foundation of health, an approach which was almost completely deposed more than half a century later by cardiovascular scientists such as Dr Kenneth Cooper of the USA, who massively downplayed the role of these fitness qualities and stressed 'aerobic' fitness as being far more important to general health. It has taken more than 25 years for the quality of strength advocated by Sandow to return to academic acceptance.

In Russia, during this same period, the eminent Polish-born physician, Vladislav Krayevsky (or Krajewski), founded the St Petersburg Amateur Weightlifting Society (1885), having visited various German towns to familiarise himself with what was already known throughout Europe as weightlifting or 'heavy athletics' (or 'Tyazhelaya Atletika', the name still used in Russia to describe this sport), because of his great interest in the use of physical culture for the prevention and treatment of illness. Many prominent scientists, artists and athletes became his pupils, including another famous strongman, George Hackenschmidt, who credited Krayevsky for teaching him all that he knew. Hackenschmidt, in his book, *The Way to Live*, added that some of the world's strongest men of that era, including Sandow, were trained according to Krayevsky's system.

Krayevsky's considerable knowledge in medicine, psychology, physical culture, methods of using exercises and organizational abilities made him an acknowledged leader in weightlifting sports (including wrestling). He not only promoted weightlifting, taught classes and organized competitions, but also lifted himself, achieving significant success in barbell lifts. Krayevsky was president of the jury at the first world championships in Vienna in 1898.

Krayevsky's personal example, enthusiasm, authority and the popularity of his group of distinguished students had a major effect on the development of weightlifting in Russia. Krayevsky wrote two of his fundamental works during the period 1896-1899, one of them being *The Catechism of Health - Rules for Athletes*. Curiously, this work was sent to press on 9 December 1899, but was never published and now is preserved only in manuscript form. His other book, *The Development of Physical Strength with Kettlebells and without Kettlebells*, however, was published in 1900 and reprinted three times (1902, 1909, 1916) after his death (1901).

Krayevsky displayed an excellent knowledge of the history of physical culture and all forms of gymnastics. He paid special attention to therapeutic gymnastics in his *Diagram of Medico Gymnastic Uses* and its accompanying detailed commentary. Krayevsky was very familiar with Swedish gymnastics and noted its therapeutic applications, but his concern with the lack of scientific substantiation of the Swedish system led him to recruit Russian experimentalists to research it.

Many of Krayevsky's methodological recommendations are still valid. These recommendations include medical control of the athlete's health, regularity of workouts and planned sequencing of increasing loads, multi-faceted physical development, psychological management, observation of wellness rules (especially sleep) and refraining from the use of alcohol and smoking. Krayevsky was especially concerned with forming correct breathing habits and methods of combating fatigue, and felt that many of the limitations imposed by heredity could be overcome by appropriate training.

Many of these early strength pioneers devised interesting and unique training weights and machines, including cable machines, variable resistance machines using cams and levers, elastic springs and cables, friction resistance devices, kettlebells, thick-grip bars, hollow-ended barbells and dumbbells whose weight could be increased by adding lead shot, odd-shaped bars, isolation machines, weighted boots and various throwing devices. Yet there are those today who lay claims of originality to designing these machines more than 50 years after their original manufacture. In addition, a large number of weight training, bodybuilding exercises and techniques which are believed to be original today had been tried and tested in that burgeoning exploration era of finding the best methods of strength training.

Interestingly, some of the earlier authors offered insights which even today tend to be ignored by some coaches. For example, Paschall (1954) wrote:

> *The main difference in physical strength between the ordinary barbell exerciser and the competing weightlifter may be traced to two things: the exerciser has been more interested in building up the 'belly' or 'lump' of the muscle than in joint or ligament strength, and also he has usually been more interested in performing a certain number of repetitions rather than one top effort. In addition to these obvious differences, there are also several intangible points, such as conditioned reflexes due to practice of certain repeated lifting motions and . . . a fuller development of the useable muscle fibres.*

It is noteworthy today that no popular Western texts on so-called plyometric training pay any attention to the fact that reflexes are not immutable and can be unconsciously or consciously conditioned by training actions.

The early names of the machines and methods mentioned above invariably were replaced by more impressive or more marketable terms and thus, the modern fitness public has been deprived of knowing the true designers and the illustrious history of the early users of strength apparatus.

The Divergence of Training Philosophies

The development of different scientific and educational cultures in the West and the East had a profound impact on the growth of the different aspects of strength and general fitness training. In the earliest days of the strength game, most of the strong men travelled extensively to learn from colleagues and teachers with different outlooks and were keen to be apprenticed to those whose knowledge attracted widespread attention. With the advent of World War I, the growth of the USA into a great power, the advent of communism and other controversial philosophies and economies, nationalism reached greater heights than ever before in Europe. The Great Depression followed a few decades later, leading to World War II and the partitioning of the world into an Eastern and a Western bloc.

The increasing ideological isolation of nations and well-protected prestige of sporting success meant that research in all fields, including sport, took different directions. During the years after both World Wars, Russia and Europe still continued to promote the virtues of physical strength and power, whereas research in the West rapidly veered in the direction of cardiovascular fitness, assuming great impetus with the running for health and 'aerobics' crazes, associated closely with Swedish endurance exercise research and popular fitness books such as Kenneth Cooper's *Aerobics*. This resulted in a vigorous promotion of the *cardiovascular doctrine*, the paradigm which maintains that cardiac and general health depends predominantly on prolonged endurance or 'aerobic' exercise. At the same time, proponents of this doctrine fairly vigorously denigrated the health benefits of strength training. For example, Cooper (1968: p25) stated that: "If it's muscles or a body beautiful, you'll get it from weightlifting or calisthenics, but not much more. . . If it's the overall health of your body you're interested in, isometrics won't do it for you, neither will isotonics or anaerobics. Aerobic exercises are the only ones that will."

It was inevitable that the accompanying high profile marketing and media campaigns, extensively underwritten by the medical profession, would make the pursuit of strength oriented sports considerably less attractive in the public eye. Olympic Weightlifting became and still is a rarity in schools in the West and strong young men are steered more in the direction of sports such as American football and rugby, games which by mere acceptance into the school curriculum ensure a huge pool of talent.

During the same period, the Russians and Eastern Europeans accumulated extensive international information on strength and sports training while developing a vast research effort into these topics, as well as establishing a vast coaching and educational sports programme. Most schools offered weightlifting and within a few decades after World War II there were at least a million Olympic lifters in the USSR alone. Besides its application in competitive weightlifting, strength training became an integral part of all sports training in Russia, whereas in the West, the attitude more often was one which claimed that weight training slowed one down, made for unnecessary bulk and reduced flexibility. Quite predictably, Russia began to dominate the Olympic Games, especially in Olympic weightlifting, at the same time that the cardiovascular doctrine began to dominate the West.

This Russian dominance often has been simplistically attributed to the extensive use of drugs such as the androgenic-anabolic steroids, but, ironically, the synthesis and sporting use of these drugs was pioneered in the West. It is more accurate to state that the use of such drugs became equally extensive in East and West and that dominance in many international sports by Eastern nations was more a consequence of several other vital factors, especially strength science and organisational systems.

The West today would appear to have reaccepted a useful role for strength training, but the proliferation of weight training facilities and personal trainers still has much more to do with commercialism than the impact of strength science, as is emphasized by the fact that the cardiovascular doctrine still dominates the fitness conscious psyche, there are few schools which offer Olympic lifting and there are fewer competitive lifters than ever before.

The Modern Era Dawns

The systems of training of the early pioneers touched upon above ultimately formed the framework of modern competitive bodybuilding and weightlifting, with some of the exercise techniques and machines being adopted into physiotherapy and the coaching regimes for other sports. Yet, serious scientific research into strength training only developed well into the 20th century and, as we have seen, even now research into cardiovascular training attracts considerably more attention from scientists.

Nevertheless, the evolution of resistance training in several different directions has produced an invaluable data base from the following distinct sources (the details in parentheses refer to the purpose of each discipline):

- Weightlifting and powerlifting (competitive performance against maximal resistance)
- Bodybuilding (resistance training to maximise muscle hypertrophy)
- Supplementary resistance training (resistance exercise to enhance fitness in other sports)
- Physiotherapy (resistance exercise for rehabilitation)
- Scientific research (analysis to understand resistance exercise scientifically).

The information in this book is selected from the above sources to present an integrated approach to the use of strength training to enhance performance in all top level sport. Throughout, the approach has been to reconcile competitive lifting and sporting performance with scientific research, for theory without practice is as limited as practice without theory. It would be premature, however, to maintain that all questions in strength training have been answered: on the contrary, the quest for a definitive science and art of strength training is still in its infancy.

The Fundamental Principle of Strength Training

The production and increase of strength both depend on neuromuscular processes. Strength is not primarily a function of muscle size, but one of the appropriate muscles powerfully contracted by effective nervous stimulation. This is the foundation of all strength training.

Several centuries ago, when electricity, less still bioelectricity, was not of much scientific interest, this principle was already anticipated by Sir Isaac Newton, who wrote in his Principia Mathematica (1687) of "a certain most subtle spirit which pervades and lies hidden in all gross bodies," and that "all sensation is excited, and the members of animal bodies move at the command of the will, namely, by the vibrations of this spirit, mutually propagated along the solid filaments of the nerves, from the outward organs of sense to the brain, and from the brain into the muscles." In other words, if we restate the terminology of those times, we will note that the central role of the mind and nervous system in human movement was already stressed by one of science's leading figures.

In the 1930s, the New York strongman, Paul Boeckmann, stressed in his treatise, *Nerve Force*, the importance of the nerves in strength training, and considered nervous control, conservation of nervous energy and the ability to generate explosive force at the time of greatest need as the foundation of physical power (Paschall, 1954). He also pointed out the great importance of using regular rest periods to enhance nervous recovery.

Physiology tells us that structure is determined by function, where muscle hypertrophy is an adaptive response to neuromuscular stimulation of a given minimum intensity. Thus, nervous stimulation produces two basic adaptive and interrelated effects in the body:

- functional muscular action (the functional effect)
- muscle hypertrophy (the structural effect).

The fundamental principle of strength training, then, is that all strength increase is initiated by neuromuscular stimulation. Although hypertrophy is the long-term result of a certain regime of neuromuscular stimulation, it is not the inevitable consequence of all types of work against resistance. Two basic types of resistance training may be recognised, namely:

- functional resistance training
- structural resistance training.

In drawing up this distinction, it should be noted that there is no such thing as purely structural training, since all training is essentially functional, which, under certain conditions, may also elicit structural changes. Moreover, the production of maximal strength depends to a great extent on the existence of an optimal degree of muscle hypertrophy.

While structural resistance training is aimed primarily at producing muscle hypertrophy (and some aspects of tissue flexibility), functional strength training is associated with many different performance goals, including improvement in static strength, speed-strength, muscle endurance and reactive ability. In other words, the former produces increases in diameter and/or strength of individual muscle fibres, whereas the latter implicates the contractions of the numerous muscle fibres to produce the appropriate performance effect. At a more detailed level, functional training involves the following processes (Fig 1.2):

1. *Intermuscular coordination* between different muscle groups. This involves the synchronisation or sequencing of actions between different muscle groups which are producing any given joint movements. Certain muscles may be inhibited from cooperating, while others may be disinhibited in contributing to the movement.

2. *Intramuscular coordination* of fibres within the same muscle group. This implicates one or more of the following mechanisms of fibre control:

    - *Number encoding*, the control of muscle tension by activating or deactivating certain numbers of fibres.
    - *Rate (frequency) encoding*, the control of tension by modifying the firing rate of active fibres.
    - *Pattern encoding*, the control of tension by synchronisation or sequencing of firing of the different types of muscle fibre (e.g. slow or fast twitch fibres).

3. *Facilitatory and inhibitory reflexive processes* in the neural pathways acting at various levels in the nervous system may be modified to optimise the development of strength, either by improving intra- and inter-muscular coordination or by promoting adaptive changes in the various reflex systems of the body.

4. *Motor learning*, which is the process of programming the brain/central nervous system to be able to carry out specific movement tasks (discussed in detail in 1.13). A great deal of the early improvement in strength and performance is a result of motor learning, this being vital to the continued efficiency of later training. Motor learning continues as the intensity and complexity of loading increases progressively, because skill under demanding conditions is significantly different from skill under less onerous circumstances.

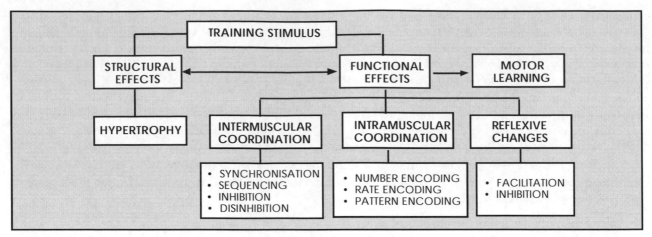

Figure 1.2 The structural and functional effects of strength training stimulation. All training, to a greater or lesser degree, affects the above and all other physical systems, including the cardiovascular, endocrine and metabolic systems. Only the major training effects of strength loads discussed in this book are shown.

In the early stages of training or during stagnation at an advanced level, the functional stages should precede the structural stages (see 1.2 and Ch 2). Thus, functionally transitional stimuli which include motor skill and coordination training are important for the beginner, and functionally powerful stimuli such as increased intensity and reflexive action are appropriate for the more advanced athlete. The need to prescribe structurally versus functionally dominant training at any stage of proficiency also should be guided by an assessment of the strength deficit (discussed after the next subsection).

Neural Changes with Training

The fact that neuromuscular stimulation is fundamental to all training is emphasized further by recent findings that sensory experience results in enlargement and other changes in the cerebral cortex. Earlier hypotheses that the central nervous system cannot change after adulthood have now been proved to be incorrect. It was generally recognised that the young brain has a great capacity to adapt to changes such as injury or disease, but that neural tissue in the mature animal is unable to display this plasticity.

Rosenzweig (1984) has concluded that the capacity for plastic neural changes is present not only early in life, but throughout most, if not all, of the human lifespan. These changes become particularly evident if one is exposed to a sufficiently enriched environment providing novel, complex and cognitively challenging stimulation, a finding which stresses the importance of not limiting one's training to simple, largely unchallenging repetitive patterns of training with exactly the same weights or machines. This is one of the main reasons why this text emphasizes the importance of planned variation utilising numerous different means, methods and exercises which draw on integrative whole-body disciplines such as physiotherapeutic PNF (proprioceptive neuromuscular facilitation), discussed in Chapter 7.

The work of Rosenzweig, Diamond and colleagues at Berkeley has not only revealed that neural changes occur in adulthood, but that these changes can occur easily and rapidly, within minutes and not years. Greenough at the University of Illinois found that these alterations in the central nervous system include not only mass increase, but other structural changes such as the formation of new cell synapses and dendrites (Hall, 1985). Other work being done with amputes, the disabled and other neurally damaged patients is revealing that the brain in effect can rewire itself and recruit areas functionally or structurally adjacent to injured areas to carry out specific tasks. For example, blind individuals who read braille have enlarged brain regions devoted to control of their index fingers. Still further work has found evidence of neural growth in the hippocampus (Gibbs, 1998).

Some of these findings are teaching better strategies for rehabilitating stroke patients. Conventionally, a patient with weak fingers, but efficient arm and shoulder movement is often advised to exercise the arm to help strengthen the fingers. However, the brain's plasticity decrees that undamaged parts of the brain take over much of the necessary functioning and the fingers grow weaker. A superior strategy is to restrict arm and shoulder movement and compel the fingers to exercise, so that the neural areas controlling the former areas will not overpower those controlling the latter. These findings have profound implications for fitness training, particularly the following:

- Fitness training not only causes physiological and functional changes in the motor and cardiovascular systems, but also in the central nervous system.

- Strength training on machines which restrict the movements of joints involved in producing a specific sporting action can modify the circuitry and programming of the brain and thereby reduce the functional or sport specific capability of many of the muscles used to execute that movement.

- The rapidity of changes produced in the brain by repeated stimuli means that even short periods of inappropriate patterns of strength training can be detrimental to sporting performance. The importance of understanding the complexities of prescribing concurrent and sequential methods of training in the short and long term then becomes obvious. This necessitates a thorough knowledge of phenomena such as the delayed training effect, the long-term delayed training effect and the conjugate sequence method, discussed in detail in later chapters.

- Over-reliance on ergogenic devices such as lifting belts, hand grips, bandages for the joints, special shoe inserts, wedges under the heels for squatting and elasticised training suits can modify the neuromuscular system to such an extent that efficient or safe training without them becomes difficult.

- The avoidance of certain exercises (such as those often condemned by popular fitness training organisations) and the use of compensatory muscle action can alter the dynamic balance between interactive muscle groups and alter neural programmes so as to reduce the capability of handling certain functional movements efficiently and safely in sport and daily activities.

- If the likelihood of total rehabilitation of an injury is remote, then the teaching of compensatory muscular action can be valuable in maintaining a high level of functional capability.

- The existence of individual style reveals that each person will programme the central nervous system in subtly different ways, so that attempts to impose stereotyped, highly general patterns of movement may prevent an athlete from ever reaching his full potential.

- Subtle differences apparently as insignificant as a change in grip, stance or head position in regular training can cause significant neural changes which control the way in which the athlete executes a given skill.

Strength Deficit

For the preceding reasons, this text is careful to distinguish between resistance training to produce functional versus structural effects. In determining whether an athlete requires a specific type of resistance training, it is useful to introduce the concept of *strength deficit* (Fig 1.1), which is defined as the difference between *maximum strength* (voluntary effort) produced in a given action and *absolute strength* (involuntary effort) of which the athlete is capable in that same action. This deficit may be defined under static or dynamic conditions, with the deficit depending on the rate at which force has to be developed in a given joint action. In the laboratory situation, absolute strength may be estimated by subjecting the muscles concerned to the maximum electrical stimulation which can be tolerated.

Since the maximum force which may be exerted depends on the load, one may define a strength deficit at different loads, according to the force-time curve shown in Figure 3.3. Zatsiorsky (1995) defines an *explosive strength deficit* as the difference between the maximum force produced under any condition and what he terms the maximum maximorum, F_{mm} (the maximum of all maxima).

Strength deficit reflects the percentage of maximal strength potential which is not used during a given motor task, but its accurate measurement is seldom performed in practice, because determination of maximum contractile strength by electrical stimulation is a difficult and potentially harmful task, and even if this were not the case, most sporting actions involve many muscles and joints, so that measurements of deficits for separate muscle groups would not necessarily relate to performance deficits in complex tasks.

The closest one can approach involuntary recruitment of as many muscle fibres in a given task is to force the body to react by reflex action to a suddenly imposed load. Thus, in a jumping or pulling activity, an approximate measure of strength deficit may be made by comparing the vertical jump achieved from a static start with knees flexed with a vertical jump preceded by a sudden dip. If there is a small difference between the two jumps, this suggests that training focuses more on nervous stimulation via the use of 'shock' and ballistic methods such as plyometrics. If the deficit is large, then strength and hypertrophy training with 5RM to 8RM (8 repetition maximum) loads using methods such as CAT (Compensatory Activation Training) is more suitable.

In general, if the strength deficit is *large* for a given muscle group, an increase in speed-strength may be produced by maximal or near-maximal neuromuscular stimulation (e.g. via weightlifting or plyometric methods). If the strength deficit is *small*, hypertrophy must be induced by submaximal loading methods as commonly used in bodybuilding, followed by maximal efforts against heavy loads.

Verkhoshansky has shown that the *strength deficit increases as the external resistance and the time of motion decrease* (see 3.2.1), indicating that training to increase maximum or absolute strength becomes more important as the time available for a movement becomes longer. Conversely, training to increase rapidity of movement (i.e. nervous system conditioning) becomes more important as the external load decreases. His work implies that estimation of *explosive strength deficit* is also more important in devising strength training regimes for athletes whose events do not allow them sufficient time to produce maximum force, in other words, for actions such as running, jumping and throwing. Chapter 3.2.1 gives further essential information on his research into the strength deficit and its relevance to training to increase power and explosive strength.

Before attempting to estimate strength deficit it is important to appreciate that *sporting performance does not depend simply on the ability to produce maximum force*, since many sporting actions take place so rapidly that it is impossible to recruit an adequate number of muscle fibres. Presuming that technical skill is adequate, performance may also be limited by the inability to produce the optimal level of strength at any given instant. In other words, *Rate of Force Development* (RFD) or *Rate of Tension Development* (RTD) in the muscles are other factors which are vital to sporting prowess. Thus, *it can be highly relevant to estimate deficits in maximal force production as well as in the Rate of Force Production* (2.2.1).

Identification of the strength deficit for the most important muscle groups of an athlete enables the coach to design the specific type of strength training more accurately than relying on the more conventional approach of fairly arbitrarily prescribing a certain number of sets and repetitions of several exercises with a given load. Development of the necessary type of sport specific fitness entails far more than this: the training programme must also pay careful attention to many other factors including the method of executing each exercise and the manner in which force is displayed relative to time and space (other factors are listed in the following section).

As stated earlier, *if the strength deficit is large* for a given muscle group, an increase in speed-strength may be produced by maximal or near-maximal neuromuscular stimulation (e.g. via weightlifting or plyometric methods). *If the strength deficit is small*, hypertrophy must be induced by sub-maximal loading methods as commonly used in bodybuilding (see Table 1.1 and Ch 7), followed by maximal efforts against heavy loads. A more enduring type of strength fitness results from a well-sequenced combination of functional and structural resistance training. However, it is important to monitor regularly any change in relative strength to ascertain if increased hypertrophy is simply adding unproductive tissue bulk which is not producing a commensurate increase in functional strength. Other useful measures of training effectiveness are the analysis of injury or soreness patterns and changes in motor skill and reaction time.

1.1 Preliminary Issues

Strength training invariably is regarded as synonymous with resistance or weight training, since the development of strength depends on the imposition of appropriate regimes of exercise against external resistance.

1.1.1 Resistance Training for Different Purposes

The regimes of resistance training classically used to produce strength, power, muscular endurance or muscle hypertrophy may be summarised in the form of Table 1.1 of recommendations based on research and experience (Note that this table refers to dynamic and not isometric training regimes).

This scheme, however, does not take into account the complexity of the phenomenon of strength or the other strength-related qualities of neuromuscular performance, such as strength-speed, explosive strength, flexibility-strength and strength-endurance.

It is the major objective of this book to investigate the scope of sport specific strength training in far greater depth than implied by the generalised scheme of Table 1.1 and thereby enable the exercise professional to apply this information in practice.

Table 1.1 Resistance training to achieve different performance goals. Endurance refers to muscle endurance.

Variable	Strength	Power	Hypertrophy	Endurance
Load (% of 1RM)	80 - 100	70 - 100	60 - 80	40 - 60
Repetitions per set	1 - 5	1 - 5	8 - 15	25 - 60
Sets per exercise	4 - 7	3 - 5	4 - 8	2 - 4
Rest between sets (mins)	2 - 6	2 - 6	2 - 5	1 - 2
Duration (secs per set)	5 - 10	4 - 8	20 - 60	80 - 150
Speed per rep (% of max)	60 - 100	90 - 100	60 - 90	6 - 80
Training sessions per week	3 - 6	3 - 6	5 - 7	8 - 14

Later in this text, it will be shown that the effective and safe prescription of resistance training should begin with an understanding of force-time and related curves concerning the patterns of force production in sport and resistance training. On this basis we can identify several major objectives of strength training, namely:

- To increase maximal or absolute strength
- To increase explosive strength (large force in minimal time)
- To increase the Rate of Force Production
- To enable the muscles to generate large forces for a given period
- To enable the muscles to sustain small forces for a prolonged period
- To increase muscle and connective tissue hypertrophy

The summary of training approaches given by Table 1.1 may be adequate for the average personal trainer or coach dealing with the average client or lower level athlete, but it needs to be expanded upon to take into account the objectives stated above. In particular, it needs to distinguish between methods concentrating on neural adaptation versus the different types of hypertrophy and muscle endurance. This is done at length in later chapters.

Methods involving a large training volume (many repetitions) are referred to as *extensive methods* and any phase which relies on a high volume of low resistance training is referred to as an extensification or accumulation phase. Conversely, high intensity, low volume methods are known as *intensive methods* and a phase comprising this type of training is referred to as an intensification phase. The early stages of training usually begin with an extensive phase to lay the foundation for the greater demands imposed by the subsequent intensive phase with heavy resistance and few repetitions (Fig 1.3). In fact, the long-term training system known as *periodisation* is based on cyclically alternating extensive and intensive phases of exercise chosen to timeously enhance given components of fitness such as strength, strength-speed and strength-endurance (see 1.14, 5.5 & 7.5).

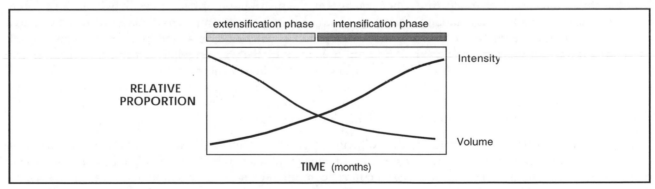

Figure 1.3 A typical basic periodisation model for early training, showing the replacement of an extensive phase by an intensive phase. Intensity refers to the average load lifted per repetition, while volume refers to the sum of (weight x repetitions) for all sets and all major exercises, which is an approximate measure of the total work done per exercise.

The traditional approaches to strength conditioning usually regard the following variables as the most important in a weight training programme:

- magnitude of the load
- number of repetitions
- number of sets

Training programmes based entirely on these variables, however, are seriously incomplete and limited in their long-term effectiveness, especially as a form of supplementary training for other sports. Factors such as the following must also be taken into consideration:

- the type of strength fitness required
- the type of muscle contraction involved (isometric, concentric, eccentric)
- the speed of movement over different phases of movement
- the acceleration at critical points in the movement
- the rest intervals between repetitions, sets and workouts
- active versus passive rest/recuperation intervals
- the sequence of exercises
- the relative strength of agonists and antagonists, stabilisers and movers
- the development of optimal static and dynamic range of movement
- the strength deficit of given muscle groups
- the training history of the individual
- the injury history of the individual
- the level of sports proficiency of the individual.

The last-mentioned factor is of exceptional importance, because the advanced athlete responds to a given training regime very differently from a novice. For instance, the exact sequencing of strength, strength-speed and hypertrophy means in a workout or microcycle is of little consequence during the first weeks or months of a beginner's training, but is very important to a more experienced athlete. Moreover, loads as small as 40% of 1RM can significantly enhance the strength of a beginner, but have no strengthening effect on an elite athlete.

1.1.2 Factors Limiting Strength Production

The production of strength in the short and long term depends on the following main factors:

- Trainability
- Neuromuscular Efficiency
- Biomechanical Efficiency
- Psychological Factors

- Pain and Fear of Pain
- Injury and Fear of Injury
- Fatigue

Trainability This refers to the potential to develop strength in response to a specific training regime and depends largely on genetic factors and pre-training status. Genetic factors determine the potential for hypertrophy, the leverage characteristics about each joint, the distribution of fast and slow twitch fibres in the different muscle groups, and metabolic efficiency. The pre-training status refers to the level of special fitness possessed by an individual before formal training begins. Physical loading imposed by work, play and casual sport has a pronounced effect on one's ability to gain strength, with the greatest relative increases being possible among untrained individuals and the smallest among elite athletes. Individual response to training at a given level of special fitness, however, is governed largely by one's genetic predisposition to increase hypertrophy, strength and power easily. Moreover, during long-term training, the blood serum levels of biologically active unbound testosterone may also be of importance for trainability (Häkkinen, 1985).

Neuromuscular Efficiency This refers to the skill with which one executes a given movement and relates to how efficiently and intensively one recruits muscle fibres in the appropriate muscle groups to produce the movement pattern accurately and powerfully. All motor action is controlled by nervous and neuromuscular processes, so that this factor should be regarded as fundamental to the functional production of strength.

Biomechanical Efficiency This relates to genetic factors such as the leverage characteristics of the body, the relative strengths of the different muscle groups controlling the movement of each limb, and the neuromuscular efficiency which orchestrates all movement patterns of the body. The efficiency of movements with and without the use of sporting apparel and equipment (such as bats, racquets and throwing implements) or in close contact with opponents (e.g. in wrestling, judo, rugby and American football) is especially important. Unlike the immutable genetic factors which predispose one person to achieve a potential which far exceeds that of another person, both neuromuscular and biomechanical efficiency are profoundly influenced by training and offer a vehicle for producing great increases in strength, as will be seen in later chapters.

Psychological Factors Sporting performance depends heavily on psychological factors such as motivation (to achieve certain goals), aggression, concentration, focus or attention, the ability to tolerate pain or to sustain effort, the perception of sensations and events in training and competition, the placebo effect, communicative skills, the ability to cope with anxiety or stress, attitudes towards events and participants in sport, attitudes towards winning and losing, learning ability, attitude, mood state, personality, alertness and vigilance, the ability to manage distractions, and the ability to relax effectively.

The role of a competent coach in assisting the athlete cannot be underestimated in this respect, because ideal physical preparation in sport will never compensate for deficiencies produced by psychological weaknesses which arise during competition. *The perception* of training loads, performance skills, strengths, weaknesses, opponents, venue, fitness state and related sporting factors is central to the efficient psychological preparation of the athlete. Fear of pain and injury are important mental factors which are discussed separately in this section.

Pain and Fear of Pain Pain seriously limits one from producing maximal strength at any given time. Here we must distinguish between *the pain of injury* and the *pain of effort* (and sometimes, the *pain of fatigue*). The pain of injury is a protective response to any activity which is causing or has caused damage to some system of the body. This pain warning must be acted upon immediately to prevent further injury, since ignoring such feedback can have serious consequences. The pain of effort is not necessarily a result of injury, but refers to one's personal interpretation of the intensity of a given effort and is sometimes assessed on a subjective scale called the rating of perceived effort (RPE). This type of scale is most commonly used to judge the intensity of cardiovascular exercise, but it may also be applied to muscle endurance and maximal strength activities (Fig 1.4).

A Rating of Perceived Exertion (RPE) was devised by Borg to enable one to estimate the intensity of cardiovascular exercise on a scale running originally from 6 to 22. This range was chosen because the average adult pulse rate varies from approximately 60 at rest to a maximum of 220 beats per minute. Borg later simplified the scale to run from 0 to 10, with cardiovascular conditioning taking place in the range between 3-5. This scale may be adapted as an RPE scale to assess the degree of effort experienced in muscle endurance, strength and power activities. Not only is the heart rate characteristically higher in muscle endurance activities and even higher in very strenuous strength movements, but muscle endurance is developed with loads of about 40-60% of the 1RM, and strength and power with loads of about 70-100% of the 1RM (see Table 1.1). Therefore, if maximal effort is rated 10 and no effort as 0, the scale may be used to rate different levels of muscular effort, as well as cardiovascular effort.

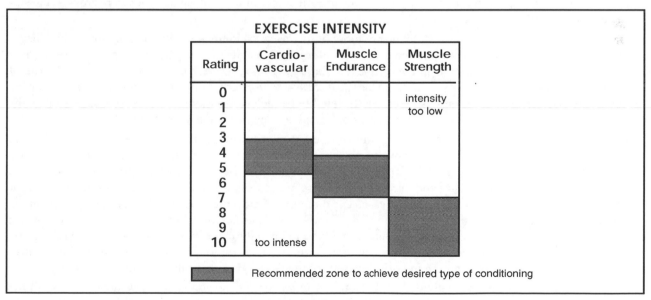

Figure 1. 4 Rating of Perceived Effort (RPE) scale for judging intensity in different types of exercise.

This can be particularly useful in preventing overtraining, because stress is determined not only by the objective magnitude of the load, but also how difficult that load feels to the athlete during a particular set and workout. Physical stress relates more to the objective magnitude (i.e. load and repetitions) of the exercise, whereas mental stress relates more closely to one's subjective perception of how demanding the load is, so that a training journal which records both the objective loading and the subjective rating offers a more thorough means of adjusting one's training programme and minimising the likelihood of overtraining and overtraining injury.

In applying any form of RPE, it should be noted that the scale is not linear, but has been found to increase exponentially (Banister, 1979). In other words, a rating of 6 does not mean that the effort is perceived as twice that at a rating of 3. Moreover, if a load is doubled, the perceived rating does not double.

Injury and Fear of Injury   It requires no sophisticated analysis to confirm that acute or chronic injury may make it impossible for one to produce maximal strength. In particular, reflex inhibition of contraction is a well-known phenomenon which produces muscle weakness when a joint is damaged (Stokes & Young, 1984). For example, it is impossible to generate maximal squatting strength if one is suffering from knee joint deterioration such as chondromalacia patellae or any other form of peripatellar damage. The importance of prescribing efficient and safe training to develop strength then becomes obvious, as does the use of appropriate rehabilitation regimens to restore the injured athlete to top-level competition. Fear of injury or pain must be recognised as a major inhibitory factor in the production of strength or any other motor qualities, for that matter. It is often largely unimportant if medical assessment pronounces rehabilitation to be complete; *return to top level performance will occur only if the athlete perceives rehabilitation to be complete* and the fear of pain or re-injury to be minimal.

Fatigue   Fatigue determines one's ability to sustain a specific type of effort, ranging from the supreme cardiovascular demands of ultra-marathon races to the short-term maximal strength bouts of weightlifters and powerlifters. Rapid fatigue is induced by the maximal and near-maximal efforts associated with strength sports (such as weightlifting and powerlifting) and slow fatigue with sports which involve low intensities of strength production (such as distance running and cycling).

Endurance may be defined as the ability to resist fatigue, *static endurance* the ability to sustain isometric activity and *dynamic endurance* the ability to sustain dynamic muscle contraction. It should be noted that dynamic endurance for the different modes of muscle action (auxotonic, isotonic or isokinetic) is not the same, nor is endurance at different velocities of motion the same. This is one reason why fitness qualities such as speed-endurance, static strength-endurance, dynamic strength-endurance and speed-strength endurance are defined.

A distinction is made between *central fatigue* and *peripheral fatigue*, where the former is associated with the central nervous system, i.e. factors outside the muscular system, and the latter refers to fatigue processes in the peripheral nervous system and the neuromuscular system. Central fatigue relates to decreased motivation, impaired transmission of spinal nerve impulses and impaired recruitment of spinal motor neurons (Bigland-Ritchie & Woods, 1984).

Fatigue at muscle cell level may affect one or more of the many excitation-contraction processes which begin with depolarisation of the muscle cell at the neuromuscular junction and end with the mechanical power stroke, the final action involved in actin-myosin interaction and force generation. Disturbance at any stage of this chain of processes will lower the capability of a muscle cell of realising its maximum force potential. The primary peripheral sites which have been implicated in muscle cell fatigue include the motor end-plate, the sarcolemma, the T tubules, the sarcoplasmic reticulum, regulatory proteins and contractile proteins (Green, 1988).

Some scientists have also suggested a significant role for ammonia in the fatigue process. Exercise-induced hyperammonemia refers to increased ammonia accumulation during exercise (Banister & Cameron, 1990). Ammonia is a ubiquitous metabolic byproduct which exerts multiple effects on physiological and biochemical systems. Depending on the intensity and duration of exercise, muscle ammonia may rise sufficiently to leak from muscle to blood, and thereby travel to other organs. The direction of movement of ammonia or the ammonium ion is dependent on concentration and pH gradients between tissues. Thus, ammonia can also cross the blood-brain barrier, although the rate of diffusion of ammonia from blood to brain during exercise is unknown. Consequently, exhaustive exercise may induce a state of acute ammonia toxicity which, although transient and reversible relative to disease states, may be severe enough in critical regions of the CNS to hinder further coordinated activity.

Peripheral fatigue has been subdivided further into *low frequency fatigue* and *high frequency fatigue*, with the distinction being made on the basis of the frequency at which fatigue occurs in response to electrical stimulation of the muscles (Edwards, 1981). If electrical stimulation is applied to a muscle directly after contraction, impairment in force production at low frequency (less than 20 Hz) has been called low frequency fatigue by Edwards. If the force decrement is detected at frequencies greater than 50 Hz, this is known as high frequency fatigue (Fig 1.5).

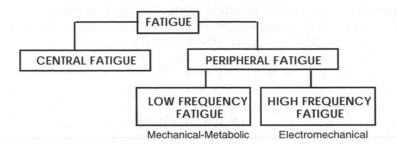

Figure 1.5 Classification of the different types of fatigue

Low frequency (LF) fatigue occurs early in exercise, without regard to the characteristics of muscle contraction, and exhibits a prolonged recovery period persisting for as long as 48 hours. It has been attributed to failure in excitation coupling due to depressed release of calcium ions (Edwards, 1981). It does not necessarily affect force output at high frequency, because the high excitation frequency may compensate for the impaired release and maximally activate the muscle fibre. Interestingly, it has been found that variable-frequency trains of impulses offset low frequency fatigue in skeletal muscle, so it appears as if such variability may exploit the catch-like property of skeletal muscle to augment force in fatigued skeletal muscle (Russ & Binder-Macleod, 1999).

It has also been shown that fatigue slows the dissociation of force-generating myosin cross bridges, since calcium ion uptake, the calcium ion-ATPase activity of the sarcoplasmic reticulum (SR) and the rates of SR calcium ion release are depressed in fatigued muscles (Williams et al, 1998). Moreover, during fatigue, the contractile apparatus and SR undergo intrinsic functional alterations, which probably results in altered force production and energy consumption by the intact muscle.

With reference to short-term maximal contractions, the reduction in neuromuscular transmission rates may be a result of a reduction in central drive rather than peripheral electrical failure (Bigland-Ritchie & Woods, 1984). This has been suggested because the reduction in firing rate may be beneficial in avoiding electrical failure and facilitating maximal mechanical response from the muscle. Intensive activation of the central nervous system through the use of training with maximal weights, maximal power or plyometrics requires a recovery period of at least 48 hours or more, if restoration means are not employed. Interestingly, the rapid force recovery following eccentric exercise is mediated at least in part by neural factors, a recovery process which may occur independently of cell disruption (Hortobágyi et al, 1998).

If we wish to understand the neural factors which contribute to fatigue, *it is incorrect to state that fatigue occurs only when a task can no longer be performed.* (Gandevia, 1998). Changes in muscle afferent feedback, motor neuronal discharge, motor cortical output, and perceived effort all develop well before an activity reaches the physiological endurance limit of skeletal muscle. During sustained maximal contractions, it has been found that the discharge of motor neurones commonly declines to below the level required to produce maximal force from the muscles, whose contractile speed usually is slowed, as a consequence. Thus, some 'central' fatigue develops. Recent findings using electrostimulation across the skull have revealed that the motor cortex is one site at which suboptimal output develops during human muscle fatigue.

The sequence of recruitment of the different muscle fibres is determined largely by the intensity and duration of loading, with the low-threshold, slow-twitch, high-endurance fibres being recruited first while the intensity of stimulation is low, and the fast twitch, low-endurance fibres being successively recruited as the intensity of activation increases (see Fig 1.21).

Other studies have revealed that changes in both recruitment pattern and increased firing frequency occur in an attempt to delay the onset of fatigue (Maton, 1981). However, different muscles may utilise different strategies to cope with fatigue, because the significance of recruitment pattern and firing frequency varies between muscles when generating isometric strength (Deluca, 1985).

The decrease in *blood flow* to the muscles with increasing intensity of muscle contraction also has a major effect on local muscular endurance. The free supply of oxygen to the muscles by the capillaries takes place only for loads eliciting less than 15% of maximal muscle tension. At greater levels of tension, blood flow is progressively more impeded by the compression of the blood vessels by the contracting muscles, until it ceases completely when a muscle generates more than about 50% of its maximum isometric strength. At this stage the muscle must rely on 'anaerobic' processes to meet its energy needs. If the dynamic activity at this level of muscular tension involves alternating phases of contraction and relaxation, as is the case with most repetitive resistance training, then blood flow will proceed during the relaxation phases and decrease the likelihood of fatigue being produced by muscle ischaemia. However, if the exercise involves isometric or quasi-isometric contractions lasting more than about 6 seconds, this circulatory cause of fatigue will be very significant. This explains why isometric activity results in more rapid and more depleting fatigue than dynamic activity (Figs 1.6a & b).

This subsection has focused on fatigue developing during short-duration strength activities, rather than the fatigue associated with cardiovascular events. The central nervous system plays a very significant role in the generation of maximal and near maximal strength and power, so that development of resistance to fatigue under these conditions necessitates suitable stimulation of the central nervous system.

The capacity for performing strenuous endurance exercise also depends on using the appropriate type of chronic training. In this case the training involves a great deal of long-duration, low resistance work, which produces extensive cardiac, respiratory and circulatory responses. However, the improvement in endurance has been attributed more to peripheral adaptation in the muscles than to these cardiovascular changes, in particular, the increased efficiency in energy metabolism, enzyme activity and fuel utilisation (Saltin & Rowell, 1980; Gollnick & Saltin, 1982).

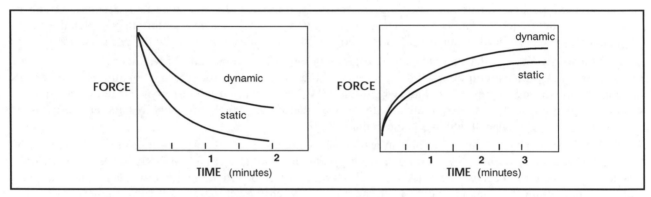

      (a) Fatigue during static and dynamic work   (b) Recovery profiles for static and dynamic work

Figure 1.6 (a) and (b) Fatigue onset and recovery profiles for static and dynamic work

The exact significance of the enzymatic and metabolic changes is not unequivocally known yet, but it has been generally agreed that fatty acids become an increasingly important fuel for muscle activity, thereby reducing reliance on stored muscle glycogen. The sparing of muscle glycogen which follows chronic training has been suggested as the main reason for fatigue resistance, although any number of other peripheral changes may be responsible. Extensive excitation-coupling and intracellular adaptations also occur with training. For instance, recent research implies that training produces both electrical and mechanical changes, as measured by muscular response to short-term electrostimulation (Duchateau & Hainaut, 1984).

Various reasons for resistance to fatigue have been propounded, such as an increase in aerobic potential (Kugelberg & Lindegren, 1979), or enhanced energetic efficiency at peripheral level, as discussed earlier. However, alterations in central nervous drive may also occur, as has been observed in strength training (Sale et al, 1982; Davies et al, 1985). In this respect, there has been little research into the role played by afferent feedback and supraspinal command in modulating motor neuron activity in either the trained or untrained state.

It us known that fatiguing muscular contractions are accompanied by a decrease in the discharge rate of alpha motoneurons (or the activation rate of motoneurons). The process whereby this activation discharge rate is modulated by the central nervous system to optimise force production by skeletal muscle during sustained muscle action has been called *muscle wisdom* (Marsden et al., 1983). Its purpose is believed to ensure that central neural drive to fatigued skeletal muscle matches that which is needed to generate the required force. During maximal voluntary contractions the activation rates decline as the muscle fatigues, while no similar decline has been observed during submaximal contractions (Binder-Macleod, 1995). In addition, muscle wisdom may be one mechanism that functions either to decrease or to postpone central neural fatigue (Enoka & Stuart, 1992). Bigland-Ritchie and colleagues (1986) have suggested that a reflex arising from fatigued skeletal muscle is at least partly responsible for muscle wisdom.

However, it has also been found that motor unit discharge rate is not associated with muscle relaxation time in sustained submaximal contractions in humans. The muscle wisdom hypothesis suggests that motor unit discharge rates decrease in parallel with the slowing of muscle contractile properties during fatigue. In a study measuring the discharge rates of single motor units and the muscle contractile properties during a sustained submaximal contraction, it was learned that most of the motor units that were active from the beginning of the task decreased their discharge rate in the absence of any slowing of muscle relaxation time. These findings suggest that the muscle wisdom hypothesis may not apply to sustained submaximal contractions (Garland et al, 1997).

Hagbarth & Macefield (1995) state that evidence points to an important role of the fusimotor system in the *muscle wisdom* phenomenon during peripheral fatigue of some voluntary contractions:

1. Muscle afferents amplify skeleto-motor output, with the only known afferent system capable of this being the muscle spindle

2. Muscle spindle firing rates decline during constant force voluntary contractions, so fusimotor support to skeleto-motor output decreases

3. This waning support can be offset by applying high frequency vibration to the fatiguing muscle, which excites spindle endings. This finding supports the use of mechanical vibrating devices that some athletes are now beginning to use in training.

4. The progressive decline in motor unit firing rates during maximal voluntary contractions is abolished by blocking muscle afferent inputs, which may be due to a progressive withdrawal of spindle support, at least in the initial stages of a contraction.

Finally, it is relevant to ascertain if one's perception of force exerted during a fatiguing near-maximal movement is based upon centrally generated sensations arising from the motor command (*the sense of effort* or RPE) or from peripheral sensations originating in the muscle (*the sense of force*). Several studies of isometric contraction indicate that the perceived rating of the force increases during sustained constant-force contractions, which is consistent with the theory that judgments of force are based on centrally generated signals (Jones, 1995). Some subjects, however, are able to dissociate effort and force and accurately judge the magnitude of forces during fatigue.

1.2 Fundamental Biomechanics of Strength

The development of strength and power would appear to be a fairly straightforward quest. Since the human constitutes an adaptive and self-regulating organism, the imposition of progressively increasing loads on the musculoskeletal system according to the well-known principle of gradual overload would be all that is required to achieve this aim. In this context, the load exerts a force on the body, which uses muscle action to stabilise or move that load, thereby giving rise to what we call strength. Once this concept of strength/force has been introduced, we can immediately draw from mechanics a number of other physical definitions which enable us to formulate a scientific framework for analysing sporting action.

Thus, *strength* may be defined as the ability of the body to produce force, *energy* may be understood to refer to that physical quality which imbues an object with the ability to exert a force, *work* may be regarded as the energy involved in moving from one state or position to another, and *power* refers to the rate at which work is done at any instant.

When a force acts on a rigid body, it produces two distinct effects, namely *translation* of the body in the direction of the force and *rotation* about some point. The concept of a *moment* is applied to the rotational effects of a force, although, strictly speaking there at least two different types of moment: the *moment of a force*, and the *moment of a couple* (a special combination of two forces).

Because force involves the movement of a limb about a joint or fulcrum, the concept of torque (the turning capability of a force) is frequently used in sport biomechanics. *Torque* is defined as the product of a force and the perpendicular distance from the line of action of the force to the fulcrum about which it acts (Fig 1.7). Sometimes, since it is defined in the same way, torque is regarded as synonymous with the *moment* of a force and, in the context of basic functional anatomy, the use of either term will not lead to any contradictions.

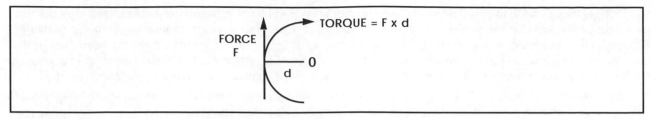

Figure 1.7 Torque or moment of a force acting at a distance d about a fulcrum or joint centre O.

A couple is defined as a system consisting of two non-collinear (not in the same straight line) equal and opposite forces. It causes pure rotation without translation, so that it possesses a moment, but no resultant force. A typical couple is illustrated in Figure 1.8, showing the two forces of equal magnitude F separated by a distance d, acting in opposite directions in the same plane. The calculations in that figure show that the moment of a couple (often simply called a 'couple') is the same about every point, unlike the moment of a force. In some texts, it is quite common to read about couples about the thoracoscapular 'joint', the pelvis and other bodily structures, because it appears as if only rotation occurs. However, the lack of obvious translation (linear movement of one of the bones relative to another) may have to do more with restraint imposed by surrounding tissues such as ligaments rather than the lack of a resultant force.

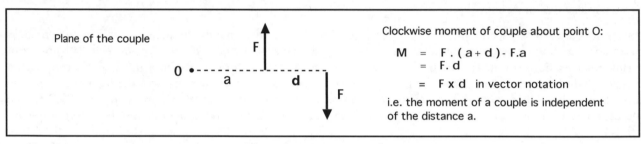

Figure 1.8 A typical couple comprising two non-collinear forces F

What is not often appreciated is the fact that resistance training is really force training, which requires the muscles to produce force against an external resistance (e.g. weights, elastic bands, water or specialised machines). If the external resistance is a weight, this force may be described by *Newton's Second Law of Motion*, expressed in its simplest form as: force $F = ma$, where m is the mass of the load and a its acceleration. Thus, it is rather irrelevant to discuss training programmes simply in terms of the load. Lighter loads can be accelerated much faster than heavy loads, so that the largest force may not necessarily be associated with heavier loads.

Biomechanics and Training

The force or torque (defined above as: torque = F x d, where F is the force and d is the perpendicular distance from the line of action of the force and the point about which the force produces rotation) acting on this load also varies throughout range of the given movement, so that the muscle tension varies constantly and it is really muscle tension and degree of coordinated neuromuscular activation rather than load lifted which determines the effectiveness of an exercise (Fig 1.7).

Even in the most basic applications of resistance training, the concept of torque (or moment) is of great practical value. For instance, the simple act of flexing the elbows will decrease the torque acting about the shoulder during dumbbell side raises, supine dumbbell flyes and bench press by bringing the load closer to the shoulder fulcrum, thereby enhancing the safety of these exercises. Similarly, keeping the line of action of the bar as close as possible to the body during the Weightlifting clean or powerlifting deadlift reduces the torque acting about the lower lumbar vertebrae and the hips, thereby enabling a greater load to be lifted with a greater degree of safety. The common error of swinging the bar away from the body during the later stages of the pull during the Olympic snatch or the javelin further away from the shoulder during the wind-up for the throw are examples of the inefficient use of torque.

The obvious implication of an understanding of torque in the case of all joints of the body is that the expression of strength and power is not merely a function of changes in soft tissue structure or neuromuscular efficiency, but also of the optimal use of torque for any sporting movements.

For instance, although the presence of a high percentage of fast twitch muscle fibres in an athlete may suggest that the latter may be well suited to sports which require production of power and speed, the existence of any inherently disadvantageous limb leverages or techniques which do not optimise torque production in specific complex joint actions may decree that any muscle fibre advantage may be of diminished importance. Occasionally, however, a disproportionate increase in strength for a given activity may tend to offset these negative factors and enable the athlete to perform quite competently, albeit in a less efficient or economic manner.

Later the issue of torque for activities involving several joints will be examined to caution us against the casual analysis of joint action according to the standard methods of functional anatomy (Ch 3). We will then learn that we are not necessarily justified in assuming that a given muscle will produce the same joint action in a multi-joint task if the anatomy charts show that it produces a certain joint action (such as flexion) when only that joint is involved in the movement. We will also learn that, in multi-joint (multi-articular) tasks, a muscle may exert a profound effect over a joint which is not crossed by that muscle.

Earlier we saw that strength is not the maximal force (or torque) which a muscle can generate; that is actually *maximal strength*. Strength, as is consistent with the definition of force according to Newton's Laws (see later), is simply the ability to generate force to overcome inertia or a load. Similarly, we can define concepts such as maximal torque and maximal power, as well as optimal torque and power (rate of doing work).

Possibly the best known curve in strength training is the hyperbolic Force-Velocity curve first described by Hill (Fig 1.9) that is widely used to reinforce the view that maximum force production can occur only at zero or very low velocities. This curve may be used to show the different effects of velocity-centred and force-centred training. Although this relationship originally was derived for isolated muscle, it has been confirmed for actual sporting movement, though the interaction between several muscle groups in complex actions changes some aspects of the curve (Zatsiorsky & Matveev, 1964; Komi, 1979).

This curve implies that velocity of muscle contraction is inversely proportional to the load, that a large force cannot be exerted in very rapid movements (as in powerlifting), that the greatest velocities are attained under conditions of low loading, and that the intermediate values of force and velocity depend on the maximal isometric force. It is misleading to take this to mean universally that large force cannot be produced at large velocities, because ballistic action involving stretch-shortening and powerful neural facilitation exist to manage such situations, as will be discussed later in more detail.

In addition, more recent research has shown that that the Force-Velocity relationship is not necessarily a continuous hyperbolic relationship during muscle shortening and that the commonly modelled force augmentation effect of muscle lengthening is incorrect, at least concerning submaximal activation of the lower back extensors (Sutarno & McGill, 1995). For instance, the erector spinae exhibit a yielding phenomenon which causes force to drop abruptly during constant velocity stretching under constant, submaximal stimulation. This study showed further that the eccentric behaviour of the lower erectors (lumbar level L3) appears to be independent of velocity and length, while that of the upper erectors (thoracic level T9) displays a dependence on length. At lower concentric velocities, a concavity in the Force-Velocity curves appeared after some sort of "threshold" velocity was exceeded.

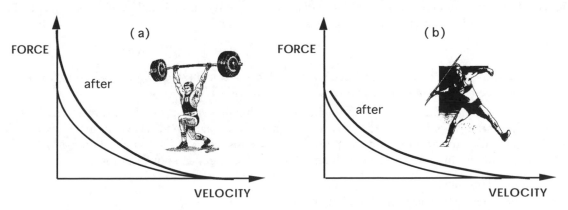

Figure 1.9 The relationship between force and velocity, based on the work of Hill (1953). (a) The dark curve shows the change produced by heavy strength training. This situation refers to 'strength-speed' training. (b) The dark curve here shows the change produced by low load, high velocity training. This situation refers to 'speed-strength' training. (after Zatsiorsky, 1995).

The influence of maximal isometric strength on dynamic force and velocity is greater in heavily resisted, slow movements, although there is no correlation between maximal velocity and maximal strength (Zatsiorsky, 1995). The ability to generate maximum strength and the ability to produce high speeds are different motor abilities, so that it is inappropriate to assume that development of great strength will necessarily enhance sporting speed.

The effect of heavy strength training has been shown to shift the curve upwards (as shown in Fig 1.9), particularly in beginners (Perrine & Edgerton, 1978; Lamb, 1984; Caiozzo et al, 1981) and light, high velocity training to shift the maximum of the velocity curve to the right (Zatsiorsky, 1995). Since, in both cases, power = force x velocity, the area under the curve represents power, so that this change in curve profile with strength increase means that power is increased at all points on the curve. The term 'strength-speed' is often used as a synonym for power capability in sport, with some authorities preferring to distinguish between *strength-speed* (the quality being enhanced in Fig 1.9a) and *speed-strength* (the quality being enhanced in Fig 1.9b).

Optimisation of force, torque, speed and power or the production of 'just the right amount at the right time' of these motor abilities sometimes seems to be forgotten, especially in the so-called strength, heavy or contact sports. All too often, the solution to most performance problems in such sports seems to be a philosophy of "the greater the strength and the greater the muscle hypertrophy, the better", despite the fact that one constantly witnesses exceptional performances being achieved in these sports by lighter and less strong individuals.

The full ramifications of the concept of power often tends to be lost in Western strength training because the term "speed-strength", directly translated from the Russian texts on strength training , is used as its colloquial equivalent. Thus, we encounter programmes on how to "increase power", which is entirely nebulous in the context of human movement, because the concept of power may appear in several different forms in biomechanics, namely 'mean power' (over a given interval), peak power (at some specific instant) and power at any given instant. Just as it is not very meaningful to develop maximal strength (force) or high mean force in every situation or stage of a movement, so it can be equally inappropriate to train an athlete to simply develop "power", irrespective of context. One of the central features of all motor skill is the ability to produce maximal power and power in the most efficient manner possible. In fact, all effective strength utilisation and training means optimally timing the magnitude of force, power and rate of force development (RFD) throughout any movement.

Since bodily motion is the result of muscle action and its underlying metabolic processes, one must distinguish between internal and external energy and work. Externally, assuming no losses by heat or sound, mechanical energy usually occurs in the form of potential energy (PE) and kinetic energy (KE), where PE is the energy possessed by a body by merit of its position and KE is the energy which a body has by virtue of its velocity.

Although external work is defined popularly as the product of the force and the distance through which it is exerted, this definition applies only if the force is constant and acts strictly along the path joining the starting and end points of the movement. The mathematical definition based on integral calculus generally is avoided in training texts, because it is felt that it may not be adequately understood by the practitioner, while the popular definition usually attracts the condemnation of the scientist, because of its limited applicability and scope. For this reason, a definition of work in terms of energy changes is given, namely:

Work   W = Final Energy - Initial Energy = Final (PE + KE) - Initial (PE + KE)

Alternatively, we could draw a graph of how the force varies with displacement; then work would be given by the area under the curve between the starting and end points of the action (Fig 1.10).

Since some of the fundamental equations used to analyse sporting movements may be expressed in the form of suitable graphs, this same graphic approach may be adopted to enable us to visualise more simply the implications of biomechanics for training and competition. In this respect, the following relationships will be seen later to play an especially important role in the biomechanics of strength and power in sport:

- Force vs Time (or Torque vs Time)
- Force vs Displacement (and Torque vs Joint Angle)
- Force vs Velocity
- Rate of Force Development vs Time

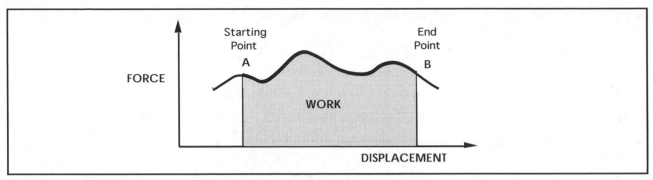

Figure 1.10 Graphical definition of work as the area under the force-displacement curve

Initial Implications of Mechanics

Because of their fundamental importance in biomechanics, Newton's Laws of Motion warrant repetition here:

Newton I (The Law of Inertia): A body will persist in its original state of rest or motion unless acted on by an external agency (i.e. a force).

Newton II (The Law of Acceleration): Newton stated it thus: "The change of motion is proportional to the motive force impressed; and is made in the direction of the straight line in which that force is impressed" (Richards et al, 1962), which in modern terms may be restated as: The rate of change of velocity (acceleration) is proportional to the resultant force acting on the body and is in the same direction as the force or, if suitable units are chosen, Force = Mass x Acceleration (F = m.a).

Newton III (The Law of Reaction): For every action there is an equal and opposite reaction.

Despite the familiarity of these laws, some of their implications appear to be forgotten in the practical setting, in particular regarding comparison between machine and free weight training. Some machine manufacturers advertise that their variable resistance machines are superior to free weights, because, in the latter case, the weight remains constant and does not change in response to altering joint leverages throughout range of any movement. Newton's first two laws show clearly that this claim is false, since a load may only be lifted if its weight (due to gravitational acceleration) is overcome by the lifter with an acceleration which exceeds that of gravity.

Furthermore, during the lift, proprioceptive feedback makes the athlete aware that the load is changing and enables him to intervene voluntarily in the loading process by accelerating or decelerating the bar to increase or decrease the force involved. This method is sometimes known as Compensatory Acceleration Training (CAT) and can be useful in altering muscle tension or movement velocity to achieve a specific training goal (see Ch 7.1).

Although the role of CAT is well known during concentric movement (in which the load is being overcome), its vital role during eccentric movement (in which the load overcomes the propulsive force) is inadequately appreciated. In non-ballistic eccentric motion in which muscle contraction continues throughout the movement, the muscles try to oppose the effects of the gravity to slow down and ultimately halt the downward motion of the bar. In ballistic motion in which muscle action is intermittent, so-called antagonistic muscle action comes into play to slow down and halt the limb to ensure that the joint is not dislocated or soft tissues are ruptured.

Even during isometric action (in which there is no external limb movement), compensatory processes are at play if no movement is to occur, since neural activation changes due to fatigue, altered mental focus or other physiological processes. This means that the athlete has to maintain adequate muscle tension for the entire duration of the isometric action, either by means of involuntary conditioned reflex action or by voluntary intervention. Thus, it might be preferable for the acronym CAT to stand for 'Compensatory Action Training'.

Mass and Acceleration Issues

The implication for the well-known Principle of Progressive Overload is that 'overload' should refer not simply to the use of progressively greater resistance over a given period, but also to the progressive increase in muscle tension, which may be produced by involuntary or voluntary processes. This change in tension may be produced in ways which relate directly to Newton II and which pose a question which is of fundamental importance to all strength training. It is relevant to examine this issue before we go any further.

Since force $F = m.a$, we may apply it to produce the same magnitude of force F in several different ways:

    (a) $F = M.a$ where the mass M is large and the acceleration is small

    (b) $F = m.A$ where the mass is small and the acceleration A is large

    (c) $F = m.a$ where both mass and acceleration are moderate

To which might be added force production under isometric or isokinetic conditions where acceleration is zero:

    (d) $F = k.R$ where k is a factor of proportionality and R is the resistance applied by the apparatus.

This might immediately suggest, since the production of an adequate level of muscle tension is necessary for strength training, that all of these methods of 'Force Training' are entirely the same and that is just a matter of one's personal choice which method is used. So, the question is: "Does it make any real difference which method of strength training is used, as long as adequate muscle tension is produced?"

If one attempts to answer this question in purely mechanistic terms, one might be tempted to reply "no" and qualify one's reply with qualifying comments about initiating movement against heavy loads with high inertia, possible detrimental effects of sustained loads on the soft tissues of the body and duration of loading.

Interestingly, practical experience from three different competitive aspects of strength training, namely Olympic weightlifting, powerlifting and bodybuilding, offers some preliminary information. Option (a) with very heavy loads is most commonly encountered in powerlifting, while the hypertrophy associated with bodybuilding generally is a product of option (c) training with moderate loads performed for about 8-12 repetitions. Option (b) is characterised by many actions in track and field events. Olympic weightlifting, which involves lifting heavy loads rapidly, appears to contradict evidence that velocity decreases with load, but this is because weightlifting is ballistic and relies on the quick movement of the lifter under the bar. It may be concluded that powerlifting is essentially strength generating, while weightlifting is maximum power generating in nature.

Option (d) occurs only under laboratory conditions using special isokinetic devices to control the motion and correlation of results obtained under these and actual sporting conditions tends to be low, although it may produce significant increase in non-specific strength (Rosentzweig & Hinson, 1972; Osternig, 1986).

The practical evidence shows that the above ways of generating force do not produce the same results and research reveals that this is because different neural, muscular and metabolic processes are involved in each case. Thus, strength and power training are not simply a matter of using some generalised form of resistance training to produce adequate physical loading and muscle tension; the principle of specificity of training is central to the entire issue.

Muscle Tension and Training Stimulus

Some coaches maintain that maximal muscle hypertrophy depends on tension time, with continuous tension times of 30-60 seconds per set of any exercise being commonly recommended. The observation that the extended use of isometric exercises of this magnitude of duration does not produce the degree of hypertrophy associated with dynamic exercise (which includes eccentric action) militates against this simplistic claim. The fact that tension fluctuates from low to high values throughout a movement also militates against this idea. Clearly, both hypertrophy and strength increase depend on the existence of some minimum level of tension, but nobody has identified what this tension threshold should be in the case of hypertrophy. Moreover, it is well known that novices to resistance training respond to much lower intensities of loading both in terms of hypertrophy and strength gains.

Research has shown that the *threshold training stimulus* necessary for increasing muscular strength in the average person should not be less than one-third of the maximal strength (Hettinger & Müller, 1953). As strength increases, the intensity of the stimulus required to produce a training effect should be increased, and reach 80-95% of the athlete's maximum. It may be appropriate that the strength of the training stimulus sometimes equals or even exceeds the level of the competition stimulus of the given exercise (Verkhoshansky, 1977).

Thus, the development of strength requires that the stimulus intensity be gradually increased. It was discovered that every stimulus has a changing *strengthening threshold*, the achievement of which fails to elicit any further increase in muscular strength (Hettinger, 1961). The less trained the muscles, the further the strengthening threshold from the beginning state. The rate at which strength increases from the initial level to the strengthening threshold, expressed as a percentage of the current maximum strength, is independent of sex, age, muscle group and the level of the strengthening threshold. After the strengthening threshold has been reached, strength can be increased only by intensifying the training.

In this regard, according to Korobkov, Gerasimov and Vasiliev (Verkhoshansky, 1977), strength increases relatively uniformly during the initial stages of training, independent of how the load is applied in training, whether large or small. Approximately equivalent increases in strength are obtained with loads of 20, 40, 60 and 80 percent of 1RM (one repetition maximum). An increase in the intensity of training in the initial stages (e.g. using a heavier load, faster tempo of movement and shorter intervals between sessions) does not always enhance the effectiveness of strength development, this becoming effective only later, as strength increases. This principle is corroborated by the training results of weightlifters (Hettinger, 1961; Verkhoshansky, 1977).

Application of Basic Biomechanics

This brings us back to the interesting and vitally important question in strength training which was raised earlier, namely: *Should a heavy weight be lifted with a small acceleration or should a lighter load be lifted with a greater acceleration to produce strength most effectively?* Or, is it preferable to train isometrically to produce maximal strength gains? In all of these cases the force produced may be exactly the same, but the training effect may be entirely different. What training effect is imposed by the duration of muscle tension, especially since the factor of strength-endurance becomes increasingly important and maximal strength becomes less important as the duration of any contraction increases?

To answer these questions, it is necessary in later chapters to apply the fundamentals of biomechanics to strength training (Fig 1.11) and draw a curve of force versus time and examine how each force-time curve or appropriate portion of this curve best matches the required strength quality, such as static strength, speed-strength, strength-endurance or strength-speed. In other words, the force-time curve may serve as one of the vital starting points for understanding the entire phenomenon of sport-specific strength and for prescribing sport-specific strength training. This curve is used in later chapters to answer the questions posed above and to act as a framework for resolving many other important strength training issues.

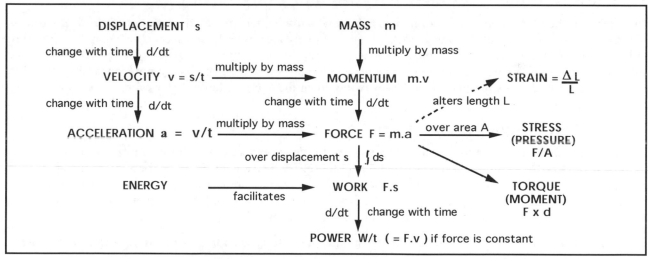

Figure 1.11 Summary of the major concepts used in sport biomechanics. Strain is the relative change in length, i.e. the change in length of a length of material L caused by a force F relative to its original length. d/dt refers to the first derivative with respect to time. ∫ ds refers to the integral with respect to displacement s.

As mentioned previously, other curves which also provide invaluable information for understanding and applying sport-specific strength training are the *force (torque) vs angular displacement* (for each joint), *force (torque) vs velocity, endurance vs force* and *endurance vs velocity* graphs. This information, together with a knowledge of which muscles are involved statically and dynamically in given complex movements, furnish the minimum requirements for drawing up an effective and safe strength training programme for any sport. It is a major intention of this text to provide the reader with a solid understanding of these and other essential processes which are central to exercise prescription for enhanced performance or rehabilitation after injury.

1.3 A Philosophy of Physical Training

The success of any training programme is closely linked to the philosophy of physical training in which it is embedded. Since this text draws heavily on Russian exercise science, it is enlightening to examine the overall education system in Russia which produced generations of the world's finest athletes in all sports. The excellence of their athletes in international competition is a direct result of carefully designed educational programmes aimed at employing sport, among other activities, to promote its national aims.   Russian sport, like any other class of education, follows the same general principles and stages. The Russians distinguish between physical education and sport, in that the latter involves specialisation, competition for improving performance, and the acquisition of maximum physical and mental drive.

Several authors (Yessis, 1987; Schneidman, 1979; Matveyev, 1981; Vorobyev, 1978)   give useful insights into the highly organised approach of the Russians, who recognise at least eight interrelated principles in scientific sports preparation:

1. The Principle of Awareness

This covers the ideology and the philosophy of Russian sport as well as the conscious awareness of all processes involved in acquiring sporting proficiency. The athlete is required to know himself and understand the physiological and psychological processes taking place in his body to enable him to control and evaluate objectively his sensations and his capacity for work.

2. The Principle of All-round Development

This entails building a solid physical and mental foundation on which to found other specialised sporting qualities. All-round development involves strength, speed, flexibility, endurance, good coordination, strong will-power, and exemplary moral and cultural development. Psychological preparation involves persuasion, explanation, example, encouragement, group influence, self-motivation and adaptation to stress.

3. The Principle of Consecutiveness (or Consistency)

This refers to the systematic overloading principle in which the intensity and the volume of physical work, as well as the degree of difficulty of motor skills, is progressively increased. In all aspects, including strength, skill and strategy, the athlete moves from the easy to the difficult, from the light to the heavy, from the known to the unknown. The same principle in reverse is advised so that physical workouts are not ended abruptly. The harmony of the body must be maintained by slowing down the exercise tempo after every workout and every competitive season.

4. The Principle of Repetition

This principle is based on Pavlov's three-stage theory for development of conditioned reflexes. Firstly, novel activities stimulate large areas of the brain and recruit muscles which are unnecessary for performing a particular movement. Next, consistent repetition diminishes spurious neuromuscular activity and enables one to concentrate predominantly on the task being learned. Finally, expertise is established and the movement becomes automatic. These are the same stages applied in teaching sporting skills, namely:

(a) *Development of knowledge* The athlete must understand fully what must be learned before attempting to master it

(b) *Development of motor ability* The athlete must acquire the ability to concentrate full attention on performance of the required physical manoeuvres

(c) *Development of automatic motor response* The athlete no longer needs to concentrate consciously on the movements to perform them efficiently. The learned skill has become an automatic, conditioned reflex.

Not only repetition of exercises, but also proper sequences of work and rest fatigue and recovery, injury and rehabilitation are vital in producing the proficient athlete.

5. The Principle of Visualisation

The athlete must be able to visualise the correct movements in order to master any sport. He must learn these patterns by observing demonstrations by his coach and other experts, studying films, slides and diagrams, and listening to clear descriptions of the kinesiology involved. This includes teaching complete movements and the same movements broken down into parts. Coaches and leading athletes are also expected to exhibit exemplary behaviour to enhance desirable learning by novices.

6. The Principle of Specialisation

Here two aspects of specialised training are recognised:

(a) Practice in the specific sport under conditions which are encountered in competition. Competition is regarded as important in the learning of specialisation, so coaches advise regular participation in selected competitions.

(b) Special exercises for perfecting motor skills, tactics and other aspects essential to performing efficiently in the sport.

Many Russian experts claim that successful performance at an early age does not necessarily ensure proficiency in adulthood. They consider that early specialisation is possible in sports such as gymnastics which emphasize coordination, agility, flexibility or speed, because of the pre-adolescent's particular ability in these respects. Strength and endurance sports are discouraged among youngsters. Research indicates that children should be admitted to sports schools according to the first column of Table 1.2, with higher levels of achievement being expected at the ages given in the last two columns.

The Russians recognise that there are individual exceptions, but they point out that the vast majority of their champions are adults. For instance, at recent Olympics the average age of Soviet participants has been about 24 years, with more than half of them between 24 and 30, and fewer than 10% under the age of 20 years.

Early specialisation at an intense level does not seem to produce an enduring athlete, hence the importance of applying the guidelines provided in Table 1.2. Few athletes match the long spans of success enjoyed by weightlifters Alexeev and Rigert or pole-vaulter Bubko. Between 1970-78 Alexeev won 22 gold medals at World championships and Olympics, while Rigert won 17. The phenomenal Bubko broke numerous world records.

Table 1.2 Ages for starting, specialising and reaching high performance in different sports (in years).

Sport	Begin the sport	Specialisation age	High performance
Basketball	7-8	10-12	20-25
Boxing	9-10	15-16	20-25
Cycling	9-10	16-17	21-24
Diving	5-6	8-10	18-22
Fencing	7-8	10-12	20-25
Figure skating	5-6	8-10	16-20
Gymnastics (women)	4-5	10-11	14-18
Gymnastics (men)	5-6	12-14	18-24
Rowing	12-14	16-18	22-24
Skiing	6-7	10-11	20-24
Soccer	5-6	11-13	18-24
Swimming	3-7	10-12	16-18
Tennis	6-8	12-14	22-25
Track-and-field	6-7	13-14	18-23
Volleyball	11-12	14-15	20-25
Weightlifting	10-11	17-18	21-28
Wrestling	10-11	15-16	24-28

7. The Principle of Individualisation

Training regimens which suit one athlete do not necessarily suit another, so Russian experts stress the importance of designing individual programmes to suit each athlete even in team sports. This entails good communication between coach and athlete, the application of scientific evaluation, the assistance of sports physicians and so on.

In all sports the Russians stress the supreme role played by the brain and central nervous system in general. They emphasize that physical fitness is determined first of all by functioning of the central nervous system. Unlike the hormonal, muscular and other slow control systems, the central nervous system exhibits a state which changes rapidly from instant to instant. Therefore, it is essential to structure training sessions and cycles carefully so as to maintain exercise intensity and nervous arousal at beneficial levels for a specific sport. Optimum stimulation levels are particularly important during pre-competition training. Russian experts assume that the highest level of preparedness for competition or the best sport condition over a given period will be reached if, together with a high level of all fitness components, the work capacity of the neuromuscular system rises in the last week before competition and if, at the time of competition, its sensitivity also increases considerably.

8. The Principle of Structured Training

All training comprises preparatory, competitive and transition stages of different duration, with various other sub-stages such as general preparation, special preparation, stabilisation, intensification and extensification. This same structure is followed at the level of the individual workout and the long-term programme. The long-term systematic training process is known as periodisation, which consists of cyclically planned microcycles, mesocycles and macrocycles that exploit the natural rhythms of adaptation, restoration and growth of the human body to enhance performance (see 1.15, 5.5 and Ch 6). Within the overall educational structure, the practice session is regarded as the basic developmental unit for every sport, a typical training session consisting of three major parts:

1. ***The initial phase*** which in turn usually comprises two subsections:

    1.1 *Introductory part* (5 minutes) during which the group is organised, is given an explanation of the session's objectives and participates in general educational drills

    1.2 *Preparatory part* (15-25 minutes) during which physical and mental preparation occurs in two stages:

    (a) general warm-up for overall preparation of the body for physical work

    (b) specific warm-up to help adapt one to the technical skills of the sport

2. ***The main phase*** (60-90 minutes) which comprises a carefully sequenced set of exercises to increase general and specific physical fitness, to teach technical and tactical skills and to impart the ability to work independently. If several types of training are to be offered in one session, the generally recommended sequence of training components is given in Figure 1.12 below (e.g Ozolin, 1971).

$$\downarrow \begin{array}{c} \text{PERFECTION OF TECHNICAL AND TACTICAL SKILLS} \\ \text{SPEED AND AGILITY TRAINING} \\ \text{STRENGTH TRAINING} \\ \text{ENDURANCE TRAINING} \end{array} \downarrow$$

Figure 1.12 Recommended training sequence in any given exercise session.

Later, however, it will be seen that low repetition strength training sometimes may precede speed or speed-strength training, because the after-effect of heavy loading can enhance speed development.

3. ***The concluding phase*** (5 minutes) during which the athlete's body is generally destressed to return to its initial condition so as to enhance recovery, growth and retention of motor skills.

The daily training may be broken down into two or more shorter separate sessions, each with a different emphasis and separated by restorative intervals to optimise the adaptation process.

Despite the fact that Russian sports training is a carefully planned operation in which the coach is blamed as much as the athlete if the expected results are not achieved, the system still receives criticism. For instance, Dembo stated in 1974 that the sports physicians (and there were over 3900 of them then) were not sufficiently utilised. He stated that "this is substantiated by the fact that the number of athletes with pathological conditions and illness has increased in the last few years" (Schneidman, 1979). With the reduced expenditure on sport necessitated by the changes taking place in Russia, this problem is deteriorating and many sports experts are seeking employment in the West.

Recognising the limitations of coaches and physical educationalists, the Russians recommended that 'responsibility for guiding the training process be placed not on one coach, but on a Coaching Council. It is necessary to attach to each coaching council, along with other committees, a committee for the implementation of scholarly findings into the practice of sport training. It is advisable to include in this committee, besides educators, specialists in physiology, biomechanics, medicine, biochemistry, psychology, and mathematics, who would be able to solve problems of sport training on a high-quality level' (Schneidman, 1979).

1.4 Specificity in Training

The main reason why the prescription of resistance training for enhancing sports performance is not at all straightforward is that strength training displays definite specificity in many respects. This is the reason why the term 'sport specific strength training' is emphasized in this book: all forms of strength training are different and produce significantly different effects on neuromuscular performance.

Fitness training for a given sport is not simply a matter of selecting a few popular exercises from a bodybuilding magazine or prescribing heavy squats, power cleans, leg curls, bench press, circuit training, isokinetic leg extensions or 'cross training'. This approach may produce aesthetic results for the average non-competitive client of a health centre, but it is of very limited value to the serious athlete. It is not only the exercise which modifies the body, or, more specifically, the neuromuscular system, but the way in which the exercise is performed. In this regard, it is vital to remember that all exercise involves information processing in the central nervous and neuromuscular systems, so that all training should be regarded as a way in which the body's extremely complex computing systems are programmed and applied in the solution of all motor tasks (among its many other roles).

For many years, there have been two opposing theories of supplementary strength training in sport. One theory proposes that strength training should simulate the sporting movements as closely as possible with regard to movement pattern, velocity, force-time curve, type of muscle contraction and so forth, whereas the other maintains that it is sufficient to train the relevant muscles with no regard to specificity. Separate practice of technical skills would then permit one to utilise in sporting movements the strength gained in non-specific training. While both approaches to strength training will improve performance, current scientific research strongly supports the superiority of the specificity principle in at least ten respects:

- Type of Muscle Contraction
- Movement Pattern
- Region of Movement
- Velocity of Movement
- Force of Contraction
- Muscle Fibre Recruitment
- Metabolism
- Biochemical Adaptation
- Flexibility
- Fatigue

In the context of training, *specificity should not be confused with simulation*. Specificity training means exercising to improve in a highly specific way the expression of all the above factors in a given sport. While simulation of a sporting movement with small added resistance over the full range of movement or with larger resistance over a restricted part of the movement range may be appropriate at certain stages of training, simulation of any movement with significant resistance is inadvisable since it can confuse the neuromuscular programmes which determine the specificity of the above factors.

Even if one is careful to apply simulation training by using implements or loads that are similar to those encountered in the sport, *there will usually be changes in the centre of gravity, moments of inertia, centre of rotation, centre of percussion and mechanical stiffness of the system which alter the neuromuscular skills required in the sport..* Features of the different specificity factors are discussed briefly below.

Specificity of Type of Muscle Contraction

Increases in voluntary strength are largely specific to the type of muscle contraction used in training. For example, the concentric-eccentric training of weightlifting increases competitive strength considerably, but produces only a small gain in isometric strength (Dons et al, 1979; Thorstensson et al, 1976) or concentric isokinetic strength (Fahey & Brown, 1973). Concentric isokinetic exercise increases isokinetic strength and power without a noticeable increase in isometric strength (Kanehisa & Miyashita, 1983a). Conversely, isometric training markedly increases isometric strength, but not concentric isokinetic strength (Lindh, 1979). Elbow extension training with weights increases triceps strength and arm girth, but isokinetic testing of the same muscles reveals no significant change (Sale & MacDougall, 1977).

It has also been found that isometric and rapid weight lifting exercises elicit different effects on evoked isometric tetanic and muscle twitch contractile properties, as well as on evoked maximal velocity of muscle shortening (Duchateau & Hainaut, 1984). Moreover, static and dynamic training cause different structural changes in the muscle (see 1.13). *Static training* produces the following changes: the sarcoplasmic content of many muscle fibres increases, myofibrils collect into fascicles, nuclei become rounder, motor end-plates expand transversally relative to the muscle fibres, capillaries meander more markedly, and the layers of endomysium and perimysium thicken. In the case of *dynamic training*, the transverse striations of the myofibrils become very pronounced, the nuclei become oval and fusiform (spindle-shaped), motor end-plates extend the length of the muscle fibres, and the layers of endomysium and perimysium become thinner (Bondarchuk et al, 1984).

Specificity of Movement Pattern

Differences in movement pattern produce significantly different results, although the muscle groups involved may be virtually the same. For instance, training with elbow flexion in the standing position increases dynamic strength considerably in this position, but only slightly in a supine position. Training with barbell squats for 8 weeks increased 1 RM squatting strength markedly, but caused a much smaller improvement in seated isometric leg press (Thorstensson et al, 1976).

Sale and MacDougall (1981) concluded that *increased performance is primarily a result of improved neuromuscular skill* and that *increased strength is apparent only when measured during the same type of movement used in training*. They also stressed that *specificity of movement seems to apply with equal validity to simple and complex skills*.

Differences have also been measured between the effects of bilateral (e.g. with a barbell) and unilateral (e.g. with dumbbells) training. The force produced with bilateral contractions usually is less than the sum of the forces produced individually by the left and right limbs (Coyle et al, 1981, Vandervoort et al, 1984), a phenomenon known as the *bilateral deficit*. The reduced force recorded in the bilateral case was accompanied by a reduced integrated EMG, suggesting that the prime movers were less activated (Vandervoort et al, 1984). This bilateral deficit is insignificant among athletes such as weightlifters who always use their limbs simultaneously in their sport. It is recommended that athletes in sports involving bilateral action of the same muscle groups should train bilaterally to minimise occurrence of the bilateral deficit (Secher, 1975).

Research indicates that the individual muscle responses depends on the direction, magnitude, and combination of external moments, as well as on the flexion angle of the knee joint (Andriacchi et al, 1984). Muscle response seems to be influenced by certain intrinsic mechanical characteristics of the knee joint that tend to change the moment arms of the muscles as the knee moves. For example, the substantial changes in quadriceps EMG activity with knee flexion with constant load, can be related to the movement of the tibial-femoral contact changing the lever arm length of the quadriceps mechanism. This indicates that the mechanics of the knee joint must be considered in attempting to interpret or predict the load response of muscles crossing the knee joint.

If contraction of the agonists is preceded immediately by a maximal contraction of the antagonists, the force and EMG produced by the agonists is increased, a phenomenon called pre-tension by bodybuilders and *reciprocal innervation* (inhibition) by physiotherapists and regularly used in PNF conditioning (see Ch 7). This pre-contraction of antagonists apparently diminishes inhibitory activity and facilitates more powerful agonist action in the subsequent contraction. The increases in low velocity concentric isokinetic strength that have been observed in the absence of muscle hypertrophy have been attributed by some researchers to neural adaptation that modifies inhibitory activity (Caiozzo et al, 1981). Strength training programmes utilising the pre-tensing technique are more effective for developing low velocity strength than those relying solely on contraction of the prime movers (Caiozzo et al, 1982).

Specificity of Region and Range of Movement

Isometric exercise increases voluntary strength maximally close to the joint angle at which training takes place, with the increase being significantly less at other joint angles (Lindh, 1979; Raitsin, 1974). The merits of training isometrically at different joint angles or quasi-isometrically over an extended range then become obvious. Other studies of dynamic and ballistic activity also reveal that there is a specific accentuated region of force production that affects the way in which strength is acquired in any movement (see 2.1.2, 4.3.2).

Research has shown that there are systematic differences between moment-length properties of the rectus femoris muscle of cyclists/speed skaters and runners (Herzog et al, 1991). In cycling and speed skating, rectus femoris is used at a shorter length than in running because of the pronounced flexion at the hip joint, this being one reason why Russian coaches caution against the regular use of any forms of cycling for any sports other than cycling. Cyclists tend to be stronger at short compared with long rectus femoris lengths, whereas the opposite is true for runners. This finding may be associated with an adaptation of the rectus femoris muscle to the requirements of cycling and running or may show an inherited difference in the muscles of the athletes that existed before they became involved in their respective sport.

Specificity of Velocity of Movement

One of the earliest observations of specificity of velocity in strength training was made by Moffroid & Whipple (1970). They found that low velocity isokinetic training distinctly enhances low velocity strength, but has minimal effect on high velocity strength. Although high velocity isokinetic training similarly improves high velocity strength, it offers a better transfer effect to low velocity strength than low velocity training does to high velocity strength (Moffroid & Whipple, 1970; Perrine & Edgerton, 1981; Kanehisa & Miyashita, 1983b).

Since the force-velocity curve for muscle contraction reveals that force decreases with velocity of concentric contraction, high velocity training may not produce a large enough force to stimulate maximal adaptation in the muscle. The special advantage of high velocity concentric training is that it conditions the nervous system, whereas lower velocity training is better suited to development of muscle hypertrophy and slow speed strength.

The force-velocity curve for eccentric contraction, however, shows that eccentric force increases with increasing velocity, thereby suggesting that high speed eccentric training (e.g. as encountered during the amortisation phase of plyometrics) may be very effective for stimulating muscular adaptation. At the same time, this benefit of eccentric training may be diminished by the increased risk of injury associated with the much greater forces of eccentric activity.

Specificity of Force of Contraction

The force of muscle contraction is a function of the load. If this load is insufficient, increase in strength will be insignificant, the effects of other intensities of load being given in Section 1.1. It is well known that it is possible to do high repetitions with light weights and very few repetitions with near maximal loads, the former method commonly being used for 'muscle definition' or muscle endurance training and the latter for hypertrophy or strength development (see Figs 1.13 & 1.14).

In fact, one can sometimes use the number of repetitions, rather than the magnitude of the load, as the primary indicator of what type of training effect will occur. We thus speak of at least 25 RM for muscle endurance, 8-12 RM for muscle hypertrophy, and 1-3 RM for maximal strength or power training (see Table 1.1). In other words, the magnitude of the load, and hence, the resulting number of repetitions, have a very specific effect on physical conditioning, a fact which has been known to bodybuilders and weightlifters for many years.

A fourth order polynomial function of the following form offers a very accurate fit to the experimental data:

Repetitions $$r = a_0 + a_1.p + a_2.p^2 + a_3.p^3 + a_4.p^4$$

where p is the percentage of 1RM and the constants are:

$a_0 = 173.5249$, $a_1 = -6.310$, $a_2 = 9.5759 \times 10^{-2}$, $a_3 = -6.742 \times 10^{-4}$ and $a_4 = 1.74962 \times 10^{-6}$ (Correlation coefficient $R = 0.9997$).

The preceding equation may be programmed into a computer to determine one's 1RM, the number of repetitions expected for a given load, or the load expected for a given number of repetitions. For those who do not wish to resort to mathematical calculations on a computer, Figure 1.14 is simply an enlarged view of the classical strength training zone with loads exceeding 60% of one's 1RM and has been given to enable anyone to read values directly off the graph.

In applying such equations, it should be noted that relatively small loads (about 40% 1RM) may produce significant strengthening in a beginner to resistance training, but considerably larger loads (over 85% 1RM) are usually necessary to enhance the strength of an advanced athlete, as discussed later (e.g. Ch 5). Moreover, a given percentage of 1RM will correspond to a different number of repetitions to failure with different lifts and for athletes with different training backgrounds, so it is vital to establish *individual responses* to loading.

It is also essential to note that this sort of prediction depends on the type of exercise, because it is well known that, because of different relative proportions of muscle fibre types, specific nervous processes and intrinsic local muscle mechanisms, every muscle group exhibits different strength, power and endurance performance. Being able to squat 5 repetitions with 95% of one's 1RM, does not necessarily mean that one can do the same number of repetitions in the bench press or standing press with the same load.

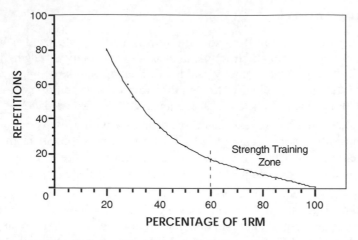

Figure 1.13 The relationship between repetitions and load in terms of 1 repetition maximum. The graph for the strength training zone is enlarged in Figure 1.9 to enable the reader to visually interrelate repetitions and load more easily.

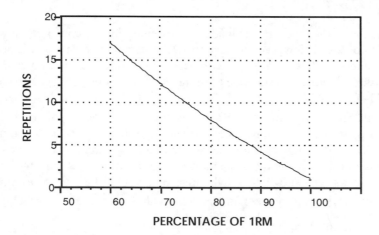

Figure 1.14 Relationship between repetitions and load for the strength training zone (> 60% 1RM)

Specificity of Muscle Fibre Recruitment

Skeletal muscle consists of different types of slow and fast twitch fibres (see 1.12). The intensity, duration and pattern of loading imposed on the muscle determines the proportion of involvement by the different fibre types and the degree to which each is conditioned by a given regime of training (see 1.12 and especially Figs 1.26-1.28). Moreover, the slow and fast twitch fibres have different viscoelastic properties and cross-bridge lifetimes, so that they make different use of the stretch-shortening cycle (see 1.7.2).

Metabolic Specificity

The metabolism of the body copes differently with the main types of physical activity: short-term maximal strength efforts, intermediate muscular endurance activity, and long-term cardiovascular endurance effort (see 1.14). Metabolism is very specific to the intensity and duration of the sporting event, to the extent that excessive development of one type of fitness may have a profoundly detrimental effect on another type of fitness. For instance, regular, in-season 'aerobic' training can significantly decrease the strength and power of weightlifters and track-and-field athletes. It is vital to understand the metabolic specificity of each sport if any training programme is to be effective and safe (see Tables 1.3 & 1.4).

Specificity of Biochemical Adaptation

Metabolic specificity, although entirely biochemical in nature, must be distinguished from adaptation that takes place biochemically in the muscles of the body (Platonov, 1988). These biochemical changes induced by training depend on the characteristics of the loads, such as their intensity, duration and load-bearing (static) components.

Endurance training involving prolonged exercise causes significant changes in the glycogen level of the skeletal muscles and in the level and activity of many mitochondrial enzymes that provide oxidative resynthesis of ATP. Here the size and number of the mitochondria increase. The ratio of the different enzymes and the enzymatic activity in the mitochondria also changes because the various enzymes do not all change to the same extent.

The potential of key enzymes in the skeletal muscles rises: the level and catalytic properties of cAMP-dependent protein-kinases increase, the resistance of cAMP metabolism to physical loading increases. In addition, the biochemical adaptation of the muscles to endurance exercises does not affect the level of myosin and its ATP-ase activity and only insignificantly raises creatine phosphokinase activity, CP levels and the intensity of glycolysis. Training causes the activity of the ATP-ase actomyosin enzyme in cardiac muscle and the contractility of the myocardium to increase concomitantly. Under the influence of general endurance training, cardiac muscle hypertrophy occurs, while a training programme aimed at increasing endurance in the skeletal muscles does not cause them to hypertrophy.

Training with *speed loads* of maximal or near-maximal intensity significantly increases the activity of glycolytic enzymes (especially phosphorylase, pyruvate phosphokinase, lactate dehydrogenase, and hexokinase), in the creatine phosphate level, and in the activity of creatine kinase and myokinase. The glycogen level, respiratory intensity, dehydrogenase activity, and the levels of myosin, myostromins, and myosin ATP-ase show smaller increases.

During training with *static strength loads*, the level of myosin and myostromins, the cross-section of muscle fibres, and the activity of myosin ATP-ase and aspartate-amino-transferase in the skeletal muscles increase very significantly. The intensity of glycolysis and respiration, dehydrogenase activity, and the levels of CP and glycogen increase less than during training with speed loads and prolonged loads of moderate intensity.

The biochemical changes depend on the type of muscle fibres and the training regime. For example, activity of the enzyme dehydrogenase b-hydroxybutyrate increases several fold in ST fibres but not at all in the FT fibres during training with prolonged endurance loads. Thus, the biochemical changes that occur in the body under the influence of training are specific and depend on the type of training. Among the different forms of skeletal muscle adaptation, it is customary to single out three basic ones in which specific biochemical changes predominate:

- increased oxidative resynthesis of ATP - for endurance work with prolonged loading
- increased non-oxidative resynthesis of ATP - for work with speed loads
- development of muscular hypertrophy - for strength work.

Specificity of Flexibility

Flexibility is a measure of the maximum range of movement of which a joint is capable. It is most commonly measured in the physical education setting by means of the seated reach-and- touch the toes test, but this measure is of little value since each joint is capable of moving in several different directions and planes. Moreover, a high degree of flexibility in one joint does not necessarily imply comparable flexibility elsewhere. Flexibility is joint specific, pattern specific and specific with respect to the type of loading. There are several different types of flexibility, including static active, static passive, ballistic and active flexibility, each of which is developed by different types of training (see 3.5.8). Training programmes must be carefully designed to maintain or enhance the specific type of flexibility required by every joint of an athlete participating in a given sport.

Specificity of Fatigue

Different types of work produce specific fatigue effects, especially during short-term exercise (see 1.1.2). Some muscle groups fatigue more rapidly than others, the different types of muscle fibre fatigue at different rates, fatigue produced by maximal effort is different from the fatigue produced by low intensity endurance activities, nervous and metabolic fatigue are two distinct phenomena, fatigue associated with muscular action is different from the fatigue associated with ligamentous support, mental fatigue produced by maximal effort and concentration on fine motor skills is largely different and the fatigue pattern produced by one movement pattern differs significantly from that produced by another movement pattern using the same joints and muscles.

The recovery rate from fatigue after different exercise regimes or using different muscle groups is also very different (e.g. see Fig 1.6). In fact, it may be stated that *the effectiveness of any training programme and the type of fitness produced depends on the specificity of fatigue as an after-effect of training*. After all, adaptation is the response of the body to cope with repeated exposure to given stressors and the fatigue induced by those stressors. Failure to adapt to fatigue in the long-term results in stagnation, deterioration or injury. It is especially important to understand the superimposition of fatigue and other after-effects of exercise, since repetition of similar exercise regimes of similar type, volume and intensity can severely exhaust the athlete, whereas variation of training and the use of programmes with different primary emphasis (see Ch 6) can facilitate recovery and enhance sport specific fitness.

Other Types of Specificity

There are possibly other forms of specificity, as well as specificities that are combinations of the above-mentioned forms. One of the more interesting observations concerns the differences between weightlifters, powerlifters and bodybuilders, all of whom train with weights in ways which may appear quite similar to the average instructor. Finnish researchers at the University of Jyväskylä examined the characteristics of these three types of strength athlete using maximum squats, squat jumps, vertical jumps and dynamometers as part of the test battery (Häkinnen et al, 1984) and found that weightlifters possessed greater values for isometric and auxotonic ('dynamic') strength per bodymass than the other two groups, as well as the highest rate of force production and greatest utilisation of stored elastic energy.

Apparently weightlifting training produces superior neuromuscular capabilities for recruiting motor units maximally. This finding has profound implications for personal trainers who may prescribe squats, deadlifts, pressing exercises and power cleans without appreciating that the manner of execution of such movements can have a profound effect on the type of strength produced in their athletes.

1.5 Strength and Fitness

Fitness is commonly regarded by the average person as synonymous with the ability to carry out endurance activities such as distance running efficiently and with minimal exhaustion. What is being referred to here is cardiovascular endurance, one of the many different types or components of fitness. Fitness actually comprises many different qualities such as cardiovascular endurance, strength, flexibility, local muscle endurance and speed. Thus, one may speak of cardiovascular fitness, strength fitness, speed fitness and so on. This type of distinction, however, disguises the fact that each fitness quality contributes to a greater or lesser extent in determining the specific type of fitness required for a given activity. For instance, a distance runner who has inadequate strength of his postural or stabilising muscles will be a less competent athlete who is more prone to premature exhaustion or injury, no matter how efficient his cardiovascular or respiratory systems may be.

It is important to note that the training programmes given in popular bodybuilding magazines and weight training manuals focus almost entirely on developing the prime movers (or phasic) muscles involved in a given exercise, but make little mention of the vital role played by the stabilising (or tonic) muscles acting during the same exercise. Since all motor actions involve a continual interplay between stability and mobility, these simplistic training programmes may be seen to be of limited value in serious sports training.

Fitness, Preparedness and Work Capacity

The ability of an athlete to perform efficiently and safely in a given sport may be described in terms of three related factors:

- Work Capacity
- Fitness
- Preparedness

Work capacity refers to the general ability of the body as a machine to produce work of different intensity and duration using the appropriate energy systems of the body. *Fitness* refers to the specific ability to use this work capacity to execute a given task under particular conditions. In general terms, *fitness may be defined as the ability to cope with the demands of a specific task efficiently and safely* (see 1.13). *Preparedness*, unlike fitness, is not stable, but varies with time. It comprises two components, one which is slow-changing and the other which is fast changing (Zatsiorsky, 1995), where the slow component is *fitness* and the fast component is exercise-induced *fatigue*.

Although the concept of fitness would seem to be intuitively obvious and well-accepted, one should note this distinction between *fitness* and *preparedness*. The term *physical fitness* refers to the functional state of the slow-changing physiological components relating to motor activity. One's fitness state does not vary significantly over any period up to as much as several days in length, but one's *ability to express fitness at any instant* may be substantially affected positively or negatively by mental state, sickness, fatigue, sleepiness and other fairly transient factors. This ability, or *instantaneous preparedness*, is defined at any given instant and varies from moment to moment.

Base preparedness or simply, *preparedness*, is the resultant of the interaction of the body's long-term fitness increase stimulated by training and the opposing short-term fatigue after-effects of training, excluding the effects of any other modifying factors such as exaggerated mental state or illness. The concepts of fitness and preparedness are discussed in more detail later in this chapter (1.16.3).

Training or conditioning is the process whereby body and mind are prepared to reach a certain level of work capacity and fitness. This involves five interdependent processes which determine **The Sports Preparation Process,** namely:

1. Physical preparation
2. Learning of motor skills
3. Psychological preparation
4. Physical and psychological restoration
5. Appropriate nutrition

Classically, the first process comprises a general phase (General Physical Preparation: GPP) and a specific phase (Specific Physical Preparation: SPP), with various transition or sub-phases (e.g. stabilisation, intensification, recuperation, conversion or competitive phases) within, between or after each of these phases. This book concentrates on the general and specific phases of preparation with special reference to all types of strength-related fitness (such as speed-strength, strength-endurance and strength-flexibility, as discussed later in detail).

Information on motor skills training for different sports and nutrition are covered in numerous specialist texts, while restoration, as applied by Russian experts for many years, is discussed in depth elsewhere (Siff & Yessis, 1992).

1.6 The Nature of Strength

The design of a successful strength training programme depends on a thorough understanding of the factors which influence the development of strength. The next task is to determine which of these factors can be modified by physical training and which methods do so most effectively and safely. Some of these factors are structural and others, functional. Structural factors, however, only provide the potential for producing strength, since strength is a neuromuscular phenomenon which exploits this potential to generate motor activity.

It is well known that strength is proportional to the cross-sectional area of a muscle, so that larger muscles have the potential to develop greater strength than smaller muscles. However, the fact that Olympic weightlifters can increase their strength from year to year while remaining at the same bodymass reveals that strength depends on other factors as well.

The most obvious observation is that a muscle will produce greater strength if large numbers of its fibres contract simultaneously, an event which depends on how efficiently the nerve fibres send impulses to the muscle fibres. Moreover, less strength will be developed in a movement in which the different muscles are not coordinating their efforts. It is also important to note research by Vredensky which has shown that *maximum strength is produced for an optimum, not a maximum, frequency of nerve firing* (Vorobyev, 1978). Furthermore, this optimal frequency changes with level of muscle fatigue (Kernell & Monster, 1982).

Determinants of Strength

In general, the production of strength depends on the following major factors:

Structural Factors

- The cross-sectional area of the muscle

- The density of muscle fibres per unit cross-sectional area
- The efficiency of mechanical leverage across the joint

Functional Factors

- The number of muscle fibres contracting simultaneously
- The rate of contraction of muscle fibres
- The efficiency of synchronisation of firing of the muscle fibres
- The conduction velocity in the nerve fibres
- The degree of inhibition of muscle fibres which do not contribute to the movement
- The proportion of large diameter muscle fibres active
- The efficiency of cooperation between different types of muscle fibre
- The efficiency of the various stretch reflexes in controlling muscle tension
- The excitation threshold of the nerve fibres supplying the muscles
- The initial length of the muscles before contraction

With reference to the concept of synchronising action among muscle fibres and groups, it is important to point out that synchronisation does not appear to play a major role in increasing the rate of strength production (Miller et al, 1981). Efficiency of *sequentiality* rather than *simultaneity* may be more important in generating and sustaining muscular force, especially if stored elastic energy has to be contributed at the most opportune moments into the movement process. Certainly, more research has to be conducted before a definite answer can be given to the question of strength increase with increased synchronisation of motor unit discharge.

Shock Training and Plyometrics

Although not mentioned in the preceding list, the connective tissues also play a vital structural role in the strength process, since they provide stability for the muscles, joints and bones, as well as the ability to store elastic energy for augmenting the working effect of muscle.

The ability to stretch the connective and elastic tissues increases the efficiency of human movement very markedly, especially as numerous sporting activities involve stretch-shortening of the muscle complex, such as running, jumping, throwing and rapid lifting.

In fact, the method now known as *plyometric training* and developed as a special speed-strength training method by Verkhoshansky relies entirely on this phenomenon (discussed in later chapters). In this process, the increase in concentric strength in response to rapid 'shock' loading is a result of increased muscle tension elicited by the powerful myotatic *stretch reflex* and the explosive release of elastic energy stored in the connective and elastic tissues of the muscle complex during eccentric muscle contraction.

It must be pointed out that the term *plyometric* has been applied more recently to what was originally called the *shock method* (udarniye metod) in Russia. Historically, it was apparently coined to mean *eccentric contraction*. In this scheme of nomenclature, *isometric* retained its original meaning of muscle contraction under static conditions, *miometric* ('muscle shortening action') was synonymous with concentric contraction, and *pliometric* (sic) referred to eccentric (muscle lengthening) contraction.

Recently, varieties of jumping drills have been introduced to Western aerobics classes (e.g. in the form of 'step aerobics') and athletics training as 'plyometrics'. Invariably, the exercises referred to as being plyometric in these contexts are fairly conventional jumps which do not produce the characteristics of true 'shock' training. Russian scientists prefer to retain the term 'shock method' when referring to general explosive rebound methods and 'depth jumps' for lower limb rebound methods. If confusion with electric shock is to be avoided, then it might be preferable to refer to explosive reactive methods as *impulsive training*. However, the persuasive appeal of popular usage will no doubt ensure that the term *plyometrics* is retained in preference to any other word, no matter how inappropriate. For instance, despite the inaccuracy of the term *aerobics* in describing exercise to music and *cross training* to describe supplementary sports training, the commercial market has decreed that these popular terms should be the definitive words to use.

All that the scientist can do is to accept the situation, but to redefine such words to the highest level of accuracy. Thus, the term *plyometrics* (as opposed to *pliometric* contraction) should be used to refer to methods in which an eccentric muscle contraction is suddenly terminated in an explosive isometric contraction, thereby producing a powerful myotatic reflex, a sharp extension of the passive components of the muscle complex and a subsequent explosive concentric contraction. Although associated with jumping, it should not refer to ordinary jumping in which there may be a significant delay and dissipation of elastic energy during a longer isometric phase between the eccentric and concentric contractions (see 5.2).

To prevent any confusion between the historical and popular usage of the words *pliometrics* and *plyometrics*, it would be preferable to apply the term *powermetrics* to that entire collection of jumping, 'shock method', rebound drills and all other methods formely casually named plyometric training (Siff, 1998).

Strength and Connective Tissue

Besides its role in ballistic and rapid movements, connective tissue can also increase the overall bulk of the muscle complex and aid it in producing usable strength. Recently, it has been found that increases in the quality (or type) and quantity of connective tissue may improve the transmission of force from individual muscle fibres to the skeletal system.

For example, an insufficiently strong or extensive sheath of connective tissue will allow the muscle to dissipate some of its force in a direction which is perpendicular to its line of action and thereby lower its efficiency in overcoming a load.

The connective tissues which are not structurally linked to the muscles, such as those in the ligaments, joint capsules, skin and cartilages play the vital role of passively stabilising the joints, facilitating contact between moving parts and absorbing shock. The importance of this passive role should not be forgotten in overall training, since it is pointless to develop bulk and strength if the remainder of the musculoskeletal system is not equipped to handle the increased strength. One must condition muscle, bone and connective tissue if overall performance and safety is to be enhanced.

Overemphasis on muscle strengthening at the expense of tendon and other connective tissue strengthening can produce a muscle complex which is prone to injury and inefficient in generating reactive strength. This is one reason why anabolic steroids are regarded as harmful: apparently they tend to hypertrophy and increase the strength of muscles relative to tendons, so that musculotendinous injuries are more common among steroid users.

Moreover, muscle tissue adapts to increased loading within several days, whereas the connective tissues (such as tendons, ligaments and joint capsules) or systems which contain a high proportion of connective tissue (such as bone and cartilage) only display significant adaptation and hypertrophy after several weeks or months of progressive loading (McDonagh & Davies, 1984). *It is vital that the prescription of training takes into account the different rates of adaptation of all the systems involved* and avoids overtraining the systems with the slowest rates of adaptation. Gradual increase in training load and avoidance of impulsive or explosive methods is essential for minimising the occurrence of connective tissue soreness and injury, particularly during the general physical preparation phase (GPP) and by relative novices to strength training.

It is important to note that most of the above factors underlying strength production are functional rather than structural. Those determined by efficiency of the nervous system are of fundamental concern to the development of strength, since the muscular 'motors' are operated by synchronised electrical impulses supplied to the muscles by the nerves. Current preoccupation with the use of anabolic steroids to produce physical bulk thus may be seen to be misplaced, unless bodybuilding bulk is the sole objective. The development of specialised training regimes to enhance nervous system conditioning would be scientifically and morally more advisable, particularly in view of the side effects of drugs and the ethics of their use.

1.7 The Muscle Complex

Muscle consists of an active contractile and a passive non-contractile component. The former consists of a system of interdigitating fibres whose purpose is to move relative to one another and produce overall contraction. The latter comprises a set of different types of connective tissues such as tendons, ligaments and sheaths around the muscle fibres. These provide a structural framework for the muscles and a network of connections between many parts of the musculoskeletal system, which both stabilises and transmits forces throughout the body. Functionally, they perform the very important role of absorbing and releasing elastic energy to enhance the efficiency of muscular action.

1.7.1 The Structure of Muscle

Skeletal muscle comprises many hundreds or thousands of small fibres, each enclosed at successive levels of size by a sheath of connective tissue and supplied by nerve fibres and a rich blood supply. Each individual muscle fibre is surrounded by a sheath called the *endomysium*. Several of these fibres are grouped together to form bundles called fasciculi or *fascicles* encased in their own sheath or *perimysium*.. Groups of these fascicles form the entire muscle, which is enclosed in a strong sheath called the *epimysium* or *fascia* (Fig 1.15).

At a more microscopic level, each muscle fibre cell contains several hundred to several thousand parallel rod-like *myofibrils* ('myo-' means muscle), each of which, in turn, comprises a chain of basic contractile units known as *sarcomeres*. The sarcomeres are composed of an intermeshing complex of about 1500 thick and 3000 thin filaments, the thick filaments consisting of *myosin* and the thin filaments of *actin*. There are small projections from the surface of the myosin filaments called *cross-bridges*. It is their temporary attachment to specific sites on the actin filaments which forms the basis for muscle contraction.

The myofibrils appear striated when examined optically or stained by dyes. Some zones rotate the plane of light polarisation weakly and hence are called isotropic or *I-bands*. Other zones, alternating with these light bands, produce strong polarisation of light, thereby indicating a highly ordered substructure composed of what are referred to as anisotropic or *A-bands*. Each of these bands are interrupted in its midsection by a lighter stripe or *H-band* (from the German 'helle' or bright), which is visible only in relaxed muscle. Each H-band is bisected by an *M-band* which interconnects adjacent myosin filaments.

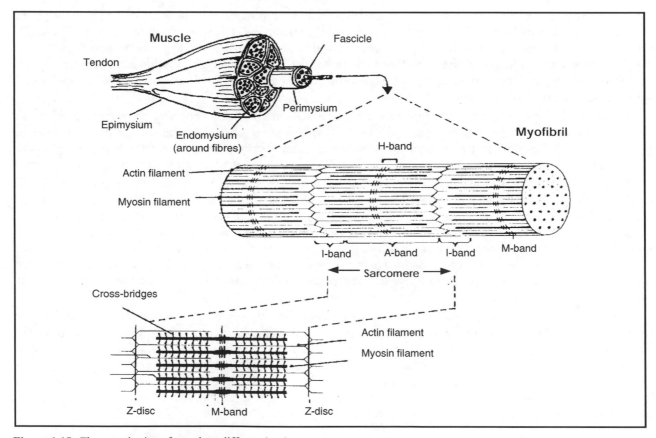

Figure 1.15 The organisation of muscle at different levels

The I-bands are intersected transversely by discs that hold the ends of the thin filaments together, the so-called *Z-discs* or membranes (from the German 'zwischenscheibe' or intermediate discs). We can now define a sarcomere to be that portion of a myofibril which lies between two successive Z-discs. Its length in a fully relaxed muscle is about 2.2 microns (1 micron = 1 millionth of a metre). Besides transverse connections being made by M-bands between myosin filaments, the connective tissue called *desmin* interconnects sarcomeres between adjacent myofibrils. Desmin is a protein located mainly in the Z discs which connect adjacent Z disks and Z disks at the edge of the fiber to the costamere in the surface membrane. Thus it contributes to the alignment of Z disks across a fiber and will also transmit lateral tension. For example, if some sarcomeres in a myofibril were damaged, longitudinal transmission of tension could still occur by lateral transmission to intact neighbouring myofibrils. In addition, elastic filaments comprising the very large-molecular weight protein *titin* interconnects the Z-discs to the myosin filaments via the M-bands. It is responsible for much of the resting tension in highly stretched fibers and plays an important role in locating the thick filaments in the center of the sarcomere. These non-contractile proteins are some of the tissues which comprise the series and parallel elastic elements (SEC and PEC), as well as the damping and sliding elements, referred to in the muscle model presented in the next section.

During contraction, the I and H-bands narrow, while the A-bands remain unchanged. This implies that, when a muscle contracts, the thin filaments are pulled between the thick filaments, thereby increasing the degree of overlap between filaments and shortening the sarcomeres. This finding led to the sliding filament theory of muscle contraction.

To understand the mechanism of muscle contraction, it is useful to begin by analyse how individual fibres are constructed. Each thick filament *(myosin)* molecule within a sarcomere consist of a rod-like tail (made of twin-stranded light meromyosin) bent up at one end to form a twin globular neck (made of twin-stranded meromyosin) and head (made of two globular protein masses). It is believed that there are two very flexible regions at the base of the neck and the base of the head called *hinges*, which allow the head/neck protrusions to flex and extend over a relatively large distances when they interact with neighbouring actin attachment sites. Approximately 200 of these molecules are bundled together to form a single myosin filament with the head/neck portions protruding from all sides of the filament (Fig 1.16). It is these protrusions which constitute the cross-bridges.

The actin filament is composed of three materials: *actin, tropomyosin* and *troponin*. The backbone of the filament is something like a special wool woven from two lengths of the same basic strand. This strand consists of fibrous actin *(F-actin)* loosely attached to an adjacent strand of tropomyosin. The fibrous actin, in turn, consists of a polymer of globular actin *(G-actin)* molecules. The two lengths are wound around one another and at regular sites along the tropomyosin a triple cluster of troponin is attached.

This cluster consists of three units, each one of which serves a different purpose (Fig 1.16). The one globule has a strong affinity for actin (troponin-I or TnI), another has a strong affinity for tropomyosin and hence is called troponin-T (TnT), whereas the third has an affinity for calcium (troponin-C or TnC).

The TnT and TnI globules of this triple cluster are believed to keep the F-actin and tropomyosin strands bonded together, while the TnC globule is thought to play a central role in interacting with the calcium ions which set off muscle contraction. It is believed that, when calcium ions interact with the TnC globule, a process occurs which exposes active sites on the actin filament where the myosin cross-bridges can attach themselves.

The sliding filament or ratchet theory of muscle contraction postulates that in the resting state the active sites on the actin filament are inhibited by the troponin-tropomyosin complex (the triple cluster system), thereby preventing the myosin cross-bridges from interacting with these sites. When the calcium ion (Ca^{++}) concentration becomes large enough, this inhibition is overcome. This occurs when an electrical impulse travels down the nerve fibres to the muscle fibre and the *sarcoplasmic reticulum* which encircles each myofibril releases a burst of calcium ions into the *sarcoplasm* (the 'plasma' within muscle cells).

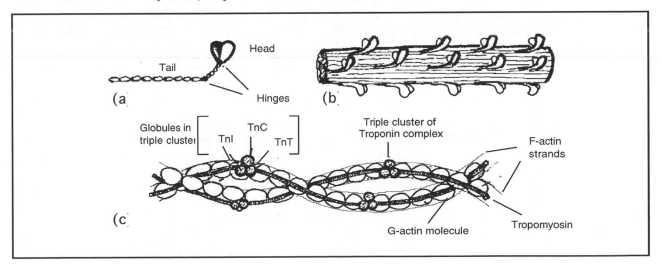

Figure 1.16 The structure of myosin and actin filaments. (a) Myosin molecule (b) Myosin filament (c) Actin filament.

The nerves which supply the stimulation are called *motor neurons*. Their cell bodies are located in the brain or spinal column and send long cables (axons) to specific muscle cells. The ends of these axons split up into several terminals as they enter the muscle, each terminal forming a *neuromuscular junction* with a single muscle fibre (Fig 1.17). This junction or *synapse* actually comprises a very narrow fluid-filled space or *synaptic cleft* between the membranes of the axonal ending and the muscle fibre. The electrical impulse causes the tiny *synaptic vesicles* (vessels) within the axonal ending to release a special chemical transmitter (a *neurotransmitter*) substance called acetylcholine which travels across the cleft and signals the sarcoplasmic reticulum to release the calcium ions.

When the concentration of calcium ions released reach a certain concentration, the heads of the cross-bridges appear to attach to the active sites on the actin filaments, tilt to a more acute angle and pull the actin filaments between the thick myosin filaments. This firmly bonded state between head and active site is known as the *rigor complex*.

An energy-producing process involving the high energy phosphate molecule ATP (adenosine triphosphate) and its breakdown by-product ADP (adenosine diphosphate) apparently occurs to establish a cycle of successive pulls by the cross-bridges, which results in the muscle shortening in progressive stages. The contribution of numerous miniature pulls exerted by thousands of myofibrils add up to produce overall contraction of the entire muscle group.

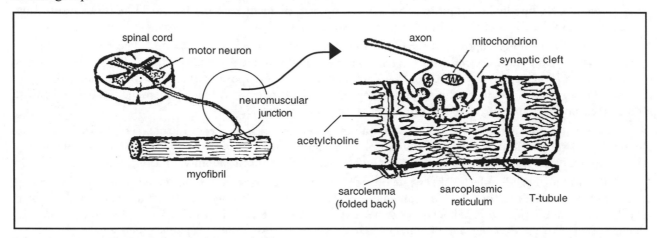

Figure 1.17 The neuromuscular junction

The postulated ratchet mechanism for contraction takes place when the head of a cross-bridge attaches itself to a nearby active site on the actin filament, flexes backwards at its hinges and tugs the actin filament with it (Fig 1.18). This action is known as the power stroke. Immediately after a full stroke, the head releases itself, tilts forwards to its original position, attaches to the next active site further down the filament and carries out another power stroke. This process is continued, pulling the actin filaments towards the centre of the myosin filament (thereby closing the H-band) and summating with the similar actions of thousands of other fibres to produce the final muscle contraction. The energy for this process is supplied in the form of ATP by the 'power-houses', or *mitochondria*, of the muscle cells.

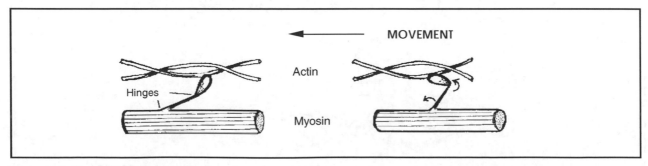

Figure 1.18 The sliding filament mechanism of muscle contraction

If the sarcomere shortens to its limits, the opposing actin filaments overlap, cross-bridging is inhibited and the Z-discs abut against the ends of the myosin, resulting in diminished strength of contraction. Any further shortening may have to be achieved by folding or spiralling of the myosin filaments (Guyton, 1984).

In addition to contraction being caused by change in the extent of overlap between actin and myosin filaments, some of the change in muscle length may also be caused by change in the length of the pitch of the actin helix (spiral). This process may be encountered under conditions of intense muscular contraction, thereby suggesting that the conditioning effect of maximal or near maximal resistance training may differ significantly from that of low intensity, cardiovascular training.

The mechanism of cross-bridge detachment is revealed by the occurrence of rigor mortis (muscle rigidity) a few hours after death. A dead body is unable to synthesize the energy molecule ATP and the calcium ions remain in the muscle cells, thereby maintaining cross-bridge bonding. In other words, cross-bridge detachment depends on the synthesis of ATP.

The occurrence of muscle cramp may be explained in a similar way. If there is inadequate ATP in the muscle or inadequate re-absorption of calcium ions into the sarcoplasmic reticulum after contraction to promote detachment of the cross-bridges, the rigor complex will persist. If this happens on a sufficiently wide scale, an entire muscle group might 'cramp'.

In summary, it may be seen that skeletal muscle fibres are composed of three structural elements, each contributing a unique aspect of muscle function, yet each 'competing' in a sense for space inside the cell (Lindstedt et al, 1998). The volume occupied by the myofibrils determines the force of contraction, the volume of the sarcoplasmic reticulum fixes the rate of onset and relaxation of a fibre's contraction and hence its contraction frequency. Finally, the volume of mitochondria sets the level of sustained performance.

Further Muscle Research

Lest it be thought that the above brief overview presents a definite or complete picture of the mechanism of muscle contraction, it needs to be stressed that considerable research is regularly modified the existing body of knowledge. For instance:

1. Force generation during muscle contraction may involve structural changes in attached cross-bridges (Hirose et al. 1994)

2. Actin filaments exhibit comparable flexibility in the rotational and longitudinal directions, but break more easily under torsional load (Tsuda et al, 1996)

3. The myosin powerstroke may be driven by the release of a strained linear elastic element (Finer et al, 1995).

4. The myosin cross-bridges may exist in two main conformations. In one conformation, the cross-bridge binds very tightly to actin and detach very slowly. When all the cross-bridges are bound in this way, the muscle is in rigor and extremely resistant to stretch. In the second conformation, the cross-bridge binds weakly to actin and attach and detach so rapidly that it can slip from actin site to actin site, offering very little resistance to stretch (Brenner & Eisenberg, 1987).

5. Huxley's original sliding filament theory has been modified to take into account filament extensibility (Mijailovich, 1996).

6. Muscle activation may cause a rearrangement of myosin cross-bridges on the thick filament surface (Sidorenko & Podlubnaia, 1995).

7. Myosin cross-bridges interacting in the slow mode do not impose a large load on the cross-bridges interacting in the fast mode, so that the magnitude of force developed and the speed of unloaded movement, differ greatly, depending on the orientation of the myosin cross-bridges (Yamada & Takahashi, 1992).

8. Rapidly reversible actin interaction of cross-bridges in force-generating states offer a mechanism for rapid detachment of force-generating cross-bridges during high-speed shortening which, in contrast with the hypothesis of Huxley (Prog. Biophys. 1957, 7: 255-318) and related cross-bridge models, does not require completion of the ATP-breakdown cycle and thus may account for the unexpectedly low ATPase activity during high-speed shortening (Brenner, 1991, 1993).

9. For a critical amount of shortening, cross-bridges may detach, rapidly reattach and generate force before the completion of the 'normal' isometric cycle of crossbridging (Piazzesi, 1993).

10. Pressure increase may perturb interaction between actin and myosin and the cycling cross-bridge in a contracting muscle (Geeves, 1991).

11. There appear to be at least two kinds of actin filament, one of which is a stiff rod, and another which is flexible. ATP exchanges with ADP in such filaments and stiffens them. Since both kinds of actin filament contain mainly ADP, the alignment of actin monomers in filaments that have bound and broken down ATP traps them conformationally and may store elastic energy. This energy could be used for release by actin-

binding proteins that transduce force or sever actin filaments, supporting other proposals that actin is not merely a passive cable, but plays an active mechanical-chemical role in cell function (Janmey, 1990).

12. Force development lags stiffness development in muscle fibres by more than 15 milliseconds and has led some investigators to postulate additional cross-bridge states (Bagni et al, 1988). Related research has shown that during activation, the attachment of myosin to actin, measured by mechanical stiffness, precedes tension generation by 10-30 ms, suggesting that series elasticity may be an important contributor to this lag between tension and stiffness (Luo et al, 1994).

13. When sarcomere length increases or when the fibre is compressed, the surface-to-surface myofilament spacing becomes lower than the head long axis, so that, in stretched or compressed fibres, some cross-bridges cannot attach, suggesting optimal relative dispositions between components of the muscle fibre. Consequently, it is probably incorrect to regard cross-bridges as independent force converters, since this idea requires cross-bridge properties to be independent of sarcomere length (Bachouchi & Morel, 1989). Related work has also shown that decrease in conduction velocity during increase in muscle length is caused mainly by a decrease in fibre diameter (Morimoto, 1986). The use of ballistic action during fully stretched muscle actions may allow one to compensate for any decrement in force production under these conditions.

14. There appear to be small perturbations in the cross-bridge configuration rather than large shifts and cross-bridges do not necessarily detach from actin during their power-strokes. Instead they may traverse the entire length of the power stroke and detached only at the end, so that cross-bridge cycling in isometric fibres is due to fluctuations in the relative positions of thick and thin filaments (Pate & Cooke, 1988).

15. When insect flight muscle is stretched, its ATP breakdown rate increases and it develops 'negative viscosity', which allows it to perform oscillatory work, so that the attachment rate is enhanced by stretching. When the muscle is stretched suddenly, the power stroke responds very rapidly, but there is a time lag before dissociation at the end of the cycle catches up with the increased attachment rate. This lag causes the delayed tension and hence also the negative viscosity (Thomas & Thornhill, 1996). Whether this sort of process occurs during explosively rapid movement in human muscle has yet to be shown.

16. The rate of decay of torque following stretch does not depend upon stretch variables and the absence of significant changes in EMG activity suggests that reflex activity does not account for the observed changes when large initial forces are involved. Time-constants of decay were much greater than time-constants of rise of isometric torque at the same muscle length, indicating that interaction of series elastic and contractile elements is not the sole cause of prolonged torque following stretch. Thus it seems that stretch temporarily enhances the intrinsic contractile properties of human muscle, rather than the nervous processes alone (Thomson & Chapman, 1988).

17. Recent research suggests that the myosin cross-bridge theory may no longer be adequate to account for certain basic facts concerning muscle contraction. A mechanism based on length changes in actin filaments might provide a simpler explanation for how the free energy of ATP breakdown can be transformed into work by muscle fibres (Schutt & Lindberg, 1993)

18. Research shows that the crossbridge structure changes dramatically between relaxed, rigor, and with time after ATP release (Hirose et al, 1994). Most crossbridges are detached in relaxed muscle, but in the rigor state, all are attached and display a characteristic asymmetric shape with a strong left-handed curvature as viewed from the M-line towards the Z-line. Immediately after ATP release, before significant force has developed (20 ms) a much more diverse collection of crossbridge shapes replaces the homogeneous rigor population. The proportion of attached crossbridges changes little over the next few hundred milliseconds, but the distribution of the crossbridges among different structural classes continues to evolve. Some forms of attached crossbridge (presumably weakly attached) increase at early times when tension is low. The proportion of several other attached non-rigor crossbridge shapes increases in parallel with the development of active tension. These findings strongly support models of muscle contraction that have attributed force generation to structural changes in attached crossbridges.

1.7.2 A Model of the Muscle Complex

It is relatively meaningless to discuss muscle action without considering the role played by the connective tissues associated with muscle. These tissues occur in the form of sheaths around muscle and its sub-units at all levels, as linkages between myosin filaments, as Z-discs at the ends of muscle filaments, and as tendons at the ends of muscles. Not only do they protect, connect and enclose muscle tissue, but they play a vital role in determining the range of joint movement (or flexibility), and improving the efficiency of movement by storing and releasing elastic energy derived from muscle contraction.

All muscle comprises a contractile component, the actin-myosin system, and a non-contractile component, the connective tissue. In mechanical terms, muscle may be analysed further (according to Levin & Wyman, 1927) in terms of a contractile component in series with a series elastic component (SEC) and in parallel with a parallel elastic component (PEC), as illustrated in Figure 1.19. Although the anatomical location of these elements has not been precisely identified, the PEC probably comprises sarcolemma, rest-state cross-bridging, and tissues such as the sheaths around the muscle and its sub-units. On the other hand, the SEC is considered to include tendon, the cross-bridges, myofilaments, titin filaments and the Z-discs. Of these elements, the myofilaments apparently provide the greatest contribution to the SEC (Suzuki & Sugi, 1983).

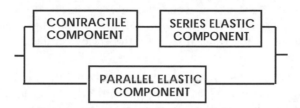

Figure 1.19 A simple mechanical model of the muscle complex

The PEC is responsible for the force exerted by a relaxed muscle when it is stretched beyond its resting length, whereas the SEC is put under tension by the force developed in actively contracted muscle. The mechanical energy stored by the PEC is small and contributes little to the energy balance of exercise (Cavagna, 1977). On the other hand, considerable storage of energy occurs in the SEC, since an actively contracted muscle resists stretching with great force, particularly if the stretching is imposed rapidly. This resistive force, exerted at the extremities of the muscle, and not the direct lengthening of contracted muscle, is responsible for the storage of elastic energy within the SEC.

Furthermore, it has been shown that mechanical strain imposed by stretching a contracted muscle is smaller in a muscle with a preponderance of ST (slow twitch) fibres, whereas the stored elastic energy is greater in FT fibres (Komi, 1984). The same study has also suggested that the elasticity of the SEC in a slow muscle is greater than that in a fast muscle. These differences are largely due to the fact that the concentration of collagen is higher in slow muscle than in fast muscle (Kovanen et al, 1984). Such findings agree with basic analysis of slow and fast movements. The high stiffness and low strain of a slow muscle clearly is most appropriate for muscle function which is intended for continuous support of posture. Conversely, the lower stiffness, greater compliance and lower elasticity of a strongly contracting fast muscle is eminently suited to enhancing speed and efficiency of movement. Further research has indicated that the differences in mechanical properties between fast and slow muscles in response to passive stretching are to a large extent due to their content of collagen.

In addition to the differences regarding the collagenous component of muscle, there are also differences in terms of the muscle fibres. Apparently ST fibres may be able to sustain cross-bridge attachments for longer periods than FT fibres. Therefore, prolonged muscle contraction would tend to be more easily maintained in slow postural (tonic) than in fast (phasic) muscles. Consequently, stretching procedures would have to be applied for longer periods on slow muscles to significantly enhance their flexibility.

The muscle fibres can also stretch passively and store elastic energy, like tendons. In this respect, the myosin cross-bridges that are considered to pull the actin filaments between the myosin filaments during muscle contraction, are known to be compliant structures which may stretch considerably before they detach from the activated sites on the actin filaments. It is believed that this compliance may be caused by rotation of the meromyosin heads of the cross-bridges and by elongation of its tail, which appears to have a helical structure that would promote extensibility (Huxley, 1974). In other words, even a contracted muscle can stretch, not only due to its collagenous component, but also due to its contractile tissue.

As stated earlier, if a relaxed muscle is stretched beyond its resting length, it is the PEC which appears to be most exposed to the resulting tension, whereas in active muscle it is the SEC which is subjected to most tension. This implies that static, relaxed ballistic and passive stretching have the greatest effect on the PEC, while tense ballistic and active stretching affects predominantly the SEC. The various physiotherapeutic PNF (Proprioceptive Neuromuscular Facilitation) flexibility techniques appear to be able to stretch and strengthen both the SEC and the PEC, as well as the associated muscles. Weight and other resistance training routines based on the same PNF principles can achieve similar results.

Further Information on Collagenous Tissue

The connective tissues comprise essentially three types of fibre, namely collagen, elastin and reticulin, with the former two fibres constituting approximately 90% of the whole. The collagen fibres (of which there are at least 10 distinct types) impart strength and stiffness to the tissue, the elastin provides compliance or extensibility under loading, and reticulin furnishes bulk (Fung, 1981). The elastic fibres occur in small concentrations in the intercellular matrix of tendons and most ligaments, but their function is not entirely clear. It has been suggested that they may play a role in restoring the crimped collagen fibre configuration after stretching or muscle contraction (Minns et al, 1973).

The behaviour of the collagenous tissues in response to mechanical stress depends on the structural orientation of the fibres, the properties of the collagen and elastin fibres, and the relative proportions of collagen and elastin. The structural orientation of the fibres differs for the various collagenous tissues and is specifically suited to the functions of each tissue.

In particular, the tendon fibres are closely packed and virtually parallel, but for a slight waviness in the relaxed state. This simplicity of structure suffices for tendon, since the latter usually has to transmit forces linearly from one point to another. In ligaments and joint capsules the fibre organisation, though still generally parallel, is less uniform and often oblique or spiral, its exact structure depending on the function of the particular ligament. Most ligaments are purely collagenous, the only elastin fibres being those which are associated with the blood vessels. Virtually the only ligaments which are mostly elastin are the ligamentum flavum of the human spine and the ligamentum nuchae of the necks of ruminating animals, both of which are composed of about two-thirds elastin fibres and therefore display almost completely elastic behaviour (Nachemson & Evans, 1968). Permanent deformation of such ligaments by traditional stretches, therefore, would be unlikely. In general, the structure of ligament has to be more complex than that of tendon, because joint ligaments have to control forces over a larger number of degrees of freedom. Thus, the stretching of ligaments requires a more extensive variety of techniques.

The collagen network of skin is a complicated three-dimensional fibrous structure which allows it to deform considerably without necessitating elongation of individual fibres.

The Structure and Function of Ligaments and Tendons

Both ligaments and tendons are similar in the manner in which their structures gradually alter as they approach their attachment sites to bone. For instance, the transition from ligament to bone is gradual, with rows of fibrocytes in the ligament transforming into groups of osteocytes, then gradually dispersing into the bone matrix by way of an intermediate stage in which the cells resemble chondrocytes (Fung, 1981). Some authorities have divided the insertion region of ligament into four zones: the collagen fibres at the end of the ligament (Zone 1) intermesh with fibrocartilage (Zone 2), which gradually becomes mineralized fibrocartilage (Zone 3). The latter complex finally merges with cortical bone (Zone 4). Thus, the stress concentration at the insertion of the ligament into the more rigid bone structure is decreased by the existence of these three progressively stiffer transitional composite materials (Fig 1.20).

Tendon differs from ligament in that only one end inserts into bone, whereas in most ligaments both ends attach to bone. Transition from tendon into bone is generally not quite as distinct as in ligament, and tendon inserts broadly into the main fibrous layer of the periosteum. Nevertheless, as in ligaments, the same type of gradual transition in four zones from collagen to bone may be identified (Fig 1.20). This structure, as before, minimizes the detrimental effects of sudden stretching or loading which would occur if there were an abrupt transition from muscle to collagen and then to bone.

Whereas ligaments are often closely associated with joint capsules, tendons occur in two basic forms: those with sheaths (called paratenons) and others without sheaths. Sheaths generally surround tendons where large frictional forces are found and provide lubrication by means of synovial fluid produced by their synovial cells. Thus, it may be seen that tendons with sheaths have a larger PEC than unsheathed tendons and any stretching in the relaxed state will probably have a greater effect on the sheath. The tendon itself comprises primarily the SEC which is tensed only when its attendant muscle is active. This again emphasizes that different stretching techniques are necessary for enhancing the extensibility of the different tissues (see 3.5.8).

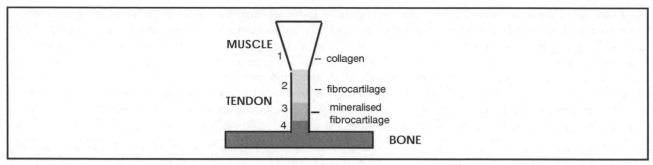

Figure 1.20 The structural transition of typical collagenous tissue to bone.

Mechanical Loading of Collagenous Tissue

Since stretching is a particular type of mechanical loading, application of stretching can be more effectively applied if the effects of loading on collagen are studied carefully. In fact, physiological stretching is possible because collagen is a viscoelastic material; that is, under rapid loading it behaves elastically, while under gradual loading it is viscous and can deform plastically.

Figure 1.21 illustrates the behaviour of collagenous tissue in response to loading to failure. The initial concave portion of the curve (Region I) has been termed the 'toe region' and applies to the physiological range in which the tissue normally functions. It probably represents a structural change from the relaxed crimped state of the tissue to a straighter, more parallel arrangement (Viidik, 1973). Little force is required to produce elongation in the early part of this region, but continued force produces a stiffer tissue in which the strain (i.e. elongation per unit length of tissue) is between 0.02 and 0.04 (Viidik, 1973). Cyclic loading up to this degree of strain produces an elastic response, while unloading from this state restores the original crimped (or planar zigzag) pattern and resting length of this tissue. In other words, mild stretching of collagenous tissue within the Region I will not produce long-term flexibility.

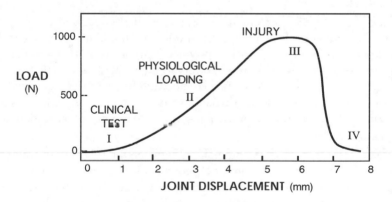

Figure 1.21 The response of typical collagenous tissue to loading to failure, showing the four characteristic regions observed during rapid loading of an anterior cruciate ligament (Frankel & Nordin, 1980).

The next, almost linear, region (Region II) shows the response to increased loading. Here the fibres have lost their crimping and are distinctly parallel, a situation which is believed to be caused by re-organisation of the fibre bundles within the tissues. Small force decreases in the curve may sometimes be observed just prior to the end of Region II, heralding the early, sequential microfailure of some overstretched fibres. At this point, the dangers of excessive stretching definitely become significant. Region III corresponds to the force imposed on the tissues from the beginning of microfailure to the sudden occurrence of complete failure (Region IV). Such a situation will occur if the stretching in Region II continues to elongate the tissues or if ballistic movements are applied in this state.

Since tendons and ligaments are viscoelastic, they also exhibit sensitivity to loading rate, and undergo stress relaxation, creep and hysteresis. For instance, Figure 1.22 represents the phenomenon of stress relaxation in an anterior cruciate ligament while it is loaded at a finite strain rate and its length is then held constant. The characteristic hysteresis curve (n = 1) in Figure 1.22(a) corresponds to the case in which the ligament was loaded to about one-third of its failure load and then immediately unloaded at a constant rate.

If the curve fails to return to its starting point it indicates that the material has become permanently deformed, a process which, if repeated regularly, can lead to ligament laxity. Prolonged, excessive stretching of this type encourages joint mobility at the expense of its stability so that the joint then has to rely more on its muscles for stability. Despite the widespread opinion that the muscles act as efficient synergistic stabilisers, it should be remembered that the musculature cannot respond quickly enough to protect a joint against injury if large impacts are applied rapidly, particularly if they are torsional. Since joint stability involves three-dimensional actions over several degrees of freedom, the necessity for appropriately conditioning all the interacting soft tissues becomes obvious. Joint stabilisation and flexibility are discussed in greater detail later (see 3.5.6).

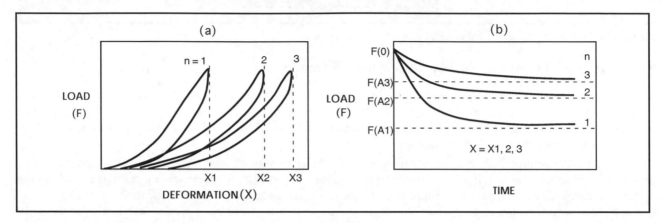

Figure 1.22 Hysteresis and stress relaxation curves of an anterior cruciate ligament (Viidik, 1973).

Figure 1.22(b) refers to the case in which the ligament was subjected to the same load F(0) and then the length was held constant, thereby revealing asymptotic relaxation to a limiting value F(A). The hysteresis loop is generally small for collagen and elastin, but large for muscle, while stress relaxation is small for elastin, larger for collagen and very large for smooth muscle.

Other loading phenomena also need to be noted. For example, if collagenous tissue is tested by imposing a successive series of loading-unloading cycles with a resting period of 10 minutes between each cycle, curves such as those indicated by n = 2 and 3 in Figure 1.22 will be produced. Figure 1.22(a) shows that the initial toe region increases in extent as the hysteresis curves shift progressively to the right. At the same time, the stress relaxation curves of Figure 1.22(b) shift upward. If the test is repeated indefinitely, the difference between successive curves decreases and eventually disappears. The tissue is then said to have been preconditioned, a state which is achieved because the internal structure of the tissue alters with cycling. This type of conditioning towards enhanced stability is the aim of stretching exercises.

The hysteresis curve also offers a way of distinguishing between the relative contributions of elasticity and viscosity to a tissue's behaviour. If the vertical distance between the loading and unloading curves (e.g. in Fig 1.22) is zero, the load-deformation graph becomes a straight line and the tissue is purely elastic, obeying Hooke's Law (i.e. elongation x is directly proportional to applied force F, or F = k.x). The larger the vertical distance between the two curves, the more viscous is the material, the more deformable it becomes and the more it dissipates imposed shocks. In addition, the slope of the hysteresis curve gives a measure of the stiffness of the tissue, with a steep slope being characteristic of a very stiff material that does not extend much under loading.

The biomechanical performance of collagenous tissues depends largely on their loading rate. For instance, if a joint is subjected to constant low intensity loading over an extended period, slow deformation of the tissues occurs, a phenomenon known as creep and which is characteristic of viscoelastic substances in general. Furthermore, collagenous tissue increases significantly in strength and stiffness with increased rate of loading, thereby emphasizing the intelligent use of training with high acceleration methods. One study found an increase of almost 50% in load of knee ligaments to failure when the loading rate was increased fourfold (Kennedy et al, 1976).

Of further interest is the fact that, at slow loading rates, the bony insertion of a ligament is the weakest component of the ligament-bone complex, whereas the ligament is the weakest component at very fast loading rates. These results imply that, with an increase in loading rate, the strength of bone (which also contains collagen) increases more than the strength of the ligament (Frankel & Nordin, 1980). Of added relevance is the finding that the tensile strength of healthy tendon can be more than twice the strength of its associated muscle, which explains why ruptures are more common in muscle than in tendon (Elliott, 1967).

These facts are directly relevant to appreciating the difference between static, passive and ballistic modes of stretching, with slow and rapid loading rates having different effects on the each of the soft tissues of the body (see 3.5.8).

The Role of Stored Elastic Energy

To superficial analysis it would appear as if dynamic contraction of the muscles of the arms and legs during activities such as running would account for a considerable amount of the expenditure of energy. Conversely, it has been found that the energetic cost of running for animals with heavy limbs is about the same as those with light limbs. This is the case because much of the energy involved is stored from step to step as elastic energy in the tendons (Goldspink, 1978). Throughout this process there is significant change in length of the tendons, but not in the muscle itself.

During active movement, the mechanical energy stored in the PEC is small and contributes little to the energy balance of exercise. Conversely, considerable storage of energy storage can occur in the SEC during dynamic exercise, since an actively contracted muscle resists stretching with great force, particularly if the stretching is imposed rapidly. The tendons play a major role in storing this energy. Explosive rebound (plyometric) training can have a significant effect on the SEC.

Whereas the SEC is implicated in activity when the muscle is contracted, the PEC exerts tension passively when the unstimulated muscle is stretched. The contribution of the PEC to total muscle tension increases with muscle length, a finding which is most relevant to integrating flexibility conditioning into an all-round strengthening programme.

The traditional view of tendons serving to attach muscle to bone presents only part of the picture. Tendons, together with other series elastic components, particularly after termination of powerful isometric or eccentric contractions, play a vital role in storing elastic energy during locomotion and other motor acts, thereby saving energy and increasing muscular efficiency.

For example, it has been found that much of the muscle activity in running is associated with tensioning of the tendons, which thereby store energy for successive cycles of movement (Cavagna, 1977). This tensioning or rewinding of the tendon fibres by largely isometric muscle contractions is achieved with very little change in the length of the muscle fibres themselves. The fact that the forces involved are derived mainly from isometric contractions means a decreased energy expenditure because isometric contractions thermodynamically are considerably less expensive than dynamic contractions. For these reasons, it is important that any stretching manoeuvres do not compromise the strength or ability of the tendons to store elastic energy throughout their range of movement (see 3.5.8). This implies again that tendon stretching exercises should be accompanied by strength conditioning against adequate resistance. Similarly, ligaments should not be overstretched to the point of diminished joint stability.

The ability to use stored elastic energy depends on the velocity of stretching, the magnitude of the stretch and the duration of the transition between termination of the eccentric and initiation of the eccentric phases of the movement. This delay between the two phases should be minimal or the stored elastic energy will be rapidly dissipated, because a more prolonged delay will allow fewer cross-bridges to remain attached after the stretch (Edman et al, 1978). Moreover, the greater the velocity of stretching during the eccentric contraction, the greater the storage of elastic energy (Rack & Westbury, 1974).

The increase in positive work associated with rapid eccentric-concentric (or plyometric) contractions is usually attributed to the storage and utilisation of elastic energy, but some of this enhanced work output is probably caused by pre-loading (or, pre-stretch) of the muscle complex. This is due to the fact that, during an impulsive eccentric-concentric action, the tension at the beginning of the concentric contraction is much greater than if the contraction had started from rest.

The Influence of Exercise on Connective Tissue

Various animal studies have produced the following findings regarding the effect of exercise or inactivity on the connective or collagenous tissues:

- Single exercise sessions and sprint training do not produce significant increase in junction strength, although sprinting produces marked increases in ligament mass and in ratios of mass per unit length (Tipton et al, 1967; Tipton et al, 1974). Hence, Tipton and colleagues have concluded that junction strength changes are intimately related to the type of exercise regime and not solely to its duration.

- Regular endurance training can significantly increase junction strength-to-bodymass ratios for ligaments and tendons (Tipton et al, 1974; Tipton et al, 1975).

- Long-term endurance exercise programmes cause significant increases in the junction strength of repaired injured ligaments (Tipton et al, 1970). In this regard, Tipton et al (1975) suggested that an increase in tissue capillarisation associated with chronic exercise may enhance the availability of endogenous hormones and stimulate blood flow to the repairing tissue.

- Long-term training significantly increases the collagen content of ligaments (Tipton et al, 1970).

- Ligaments become stronger and stiffer when subjected to increased stress, and weaker and less stiff when the stress is decreased (Tipton et al, 1970; Noyes, 1977).

- Ageing reveals changes in collagenous tissues similar to those caused by immobilisation, with reduction in strength and stiffness of ligaments occurring with advancing age. These changes may be due not only to the degenerative process, but also to reduced physical activity, superimposed disease states and other unidentified processes (Frankel & Nordin, 1980).

Studies of the mechanical and biochemical properties of tendon reveal a close relationship between tensile strength and the amount of collagen. Similarly, the concentration of total collagen is higher for slow muscle than for fast muscle. This difference also appears at the level of individual muscle fibres, with the concentration of collagen in slow twitch fibres being twice that in fast twitch fibres (Kovanen et al, 1984).

The tensile properties of collagenous tissues are determined by the type, structure and amount of collagen. There are at least ten distinct types of collagen, each with a different chain composition and occurring in various forms in different subsystems of the body (von der Mark, 1981). At a microscopic level, the characteristic mechanical strength of collagen depends largely on the cross-links between the collagen molecules. It has been shown that the type of exercise can affect the properties of muscle, a fact which relates to these collagen cross-links, rather than merely to the actin-myosin complex. For example, muscle endurance training increases the tensile strength of both slow and fast muscles, as well as the elasticity of the former (Kovanen et al, 1984). Other studies have shown that prolonged running also increases the concentration of collagen in tendon and the ultimate tensile strength of tendon (Woo et al, 1981). This finding is relevant to the limited prescription of off-season transitional or general physical preparation (GPP) training.

In contrast with this finding, the concentration of collagen in muscle is not altered by endurance training. However, the increase in elasticity and tensile strength of the more collagenous slow muscles after training suggests that collagen must undergo some structural changes. In this respect, it is possible that these changes in the mechanical properties of slow muscles are related to stabilisation of the reducible cross-links of collagen (Kovanen, 1984).

With more specific reference to muscle tissue, it has been proposed that ST fibres may be able to sustain cross-bridge attachments for a longer period than FT fibres (Bosco et al, 1982). Therefore, the former would utilise the elastic energy stored in their cross-bridges more efficiently during slow movements. In addition, this process may be augmented by the behaviour of the connective tissue in each given muscle in determining the ability of the slow and fast muscles to perform different types of work (Kovanen et al, 1984). Slow muscles with their greater content of strongly cross-linked collagen would then be more adapted to slow contraction, since the fairly rigid collagenous connective tissue would resist fast contraction. The less rigid connective tissue in fast muscle, on the other hand, would facilitate fast movements with greater changes in form.

The differences noted in the collagenous components of different muscle types could also imply that a slow muscle can store relatively more elastic energy in its collagenous tissue than fast muscle, thereby explaining the efficiency of slow muscle in postural and endurance tasks.

A Modified Muscle Model

Modern advances in training deem that it is necessary to modify the Levin-Wyman muscle model. It is too simplistic to regard the muscle complex as comprising only contractile and elastic elements, since its various components exhibit other mechanical properties such as damping and deformation. The fact that several of the components, including the connective tissue and interstitial fluids, of the muscle complex are viscoelastic immediately suggests that damping must form an important part of any muscle modelling.

For instance, force plate analysis revealed that vibrations of the muscle complex dissipate in the form of damped simple harmonic motion, indicating that the SEC and the PEC are associated with efficient damping mechanisms which absorb energy and smooth out movements, thereby offering protection from injuries linked with resonant loading at certain rates (Siff, 1986). Moreover, the connective tissue within the muscle complex has a specific damping ratio and mechanical stiffness (or spring stiffness) which is different for subjects of different genders, injury state and athletic background (Siff, 1986).

Moreover, the spring stiffness tends to decrease or remain approximately the same after exercise, while the damping ratio invariably increases after slow, sustained or explosive exercise in males and females (Siff, 1986). This change takes place possibly to ensure that the potential dangers of neuromuscular or local muscular fatigue are offset by improved damping of subsequent stresses. The damping ratio and stiffness both tend to increase in subjects loaded with additional mass, again an adaptive response which tends to maintain stability under a wide range of exercise conditions. Damping ratio also tends to increase with bodymass and to be higher in females (Siff, 1986).

Similar work by Greene and McMahon, requiring subjects to bounce with different degrees of knee flexion on a flexible board at different frequencies, revealed that the spring stiffness of soft tissue is a function of joint angle. For instance, for the knee joint the stiffness decreases from about 120kN/m at an angle of 0° to 30kN/m at 75°, so that the contribution of the SEC drops dramatically as the amount of knee flexion increases. This has profound implications for the prescription of plyometric training, in particular the limiting of joint angle to ensure the adequacy of the 'shock' loading on the muscle complex.

The damping ratio measured by the technique of Greene & McMahon (0.34) was approximately three times greater than the value obtained by Siff (0.12), since their method constrained the subjects to maintain a high level of isometric tension in the quadriceps while they were oscillating on the flexible board. This indicates that the damping ratio varies with the intensity of muscular tension.

It is relevant to note that *the lifetime of the cross-bridges between actin and myosin strands is limited*, varying from 15 to 120 milliseconds. Thus, for utilisation of stored elastic energy, it is important that the period of stretching and the transition period between stretching and subsequent shortening (concentric contraction) is short. A long stretch simply causes slippage between the components of the muscle complex and the elastic potential of the cross-bridges will be wasted. A brief coupling time produced by short-range pre-stretch, however, will prevent detachment of the cross-bridges and will facilitate better use of the stored elastic energy during the shortening phase, which is of particular importance in activities such as jumping, the weightlifting jerk and plyometrics.

It also appears that the slow twitch (ST) and fast twitch (FT) muscle fibres have different viscoelastic properties, which enables them to make different use of the stretch-shortening cycle (see 1.9). For example, vertical jump tests show that rapid, short-range execution of the stretch phase was maximally beneficial to vastus medialis muscles which are rich in FT fibres. The knee extensor muscles of subjects (e.g. distance athletes) with a larger proportion of ST fibres benefitted more from slower, larger amplitude jumps with a longer transient period between stretch and shortening. Bosco et al (1982) consider this difference to be a consequence of differences in cross-bridge lifetimes between FT and ST fibres.

This research suggests that the Levin-Wyman model should be modified as in Figure 1.23 to include non-linear damping elements (since the muscle components move in a fluid) and a slider element (an element which allows for the uncrimping of the slack in unstressed connective tissue and for slippage when the tension in the system reaches a critical value).

Furthermore, the variation of stiffness with joint angle shows that the spring characteristics of the SEC and PEC are also non-linear. In other words, these components do not simply obey Hooke's Law (i.e. force F is directly proportional to the extension x produced by the force, or F = k.x, where k is the spring stiffness). Thus, twice the range of extension will not necessarily be associated with twice the tension in the tissues. A damping element has not been associated with the PEC, because there is minimal movement between structures such as the sarcolemma and sheaths around the muscle fibres which are considered to comprise the PEC.

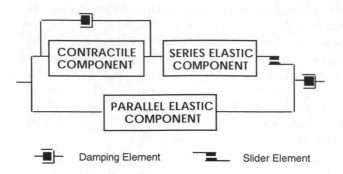

Figure 1.23 An extended model of the muscle complex

The muscle models presented in this text emphasize that fitness training should focus not only on muscle development, but also on conditioning all the connective tissues associated with stability and mobility. This is further borne out by recent findings that *increase in strength may not be related only to increase in density of the contractile protein elements of muscle, but also to improvement in the transmission of force from the muscle fibres to the skeletal system.* In this respect, increase in connective tissue strength and improved rigidity of the muscle complex may decrease the dissipation of force generated by individual sarcomeres into the surrounding tissues. Research into this issue was instigated to probe the reason why muscle strength can increase without increase in muscle size or density of muscle filaments (see earlier subsection entitled 'Strength and connective tissue').

The hypertrophy produced by strength conditioning and the enhancement of neuromuscular efficiency by appropriate speed-strength and impulse training can also influence the storage and use of elastic energy. Since this hypertrophy is associated with an increase in the quantity and strength of connective tissue and an increase in the number of cross-bridges, the potential for storage of elastic energy can also increase, especially if the training has included suitable neuromuscular stimulation. This can be very important for improving performance both in acyclic power sports such as weightlifting and field athletics, as well as in cyclic endurance events such as distance running and cycling.

1.7.3 Implications of the Muscle Model for Flexibility

Mobility and stability both rely heavily on flexibility and strength-flexibility, so it is important to understand the implications of the integrated muscle complex model for actions which involve stretching of the soft tissues of the body. This model reveals that the different types of stretching have specific effects on the different components of the muscle complex and that all-round preparation of the athlete depends on using the various types of stretch conditioning during the appropriate periods. This issue is covered in detail in Section 3.5.

1.7.4 The Relationship between Stability and Mobility

The fundamental principle of animal motion is that *all activity is the result of balance between stability and mobility* in the body. All sporting performance and training involve the learning and perfection of processes which produce the appropriate and effective interaction of mechanisms which stabilise and those which mobilise the joints from instant to instant during a given activity. As discussed in the next section, certain muscles act in a phasic role as prime movers or assistant movers, while others act in a tonic or postural role as stabilisers. Sometimes the roles of the muscles will interchange during certain activities and stabilisers will become movers and vice versa. The balance between stability and mobility depends on the neuromuscular integration of factors such as strength, endurance and range of movement, as well as the mechanical properties of the tissues involved (in particular, mechanical stiffness and damping ratio). This process is summarised graphically in Figure 1.24.

Neuromuscular processes, including the various reflexes of the body, orchestrate the overall interplay between stability and mobility to produce motor skill. Range of movement and stiffness are intimately related to flexibility, where the 'stiffness' referred to here is the mechanical stiffness of the tissues comprising the muscle complex (the spring constant k in the Hooke's Law equation relating force F to extension x: $F = k.x$) and not 'joint stiffness' which is a popular synonym for inflexibility. Stiffness also determines the ability of the deformable tissues to store elastic energy ($EE = \frac{1}{2} k.x^2$). Damping efficiency, the ability to absorb and dissipate shock or vibration, plays a major role in the storage and utilisation of elastic energy, as well as the prevention of injury during activities involving rapid acceleration and deceleration. Although only strength is illustrated in the figure, the term includes all the different types of strength, while endurance refers to both muscular endurance and cardiovascular endurance, factors which relate directly to the onset of fatigue during stabilisation or mobilisation.

The relationship between stability and mobility forms a vital part of physiotherapeutic PNF (proprioceptive neuromuscular facilitation), whose means and methods of physical conditioning may be extended to offer an extensive system of strength training (see Ch 6).

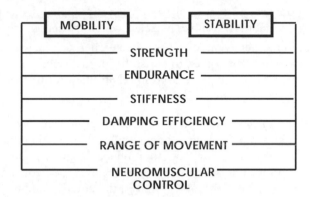

Figure 1.24 The interrelation between stability and mobility in human activity.

1.8 Classification of Muscle Actions

In producing the various directions of movement, many muscles are simultaneously involved in controlling the action from its beginning to its end. This orchestration of diverse contributing muscles has led to different roles being allocated to each muscle group. One of the typical classification schemes recognizes the following traditional roles:

• *Agonists*: Muscles acting as the so-called prime movers of the action. *Prime movers* produce the most significant contribution to the movement, while *assistant movers* play a more secondary role in assisting this prime action. Some authorities recognise *emergency muscles* as a special class of assistant movers which come into play only when maximal force must be generated during a particular movement. In physiotherapy, the phenomenon of assistant movers being recruited by significant increases in loading is referred to as *overflow*. The value of training periodically against near maximal or maximal resistance then becomes obvious.

• *Antagonists*: Muscles acting in direct opposition to the agonists. As emphasized by Basmajian (1978), this action does not necessarily accompany every agonistic contraction, but only under certain circumstances. *Central nervous processes are sufficiently refined to control agonist activity without routine reliance on opposition by antagonists*. After all, in engineering situations it is rarely necessary to use two motors in opposition to offer sophisticated control of any movement. All that is necessary is a single sufficiently powerful motor with rapid feedback processes to ensure accuracy, control, appropriate force and appropriate speed throughout the defined movement range.

Moreover, it is important to note that *reciprocal inhibition* of the antagonist usually occurs whenever an agonist is strongly activated (see 3.5.3). In other words, the antagonist invariably relaxes when the agonist contracts, except when the action is extremely rapid and some 'antagonists' come into play to prevent joint damage due to the large momentum of the moving limb. The inappropriate activation of 'antagonists' to oppose strongly contracting agonists, however, is recognised as one of the causes of musculoskeletal injury. For instance, the hamstrings can rupture if they contract to oppose the quadriceps while an athlete is sprinting or kicking. Russian researchers have shown that *antagonist inhibition occurs most readily during rhythmic activity associated with motor learning*.

So-called 'antagonists' may act continuously or in periodic spurts throughout a movement. Moreover, the presence of antagonist activity may be due to motor learning and not inherent reflexes. Sometimes, the existence of antagonistic activity is a sign of unskilled movement or nervous abnormality. Clearly, the automatic labelling of specific muscle actions as antagonistic needs to be tempered with caution, unless confirmed by careful electromyography (recording of electrical signals from the muscles).

• *Stabilisers*: Muscles stabilising or supporting a body segment statically or dynamically while other muscles carry out a movement involving other joints. During *static stabilisation*, the muscles either contract isometrically or quasi-isometrically (very slowly). An example is the action of the spinal erectors (erector spinae) during pushups. They maintain an isometric contraction to prevent the spine from hyperextending (sagging) while the pectoral and anterior deltoid muscles produce the up and down movement of the upper body relative to the ground. During *dynamic stabilisation*, the muscles are in continuous contraction while simultaneously carrying out a mobilising role. For instance, during running and walking, the quadriceps contract not only to extend the knee, but also to stabilise it during the ground contact phase of each stride. Stabilising muscles often augment the action of ligaments, which are *passive* stabilisers (unlike muscles, which are *active* stabilisers).

In keeping with the concept of emergency muscles described earlier, one may also recognise the existence of *assistant or emergency stabilisers* which are recruited to assist the 'prime' stabilisers during very intensive effort by the prime and assistant movers. This principle is used in rehabilitation by physiotherapists to recruit 'lazy' muscles.

• *Neutralisers*: Muscles counteracting the unwanted actions of other muscles by tending to produce opposite movements. An example is offered by situps, in which the internal and external obliques contract simultaneously to produce trunk flexion. Singly, these muscles tend to produce lateral flexion and rotation of the trunk. Simultaneously contracting, they oppose one another to cancel these movements and thereby assist the rectus abdominis muscles in producing pure trunk flexion. Similarly, the anterior and posterior heads of the deltoid muscles neutralise one another's tendencies to elicit medial/lateral rotation and horizontal flexion/extension, thereby assisting the medial head in producing pure abduction (raising of the arm laterally).

Variations on these categories exist, such as the division of muscles into two classes: *synergists*, which cooperate to produce a movement, and *antagonists* which act in opposition to the direction of movement. However, it must be emphasized that *all muscles operate synergistically* in the normal person; they all cooperate by contributing forces in the most appropriate directions to produce the desired motion, although not necessarily with maximum efficiency. It is preferable to remember that all muscles interact to produce the two fundamental characteristics associated with all human movement: *stability* and *mobility* (see 1.7.4). To do this, the same muscle may act as a mover at one time and a stabiliser at another. It is inappropriate to identify a muscle as one of the above types under all circumstances. Accurately speaking, *a muscle may only be identified as carrying out a specific role in a specific situation.* Thus, it is imprecise to refer to specific muscles as being agonists, antagonists, stabilisers, synergists and so forth: it is more accurate to state that each muscle plays a specific role at a given moment (or during a certain movement phase) in a given situation.

Muscles are also categorised as being *tonic* (postural or anti-gravity) to offer stability and resist gravity, or *phasic* (dynamic) to provide movement. *Tonic* muscles are usually penniform, contain a higher proportion of slow twitch muscle fibres, generally cross only one joint, lie deeper below the surface and perform extensor actions including abduction or lateral rotation. *Phasic* muscles usually occur more superficially, contain more fast twitch muscle fibres, often cross more than one joint and perform flexor functions, including adduction and medial rotation.

1.9 Cocontraction and Ballistic Movement

In general, muscles will cooperate to produce two kinds of action: *cocontraction* and *ballistic* movement (Basmajian, 1978). In *cocontraction*, agonist and antagonist muscles contract simultaneously, with dominance of the former producing the external motion. *Ballistic* movement involves bursts of muscular activity followed by phases of relaxation during which the motion continues due to stored limb momentum. The term 'ballistic' is used, since the course of action of the limb is determined by the initial agonist impulse, just as the flight of a bullet is determined by the initial explosive charge in the cartridge.

Skilled, rapid ballistic and moderately fast continuous movements are preprogrammed in the central nervous system, whereas slow, discontinuous movements are not. The ballistic action rarely involves feedback processes during the course of the movement. *Feedback* from the muscles and joints to the central nervous system permits the ensuing motion to be monitored continuously and to be modified, if necessary. The resulting movement becomes accurately executed and the relevant soft tissues are protected from injury by changes in muscle tension and by the activation of appropriate antagonists to control and terminate the motion.

If no sensory or proprioceptive feedback is implicated, the mode of control is termed *feedforward* or 'open-loop' control (Smith & Smith, 1962; Green, 1967). Here, control is preprogrammed into the central nervous and neuromuscular systems by the visual and auditory systems before movement begins, so that ongoing monitoring mechanisms are not involved. The first sign of impending programmed action is the inhibition of antagonist contraction preceding agonist action, as revealed by the electromyograph. Premature activation of the antagonists may not only diminish skill, but it can cause muscle injury. During ballistic and other rapid movement, antagonist contraction is appropriate only to terminate further motion of the limb concerned. Not only is there no antagonist activity during ballistic movements, but it is also absent during discontinuous motion (Brooks, 1983). The advantage offered by feedforward processes is speed of action, whereas its main disadvantage is the lack of flexibility which can be offered by feedback. Nevertheless, the importance of feedforward processes in human movement should not be underestimated, as implied by the Russians in using regimes of visualisation and autogenic training in sports preparation.

1.10 Types of Muscle Action

Traditionally, the following types of muscle "contraction" (or, more accurately, "action") beginning with the prefix '-iso' (meaning 'the same') are defined: *isotonic* (constant muscle tension), *isometric* (constant muscle length), *isokinetic* (constant velocity of motion) and *isoinertial* (constant load). In addition, movement may occur under *concentric* (so-called "muscle shortening") and *eccentric* (so-called "muscle lengthening") conditions. Before these terms are unquestioningly applied to exercise, it is important to examine their validity.

In all of the above cases, it is more accurate to speak about muscle action taking place under various movement conditions. It is well known that a muscle can only contract or relax relative to its resting or inactivated state, so that it is a misnomer to refer to eccentric muscle action as a "contraction" in which a muscle contracts and lengthens simultaneously. Actually, this means that a muscle which has contracted under concentric or isometric conditions is simply returning under eccentric conditions to its original resting length. To avoid confusion like this, it is preferable to define muscle action as follows:

- Concentric - Action in which the proximal and distal muscle attachments move towards one another
- Eccentric - Action in which the proximal and distal muscle attachments move away from one another
- Isometric - Action in which the proximal and distal muscle attachments do not move relative to one another

Isometric literally means 'same length', a state which occurs only in a relaxed muscle. Actually, it is not muscle length, but joint angle which remains constant. Contraction means 'shortening', so that isometric contraction, like all other forms of muscle contraction, involves internal movement processes which shorten the muscle fibres. Isometric contraction may be defined more accurately to mean muscle action which occurs when there is no external movement or change in joint angle (or distance between origin and insertion). It occurs when the force produced by a muscle exactly balances the resistance imposed upon it and no movement results. Although not incorrect, the term *isometric* may be replaced by the simple word *static*, without sacrificing any scientific rigour. It is interesting to note that, during isometric action, mechanical work, some of which is absorbed by the tendinous tissue, is generated by the shortening of muscle fibres (Masamitsu et al, 1998).

The term *isotonic*, however, should be avoided under most circumstances, since it is virtually impossible for muscle tension to remain the same while joint movement occurs over any extended range. Constancy is possible only over a very small range under very slow or quasi-isometric (almost isometric) conditions of movement for a limited time (since fatigue rapidly decreases tension). Naturally, constant tone also exists when a muscle is relaxed, a state known as resting tonus. Whenever movement occurs, muscle tension increases or decreases, since acceleration or deceleration is always involved and one of the stretch reflexes may be activated.

European and Russian scientists prefer the term *auxotonic*, which refers to muscle action involving changes in muscle tension and length and thus is often synonymous with isoinertial action (note that 'auxotonic' applies to action of the muscle whereas 'isoinertial' applies to the load). Other authors use the term *allodynamic*, from the Greek 'allos' meaning 'other' or 'not the same'. These terms are all more accurate than isotonic in this context.

Isotonic action is most likely to occur under static conditions, in which case we have *isotonic isometric* action. Even then, as is the case with all muscle activation, there is rise time of tension build up, an intermediate phase of maximal tension and a final decay time of tension decrease. For any prolonged action, the tension oscillates irregularly over a range of values. If the load is near maximal, the muscles are unable to sustain the same level of static muscle tension for more than a few seconds and the situation rapidly becomes *anisotonic isometric*. In general, the term *isotonic* should be reserved for the highly limited, short-movement range situations in which muscle tension definitely remains fairly constant.

The word *isokinetic* is encountered in two contexts: firstly, some textbooks regard it as a specific type of muscle contraction, and secondly, so-called isokinetic rehabilitation and testing machines are often used by physical therapists. The term *isokinetic contraction* is inappropriately applied in most cases, since it is impossible to produce a full-range muscle contraction at constant velocity. To produce any movement from rest, Newton's first two Laws of Motion reveal that acceleration must be involved, so that constant velocity cannot exist in a muscle which contracts from rest and returns to that state. Constant velocity can occur only over a part of the range of action.

Similarly, it is biomechanically impossible to design a purely isokinetic machine, since the user has to start a given limb from rest and push against the machine until it can constrain the motion to approximately constant angular velocity over part of its range. The resistance offered by these devices increases in response to increases in the force produced by the muscles, thereby limiting the velocity of movement to roughly isokinetic conditions over part of their range. They are designed in this way since some authorities maintain that strength is best developed if muscle tension is kept at a maximum at every point throughout the range, a proposition which is neither proved nor universally accepted with reference to all types of strength. Moreover, research has shown that torque (and force) produced under isokinetic conditions is usually much lower than that produced isometrically at the same joint angle (see Figs 2.8, 2.9). In other words, it is impossible to use isokinetic machines to develop maximal strength throughout the range of joint movement.

The presence of any acceleration or deceleration always reveals the absence of full-range constant velocity. Isokinetic machines should more accurately be referred to as quasi-isokinetic (or pseudo-isokinetic) machines. One of the few occasions when isokinetic action takes place is during isometric contraction. In this case, the velocity of limb movement is constant and equal to zero. Approximately isokinetic action also occurs during very brief mid-range movement phases in swimming and aquarobics, with water resistance serving to limit increases in velocity to a certain extent. However, even if a machine manages to constrain an external movement to take place at constant velocity, the underlying muscle contraction is not occurring at constant velocity.

Two remaining terms applied to dynamic muscle action need elaboration. *Concentric* contraction refers to muscle action which produces a force to overcome the load being acted upon. For this reason, Russian scientists call it *overcoming* contraction. The work done during concentric action is referred to as *positive*. *Eccentric* action refers to muscle action in which the muscle force yields to the imposed load. Thus, in Russia, it is referred to as *yielding* or succumbing contraction. The work done during eccentric action is called *negative*.

Concentric contraction occurs, for example, during the upward thrust in the bench press or squat, while eccentric contraction occurs during the downward phase. Apparently, more post-exercise soreness (DOMS - Delayed Onset Muscle Soreness) is produced by eccentric action than the other types of muscle action. However, it should be noted that adaptation processes minimise the occurrence of DOMS in the musculoskeletal systems of well-conditioned athletes. Apparently, microtrauma of connective tissue plays a significant role in the DOMS phenomenon, but the relationship between the intensity and volume of eccentric muscle activity, biochemical changes, the influence of adaptation processes and the extent of DOMS is still poorly understood.

A little appreciated fact concerning eccentric muscle action is that the muscle tension over any full range movement (from starting position through a full cycle back to the starting position) is lower during the eccentric phase than the isometric or concentric phases, yet eccentric activity is generally identified as being the major cause of muscle soreness. Certainly, muscle tension of 30-40% greater than concentric or isometric contraction can be produced by *maximal* eccentric muscle contraction, as when an athlete lowers a supramaximal load in a squat or bench press (but can never raise the same load), but this degree of tension is not produced during the eccentric phase of normal sporting movements. Clearly, it would be foolhardy to assume that our current understanding of all aspects of muscle action is adequate for offering optimal physical conditioning or rehabilitation.

Quasi-Isometric Action

Since any resistance training with heavy loads constrains the athlete to move very slowly, it is relevant to define this type of slow, dynamic isometric action as *quasi-isometric*. Recognition of this discrete type of activity is necessary, because cyclic and acyclic force-velocity curves at near-maximal loads deviate significantly from the hyperbolic relationship displayed at higher velocities (see 3.3.2). Unlike isometric activity which occurs at a fixed joint angle, quasi-isometric activity may be executed over much of the full range of movement. Therefore, its training effects, unlike those of true isometrics, are not produced predominantly close to a specific joint angle. This quasi-isometric activity may be executed in either the concentric or the eccentric mode (*concentric quasi-isometrics* and *eccentric quasi-isometrics*) and is highly relevant to training for maximal strength, muscle hypertrophy and active flexibility (see 3.5.8), rather than maximal power or speed.

One does not necessarily have to try to produce quasi-isometric activity; it is a natural consequence of all training against near-maximal resistance and it takes place with most bodybuilding and powerlifting exercises, provided the lifter avoids any tendency to allow the load to drop rapidly and involve the use of momentum or elastic rebound.

The different types of muscle action/contraction are summarised in Figure 1.25 (see also 4.2.4 for further categories of isometrics and Fig 3.1 for classification of the types of muscle action).

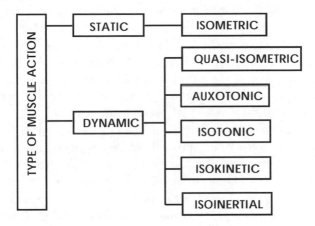

Figure 1.25 The different types of muscle action under various movement conditions.

A concluding comment is necessary about all the types of muscle contraction. A careful distinction has to be made between the characteristics of the machine or device against which the athlete is working, the external movement produced by muscle action and the internal muscular processes. A device may well be designed which constrains its torque or the force in its cables (of transmission system) to remain constant over most of its range, but this does not mean that the force or torque produced *about a joint* by a given muscle group remains the same when working against this machine.

In this respect, *it is essential to distinguish clearly between force and torque*, since a muscle may produce constant torque about a joint over a certain range, but the force or muscle tension causing the action may vary considerably. Conversely, relatively constant muscle force or tension may produce significantly changing torque. This is because torque is the vector product of the force and the perpendicular distance from line of action of the force to the fulcrum about which it acts ($\mathbf{T} = \mathbf{r} \times \mathbf{F}$). So, if either the force or the distance changes, there will be a change of torque.

This is of importance in understanding some of the new devices which are claimed to offer iso-acceleration working conditions. There is essentially no difference between an 'iso-force' (constant force) device and an 'iso-acceleration' device, since acceleration and force are directly proportional to one another, according to Newton's Second Law. It is even more important to stress that action about a joint is always associated with two mutually perpendicular accelerations or force: *radial acceleration* directed towards the fulcrum, and *tangential acceleration* acting at right angles to the radial acceleration. In designing a constant acceleration or force device, we usually wish the *angular acceleration* about the joint to remain constant. As with isokinetic devices, it is not possible to create a truly iso-acceleration device, since joint action always involves changes from clockwise to anti-clockwise direction. At some stage the limb must decelerate to rest, maintain a brief phase of isometric tension or recruit elastic recoil, then accelerate in the opposite direction.

Numerous researchers use isokinetic or iso-acceleration devices to measure strength, endurance and work, yet they never correct for phases of non-isokinetic or non-isoacceleration activity. Scientifically, one cannot simply ignore phases of isometric, concentric or eccentric work because they are of short duration. Yet this is exactly what has happened with a great deal of research into muscle action, a situation which undoubtedly has distorted our understanding of strength, endurance and work, particularly in the therapeutic setting.

1.11 The Triphasic Nature of Muscle Action

It is fairly universally recognised that dynamic movement is the result of a *concentric* action, in which muscle action supplies enough force (or tension) to overcome the load, and an *eccentric* action, in which the force of muscle action is overcome by the load. Consequently, dynamic muscle action has sometimes been described as biphasic, a term which oversimplifies the complex nature of muscle action.

Classical categorisation of muscle action states that there are two broad classes of muscle action: static (isometric) and dynamic (concentric and eccentric). This neat, but somewhat naïve schema, however, obscures a very important fact, namely that *all dynamic action has to involve a static phase*. It is impossible to initiate, terminate, then repeat any movement without the intervention of the static muscle contraction of some or all of the muscles responsible for the movement. This is not merely a matter of scientific pedantry; it is a matter of central importance to an understanding of all muscle movement and it is essential that its role be recognised in all kinesiological analysis and muscle conditioning.

In all human activity, a muscle has to contract from its resting state before movement becomes possible. This action always occurs under isometric conditions. Only once sufficient tension has developed in the muscle fibres, can dynamic action begin. In other words, the muscle tension developed just manages to counterbalance the external load. If the muscle produces sufficient tension to overcome the external load, a concentric action occurs. If the muscle does not produce the necessary tension, eccentric action ensues.

Thus, *all dynamic muscle action is triphasic*. The initiating phase from a state of rest is always isometric. This will be followed by either a concentric or eccentric phase, depending on the specific movement. When this phase is completed, the joint will come to rest for a certain period of isometric activity, after which it will be followed by an eccentric or concentric phase to return the joint to its original position.

During ballistic movement, the transition isometric phase between the concentric and eccentric phases is very brief, whereas it may be much longer during slower maximal efforts produced, for instance, by a powerlifter performing the squat or bench press. The brief isometric action between the eccentric and concentric phases of a plyometric movement is of particular importance in speed-strength training. This is one of the ways of producing *explosive isometric* action, as distinct from slow isometrics (see 4.2.4). It is associated with the generation of great muscular power during movements such as the weightlifting jerk, shotput or high jump, which combine a maximal voluntary concentric thrust of the knee extensors, in particular, with the reflexive contribution of explosive isometrics produced by the knee dip.

The slowing down and ultimate halting or reversal of a joint action is not as simple as is sometimes suggested by the brief kinesiological descriptions given in popular muscle magazines and many textbooks. Frequently, the termination or reversal of a movement is attributed to the initiating action of agonists being opposed by the action of antagonists, neutralisers or similar categories of muscle.

EMG (electromyographic) recordings, force plate studies and video analysis reveal that this is but one of several mechanisms which control patterns of joint action. It may be deduced from work by Basmajian (1978) and Siff (1986) that other possible actions include:

- eccentric action of the agonists (primary and assistant movers)
- isometric action of the agonists
- concentric action of the antagonists
- isometric action of the antagonists
- isometric action of certain stabilisers of the relevant joint or nearby joints
- concentric action of other stabilisers of the relevant joint or nearby joints
- eccentric action of other stabilisers of the relevant joint or nearby joints
- passive tensioning of connective tissue of the relevant joint (simple harmonic damping)
- passive harmonic damping by connective tissue of nearby joints.

No matter which action or combination of actions is implicated in decelerating, terminating and reversing a specific joint movement, Newton's Laws of Motion decree that there will always be a moment when the system comes to rest before moving in the opposite direction.

An isometric muscle action will occur either concurrently with the rest state or a short period afterwards, depending on whether the movement is slow or ballistic. If the movement produces a recoil due to high initial momentum, the release of stored elastic energy will contribute strongly to the subsequent motion. Nevertheless, the elastic recoil will at some stage be augmented by the onset of muscle action initiated under isometric conditions preceded by eccentric stimulation of the myotatic stretch reflex. If the movement is not accompanied by any ballistic recoil, then the limb will come to rest and isometric muscle action will be the sole initiator of the subsequent movement.

Clearly, the existence of an isometric phase during all joint movement must be recognised in analysing movement and prescribing exercise. Isometric action should not be thought of as a separate type of muscle training which occurs only under special circumstances, but a type of muscle action which is involved in the initiation and control of all dynamic movement.

1.12 Types of Muscle Fibre

Skeletal muscle does not simply comprise an extremely large number of the same type of fibre, further subdivided into actin, myosin and other components. Research has revealed that muscle fibres may be classified in terms of factors such as colour, contractile properties, content of myoglobin (the pigment which binds oxygen in the blood), relative content of metabolic enzymes, and the content of mitochondria.

Slow and Fast Twitch Muscle Fibres

Earlier we discussed the actin and myosin components of muscle. We now note that the myosin plays a special role in determining the contractile characteristics of the muscle via one of its specific components, namely the myosin heavy chain (MHC). This chain appears in three different varieties or isoforms, referred to as type I, IIa and IIx isoforms, as are the muscles fibres which contain them (i.e., I, IIA and IIX). Type I fibres are also referred to as slow fibres, while the other two fibres are known as fast fibres, because the latter contract far more rapidly than the former (type IIX fibres contract approximately 10 times faster than type I fibres, with the contraction velocity of IIA fibres lying intermediate to types I and IIX (Andersen et al, 2000).

The type I, IIA and IIX fibres or pure fibres are not the only form in which the various isoforms express themselves: there are also hybrid fibre types which contain mixtures of slow and fast myosin isoforms. Interestingly, these hybrid fibres are scarce in young people, with vastus lateralis studies showing that the latter exhibit less than 5% of this variety. On the other hand, in older adults this value rises to over 30% and becomes the dominant fibre type in very old adults (Andersen et al, 2000).

Research indicates that all muscle fibres appear to lie on a continuum which extends between the slow contracting, slow fatiguing fibres at one extreme and the fast contracting, fast fatiguing fibres at the other. Most classification schemes refer to the these extremes as Type I red, slow twitch (ST) fibres and Type II white, fast twitch (FT) fibres, where the difference in colour is due to the fact that red fibres have a higher content of myoglobin. Since slow fibres rely largely on aerobic metabolism and fast fibres depend more on anaerobic metabolism, endurance athletes are heavily reliant on a large percentage of slow fibres and short distance or strength athletes require a large percentage of fast fibres.

In general, *ST (Type I)* fibres are slow contracting, slow fatiguing reddish fibres with a small diameter, high oxidative capacity and low glycolytic capacity (ability to rely on stored glycogen as an energy source for resynthesizing ATP). They are efficient in maintaining posture and sustaining prolonged, low intensity activity such as distance running, particularly since they usually contain a large number of mitochondria and use ATP slowly. These fibres may be tonically or phasically active for prolonged periods, being known to fire at fairly low rates for as much as 20-35% of the day (Edstrom & Grimby, 1986).

FT (Type II) fibres have usually been subdivided into several sub-classes, the most frequently mentioned being FTa (Type IIA) and FTb (Type IIB or IIX in humans). *Type IIA (FTa)* fibres are also called fast twitch, oxidative-glycolytic (FTOG), since they are able to draw on oxidative and glycolytic mechanisms for energy. They are apparently suited to fast, repetitive, low intensity movement and are recruited next after Type I (ST) fibres. They possess fairly large numbers of mitochondria and therefore tend to be reasonably resistant to fatigue and can recover fairly rapidly after exercise. Some authorities believe that they are Type II (FT) fibres which are adapted for endurance activity. Bodybuilders often tend to have a high relative percentage of these fibres, which has led some researchers to propose that these fibres may be especially able to adapt to hypertrophy in response to suitable training stimuli (Jurimae et al, 1997).

Type IIX (IIB or FTb) fibres are fast contracting, whitish, low myoglobin fibres with a large diameter, high glycolytic capacity, low oxidative capacity and few mitochondria. They are suited to high power output and are usually recruited only where very rapid or very intense effort is required, as in field athletics and weightlifting, where athletes in these sports exhibit high percentages of these fibres (Abernethy, 1994; Tesch, 1998). They fatigue rapidly and replenish their energy supplies mainly after exercise has ceased. Interestingly, some studies reveal that bodybuilders often display a smaller percentage of type IIX/B Myosin Heavy Chain (MHC) isoforms than untrained controls or even endurance-trained subjects (Jurimae et al, 1997).

While the above classification is widely referred to in exercise physiology as a matter of convenience, some controversy still surrounds skeletal muscle fibre nomenclature and classification (see the next section on Muscle Isoforms). For instance, the slow twitch fibres have been subdivided into types I and IC, while the fast-twitch fibre population has been subdivided into types IIA, IIB, IIC and even types IIAB and IIAC to form part of an entire fibre continuum (Staron & Hikida, 1992). The possible transformation between fibre types or characteristics by specific types of exercise is currently an area of prolific research. Another older classification scheme which may be remembered readily recognizes the following fibre types, organised on the basis of their fatigue properties and degree of 'sag', or decrease in force production after an initial rise during the frequency-tension response (Burke, 1981):

- S - slow contracting
- FR - fast contracting, resistant to fatigue
- FI - fast contracting, intermediate fatiguability
- FF - fast contracting, fast fatiguing

Identification of muscle type is performed by removing a sample core (biopsy) of muscle tissue from the chosen muscle with a fairly broad injection needle, which commonly is the vastus lateralis muscle of the thigh.

Every muscle group contains a different ratio between fast and slow twitch fibres, depending on their function and training history. For example, muscles such as the soleus of the calf usually have a higher content of ST fibres than gastrocnemius, whereas the arm triceps generally have a higher proportion of FT fibres.

Lest the impression be created that the different fibre types are discretely packaged into zones that are dominantly slow or fast twitch in nature, it is important to appreciate that muscle fibres usually tend to be surrounded by fibres of a different type rather than concentrating in the immediate neighbourhood of one other. As stated elsewhere in this text, the superficial layers of muscle tend to contain a greater percentage of faster fibres, whereas slower fibres seem to predominate in the deep muscle layers (Grotmol et al, 1988; Kernell et al, 1998). It has been suggested that the separation of muscle fibre types in the same and different layers of muscle may enhance mechanical efficiency during demanding activities. Interestingly, as one grows older, II fibres seem to preferentially atrophy, but it is not yet known whether this is due to physical inactivity or biological ageing (Enoka, 1996; Staron, 1997). The responsiveness of these fast fibres to strength training supports the value of this type of exercise to older adults.

Technological advances more recently have facilitated research into the microstructure of muscles, with analysis focusing on the adequacy of the original sliding filament model, the cross-bridging process and the structure of the actin and myosin sub-units (see 1.7). The myosin molecule has now been recognised as comprising several different heavy myosin chains (MHC) and several light myosin chains (MLC), each chain consisting of various polypeptides (Staron & Johnson, 1993). Other work has suggested that there may not just be a single binding state between the actin and myosin filaments, but there may be distinct weak and strong binding states, with the myosin powerstroke (Fig 1.18) being driven by the release of a strained linear elastic element (Finer et al, 1995).

Muscle Protein Isoforms

All muscle fibres contract according to the same cross-bridging or sliding filament action (see 1.7.1). The distinction between the different fibres lies in the rate at which cross-bridging occurs and their ability to sustain a cross-bridging cycle. Goldspink (1992) has found that the rate at which cross-bridging consumes the high-energy phosphate ATP varies considerably with each type of muscle fibre. Cross-bridging takes place far more rapidly and consumes more ATP in fast twitch muscle fibres than in slow, postural muscles.

Apparently, the difference in response between fibres lies in the diversity of forms in which muscle fibre is synthesized. Instead of occurring in one identical form for all muscle fibres, many of the protein building-blocks of muscle exist in a variety of subtly different forms, known as protein *isoforms*. Research reveals that a muscle will manifest itself as 'slow' or 'fast' on the basis of precisely which protein isoforms it is manufacturing, in particular which isoform of the heavy myosin filament is being formed (Goldspink, 1992). The role of the myosin is very important, not only because of its size, but also of its diversity of function. Besides providing muscle fibres with cross-bridges, it also reacts with ATP to harness the energy released by the mitochondria for contraction.

Geneticists have discovered that different members of the myosin gene family are activated at different stages of human development from embryo to adult. The reason for this is not yet known, but the fact that embryonic muscle continues to grow in the absence of contraction or mechanical stimulation suggests at least one hypothesis. It is possible that the embryonic form of the myosin heavy chain liberates muscle fibres from dependency on mechanical stimulation for growth. Evidence for this proposal comes from the observation that the cells of damaged muscle fibres revert to synthesising the embryonic form of the myosin protein in an apparent attempt to assist in tissue repair.

Four myosin heavy chain (MHC) isoforms, MHC I, MHC IIa, MHC IIb, and MHC IId(x), have been identified in small mammals and are regarded as the building blocks of the histochemically defined muscle fibre types I, IIA, IIB, and IID(X), respectively (Hamalainen & Pette, 1995; Schiaffino & Reggiani, 1994). These fibres express only one MHC isoform and are called *pure fibre types*. Hybrid fibres expressing two MHC isoforms are regarded as hybrid or transitional fibres between the different pure fibre types. The existence of pure and hybrid fibres even in normal muscles under steady state conditions creates a wide spectrum of possible fibre types.

The variety of fibre types is even greater when myosin light chains are taken into account. A large number of isomyosins results from the combinations of various myosin light and heavy chains isoforms, thereby further increasing the diversity of muscle fibres. As shown by comparative studies, different fibre types varies in a muscle-specific and a species-specific manner.

Furthermore, research has shown that the previously classified IIb muscles fibres in human muscle should more accurately be classified as IIx fibres, with the analogous IIb fibres being present in species other than humans (Ennion, 1995). Several members of the sarcomeric myosin heavy chain (MHC) gene family have been mapped in the human genome but many of them have not yet been identified. The distribution of beta/slow, IIa, and IIx MHC transcripts defines three major muscle fibre types - either beta/slow, IIa, or IIx MHC mRNA, and two populations of hybrid fibres co-expressing beta/slow with IIa or IIa with IIx MHC mRNA. Fibre typing by histochemistry shows that IIa MHC transcripts are more abundant in histochemical type IIa fibres, whereas IIx MHC transcripts are more abundant in histochemical type IIb fibres (Smerdu et al, 1994).

The IIa-, IIx-, and IIb-MHCs were first detected in the muscles of newborn babies, with their expression in developing and adult muscle being regulated by neural, hormonal, and mechanical factors. The functional role of MHC isoforms has been in part clarified by biochemical-physiological studies on single skinned fibres which indicate that both MHC and MLC isoforms determine the maximum velocity of shortening of skeletal muscle fibres.

The existence of numerous different forms of the myosin chain endows muscle fibres with an inherent plasticity, thereby enabling them to modify their myofibrils to produce muscles with different contractile properties. Unlike other genes, which are generally switched on and off by the indirect action of signalling molecules such as hormones or growth factors, *muscle genes are regulated largely by mechanical stimulation*. Goldspink (1992) has shown that passive stretching and electrical stimulation separately have only a mild effect on the myosin genes, but together they virtually halt synthesis of the fast myosin chain, thereby reprogramming fast twitch muscles to express themselves as slow twitch muscles. He also found that immobilisation causes the normally slow-twitching soleus muscle to become fast twitching: apparently it requires repeated stretching to sustain synthesis of the slow myosin chain. In other words, the 'default' option for muscles seems to be the fast myosin chain. Moreover, training apparently can alter the contractile properties of muscle by modifying one type of fibre to act like or become another type of fibre or by enhancing the selective growth of a particular fibre type (Goldspink, 1992).

Muscle Fibres and Training

Fibre types differ considerably between individuals, especially between endurance and strength athletes. For instance, vastus medialis biopsies reveal that the proportion of FT fibres in field athletes and weightlifters can be over three times (i.e. over 60% FT fibres) greater than that of marathon runners (approximately 17% FT fibres) and 50% greater than that of bodybuilders, cyclists and race walkers (all about 40% FT fibres). The importance of fast fibres in short duration explosive or maximal strength efforts is underscored by the fact that fast type IIx fibres contract 10 times faster than slow type I fibres (Andersen et al, 2000).

Near-maximal and explosive resistance training also produce greater hypertrophy of FT fibres than ST fibres (Häkkinen, 1985). In this respect it is noteworthy that maximal muscle power output and potential for explosive movement is determined strongly by the proportion of FT fibres in the relevant muscles (Häkkinen, 1985). Moreover, endurance training reduces vertical jump power, explosive speed and similar FT fibre activities, possibly because endurance training may degrade FT fibres, replace them with ST fibres or cause enzymatic and neuromuscular changes more appropriate to slow endurance activities (Armstrong, 1987).

Although research indicates that fibre distribution is strongly determined by genetic factors, it appears as if these differences may also be strongly influenced by the type, intensity and duration of training, as well as the pre-training status of the individual. This becomes particularly evident if the muscle fibre distribution is compared between weightlifters and bodybuilders. Weightlifters have a considerably higher proportion of FT fibres, a fact which cannot be explained by the contention that specific genetic types excel at specific sports. Bodybuilders have about 10% fewer FT fibres (or 10% more ST fibres) than untrained subjects, while weightlifters have about 10% more FT fibres. It is apparent that even the specific type of strength training may influence the relative proportions of FT and ST fibres and their hybrid sub-types. The difference between weightlifters and bodybuilders probably lies in the fact that weightlifters usually execute considerably more low repetition, maximal effort, explosive training than bodybuilders, who often use moderate loads slowly to failure.

Hather et al (1991) reported that 19 wk of heavy resistance training caused a decrease in the percentage of type IIX/B and an increase in the percentage of type IIA fibres in vastus lateralis, suggesting that resistance training had caused transformation among the fast-twitch fiber subtypes. This was confirmed by further work which also showed that neither MHC I composition nor type I muscle fibre percentage changed with training (Adams et al, 1993).

One has to be cautious in simplistically analysing different activities and athletes on the basis of percentage differences in muscle fibre type, since the cross-sectional area of all fibres is not the same and we know that force generated by a muscle depends on its cross sectional area (as well as its level of excitation at any given instant). FT generally are about 30-40% larger in cross-sectional area than ST fibres (although there are notable exceptions which are discussed later). This means, even if a muscle comprises equal 50% percentages of FT and ST fibres, that the overall percentage FT contribution to total cross-sectional area of the muscle can exceed 65%, depending on the degree of hypertrophy (Pipes, 1994; Tesch et al, 1983). In individuals and muscle groups with a tendency to contain more FT fibres, this value can be even higher.

Furthermore, it has been found that heavy resistance training enlarges type II fibres twice as much as in slow fibres, which shows that strength training can increase the relative cross-sectional *area* of FT fibres without increasing the relative proportion of FT fibres in the muscle (Andersen & Aagaard, 2000; Andersen et al, 2000). Since the velocity of muscle contraction depends on the area covered by fast fibres, an athlete may use intense strength training to increase strength and power, even if one cannot change the actual proportion of fast fibres in the muscles.

Another interesting finding is that, after a period of resistance training, MHC IIX content decreased from 9.3 to 2.0%, with a corresponding increase in MHC IIA from 42.4% to 49.6% (Andersen & Aagaard, 2000). After a detraining period of 3 months, the amount of MHC IIX reached values that were 17% higher than before and after resistance training, revealing what the researchers call *MHC IIX Overshoot*. This seems to suggest that, if an athlete wishes to increase the relative amount of fast muscle fibre isoforms, a logical method would be to decrease the training load and allow the fastest fibres to express themselves a few weeks later. This finding appears to lend some support to the practice of training 'tapering' that has been implemented for many years among strength and sprint athletes. It is important to note that this study was carried out on sedentary subjects and the situation might be very different among elite athletes. At this stage the use of a 3 month tapering period would be regarded by all athletes as being excessive, so, if we are to be guided by the trial and error experiences of athletes, it might well be found that the detraining period needs to be considerably shorter for trained competitors whose ability to adapt to demanding stimuli already is far superior to that of the general public. Moreover, one needs to distinguish between the different components of detraining, namely the perceived and actual levels of intensity and volume. In the case of heavy strength activities, it is usually excessive volume which tends to have a more profound effect than occasional very heavy loads on competitive impairment. One also needs to be appreciate that the volume and intensity as calculated on a typical training card may not concur with the perceived impact of these variables, so that one should also be guided by the athlete's perception of his condition.

Some researchers have suggested that *there may be an optimal or maximum size for individual muscle fibres undergoing training hypertrophy*, since efficiency of strength, power and work production decreases if muscle cross-sectional area is too small or too large (MacDougall et al, 1982; Tesch & Larsson, 1982). Other work tends to corroborate this conclusion (Häkkinen, 1985). This study noted a significant increase in the maximal isometric strength of non-athletes, but no hypertrophy of ST or FT fibres, between weeks 12-20 of a 24 week-long strength training routine using variable intensity rates of concentric and eccentric exercise. The significant strength increase during weeks 12-20 was attributed to increased neural activation. In highly trained athletes, the increase in muscle hypertrophy is even more limited, thereby emphasizing the importance of using high intensity, rapid transition techniques for stimulating their nervous systems.

The existence of possible optimal fibre size, the limited ability of advanced athletes to experience muscle hypertrophy, and the lack of correlation between hypertrophy and strength gain stresses the futility of prescribing hypertrophy training for highly qualified athletes. This type of training is suitable for novices, but its regular use may be seriously detrimental to the strength and strength-speed performance of elite athletes.

There is also considerable evidence to indicate that cardiovascular ('aerobic') endurance exercise performed at low intensity for long periods during the same stage of a conditioning programme as strength training seriously compromises the development of strength and power. This is probably partly due to the fact that it is relatively easy for the faster twitching fibres to become or behave like slow twitch fibres with prolonged low intensity training. Furthermore, studies of the gastrocnemius muscles of distance runners have shown that prolonged distance training produces muscle necrosis and inflammation which can be detected at least 7 days after a marathon (Hikida et al, 1983). Comparative muscle biopsy studies of weightlifters, sprinters and rowers after strenuous training sessions do not show any of these abnormalities.

These findings have important consequences for the design of sport specific strength programmes, since some instructors and machine manufacturers maintain that continuous circuit training (CCT) regimes simultaneously develop cardiovascular endurance and strength. Research does not support this belief. On the contrary, it shows that it is more appropriate to prescribe cardiovascular training separately in limited amounts during the early off-season and high intensity resistance training at a later stage. In addition, interval circuit training (ICT) using high intensity loading and regular rest intervals is more suitable for development of strength and strength-endurance.

The sequence of recruitment of muscle fibres by exercise also has important consequences for training. The ST (Type I) fibres are recruited first for muscle tensions up to about 25%, the FTa (Type IIA) are recruited next and the FT (FF or Type IIX) fibres last, as the intensity of the activity increases towards a maximum or as the ST fibres become seriously energy depleted (Fig 1.26). Therefore, if the intention is to train FT fibres for a particular sport, it is vital that high intensity training be concentrated upon.

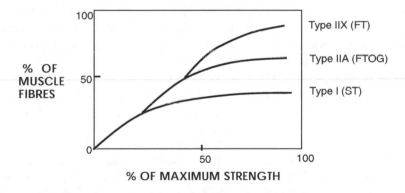

Figure 1.26 Dependence of the recruitment sequence of the different muscles fibres on intensity of exercise

Further research reveals that this high intensity is not necessarily dependent on the use of 1RM (1 repetition maximum) or near 1RM loads, but the degree to which the relevant muscle fibres are recruited during the effort. In this respect, the terms *fast twitch* and *slow twitch* do not necessarily mean that fast movements recruit exclusively FT fibres and slow movements ST fibres. To analyse the involvement of different fibre types, it is vital to determine the force that needs to be produced. If large acceleration of the load is involved, Newton's Second Law of Motion decrees that the resulting force will be large. Thus, the maximal force generated during rapid acceleration of a 100kg bench press easily can exceed the maximal force produced during a slowly accelerated 150kg bench press. Both a small load accelerated rapidly and a heavy load accelerated slowly strongly involve the FT fibres. Likewise, explosive movements rely heavily on the action of FT fibres.

Moreover, rapid movements often recruit the muscle stretch (myotatic) reflex, which can elicit a powerful contraction. Relevant to this process is Starling's Law, which states that the strength of contraction is proportional to the original length of the muscle at the moment of contraction. The ideal relationship between tension and length in a sarcomere occurs when the muscle is slightly stretched and the actin and myosin filaments just overlap slightly. However, in applying this law, it has to be remembered that the advantage offered by the stretching may be diminished in cases where this stretching occurs at large joint angles which provide poor leverage. The well-known *prestretch* principle in bodybuilding training and the plyometric method in speed-strength training rely on this phenomenon. Many gymnasium machines are seriously limiting in that they do not allow the user to begin a movement with a pre-stretch. Not only does this diminish the force which can be generated, but it also exposes joints to a greater risk of injury because the movement begins without muscular support for the ligaments.

The importance of the nervous system in developing strength cannot be ignored. As stated earlier, the development of strength is related to the number of appropriate muscle fibres firing simultaneously, which is entirely a function of the nervous system. An additional finding is that, if the nerve which normally supplies a ST muscle fibre is surgically interchanged ('cross reinnervated') with one which supplies a FT fibre, the ST fibre will behave like a FT fibre (e.g. Bacou et al, 1996; Barjot et al, 1998). These studies, carried out on rabbits, suggest that sensitivity to motor innervation increases from the glycolytic to oxidative types of fibre, in the order: IIB > IIX/IID > IIA> I (where the IID, like the IIB fibre types occur in small mammals as analogues of the human IIX type). In other words, the behaviour of muscle would appear to be determined by the activity of the nerve fibres which supply it, a deduction which is discussed further in the next section.

The rate and number of fibres firing depends on voluntary and involuntary processes, the voluntary ones being related to personal motivation and biofeedback techniques, and the involuntary ones to feedback information from the proprioceptive system, including the various stretch reflexes.

Thus, the simple act of motivating or emotionally willing yourself, through methods such as self-talk or guided imagery to produce greater or faster efforts can recruit a greater number of muscle fibres at an increased rate of firing. Encouragement by a training partner can also play a useful role in this regard, if done at appropriate stages during an exercise. Interestingly, the method of training with progressively heavier loads or at larger accelerations is a valuable way of learning how to motivate yourself at progressively higher levels of performance. The carry-over of this may well benefit one in all aspects of daily life.

Further Aspects of Muscle Plasticity

A great deal of ongoing research is investigating the plasticity, or structural-functional change, of muscle in response to various conditions, such as active and passive loading, different types of neural activation, lack of loading and electrical stimulation. Some of this work has been reported elsewhere in this book, but it is relevant to include some further information on other recent findings in this regard.

One of the prominent hypotheses is that the pattern of neural activation determines the quantity and quality of contractile proteins (myosin and actin isoforms) and metabolic proteins (glycolytic and oxidative enzymes) which the muscles express (Roy et al, 1991). This thesis emerged from studies which showed that typical FT muscle after very prolonged daily low frequency stimulation (24 hours a day) produces physiological, biochemical and structural changes which resemble those found in ST muscle (Lomo et al, 1974; Pette & Vrbova, 1985). This seemed to reinforce work first done by Buller et al (1960), who crossed nerves over from one group of muscle to another and found that this apparently caused the muscle fibres to change their type. They pointed out, however, that "the neural influence on muscle speed is not exerted by nerve impulses as such", but could also have been due to neural growth processes associated with hormonal factors (e.g. thyroid hormone and testosterone).

Hormonal effects generally seem to depend on the type and level of activity of the muscle fibres involved. The muscle fibre types involved in the anabolic properties of estrogens have not yet been clearly described, but in the case of growth hormone and insulin, mainly the ST type is affected, partly via an increased secretion of somatomedins (Insulin-like Growth Factors - IGFs) or by interaction on IGF receptors (Vigneron et al, 1989). The other hormones in the body tend to produce a shift toward more vigorous fast contracting activity, which increases the percentage of fast glycolytic fibres. Anabolic hormones such as the androgens, catecholamines and beta-agonists enlarge these fibres, whereas excess quantities of thyroid hormones or glucocorticoids promote their catabolism ('break down').

The powerful influence of androgenic and anabolic steroids such as testosterone on muscle hypertrophy and function are well known, which has led directly to their huge abuse in sport. Less well known is the potent effect of thyroid hormone in this same regard. The first study to reveal this was conducted by Gold et al (1970), who showed that thyroid state influences the contractile properties of slow skeletal muscle. They found in rat soleus muscle that the hypothyroid state decreased the normal shortening velocity by 60%, while hyperthyroidism increased this velocity by 20%. Other work revealed that in the soleus muscle hyperthyroidism converts some slow Type I fibres to Type IIA and IIX fibres and shifts the force vs frequency curve to the right (Caiozzo et al, 1991). At the same time, hypothyroidism completely suppresses the expression of FT fibres in soleus. Even though soleus comprises only about 15% of FT fibres, this FT to ST conversion produces significant changes in the soleus force-frequency curve, which implies that the small relative population of FT fibres in soleus plays a vital role in determining the mechanical properties of this muscle (Caiozzo & Haddad, 1996). Thyroid state, however, has far less effect on FT muscles, such as plantaris (Caiozzo et al, 1991).

Hypothyroidism also retards the rate and extent of muscle growth, although the change in maximal muscle tension per unit cross-sectional area is insignificant. Another aspect of this work is the fascinating discovery that there appears to be a subset of the ST fibre group which is unresponsive to hormonal, mechanical or electrical stimuli and which have been called refractory Type I fibres (Caiozzo et al, 1993).

In summary, this research, which is part of an effort to understand altered gene expression for specific isoforms as a central process in muscle adaptation, shows that thyroid hormone and mechanical activity can produce rapid qualitative and quantitative changes in muscle protein expression and possibly also on overall muscle function (Caiozzo & Haddad, 1996). Although any suggestion of athletes experimenting with ingestion of thyroid hormone in a private quest for enhanced performance should be deemed as potentially very hazardous, this research implies that significant alterations in one's natural thyroid hormone status may be associated with undesired changes in muscle performance.

Other recent research concerning the plasticity of muscle has shown that (Roy et al, 1991):

1. Muscle atrophy produced by lack of stimulation, nerve damage or reduced gravity proceeds in the following order: atrophy in the slow extensors is greater than in the fast extensors, which in turn is greater than in the fast flexors. Conversely, regular progressive overloading increases the mass of fast muscle more than slow muscle, with fast extensors hypertrophying more than fast flexors. Possibly this is a rational manifestation of some survival mechanism, since rapid extensor actions, which are associated with striking an assailant or thrusting him away, generally are involved more in self defense processes than flexion activities.

2. Muscles display regional change in response to the effects of activation or deactivation. Typically, the deeper regions of the muscle, namely those with the highest proportion of oxidative (ST) fibres, tend to atrophy more than the superficial regions, while the same regions also seem to show the greatest hypertrophy after functional overload.

3. The concept of variation in muscle fibre size as a function of fibre type fails to take into account the existence of many exceptions to this often proliferated rule. Popularly, FT (Type II) fibres are assumed to consistently have larger diameters than Type I, an observation which seems to be borne out in the superficial muscle regions, but not in deeper regions, where the two fibre types have similar diameters. Moreover, in predominantly slow muscles such as soleus, vastus intermedius and adductor longus, animal studies show that the fast fibres are consistently smaller than the slow fibres. In human males, the Type II (FT) fibres of vastus lateralis are larger than the ST fibres, but the opposite tends to occur in females (Saltin & Gollnick, 1983).

4. The largest muscles tend to atrophy and hypertrophy the most, irrespective of fibre type. When this change is calculated in the form of a relative percentage, it is often the same in slow and fast muscle.

5. The fastest rate of muscle atrophy takes place in the initial 1-2 weeks of inactivity, especially regarding the degradation of contractile proteins (like slow myosin in soleus), after which this rate progresses more slowly. The situation concerning hypertrophy is more complicated. Muscle mass increases markedly within a few days of functional overload (despite the assumptions that all initial changes are mainly neural), but, during the first week or so, this increase in cross-sectional area offers little or no increase in strength. After this initial latency period during which relative muscle strength decreases, this trend reverses and normal concurrent increases in hypertrophy and strength proceed for several weeks or months. After about 2-3 months, the rate of increase slows down, as is the case with atrophic changes after a similar period.

6. Prolonged muscle stimulation does not increase muscle strength and hypertrophy, but can actually decrease both after several weeks of electrical stimulation (Eisenberg et al, 1984). Moreover, fibres that are the least active, as based on the sequence of accepted recruitment patterns, usually are the largest fibres in normal mammals. This raises questions about the practice of continued long periods of intense resistance training. These findings suggest that excessive strenuous training can produce stagnation or decrease of hypertrophy and muscle function and that *the condition which optimally promotes hypertrophy and strength increase is the production of some minimum level of force for some minimum amount of time.*

7. There is a close association between enzymes associated with myosin ATP metabolism and those involved with glycolysis, suggesting that there may be some functional advantage for the maximal rates of glycogen and ATP breakdown to coincide, as happens during intense muscle contraction. Since this would match the rate of energy expenditure during myosin activity with an immediate replacement of energy by glycolysis, this concept seems logically compelling. This idea is supported further by the fact that fast myosin hydrolyses ATP twice as rapidly as slow myosin, which is reflected by very a marked increase in the flux of energy substrates via the process of glycolysis. It would not be unexpected to find that the expression of proteins associated with specific myosin type and the glycolytic capabilities of a fibre indeed are closely linked.

8. Muscles and motor units can atrophy without altering their fatiguability, with slow muscle fibres showing prolonged capacity to metabolically support the amount of contractile proteins left in the atrophying muscle cells. However, if the whole body is involved in producing strength output, the atrophied muscles will become more easily fatigued because of recruitment of larger numbers and types of muscle fibres, many of which may well be susceptible to fatigue.

9. Although most research has stressed that training increases the size of muscle fibres, some studies show that muscles adapt sarcomere number and rest length in response to different patterns of use. For instance, fixing a joint in a flexed or extended position that lengthens some muscles and shortens others causes the muscle fibres to lengthen or shorten to establish a new mean sarcomere length which ensures that active force production is maximal at the maintained joint position (see review by Lieber R, "Skeletal Muscle Structure and Function".) Work done by Morgan and colleagues (Lynn & Morgan, 1994) on rat vastus intermedius muscle fibres revealed that eccentric exercise produces a greater increase in sarcomere number than concentric training, but Koh and Herzog (1998) found no significant increase either in sarcomere number or muscle length in rabbit dorsiflexor muscles in response to eccentric training. The differences between these two studies may relate to species differences, or different exercise regimes, stressing that more work needs to be done in this area.

These findings collectively add further support for the view (stated in the previous section by Goldspink and others) that the relative expression of isoforms of myosin in skeletal muscle is strongly influenced by the degree of mechanical or gravity-related stress imposed on muscle.

The Implications of Ballistic Research

Most of the studies of force generated by muscle have been carried out under isokinetic conditions, which rarely occur in sport. Consequently, Bosco and Komi (1979a) re-examined the force-velocity curves under ballistic conditions, particularly with respect to the involvement of the different muscle fibre types. This was done by using a force-plate to examine the relationship between force and knee angular velocity in subjects who performed maximal vertical jumps with barbells of different weight on their shoulders (Fig 1.27). In another study, they concluded that vertical jump performance is related to the percentage of FT fibres (Bosco & Komi, 1979b).

More recently, it was found that there is a significant relationship between FT% and the power output of the leg extensor muscles when working dynamically at loads exceeding 23% of the maximal isometric force F_{max} (Thihanyi et al, 1982). However, when the load increased to over 40% of F_{max}, this relationship disappeared.

It would seem that the FT fibres are the main contributors to force production in pure ballistic motion with maximal voluntary effort, while the ST contribution rises as the muscle contraction time increases from 100 to 1000 milliseconds. This deduction agrees with the relationship found between FT% and the time taken for the force to increase from 10 to 30% of F_{max} (Viitasalo & Komi, 1978, Viitalaso et al, 1982). This relationship between fibre composition and contraction time is not exhibited when the time taken for force to increase from 60% to 100% of F_{max} is measured. Moreover, no definite relationship has been found between F_{max} and muscle fibre composition.

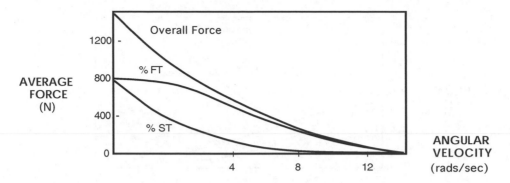

Figure 1.27 The relationship between average force and angular velocity of the knee, obtained from subjects performing squat jumps with different weights on the shoulders. The percentage contributions of the different fibre types are shown, as suggested by Bosco. Graphs based on the work of Bosco & Komi (1979a).

Therefore, muscle cross-sectional area may be most important for production of maximal strength, regardless of muscle composition (Ikai & Fukunaga, 1968), whereas power or explosive maximal strength depends more on FT% (Bosco & Komi, 1979b). It should be noted that ST fibres appear to predominate in most graded movements requiring less than approximately 20% of the maximum force capability of the given muscles and produced at submaximal speeds (see Fig 1.26).

However, if the movements involve producing large forces of short duration at very high velocity, then the FT fibres appear to be recruited, while some inhibition may be exerted over ST fibres (Minagawa et al, 1978). Therefore, the pattern of muscle fibre recruitment is related to the mechanical pattern of muscle contraction and the plasticity of the central nervous system enables the body to select the most efficient pattern of muscle activation to carry out a wide variety of movements of different intensity, duration and speed (Bosco, 1982).

Bosco (1982) compares the patterns of muscle fibre recruitment in different cases to illustrate the limitations of the recruitment scheme of Figure 1.26. Firstly, he points out that walking at moderate speed (ground contact time about 700ms) produces a vertical ground reaction force of over 700 Newtons, relying entirely on ST action according to Figure 1.26.

Secondly, if a person pushes a car from rest, the development of force is graded and progressively involves more and more FT fibres (see Fig 1.26). Finally, if a subject lies supine with knees flexed to 90º and then performs a maximal effort knee extension by thrusting against the foot plate of a horizontal leg press machine, the muscles approach their highest shortening velocity. However, the force produced in this case is usually less than the force developed during walking although it is the result of entirely FT action. Bosco concludes that the schema presented in Figure 1.26 may be suitable for graded, progressive loading, but it is unsuitable to describe ballistic motion. He suggests that Figure 1.27 may be more appropriate under these circumstances. He remarks on the implications of this for isokinetic training.

He notes that the velocity of efficient isokinetic apparatus is adjustable to enable it to more closely match the requirements of specific sports, but cautions that this type of training is not advisable for athletes engaged in any sports involving predominantly ballistic motion (Bosco, 1982). Much of the international literature contends that the isokinetic training method is the most effective for neuromuscular reasons, whereas dynamic auxotonic training is highly effective for promoting power development and muscle hypertrophy, an hypothesis which has caused considerable confusion among training specialists. It must be pointed out that maximal effort on an isokinetic device usually produces the same maximal motor unit activation for both concentric and eccentric contraction (Komi, 1973b), even though prolific research reveals that fewer motor units are recruited during maximal eccentric work to produce greater muscle tension than during concentric work.

Similarly, no change in myoelectric activity was found during maximal vertical jump performance performed with or without additional loads (Bosco et al, 1982). This means that maximal motor unit activation can be elicited by ballistic action, regardless of muscle shortening velocity and pattern of force production during concentric work (Fig 1.28).

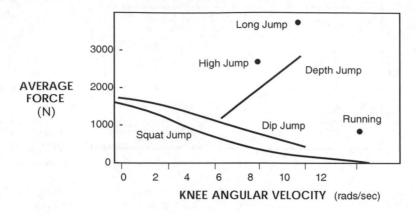

Figure 1.28 Force-Velocity curve for different types of jump (Bosco, 1982). In the squat jump, the contractile component of the muscle is primarily responsible for force production, whereas elastic energy plays a central role in dip (counter movement) jumps and depth jumping. The calculated values of F and V for high jump, long jump and sprints are also shown.

This figure also shows that jumping with a preliminary dip (or, counter movement) causes the F-V curve to shift upward away from the more conventional hyperbola-like F-V curve recorded under isokinetic conditions or with squat jumps. For depth jumps, the resulting graph displays a completely different trend where the force is no longer inversely proportional to the velocity of movement. The coordinates describing the more rapid actions of running, high jumping and long jumping also fall very distant from the traditional F-V curve.

The reason for these discrepancies lies in the fact that movement under isokinetic and squat jumping conditions involves mainly the contractile component of the muscles, whereas the ballistic actions of the other jumps studied are strongly facilitated by the release of elastic energy stored in the SEC during the rapid eccentric movement immediately preceding the concentric movement in each case (see 1.7.2).

Studies of F-V curves under non-ballistic and ballistic conditions (Bosco, 1982) further reinforces the above findings that the traditional F-V curves do not even approximately describe the F-V relationship for ballistic or plyometric action (Fig 1.29). The theoretical basis for the traditional F-V curves is discussed in detail in Section 3.3.2, but the non-applicability of these curves to ballistic motion should be carefully noted, especially if testing or training with isokinetic apparatus is being contemplated for an athlete.

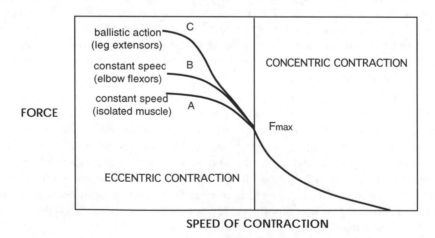

Figure 1.29 Force-Velocity curves for concentric and eccentric muscle contraction under different conditions (Bosco, 1982). Curve A refers to isolated muscles stretched at constant velocity by constant intensity electrical stimulation; curve B was obtained by isokinetic analysis of elbow flexion; curve C gives the F-V relationship for eccentric work produced by drop jumps from different heights.

Other work reveals that the jump height reached and the force produced increase after training with depth jumps (Bosco, 1982). Whether this is the result of positive changes in the myotatic stretch reflex, the structure of the SEC of the muscle or in both is not precisely known yet. What is obvious is that the normal protective decrease in muscle tension by the Golgi tendon organs does not occur to the expected extent, so it seems as if plyometric action may raise the threshold at which significant inhibition by the Golgi apparatus takes place. This has important implications for the concept and practical use of plyometrics (discussed later in detail in 5.2.4).

1.13 The Mechanism of Muscle Growth

Living tissue grows by increase in the size of its components (*hypertrophy*) or by increase in the number of its components (*hyperplasia*). This growth in structure is an adaptation to the functional demands placed on the given system, where adaptation occurs at a molecular level within the genetic structure of the cells.

Research by Meerson discovered a link between the volume of loading imposed on the cells and their genetic structure. He learned that stimulating cellular function activates the genetic apparatus and increases the speed of transcription, translation, protein synthesis and build-up of certain structures (Nikituk & Samoilov, 1990). He propounded the concept of *intensity of functioning of structures* (IFS), which posits that the functional capacity of a system is related to its mass. Thus, the more intense the required function, the greater the mass of the working structure needed to perform the function. In the light of the discussion in Section 1.6, the mass involved should be understood to be the 'active mass'.

We are now in a position to examine the increase in muscle mass as an adaptation to resistance training. In the case of muscle fibres, the occurrence of *hypertrophy* in response to strength training is a well-established fact, but there is considerable debate concerning muscle *hyperplasia*. Gonyea (1980) has presented evidence of hyperplasia in cats subjected to heavy resistance training, but other researchers have criticised this work, pointing out that there may be fibre splitting, but not proliferation of new fibres. Certain Russian research also suggests that increase in muscle mass occurs not only through hypertrophy of muscle fibres, but as a result of an increase in fibre number by means of the splitting of hypertrophied muscle fibres and the development of muscle fibres from muscle 'buds' and satellite cells (Gudz, 1968, 1976). In addition, it has been suggested that muscle hyperplasia may occur with extremely intense resistance training, but current evidence from human subjects is still by no means unequivocal.

However, the contention that skeletal muscle enlargement in adult animals is solely due to changes in fibre is now being seriously challenged by recent evidence which suggests strongly that fibre hyperplasia may also contribute to muscle mass increases in mammals under certain extreme conditions (Antonio & Gonyea, 1993). Research involving direct counts of muscle fibres using nitric acid digestion techniques have shown that both exercise and stretch overload result in significant increases in the number of muscle fibres, plus indirect fibre counts using histological measurements of muscle cross-sections have suggested fibre hyperplasia. In addition, the expression of embryonic myosin isoforms has furnished indirect evidence for the formation of new fibres in bird flight muscles subjected to long-term stretch overloading (with weights attached to their wings). Moreover, satellite cells, which can activate new cell formation, have been shown to be involved in muscle fibre hyperplasia in stretching and dynamic exercise. Hyperplasia may also occur due to fibre splitting of large fibres that subdivide into two or more smaller fibres (Hather et al, 1991; Tamaki et al, 1992; Antonio & Gonyea, 1994).

With regard to hyperplasia in humans, Antonio states that evidence for its occurrence is indirect. He points out that one study showed that elite bodybuilders and powerlifters had upper arm circumferences 27% greater than normal sedentary controls, although the cross-sectional area of their triceps muscle fibres were not different from the control group (Yamada et al, 1989). Larsson and Tesch (1986) found that bodybuilders displayed thigh circumference measurements 19% greater than that of control subjects, yet the average size of their muscle fibres were not significantly different from that of the controls. Furthermore, Nygaard and Neilsen (1978) did a cross-sectional study in which they found that the overall size of deltoid muscles was greater in swimmers than in controls, despite their having smaller Type I and IIA muscle fibres.

Furthermore, Alway et al. (1989) compared the biceps brachii muscle in elite male and female bodybuilders and found that the cross-sectional area of the biceps muscle correlated to both fibre area and number, unlike other workers who have shown that bodybuilders have larger fibres instead of a greater number of fibres when compared to a control population (Haggmark et al, 1978; McDougall et al, 1984; Schantz et al, 1981). Some scientists counter these findings by suggesting that many bodybuilders or other athletes have the same sized or smaller muscle fibres versus untrained controls is because of a greater genetic endowment of muscle fibres. In other words, they must have been born with more muscle fibres. Antonio points out that, if this were true, then the prolonged periods of intense training performed by elite bodybuilders and other strength athletes has produced at best average size fibres. This implies that they were born with a system of below average size fibres that training simply enlarged to average size, which is a generally unlikely and implausible.

Antonio considers that the question which needs to be asked is not whether muscle fibre hyperplasia actually occurs, but rather under what conditions it does occur. The prolific amount of evidence which shows that increase in muscle mass most commonly is associated with an increase in muscle cross-sectional area certainly emphasizes that hyperplasia does not take place as a simple matter of course, but under very special conditions which warrant further research.

Although the existence of hyperplasia of muscle fibre may be uncertain or rare, *hyperplasia of structures within the muscle fibre and cell does occur*. Nikituk and Samoilov (1990) identify two types of subfibral hyperplasia:

* *Sarcoplasmic hyperplasia*, which involves an increase in the number of sarcoplasmic organelles
* *Myofibrillar-mitochondrial hyperplasia*, which involves increase in the number of myofibrils and mitochondria.

Increase in muscle diameter is due to enlargement of individual muscle fibres by an increase in the number and size of individual myofibrils (Goldspink, 1980), accompanied by an increase in the amount of connective tissue (McDonagh & Davies, 1984), as discussed in Section 1.6. This increase in muscle protein is produced by increased protein synthesis and decreased protein degradation (Goldberg et al, 1975). Two types of muscle hypertrophy may occur (Fig 1.30):

* *Sarcoplasmic hypertrophy.* In this case, the volume of non-contractile protein and semifluid plasma between the muscle fibres increases. Although the cross-sectional area of the muscle increases, the density of muscle fibres per unit area decreases and there is no corresponding increase in muscle strength.

* *Sarcomere hypertrophy.* Here there is an increase in the size and number of the sarcomeres which comprise the myofibrils. These may be added in series or parallel with the existing myofibrils, although only the parallel growth will contribute to an increased ability to produce muscle tension. The area density of myofibrils increases and there is a significantly greater ability to exert muscular strength.

Except for a few sports, such as bodybuilding and sumo wrestling, in which an increased bodymass without greater relative strength may contribute to performance, sarcomere hypertrophy is far more important than sarcoplasmic hypertrophy in most athletic activities.

The exact biochemical mechanism whereby hypertrophy is stimulated by resistance training is not yet known and existing theories are incorrect or incomplete (McDonagh & Davies, 1984). Post-exercise enhancement of protein synthesis has been attributed variously to triggering by ATP depletion, altered blood acidity, muscle hypoxia or rebound increase in blood circulation after intense contractions, but none of these mechanisms is adequately supported by research.

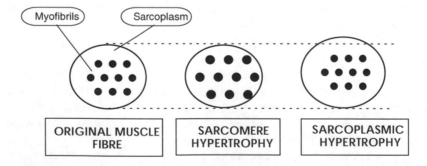

Figure 1.30 The different types of muscle fibre hypertrophy

Although not thoroughly corroborated, the *energetics theory of muscle hypertrophy* appears to be more acceptable than the other theories, especially as seriously depleted ATP levels have not been detected even in completely exhausted muscles and changes in blood or nutrient flow have not been shown to stimulate muscle growth. This theory proposes that hypertrophy results from the 'supercompensation' of protein synthesis after high intensity exercise, analogous to the supercompensation of muscle glycogen after prolonged lower intensity exercise.

Since glycogen supercompensation is a transient effect, lasting only long enough to facilitate prolonged exercise in endurance events, it is relevant to refer to our later remarks on the use of the term *adaptive reconstruction* instead of supercompensation (see 1.16).

The acute shortage of cellular energy after strenuous activity is held to be the trigger for the eventual supercompensation (or adaptive reconstruction) during the subsequent low intensity or rest phases. Since each cell possesses only a fixed quantity of energy at any given instant, it has to be distributed between protein metabolism and mechanical work. Under conditions of rest or recovery, most of the energy is directed to protein synthesis, whereas most of it is devoted to muscle contraction during intense exercise (Fig 1.31). The lack of energy for protein growth and maintenance during heavy exercise apparently produces protein catabolism (breakdown), which stimulates protein supercompensation during later rest periods.

The prescription of any type of resistance training to produce a given functional change depends on examining the concurrent effects of the training regime on muscle hypertrophy and subfibral hyperplasia. The popular view is that the greater the intensity of the load, the greater the activation of the motor apparatus, so that the *intensity of functioning of structures* (IFS) and hence, the amount of active muscle tissue grows. This is supported by the fact that muscle genes are regulated largely by mechanical stimulation (see 1.12). Despite abundant earlier research indicating that intense physical loading apparently causes sarcomere hypertrophy, more recent findings, however, reveal quite the opposite result (Nikituk & Samoilov, 1990).

The data shows that the longer and more strenuous the submaximal loading (but not the rapid, near maximal low-repetition loading of Olympic weightlifting), the less there is sarcomere hypertrophy and the more there is sarcoplasmic hypertrophy. Although increase in load intensity and speeding up of its rate of increase promotes overall muscle hypertrophy, it is accompanied by a greater breakdown of muscle fibres and a decrease in the number of contractile structures. The hypertrophied muscle contains fewer sarcoplasmic organelles, myofibrils and mitochondria, so that the increased diameter of the muscle fibres is due largely to an increase in the volume of sarcoplasm (i.e. sarcoplasmic hypertrophy).

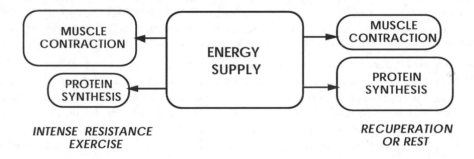

Figure 1.31 The distribution of cellular energy during intense resistance exercise versus rest. Note that prolonged intense resistance work can diminish the availability of energy for protein synthesis and halt any increase in hypertrophy of the muscle fibres.

Other research has found that *hypertrophied muscle fibres need a significantly larger tissue volume to perform a given quantity of work*. With the development of non-functional hypertrophy, the increase in muscle mass outstrips the development of the vascular system. This results in diminished nutrition and oxygenation of the muscle, slowing down of metabolic processes in the muscle and less efficient disposal of metabolic waste products from the musculoskeletal system (Zalessky & Burkhanov, 1981).

Furthermore, *adaptation occurs more slowly in connective tissue* (such as tendons and ligaments) than in muscle and any increased tension made possible in the musculotendinous complexes by the increased muscle mass can cause damage to these structures (Zalessky & Burkhanov, 1981). Thus, *excessive hypertrophy usually leads to slower muscle recovery after exercise, deterioration in speed, speed-strength and speed, as well as an increased incidence of injury.*

This might suggest that all muscle fibre hypertrophy lowers work capacity. Hypertrophy is an adaptive response to physical stress and does offer the benefit of increased mitochondrial surface area, which provides for more efficient energy processes than would an increased number of mitochondria. With a rapid increase in loading, the size of the mitochondria continues to increase markedly, but their number decreases and the concentration of ATP drops, thereby diminishing the partial volume of the contractile myofibrils. The resulting energy deficit soon inhibits the formation of new structures and the decreased amount of ATP stimulates various destructive processes associated with decrease in the number of myofibrils. This process is referred to as *irrational adaptation.*

Growth of any living structure is related to the balance between its volume and its surface area. When muscle hypertrophy occurs, the surface of the fibres grows more slowly than their volume and, according to Hartwig and Mezia, this imbalance causes the fibres to disintegrate and restructure in a way which preserves their original thermodynamic state (Nikituk & Samoilov, 1990). It would appear that light and medium increases in loading require less energy, facilitate cell repair, minimise the occurrence of destructive processes and stimulate the synthesis of new, non-hypertrophied organelles. Medium loads applied with a medium rate of increase in loading produce intense muscular development, the process in this case being referred to as *rational adaptation.*

The fact that conventional isometric training improves performance in static, rather than dynamic, exercise may be due to the different structural effects of isometric training. Gudzia has discovered that *static training* produces the following changes: the sarcoplasmic content of many muscle fibres increases, myofibrils collect into fascicles, nuclei become rounder, motor end-plates expand transversally relative to the muscle fibres, capillaries meander more markedly, and the layers of endomysium and perimysium thicken. In the case of *dynamic training*, the transverse striations of the myofibrils become very pronounced, the nuclei become oval and fusiform (spindle-shaped), motor end-plates extend the length of the muscle fibres, and the layers of endomysium and perimysium become thinner (Bondarchuk et al, 1984).

The above work seems to corroborate the hypothesis referred to earlier that *there may be an optimum size for muscle fibres undergoing hypertrophy* (MacDougall et al, 1982; Tesch & Larsson, 1982). The importance of prescribing resistance training regimes which produce the optimal balance between hypertrophy and specific strength then becomes obvious. Thus, it is not only prolonged cardiovascular training which can be detrimental to the acquisition of strength, but multiple fairly high repetition sets of heavy bodybuilding or circuit training routines to the point of failure may also inhibit the formation of contractile muscle fibres.

Therefore, it is vital to monitor regularly changes in muscular structure and function alongside changes in size and mass. In most cases the taking of biopsies is not possible or financially practical, so that indirect assessment of the adaptive processes is necessary. Increase in hypertrophy of a given muscle zone may be assessed from muscle girth and skinfold thicknesses at that site, while factors such as relative strength, maximal strength and the strength deficit (discussed early in Ch 1) serve as useful indicators of functional efficiency.

Bosco (1982a) cautions against the indiscriminate use of resistance training that typifies much of the 'cross training' prescribed with weights and circuits by Western personal trainers and coaches. He emphasizes that, although heavy resistance training serves as a powerful stimulus for the development and hypertrophy of both ST and FT fibres, the invaluable role played by FT development can be impaired by the accompanying growth of ST fibres, because the latter appear to provoke a damping effect on FT contraction during fast movement. This is due to the fact that, during high speed shortening of muscle, the sliding velocity of ST fibres can be too slow and therefore, may exert a significant damping effect on the overall muscle contraction. He concludes that the central role played by the storage and release of elastic energy by the connective tissues of the muscle complex should never be ignored in sport specific training programmes (see 1.7.2 and 5.2.4).

Effects of High versus Moderate Intensity Exercise

Besides the adaptive effects of the different regimes of strength training discussed above, there are other effects worthy of mention which refer to the different outcomes produced by high intensity versus moderate or submaximal resistance training.

Besides enhancing muscle hypertrophy, low volume high intensity resistance exercise also increases the cross-sectional area of fast and slow twitch fibres, with a greater relative hypertrophy occurring in the fast-twitch fibres (McDougall et al, 1980; Tesch et al, 1985; Thorstennson, 1976). A comparison of strength- and endurance-trained subjects revealed that the area of both fast and slow twitch muscle fibres was greater in the strength-trained group (Alway et al, 1988). Tesch et al (1987) showed that a six month-long, heavy resistance training resulted in a decrease in the activity of enzymes involved in 'aerobic' metabolic pathways (hexokinase, creatine kinase, myofibrillar ATPase, citrate synthase, myokinase and phosphofructokinase). Other research revealed that citrate synthase activity is lower in weightlifters and powerlifters than in bodybuilders and non-athletes (Tesch, 1988). This difference is probably due to the fact that weightlifters and powerlifters regularly train at near maximal intensity with few repetitions, whereas bodybuilders train at moderate intensity and fairly high volume. Five months of heavy resistance exercise was also shown to significantly increase the levels of the energy substrates glycogen, ATP, creatine phosphate and creatine (MacDougall et al, 1977).

Moderate intensity, high repetition resistance exercise, as commonly used in bodybuilding and circuit training, can also convert fast-twitch to behave more like slow-twitch fibres, apparently in an adaptive attempt to resist the fatigue of the repeated efforts (Timson et al, 1985; Baldwin et al, 1992; Noble & Pettigrew, 1989). Under these conditions, the transitional muscle fibres exhibit contraction times similar to those of fast fibres, but with fatigue resistance more like slow fibres. Thus, the capacity for strength-endurance seemed to increase.

A mechanism for this muscle adaptation was offered by Hoy et al (1980), who found that the fast isoforms of myosin disappear and are replaced by isomyosins that are characteristic of slow muscle after chronic overloading. This fibre transformation caused by chronic stimulation is regulated primarily at the genetic transcriptional level of regulation (Heilig & Pette, 1983). This process is associated with the presence in fast-twitch muscle of a myosin light chain component that is usually observed only in slow-twitch fibres (Samaha et al, 1970). For these reasons, it would appear that high volume, moderate resistance training is actually high intensity, general endurance training.

Several studies of male and female bodybuilders have discovered that female muscle appears to adapt to resistance training in a different way from male muscle (Bell & Jacobs, 1990; Alway et al, 1992). Although the cross-sectional area of fast and slow twitch muscles increased in both male and female bodybuilders, the fast-twitch muscles of the males had a significantly greater area than the slow-twitch muscles, a trend which was not found among the females.

1.14 Neurophysiological Aspects of Exercise

All-round preparation of the athlete necessitates physical and psychological training, not as separate components, but as closely interrelated aspects of human performance. The mental and physical systems interact continuously and it is vital to remember that the highly-skilled, superbly conditioned body is of little value in competition without the right frame of mind. For instance, an emotional upset can prevent the athlete from relaxing or concentrating to produce the necessary degree of physical efficiency. Similarly, a slight physical injury may disturb one sufficiently to diminish confidence, concentration and skill.

The body may be viewed as a living cybernetic (control and communication) system in which the central nervous system, including the brain and spinal cord, controls the functions of the body via two major communication systems: the nervous system (autonomic and voluntary systems) and the hormonal system (endocrine glands).

The hormonal system is involved with control of the slower bodily processes such as growth, metabolism, sexual function, excretion and temperature regulation. The nervous system is concerned mainly with rapid processes such as sight, hearing, thinking and muscular contraction. However, these two systems interact in numerous processes, the link between them being the hypothalamus, situated near the middle of the brain. The hypothalamus is linked with the brain's limbic system (intimately connected with emotion) and the pituitary gland (sometimes called the master gland of the body). It may be inferred immediately that physical efficiency depends on proper utilisation of thought processes, emotions and muscles.

This may be seen from Figure 1.32 which illustrates how external stimuli from the environment and internal stimuli from within the body are received by the specialised transducers of the sensory systems and relayed to the relevant parts of the central nervous system for further processing. Not only does the latter system activate the muscular system to produce appropriate patterns of movement, but it also relays information to the hypothalamus which may produce emotional and glandular responses.

This model offers a simplified foundation for the psychology of sport. The remainder of this section is devoted to analysing the different systems of the body and applying this information to physical training and competition.

1. The Sensory System

The sensory systems (see Fig 1.32) provide man with information about his environment and his body. The traditional view refers to the 'five senses' (sight, hearing, touch, smell and taste), but neglects the vital 'inner senses' known as the kinaesthetic sense (sense of the position and movements of the body and its limbs) and the visceral sense (sense of operation of the inner organs such as heart and digestive system).

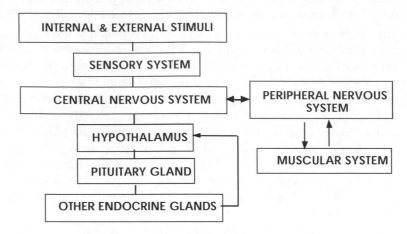

Figure 1.32 Interaction between central nervous, endocrine and muscular systems

The kinaesthetic sense depends on information coming from the touch receptors in the skin, from the balance and gyroscopic centres of the inner ear and from the proprioceptors in the joints, muscles and tendons. This sense provides essential information to the brain to enable movements to be performed by the relevant muscles and limbs in specific patterns at a certain velocity and intensity. The importance of the proprioceptors may be appreciated when one realises that proprioception is second only to pain in causing the most intense and widespread electrical activity in the brain.

The eyes are undoubtedly extremely important in guiding the athlete in execution of the correct movements, while the ears may assist him in timing phases of the manoeuvre via feedback of any sound produced by the body or apparatus. However, without the kinaesthetic sense, skilled physical activity would be impossible. The following is a summary of the main subsystems which contribute essential data to the kinaesthetic sense:

Joint receptors This network of nerves in the ligament capsule surrounding movable joints gives information about the angle between the bones of the joints and the rate at which this angle is changing.

Muscle spindles These coiled nerves stretch as the muscles stretch, relaying information back to the central nervous system about the relative lengths of and degree of tension in the muscle.

Golgi tendon apparatus This nerve network, situated in the tendons of the muscles, continuously monitors tension and contributes to coordination of the actions of many cooperating muscles. This system is important for protecting muscle fibres from excessive loading by decreasing muscle tension after it reaches a critical value.

Vestibular apparatus This system, located close to the inner ear, constitutes an inertial guidance or gyroscopic balance mechanism which is sensitive to any changes in position, velocity and acceleration of the head, and consequently, of the entire body. The three semicircular canals monitor position and angular velocity, since they are too slow to respond to angular acceleration, whereas the hair-and-jelly-like structure of the utricle measures acceleration.

The following two types of receptor are not traditionally kinaesthetic senses, but are also very important in the control of skilled movement:

Touch receptors These pressure receptors, which work closely in cooperation with the proprioceptive system, cover the surface of the entire body and supply information to the brain of the contact of any part of the body with an outside object.

Pain receptors Specific or non-specific pain receptors throughout the body inform the brain about the dangers of overstressing or damaging any part of the body. Moreover, certain foci in parts of the brain such as the limbic system (also involved with emotion and motivation) receiving stimulation from all the other senses play an important role in the perception of pain.

In the early stages of learning skilled movement, the athlete has to use the voluntary nervous system to assist in integrating the huge amount of information from all of the kinaesthetic systems. Eventually he should be able to rely almost entirely on automatic, reflexive processes to manage the same task. In fact, it has been discovered that the unskilled athlete not only produces inefficient patterns, intensities and timing of movements, but he also recruits muscles which serve no purpose in controlling those movements. Moreover, the existence of tension in muscles which are supposed to be relaxed or performing a different degree or pattern of tension, may well be a cause of muscular injury. Hence, learning correct technique is essential not only for efficiency but also for preventing injury. Neglect of this basic rule is commonplace among many athletes who strain inefficiently using brute force to perform a manoeuvre which would take place effortlessly if more attention were to be paid to perfecting technique.

2. The Central Nervous System

The central nervous system (see Fig 1.32) is the complex central computing facility of the brain and spinal column which processes incoming information and sends out commands to the rest of the body (including the muscles) via the peripheral nervous system (see Fig 1.33).

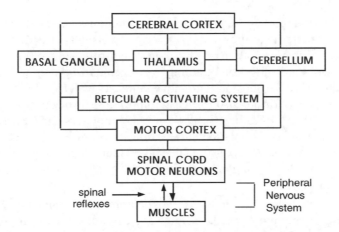

Figure 1.33 A simplified representation of the major components and interconnections of the central nervous system involved with the control and execution of motor activity.

Scientific understanding of the brain has made massive strides recently and the simple view offered here is not intended to provide a thorough physiological treatise. Instead, the more important theories and findings are given to enable the reader to base his training methods on a more solid scientific foundation.

At the outset it should be noted that in certain emergency situations the muscles have to react very rapidly and, therefore, time cannot be spent in having the input signals pass through the entire computing facility of the central nervous system. The body provides for this with its system of reflex loops. For example, if one's hand accidentally touches a hot object, reflex action managed solely at the level of the spinal cord compels one to withdraw the hand almost immediately and prevent further injury. During voluntary movements reflex action also occurs at the level of the motor cortex and not merely at the level of the spinal cord (Evarts, 1979).

The Russian psychologist Pavlov was the first researcher to recognise that conditioned reflexes could be learned by proper methods of reinforcement. In other words, programmes of correctly repeated movements can eventually enable these movements to become automatic. This is particularly important in the case of all manoeuvres which have to be executed rapidly and cannot accommodate delays caused by active thinking about the process.

Repetition of incorrect movements will eventually result in their becoming built-in reflexes which are difficult to erase. Any attempt to change faulty technique usually results in a feeling of awkwardness and an inability to perform as comfortably as before. This is because the body has adapted to its inefficient movement patterns, and the emotional distress caused by apparently useless new techniques can prevent the athlete from implementing any changes. Often one will hear a coach or colleague shouting instructions to a competitor to correct faulty technique during rapid movements. This is little more than useless because it is not possible consciously to change the course of any movement which lasts less than 0.4 second (Thomas, 1970). Moreover, the well-known phenomenon of *paralysis by analysis* may result if the athlete tries to correct or advise himself immediately before or during a skilled manoeuvre.

It is rare for any movement sequence to be controlled entirely by reflex loops; instead, reflexes operate together with the entire control system depicted in Fig 1.33. The traditional view was that the motor cortex, guided by the cerebellum as a mere servo-control device, is the highest centre for motor integration. Moreover, it was assumed that control begins together with or just after initiation of any movement (i.e. via *feedback*). Instead, research has now discovered that the motor cortex is at a lower level of control, more directly connected to spinal-cord motor neurons than either the cerebellum or the basal ganglia. It was also found that the cerebellum, the basal ganglia and the motor cortex all become active before any movement begins (Evarts, 1973, 1979). Furthermore, a specific brain rhythm of about 9 Hz (the mu rhythm) is blocked in advance of any physical movement (Siff, 1977). There is also an increase in muscle tone and other changes in activity of the cerebral cortex (such as the 'orientation response' and 'expectancy waves') preceding the commencement of a motor response (Siff, 1977).

It is also known that the cerebellum does not initiate movement, but corrects or reorganizes motor commands before they reach the muscles, thereby implementing inner *feedforward mechanisms* to ensure maximum external muscular efficiency. The cerebellum can even coordinate movement in the absence of all information from the periphery of the body (Llinas, 1975).

These findings clearly are most important for devising correct training methods. Since brain activity precedes movement, it is vital that correct patterns of movement are correctly visualised even before practice begins. In fact, the technique of visualisation by observation of films, top weightlifters and coaches, combined with proper mental rehearsal, forms an integral part of Russian training. *Autogenic training* in which the athlete visualises himself in action, feeling all the muscular tensions and movements, as well as the physiological and emotional changes actually encountered in competition, also forms an important part of the advanced training of Russian athletes. Sometimes, devices such as an ECG, EMG, blood pressure monitors and GSR (Galvanic skin response) meters are attached to the athlete to ensure that the visualisation is accurately simulating the conditions of the sporting action. *Feedforward* mechanisms (see 1.9) established by mental mapping of intended manoeuvres and by regular use of autogenic training should be more familiar to coaches than they are at present. In other words, 'mental and physical practice makes perfect'.

The same research has revealed that the *motor cortex* determines the amount and pattern of muscular contraction, rather than the displacement produced. Moreover, the motor cortex is involved with both slow and fast movements, whereas the *basal ganglia* seem to be preferentially active in slow movements. It has further been suggested that the major role of the *cerebellum* is to preprogramme and initiate rapid ballistic movements (Evarts, 1973). In the overall scheme of events, the basal ganglia and the cerebellum receive information from the intero-receptors (proprioceptors and other inner sensors) and the exteroceptors (eyes, ears and other external receptors) of the cerebral cortex (the supreme thinking control centre), transform this information and then send an appropriate pattern of signals to the motor cortex. Information about the state of the muscles is constantly fed back from the proprioceptors to the CNS, otherwise control of movement would be impossible.

The primary function of the cerebellum in fine motor control has recently been challenged by research showing that it may also be involved in perception, cognition, visualisation and memory storage (Rapoport et al, 2000; Kenyon, 1997). An alternative hypothesis is that the lateral cerebellum is not activated by the control of movement per se, but is strongly engaged during the acquisition and discrimination of sensory information (Jia-Hong Gao et al, 1996). These findings suggest that the lateral cerebellum may be active during motor, perceptual, and cognitive performances specifically because of the requirement to process sensory data.

The cerebellum also appear to play a role in the visualisation of movement and feedforward processes. Analysis of cortical activity has already supported the hypothesis that motor imagery and motor performance possess similar neural substrates. The differential activation in the cerebellum during executed and imagined movements is in accordance with the assumption that the posterior cerebellum is involved in the inhibition of movement execution during imagination (Lotze, 1999).

The thalamus and reticular activating system situated deep within the brain play a vital role in activating different parts of the brain acting as relay stations, and in integrating emotional and hormonal responses with the more mechanical functions. It is at this level that the hypothalamus generally becomes involved (see Fig 1.30).

Even though the same muscles may be involved in a movement, they may be controlled by different parts of the brain, depending on the speed of movement. Yet, it is not only speed which may determine the brain mechanisms required. There is strong evidence that two different control mechanisms are involved in the cardiovascular response to exercise (Med Chron, 1978). This means that isometric and dynamic exercise recruit different brain mechanisms, because isometric exercise causes a marked increase in blood pressure, but little increase in blood flow. Dynamic exercise, however, generates an oxygen demand that is met largely by an increase in the volume of blood pumped and a decreased resistance to its flow.

To further complicate the issue, slow, as opposed to, rapid execution of the same movement might involve different muscle groups (Basmajian, 1978). For instance, experiments with arm curls reveal that both slow and rapid movements activate the biceps and brachialis muscles but, in addition, rapid curling also recruits the brachioradialis muscle.

These findings have profound implications for sport. For example, perfection of a movement at slow speed may not necessarily result in perfection at high speed. Isometric or isokinetic training of any muscle which should be producing efficient auxotonic movements may result in inefficiency of technique. High repetition stamina-type exercises may well be disadvantageous to the person whose sport places little reliance on sustained series of movements. Moreover, any movement may be influenced by other movements which precede it. In fact, efficiency in the weightlifting snatch can suffer if one has performed repetition snatches as long as 24 hours previously. Inappropriate stretching or warming-up may be detrimental to proper execution of the actual movements required in a competition. Fatigue has a pronounced effect on skill, and different skills have to be learned for operation in the fatigued state.

Simulation training which involves imitation of a specific movement using more resistance than encountered in actual performance compels the body or its limbs to operate at a different speed, recruit different muscles and use different patterns of muscular activity as compared with the competition movements. Simulation training in tennis, for instance, might involve practice of the backhand stroke with weights or pulley machines offering additional resistance to the playing arm. Unless simulation takes place over a small, well-controlled segment of a complicated movement or with very small differences in loading, it should form no part of an athlete's routine. Strength and skill are different aspects of training and generally should be developed separately, except in sports such as weightlifting, gymnastics and shotputting which integrate both factors in explosive, single movements.

At the level of the muscles, it should be remembered that the force produced by a group of muscles is proportional not only to the cross-sectional area of the muscles but also to the number and efficiency of appropriate muscle fibres contracting simultaneously (see Section 1.6). This is a consequence of mental factors and technical expertise rather than of muscle mass or size, so no athlete should ever focus largely on the latter qualities at the expense of the former.

Technical perfection depends, inter alia, on acquiring mastery of the appropriate modes of driving the muscles: either cocontraction or ballistic action (see 1.9). No matter which mode is involved, ultimate control resides in the motor systems of the brain.

Contrary to common belief, dynamic cocontraction is not the primary action implicated in continuous exercises such as running. Much of the energy is stored from step to step as elastic energy in the tendons which undergo considerable change in length, unlike the muscles which rewind the tendons after each movement. This system of initial isometric contraction followed by ballistic swing is far more efficient than continuous dynamic activity, which requires much more energy (Green, 1967). Cybernetic processes in the CNS, based on practice of correct technique, are responsible for ensuring this standard of efficiency.

The states described as mental effort, motivation and concentration are closely related to the functioning of the reticular activating system (RAS - see Fig 1.31) and the limbic system, which includes parts of the thalamus, basal ganglia and the hypothalamus (Fig 1.33). Specific pain and pleasure centres have been located throughout these systems, which may provide some basis for motivated behaviour. According to current theory, emotional response depends partly on the limbic system controlling the pleasure-pain and the approach-avoidance reactions, and partly on the RAS controlling the intensity of activation.

The hypothalamus influences a wide series of activities: temperature regulation, water balance, growth, appetite, the metabolism of sugar, fats and electrolytes, respiration, sleep, digestion, and the activity of the heart and blood vessels. Changes in these activities may provide a secondary source of information concerning bodily feelings by transmitting information back to the brain to contribute to the experience of an emotional state.

1.15 Bioenergetics and the Energy Systems

Fitness has been defined earlier as the ability to cope efficiently and safely with the demands of a specific task or activity. There is not simply one type of 'fitness'. A different type of physical fitness is required for cardiovascular, strength, and muscle endurance activities. The existence of these different types of 'fitness' is largely a consequence of the different metabolic processes which are responsible for providing energy in response to the special demands imposed by the specific activity.

1.15.1 The Energy Systems and Types of Activity

All physical activity may be distinguished essentially on the basis of two major factors: intensity and duration. These factors are not independent, since high intensity activity cannot be sustained for long periods before exhaustion interrupts it. High intensity activity can proceed only in short spurts interspersed with regular rest intervals to facilitate recovery. Conversely, low intensity activity can continue for prolonged periods. Thus, the *duration of exercise is inversely related to its intensity*. In other words, the intensity of the exercise plays the dominant role in determining the maximum duration of the exercise.

The physics concept of *power* (i.e. work done per unit time, where work, roughly speaking, is the force multiplied by the distance through which the force acts) combines the factors of intensity and duration, and can serve as a useful alternative measure of which energy pathway or system predominates during a specific activity.

High intensity or high power output activity places strong demands on specific muscle groups, whereas low intensity or low power activity places small demands on the muscles. Intensity thus may be assessed in terms of the proportion of fibres in a specific muscle group contracting simultaneously. Intense or powerful activity may be divided into two types:

- maximal or near maximal, very short duration activity
- sub-maximal, longer duration activity.

The former refers to explosive or powerful actions such as kicking, jumping, clean-and-jerking a weight and throwing, whereas the latter refers to muscle endurance activities which require particular muscle groups to produce fairly strong contractions over periods characteristically as long as several minutes in duration. These contractions may be produced under static or dynamic conditions, so that one may distinguish between static and dynamic muscle endurance.

High intensity activity characteristically is associated with rapid changes in heart rate and blood pressure. It often elicits the *Valsalva manoeuvre*, or forced breath-holding against a closed glottis (in the lower larynx) and restricts local blood flow. Low intensity activity may be assessed in terms of the demands it places on the cardiovascular and circulatory systems of the body. Two different types of low intensity activity (excluding the sedentary state of minimal intensity) may be distinguished:

- low intensity actions which elevate the heart rate minimally, such as slow walking
- low intensity actions which elevate the heart rate into a zone known as the heart training zone and keeps it at that level for at least 15 minutes.

The former produces minimal fitness of any type. At best, it encourages circulation of blood and lymph around the body and may serve as a form of mild active recuperation and relaxation. It does not produce cardiovascular fitness. The latter, if continued over a period of weeks or months, enhances cardiovascular fitness and produces a lower resting pulse and a pulse rate which returns to its resting value rapidly after exercise. Unfortunately, prolonged cardiovascular training interferes with the development of strength or power. The body caters for the demands of these different types of fitness by utilising three overlapping and interacting energy systems:

- The high intensity, short duration (or high power output) system
- The medium intensity, medium duration (or medium power output) system
- The low intensity, long duration (or low power output) system.

The first two systems produce energy under conditions which do not rely on oxygen and used to be called anaerobic systems. They are now more accurately referred to as *oxygen-independent systems* or pathways. (Some authorities prefer the terms *non-aerobic*). The last-named system, formerly known as the aerobic system, is now called the *oxygen-dependent system* or pathway (some still use the term *aerobic* to mean the same thing).

The terms *oxidative* and *non-oxidative* scientifically are more accurate than *aerobic* and *anaerobic* or non-aerobic, since oxidation does not refer only to the process whereby oxygen combines with other elements or compounds. Oxidation also occurs in a reaction in which hydrogen atoms are removed from a compound. The acquisition of oxygen atoms and the loss of hydrogen atoms are both characterised by the oxidised substance losing negatively charged entities known as electrons. Thus, *oxidation refers to any reaction in whereby a chemical compound loses electrons*.

The high intensity, short duration system produces energy from processes relying on the high energy phosphate compounds ATP (adenosine triphosphate) and CP (creatine phosphate). It is known as the *phosphagen, high energy phosphate or ATP-CP system*. A former name was the alactic anaerobic energy system.

The intermediate system, formerly known as the lactic anaerobic (or anaerobic glycolytic) energy or lactic acid system, is now referred to as the *oxygen-independent (or non-oxidative) glycolytic system*. The process of glycolysis ('*-lysis'* means 'loosening' or 'breaking down') refers to the breakdown or conversion of glucose into pyruvic acid and ATP. Lactic acid, or rather, lactate, is also produced under these conditions and can serve as an additional energy source. Contrary to former opinion, glycolysis does not take place only when there is inadequate oxygen present. For instance, glycolysis is a dominant process during sprinting, even though the muscles have sufficient oxygen during these short events.

The long-term system relies on the continuous use of oxygen for the oxidation of glycogen (stored in the muscles and liver) or fatty acids (from stored body fats). Therefore, it became known as the aerobic energy system, a term which led to the name *aerobics* to describe the emerging fitness-to-music industry. Regrettably, this term continues to be applied erroneously to all types of aerobics class, including stretching, despite the fact that many of these classes do not rely predominantly on aerobic processes. The term 'fitness class' would be preferable and more accurate. This long-term energy system or pathway is now referred to more correctly as the *oxygen-dependent (or oxidative) system*. It is this system which predominates during prolonged cardiovascular events such as distance running or cycling.

It is important to correct the misconception that oxidative processes involve the direct and immediate combustion of nutrients with inhaled oxygen. It has led to the difficulty the lay person has with understanding sprinting is not an aerobic (oxygen-dependent) event and that the oxygen inhaled vigorously during sprinting (an 'anaerobic' event) is not utilised immediately and directly to produce energy. *Cellular oxidation* by direct reliance on molecular oxygen (O_2) *occurs only at the end of a series of metabolic processes* which remove hydrogen atoms in successive stages from the original energy-producing substances.

It is also important to note that all movement involves muscle actions which simultaneously stabilise and move the limbs, so that the body may rely on cardiovascular processes for its overall movement in a particular event, while the postural muscles are fuelled by oxygen-independent processes. Thus, oxidative processes might be dominant systemically, whereas locally, non-oxidative processes also might be highly active. It is incorrect to state that only one energy system or pathway is active during a specific activity. Even at a general systemic level, there is an overlap between the three energy systems described above (Fig 1.34).

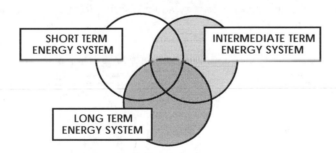

Figure 1.34 The overlap between the different energy systems at any instant

1.15.2 Energy Mechanisms

Bioenergetics refers to the series of processes whereby energy is produced to sustain biological activity and to fuel muscular movement. This energy cannot be derived directly from food. Instead, different chemical pathways in the body break down the food to produce building materials for repair, maintenance and growth of the cells, as well as for providing energy to carry out all of these processes.

The production of energy from nutrients is known as *metabolism*. This, in turn, consists of two types of biochemical reaction: *anabolic* reactions, in which large or more complex molecules are assembled from smaller or simpler ones, and *catabolic* reactions, in which larger or more complex substances are broken down into simpler ones. For instance, the breakdown of protein foods during digestion is catabolic, whereas the building up of muscle tissue from amino acids and the synthesis of the complex carbohydrate, glycogen, from glucose is anabolic. Another group of reactions which is catabolic is *cellular respiration*, whereby fatty acids, glucose and amino acids are broken down in the cells to release energy and form ATP.

All energy-requiring processes in the cells rely ultimately on the basic energy molecule of the body, ATP (adenosine triphosphate). This molecule consists of adenosine (a combination of *adenine* and the sugar *ribose*) linked with three phosphate molecules by high-energy bonds, in particular the two outermost phosphate bonds (Fig 1.35). When the latter two bonds are broken, a burst of energy is released and the ATP is broken down to ADP (adenosine diphosphate). The ATP is applied directly to the muscle cross-bridges to activate and maintain the process of cross-bridging between the heads on the myosin filaments and the active sites on the actin filaments of the muscle fibres (see 1.7).

This energy is produced in the tiny *mitochondria*, the so-called 'powerhouses' of the cell, whose major responsibility is to power muscle contractions. These energy generators produce ATP only in the presence of adequate oxygen, so that there needs to be an emergency back-up system to generate ATP under oxygen deficient circumstances. Such a system, indeed, exists in the cells. It was mentioned above as the oxygen-independent glycolytic system. It depends on a group of enzymes or specialised biological catalysts which facilitate the oxygen-independent breakdown of stored glycogen and blood glucose in the cell and provide the necessary energy for muscle contraction.

The Concept of Oxygen Debt

Exercise under these conditions of high intensity effort is followed by a period of accelerated breathing, which used to be thought of as a mechanism employed to pay back an *'oxygen debt'* incurred by relying on non-oxidative processes and depriving the body of oxygen during the exercise. Nowadays, the concept of an oxygen debt is considered as outmoded. Instead, the post exercise period is now known to reflect recovery oxygen consumption to regenerate cellular ATP (and CP) and to return the respiratory, ionic, circulatory, hormonal and thermal processes to their resting state (McArdle, Katch & Katch, 1991).

1.15.3 The Short-term Energy System

The energy for high intensity, high power or very rapid activity comes largely from the high energy phosphagen stores (ATP and CP). The initial energy is furnished by the breakdown of ATP into ADP and inorganic phosphate Pi in the presence of water and the enzyme *adenosine triphosphatase* (Note: the suffix *'-ase'* refers to a compound serving as a biological catalyst to facilitate or control a biochemical reaction). Each mole of ATP produces about 7.3 kilocalories (35 kilojoules) of energy and a residue of ADP, which has to be upgraded to ATP from the CP (creatine phosphate) stores (Fig 1.35).

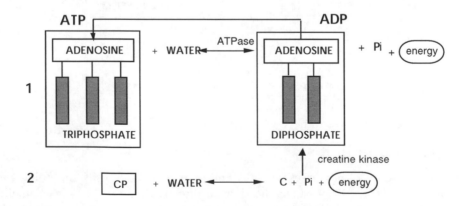

Figure 1.35 Energy processes involving ATP, ADP and CP

The small quantity of ATP in the muscle cells is depleted within a few seconds of strenuous all-out activity and muscle action would cease but for the fact that energy is transferred rapidly to the ADP by the CP reservoir in the cells. There is some three to five times as much CP as ATP in the cells, which enables the phosphagen system to fuel intense effort for a maximum of 20-30 seconds. The enzyme *creatine kinase* catalyses this reaction. After this, the exercise intensity has to drop to enable the phosphagen stores to be replenished by the other energy systems. Any increase in the concentration of ADP in the cell signals the need for more energy to be made available from the breakdown of carbohydrates, fat or protein in order to restore the levels of ATP.

1.15.4 The Intermediate Energy System

Both the intermediate and long term energy systems derive energy from stored or circulating nutrient substrates derived from ingested carbohydrates, fats or proteins. The difference between these two systems or pathways is that the *intermediate system* derives energy *non-oxidatively* from glycogen, whereas the *long-term system* releases energy *oxidatively* from glycogen or fatty acids. Another difference is that lactate (or 'lactic acid') is produced in the intermediate system, which may also serve as another energy substrate.

In both cases, energy is released essentially by the same process after the carbohydrates, fats and proteins have each been processed through different preliminary reactions to produce a suitable fuel for acceptance into the main part of the metabolic cycle, known as the *Krebs cycle* or citric acid cycle (Fig 1.36).

It is important to note that all carbohydrates in food are eventually transformed to *glucose* as a major body fuel. Although fats can also act as a source of fuel, certain cells, such as those of the brain and blood, rely almost exclusively on glucose for their energy. Thus, if blood glucose levels drop and the brain is even temporarily deprived of glucose, functioning of the nerve cells can be seriously disrupted and one's state of consciousness can be profoundly disturbed. Usually, a decrease in blood glucose precipitates a feeling of hunger. Mild deficits of glucose lead to fatigue, faintness, dizziness or disorientation, which commonly happens in anyone exercising whose blood sugar or blood glucose levels drop below a certain threshold concentration. This state is known as *hypoglycaemia* ('hypo-' means low; 'glyc-' refers to glucose). Greater deficits can lead to collapse, coma or death.

When carbohydrates are ingested, the hormone *insulin* is released by the pancreas into the blood, with a particularly large increase in secretion occurring after the ingestion of sugars, a phenomenon sometimes referred to as 'insulin shock'. Insulin levels then remain elevated for some 60 - 90 minutes and inhibit the release of energy from glycogen in the liver and from fatty acids, which are a major energy source during prolonged cardiovascular exercise. This compels the body to rely on the limited amounts of glycogen stored in the muscle or blood, thereby leading to premature hypoglycaemia and systemic fatigue. This is why insulin is sometimes called the 'anti-exercise' hormone. This is also a good reason why sucrose should not be regarded as a suitable or effective fuel for prolonged cardiovascular exercise, despite regular advertising to the contrary. More complex carbohydrates or starches which do not produce the same rapidity of insulin release are preferable (with lower glycaemic index, GI).

As ATP and CP are depleted by intense activity, so the intermediate energy system becomes increasingly important in generating energy for sustaining muscle action. For example, an athlete sprinting at the end of a 1500 metres race depends heavily on regenerating phosphagens by the non-oxidative breakdown of glycogen.

In this system, glycogen stored in the liver or muscles undergoes *glycolysis*, that is, the hydrolysis (breakdown in the presence of water) of glycogen, first to a special derivative of glucose, *glucose 1-phosphate*, and then to another derivative, *glucose 6-phosphate*, in a reaction regulated by the enzyme, *phosphorylase*. In the liver, another enzyme, *glucose 6-phosphatase*, converts the glucose 6-phosphate to glucose for delivery to the bloodstream and thence to the muscles, brain, red blood cells and kidneys. During exercise, skeletal muscle becomes the main site of glucose uptake. The end-product of glycolysis is called *pyruvate*, most of which crosses the mitochondrial membrane, in which is embedded the enzyme, *pyruvate dehydrogenase* ('dehydrogen' means 'removes hydrogen'; '-ase' indicates that this is an enzyme - in other words, this is an enzyme for removing hydrogen from pyruvate).

When sufficient oxygen is present, pyruvate is able to enter the Krebs cycle and the pyruvate hydrogenase converts the pyruvate mainly to *acetyl-CoA*, the necessary end-product for entry into the Krebs cycle. Acetyl-CoA is a sulphur-containing coenzyme derived from the B vitamin, pantothenic acid, where a *coenzyme* is defined as a non-protein substance which is associated with and activates an enzyme. This process is known as *oxygen-dependent glycolysis* and is directly relevant to the discussion of the long-term energy system described in more detail in the next section (Fig 1.36).

When there is an oxygen deficit, the pyruvate is reduced mainly to lactate (or lactic acid), a process which is called *oxygen-independent glycolysis*. During mild exercise, sufficient oxygen is available to the cells and the rate of lactate removal equals its rate of formation, so that there is no accumulation of lactate.

Contrary to popular belief, *lactate is not a toxic by-product or waste-product of metabolism* accelerated by exercise. Lactate is produced even under conditions of rest and actually can serve as a valuable extra substrate (or source) of energy. When sufficient oxygen again becomes available via rest or decrease in exercise intensity, lactate is reconverted to pyruvate for use as an energy source. In addition, the lactate and pyruvate formed in muscle during exercise can be used to manufacture glucose by *gluconeogenesis* ('neo-' means 'new'; '-genesis' refers to 'making', so this word means 'making new glucose') in a process known as the *Cori cycle*. This supplements any existing blood glucose and muscle glycogen.

Moreover, *muscle fatigue* is not due to 'lactic acid poisoning' of the muscles. The formation of lactate (or lactic acid) is accompanied by the presence of positively-charged hydrogen ions (H^+) or protons. These electrical charges, which increase the acidity of the blood, can interfere with the muscle contraction process and the efficiency of the enzymes involved in energy production. Neither should lactic acid be regarded as the cause of *muscle soreness*, since blood lactate levels return to normal within an hour or so of strenuous interval training.

Furthermore, the most pronounced muscle soreness occurs after prolonged endurance events performed at speeds which keep lactate levels below the lactate threshold. Current theories favour the explanation that the soreness is due to transient damage of muscle cells or connective tissue.

Hydrogen is released at various stages of glycolysis and transferred to another metabolic system, the *electron transport chain*, which employs iron-containing proteins called *cytochromes* (in the mitochondrial membrane) to produce mitochondrial ATP. Oxygen ultimately combines with these hydrogens to form water, a major by-product of metabolism, along with carbon dioxide produced by processes such as the Krebs cycle (Fig 1.36).

Lactate does not accumulate to a significant degree until exercise intensity reaches about 55% of the healthy, untrained subject's maximum capacity for oxidative metabolism. The rate of lactate accumulation now exceeds its rate of removal and fatigue is initiated. The intensity of exercise has to be decreased if the activity is to continue. The point at which this occurs, formerly known as the anaerobic threshold, is now referred to as the *blood lactate threshold* (or turnpoint) or *OBLA* (Onset of Blood Lactate Accumulation).

The superior ability of the trained endurance athlete at higher levels of prolonged exercise intensity is largely due to the fact that :

- this threshold occurs at a higher percentage of one's oxidative (aerobic) capacity
- the athlete removes lactate more rapidly or converts it more efficiently to glucose.

It has also been proposed that lactate in one region of the working muscle of a trained athlete may be oxidised in the same or neighbouring less active muscles.

1.15.5 The Long-term Energy System

The long-term ('aerobic') energy system implicates metabolism under oxidative conditions and, as discussed earlier, may use either carbohydrates or fats to produce the necessary ATP for energy release in the muscles. Since all food carbohydrate is ultimately converted to glucose, carbohydrate metabolism may be understood in terms of glucose metabolism, a topic which was discussed earlier.

Protein sometimes may also be used as an energy source. After ingestion, the amino acids from the protein are stripped of their amine groups (NH_2) in a process called deamination and converted to pyruvate or other substances (keto acids), which can then enter the Krebs cycle (Fig 1.36).

The neutral fats (or lipids) which act as an energy source are triglycerides, which comprise a glycerol molecule to which are attached three fatty acid molecules. A process known as *lipolysis* ('lipo-' means 'fat'; '-lysis' means 'breaking down') breaks down the triglyceride into its constituent fatty acids and glycerol, via the intervention of the enzyme, triglyceride lipase. The *fatty acids* then undergo *beta oxidation*, a series of biochemical events which eventually produces *acetyl CoA* for entry into the Krebs cycle. After processing via other mechanisms, the glycerol molecule may be converted to glucose or fed into the Krebs cycle.

It has been said that 'fats burn in a carbohydrate flame', since the combustion of fats in the body relies on an adequate supply of carbohydrates. When there is a carbohydrate deficiency, fat oxidation is incomplete and the liver converts the acetyl CoA into by-products called *ketones*, which are released into the blood stream. If these ketones accumulate faster than they can be used as fuel by the cells and large quantities are secreted in the urine, *ketosis* occurs. Since ketones generally are strongly acidic, the acidity of the blood increases markedly and metabolic acidosis becomes evident. The person's breath displays a fruity (or nail varnish) smell as acetone is released from the lungs and breathing accelerates. Untreated serious cases of metabolic acidosis can lead to coma and death.

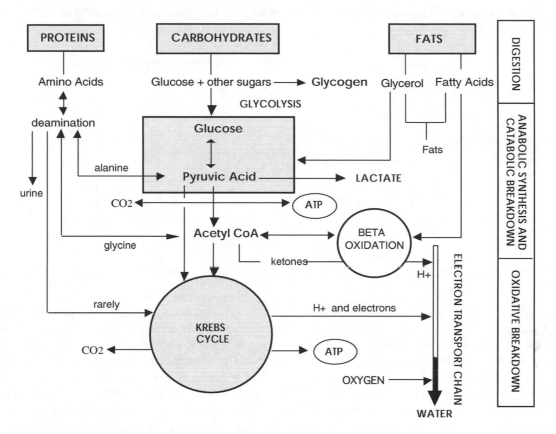

Figure 1.36 The metabolism of nutrients and the different stages of energy production

Interestingly, fats are the preferred energy fuel of the resting muscles and the liver. More specifically, the metabolism of fats furnishes about two-thirds of the energy we require at rest. They also become a more important energy source as the duration of the exercise increases, since exercise lowers insulin levels and raises adrenaline levels. Conversely, large intake of carbohydrates, in particular the simple sugars such as glucose, produces the 'insulin shock' discussed earlier and inhibits the oxidation of fats.

Although 1 gram of fat contains more than twice the amount of energy as 1 gram of carbohydrate, fat metabolism requires more oxygen than carbohydrate metabolism. At rest, this poses no limitation to the production of ATP, but as the intensity of exercise increases, so does reliance on glycogen as the prime energy source increase. There is a limit to the maximal volume of oxygen that the body can use per unit time, so it is logical that energy production should implicate processes which make more efficient use of oxygen.

1.15.6 Implications for Physical Conditioning

Our discussion of bioenergetics commenced with a definition of fitness. It is now appropriate to examine the implications of the above information for enhancing some of the components which underlie fitness: strength, muscular endurance, speed and cardiovascular endurance. The preceding analysis reveals that the development of a specific fitness component depends on adjusting the intensity, duration and type of training. In general, power and strength rely heavily on the high energy phosphagen system, muscle endurance on the oxygen-independent glycolytic system, and cardiovascular endurance on the oxygen-dependent energy system.

The single maximal muscular contractions characteristic of maximal power developed over a period which may last a fraction of a second rely entirely on stored ATP. This process does not increase blood lactate levels and the limitation to continued effort lies largely in the availability of ATP.

After a few seconds, CP is drawn upon to replenish the rapidly dwindling ATP. The CP contribution reaches a peak after 5-7 seconds, during which time *oxygen-independent glycolysis* has already commenced (Fig 1.37). Extraction of energy from the CP system also does not cause a build-up of lactate and protons, so that the main limitation to continued effort is the availability of the enzyme (creatine kinase) which resynthesizes ATP

(Fig 1.35). Maximal force development no longer becomes possible and muscle endurance becomes the dominant fitness component.

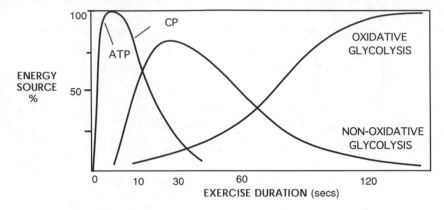

Figure 1.37 The contribution of the different energy systems to maximal exercise of increasing duration (based on van Handel & Puhl *Clinics in Sports Medicine* 1983, 2: 19-30)

Strenuous exercise lasting between approximately 6-30 seconds activates oxygen-independent glycolysis maximally, but appropriate rest intervals will prevent a serious increase in blood lactate. This is the rationale behind the value of interval and fartlek (repeated jog-sprint) running, and interval circuit training with weights or machines. In the gymnasium setting, development of endurance in specific muscle groups is facilitated by ICT (interval circuit training), which permits the use of fairly heavy loads, alternating with rest phases of 30-60 seconds between stations. The sub-maximal nature of most ICT, however, does not enhance strength and power sufficiently to meet the specific needs of strength and speed sports, except possibly during the early off-season.

Oxygen-independent glycolysis reaches its peak after about 30-40 seconds, and after 90-120 seconds its contribution becomes minimal, being replaced by *oxygen-dependent glycolysis* (Fig 1.37). This process becomes the dominant energy-producer for all long duration, low intensity activities such as distance running and cycling. If the exercise intensity is kept below the blood lactate turnpoint, the lactate and protons will be removed at the same rate as their production so that prolonged muscle activity becomes possible.

Tables 1.3 and 1.4 summarise the contributions of the different energy systems in various physical activities which traditionally have been used to offer a rough guide to anyone who devises sport specific training routines to meet the appropriate requirements for each sport.

Table 1.3 The effect of different types of training on the energy systems of the body. Based on Fox E & Mathews D (1974).

Type of training	Short-term System	Intermediate System	Long-term System
Long distance walking, running, swimming or cycling at a slow pace	2	5	93
Alternate 50m sprints and 50m jogs for a total distance of 5km	20	10	70
Interval training - repeated bouts of work alternating with rest periods (the longer the rest, the more 'anaerobic' the exercise)	0 - 80	0 - 80	0 - 80
Jogging, continuous walking or running at a slow pace over 3km	0	0	100
Fartlek - alternating fast and slow running with incomplete rest between	20	40	40
Fartlek - repeated sprints at maximal speed with complete recovery between bursts (e.g. walk back to start in between)	90	6	4

Table 1.4 Contribution of the different energy systems to different sports, as classically estimated. Adapted from Fox E & Mathews D (1974) *Interval Training for Sports and General Fitness* W B Saunders Co

Sport	Short-term System	Intermediate System	Long-term System
Badminton	80	10	10
Baseball	80	20	0
Basketball	85	15	0
Cricket	80	20	0
Fencing	90	10	0
Field hockey	60	20	20
American football	90	10	0
Golf	95	5	0
Gymnastics	90	10	0
Ice hockey : forwards, defence	80	20	0
Ice hockey : goalie	95	5	0
Lacrosse : goalie, defence, attack	80	20	0
Lacrosse : midfielders, man-down	60	20	20
Rowing	20	30	50
Rugby	90	10	0
Skiing : slalom, jumping, downhill	80	20	0
Skiing : cross-country	0	5	95
Skiing : pleasure skiing	34	33	33
Soccer			
• goalie, wings, strikers	80	20	0
• half-backs or link players	60	20	20
Squash	50	30	20
Swimming and diving			
• 50m, diving	98	2	0
• 100m	80	15	5
• 200m	30	65	5
• 400m	20	40	40
• 1500m, 1 mile	10	20	70
Tennis	70	20	10
Track and Field			
• 100m, 200m	95	5	0
• Field events	90	10	0
• 400m	80	15	5
• 800m	30	65	5
• 1500m, 1 mile	20	55	25
• 3000m	20	40	40
• 5000m	10	20	70
• 10 000m	5	15	80
• Standard marathon	0	5	95
Volleyball	90	10	0
Weightlifting	95	5	0
Wrestling	90	10	0

It should be noted that the figures for longer duration events such as the 1500m run have been modified by other researchers and their accuracy needs to be re-examined. In fact, the highly determinate nature of this whole scheme, compiled several decades ago, has been questioned more recently, so that it should not be used casually without examining other factors which are important in determining human performance.

For instance, these figures reflect the average contributions made by three concurrently operating metabolic systems (all of which ultimately depend on the breakdown and resynthesis of ATP, anyway) for an average athlete in each of the listed sports. This disguises the fact, for instance, that the metabolic demands often differ from instant to instant during every type of activity taking place in each sport.

Thus, although Table 1.4 indicates that endurance events such as distance running, swimming and cross country skiing rely largely on the long-term energy system, there are stages of acceleration and increased muscular effort which make significant demands on the short-term 'anaerobic' and the intermediate energy systems. Moreover, while we may consider that the body as a whole or the cardiocirculatory and respiratory systems may be relying largely on 'aerobic' processes, we cannot ignore that strongly contracting postural and propulsive muscles may be strongly dependent upon 'anaerobic' processes at the same time. The implications of this are that exercise prescription should not rely on the analysis of just one aspect of sporting performance. Therefore, it would be logical to include some regular bouts of high intensity and high speed training even for so-called endurance sports.

The duration of this exercise depends ultimately on the amount of glycogen stored in the liver and skeletal muscles, as well as the efficiency of deriving energy from fatty acids. Glycogen storage may be enhanced by means of 'carbo-loading', which relies on a few days of moderate carbohydrate depletion followed by the large intake of complex carbohydrates before a major event in order to promote some *glycogen supercompensation*.

Research shows that the rate of glycogen synthesis after endurance exercise is strongly influenced by the timing of carbohydrate ingestion (Ivy et al, 1988). It was discovered that drinking a 23% carbohydrate solution (2gm per kilogram of bodymass) instead of water directly after exercise produced a 300% increase in the rate of glycogen synthesis above the basal rate during the first two hours of recovery. A delay in carbohydrate ingestion by only two hours resulted in a 47% slower rate of resynthesis.

This emphasizes that efficient physical conditioning is a consequence of balanced nutrition combined with an exercise schedule of appropriate intensity, duration and type, carefully periodised over a prolonged period which includes suitable restoration phases to regenerate energy stores, repair the cells and promote regular supercompensation.

1.15.7 Hormonal Factors and Strength Training

Both acute and long-term exercise influence the endocrine system, with decreases in testosterone levels being measured in distance athletes and increases occurring among certain athletes using resistance training (see review by Terjung, 1979). The implications of such findings are of importance to strength and hypertrophy training, since both of these factors are positively affected by the levels of growth-promoting substances, such as testosterone, in the blood. This is the main reason why the abuse of artificial anabolic agents is so widespread in sport today.

Some studies of training programmes have yielded equivocal results, largely because of the difficulty in prescribing the exercise precisely in terms of intensity, volume, rest periods and long-term periodisation. Short-term strength training has been shown to produce no changes in the level of anabolic-androgenic hormones in the body (Young et al, 1976; Hetrick & Wilmore, 1979), but intensive training for maximal strength over a period of some 20 weeks has resulted in an increase in the testosterone/cortisol ratio (Häkkinen, 1985). This demonstrates the increase in anabolic activity stimulated by prolonged strength training of optimal intensity. This ratio is regarded as a useful indicator of growth, because testosterone is associated with stimulation of growth, while glucocorticoids such as cortisol have a catabolic effect on tissue.

Longer periods of intensive strength training tend to stabilise the testosterone/cortisol ratio at a certain plateau level, although large variations occur for individuals, with some athletes gaining and others losing strength (Häkkinen, 1985). In all cases, however, increases in strength correlate directly with high values of the testosterone/cortisol ratio. Other studies have revealed short-term changes in this ratio in response to heavy resistance training, with a peak characteristically being reached after about 45 minutes of training. This finding lends support to the Russian and Eastern European scheme of using several short training sessions per day interspersed with recuperation periods to facilitate recovery of work capacity for each intensive module of a few well-chosen strength exercises.

1.16 Adaptation and the Training Effect

The phenomenon of increase in strength and all other fitness factors in response to training is clear evidence of biological adaptation to stress. In fact, *fitness may be defined as the ability of the body to cope with a specific task under specific conditions,* where the task is characterised by a set of particular physical and psychological stressors. Training may thus be defined initially as the process of imposing physical loading in a particular way to achieve a specific type of fitness. Here it must be noted that the concept of fitness is not the only one relating to the ability of an athlete to perform efficiently and safely. One has to distinguish between the related factors of *work capacity, fitness* and *preparedness*, as introduced earlier (1.4). Training and environmental factors affect all of these abilities and the models discussed here relate to all of them.

As was discussed earlier (1.3), training is highly specific to the methods being used, a fact which has been formulated as the well-known *SAID principle* (Specific Adaptation to Imposed Demands). Simply stated, this means that the body adapts with a specific type of fitness to any demands which may be regularly imposed on it, provided the loading does not exceed the adaptive capabilities of the body at that time.

The Effects of Stress

The nature and effects of stress were extensively researched by Hans Selye, who devised a comprehensive model to describe the response of living systems to sources of stress (stressors) in the environment (Selye, 1956). This model, which he termed the *General Adaptation Syndrome (GAS)*, has been widely used to explaining the process of strength development and is summarised here mainly because of its historical significance and its early impact on training theory. Selye identified two forms of stress: *eustress*, beneficial stress which produces growth, and *distress*, detrimental stress which can cause decay, damage, death or disease (Fig 1.38).

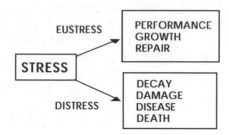

Figure 1.38 The different types of stress and their possible consequences (after Selye)

Well-planned training is characterised by the continued operation of eustress processes, whereas stagnation, soreness and persistent minor injuries are early indicators of distress. Later we will see that the *Two-Factor Model of Training* would describe this process as a consequence of the situation where the fatigue factor tends to be outweigh the fitness factor over prolonged periods (1.16.3).

Although Selye's model has been applied more recently to explain sports adaptation and supercompensation, the concept of supercompensation (Weigert's Law) was formulated at least a decade before Selye's work (Folbrot, 1941). Moreover, the relationship between adaptation and exhaustion-recovery processes under different types of loading was researched in the early 1950s by Yakovlev (1955).

1.16.1 The General Adaptation Syndrome

Selye's theory postulates that all animals exposed to periods of stress undergo three phases of the GAS: initial alarm, resistance and exhaustion. The energy for resistance or adaptation comes from the readily available *superficial adaptation energy* source or the emergency *deep adaptation energy* source, depending on the level of exhaustion or depletion of energy at any instant. In Russian texts, the former energy source is referred to as the *Current Adaptation Reserves* (CAR), a term which is used extensively in later sections of this text. The capacity of these reserves is not fixed, but alters in response to the demands placed on them by stresses such as training. The importance of this will become clear when the concept of supercompensation and its applications in achieving a training effect are discussed later (especially in 1.16.2, 5 and 6).

The initial stage may be termed the flight, fight or freeze (paralysis) response, during which the body experiences a temporary reduction in its ability to cope with the stressor. Feedback systems then rapidly signal it to resist the stressor by drawing on the appropriate energy source, systems and processes. *Training may then be described as the process whereby the body is systematically exposed to a given set of stressors to enable it to efficiently manage future exposure to those stressors.* This definition implies that the training process enables essential systems of the body to recover and grow during the rest phases following exhaustion.

Strength training would then refer to training which enables the body to increase the general strength output of its muscles, with similar definitions being applicable to all the different types of training. Strength-related forms of fitness require the body to competently resist high intensities of stress at a particular time, whereas endurance-related forms of fitness require it to withstand lower intensities of stress over prolonged periods.

Research and experience in sport indicate that the GAS model has to be modified to account for the fact that training (i.e. planned exposure to specific stressors) can allow one to adapt to increasingly higher levels of stress due to various structural and functional changes. This is what is referred to as *progressive overload*. However, it is inappropriate to apply this principle literally, since research has revealed that *optimal progress is made if the increased loading phases are alternated periodically with decreased loading phases* (see Ch 6). Continual monotonic (non-decreasing) increases from workout to workout or week to week may lead to overtraining, stagnation or injury. It is vital to remember that tissue repair and growth occur predominantly during the restoration and transition periods between training sessions and not during the heavy loading phases.

It has also been deduced that adaptive processes apparently do not just constrain bodily processes to always produce the same, predetermined maximal level of resistance. It has been hypothesised that they cause the body to over-adapt, or *supercompensate*, to a somewhat higher level, in physiological anticipation of repeated exposure to the same stressor (Fig 1.39).

This supercompensation is associated with an increase in the capacity of the Current Adaptation Reserves (CAR) and forms the foundation for all methods of programming training (Ch 6). At the nutritional level, the well-known method of increasing bodily stores of glycogen with significantly increased intake of carbohydrates after an exhausting stage of aerobic training may be termed 'glycogen supercompensation'. Unlike the process of fitness improvement, successive periods of 'carbo loading' do not produce progressively increased storage of glycogen. It should also be noted that *enhanced performance is not simply the result of increased stores of bioenergetic substances, but also of structural changes in muscle and other tissues*, as well as enhanced efficiency and rates of bioenergetic and neuromuscular processing (see 1.12). This is a major reason why Russian scientists prefer to use the term *adaptive reconstruction* to describe the body's response to physical training.

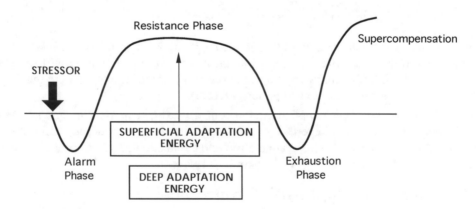

Figure 1.39 Selye's General Adaptation Syndrome model. The Deep Adaptation Energy is often referred to as the Current Adaptation Reserves (CAR) by Russian authors.

Despite these shortcomings, this theory of supercompensation had a profound impact on sports training, since it could readily be related to the system of carefully planned cyclical conditioning known as *periodisation* (Ch 6). In brief, periodisation involves organising all components of training (such as strength, strength-speed, cardiovascular endurance and strength-endurance) into carefully sequenced phases (micro-, meso- and macro-cycles) of low, medium and high intensity and volume, and regular recuperation to enable the athlete to reach specific performance goals in given competitions over a prolonged period.

Both Selye's theory and the principle of periodisation concur in that the planning of each cycle and training session depends on optimally imposing repeated loads of appropriate intensity and duration with adequate recovery time between training stimuli. If the training stimulus (stressor) is inadequate, the alarm response will be minimal and the body will perceive no need to supercompensate or adaptively reconstruct, as discussed later (1.16.2).

Adaptive Reconstruction versus Supercompensation

As emphasized earlier, it is preferable to use a term such as *adaptive reconstruction*, rather than supercompensation when referring to adaptation to training loads by the body. Thus, although the energy systems or adaptation reserves would appear to have superadapted, supercompensated or overcompensated in magnitude, there are trophic and many other changes elicited by training which are not directly related to changes in size of energy stores. Training induced changes in muscle tissue (1.12 and 1.13) and connective tissue (1.7.2) such as increased tissue hypertrophy, altered muscle fibre characteristics, intensified protein synthesis, stimulated enzyme activity, activation of the genetic apparatus of muscle cells and increased rate of energy release have already been discussed. More of these changes will be examined in greater detail in the following section to enable us to present other models of training later in this book.

1.16.2 The Biochemistry of Adaptation in Sport

Adaptation is primarily dependent on the interrelation between a cell's function and its genetic apparatus, which constitutes the constantly active mechanism of intracellular regulation.

Unlike immediate adaptation reactions, the process of prolonged adaptation to systematic muscular activity typically involves significant intensification of the biosynthetic processes, primarily those of protein synthesis, as well as the emergence of marked structural changes in the tissues.

The use of radioactively labelled amino acids has revealed that training intensifies the synthesis of proteins in the myofibrils, mitochondria, sarcoplasm, and microsomes of the skeletal muscles and the heart (Platonov, 1988). The synthesis of DNA and RNA precursors also intensifies, indicating activation of the genetic apparatus of the muscle cell, while RNA synthesis in the cardiac muscle also increases during training. In this respect there is increased activity of enzymes which are structural components in the synthesis of nucleic acids.

Training intensifies the formation of all cellular material including the mitochondria, myofibrillar proteins, endoplasmic reticulum and various enzymes. The motoneurons also thicken, and the number of terminal nerve shoots increases, as does the number of nuclei and myofibrils in the muscle fibres. In addition to the intensified synthesis of structural proteins, synthesis of enzymatic proteins (especially skeletal-muscle aspartate-amino-transferase) is increased during training.

The nucleotides (ADP, AMP - adenosine monophosphate), creatine, inorganic phosphate, and some amino acids, as well as the ADP/ATP and the creatine/CP ratios, play an important role in activating protein synthesis elicited by training. It appears that the accumulation of metabolites formed during muscle activity, as well as the decreased ATP and CP levels, might signal activation of the genetic apparatus of the muscle cells. The change in the metabolism of hormones such as glucocorticoids, somatotropin, androgens, insulin and the thyroid hormones is very important in intensifying protein synthesis during training. Thus, adaptive synthesis of proteins as a result of training is induced by both hormonal and non-hormonal components.

The overall process of intensifying enzymatic and structural adaptive biosynthesis that ultimately leads to their supercompensation is most important in biochemical adaptation during physical load training.

In the skeletal muscles, training increases the levels of energy substrates (glycogen, CP, and creatine), muscle proteins (e.g. myosin, actomyosin, sarcoplasmic and mitochondrial proteins), phospholipids, vitamins, minerals (e.g. iron, calcium, magnesium), dipeptides (carnosine, anserin) and nucleotides (Platonov, 1988).

However, the concentration of ATP does not increase under the influence of training, probably due to accelerated metabolism of ATP in the muscles that involves intensification of its synthesis and breakdown. The increased activity of a number of enzymes that catalyse the energy metabolism reaction is an integral component of biochemical adaptation during training, especially the activity of glycolytic enzymes (e.g. hexokinase, phosphorylase and pyruvate-kinase) and enzymes in the oxidative resynthesis of ATP.

Thus, as a result of training, supercompensation of some of the energy sources takes place, enzyme activity increases, and the activity ratios in the enzyme systems change. In turn, the state of energy supercompensation serves as a starting point for intensifying adaptive protein synthesis, which requires a large quantity of ATP.

The Specificity of Biochemical Adaptation

Biochemical adaptation is not simply a generalised and summated response of physical systems to training stress. Many components and processes of the muscular system display a definite specificity of adaptation to loading, as discussed earlier in some detail (1.16).

The Sequence of Biochemical Changes during Training

The many biochemical changes that take place in the body during and after training (as well as overtraining) do not occur simultaneously. A definite sequence in the biochemical adaptation to training is discerned (Platonov, 1988). First, the potential for oxidative resynthesis of ATP and the level of glycogen increase. Next there is an increase in the level of structural protein in the muscles (myosin) and in the intensity of non-oxidative ATP resynthesis (glycolysis), following which the level of CP rises.

In overtraining the typical changes of biochemical adaptation acquired through training are gradually lost and work capacity decreases. The biochemical indices during overtraining change in an order that is the reverse of the order seen during training. Naturally, the dynamics of developing and losing the biochemical changes of adaptation depend on the characteristics of the previous training. In general, the longer the training period, the more thorough is the reorganisation by the adaptation mechanisms and the longer the accompanying biochemical changes last in the body after cessation of training, especially regarding glycogen and CP levels. Thus, the biochemical changes during immediate and long-term adaptation to systematic muscle activity are reversible, with the process of direct and reverse development of these changes being heterochronic.

During overtraining, the chemistry of the muscles and, above all, the oxidative processes are disturbed. Here the glycogenolytic activity of the muscle tissue diminishes, and levels of ascorbic acid, glutathione, and glycogen in it decrease (Platonov, 1988). Dysproteinaemia of the blood plasma is noted, and the blood levels of glycoproteins, sialic acids, and urea increase. With prolonged chronic fatigue, athletes have reduced functional potential of the sympathico-adrenal system, which is closely linked to a disruption of the acid-base balance.

When training loads exceed the adaptation potential of the body and cause fatigue, another type of sympathetic nervous system reaction takes place: in fatiguing endurance events, a physical load that was previously of relatively little significance for the athletes causes a sharp increase in the excretion of catecholamines, their biological precursors, and the products of degradation, i.e. a particular hormonal reaction to the test load occurs. It is clear, then that the above-mentioned biochemical changes during overtraining exert an unfavourable influence on work capacity and the level of sports results.

The biochemical rules governing bodily adaptation may be used to verify various principles of sports training such as the continuity of the training process, the undulatory nature of load dynamics, the cyclical nature of the training process, the unity of general and special preparation, the gradual increase in loading and the progression toward maximal loading.

A single physical load can cause an immediate biochemical effect, but this rapidly subsides. If a subsequent physical load is performed after the traces of the adaptation effect of the first load have completely disappeared, a summation of the biochemical changes does not take place. Therefore, the training process must be repetitive in order to develop long-term progressive changes in the energy reserves and the metabolism-regulating systems.

The rules governing fatigue and restoration, the specific nature of biochemical adaptation, and the sequence in which the biochemical components of adaptation are developed and lost underlie the principles of the undulatory nature of load dynamics, the cyclical nature of the training process, and gradual increase in the volume and magnitude of the training loads.

Scientifically substantiated use of diversified training regimes for alternating work and rest has become possible as a result of creatively combining these biochemical principles, sports pedagogy and the experience of the coaches. The need to increase loads and progress towards maximal loading is based on the thesis that physical loads which are most capable of significantly disrupting homeostasis elicit the greatest training effect.

The biochemical changes caused by a physical load immediately after it is performed (immediate training effect - see 6.7.1) are capable of activating the genetic apparatus of the cells. When physical loads are systematically repeated, there is an accumulation of immediate training effects which assures their transfer to long-term adaptation (the cumulative training effect - see 6.7.1). Thus, the following important fundamentals of the trained body's biochemical adaptation may be identified:

1. Improvement of nervous, endocrine, and adenylatcyclase processes to increase metabolic efficiency
2. Adaptive biosynthesis of enzymatic and structural proteins.
3. Supercompensation of energy substances and proteins.

All of the foregoing indicates that significant changes in metabolism occur in the body during training. As muscle work is performed, catabolism intensifies, but during the restoration period anabolic processes intensify.

All of these changes are closely related to nutrition. The increased energy expenditure during muscle activity demands adequate replenishment; increase in need for vitamins demands an increased intake of them; and increased mineral losses during sports activity necessitate compensating for them.

A number of other specific problems also arise: nutrition over a long period and during restoration stages; the athlete's feeding frequency; and the application of biologically-enriched sports nutrition products. Planning diets for athletes also requires a new approach to organising nutrition at different stages of the annual cycle of training and competitions, especially concerning the quantities of food components, the interaction between different nutrients and optimal timing of ingestion of specific substances (chrononutrition). We must achieve the maximal correspondence between all the goals of sports training and the effect of diet on the body. In this respect, the biochemical processes underlying sports training form the theoretical basis for scientific sports nutrition.

1.16.3 General Theories of the Training Process

It has been stated previously that almost any regimen of resistance training can be successful with a novice, but in the long term, the body habituates to the stimulus, progress slows down and halts as stagnation sets in and performance deteriorates (Fig 1.40).

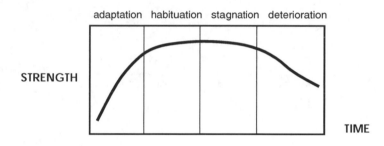

Figure 1.40 The effect of random, casual resistance training over the long term

The gains in strength are rapid during the first few months, a period of several months of fairly stable performance follows, until stagnation ensues, especially if there is unskilled use of progressive loading and inadequate training variety. Finally, the individual becomes unable to maintain sufficient motivation and central nervous stimulation to make further progress. This entire process of adaptation or failure to adapt to physical training has been explained by two theoretical models:

- Single-Factor Model of Training (The Supercompensation Model)
- Two-Factor Model of Training (The Fitness-Fatigue Model)

Single-Factor Model of Training

The single-factor model may be better understood in the light of Selye's GAS model, which provides a theoretical foundation for the *principle of supercompensation* (Fig 1.41), whereby bodily processes are hypothesised to adapt to a higher level of functioning in response to the repeated physical stresses of training. The immediate after-effect of training is assumed to deplete certain biochemicals whose amount increases above their initial levels during the training period. If subsequent loading is imposed too soon during the recovery stage (at point A), then supercompensation fails to occur and performance continues to decrease (Fig 1.41b).

If a conservative approach is followed and successive bouts of loading are too infrequent or imposed too late (at point C), then supercompensation is minimal and performance tends to stagnate (Fig 1.41c). Loading is optimal if it is imposed when supercompensation has peaked (at point B); this enables the load to be increased regularly without causing stagnation or overloading (Fig 1.41d). This principle forms the basis of correct design of training loads and volumes at the level of the microcycle (about a week), the mesocycle (several months) and the macrocycle (about a year), thereby establishing the long-term training principle defined earlier as periodisation.

Although the supercompensation model has been popular for many years among scientists and coaches, its theoretical foundation has not been comprehensively studied or proved. The depletion of glycogen after specific types of training and a carbohydrate loading process leading to increased glycogen storage in the body have both been experimentally measured, but have not been observed to occur on an ongoing basis from workout to workout, thereby leading to long-term supercompensation of glycogen. On the contrary, ATP levels have never been shown to deplete significantly, even after very strenuous exercise. No supercompensation has yet been observed to occur among any of the other biochemicals involved in the various bioenergetic processes in the body. Moreover, return to their initial levels by each of these substances after changes have been elicited by physical stress takes a different period of time, so the timing of subsequent loads to stimulate the appropriate type of supercompensation remains indeterminate.

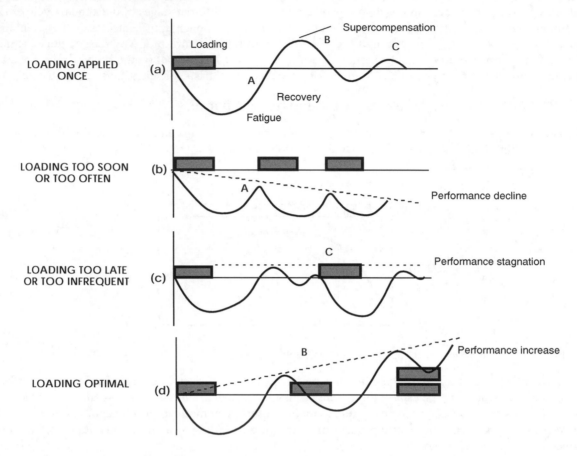

Figure 1.41 Application of the principle of supercompensation for producing optimal training

In addition, various other structural and biochemical factors relating to the adaptation of the body to training have been discussed in the previous section. These problems with simple supercompensation theory have led to increased criticism and decreased popularity in applying it to explain the training process.

Two-Factor Model of Training

The Two-Factor Model (or Fitness-Fatigue Model) of the training process involves the superimposition of two after-effects following the application of a training load (see 6.7 and especially Figure 6.14), as alluded to earlier in the work of Yakovlev (see 1.16):

- A long-term *fitness after-effect* which leads to an increase in specific fitness
- A short-term *fatigue after-effect* producing a specific type of fatigue

These after-effects interact to produce what is termed *physical preparedness*. The first factor is slow-changing and longer lasting, leading to progressive, delayed increases in physical fitness, whereas the fatigue after-effect is a shorter-lasting negative factor that decreases preparedness (Fig 1.42).

The fatigue effect, though relatively short in duration, displays a greater magnitude than the fitness effect. *Preparedness* at a given time, $P(t)$, is the initial preparedness $P(0)$ before the workout plus the increase in preparedness, ΔP, produced by the summation of the fitness and fatigue after-effects (Fig 1.42). Research has described the fitness-fatigue relationship in terms of equations such as the following (Banister et al, 1992):

Preparedness at a time t = Initial Preparedness + Change in Preparedness due to one workout

$$= P(0) + (\text{Fitness} - \text{Fatigue}) \text{ for 1 workout}$$

Preparedness at time t: $P(t) = P(0) + A.e^{-t/T_1} - B.e^{-t/T_2}$

where A is the fitness constant, B is the fatigue constant, T_1 is the fitness decay time constant and T_2 is the fatigue decay time constant. This type of equation varies with individual, situation and phase of training, so that new constants have to be determined periodically by the use of successive iterations.

Some of the earliest work on the concept of the balance between fitness and fatigue was done by Banister and Calvert (1980) who quantified the contribution of cardiorespiratory endurance and strength to elite performance in swimming in terms of a unit of training termed the *Training Impulse* (TRIMP). They used the Training Impulse to construct a model for predicting performance in swimming based upon the balance between fitness and fatigue.

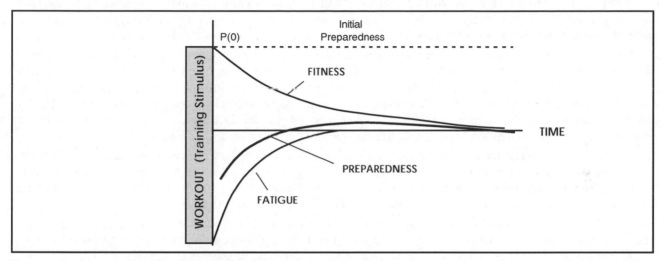

Figure 1.42 Two-Factor Model of the Training Process, showing Preparedness as the summation of the opposing fitness and fatigue processes produced by a single workout (based on Zatsiorsky, 1995).

Zatsiorsky (1995) has stated that, with respect to one training session of average intensity, the fitness effect endures roughly three times longer than the fatigue effect (i.e. $T_1 = 3.T_2$). Thus, if the last negative traces of fatigue of a given workout have faded after 2 days, then the positive fitness traces will persist for about 6 days. In applying such a model, it is relevant to note that different muscle groups recover at different rates (heterochronically) and that the characteristics of the fatigue process may be modified by other adjunct training or restoration. Some Russian restoration specialists, therefore, advocate that restorative procedures (such as massage) should not always be used on all muscle groups after each session or in the same sequence, because supercompensation tends to be more pronounced on a basis of partial restoration (see Ch 8).

More recently, a considerable amount of research has examined the relationship between fitness and fatigue and has produced a variety of systems models to enable the training process to be devised more accurately, especially with regard to the *tapering process* before competitions (Busso et al, 1994; Mujika et al, 1996; Busso et al, 1990; Houmard 1991)

Some of this work has suggested that presently accepted forms of tapering for competition may remain too rigorous and short to achieve the best result possible from the training undertaken (Fitz-Clarke et al, 1991). These results demonstrate that proper placement of training *volume* during taper is a key factor in optimising performance for a specific competition, with a high volume of training in the immediate days preceding an event possibly being detrimental to optimal performance (Zarkadas et al, 1995; Mujika et al, 1996; Shepley et al, 1992).

The Concept of Progressive Overload Training

The concept of progressive overloading is proliferated probably more vigorously than any other principle in fitness training.   This ancient principle states that strength and all other components of fitness increase if the training gradually becomes more demanding.

It was known to the legendary Grecian-Italian hero, Milo, who at an early age began lifting a newly-born bull. As the bull grew, the growing Milo had to lift a progressively heavier load, until eventually he was lifting a fully-grown beast. This, according to legend, is why Milo became so powerful. Today, essentially the same training principle, now known as gradual overload or progressive gradual overload, is followed by most serious athletes.

This story or its underlying principle appears in numerous textbooks, without much critical analysis, despite the fact that the methodology of periodisation actually contradicts this principle in important respects. The major limitation of the gradual overload principle is obvious, namely that a stagnation point is reached, despite further increase in loading. The performance growth curve flattens out and a limit to further growth is reached. This phenomenon is what prevents the same person from constantly breaking world records.

Closer examination of the Milo tale reveals an incomplete ending. Milo, being an enterprising strongman, obviously would have sought further strength increase by lifting progressively heavier bulls. If he had progressed very gradually, the implications are that he should have been lifting well over 500kg after a few years. Similarly, if you began your first bench press with 60kg at the age of 16, then increased the load by only one kilogram per week, you should be lifting 580kg at the age of 26 and 1100kg at the age of 36 years. That this will not happen is obvious. In other words, progressive overloading produces diminishing, and ultimately zero, returns.

Research and clinical records also reveal that more intensive loading produces an increase in injury rate well before one's physical limits are reached. This is why Russian research produced periodisation models which involve phases of decreased loading, so that the curve of training intensity fluctuates upwards and downwards in a specific wave shape for each sport, with a gradual overall tendency to increase over a given macrocycle. Regular phases of lighter loading are prescribed to facilitate recovery and growth, since increases in loading are associated with tissue stress and breakdown, whereas decreases in loading promote repair and restoration.

In other words, the gradual overload principle should be understood to be a *fluctuating overload system*, where monotonic increases in loading do not occur for any prolonged period. The expression *monotonic increase*, borrowed from mathematics, means continual increase without any decrease. Thus, monotonic increase training imposes a load which always increases, though not necessarily at the same rate all the time.

The rate of increase may be rapid at certain times and slow at other times, but the curve of progress at no stage dips below the level reached at an earlier stage (Figure 1.43a). Non-monotonic training is characterised by a fluctuating curve which can dip below levels reached at earlier stages of the training cycle (Figure 1.41b) .

The gradualness aspect of the principle also warrants further comment, since some periodisation models, such as those of Vorobyev and Verkhoshansky, sometimes involve phases of sharp or concentrated loading to achieve a specific training purpose or to shock the body out of a state of stagnation or habituation. These scientists are well aware that sudden increases in the rate of loading are potentially more risky, but they never recommend such regimes without careful consideration of the state of preparedness of each individual athlete.

In summary, the gradual overload principle should more correctly be applied as a *fluctuating overload system*, where the direction of loading is positive in the long term, but alternating between positive and negative at microcyclic and mesocyclic levels (Figure 1.44). The rate of loading generally is gradual, but may be more rapid to provide an adequate training stimulus, depending on the particular athlete and the phase of the training cycle. The practical details of the various methods of loading, unloading, concentrated loading and the different types of periodisation are discussed in great detail in Chapter 6.

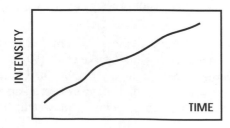

Figure 1.43 (a) Monotonic increase training

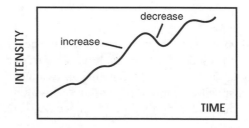

Figure 1.41 (b) Non-monotonic training

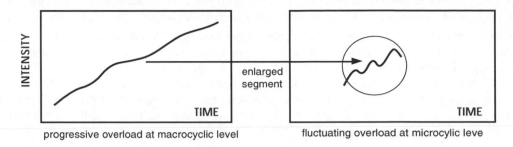

progressive overload at macrocyclic level   fluctuating overload at microcylic leve

Figure 1.44 Fluctuating overload training

1.16.4 A Model of Physical Fitness

The definition of fitness given earlier needs to be expanded to incorporate all the essential factors which contribute to this state. Fitness comprises a series of interrelated structural and functional factors which conveniently may be referred to as the basic S-factors of fitness: *Strength, Speed, Stamina* (general systemic endurance or local muscular endurance), *Suppleness* (flexibility), *Skill* (neuromuscular efficiency), *Structure* (somatotype, size, shape) and *Spirit* (psychological preparedness). Within the scope of skill, there is also a fitness quality known as *Style*, the individual manner of expressing a particular skill.

Unlike work capacity (1.5), fitness is described not simply by laboratory measurements of qualities such as cardiovascular function, muscle strength and flexibility, but also by the *specificity* of fitness required for each activity or sport, which depends to a major extent on neuromotor skills. It is the primary purpose of this book to concentrate on the specificity associated with all of the fitness factors related to strength, to analyse how these factors interact to provide a form of fitness which is fairly specific to each sport, and to show the reader how to devise appropriate models for designing strength training programmes for a given sport.

A comprehensive model of physical fitness may be constructed from the functional motor elements of fitness, as shown in Figure 1.45. The model may be developed in two stages: firstly, as a triangular model which interrelates strength, stamina (muscular endurance), speed and suppleness (flexibility), and secondly, as a more complete pyramidal model which interrelates all of these factors with the process which makes all movement possible, namely *neuromuscular control* or skill.

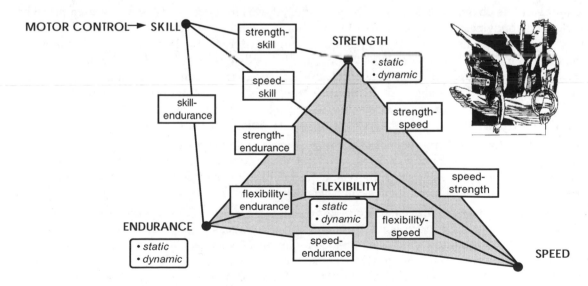

Figure 1.45 Pyramidal model comprising the major elements of musculoskeletal fitness

The diagram illustrates that strength, endurance and flexibility may be produced statically or dynamically, unlike speed, which changes along a continuum from the static (speed = 0) to the dynamic state. However, this convenient picture could be complicated by including the quasi-isometric state which can influence production of any of the motor qualities at very slow speeds (see 1.10). For this and other reasons, this model should be viewed as one which is representational or descriptive rather than scientifically analytical.

The quality of flexibility has been place at the centre of the base of the pyramid, because the ability to exhibit any of the other qualities depends centrally on range of movement (ROM). It should be noted that static or dynamic flexibility refers to the maximum ROM that may be attained under static or dynamic conditions, respectively. The line joining all adjacent pairs of primary fitness factors depicts a variety of different fitness factors between each of the two extremes. The model (which receives further scientific corroboration in 3.3.3, especially in Fig 3.21) thus allows us to identify an extended list of fitness factors, as follows (the factors bearing an asterisk are various types of special strength):

- static strength*
- static strength-endurance*
- dynamic strength*
- dynamic strength-endurance*
- strength-speed*
- speed-strength*
- speed-strength endurance*
- strength-speed endurance*
- speed
- endurance

It is sometimes convenient to identify various flexibility qualities, namely:

- flexibility (static and dynamic)
- flexibility-strength*
- flexibility-endurance
- flexibility-speed

A series of skill-related factors may also be identified, although it should be noted that skill forms an integral part of the process of exhibiting all of the above fitness or motor qualities:

- skill
- strength-skill* (Diachkov, 1961; Kuznetsov, 1970)
- flexibility-skill
- speed-skill
- skill-endurance

All of the primary and more complex fitness factors should be viewed as convenient descriptors of qualities which are involved in different proportions in a particular physical activity. Nevertheless, this pyramidal model enables us to understand sport specific fitness and training far more effectively than with a simplistic model based only on the primary functional fitness factors of strength, endurance, speed and flexibility.

At the beginning of this chapter the concept of relative strength was introduced. The improvement in other fitness factors relative to bodymass is also sometimes highly relevant. For instant, *relative power* (relative speed-strength and relative strength-speed) or the power per unit bodymass (Berger, 1982) is very important in cases where the athlete has to increase his power without increasing his bodymass (e.g. a weightlifter or boxer in a specific bodymass division). In sports which require the athlete to increase endurance without increasing body-mass, *relative endurance* needs to be enhanced. In this case, one might even distinguish between relative static endurance and relative dynamic endurance. Depending on the sport, improvement of *relative speed-strength endurance* (or relative strength endurance) under cyclic or acyclic conditions, may also be relevant.

Many studies of the effect of certain regimes of training on increase in factors such as strength or power are deficient in that they often fail to examine changes in relative terms. Since strength is not linearly related to bodymass, it is sometimes preferable to use appropriate correction formulae (based on weightlifting and pow-erlifting performances) to compare changes in more equitable relative terms (see 3.3.5).

Some of the above terms may require elaboration. For example, *static strength-endurance* refers to muscle endurance under isometric conditions; *strength-speed* and *speed-strength*, synonymous with the ability to develop great power, refer to qualities which simultaneously involve aspects of strength and speed; *speed-strength endurance* refers to the ability to produce great power continuously without serious decrement; *flexibility-speed* refers to flexibility which must be exhibited at high speed; and *speed-skill* refers to an action which must be produced skillfully at high speed.

Lest each hyphenated term imply that the complex quality is some type of mixture of the relevant primary factors, it must be emphasized that many of these qualities can be identified as fairly distinct factors in their own right. It is inappropriate to enter into a detailed study of these factors here, because the analysis and practical application of the major special strength fitness factors form the essence of later chapters. The functional fitness model was presented at this stage to enable the reader to appreciate the scope and complexity of special strength training and to understand the philosophical basis of the terminology and approach used in this book.

It is also important at all stages of training to recall the differences between work capacity, fitness and preparedness (1.4), since *a high level of work capacity and sport specific fitness will not guarantee exceptional performance*. Instead, the ability to exhibit a maximal level of preparedness, as the summated ongoing resultant of fitness and fatigue, is essential if such performance is to be more likely (1.16.3).

From the number of factors bearing an asterisk, it becomes apparent that strength-related qualities are very important in any sport specific training programme. The subtitle of this text may then be appreciated more fully: *Strength Training for Sporting Excellence* refers to training which efficiently develops the appropriate balance of strength-related factors for any sport (or any other physical activity such as dance).

SPORT SPECIFIC STRENGTH TRAINING

Special Strength Training

Strength training has become vital for successful sports preparation. However, it is only of value if a specific methodology can be devised on the basis of scientific research, detailing the role and place of strength conditioning in the training process in the short and long term.

Regrettably, its historical links with physique training and the traditional view of muscle-bound gymnasium patrons have created the faulty impression that strength training retards athletic performance. Current emphasis on research into heart disease and cardiovascular physiology has served to consolidate this view by popularising the belief that fitness and cardiac health in general are well served by 'aerobic' or cardiovascular exercise and endangered or minimally enhanced by training against resistance. The 'aerobics' community has confounded the picture further by empirically categorising many strength conditioning exercises as dangerous and generally regarding aerobic activity as superior to all other forms of exercise.

It often seems to be forgotten that fitness is a complex state determined by several interacting components (the fitness factors discussed in 1.14.3), each of which requires specialised training for optimal development. Strength processes play a particularly important role in controlling the stability and mobility of the body in sport.

Fortunately, a sizeable community of 'strength scientists' has emerged to challenge the above preconceptions and examine the part played by strength and strength conditioning in human performance and injury rehabilitation. Some of their work is now revealing that muscle strength and endurance may play key roles in ensuring superior performance even during long duration events such as marathons. For instance, research into the biomechanics of the soft tissues has indicated that performance in distance running also may be enhanced by (Siff, 1986):

- improving the ability of the SEC (series elastic component) of the muscle complex to store and release elastic energy

- modifying running technique to improve the ability of the athlete to utilise the stored elastic energy and to spare muscular energy.

As detailed in Chapter 1, the mechanical properties of connective tissues (such as elasticity, strength and damping ratio), as well as neuromuscular efficiency (discussed in later chapters), can be beneficially altered by using appropriate regimes of resistance and plyometric training.

The striking success achieved by Russian and Eastern European coaches in applying specialised strength training in preparation for most sports has also stimulated the rest of the world to take this type of conditioning far more seriously. Considerable experience has now been gained in the use of special strength training to facilitate adequate analysis and identify some general principles. However, it has been insufficient to form a definitive methodological foundation for the special strength training of athletes. The role and place of special strength training can be established only through scientific research in two main directions:

- Further study of the principles governing the *general* conditioning of the body to determine scientific means of achieving one's physical potential

- Intensive study of the principles determining the *specific* long-term sports training process.

Scientific research in the first direction already has yielded a wealth of information, whereas serious work in the second direction has commenced only recently, so that its findings are still rather limited. Nevertheless, they enable one to formulate important principles concerning *special strength training*, where the latter term refers to the specialised application of strength training to sport. It is synonymous with *sport specific strength training*, and both expressions may be used interchangeably to distinguish it from general weight training or bodybuilding for aesthetic or casual fitness purposes.

At the outset, it must be emphasized that the phenomenon of strength should not be viewed simplistically in terms of the classical definition as 'the ability to produce force by action of the muscles'. *Strength is highly context dependent.* This point will be stressed throughout this book, since strength can manifest itself in many forms, such as static strength, dynamic strength, strength-speed and strength-endurance. The accurate modelling of the strength and other fitness characteristics of a particular sport is what transforms *general* strength training into *special* strength training to produce consistent improvement in sports performance.

The Russian System of Classifying Athletes

Before going any further, it is relevant to remark on the use of the terms *Sports Mastery* or *Mastery in Sport.* These terms have been used for many years in Russia and Eastern Europe to describe the process of reaching the highest possible level of sporting prowess.

They are also closely related to the categorisation scheme used to identify athletes of different qualification. In this scheme, competitors at the most basic level fall into Class III, athletes of intermediate standard into Class II, and advanced athletes successively into Class I, Candidate for Master of Sport, Master of Sport, Candidate for International Master and International Master (or, Master of Sport, International Class). The last two categories refer to athletes such as world record holders, world champions and world champions of several years' standing. Specific norms are set for all individual and team sports, based on times, distances, scores, lifts, number of times of selection at a given team level or special achievements. The classification system does not rank beginners, since ranking is based on specific achievements.

It is one of the objectives of this book to present information which will assist the athlete to progress via the use of appropriate and effective strength training through all the stages of Mastery to the highest possible level dictated by his/her inherited potential.

It should be noted that the Russian system of classifying athletes begins not with formal competitions, but with the GTO (Readiness for Work and Defence) badge, which recognizes the minimum standards of physical fitness for anyone in the population. The GTO norms apply to children from about 10 years of age and progress into late adulthood (over 65 years of age). The GTO tests involve several sports and serve to identify levels of athletic prowess in the formative years. Those whose intention is to progress beyond the GTO IV, III, II and I badges have to pass more rigorous requirements to lead them through the various Classes of Mastery as detailed above. Before one reaches the adult classification system, there are also junior rankings (Class III up to Class I) for athletes of up to 19 years.

The classification of athletes should not be regarded as a regimented system with strict application only in the Russian context, but a fundamental principle for the scientific preparation of athletes in all countries. Since *athletes of different levels of proficiency and training experience respond very differently to strength conditioning programmes*, it is vital that competitors be periodically tested and graded to enable coaches to set up the most appropriate training regimen for each individual during a specific phase of development.

The Early Stages of Strength Training

A few remarks are necessary about the early stages of strength training. *Virtually any methods of strength training will enhance the strength of a novice during the first few months*, provided the intensity, in particular, is kept at a safe level. This is a major reason why it is misleading and counterproductive to apply the results obtained from scientific studies of less than at least six months' duration. It is also a major reason why relatively inexperienced coaches manage to have initial success with athletes and thereby continue to attract clients. Moreover, it has been discovered that *each individual displays a different rate, degree and efficiency of responding to the same type, quality and quantity of physical training.* In other words, the identical training programme will have different effects on different people. The achievement of higher levels of mastery is a complex process which requires the careful application of the appropriate means and methods of training at the different stages of sports preparation for each individual.

In approaching strength training for the first time, it is important to remember that the increase in strength in relative newcomers is due primarily to a learning effect which is neuromuscular in nature. Such increases in strength related to performance factors such as the improvement in skill in executing a specific exercise can even take place *within the first training session.* This type of improvement generally will be experienced with any exercise which is novel to the user. After that, strength changes occur in the following typical pattern (though the qualifying discussion in Section 1.12 should be noted):

1. *Increase in intermuscular coordination.* This functional improvement in the overall co-operation among different groups of muscles takes place over the first 2-3 weeks of training.

2. *Increase in intramuscular coordination.* This next functional improvement, caused by enhanced cooperation between the fibres in a specific muscle group, continues for the following 4-6 weeks.

3. *Increase in muscle hypertrophy.* This first structural phase of significant increase in strength due to growth in muscle tissue becomes prominent during the next 6 to 12 weeks.

4. *Stagnation.* The rate of improvement for functional and structural reasons now decreases markedly. For continued progress, it now becomes necessary to determine whether the stagnation is due to neuromuscular or muscle growth factors and then modify the training programme accordingly. At this point, the knowledge of a highly skilled coach becomes necessary, especially as haphazard trial-and-error programmes initiated at the onset of the stagnation phase can diminish overall sports performance and lead to pain or injury.

Earlier sections of Chapter 1 (especially 1.6) and the immediately preceding section relate increases in strength to two broad physiological processes, namely hypertrophy and neural adaptation. More detailed analysis has associated more strength gain with hypertrophy of type II muscle fibres, with further information on changes in the different types of muscle fibre due to activation or inactivity appearing in Section 1.12.

Some caution is necessary before one overemphasizes the role of neural adaptation at the expense of other possible mechanisms of strength increase. Gains in peak force or joint torque after strength training have been documented in the absence of any changes in neural drive, as shown in studies which relied on training with electrical stimulation of the motor nerve or muscle, a process which ensured that the observed adaptations in peak torque were independent of neural, learning or motivational effects.

Even though a relatively amateurish approach may produce strength increases during the first year of training, this may not be entirely beneficial to the athlete, because the improvements may not be sufficiently sports specific. From the beginning, it is vital to identify exactly which strength-related qualities (such as speed-strength, skill-endurance or strength-endurance) need to be enhanced in a given individual executing a specific series of tasks in a particular sport. Both short- and long-term progress has to carefully planned if the path to Sports Mastery is to be efficient and largely injury-free.

2.1 Schemes for Perfecting Movements

Athletic performance may be described in terms of a complex interaction of many movements, so that the fundamental phenomenon underlying all sports tasks is movement. *Sport then becomes a problem-solving activity in which movements are used to produce the necessary solutions.* These movements are controlled by the neuromuscular system, whose performance is the result of innate characteristics and the long-term acquisition of skills through training.

The perfecting of athletic movements during long-term training is realised primarily by enhancing the efficiency of the neuromuscular system to competently solve specific motor tasks. The ability to effectively use one's motor potential to achieve success is the essence of sports mastery. This ability is realised by means of a specific system of movements, the composition and organisation of which are determined by the type of athletic activity and the rules of competition. The sports training process as a whole is a phenomenon of exceptional complexity. In the context of this book, it is therefore appropriate to limit the study largely to those training schemes which relate most directly to muscular strength and the kinesiological organisation of movement in space and time, namely:

- Increasing the working effect of movements
- Perfecting the motor pattern of movements
- Perfecting the kinesiological pattern of movements.

2.1.1 Increasing the Working Effect of Movements

The *working effect* of a movement is the result of interaction with objects in the environment, where speed and direction of movement depend upon the character of the force developed.

If the movement is to be analysed mathematically, then the force developed at any instant, $\mathbf{F}(t)$, may be depicted graphically (see Fig 2.1). In almost all athletic movements the beginning and end of the force curve lie on the horizontal axis, because the movement begins and ends with zero velocity. The working-effect of the effort is given by the area under the curve F(t) over the time interval t during which the weight W is overcome (the shaded area) or as the integral $\mathbf{p} = \int \mathbf{F}(t).dt$, where $\mathbf{p}$ is the momentum (m.v) of the body attained over that interval (see 5.1 for definitions and derivations). An increase in the working-effect of the movement is achieved in principle by increasing this area (i.e. its momentum). This, in brief, is one of the major goals for perfecting athletic movements. Other major goals include increase in the maximum force (the peak of the $\mathbf{F}(t)$ graph), increase in the rate of maximum force production (the upward slope of the $\mathbf{F}(t)$ graph in Fig 2.1), and production of maximum force at the appropriate instant. When a force is applied explosively over a very brief time interval, the resulting rapid change in momentum is known as the *impulse* of the force (detailed in 5.1).

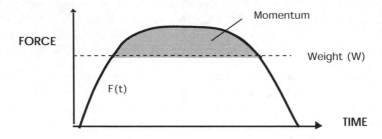

Figure 2.1 Force - time curve for a weight W being overcome by a force F(t)

As sports proficiency increases, the pattern of the effort produced undergoes specific changes in space and time which can be clearly displayed even within a relatively short period of training. For example, the graphs describing explosive force, $\mathbf{F}(t)$ and $\mathbf{F}(s)$, obtained before and after 6 months of training respectively are shown in Figure 2.2, produced by an individual for a leg movement in the seated position. $\mathbf{F}(t)$ refers to the force as a function of time and $\mathbf{F}(s)$, the force as a function of displacement.

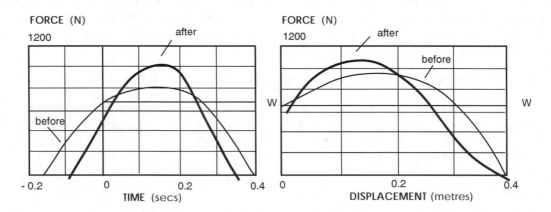

Figure 2.2 The force-time, F(t), and force-displacement, F(s), graphs for explosive force, before and after 6 months of strength training. W is the weight being overcome (Siff & Verkhoshansky, 1999).

Their coincidence on the vertical axis corresponds to the instant when the magnitude of the force is equal to the weight of the load displaced. $\mathbf{F}(t)$ graph displays several features:

- there is a decrease in the time taken to produce maximal force
- there is an increase in the maximum force
- maximum effort is produced at a point closer to when muscle tension begins
- there is a decrease in the general duration of the effort.

The changes in the profile of the graph reflect the general patterns in perfecting sporting movement which were identified in research with athletes of different specialisation and qualification using different regimes of muscular work, as well as with the same athlete during training over different lengths of time (Verkhoshansky, 1977). The experimental results show that, during long-term training, the perfecting of athletic movement proceeds as follows (Fig 2.3):

1. Initially there is a relatively uniform increase in force (compared with the initial level of curve l), with an insignificant decrease in its duration (Fig 2.3a, curve 2)

2. There is then a significant increase in maximum force and a noticeable decrease in the duration of the movement (Fig 2.3a, curve 3)

3. Finally, there is an increase in the force developed at the beginning of the effort, with some increase in its maximum and a decrease in the time taken to reach the latter (Fig 2.3a, curve 4).

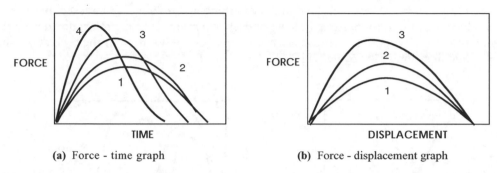

(a) Force - time graph   (b) Force - displacement graph

Figure 2.3 Changes in F(t) and F(s) during training (details are described in the text). (Verkhoshansky, 1977).

The change in the dynamics of an athletic movement, relative to its working amplitude, follows a regular sequence, namely (Fig 2.3b):

1. The movement initially displays a flattened distribution of force over much of the working range, which is associated firstly with insufficient strength and, secondly, with the inability to use it efficiently (curve 1).

2. Next, with exercise, the maximum dynamic force increases and tends towards localised peaking in the working range, whose location depends upon how the movement tasks are resolved (curve 2).

3. In ballistic types of speed-strength movement against relatively small resistance, the force is concentrated near the beginning of the working amplitude (curve 3).

The force near the beginning of the movement is produced to a smaller degree when the resistance is large. In this case there is a tendency to develop force quickly, although the high initial inertia decrees that maximal force cannot be displayed with minimal delay. There is then some increase until it reaches a maximum near the middle of the second part of the working range.

Thus, the perfecting of the working effect is associated with the production of a large maximum force over a shorter period of time. This finding by Verkhoshansky, (1961, 1963) is corroborated by studies of the dynamics of movements of athletes of different qualification (Papysheva, 1966; Gomberazde, 1970; Semyenov, 1970; Tatyan, 1974).

It must be remembered that different regimes and external conditions of muscular work in athletics undoubtedly influence this pattern. Thus, in movements associated with overcoming significant external resistance (as in gymnastics, wrestling and weightlifting), the perfecting of the working-effect is realised primarily by an increase in the maximum force developed and some decrease in the time taken for its production (Fig 2.4).

In *ballistic movements*, fencing, and some aspects of throwing, perfecting of the working-effect is associated with concentration of force near the beginning of the movement. With this significant increase in maximum force, it shifts closer to the beginning of the movement and takes less time for its achievement (Fig 2.5).

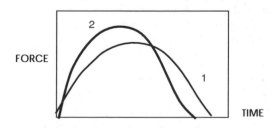

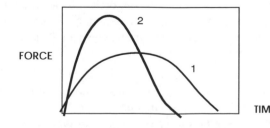

Figure 2.4 Displacement in force during explosive isometric contraction before training (1) and after training (2). (Siff & Verkhoshansky, 1999).

Figure 2.5 Displacement in force during a ballistic movement before training (1) and after training (2) (Siff & Verkhoshansky, 1999).

In exercises involving a combination of muscular work regimes, the working force is preceded by a phase of muscular stretching (e.g. jumping in track-and-field, figure skating and acrobatics). Thus, the perfecting of the movement is achieved by improving the ability of the muscles to generate great force during the transition from eccentric to concentric work. This rapid transition from stretching to contracting causes some decrease in the working amplitude, i.e. there is a decrease in the angle of the working joint during flexion (Fig 2.6).

The working-effect in *cyclic exercises* (e.g. running, swimming and rowing) is increased by improving the ability to quickly produce maximum force from the state of deep and rapid muscular relaxation during the passive phase of the movement. There is a simultaneous increase in the relative duration of the relaxation phase and a shortening of the absolute duration of the cycle (Fig 2.7).

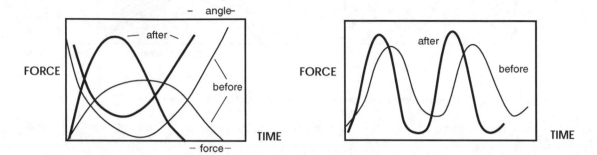

Figure 2.6 Variation in dynamic force & angular displacement for reactive-ballistic movement before and after training (Siff & Verkhoshansky, 1999).

Figure 2.7 Dynamics of a cyclical movement before and after training (Siff & Verkhoshansky, 1999).

Thus, during the course of achieving sports mastery, the process of increasing the working-effect of the movement is independent of the regime, while the external work of the motor apparatus displays a specific pattern. This pattern is characterised principally by:

- an increase in maximum force
- displacement of the instant of maximum force closer to when muscle tension begins
- an increase in the working amplitude of the movement
- a decrease in the time of production of the force.

In each case, the magnitude of these changes is specific to the type of sport involved.

2.1.2 Perfecting the Motor Pattern of Sports Movements

The effectiveness of movement is associated primarily with the appropriate use of the working mechanisms of the body. This produces mechanical energy for effective use in response to external conditions. Such working mechanisms are complex and are largely inherited by each individual. Sports training adds nothing new to them, but only directs them to a high level of proficiency, improves their coordinated use and increases energy capabilities. The working mechanisms of the body include:

- The contraction of muscles transformed into external force via limb leverages
- The synergism and antagonism of muscle groups at the joints and in the musculoskeletal system as a whole
- The neuromuscular reflexes
- The elasticity of muscle and connective tissue which stores and uses elastic energy
- The strengthening of a basic movement by excitation from other collateral movements
- The sequential involvement of muscles with different functional qualities
- The tonus of the muscular system.

Biomechanically, it is appropriate to consider a motor complex which is organised with respect to the structural and functional characteristics of the body and facilitates optimal use of the working mechanisms under real sporting conditions. The body's mechanisms determine the form of the interaction during the execution of a given motor task and how systematic training uses them to produce efficient performance. It is useful to study the functional properties of the body's mechanisms and how they enhance specific performance at the following levels:

- The level of the kinematic pair (two actively combined adjacent links)
- The level of the kinematic chain (the sequential combination of several links)

- The level of the kinematic system (the combination of several kinematic chains).

The Kinematic Pair

The perfecting of movement at the kinematic pair level depends on its linking purpose, development of the ability to produce large motor force, and the execution of movement with high angular speed, or on all of these and other factors simultaneously. The process of perfecting a movement is determined by the anatomical characteristics of the musculoskeletal system.

Many studies indicate that, in all of the diverse isolated single-joint movements, changes in strength apparently depend upon the role and functions of the joint mechanisms and the relative disposition of the body's links relative to one another (Zatsiorsky, 1966; Verkhoshansky, 1970). Changes in joint angle alter the conditions of muscular work, since muscle length and angle of pull are changed. Muscular strength and leverage change, and consequently, so does the torque (i.e. moment of force) produced by the muscles about a joint.

Therefore, the maximum external force developed by the muscles corresponds to a specific joint angle in each case (Figs 2.8, 2.9). Thus, maximum force (measured isometrically at different joint angles) is achieved at a joint angle of approximately 90° for elbow flexion, at 120° for elbow extension, at 60°-70° for extension at the shoulder joint and at an angle of 60° for extension at the knee joint. Trained athletes can produce maximum force at a number of angles close together (Kosilov, 1965; Dorofyev, 1966; Hansen & Lindhard, 1923; Wilkie, 1950).

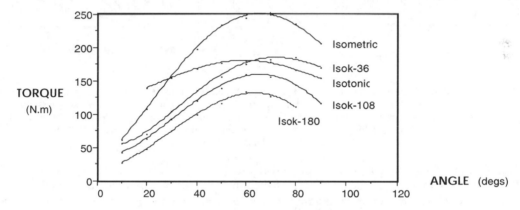

Figure 2.8 Variation of torque during seated knee extension for different regimes of muscle action for male subjects (based on Knapik et al, 1983). Isok-36 refers to isokinetic contraction at 36° per second, isok-108 at 108° per sec, and isok-180 at 180° per sec.

Graphically, the dependence of strength on joint angle can be classified into three types: *ascending, descending* (maximal and minimal forces corresponding to the extreme parts of the angular amplitude of joint movement respectively, Fig 2.10, graph F) and *ascending-descending* (minimal force is at the extreme ends and maximal force near the middle of the angular amplitude).

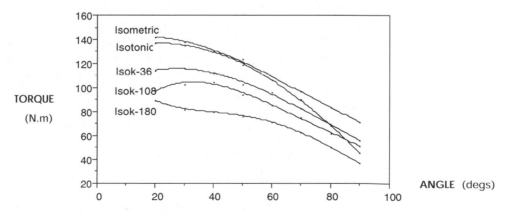

Figure 2.9 Variation of torque during seated knee flexion for different regimes of muscle action for male subjects (based on Knapik et al, 1983). Isok-36 refers to isokinetic contraction at 36° per second, isok-108 at 108° per sec, and isok-180 at 180° per sec.

A number of Verkhoshansky's studies have established that the ability to express explosive strength (i.e. Se, sometimes calculated by dividing one-half the maximum isometric tension by the time taken to reach it: see 2.2.1) changes unidirectionally with the change in external muscular force (Fig 2.10, graph Se). A decrease in the Se index with change in joint angle is associated simultaneously with a decrease in muscular tension and an increase in the time required for its production (Fig 2.11).

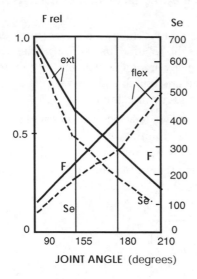
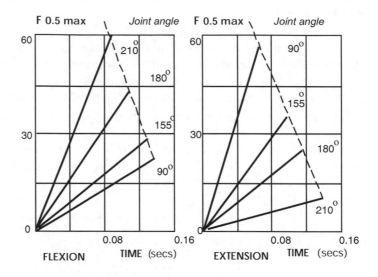

Figure 2.10 Changes in relative strength (Frel) and explosive strength (Se) with changes in hip angle for qualified women sprinters for extension (ext) and flexion (flex). (Siff & Verkhoshansky, 1999).

Figure 2.11 Change in rate of a gradually applied isometric force with changes in hip angle for qualified women sprinters for flexion and extension. Note that F0.5max = 0.5 of max isometric force, which provides an approximation of the explosive strength Se. (Siff & Verkhoshansky, 1999).

The force-angle graph does not change its form fundamentally with the increase in muscular strength produced by training. However, a number of studies have established that the increase in strength over the entire amplitude of single-joint movements depends on the joint angle at which maximum muscular tension is exerted during training (Zatsiorsky & Raitsin, 1974; Raitsin & Sarsania, 1975). If it is produced at an angle corresponding to the muscle's greatest length (i.e. the smallest degree of flexion in the joint for active muscular flexion or the least degree of extension for muscular extension), then the transfer of strength to the other joint angles is relatively uniform.

The reverse is true if maximum muscular force is produced when the joint is significantly flexed and the muscles are in a shortened state; in this case the increase in strength is larger. However, the transfer of the training effect to other joint angles is comparatively small and, the further from this angle, the smaller the transfer of maximum strength. It is interesting to note that, for the joint angle at which maximum force is produced in training, there is a relatively larger increase in strength than there is at adjacent joint angles.

The perfecting of movement at the kinematic pair level is still associated with increasing the amplitude of movement through greater mobility of the joint. However, this applies primarily to kinematic pairs, namely those joint combinations which involve two or three planes of movement (e.g. the ankle, shoulder and hip joints).

It is relevant to point out that the force-angle graphs reproduced in most textbooks are not obtained under continuously varying dynamic conditions. They are obtained by using a dynamometer to measure the maximum isometric force at a series of successive angles. A curve is then fitted to the resulting set of points which, strictly speaking, allows one to predict the expected maximum isometric force or torque at a particular joint angle. Research by Siff and mechanical engineering students at the University of the Witwatersrand using high speed video and tensiometers to measure the changes in torque under non-isokinetic dynamic conditions has confirmed the work of Knapik et al (1983) showing that the resulting dynamic curves for a particular joint are significantly different from the curves obtained statically (Figs 2.8, 2.9).

This research also shows that the profile of the curve changes with load, velocity of movement and orientation of the joint. For instance, the maximum torque for auxotonic elbow flexion does not occur near the 90° measured isometrically, but nearer full flexion. Moreover, if the myotatic stretch reflex is evoked by using a ballistic start near full elbow extension, yet another profile of curve results. The torque curves produced dynamically on isokinetic apparatus also differ radically from those measured biomechanically under unrestricted auxotonic conditions, using free weights or pulley systems.

This does not negate the value of research done on isometric force-angle curves, which gives a fairly accurate picture of slow movement against very large resistance. It emphasizes that there are specific force-joint angle curves for each joint, determined by the type of muscle contraction, the velocity of movement, the starting conditions, the load and the orientation of the joint. The phenomenon of specificity again becomes apparent. Clearly, it is important to model the strength characteristics of each sports movement accurately to allow one to select the appropriate training regime.

The Kinematic Chain

The working movements of the body are produced by a system of links in a kinematic chain where the angles in each joint combination change simultaneously. The fundamental working functions of the kinematic chains in the motor apparatus consist of transforming rotational joint movements to linear movement (by lengthening or shortening the system's levers) or angular movement at the distal end of the system's links (relative to the proximal joint).

The working effect of the movements executed by the kinematic chain varies to a great extent, depending on specific conditions of the system at a given time (e.g. relative disposition of the links and the motor potential of given muscle groups). In addition, the working effect of exercises in kinematic chains is associated with larger qualitative and quantitative changes than in kinematic pairs. Perfecting of movement through the kinematic chain is secured by three basic factors:

- an increase in the working amplitude of the movement
- concentration of dynamic force at a certain part of it
- optimal interaction among the muscles involved.

An increase in the working amplitude is achieved by a large range of motion in the joint and by an increase in the elasticity and strength of the corresponding muscle groups and their associated connective tissues (Topolyan, 1951; Ivanitsky, 1956; Donskoi, 1960). The amplitude of movement increases in two directions of the kinematic chain, namely the beginning and end of range. This is realised in the first case by an increase in muscular strength and the ability of the muscles to develop a powerful force during the movement, as well as an increase in the elasticity of the functional antagonists. The force produced shows two clear characteristics over the course of a movement:

1. A decrease in muscle tension at the end of the movement, especially with ballistic work (which is more pronounced for faster movement and smaller external resistance)

2. There is an increase and a concentration of working force at a certain part of the range of the movement.

The first characteristic is an obvious protective reflex as expressed by the inhibitory action of muscle antagonists, which is associated with the survival role of the motor system (Pierson, 1965). This mechanism does not change with growth in sports proficiency, which concerns the second characteristic, correlating directly with the process of producing a biomechanically appropriate movement, as discussed earlier.

The working force of a kinematic chain is produced by the coordinated work of the muscle groups serving each of its joints. The coordination of force and the function of certain muscle groups have their own characteristics in this context. It is noteworthy that the following two examples have not yet been adequately analysed in the sporting literature:

(a) The resulting force is less than the sum of the forces of the muscles each kinematic pair is capable of producing (Verkhoshansky, 1961, 1965, 1970; Yegorov, 1966). For example, in isolated elbow flexion, strength increases as elbow joint angle decreases and reaches an isometric maximum at about 90°. However, with isolated flexion at the shoulder, there is no significant difference in isometric strength in the 0° to 160° range (Campney & Wehr, 1965). If the entire arm executes stretching work (simultaneous extension at the shoulder and forearm flexion with the working point at the hand), then maximum isometric force is produced at about 160° in the elbow joint. If propulsive work is executed by the entire upper extremity (i.e. involving shoulder and elbow action), maximal isometric force is developed with the elbow near full flexion, i.e. near the beginning of the push-off.

(b) With isolated extension involving only the knee, maximal force is produced (with little variation) in the range 80°-130° and then quickly drops (Campney & Wehr, 1965; Williams & Stutzman, 1959). However, with propulsive work when the system's links lengthen (ex-tension at both hip and knee), maximal force occurs when the hip angle is near maximum extension and when the knee angle is close to 160° (Dorofeyev, 1965; Yegrov, 1966).

These examples illustrate the adaptation of the body to cope with bipedal ambulation. Thus, the latter example of maximal knee extension force occurring with a nearly fully extended hip is probably associated with the dominance of the human erect gait.

Semyenov and Tatyanov (1976) have established that there is a smaller correlation between improvements in running or jumping exercises and the individual maximum torque about each joint of the lower extremity, than with the force produced by the extremity as a whole. This correlation increases noticeably with the growth in proficiency, which indicates that efficiency of movement is determined by one's ability to optimise muscular potential, i.e. when any functional deficiencies are strongly overcome by other physical advantages.

Careful analysis of muscle group combinations under various work conditions in the kinematic chain enables one to identify certain biomechanical characteristics. Depending upon the activities, the athlete involuntarily orients the links relative to one another in the kinematic chain to ensure that the required working-force simultaneously or sequentially uses the angles of maximal strength for each joint involved (Verkhoshansky, 1977).

The first case (a) is associated with overcoming large external resistance, such as isometric tension (for instance, the attempt to move a heavy object). The second case (b) is typical of movements which necessitate imparting as large as possible a velocity to an external object or bodymass under conditions of limited working amplitude (e.g. the take-off in jumping).

This functional relationship between the muscle groups involved in the kinematic chain is such that the movement is begun by the most powerful muscles of the proximal joints (the key muscles in the chain) and is achieved with the support of the distal links and the joints which are rigidly fixed. The distal links then participate in the work, while at the proximal links, fixation begins in the joints to produce a stable base for the movements of the distal links.

Thus, the athlete always strives to begin the working-force by using the joint-angle zones of maximum strength for the specific situation. It can be assumed that sports technique evolved over many decades on precisely this basis to ensure the most favourable conditions for exerting maximal force at the appropriate time and position. However, in certain cases, there may be a conflict between these mechanisms and the requirements of the movement during the sports activity. This reveals in particular the need to increase the working amplitude of a movement, especially if it is necessary to exert maximum strength in the range where this strength cannot be produced primarily on the basis of anatomical structure.

Nevertheless, the body's high adaptive capability enables one to find the optimal solution to such conflicting situations. This is possible, for instance, when the corresponding muscle groups (prior to beginning the working-force) possess some additional tension accumulated during the *preparatory movement phase*. Thus, during the *amortisation phase (shock absorption phase)* of the vertical jump, some of the elastic energy accumulated at the end of this phase facilitates the subsequent extension of the knees.

Therefore, it is possible to begin from certain joint angles where maximal strength is produced and achieve the greatest gain in amplitude of movement compared with jumping from an initial half-squat position (i.e. without the amortisation phase). There is a tendency for the amplitude of amortisation during knee flexion to decrease after a depth jump. There is an obvious effort towards operating near the angles of maximum strength in certain joints because of the large dynamic loading encountered there. Some of the loss in amplitude of the movement is compensated for by the additional elastic energy stored in and released by the muscle complex. Thus, *there is a specific sequence in the process of perfecting of movement at the level of the kinematic chain* (Verkhoshansky, 1977):

1. The choice of the optimal working amplitude of a movement based on interrelating the angles of maximum strength for each joint, the motor potential of the muscles and the conditions facilitating resolution of the motor task, as follows:

   (a) for small external loads there is a characteristic attempt to increase the amplitude of movement independent of the zones of maximum strength for each joint

(b) for large external loads where additional reserves of strength are lacking, the movement characteristically is facilitated by decreasing its working amplitude in conjunction with an effort to execute actions near the zone of maximum strength

(c) for large external loads and additional sources of movement (e.g. force of inertia and elastic energy of the muscles and connective tissues), there is the possibility of some increase in the working amplitude outside the joint zones of maximum strength

(d) in all cases a forcible decrease in the amplitude of movement is compensated for by storage of elastic energy in the muscle complex, accumulated during the preparatory phases of the movement, which ensures a powerful initial muscular contraction.

2. An increase in the maximal motor force and its concentration primarily at the beginning of the working zone.

3. Participation of the muscles in the kinematic chain in the work in a suitable sequence which enables them to produce powerful force and speed of contraction throughout the movement.

4. An attempt to execute the movement within the zones of maximum strength in each joint and simultaneously enhance its efficiency by storing elastic energy during the preparatory phase.

The Kinematic System

The *kinematic system* possesses many linear and rotational degrees of freedom. Therefore, the process of perfecting movement, from a level of kinematic pairs to that of a kinematic system, is closely associated with the efficient organisation and control of the motor action. Nevertheless, biomechanical factors continue to play an important role.

The characteristics of perfecting the movement considered earlier are associated with the sequence of muscular actions generated in the kinematic chain and intimately involve the kinematic system. The only difference is in the number of functionally interacting muscle groups. This interaction involves chiefly the work of the strongest muscle groups of the legs and torso, followed by the muscles of the shoulder girdle.

Thus, the perfecting of movement is associated with determination of the most effective method of uniting individual kinematic chains and their working mechanisms into a single working system. The logical organisation of such mechanisms may be referred to as the *kinesiological pattern* of a complex motor event, which is discussed separately because of its special significance.

2.1.3 Perfecting the Kinesiological Pattern of Movements

The motor programme underlying a sports exercise involves certain cause-effect relationships between its individual elements, with their pattern of force production depending on neuromuscular processes. In the course of achieving sports mastery these relationships change continuously while the body searches for a more efficient interaction between the elements of the motor complex, and its kinesiological pattern acquires further information for enhancing this process.

This pattern constitutes the basic framework of the movement system, determining its spatio-temporal characteristics and the functioning of the working effect. Therefore, the *kinesiological pattern* of a specific sport exercise is an extremely important condition for successfully solving the problem of special strength training. With respect to the kinesiological pattern of a sports action, the strength field, which is a result of the athlete's interaction with external objects, is divided into phases of voluntary action and reflexive reaction (Verkhoshansky, 1958, 1963, 1966, 1968).

Note that the term *kinesiological pattern* is used in preference to "biomechanical pattern" or "biomechanics" to emphasize that we are not simply referring to the action of force as an entity in physics, but as an active motor process which involves a complex of psychological and physiological factors.

Initially these dynamic elements are expressed weakly and are irregularly distributed over the strength field (Fig 2.12a). Not only does coordination in space and time vary widely, but the motor act as a whole is still dynamically unstable and its final effect is inefficient and unstable. Then, as adaptation to the situation takes place, the athlete develops the ability to more effectively manage the motor tasks. This is associated with distinctions between and increases in the dynamic accentuations, clearly localising them within the limits of the motor complex and unifying them into a specific, distinctly interrelated system (Fig 2.12b). Now, with repetition of a motor act, the range of variation of its elements decreases, the process can be executed accurately over a shorter period and its elements do not simply sum in space and time, but interact in a specific pattern of simultaneous and sequential actions.

The correlation between the dynamic elements is such that any change in the characteristics of one of them is reflected in the others, even if far removed in space and time. The interrelation of elements establishes a hierarchical scheme which involves the dominant roles of some and the subordinate roles of others. Thus, one can separate the key elements crucial for managing the motor tasks, as well as organise the elements acting as the fundamental components of the kinesiological pattern, and thereby increase the functional value of these key elements (Verkhoshansky, 1977).

Thus, the kinesiological pattern of a motor action enables an athlete to effectively use his motor potential to execute specific physical tasks. As the motor system becomes an integrated whole, it reacts and functionally evolves as a whole. When a kinesiological pattern is firmly established, a motor act is reproduced at a new, higher level of efficiency, increasing its working effect by optimal use of the body's motor potential.

As has already been discussed, the kinesiological pattern is constantly perfected by refining the connections between the elements of the motor complex. However, the motor complex possesses a certain flexibility in specific situations and an ability to cope with strong external influences without disrupting its functional effectiveness. This becomes possible because of the kinesiological pattern's ability to adapt to external events.

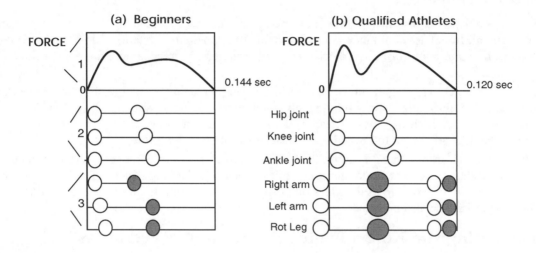

Figure 2.12 Sequence of accentuated active and reactive dynamics of the motor system for the second take-off in a triple jump: 1. resulting force-time curve; 2. accentuation in the tension of the relevant muscles of the hip, knee and ankle joints of the support leg (measured with a myotensiometer); 3. accentuation of active and reactive (shaded circles) dynamics of rotary movement associated with the swinging arms and leg. a = beginners and b = qualified athletes. The open circles refer to active, concentrated voluntary effort. (Siff & Verkhoshansky, 1999).

It should be pointed out that the principle of dynamic organisation applies to any complex motor act. However, *acyclic exercises* demand the production of significant force over a minimal time, so that the concept of training consists of forming and perfecting the kinesiological pattern. On the other hand, *cyclic exercises* require the prolonged maintenance of work output. In this case, the kinesiological pattern develops significantly more rapidly, its composition is simpler and the concept of training consists primarily of perfecting the contributions of the involuntary functions of the body.

The kinesiological pattern is part of the *general strength field*, i.e. the sum of all the external and internal forces involving the body while it undertakes a given motor task. The force producing movement is the geometric sum of external, internal and reactive strengths. If this classification is based upon the character, origin and direction of force, the components of the *strength field* may be recognised as follows (Verkhoshansky, 1977):

1. The active driving force produced by muscular contraction.
2. The reactive force, which arises as a result of the interaction of the active muscles with the environment.
3. The force stored in the muscle complex as elastic energy during the preparatory phases of a movement.
4. The force of inertia of the body or its links.
5. The weight of the body or its links.

Each of these factors is involved in the process of solving motor tasks and has a distinct influence on the results. Therefore, each must be considered when one is analysing the kinesiological pattern of the movement system and selecting the special strength-training means. These forces, depending upon the place and point of application, can be external or internal to the body; and depending upon the direction of movement of the body, they may assist or resist movement. It is necessary to identify further characteristics of the strength field. Relative to the body, the strength field consists of two systems (Verkhoshansky, 1977):

- the *external interaction* with the motor apparatus
- the *internal interaction* with the motor apparatus.

These systems appear simultaneously and in several aspects act independently of each other, but they obviously influence each other, to an extent which increases as sports proficiency improves. The composition of the system of external interaction decisively influences the structure of the internal strength system, whereas the internal interaction system depends on the magnitude and direction of the resulting movement and its change over time.

Hence, the kinesiological pattern of a sports action can be the appropriate concept only if it represents part of the general strength field. At the same time, control of the external interaction of the motor apparatus is possible only through the internal kinesiological pattern. Consequently, when referring to control of the athlete's movements, one must consider not so much the movement (i.e. the relative shifting of the body's links), as the kinesiological pattern and its influence on the working-effect of the movement. This forms the pedagogical basis of the problem of controlling human movement.

2.2 Specialisation to Develop Sports Mastery

One of the main features of the sports training process (STP) is the steady perfecting of the athlete's physical system, which occurs with a certain regularity. In the beginning, the body reacts fairly generally to any new motor regime with all of its systems and this is sufficient for the initial sporting successes. However, subsequent adaptation tends to be more selective, conditioned by the motor specifics and the peculiarities of the external factors. Under such conditions, one of the body's systems may receive considerable development, whereas another may receive less, depending upon their respective roles in meeting the requirements of the motor activity.

Adaptation has been examined in sufficient detail in various texts on the anatomy, physiology, medicine, biomechanics and biochemistry of sport. However, the character and tempo of the adaptations and their interrelation in the STP have not yet been studied adequately. This is an important problem in applied exercise science and constitutes the scientific foundation for any theories of sports training. Some characteristics of adaptation of the athlete's motor apparatus during long-term preparation to develop strength are discussed below.

2.2.1 Specific Forms of Producing Muscular Strength

Depending upon the primary coordination pattern of the motor activity, muscular strength acquires a specificity which becomes more apparent as one's level of sports mastery grows. Some of the fundamental specific forms in which strength is displayed in athletic activities are: *absolute strength, explosive strength* and *strength-endurance*.

Maximum strength characterizes the athlete's strength potential and is a measure of the maximal voluntary isometric muscular force which can be produced without a time limit or a limit to the amount of weight lifted. The term *absolute strength* is often regarded in other books as synonymous with maximal strength, but this text confines it to mean maximum involuntary strength (see Ch 1).

The *relative strength* of an athlete (i.e. amount of force produced per kilogram of bodymass or sports apparatus) is also defined in sport. This index is sometimes used for comparing the strength of athletes of different bodymass, although it is scientifically preferable to reserve its use for assessing changes in an individual with time. Comparison of the strength of individuals of different bodymass is far more accurate by applying the adjustment equations detailed in the next chapter (see 3.3.5).

Speed-strength characterizes the ability to quickly execute an unloaded movement or a movement against a relatively small external resistance. Speed-strength is assessed in terms of the speed of the movement.

Explosive strength characterizes the ability to produce maximal force in a minimal time. The index of explosive strength IES is often described roughly by dividing the maximum force by the time t_{max} taken to produce this level of force (Fig 2.13a), thus (Zatsiorsky, 1995):

$$IES = F_{max} / t_{max} \quad \text{(Newtons per second)}$$

although mathematically, it is given by the maximum value of the slope of the force-time curve.

Explosive force production is also described by another index called the *Reactivity Coefficient*, RC, which is the explosive strength index relative to body weight or the weight of the object being moved (see 3.2.1):

$$RC = F_{max} / (t_{max} \cdot W) = RFD_{max} / W$$

The most accurate way of assessing force development at any instant is to plot the slope (tan θ) of the force-time graph versus time or to use a computer to simultaneously display the curves of force versus time and the slope of the F-t curve (i.e. the Rate of Force Development) versus time. The maximum of this Rate of Force Development (RFD) curve gives a precise measure of explosive strength (Fig 2.13b). In addition it may be noted that the smaller the value of t_{max}, the more explosive the movement. Analysis of the F(t) curve of explosive force reveals three further characteristics of the movement, namely (Verkhoshansky, 1966, 1970, 1972):

- The *maximum strength* of the muscles involved (F_{max})

- The *starting-strength*, or ability of the muscles to develop force at the beginning of the working contraction before external movement occurs

- The *acceleration-strength*, or ability over time to quickly achieve maximal external force while developing muscle tension isometrically or at the beginning of a dynamic contraction.

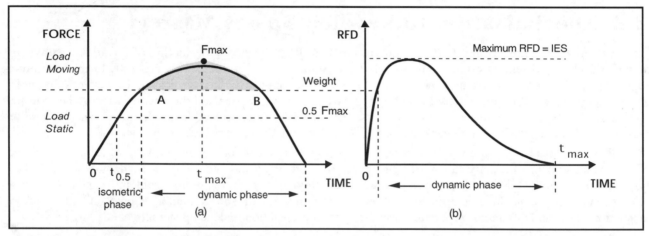

Figure 2.13 **(a)** Force-time curve illustrating a method for determining explosive, starting and acceleration strength. W is the weight being overcome by the force F(t). Movement occurs only when the force exceeds the weight W of the object. **(b)** Rate of force development (RFD) curve up to t_{max} obtained by plotting the slope of the force-time graph versus time. The maximum rate of force development represents the explosive strength, ES.

The following formula is used to calculate an index of *starting-strength* ISS (or the S-gradient), which is exhibited during the contraction just preceding the movement of the load (Zatsiorsky, 1995):

$$ISS = 0.5 F_{max} / t_{0.5} \quad \text{where } t_{0.5} \text{ is the time taken to reach one half } F_{max}$$

The index of acceleration strength IAS (or the A-gradient), usually used to quantify the rate of force development (RFD) during the late stages of developing muscular force, is described by the formula:

$$IAS = 0.5 F_{max} / (t_{max} - t_{0.5})$$

Explosive strength is most commonly displayed in athletic movements when the contraction of the working muscles in the fundamental phases of the exercise is preceded by mechanical stretching. In this instance, the switch from stretching to active contraction uses the elastic energy of the stretch to increase the power of the subsequent contraction. This specific quality of muscle will subsequently (3.2.1) be called its *reactive ability* (RA).

Strength-endurance characterizes the ability to effectively maintain muscular functioning under work conditions of long duration. In sport this refers to the ability to produce a certain minimum force for a prolonged period. There are different types of muscle functioning associated with this ability, such as holding a given position or posture (*static strength-endurance*), maintaining cyclic work of various intensities (*dynamic strength-endurance*) or repetitively executing explosive effort (*explosive strength-endurance*).

2.2.2 Sports Implications of Strength Indices

To progress beyond these dynamometric analyses of strength and to better understand the role of strength in sport, it is relevant to commence with an analysis of a typical force-time curve in lifting a free weight from a given position and returning it to that position (Fig 2.14).

Starting-strength, as introduced earlier, refers to the ability to build up working force as rapidly as possible once muscle contraction has begun and it is always produced under conditions of isometric muscle action. This fact alone has important consequences for strength training, because it dispels the opinion that the once-popular method of isometric training should be completely abandoned in modern training. On the contrary, the ability to generate starting strength rapidly can exert a profound effect on the dynamics of an entire movement, not only in terms of the magnitude of the impulse, but also regarding the psychological sensation of "lightness" that it creates during the crucial initial stage of a highly resisted movement.

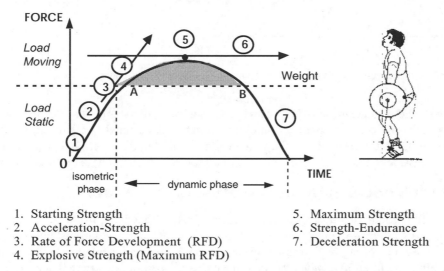

1. Starting Strength
2. Acceleration-Strength
3. Rate of Force Development (RFD)
4. Explosive Strength (Maximum RFD)

5. Maximum Strength
6. Strength-Endurance
7. Deceleration Strength

Figure 2.14 A typical force-time curve describing the lifting of a free weight from a given position and returning it to it to rest. Movement occurs only when the force exceeds the weight of the object, namely over the shaded portion of the curve.

If the load is near maximal, then the initial slope of the Force-Time curve is small and the time taken to produce movement is prolonged. This requires the exhibition of the motor quality of *static strength-endurance*, as opposed to *dynamic strength-endurance*, which refers to the muscle endurance required to maintain movement over a given interval. This quality may be involved in carrying out a set of repetitions with a load or by maintaining cyclic work of various intensities   One may also identify a property known as *explosive strength-endurance* which involves the repetitive execution of explosive effort. As we learned above, *acceleration-strength* describes the ability of the muscle to build up force as rapidly as possible under dynamic conditions once the contraction has already begun:

Finally, we recall that *explosive strength* is the ability to produce maximal force in a minimal time. It is most commonly displayed in athletic movements when the contraction of the working muscles in the fundamental phases of the exercise is preceded by mechanical stretching. In this instance, the switch from stretching to active contraction uses the elastic energy of the stretch to increase the power of the subsequent contraction, a process that is central to the so-called stretch-shortening cycle and 'plyometric' or rapid rebound action. This specific quality of muscle is called its *reactive ability*.

Suppose that we now wish to use the information from Figure 2.14 to compare the performances of two different athletes in executing the same exercise. They have both been instructed to perform a single maximal repetition of this exercise as rapidly as possible and to hold the load for as long as possible until fatigue forces them to stop. Their resulting force-time curves (Fig 2.15) show that athlete B exerts a greater maximal force and continues to produce force for longer than athlete A. However, at any instant T_1 between 0 and time T_2, athlete A is able to exert greater force than athlete B. If the sport concerned requires rapid RFD (Rate of Force Development), then athlete A will have the advantage.

This quality is essential in any sports which involve jumping, striking or throwing, such as basketball, martial arts and track-and-field. In this case, any training aimed at increasing B's maximal strength or bulk will be misdirected, because he needs to concentrate on explosive strength (RFD) training. If the sport requires a high maximal force or a large amount of momentum to be exerted irrespective of time, then athlete B will prove to be superior. Athlete A will not improve unless he trains to increase maximal strength.

The area under the curve (i.e. momentum) which describes athlete B's performance is greater than the corresponding area for athlete A, like the total duration of his curve (i.e. reflecting muscle endurance), so that B has a distinct advantage in any activity that requires great momentum or great muscle endurance during a single heavy effort. This situation occurs in events like wrestling, powerlifting, rugby scrumming and judo.

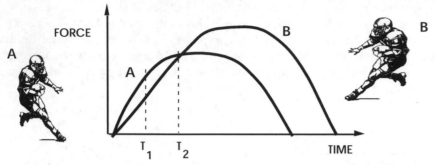

Figure 2.15 Force curves produced by two different athletes in attempting to produce optimal motor output or force-time patterns in a given exercise.

This type of analysis also reveals the limitations of using isometric or isokinetic dynamometers to assess muscular strength and performance. These devices are unable to measure functional maximal strength, Rate of Force Development or explosive strength, so it is futile to use them in an attempt to identify functional characteristics or deficiencies in such a way as to have any accurate bearing on analysing sporting preparedness or progress.

2.2.3 The Functional Topography of the Muscular System

Observations of some of the functional qualities of certain muscle groups, adopted from work physiology (Uflyand, 1965), have enabled us to determine the functional topography of the muscular system. Usually the basic observations concern the maximal strength of certain muscle groups. Visual representation of the topography of muscular strength produces the so-called *dynamometric profile* (Uflyand, 1965), constructed according to the dynamic record of the strength of various muscle groups (Fig 2.16).

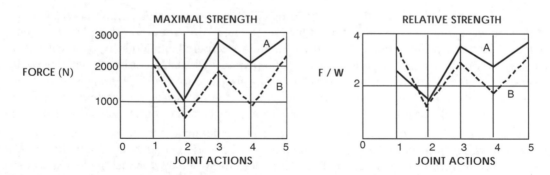

Figure 2.16 Dynamometric profile for high jump (A) and distance running (B), giving different joint actions: trunk extension (1), trunk flexion (2), thigh extension (3), ankle plantarflexion (4) and ankle dorsiflexion (5). Force is in Newtons and relative strength is the ratio of force to bodymass (Siff & Verkhoshansky, 1999).

The dynamometric profile enables one to compare the strength fitness of individual athletes. Of particular interest is the study of the *general dynamometric profile* which characterizes the strength topography of representative muscle groups of athletes of different specialisation, as well as the changes in the general profile with growth of sports mastery. Such a general profile reflects the characteristics of the strength fitness of athletes in a given sport and can serve to some extent as a standard for controlling the training process.

Semyenov et al (1971) showed that the general dynamometric profile of athletes of one specialisation is preserved as sports mastery increases (Fig 2.17). However, there is always some irregularity in the rate of strength development of certain muscle groups at novice and higher training levels. This is characteristic of sporting development and is associated with the changing conditions of the athlete's interaction with external objects, which decrees that some muscle groups display a large potential for development, and others, less.

Thus, the dynamometric profile clearly expresses the specialised character of the perfecting of the motor action of a competitor in a particular sport (Verkhoshansky, 1977).. However, muscular strength is only one of the characteristics of the functional specialisation of the motor apparatus. *People with identical dynamometric profiles demonstrate different sports results.* The cause of this is the different levels of development of indicators such as the ability to rapidly produce external force from the commencement of muscular tension.

For instance, two women sprinters may be roughly equal in relative strength (Fig 2.18). However, one of them runs the 100m in 12.1 seconds and the other in 12.4 seconds. The reason for this is the differences in the speed qualities of the muscles as characterized by their ability to quickly develop maximum working force (the ratio of maximal strength to the time of its display for explosive-isometric muscular tension).

From this it is obvious that the characteristics reflecting the topography of the athlete's muscular system should include its diversity, and those qualities of muscle essential to the given sport. This enables one to obtain a comprehensive idea of what may be termed the *functional profile* (sometimes called the *polyfunctional profile*) of the athlete's muscular system, which has important significance for determining the objectives of his special preparation (Verkhoshansky, 1977).

Figure 2.17 depicts a portion of such a *functional profile* of women sprinters of different qualification, giving chiefly the speed-strength characteristics. The basic differences in the women's speed-strength with increase in the level of mastery may easily be seen in the lower two graphs, in particular the last one.

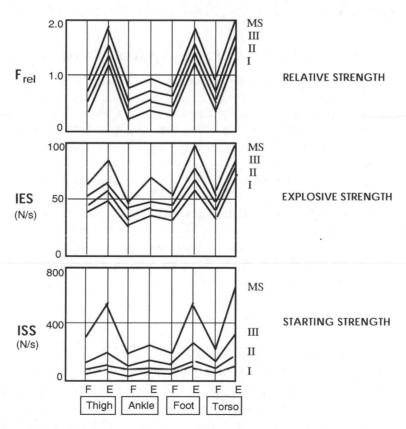

Figure 2.17 General functional profile of muscular systems of women sprinters. The labels I, II, III, and MS refer to Class III, Class II, Class I and Master of Sport, respectively. F and E refer to flexion and extension, respectively. Frel = relative strength. (Siff & Verkhoshansky, 1999).

The functional profiles clearly indicate that the specific adaptation of the motor apparatus involves chiefly those of its segments with which the sports performance is primarily achieved. The nature of such adaptation reflects the specific characteristics of the work regime and, with the growth of mastery, this is displayed even more strongly. Thus, the *functional profile* of the muscular system is a prerequisite for formalising the objectives of special strength training, since it enables one to determine which muscle groups are underdeveloped and need additional work.

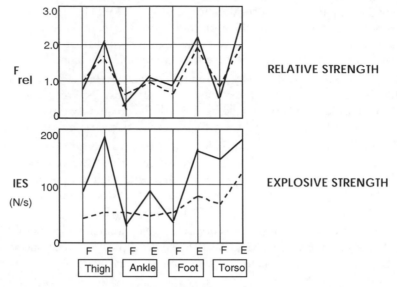

Figure 2.18 Strength fitness of two 100 metre woman sprinters with times of 12.1 sec (continuous line) and 12.4 sec (dashed line). (Siff & Verkhoshansky, 1999).

2.2.4 Motor Specialisation in Developing Sports Mastery

The special strength fitness of athletes of different qualification gives an idea of the most general characteristics of the motor apparatus in long-term training. For example, there is a relationship between an increase in the reactive ability (RA) of the neuromuscular apparatus and improvements in the long jump and triple jump (Fig 2.19). Here it should be noted that the abilities assessed by the standing triple jump and the back squat display a more complex form of correlation with the triple jump. An analogous pattern in the dynamics of the control indices can be seen in Olympic weightlifting.

One should remember, however, that in the given case, the dynamic indices being examined are produced by a particular combination of specific motor abilities. The rate of perfecting each of them individually can reflect different relationships, an understanding of which is vital for solving the problems of organising special strength training in sport (Verkhoshansky, 1977).

A detailed study of this question reveals five variants which describe the relationship between the indicators of adaptation of the body and athletic performance (Fig 2.20). This relationship can be described by the following mathematical functions which are commonly applied in biology:

- linear (1)
- exponential with slowed growth (2)
- exponential with accelerated growth (3)
- logistic, Gompertz and other sigmoid functions (4)
- power law and third order parabolic functions (5).

The first variant (1) is characteristic of the key motor abilities, i.e. the dominant abilities which determine success in the sport. The second variant (2) is characteristic of those non-key motor abilities which are indicators of general physical fitness. They play an important role in the initial stages of the sports training process to secure conditions for the harmonious development of the body and to provide a foundation for perfecting specific motor abilities. The third variant (3) is characteristic of the specific adaptation which determines chiefly the developmental level of the key motor abilities, and consequently the success of the athletic achievements as a whole. The form of this relationship indicates that the growth of sports performance requires the accelerated development of the key motor abilities. The correlation of the latter with athletic results increases significantly with the growth of sports mastery. The fourth (4) and fifth variants (5) are characteristic of the variety of dynamic non-essential and key motor abilities in the sports training process.

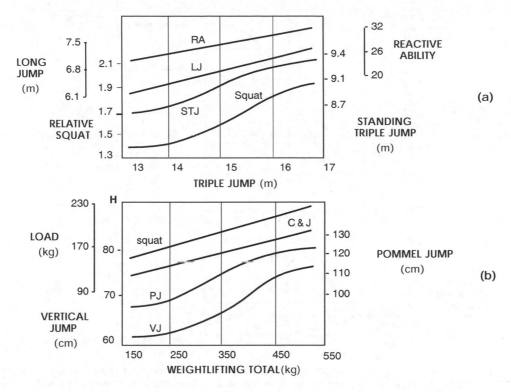

Figure 2.19 Dynamics of control exercises relative to the sports results of triple jumpers and weightlifters. The weightlifting data applies to the period up to 1971 when competition comprised the triathlon, i.e. the press, snatch and clean-and-jerk (C & J). RA = reactive ability, STJ = standing triple jump, PJ = jump onto a pommel horse, VJ = standing vertical jump, and squat refers to the back squat. (Siff & Verkhoshansky, 1999).

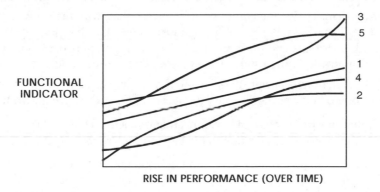

Figure 2.20 The different types of relationship between physical adaptation and performance. (Siff & Verkhoshansky, 1999).

Heterochronicity

It has been established that, as sports proficiency grows, a key ability for achieving a movement can be transferred from one group of muscles to another. Specific regularities in the process of functional specialisation of key muscle groups are observed particularly in what may be called the *heterochronicity* of the rate of developing specific motor abilities (Verkhoshansky, 1977). In the absence of a term existing to describe the phenomenon, this word was coined to describe the process in which specific events do not occur simultaneously or asynchronously, but in a complex sequence of distinct steps or actions, each of which lays the foundation for the next one.

Thus, Nikonov and Verkhoshansky found an irregular strength development of certain muscle groups of pole vaulters. If the strength curves are compared (Fig 2.21a), as well as the derivatives (with respect to height) which describe the rate of strength increase relative to athletic achievements (Fig 2.21b), then it is easy to notice that the shoulder flexors (1) prolong the functional perfecting begun by the abdominal muscles from the moment when the strength of the latter begins stabilisation.

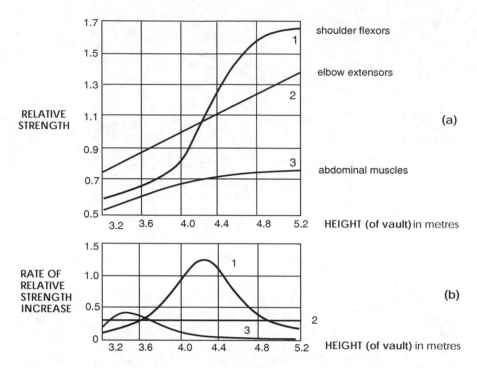

Figure 2.21 **(a)** Increase in relative strength of the shoulder flexors (1), elbow extensors (2) and the abdominal muscles (3) of pole-vaulters with growth of sports mastery. **(b)** Increase in rate of change of relative strength relative to height achieved, for the same muscle groups of pole-vaulters. (Siff & Verkhoshansky, 1999).

This continuity is easily explained. Novice athletes raise their bodies up the pole with their abdominal muscles, but with increase in mastery, this raising is executed quickly by the arms and shoulders. The strength of these muscles increases significantly at the same time as the strength of the elbow extensors (2) increases uniformly.

In a study conducted by Verkhoshansky and Purvin, it was discovered that, with the growth of mastery in the shot put, the key role gradually shifts from the shoulder to the leg muscles (Verkhoshansky, 1977). For beginners, the correlation between athletic achievements and the strength of the arm muscles is 0.83, and with leg strength 0.37. The corresponding figures for highly qualified athletes are 0.73 and 0.87, respectively.

A more detailed analysis of the functional specialisation of the key muscle groups (in the example of jumpers and sprinters) also reveals the heterochronicity phenomenon. It appears in the given case in two forms:

- the non-coincidence of the initial rate of increase of specific strength factors (Fig 2.22a)
- the characteristic sequence of functional specialisation in the key muscle groups (Fig 2.22b).

Thus, *maximum strength* and *absolute strength* (So) increase from the beginning of training, then *explosive strength* (Se) begins to increase and only later does *starting strength* (Ss) rise significantly. It should, however, be noted that approximately linear increase in maximum and absolute strength is typical only of those sports where the athlete overcomes relatively small resistance, and where the speed of producing working force and not the magnitude of the external force is most important. In the higher stages of sports mastery, there is typically some slowing of the rate of strength increase.

The second form of heterochronicity appears in the non-coincidence of the initial acceleration of growth in the key muscle groups of specific abilities such as starting-strength (Fig 2.22b). They are revealed first at ankle flexion, then thigh extension and finally, thigh flexion.

It is easy to trace the connection between the above-mentioned forms of heterochronicity in perfecting the action of certain muscle groups, by examining the changes in the work capacity of the motor system in long-term training. The commencement of training produces an immediate increase in absolute strength. Explosive strength then begins to increase with the introduction of speed-strength training. Finally, the increase in special strength training within the general volume of means (including the execution of the fundamental sport exercises with an intensity close to competition intensity) leads to a quick increase in starting-strength.

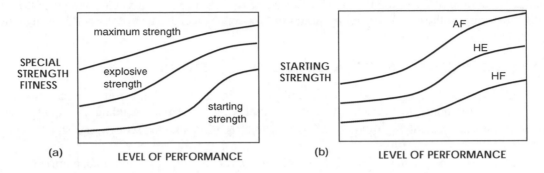

Figure 2.22 Dynamics of speed-strength (a) and starting strength (b) relative to sporting results. AF = ankle flexion, HE = hip extension, HF = hip flexion. (Siff & Verkhoshansky, 1999).

The *heterochronicity phenomenon* in the process of functional specialisation of the support apparatus depends first on the differing rates of development of starting-strength in certain muscle groups. Later it involves other factors. For example, the flexors of the joints of the feet are subjected to the most intense loads at the onset of training. Therefore, specific functional improvement is discovered in them first, as expressed by the increase in the starting strength of the ankle flexors (Fig 2.22b). Then, as the extensor force (for pushing off) increases, adaptation in the hip and knee joint extensors begins to intensify.

These muscles act to oppose the force of gravity and the inertia of the body's mass obviously requires them to produce significant tension. On the other hand, the flexors of the hip have to overcome only the force of gravity and the inertial resistance of the mass of only one leg. Consequently, they require less emphasis on functional perfecting. Therefore, the hip flexors are significantly weaker and display motive force more slowly than the hip extensors. In addition, their starting-strength increases later, but is distinguished by a less intense increase.

Specialisation Processes

We should turn our attention to the fact that the *starting-strength* and *explosive strength* (see 2.2.1) increase slowly in the advanced sports mastery stage (Fig 2.22). As was shown previously, this is associated with a decrease in the effectiveness of the means of special strength training, which appears to be one of the reasons for the decrease in the growth of sporting performance. It can be assumed that the fundamental means of special-strength training in such a case is the sports exercise itself, executed at near-maximal intensity. Thus, *the functional specialisation of the motor apparatus* in the sports training process proceeds in a particular pattern, which may be expressed as follows (Verkhoshansky, 1977):

1. In the heterochronicity process, beginning with significant functional adaptation of certain muscle groups
2. In the different rates of functional adaptation of these muscle groups
3. In a specific sequence for developing the required motor abilities.

The functional specialisation of the body in the sports training process occurs in two basic forms:

- Specialisation of the motor apparatus (certain parts of which display strong adaptation, i.e. principally those which handle the heavy fundamental work during the sports activity)

- Specialisation of the body as a whole and especially the isolation of the above-mentioned parts in developing those specific motor abilities which are necessary for success in the given sports activity.

Thus, it is a matter of specialisation of the body by the physiological system on the one hand and by motor ability on the other. *Specialisation by physiological system* is clearly local, restricted to specific muscle groups and their functional units. *Specialisation by ability* is expressed in the development of such qualities of the body as a whole and chiefly the key working systems which primarily determine the level of its specific work capacity. As sports proficiency grows, the local character of the body's functional specialisation and the specificity of the motor abilities becomes more evident (see also 5.4.2, 5.4.3).

The pattern of long-term functional specialisation reflects essentially the natural course of adaptation (i.e. it is not really controllable, because its characteristics are largely unknown). It may be assumed that the time and other quantitative parameters of the stages and the trends in the functional specialisation of the body are not precisely definable at present. To enhance the effectiveness of long-term training, these parameters thus may be changed within reasonable limits to produce optimal results. In other words, it is the controlled achievement of the adaptive regularities which determines the character and dynamics of functional specialisation of the body during long-term special-strength training.

2.3 Characteristics of Physical Fitness

Sports activity is characterised by the introduction of a physical regime to which the body is unaccustomed. The body attempts to accommodate to it with its entire complex of systems, including the central nervous, neuromuscular and muscular systems. Interaction between the various responses to these systems establishes the working efficiency of the body as a whole.

Thus, it is the form of the athlete's physical fitness (i.e. the structural and functional adaptation of the body) that determines work capacity. The body's work capacity acquires a certain specificity which depends on the type of sport. So, one can speak of the primary development of the ability to display qualities such as strength, speed and endurance, and call this key characteristic his motor function.

Each key function experiences a typical adaptation. It is largely inherent to any athlete of a given specialisation, although it can have an individual character in each case. Significantly distinct, individual differences can occur in the structure of strength fitness. Different athletes can obtain the same results using different contributions of work by the basic muscle groups, their different abilities to contract quickly, and their tendency to compensate for the functional lag of one muscle by more pronounced development of other muscles. Hence, the concept of the structure of strength fitness has great significance for organising strength training and especially for selecting effective means of developing muscular strength.

2.3.1 The Structure of Physical Fitness

The concept of the structure of physical qualities in general, has been formulated in a number of studies, but only as a statement of the problems involved (Zatsiorsky, 1961, 1965; Verkhoshansky, 1963, 1970, 1972). Until now a sufficiently thorough analysis has not been undertaken. At the same time, findings concerning the structure of physical fitness have been extensively covered in the literature, in particular concerning the interrelation between physical qualities (during their development); and the transfer of these qualities from one type of activity to another (Zimkin, 1965; Yakovlev et al, 1960; Zatsiorsky, 1965; Hebb 1949; Lindeburg, 1949; Nelson, 1957; Woodworth, 1958; Cratty, 1964). These studies have established that:

- The transference of physical qualities decreases with an increase in specific fitness (Zimkin, 1965; Zatsiorsky, 1965)
- The transference mechanism is to a great extent specific (Cumbeca et al 1957; Nelson 1957; Bachman, 1961; Cratty, 1968; Lawther, 1968; Barrow, 1971)
- The interrelation between physical qualities can be positive, negative or neutral (Zimkin, 1956)
- Positive transference of certain qualities during the initial stages of training can lead later to negative transference (Korobkov, 1958).

It has often been claimed that complex training consisting of exercises which collectively involve speed, strength and endurance activities develops each of these qualities better than training each of them individually, even if the load is increased for the separate activities (Ozolin 1949, 1970). The validity of this assertion is examined later in this and later chapters.

The development of each quality positively influences the development of the others, and conversely, a lag in the development of one or more qualities limits the development of the others (Krestovnikov, 1951; Kaledin, 1961). For example, the development of strength and speed develops the ability to display speed-strength (Zimkin, 1956; Kuznetsov, 1970).

Here the theoretical explanation is based on the mechanism of the conditioned reflex which underlies learned muscular activity. Training leads to the formation of an extensive background of *temporary connections*, which serves as a foundation on which various combinations of the motor activities can arise, depending upon the emphasis of training. It is assumed that, in the beginning, the training means should develop the motor qualities separately. They are later integrated on the basis of the sports movements which are structurally similar to them.

Recent developments have supplemented the 1930s' concept of the specificity of human motor abilities, based upon considerable research (Downey, 1923; Allport, 1933; McCloy, 1937; Verkhoshansky, 1970, 1972). This emphasizes the highly complex relationships between motor abilities, the development of various means for the different kinds of muscle activity, and the consequent low degree of generality, high degree of specificity and poor transference from one type of activity to another.

The existence of general and specific abilities supports this concept. *General abilities* form the basis for the ability to execute several different tasks, as they are constant relative to any fluctuations of the conditions under which the task is executed. The general motor abilities provide the foundation for the execution of motor tasks and determine the relative stability of the neuromuscular system. They are regulated by heredity, physical structure and physiology.

Specific abilities reflect the functional specifics of performance in complex motor tasks, and are the chief results of motor experience gained by interaction with the environment. If general abilities facilitate the execution of several similar types of task, then specific abilities will be largely independent, enhancing only one specific activity. Attempts have been made to formulate theories explaining the physiology of specificity and the functional independence of different motor abilities with respect to neuromuscular coordination (Pitts, 1954; Henkey, 1960; Henkey & Whitlec 1960; Smith, 1962). However, these attempts remain largely speculative, since they are based on fairly rudimentary research.

Despite numerous studies, much is still unclear and contradictory regarding the nature of strength abilities. Analysis of the literature identifies some of the conclusions on which specialists generally tend to agree (Verkhoshansky, 1970, 1972). In this respect, many articles assert that muscular strength developed by one means does not have universal application, that there is no correlation between absolute muscular strength and speed of movement, that strength exercises decrease the speed of movement, that there is no relationship between static and dynamic strength, that there is no carry-over from isometric training to dynamic activity, and that dynamic strength relates more closely to motor performance than isometric strength.

However, it should be noted that such conclusions on the interrelation of motor abilities are often based on data obtained from subjects of low sports qualification and where the process of achieving sports mastery is not taken into consideration. It is therefore necessary to be very cautious about these conclusions and limit their applicability to those categories of athletes from which they were obtained and not to generalise prematurely.

The concept of the structure of an athlete's physical fitness (in particular, strength fitness) must be based on research and competitive performance. With respect to this, it is appropriate to distinguish between the *composition* and *structure* of the athlete's physical fitness (Verkhoshansky, 1977). The *composition* refers to the collection of all specific forms of the work capability which determine prowess in a given sport (e.g. strength, speed-strength, speed-endurance and other factors detailed in Section 1.15.4 and Table 8.1), whereas the *structure* refers to that complex interrelationship which functionally unites these independent motor abilities and determines the body's capability in that sport.

2.3.2 The Interrelation between Motor Abilities

Research enables us to recognise the following connections between motor abilities: general and partial, essential and non-essential, positive and negative, direct and indirect (Verkhoshansky, 1970, 1972 ; Semyenov, 1971; Tatyan, 1974; Khodykin, 1976).

General and Partial Connections

A *general connection* is characterised by the interaction between any two motor abilities, including the influence of all other abilities, whereas a *partial connection* involves only the indirect interaction between two abilities. Calculation of the general and partial correlations is used for quantitatively assessing these types of connections. Studies of the general and partial connections, using athletes of different specialisation and qualification have established that (Verkhoshansky, 1977):

1. Depending upon the abilities compared, the contribution of the partial connections can be lower (the most typical case) or higher than the contribution of the general connections.

2. The contribution of the partial connection between the same abilities in different sports is more stable than the contribution of the general connections.

Essential and Non-Essential Connections

These connections are characterised to a greater or lesser extent by the interaction of the motor abilities in sport. Research indicates that *essential connections* (without which efficient sporting action is impossible) are more stable

116

than *non-essential connections* (spurious connections which may contribute to or detract from movement efficiency) and can display a non-essential character which conceals the influence of the other abilities.

Positive and Negative Connections

These connections are also characterised by the relationship between motor abilities, where one of them may assist (positive connection) or hinder (negative connection) the other. Research (Verkhoshansky, 1977) indicates that:

1. The *positive connection* is the most characteristic of the complex of motor abilities
2. The *negative connection* appears primarily at the level of the partial connections
3. The positive connection, at the general correlation level, can become negative at the partial correlation level.

It should be noted that a negative connection has been repeatedly identified between such abilities as short and long distance running, as well as absolute strength, speed of movement, and the ability to produce explosive force against a relatively small external resistance.

Direct and Indirect Connections

The *direct connection* is characterised by a relationship between two abilities and can express any of the previously-described types of connections (Verkhoshansky, 1977). The *indirect connection* is also a relation when there is an essential, direct connection between two abilities. For example, there is no correlation between abilities A and B in Figure 2.23(a), but they are nevertheless connected through the third ability (C).

The latter connection is the most characteristic structure of physical fitness. For example, there is no direct, significant connection between running speed and a sprinter's absolute leg strength (it has already been mentioned that this connection is negative at the partial level). However, there is a close connection with jumping exercises, which are also rather closely connected with running speed. This emphasizes how important it is to have a clear representation of the structure of an athlete's special strength fitness and use this to determine tasks and prescribe the means of special strength training.

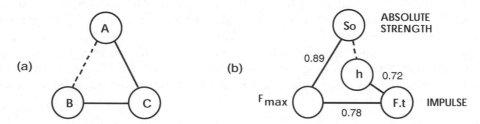

Figure 2.23 Types of connections between motor abilities: theoretical model (a) and practical example (b) (Siff & Verkhoshansky, 1999).

The *indirect connections* between motor abilities can be more complex. Thus, there is no direct, significant connection (Fig 2.23b) between the height achieved in a vertical jump (h) and the absolute strength of the legs (So). However, absolute strength determines the magnitude of the maximal force of the take-off (Fmax) which, in turn, influences the magnitude of the impulse (F.t) of the push-off, and ultimately, the height of the jump.

The interdependence of the motor abilities changes both qualitatively and quantitatively with growth in sports proficiency. The most typical dynamics of the connections are changes in the proportion of the above types of connections between the separate abilities. In some cases, these involve a clear switch from one type of connection to another. Thus, while the *partial connection* is preserved, the *general connection* between individual abilities can increase or decrease, because the *non-essential connection* can acquire vital importance and vice-versa (Verkhoshansky, 1977). For example, triple jumpers lose some of their ability to execute the standing long jump (or standing triple jump) and, conversely, increase their sprinting speeds (at 30m and 100m).

Positive and negative connections represent a special case. The changes in them are primarily one-sided with growth in sports proficiency, i.e. from positive to negative (mainly at the partial correlation level), although a complete switch from one type to another is apparently impossible because of the influence of the third (levelling) ability.

In the initial stages of training, the principle that 'all means are effective', is justified. However, as far as the development of physical fitness is concerned, the negative correlations between abilities appear more strongly than they should, but owing to the third ability, they level out. Levelling proceeds according to a principle of averaging, because of which the optimal correspondence between a number of abilities is achieved, facilitated by a decrease in both the direct and indirect connections (Verkhoshansky, 1977).

For example, the negative correlation between the 100m and the 1500m runs becomes even more apparent in decathlon athletes as the level of proficiency grows. However, because of the improvement in the ability to run 400m, this correlation levels out by a decrease in the closeness of the connection between running the 400m and 1500m, while it increases between the 100m and 400m run.

Direct and indirect connections between abilities display the smallest qualitative changes. They always characterise the structure of physical fitness, they are its specific properties, and changes are primarily quantitative. From the standpoint of quantitative changes, the connections between the individual abilities display two principal trends (Verkhoshansky, 1977):

- a decrease or increase in the closeness of the connection
- a linear or non-linear change of its indicators.

These trends may be illustrated concisely by means of a model of the correlational structure of the specific physical fitness of triple jumpers (Fig 2.24). This model analyses the connection between performance tests to determine the level of the jumper's sprinting, strength and jumping fitness.

The interconnecting lines between boxes in the diagram give the three coefficients of correlation (expressed as a percentage) relating to the performances of three groups of athletes of different levels of mastery in the triple jump. The first correlation coefficient refers to the jumping range of 13.50-14.49m for group 1, the second to the range of 14.50-15.49m for group 2, and the last to the range of 15.50-16.70m for group 3, respectively (there were 40 men in each group).

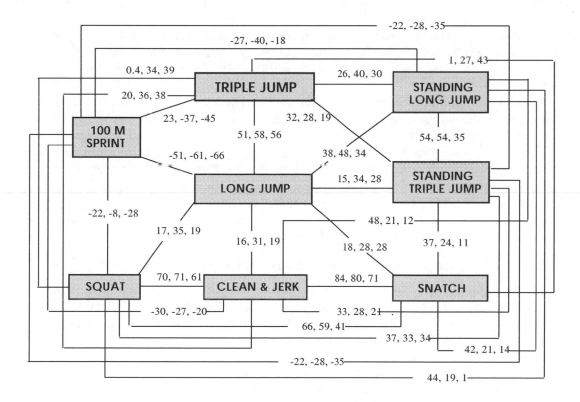

Figure 2.24 Correlation flowchart of exercises for special physical preparedness of triple jumpers. The group of three numbers in each case refers to the correlation coefficient expressed as a percentage for triple jumpers of increasing levels of sports mastery (Class 3, 2, 1, respectively). (Siff & Verkhoshansky, 1999).

2.3.3 The Structure of Motor Abilities

Very interesting data for understanding the structure of physical fitness were obtained in studies using factor analysis in a complex of tests to assess the motor abilities of junior and senior athletes of different levels of qualification in a variety of sports (Verkhoshansky, 1977). The experimental data of training for various lengths of time of one group of athletes was analysed in specific cases. The factor structure of the athlete's physical fitness in a specific event, as well as the important changes in the structure connected with the growth in sports proficiency, were examined.

The number of factors increases with growth in proficiency and are distinguished from the average characteristics by which motor abilities are assessed. This is expressed in the separation of one or two factors. For example, the change in the structure of physical fitness of triple jumpers with growth in proficiency is connected with subdivision of the first factor into separate components (a 30m sprint, a standing long jump and a standing triple jump). Thus, if the factor composition of a junior jumper's physical fitness can be identified as *special sprint-jump fitness* and *strength fitness*, then a new factor must be added for more advanced jumpers, namely *explosive jumping strength* (the specific factor).

The division of one relatively general, primary motor ability into two specific abilities is typical of the process of forming the structure of the athlete's physical fitness (Verkhoshansky, 1977). For instance, practical investigations have analysed the separation of the snatch and the clean-and-jerk from squats and clean pulls as performance indicators in weightlifting, the separation of absolute strength and relative strength as indices of performance in volleyball, and the separation of the abilities to run with a running start and a regular start, as well as running 30m and 100m from a regular start in sprinting and jumping.

Factor analysis enables one to quantitatively assess the contribution of each factor in the general profile of factors. This method was used to observe the changes in the relative importance of a specific factor with growth in proficiency. It has been established that, concurrent with the change in the factor *composition* (and consequently the motor abilities which determine sporting success), there is a definite overestimation of their significance as proficiency grows.

One of them displays a greater significance, while another becomes less important. For instance, there is a general tendency in speed-strength sports for muscular strength to decrease and the ability to produce explosive force to increase (with the exception of weightlifters, because they experience a sharp increase in relative strength with growth in proficiency).

The fitness factor proportion of the individual motor abilities (such as absolute strength, starting strength and acceleration strength) changes concurrently with growth in proficiency, i.e. the degree of correlation of proficiency with the given factor. Two fundamental tendencies are observed here: an increase or a decrease in the correlation of the individual fitness characteristics with the corresponding level of sports proficiency. This clearly corroborates the above-mentioned decreasing role of absolute strength activities in enhancing speed-strength.

Research also shows that the most important changes in the composition and structure of physical fitness occur primarily during the beginning stage of training. At the high sports mastery level, significant changes in the structure of physical fitness do not occur, thereby emphasizing the stability of the advanced neuromotor programmes and the contributions by the individual fitness factors.

2.3.4 General Concepts of the Structure of Physical Fitness

In research and sports practice it is appropriate to divide *motor abilities* into general and special abilities. However, it should be emphasized that sporting performance is determined by a complex of motor abilities which are qualitatively specific. They are relatively independent in both their manifestation and development, and may serve as determinants for a whole series of motor actions, all based on physiological processes.

Taking into account the functional role of the determinant motor abilities, it is appropriate to divide them into *specific, non-specific* and *levelling abilities*. The levelling abilities ensure the effective development of the key motor ability, which expresses the motor requirements of the specific sporting action. The levelling abilities, as will be seen later, balance out and smooth the interaction between all other abilities.

The role of *specific abilities* is to secure the productivity of the key motor abilities. The *non-specific ability* does not satisfy the particular motor requirements and therefore participates as an assisting factor (Verkhoshansky, 1977). The role of the non-specific ability becomes apparent where the specific ability is displayed under difficult conditions. For example, if speed of movement (the specific ability) is the primary requirement, but displaying it to a high level is difficult because of external resistance, then muscular strength (the non-specific ability) acts as an assisting factor. On the other hand, if the level of explosive strength decreases due to increasing fatigue, for example, then the required motor effect can be maintained by special endurance processes.

The *non-specific ability* can often negatively affect the key motor ability. For example, the excessive development of absolute strength has a negative influence on speed.

Levelling abilities play an important role in refining the key motor ability and in determining the structure of general physical fitness. They smooth out clashes between the specific abilities and neutralise the influence of the non-specific abilities if the latter act negatively against the specific abilities. Considering the diversity of motor functions, where the formation of a whole series of non-specific motor abilities is possible, it should be recognized that the levelling role of certain functions acquired by the body is vital for facilitating a high level of performance under varying conditions.

Finally, it should be noted that determinant motor abilities display their own complex combination of the elementary motor abilities. Thus, with respect to physical fitness, the key determinant abilities and the elementary abilities should be distinguished hierarchically (Verkhoshansky, 1977). Based on studies of the types of connections between abilities (see 2.3.2), the principal structure of physical fitness may be represented as follows (Fig 2.25):

1. The key motor ability (KMA) is the result of the integrated development of a complex of determinants, primarily the specific (SA) and non-specific (NSA) ability in each specific case.

2. The *levelling motor abilities* (LMA) participate in the process of motor integration as follows:
   - to smooth out the negative correlation between specific and non-specific abilities
   - to improve the connection between specific and non-specific abilities
   - to expand the functional range and the accommodative potential of the key abilities.

3. Each of the determinant abilities is represented as a complex of elementary abilities (EA).

Underlying the development of physical fitness is the organisational unity of the differentiation and integration of the motor abilities. As a result, a new ability arises which is able to produce a strong working effect under a wide range of conditions. This emerging ability displays a functional potential which is greater than the sum of the properties of all the individual abilities.

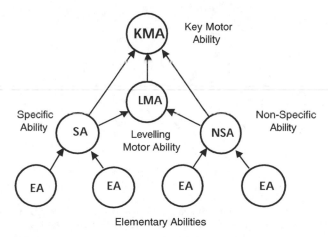

Figure 2.25 Model of the physical preparedness of an athlete (Verkhoshansky, 1977).

The development of the specific motor abilities is one of the conditions for establishing the structure of physical fitness. Before making assumptions about the mechanism of the specific motor abilities, it is necessary to consider the following points (Verkhoshansky, 1977):

1. The elementary motor abilities are functionally independent, are not transformed into the key abilities (specific) and preserve their own individuality with increase in fitness.

2. The specific motor ability (for example, explosive-strength) is, in general, largely an innate property of the motor apparatus.

3. The specific motor ability is developed only by a particular motor regime.

Two hypotheses arise here: either the specific motor ability is functionally unrelated to the elementary motor abilities or it is determined by a specific neuromotor structure which integrates part of the mechanisms of the separate elementary forms of the motor abilities into a functional whole.

It is difficult to accept the former hypothesis. Research and practical experience indicate that the formation and development of specific motor abilities is not based upon the synthesis of the motor abilities developed individually or the gradual transformation of some abilities into others. Instead, motor abilities retain their separate characteristics and a specific neuromotor programme is established by rational training which integrates the contributions of other motor abilities.

This hypothesis can be expressed in the form of the principal scheme of the structure of explosive strength (Fig 2.26). This scheme emphasizes that the development of this ability, occurs under the control of a specific motor programme (SMP), which influences the components of explosive strength (*starting strength, absolute strength, acceleration-strength,* and the *reactive ability* to quickly produce unloaded movement, RA), and forms its *specific neuromuscular structure* (SNS). The latter is the fundamental condition for developing explosive strength, its specific neuromuscular structure displaying a particular functional form.

It should be noted that there is a principal distinction between the mechanism which forms the structure of physical fitness as a whole, and the mechanism of the key and specific motor abilities. In the former case, the advantageous process of integration forms the foundation; in the latter case, the process of adaptive perfecting already possesses a functional structure. The structure of physical fitness and the key motor ability is more flexible and is formed on the basis of the wide diversity of the motor regimen. The specific motor abilities are more conservative and their neuromuscular structure is developed only by a narrow range of means.

It is necessary to control the formation of the structure of physical fitness, a problem which is of exceptional complexity in the theory of sport. This complexity is due to the fact that the physiological processes of integrating the motor abilities is as yet not sufficiently clear. Therefore, it is extremely important to determine the statistical characteristics of the structure of physical fitness to serve as the basis for objectively assessing and controlling factors which influence it.

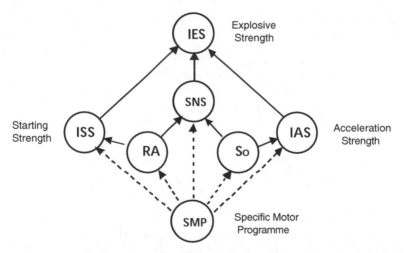

Figure 2.26 Model of the specific motor structure of explosive strength. RA is the reactive ability to quickly produce unloaded movement, So is absolute strength and SNS is the Specific Neuromuscular Structure (Verkhoshansky, 1977).

So, the material examined in this chapter indicates that adaptation in sport seems to display various contradictions. This is displayed by tendencies such as the integrative and separating character of the adaptive reaction, the generality and specificity of adaptation, and the unity of divergent and convergent processes during adaptation.

The tendencies mentioned express themselves in the local specialisation of the motor apparatus and the intensive development of specific motor abilities against the background of an increase in performance (Verkhoshansky, 1977). Functional adaptation begins with the body as a whole, then proceeds according to two interdependent paths, namely *general adaptation* and *specific adaptation*. At the same time adaptation develops independently because of the differentiating and separating character of physiological processes.

Observations of adaptation in the body and its external relationships during long-term training show that measures of adaptive processes tend to correlate with sporting results (e.g. see 2.2.3). This assists in identifying the most typical dynamic and structural regularities of the sports training process (Verkhoshansky, 1966, 1970). The dynamics of the four fundamental components of sports proficiency relative to sports results (i.e. special work-capacity, ability to utilise motor potential, general fitness and specific fitness), may be expressed by the scheme illustrated in Figure 2.27.

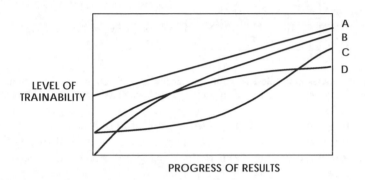

Figure 2.27 Typical changes in the fundamental components of sports mastery over time. A is the athlete's special work capacity, B is the athlete's ability to fully utilise his motor potential in sport, C refers to general fitness and D refers to special fitness. (Verkhoshansky, 1977).

Growth of special work-capacity chiefly determines sporting success; it improves steadily and correlates linearly with sports performance (A). Perfecting the ability to effectively utilise motor potential can be depicted as a monotonically growing curve, converging asymmetrically on the line describing the increase in the key motor ability (B). Improvement in the general work-capacity of the body can be expressed as a monotonically growing curve (C), and special fitness as a sharply rising and plateauing parabola (D).

The closeness of correlation between the various components of sports mastery differentiates, and determines to a large extent the motor specificity of the sporting movements (Verkhoshansky, 1977). Despite specific differences between some components, a certain regularity is observed in the dynamics of certain connections relative to improvement in performance. The principal changes in direction generally may be expressed graphically in the form of a *vector correlation matrix* (Fig 2.28)

This scheme, which may be used to depict changes in the correlation between different components of sports mastery in a given sport, does not pretend to quantitatively express the dependencies precisely and it probably oversimplifies reality. However, it is sufficient to illustrate the characteristics of the dynamics of the fundamental components of the sports training process. It can serve as a starting point for long-term planning of training and as an ongoing indicator of the effects of an existing training programme, at least until there is a more rigorous mathematical analysis to yield more precise and reliable results.

It is relevant to make a few concluding remarks about sports technique which results from recognising certain regularities in the dynamics of the sports training process. The working-effect of a sporting movement is simply the result of the specific form of organisation and control of one's interaction with the environment. However, the fundamental concept of sports technique appears not merely as the organisation of the motor components of the sporting movement, but also as the athlete's ability to manage the external conditions competently and exploit the possibilities which they offer.

This ability is the result of many years of perfecting the motor functions and optimising use of all the body's systems. If this is so, then sports technique is the result of a certain form of the process developing over time, and consequently, as a specific scientific concept, it includes time coordinates. This determines an important principle, namely that sports technique is not a constant which can be achieved once, but is the result of continued progress from a lower to a higher level of perfection (Verkhoshansky, 1977).

This suggests that sports technique is widely understood in theory and practice as a means of solving motor problems. Strictly speaking, sports technique is a system of movement, representing not so much a means of solving motor problems, as the specific motor problem itself, which the athlete must solve every time he executes a sports exercise. Consequently, sports technique consists of the search for and the learning of relevant motor methods that provide the best way to use the one's motor potential.

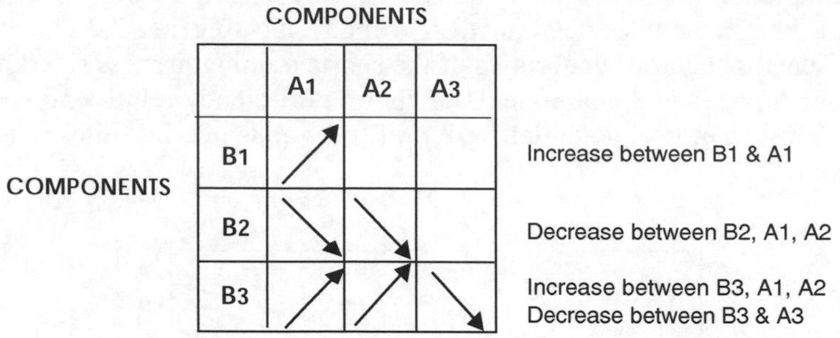

COMPONENTS

	A1	A2	A3
B1	↗		
B2	↘	↘	
B3	↗	↗	↘

COMPONENTS

Increase between B1 & A1

Decrease between B2, A1, A2

Increase between B3, A1, A2
Decrease between B3 & A3

Figure 2.28 Vector correlation matrix of changes in the closeness of the connections constituting the sports training process. The arrows depict the trend in the changes of the various connections (up refers to an increase, down to a decrease). (Verkhoshansky, 1977).

Therefore, the ability to achieve one's real potential in specific motor tasks by maintaining a particular system of movement is the essence of sporting proficiency. Continual improvement in this ability is fundamental to the training process and the degree to which motor potential is realised is the criterion of its effectiveness.

FACTORS INFLUENCING STRENGTH PRODUCTION

It was not very long ago when the athlete did not seriously consider the intricacies of strength development that are so important in today's training. The question of strength superiority was decided simply on the basis of lifting the heaviest weight or recording the highest reading on an isokinetic or isometric dynamometer. However, experience and scientific experimentation have uncovered facts which indicate how primitive those evaluations of strength were. This resulted in the necessity to consider the question of strength preparation in sport more carefully and to define the concept of strength more precisely.

The general definition of strength presented in Chapter 1 needs to be expanded to cover its specifics in actual sporting activities. The concept of strength must be sought in physics and physiology. In physics it concerns the interaction of bodies to cause their movement. Therefore, as the ability to produce force, the concept of strength is used to analyse quantitatively the body's interaction with external objects. In other words, when assessing the force as a cause of movement, we are examining its working effect.

In physiology, strength refers to the ability of muscle action to move the body or any of its linkages in a specific situation. Further, the concept of strength is used as one of the characteristics of voluntary movement to execute specific motor tasks. Here, in conjunction with fitness factors such as speed, endurance and skill, strength is a concept used to describe the qualitative aspects of movement.

The great diversity of human movements makes it necessary to evaluate the strength components of movement (sub-maximal strength, maximal strength, impulse strength, work and power), analyse the ability to produce strength (absolute strength, relative strength, and the moment of the force of muscular contraction about a joint), and to comparatively evaluate the strength components of movement (explosive strength, speed-strength movements, strength-endurance and others) which reflect the specificity of movements. Hence, one is able to select appropriate methods for developing strength fitness.

Thus, muscular strength is a specific motor quality and it is involved functionally under extremely diverse conditions in sport. Therefore, before discussing the methods of special strength preparation, the fundamental characteristics of producing muscular strength in sports movements must be examined.

3.1 Regimes of Muscular Work

Many studies have been devoted to the different regimes of muscular work. Based on the purpose of the work, they can be divided into two groups. One group is devoted to determining the conditions and regimes which increase the working effect of muscular strength, the other to finding the regime which most effectively develops muscular strength. Unfortunately, many of these investigations have led to confusion and contradictions.

For example, some researchers maintain that the largest strength gains are made with dynamic (concentric) actions, others with isometric tension. Moreover, careful analysis of the experimental design reveals that similar contradictions are associated with invalid generalisations of results obtained in different laboratories, under unnatural conditions, on different muscle groups of subjects of different standards, using different loads and movement speeds. For instance, it was established that, with maximal isometric tension of the biceps (with the elbow flexed at 90°), subjects were able to develop a force 6.5-10.0 kg greater than the maximal weight that could be lifted concentrically.

However, this changes with a decrease in load and an increase in speed of movement. The electrical activity in the biceps muscle while lifting a weight of 50-80% of maximum is significantly greater than it is during the period when it is subsequently held statically, both in magnitude and the production of strength (Stepano & Burlakov, 1963; Monogarov & Laputin, 1966; Scheraev 1954, 1957; Rasch & Pierson, 1960; Yanchevsky & Steklove, 1966).

Thus, there is an important difference in the characteristics of the muscular force displayed, depending upon the magnitude of the load and the speed of movement. It should be pointed out that the torque produced by the muscles increases approximately four-fold up to an angle of 90° during elbow flexion. Therefore, for example, if you compare the force of a maximal isometric action developed at an angle of 90° and the maximum weight which can be raised from an angle of 180°, then the force in the first case is greater.

Consequently, if one is referring to the development of muscular strength, then to discuss superiority in the dynamic versus the isometric regime is scarcely appropriate, because the biomechanical conditions for the production of strength are not comparable. If it is necessary to compare the training effect of a certain regime, then you must first establish which kind of strength is being measured.

A similar approach is necessary when comparing the advantages of eccentric and concentric muscular work. Bethe (1929) showed that the force a muscle develops with a maximal overcoming action (*concentric strength*) is between 1.2 and 1.6 times less than the resistance strength the contracting muscle displays when it is stretched (*eccentric strength*).

Some examples of the superiority of eccentric strength over concentric strength for some muscle groups are as follows: 22% for the arms, 46.8% for the forearms and 50% for the knee extensors. According to Semyonov's study of untrained subjects (1968), the maximal isometric force developed by the knee extensors at an angle of 120° is 465 Newtons and 401 Newtons in the concentric regime. For combined regimes, the largest strength (504 N) was recorded for slow eccentric action exerted after preliminary maximal isometric tension (under conditions of equivalent forced knee flexion using an electric motor to offer resistance), and 453 N produced for eccentric action exerted after preliminary concentric work.

The myotatic stretch reflex has great significance for increasing the working effect of eccentric work. Experiments on animals and humans have established that the greater the rate of muscle stretch, the stronger the myotatic reflex (Samoyloff & Kisseleff, 1928; Foerster & Altenlurgey, 1933; Lippold, 1957). It has been noted, that *the better trained the athlete, the more precise and efficient the use of the reflex muscle tension during eccentric work* (Zakharyents, 1962).

Eccentric work uses significantly less energy than concentric work. It has been demonstrated by replacing concentric with eccentric actions that the expenditure of energy is almost halved when movement velocity does not exceed 0.12 metres/second (Chauveau, 1904). These conclusions have been corroborated more recently. It has been revealed that more energy is expended by the concentric versus the isometric action of a muscle. The energy expenditure for muscle lengthening is also less than that for isometric action (Fenn, 1924, Hartree & Hill, 1928; Hill, 1930; Cattel, 1983). However, it should be emphasized that this *advantage of eccentric work is displayed only with slow movements and large loads*. Therefore, there is no reason to associate these advantages with the potential to develop the ability for quick and powerful movements in concentric work.

It should be remembered that this is only a brief survey of the important mechanical and physiological differences relating to the different forms of muscular activity. Nevertheless, it suffices to emphasize that the quest for a universal regime of muscular work to develop strength is as futile as it is to discuss the advantages of a specific regime without considering the type of sports activity and the specific nature of the muscle contraction.

Before proceeding to the next section, it is necessary to define more precise terminology for the diverse forms of muscular work. This is associated with the types of mechanical work and their corresponding regimes of muscular tension. We do not pretend to have classified all the forms in which the working activity of muscles are expressed in Figure 3.1. It is obviously only for convenience and for systematising the concepts which apply within the scope of this book. However, it should be pointed out that the same principles can be used to devise a stricter and more representative classification.

Thus, to evaluate the external form of muscular activity, one must differentiate between the four basic types of *muscular work*: overcoming (positive or concentric), yielding (negative or eccentric), holding (static or isometric) and combined (Fig 3.1a). To avoid confusion, it should be noted that the terms 'concentric' and 'eccentric' for types of muscular work are also sometimes used to refer to the equivalent types of muscular tension. This usage is to be expected, since all muscular work is a function of muscular tension.

In specific cases, when talking about moving the body (plus external objects) or maintaining a posture with muscular force to manage bodyweight or external loads, one can discuss the relationship between dynamic and static muscular work. In the latter case there is no work in the physical sense, since there is no movement. Therefore, to calculate static work, the action of force over a distance and the corresponding basic formula: [work = force x displacement] cannot be used. Instead, assessment is based on the physiological definition of work, so that the production of force, the time of its action and biological energy expenditure are used.

Muscular tension should be considered a physiological phenomenon distinguished by the following basic regimes (see 1.10): *isotonic*, where there is a change in muscle length, but the tension remains constant; *isometric,* where tension is developed without a change in muscle length; *auxotonic*, where there is a change in muscle tension and length; *isokinetic*, where varying muscle tension is produced at constant velocity; and *quasi-isometric*, where muscle tension and length change at very slow velocity (Fig 3.1b). However, these regimes do not exhaustively cover all types of muscle tension and do not describe characteristics of an athlete's movements, such as the speed of production and magnitude of the tension, or the dependence of the tension upon interaction of the motor system with external objects.

Therefore, taking into consideration the diversity of sports activities, it is necessary to identify the specific character of the muscular tension, in particular, the different speeds with which tension is developed, its magnitude, duration and number of repetitions, as well as the state of the muscle preceding the working tension. To analyse all this diversity in sporting movements, muscular tension may be conveniently divided into at least eight types (Fig 3.1c). This classification is central to the subsequent discussion of special strength training in sport (Siff & Verkhoshansky, 1999).

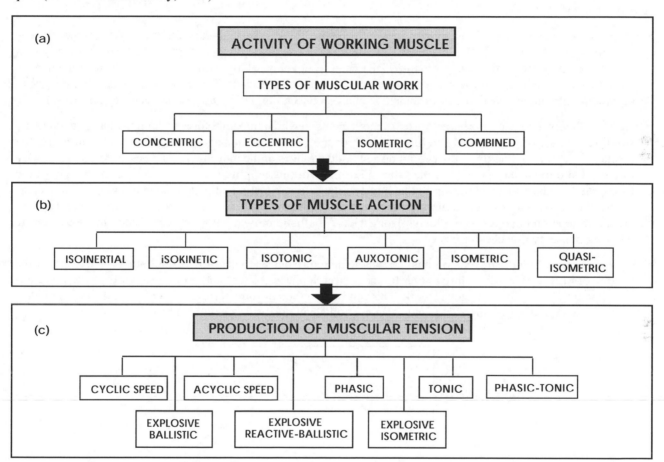

Figure 3.1 Classification of the types of muscle action (see also Ch 1.10 and Fig 1.23). (based on Siff & Verkhoshansky, 1999).

- *Tonic muscular tension* is characterised by significant and relatively prolonged muscle contraction. The speed with which it is developed, however, does not have major significance. This type of tension may be observed in wrestling when one athlete pins another to the mat, in weightlifting when the lifter holds a barbell overhead, and in many highly controlled gymnastic manoeuvres. In all these cases, the muscles are working at the limit of their force capabilities. However, tonic tension can be of a much smaller magnitude when it is necessary to hold a pose (e.g. in pistol shooting or gymnastics). Depending upon the type of sport, the characteristics of the strength displayed by tonic tension are determined by strength-endurance or absolute strength.

- *Phasic tension* refers to dynamic muscular work in exercises requiring production of a driving force of a given magnitude. Such exercises are very frequently cyclic movements where each cycle has its own changing rhythm of muscular contraction, relaxation and frequency of repetition. Here, the speed with which maximal motor force is developed is not so important, but strength or speed-strength endurance play a vital role. The type of exercise, the magnitude of tension (e.g. in rowing), the tempo of cyclic movement (e.g. in swimming or speed-skating), or both tempo and tension (e.g. in cycling) can have major effect on the working of the muscles. It is also possible to develop the ability to carry out phasic work of long duration at moderate tension (e.g. in distance running and swimming).

• *Phasic-tonic tension* occurs when dynamic work changes to stabilisation or when stabilisation changes to movement as a result of different musical rhythms or tempos of activity (as in gymnastics, judo, wrestling and ballet). The qualitative aspects of strength preparation in these cases are very complex and multi-faceted. One type of sport or even one sports exercise may require both tonic and phasic tension involving a rapid transition from one type of tension to another at a high intensity of effort in each of them. This occurs in gymnastics during the switch from the dynamic to the static or stabilisation elements, or when a boxer quickly attacks resistance imposed by his opponent.

Explosive force is inherent to the following types of muscular tension: *explosive-isometric*, *explosive-ballistic* and *explosive-reactive-ballistic*.

• *Explosive-isometric tension* is inherent to movements in which significant resistance is overcome (e.g. snatching or jerking a barbell, some elements in gymnastics and wrestling, or throwing a heavy projectile). A basic characteristic of these movements is the need to develop a large working-force whose maximum is achieved isometrically at the end of the movement (see also 4.2.4). This type of tension also occurs in plyometric activities during the brief transition phase between rapid eccentric and concentric contraction.

• *Explosive-ballistic* tension is characteristic of movements in which maximal force is applied against a relatively small resistance (e.g. shotput, javelin, baseball, or the serve in tennis and squash). Here the motive force reaches a maximum quickly in the beginning and middle ranges of the movement, then begins to diminish. Due to inertia and muscular force (which at the end of the working amplitude does not exceed the weight of the load), the load has no acceleration but is only maintaining its existing velocity. The typical kinematic characteristics of ballistic movements are presented in Figure 3.2. As the resistance increases, this type of muscular tension changes to explosive-isometric. A ballistic movement may be preceded in its concentric working phase by muscle stretch.

• *Explosive-reactive-ballistic* tension has the same characteristics as the explosive-ballistic type except for the regime of muscular work. Here the preliminary stretch phase is sharp and pronounced, after which there is an immediate change to concentric work. This can be observed in some throwing events, and during individual elements of wrestling, gymnastics, figure skating, volleyball, tennis or kicking in football.

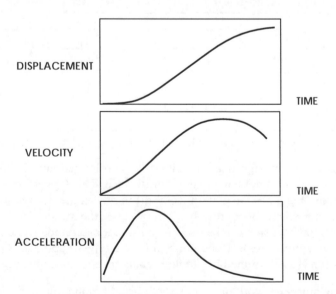

Figure 3.2 Typical dynamic characteristics of a ballistic movement

In speed movements involving rapid changes in position of the entire body or its links, the type of tension produced is a quick, momentary muscular contraction (e.g. a boxing punch or the prick in fencing), or a repetition of actions at a specific fast tempo (e.g. in sprinting). The first case is an example of speed of the *acyclic* type of tension, whereas the second is an example of speed of the *cyclic* type.

The speed type of tension is inherent to movements where the force developed resists the inertial force of the system's working links and a light additional load (e.g. a rapier or racquet). Therefore, they do not require that tension be developed quickly in the form of a brief transient impulse. *Speed-cyclic* types of tension require that the level of the working effect be maintained throughout each repeated cycle of tension. This necessitates a highly-developed ability of the muscles to relax after each working movement under these conditions.

Many movements in sport are superficially similar in spatial structure and are executed with many of the same muscles (e.g. punching in boxing, putting the shot, the bench press, the spike in volleyball, the serve in tennis and javelin throwing). Even the experienced eye cannot discern the essential differences between the kinematic patterns of some of them. The reverse is true for other movements. The differences in speed, amplitude, direction, beginning conditions and magnitude of strength displayed are strikingly obvious to the naked eye. A more detailed analysis with scientific instrumentation reveals further nuances such as the variations in intensity and type of muscle activity, the sequence and speed of muscle involvement in the work, energy expenditure, and reliance on each of the different energy sources.

The diversity in sporting exercises may be divided into a number of groups in which they are unified according to the primary characteristics of the muscular activity. Such an approach is clearly practical when the training methods are selected on the basis of identifying the major characteristics of muscular work for the given sports group, the specific character of this work at the speed with which tension is developed, its magnitude, duration and number of repetitions, as well as the state of the muscles and the preceding muscle tension.

3.2 Qualitative Characteristics of Strength

The diversity of the conditions under which muscles work in sport is responsible for the differences in motor activity and, consequently, the development of a specific strength capability. Categorisation of strength capabilities into four discrete types (*absolute strength, speed-strength, explosive strength* and *strength-endurance*) can be somewhat restrictive, because all of them are interrelated in their production and development, despite their inherent specificity. They are rarely, if ever, displayed separately, but are the components of every movement.

The strength ability most characteristic of sporting activities is *explosive strength* (see Fig 2.24), as displayed in acyclic and cyclic movements. Acyclic movements are distinguished by brief episodes of powerful muscular work, and cyclic movements by the maintenance of optimal power for a relatively long time. If attention is paid to the fact that the explosive character with which strength is displayed is determined by the presence of *absolute strength* or *speed-strength* (depending upon external conditions), then two general abilities, namely *explosive strength* and *strength-endurance*, are the basis for the production of all sporting movements.

3.2.1 Explosive Strength

Explosive muscular force is determined by the external resistance which is to be overcome. Therefore, it is logical to consider the characteristics of explosive force during dynamic muscular work by examining what happens with loads of various weight being moved as rapidly as possible (Fig 3.3). The graphs display several characteristics. In all instances the maximum dynamic force is less than the absolute strength S_o, the closest value to S_o being the maximum force of explosive isometric tension (F_{isom}). In the dynamic regime, the difference between S_o and F_{max} (i.e. the strength deficit, as defined in Ch 1) increases as the resistance decreases (Table 3.1). In other words, with decreasing external resistance, the realisation of the strength potential of the muscles for explosive force is diminished, as shown by the decreasing correlation between S_o and F_{max}.

Despite the differences in magnitude of muscular force $F(t)$ for different loads and for isometric tension, the various curves are precisely superimposed upon each other at their beginning (Fig 3.4). Thus, if *explosive force* depends entirely upon external conditions and its maximum on the level of *absolute strength*, then the initial portion of the graph $F(t)$ is determined by the special ability of the neuromuscular apparatus referred to earlier as *starting-strength* (Verkhoshansky, 1968, 1970). It may be assumed the degree to which this ability is expressed is determined by the efficiency of the biochemical processes in those muscles which are responsible for the rapid development of initial tension. The intensity of these processes during maximum voluntary effort characteristically is constant for a given functional state and the athlete's level of fitness. It is independent of the external resistance, its character and the regime of muscular work (dynamic or isometric).

Table 3.1 The relationship between resistance and strength production (Siff & Verkhoshansky, 1999).

Resistance (as % of So)	Fmax (as % of So)	Strength Deficit	Fmax : So Correlation
80	94.0	6.0	0.822
60	82.7	17.3	0.798
40	64.4	35.6	0.657
20	47.7	52.3	0.316

During *explosive-isometric tension* and dynamic effort with loads of 60% and 80% of So, the external force quickly reaches a certain level through action of the starting-strength and continues to grow more slowly to maximum (Fig 3.3). For dynamic muscular work, changes in F(t) occur at the instant when the force equals the weight of the load. It would appear that, when the movement begins, it is mediated by involvement of some other physiological mechanism, mobilised from additional resources to increase muscular strength. It is this which determines the ability of the muscles to display power of movement.

The *acceleration-strength* of muscle has been defined as the ability which produces acceleration of a moving object (see 2.2.1). The quality known as *explosive strength* is distinguished from other speed-strength types of action as that which produces the greatest possible muscular tension in the shortest time over a given path. It also describes the ability to rapidly build the working force up to a maximum (see 2.2.1). *Starting-strength* is the ability to quickly develop the greatest possible force at the initial moment of tension, while *acceleration-strength* is the ability to build up working force as rapidly as possible once the contraction has begun (2.2.1).

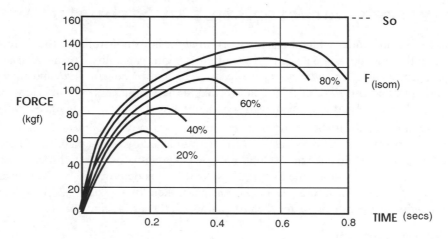

Figure 3.3 The force-time graph of explosive-isometric tension F(isom) and dynamic work with 20, 40, 60 and 80% of maximum strength for a leg-press movement (Siff & Verkhoshansky, 1999).

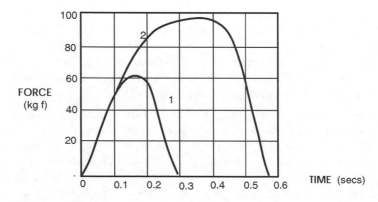

Figure 3.4 Force-time graph of maximal voluntary effort for a leg press. Graphs of the explosive force at values of 40% of maximum strength (curve1) and 70% of maximum strength (curve 2). (Siff & Verkhoshansky, 1999).

129

It is not difficult to conclude that, during dynamic-explosive force with 20-40% of So, the F(t) curve characteristically is determined entirely by the *starting-strength* of the muscles. With a resistance of 60-80% of So, their functional characteristics change significantly. As in the previous case, the beginning of the F(t) curve is determined by *starting-strength*. Further on, however, it is increasingly connected with the ability of the muscles to quickly produce the maximum possible strength, i.e. *acceleration-strength*.

Some studies indicate that there is a small correlation between *starting-strength* and *acceleration-strength*, and that they are qualitatively specific motor abilities. Thus, based on a factor analysis, the F(t) curve of explosive force in the isometric and dynamic regimes indicates these abilities are distinguished by different factors, in particular absolute strength So, Fmax, tmax, starting-strength, explosive strength and acceleration-strength. The distinguishing factors are easily identified as follows:

1. The general ability to display *explosive strength*
2. The *absolute strength* (strength potential) So of the athlete
3. The ability of the muscles to rapidly display *starting-strength*
4. The ability of the muscles to quickly develop *acceleration-strength*.

In experiments where the absolute speed was recorded (the average velocity of an unloaded movement, Vo, over a given interval), acceleration-strength was identified as an independent factor. Thus, the working effect of a sporting movement, executed with maximal voluntary muscle tension, is determined to a greater or a lesser degree by the four special strength abilities: *absolute strength* (So), *starting-strength* (SS), *acceleration-strength* (AS) and *absolute speed* of muscular contraction (Vo).

To a varying degree these abilities are intrinsic to all athletes of different levels of fitness and specialisation during the execution of isometric and dynamic regimes of muscular work. It has been established that training does not change the above factor structure of the speed-strength abilities. However, the relative importance of each factor, the need for a particular strength ability, and the contribution of each factor to the overall fitness profile alter, depending on the character and especially the emphasis of training (Verkhoshansky 1972, 1973).

To solve the problem of special strength fitness, it is relevant to focus on the principal relationships between the strength abilities and their role in sports movements under given conditions. The larger the resistance, the greater the correlation between *absolute strength* So and *maximal explosive force* Fmax. As external resistance increases, the percentage *generality* of the individual differences between absolute strength So and Fmax increases (Fig 3.5, curve 1). As external resistance decreases, the percentage *specificity* of the differences between them increases (Fig 3.5, curve 2).

Note: Determination of the generality (generality - R^2) and specificity (specificity - K^2) factors is based on the motor task (calculated from the correlation coefficient between the indicators). Squaring the correlation coefficient and multiplying by 100: i.e. (R^2 x 100) gives the percentage *generality* of the individual differences, determined as the sign of similarity for the two shifting magnitudes. The quantity characterising the *specificity* for both of the shifts (K^2), is determined from the equation (R^2 x 100) + K^2 = 100. It is acceptable to consider that the specificity of the sign is significant if K is larger than R (Lotter 1961, Bachman 1961).

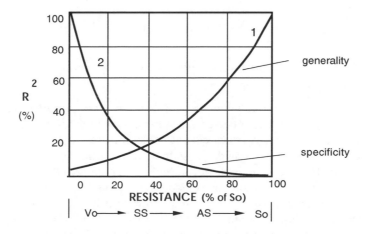

Figure 3.5 Change in the power of individual differences (R^2) between the maximum explosive force Fmax and absolute strength So with external resistance. SS = starting-strength, AS = acceleration-strength. (Siff & Verkhoshansky, 1999).

The mean *generality* of the individual differences between So and the value of the beginning portion of the F(t) curve is 20-25%, while the *specificity* is 75-80%. It should be pointed out that the connection between absolute strength and the values of the dynamic strength curve F(t) at its initial point for relatively untrained people is significant, but with an increase in fitness, this becomes an unreliable measure. The degree of generality between So and the initial part of the F(t) curve diminishes noticeably as a result of even short-term training (30-36 workouts).

Not only is there no correlation between the absolute strength So and absolute speed (average velocity Vo), it is negative. The connection between absolute strength and the speed of a movement against external resistance has a significant generality (up to 40% of So), which then displays an approximately linear dependence on the external resistance (Fig 3.6).

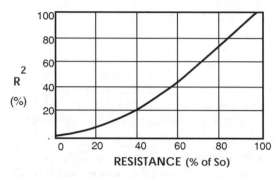

Figure 3.6 Change in the correlation of individual differences between absolute strength and the speed of a resisted movement, depending on external resistance. (Verkhoshansky, 1977).

Thus, *absolute strength* So determines neither the working effect at the initial instant of muscular tension nor the maximum force in movements against small external resistance. It is connected with maximum explosive force only if the external resistance is large. Not only does absolute strength not ensure the development of absolute speed of movement, but it tends to exert just the opposite effect. However, if the movement is executed against an external resistance, then the larger the resistance, the more the speed depends on absolute strength. There is an exceptionally low degree of *generality* between the absolute speed of movement (Vo) and its speed, if it is carried out against an external resistance. In this instance, even with a resistance of 20% of So, the *specificity* of the individual differences reaches 70% (Fig 3.5, curve 2).

Consequently, the absolute speed (average velocity) of movement has a very moderate influence on the speed of explosive force if the external resistance is in the range of 10-20% of So. The correlation between the gradient characteristics of the dynamic strength curve F(t) is different, namely:

• The mean correlation between the *explosive strength* (IES) and *acceleration-strength* (IAS) gradients is 84% (with a degree of specificity of 16%)

• The mean correlation between the *explosive strength* (IES) and *starting-strength* (ISS) gradients is 52% (with a specificity of 48%)

• The mean correlation between the *starting-strength* (ISS) and *acceleration-strength* (IAS) gradients is 27% (with a specificity of 73%).

The gradient forces (ES, SS, AS) are related moderately to *absolute strength* (explosive strength ES and *acceleration-strength* AS are related to a larger degree, and *starting-strength* SS to a lesser degree) and to *absolute speed* (starting-strength SS is related to a larger degree, and explosive strength ES and acceleration-strength AS to a lesser degree). Here the correlation depends on the magnitude of the external resistance, the degree of generality averaging 20% and the specificity 80%. The gradient forces and the corresponding values of the dynamic strength F(t) with respect to time have a typically higher correlation, reaching an average of 64%. As a result of training, the power of the gradient forces from So decreases significantly (particularly SS) and the dynamic strength F(t) increases, but the absolute speed changes minimally. *Starting-strength* and *acceleration-strength* depend weakly upon each other, while *starting-strength* and the general ability to display explosive force have little in common (see Fig 2.24). The general abilities to display *explosive strength* and *acceleration-strength* are determined to a significant degree by a combination of different causes.

Not all of the component abilities contribute equally to the working effect of explosive strength. Depending upon conditions, one or the other plays a dominant role and consequently exhibits the main potential for producing intensive development. Participating to a greater or lesser extent during the execution of powerful motor acts, the component abilities, due to their relative neuromuscular independence, unite not structurally, but functionally. In other words, they integrate to produce some new general ability, regulating the interaction, solving general motor tasks and at the same time maintaining their individuality and ability to enter into any functional union demanded by the changing conditions of the activity. Depending upon the character of the movement, a motor programme is established through which the component abilities are realised simultaneously and sequentially.

The general tendency here may be expressed thus: the smaller the external resistance (consequently, the faster and briefer its execution), the greater the role of abilities such as *starting-strength* and the ability to display high *absolute speed.* Conversely, the larger the external resistance, the greater the importance of *acceleration-strength* and *absolute strength*. With reference to these component abilities (which determine the working-effect of explosive force), one can identify the following sequence: $V_o > SS > AS > S_o$, each component of which correlates specifically with the external resistance imposed, as depicted on the horizontal axis in Figure 3.5. This sequence reveals certain characteristics:

1. The development of component abilities takes place independently of each other, growth of one of them being associated with insignificant development of the others. The further the abilities are from each other in this sequence, the smaller their interaction.

2. The development of each ability requires a specific training regime. A training programme directed primarily at enhancing one ability has very little or no effect on the other abilities.

3. The relative independence of the component abilities in their production and development becomes even more obvious with increase in fitness.

4. The component abilities require different amounts of training. The abilities (AS, S_o) on the right side of the sequence are easier to perfect than those on the left (V_o, SS).

In a practical sense, since sports movement is always associated with overcoming an external resistance, primarily two component abilities determine the working effect of explosive force, namely *starting-strength* and *acceleration-strength*. To examine their role in the execution of speed-strength movements we must refer to Figure 3.3. It is obvious that, when overcoming insignificant external resistance (up to approximately 40% of S_o), one cannot display full strength potential. In this instance, the impulsive force producing the movement is developed chiefly by *starting-strength*. With a large resistance (more than 60% of S_o), the impulsive force producing the working movement is developed primarily by *acceleration-strength* and *absolute strength* (or maximum strength).

Starting-strength plays an assisting role here. Thus, for the working muscular tension to reach a certain level as quickly as possible, starting-strength is the underlying mechanism crucial to the production of acceleration-strength. It follows that:

• With external resistance, *starting-strength* is displayed isometrically (especially as the resistance increases), whereas *acceleration-strength* is displayed dynamically.

• The higher the level to which *starting-strength* is developed, the more rapidly the *acceleration-strength* can be produced. The latter point needs to be strongly emphasized, since there is a limited time for the execution of all speed-strength movements in athletics.

Quickness and Reactive Ability

It is necessary now to discuss the particular ability of the muscles to produce movement rapidly. This neuromuscular process manifests itself in essentially two forms: *reactive ability* and *quickness*. Although Verkhoshansky (1996) distinguishes between *quickness*, which describes a rapid movement involving little resistance or muscular effort, and *velocity*, which he relates to movements requiring considerable energy output against large resistance, this sort of distinction is avoided, because velocity has a highly specific and well-established meaning in biomechanics. It is entirely unambiguous to apply the term velocity to the actual movement of the limb, body or implement concerned without confusing it with events between stimulus and final response of the body.

Rather, *quickness* may be referred to the ability of the central nervous system to contract, relax or control muscle function without involvement of any preliminary stretch. Its primary role is to produce high-speed movement which do not encounter large external resistance or require great strength, power or energy consumption. It is measured as the time interval or *reaction time* between stimulus and response (or initiation of movement). This time must be distinguished from the *movement time*, which is the interval from the end of the reaction phase to the end of the movement (i.e. from beginning to end of movement). It is important to note that no correlation between reaction time and movement time has been demonstrated (Harbin et al, 1989). The reaction time consists of two stages: a *latency phase* between receiving of the stimulus and the appearance of electrical activity in the relevant muscles, and a *response phase* between the appearance of the EMG signal and the motor action. There are two electrical transmission lags associated with the reaction time (excluding any central processing time):

- the time taken for the sensory input to reach the central nervous system
- the time taken for a motor impulse to travel from the central nervous system to the muscles.

Average reaction times for simple tasks are (Harbin et al, 1989):

- 0.142 second for auditory stimuli
- 0.155 second for tactile stimuli
- 0.194 second for visual stimuli.

Since the early research of Helmholtz, it has been known that reaction times are long and variable, and that nerve conduction velocities do not account for the length and variability of times. Work by Hanes and Schall (1996) examined changes in firing rates in monkeys deciding to initiate eye movements and found that the variability in reaction time is due to the variability in how rapidly the neuronal rate of firing reaches a fixed threshold, at which point movement is initiated. In another experiment, they found that movement was not initiated until the firing rate actually cross the threshold level.

Apparently the latency period is determined largely by genetics and is minimally affected by training, so that improvement in quickness has to focus on modifying the response or movement phase. For example, the average movement time of a simple unidirectional task of an extremity is 0.3 second, which can decrease by more than 50% in the case of highly trained subjects. It should be noted that the above reaction times may be considerably slower for more complex or less predictable tasks. For instance, *completely unpredictable visual signals* result in reaction times in excess of 0.5 second (Fogel, 1963). The regular practice of neuromuscular skills, therefore, is of paramount importance in determining sporting prowess.

It has been shown that the ability to strike, catch or block a rapidly moving object (as in tennis, squash, baseball or boxing) also depends strongly on one's *ability to accurately anticipate* the likely trajectory of the projectile rather than on a rapid reaction time alone. Clearly, the competitor in any sports which require these skills must acquire the ability to visualise and execute all necessary motor patterns. *Enhanced strength is of little value if the athlete does not maintain or improve neuromuscular ability*.

When an extremely rapid reaction is necessary, for example in a self-preservation situation, the nervous signals do not travel to the brain for conscious interaction, but follow a much quicker reflex arc via the appropriate level of the spinal cord. Such reflex activity is an essential aspect of all sport, but in many cases, reaction time also involves subconscious decision-making or conscious decision-making at a cognitive level. In these cases, reaction time comprises a *sensing time* and a *decision time*, with the latter in particular improving through the regular application of neuromuscular skill training.

Movement time is strongly influenced by motor coordination or precision of movement, where *precision* refers to the ability to execute a single goal-directed task with the smallest degree of error or the least number of random moves during performance of the task.

The monitoring of reflexes and reactive processes is important not only for training healthy athletes, but also for rehabilitating injured athletes, where rehabilitation refers to the return of the patient to full functional fitness (e.g. in terms of strength, power, endurance and flexibility) and motor proficiency (in terms of coordination, reactive efficiency and skill). *Strength or endurance measurements on isokinetic or other dynamometers do not necessarily ensure that the athlete is completely rehabilitated and prepared for return to competition.*

Improvement in movement time, agility and motor skill is also essential, with oculomotor, sensorimotor and auditory-motor coordination being paid special attention.

A distinction may also be made between quickness in simple and complex tasks, as well as quickness in single versus repeated actions. In boxing or martial arts, simple quickness would involve thrusting out a fist from rest to execute a punch, or a judoka or wrestler pulling an arm away from an opponent's grasp in anticipation of a throw or hold. Examples of quickness in repeated actions are dribbling in soccer, hitting a rapidly returned shuttle in badminton or a flurry of offensive blows in boxing. In the latter examples, as well as in tennis, table tennis and squash rallies, quickness would also refer to the frequency of repeated movements.

Complex motor responses necessitate evaluation of the entire situation and selection of a suitable response, involving a decision time, as discussed above. Variation in the components of movement production also occur over the annual training cycle, so that if training programmes enhance sports skills efficiently, so they will also decrease the time needed to perceive and respond to the stimulus. Even an apparently trivial process such as breathing can affect one's speed of movement. For instance, in boxing, the rate of movement is directly related to breathing rhythm and the boxer's ability to control this rhythm (Verkhoshansky, 1996).

Reactive ability was defined earlier as the neuromuscular ability to generate explosive force (2.2.1), a quality which relies on both preliminary stretch and rapidity of reaction. This depends heavily on the specific ability to display a powerful driving force immediately after an intense, mechanical muscular stretch, i.e. when there is a rapid change from eccentric to concentric work at the instant when a maximal dynamic load is encountered. The preliminary stretch causes elastic deformation of the muscles, thereby storing potential energy which is transformed into kinetic energy as the muscles begin to contract. This is added to the force of the muscle contraction and increases the working effect.

Reactive ability, as a specific quality of the human working apparatus, is explained by some of the principles of neuromuscular physiology. It is known, for example, that preliminary stretching of a muscle increases the working effect of its subsequent contraction. It has been established that the concentric work of a muscle which begins contracting quickly after a preliminary stretch is larger than the concentric work of the same muscle after executing an isometric contraction (Abbott & Aubert, 1952; Cavagna, 1965, 1968) .

The additional strength achieved as a result of stretching increases, depending on its speed and muscle length (Hill, 1938; Katz, 1939; Wolker, 1953): the faster the stretch, the greater being the additional strength (Cavagna, 1965). Practical application of this effect was done in work activity (Setchenov, 1901) and sporting movements (Fenn, 1930; Cavagna, 1964). The results obtained from the study of sports exercises showed, in particular, that the use of a preliminary stretch ensures that the execution of the motor task will be more effective (Ozolin & Chkhaidze, 1951; Verkhoshansky, 1961, 1963). The regime in which an external resistance is actively overcome after being preceded by a sharp preliminary muscular stretch is the most effective for training *explosive strength* (Verkhoshansky, 1963). This technique is sometimes referred to as shock or plyometric training (see Ch 1).

The basic characteristics of the reactive ability of the neuromuscular apparatus were demonstrated clearly in an experiment which modelled the muscular work involved in propelling a dropped load. Subjects threw a load upward along guiding rails after it had dropped from different heights. The height of the drop and the throw were recorded. The path was plotted and the time taken to reach different heights was recorded (Fig 3.7).

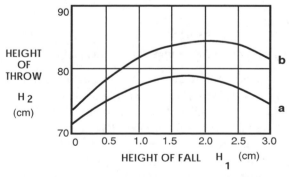

Figure 3.7 Height attained by a load thrown upwards after falling from different heights. Dependence of height (H_2) attained by a 6 kg load thrown vertically upwards after falling from different heights (H_1): (a) before training; (b) after training. (Verkhoshansky, 1977).

The resulting curves indicate that, with increasing strength of the stimulus (characterised here as the kinetic energy of the falling load), the working effect (height of the subsequent flight of the load) increases, then stabilises as the strength of the stimulus exceeds some optimal limit, and finally begins to decrease. With training, the height of the reactive curve above the horizontal axis increases, and its plateau and descending portion are displaced to the right. In other words, the neuromuscular system is able to respond positively to a stimulus whose intensity initially causes the working effect of the movement to diminish.

Another detail must be analysed, namely the trajectory of the load with respect to time (Fig 3.8). The movement has an *amortisation (braking) phase* during which the speed of the load's preliminary fall is cancelled out and an *active thrust phase* in which a vertical velocity is imparted to the load (where the motor purpose is to thrust the load as high as possible).

The slope of the graph between the descending and ascending parts indicates that the transition from eccentric to concentric work is preceded momentarily by isometric work. Its duration varies, but on the whole it tends to shorten in conjunction with increasing strength of the stimulus. As a result of specific training, the movement is generally executed more quickly and more energetically, with a faster transition from eccentric to concentric work, and with a large velocity of muscular contraction during the thrust phase. The working effect of the movement is greater when the preliminary muscle stretch has a sharp, shock-like character.

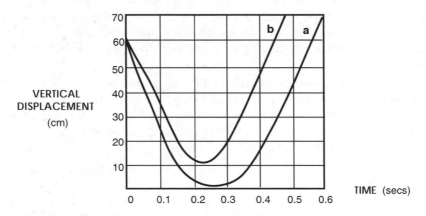

Figure 3.8 Displacement-time graph of a 6 kg load thrown upwards after falling from a height of 2 metres: (a) before training; (b) after training (Verkhoshansky, 1977).

In studies of reactive ability, the question arises as to how this can be quantitatively evaluated. This following formula may be applied:

Reactivity Coefficient $RC = K_2 / K_1$

Here K represents any suitable characteristic of muscular work in the stretching or active thrust phases, e.g. the power generated by the working-force (K_1 and K_2 are two different characteristics such as momentum or energy which describe the actions directly before and after the overall movement). However, the complexity of analysing activity in these phases restricts the use of this type of RC determination to the biomechanics laboratory.

The formula $RC = F_{max} / (t_{max} \cdot W)$ first introduced in 2.2.1

$\qquad\qquad = F_{max} / (t_{max} \cdot mg)$ is more convenient for practical applications,

where F_{max} is the maximum force, t_{max} is the time taken to reach this maximum, m is the mass of the moving object or the athlete's bodymass and g is the gravitational acceleration (9.8 m/s^2). RC consists primarily of assessing the overloading of the working part in units of movement time (Verkhoshansky, 1963). This coefficient has found widespread application in research (Chudinov, 1966; Papysheva, 1966; Kuznetsov, 1966; Kharabuga, 1967; Chereshneva, 1967; Polmachev, 1968; Kuznetsov, 1970; Semenov et al, 1971).

To objectively evaluate reactive ability Verkhoshansky and colleagues devised the so-called reactivity test, which consists of a series of vertical jumps (without use of the arms) after a depth-jump (h = 0.4 meters), without loads and with loads of 10, 20, 30, and 40 kg. The height of the jump and the duration of the support period were measured, then the height of the jump was plotted against the mass of the individual plus the additional load (Fig

3.9). The coefficient of reactivity was determined from the length of the support period and analysis of the mean take-off force (based on the drop height and the height of the jump).

A number of investigations studied the interdependence of reactive ability (evaluated with the reactivity test), muscular strength and functional speed. It was found that the correlation between *reactive ability* and *strength* increases with an increase in load. However, a high correlation (R = 0.95) was observed only with loads that are large for the muscle groups concerned (30 kg and 40 kg). The largest correlation between *reactive ability* and *speed* (determined from the duration of the support period) was observed only between the reactivity coefficient RC and time t, measured for one specific movement. In addition, the correlation between RC and time t is by far higher than that between the RC and the force F in all the tests. The correlation between the length of the support period and strength tends to increase in proportion to the mass of the load, but it is significant only with large loads (30 kg and 40 kg).

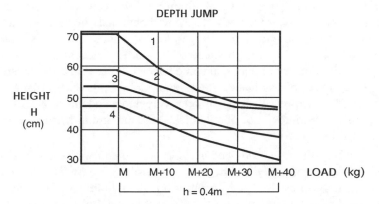

Figure 3.9 Results of practical testing of reactive ability for jumpers (1), throwers (2), short distance runners (3) and middle distance runners (4). M = the mass of the athlete. (Verkhoshansky, 1977).

In addition, the correlation between RC and time t is by far higher than that between the RC and the force F in all the tests. The correlation between the length of the support period and strength tends to increase in proportion to the mass of the load, but it is significant only with large loads (30 kg and 40 kg). The correlation between the speed of muscle contraction and maximal strength depends upon the conditions of the take-off. With a relatively small load (depth jumps without added weight), *absolute strength has a negative effect on the speed of muscular contraction, but it has a positive effect with relatively large loads* (depth jumps with 40 kg). On the other hand, *great relative strength has a positive effect on the speed of muscular contraction with light loads, and a negative effect with heavy loads.*

Research reveals that *reactive ability is a specific neuromuscular characteristic which can be improved by training*, the motor regimes in sport determining the level to which it can be developed (Fig 3.10).

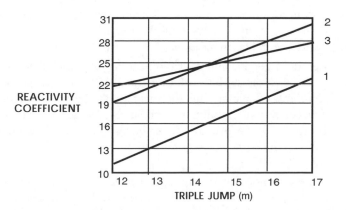

Figure 3.10 The relationship between reactive ability and performance in the triple jump (1 = first, 2 = second, and 3 = third take-off). The reactivity coefficient is calculated from the equation quoted earlier, $RC = F_{max} / mg.t_{max}$ (Verkhoshansky, 1977).

Of all the sports examined, the highest level of reactive ability was demonstrated by jumpers and the lowest by middle-distance runners.

Reactive ability is to a significant degree fundamental to triple jumping, which is obvious from its linear relationship with athletic results (Fig 3.10) and the high correlation between them (approximately 0.95). Reactive ability also has a great relative importance in the complex of biomechanical characteristics of the take-off in the triple jump.

Speed, Speed-Strength and Quickness

Traditionally, it was assumed that one could develop each fitness quality separately, then summate them or other abilities and obtain some specific performance end-product from them. However, recent practical and scientific achievements reveal such traditional concepts to be antiquated.

In reality, we find that the characteristics of the resultant working-effect of sports movements reflect the complex non-linear sum of many functions of the body. These will obviously be such characteristics as the rate of initiating the movement or the speed of the movement. Regardless of whether one is a sprinter or distance runner, a boxer throwing a punch or a thrower accelerating his projectile, sporting success depends upon the speed of execution. Nevertheless, this certainly does not mean that some speed quality is the sole basis for their success. In its basic forms, speed is displayed in simple, unloaded single-joint movements (e.g. thrusting or swinging the arms and legs in different planes) and is expressed in such relatively independent forms as motor reaction time, individual movement time, ability to initiate a movement quickly and maximum frequency of movement (Henry et al, 1960, 1968; Zimkin, 1965; Godik, 1966).

However, *the speed of similar, simple actions has nothing in common with the speed of executing complex sports movements*. This is clearly emphasized by the lack of correlation between elementary forms of speed activity and the speed of movement in cyclic sport locomotion (Gorozhanin, 1976). This is because far more complex neurophysiological control mechanisms and their associated metabolic processes are the basis for speed of movement in *cyclic locomotion*. For example, a number of qualities determine sprinting ability, including explosive strength, quick acceleration ability at the start, the development and maintenance of maximum movement speed, and resistance to fatigue (Henry & Trafton, 1951; Semyonov, 1966; Primakov, 1969; Lapin, 1971). The speed with which one copes with *longer-duration activity* depends on increasing the body's energy resources and their efficiency (Farfel, 1939, 1949; Volkov, 1966; Mikhailov, 1967; Margaria, 1963; Astrand, 1956). The speed of execution of *acyclic locomotion* is determined by the ability of the muscles to overcome significant external resistance (Farfel, 1939; Zimkin, 1955; Donskoi, 1960).

Speed in sport movements comes primarily from strength and endurance, although this does not exclude the role of quickness as a functional quality of the body. The latter is just as inherent as strength and endurance, but is displayed fully only when the external resistance of the movement does not exceed 15% of maximal strength (Verkhoshansky, 1973).

In comparison with work on strength and endurance, research concerning speed and methods of developing it have undergone significantly less development. This is especially true of attempts to correlate speed of movement with the activity of the nervous system and the reasons why it stabilises at a so-called *'speed barrier'*, which occurs as a result of the monotonous repetition of movement with maximum effort, a phenomenon for which research has not found convincing experimental corroboration.

However, some research has identified genetic and physiological factors which determine and limit speed and its response to training. Therefore, based on studies (Orlovsky, 1970) of the neurodynamic mechanisms determining the speed of cyclic locomotion of animals, and their general similarity to human striding (with respect to angular amplitudes, speed and acceleration of joint movements), it appears that *very fast sprinters are distinguished by more efficient organisation of the locomotor control systems*. This is expressed principally by the relationship between certain central nervous systems (e.g. the reticular and spinal cord systems) and their high frequency of discharge (Gorozhanin, 1973, 1977).

The ability to relax muscle is very important for rapid movements, especially in cyclical actions which involve resynthesis of ATP during the phases between muscle contractions. It has been found that muscle relaxation time decreases markedly as the athlete's skill improves (Verkhoshansky, 1996). In some sprinters, improvement in performance is largely a consequence of strength increase while the ability to relax muscle remains much the same, whereas some talented sprinters improve more because of an increase in their capacity for efficient muscle relaxation.

The adequate retrieval of elastic energy stored in the muscle complex, together with the stretch-shortening potentiation of force output, are valuable prerequisites for efficient high velocity cyclic and acyclic movement. Verkhoshansky (1996) reports that economical sprinting activity can result in the recovery of about 60% of the total mechanical energy expended in the movement cycle, with the remaining 40% being replenished by metabolic processes during the following cycle. He adds that there is a high correlation (r = 0.785) between the muscular capacity to store potential (elastic) energy and the performance of distance runners, with an increase in the contribution from non-metabolic energy sources taking place with increase in running velocity.

Although speed training produces both structural and functional changes in the body, the adaptive central nervous changes develop much more slowly than the changes associated with increases in strength and endurance and can be maintained only for short periods of time. In devising a training program, it must be realised that the adaptive changes produced by strength and speed training are very similar, the major difference being essentially quantitative. In both cases muscle myoglobin increases as an apparent adaptation to an oxygen deficit, while there is also a increase in myosin ATPase and calcium ion utilisation in the sarcoplasmic reticulum, which facilitates fast muscle contraction, as well as greater development of muscle tensile strength (Verkhoshansky, 1996).

Each phase of a rapid movement is functionally different. The initial acceleration from rest, for example, is determined primarily by stride length through a high level of explosive and maximal strength of the propulsive muscles. This initial acceleration is a specific motor skill determined by the body's maximum anaerobic power and does not correlate with the rest of the sprint performance. More specifically, the correlation between the strength of the hip flexors and initial acceleration is high, but this is not the case with respect to running speed during the rest of the race. Maximum anaerobic power, maximum muscle strength and the athlete's ability to produce intense effort are all closely interrelated, with maximal anaerobic power best being developed by event specific strength training.

In cyclic events, speed is determined by the relationship between stride rate (R) and length (L), where *movement velocity* V = R x L, although in practice, the overall economy of energy expenditure decides the final racing outcome. In some events, such as swimming, inertia plays a major role in the entire process, unlike in running, where the specificity of movement depends on horizontal thrust and the vertical oscillation of the athlete's centre of gravity.

The stride length/rate ratio varies considerably even among athletes of similar rank and though some coaches believe that the optimal ratio will emerge automatically as the athlete grows in experience, research into running, cycling and swimming has not shown this to be universally true, especially since unpredicted challenges from opponents will cause one to vary one's running characteristics. This would suggest that training should be varied in such a way as to prepare the athlete not only to develop explosive power and movement efficiency, but also the ability to cope with unexpected changes in rhythm and power production.

As discussed in detail in Chapter 1, speed of movement is associated largely with the fast and slow fibre composition of the muscles, which possess different contractile and metabolic qualities (Astrand & Rodahl, 1977; Komi, 1979). It has been established that athletes who possess a large proportion of fast fibres in their muscles, under equal conditions, display greater movement speed and ability to generate force (Rusko, 1976; Costill et al, 1976; Forsberg et al, 1976; Komi et al, 1977). It has been shown that the propulsive muscles of sprinters contain more (up to 75%) fast-contractile fibres (Gollnick, 1972; Thortensson et al, 1977) and that long-distance runners have more (up to 90%) slow contractile fibres (Costill, 1973).

In addition, excitability of the nervous system is a factor which governs individual speed level (Teplov, 1961; Nebylitsyn, 1966; Rozhdestvensky et al, 1969; Rusalov, 1972). It has been shown that people with high excitability of the nervous system are distinguished by great speed of movement (Gorazhanin, 1977; Sultanov, 1979; Ilin & Malchikov, 1979; Tabachnik et al, 1978). Thus, speed, as a characteristic of motor potential, has an upper limit that is largely predetermined by genetics, and its enhancement in training tends to be restricted to this limit. Therefore, the preparation of high-class sprinters is associated not so much with the absolute development of speed as it is with the selection of genetically gifted people and the efficient organisation of training to enable them to utilise their natural ability maximally. The halt in improvement of results in sprinting is not due to the existence of a 'speed barrier', but to reaching the limits of one's speed potential.

Further experiments are necessary before all factors determining speed of movement are identified and understood. It is also necessary to be critical of plausible hypotheses that for years have limited research in exercise physiology and frequently misguided sports coaches.

It is important to point out that maximum speed can be produced only if the corresponding movement receives sufficient energy for its execution. Consequently, in those sports where competitors achieve high speeds, oppose significant external resistance or resist fatigue, it is necessary to examine not so much the development of speed, but the refinement of those functional systems which make it possible for one to execute the motor task with the greatest speed possible. It depends on the strength potential of the muscles and the effectiveness of the metabolic processes determining their capability to do endurance work. In those instances where speed of movement does not require great strength or endurance, it is necessary to approach this quality cautiously and not impair it by training with large volumes of useless work. Regarding this, it is interesting to note the surprisingly low training volumes which typify many distinguished sprinters.

Thus, it may be seen that quickness and speed are different characteristics of the motor system. *Quickness* is a general quality of the CNS, being displayed most powerfully during protective motor reactions and the production of the simplest unloaded movements. The individual characteristics of quickness in all of the forms in which it is displayed are determined by genetic factors, and therefore the potential for its development is limited.

Speed of movement or displacement is a function of quickness, reactive ability, strength, endurance and skill to effectively coordinate one's movements in response to the external conditions under which the motor task is to be executed (Fig 3.11). Unlike quickness, there is far greater potential to enhance speed of movement.

It is important now to turn our attention to the fact that different conditions in sport rely on the same major system (the motor apparatus) and the same regulatory centres. The body is not provided with a collection of narrow, specialised mechanisms for satisfying each motor requirement, but is endowed with broad, general methods of response over a wide range of possibilities and a large supply of motor abilities to cope with external influences. The body's remarkable ability to adapt to unusual environmental conditions is the result of the functional growth of those systems which resist extreme stresses, such as those encountered in sport.

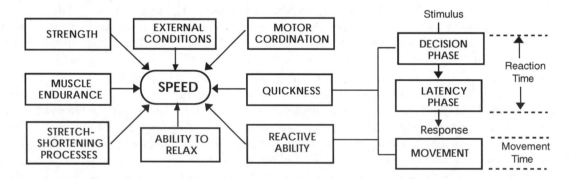

Figure 3.11 Factors which determine speed of movement. A decision phase occurs only if the action is cognitive rather than reflexive.

Consequently, highly specific mechanisms which are crucial only for speed, strength or endurance do not exist. All sport activities are governed by the same functional systems of the body. However, as a result of correct training, these systems specialise in accordance with the chief emphasis of the motor regime which characterises the given sport activity. Thus, increase in the athlete's special work-capacity is associated, not with the development of fitness qualities alone, but with the functional specialisation of the body in that direction necessary for producing a high degree of strength, speed or endurance. This information enables one to establish more effective methods for the special physical preparation of athletes.

Functional specialisation of the body in a given sport requires the development of different types of strength and endurance, a process that begins with the neuromuscular apparatus (see Ch 1). It is expressed as the functional hypertrophy of the muscles, enhanced control of intramuscular and intermuscular processes, and an increase in the efficiency of metabolism. Enhancement of muscular potential increases absolute strength, the power of explosive effort and the ability to execute work for a prolonged period.

Muscle hypertrophy is characterised by an increase in the diameter of the muscle due to a thickening of the fibres and an increase in the number of capillaries to the muscle (see 1.11). When maximum or explosive effort is required, functional hypertrophy is associated with an increase in the volume of the myofibril (i.e. the contractile apparatus proper of the muscle fibres) and particularly in the large, high-threshold motor units. However, muscle volume may increase insignificantly because of increased myofibril density in the muscle tissue (see 1.11).

Thickening of the muscle fibres as a result of endurance work occurs via an increase in capillary volume (i.e. the non-contractile parts of muscle fibres), which increases the metabolic reserves (glycogen, creative phosphate, myoglobin, etc.) and improves the oxidative qualities of the muscles. Training for strength or endurance can result in selective hypertrophy of the fast or slow fibres (Saltin, 1973; Skinner & McLellan, 1980). However, the ratio of both fibre types and their contractile qualities does not appear to change, despite the enhanced oxidative capabilities of the muscles (Gollnick et al, 1973). Examination of the possibility of altering the individual differences in the fast and slow fibre ratio as a result of training suggests that a change in the contractile qualities of the fibres is more likely (Costill et al, 1976; Astrand & Rodahl, 1977; Komi et al, 1977).

Increased strength occurs by improved functioning of the intramuscular processes via an increase in the number of motor units involved in muscle contraction, via increased motor neuron impulse frequency and via enhanced firing synchronisation. This is associated with an increase in intensity of the excitation to which the motor neurons are exposed from the neurons and receptors of the higher motor levels (the motor cortex, subcortical motor centres and intermediate neurons of the spinal cortex).

Maximum strength is increased chiefly by involving large (high-threshold) motor units in the contraction, whereas endurance work requires the activation of small (low-threshold) units. In the latter case it is possible to alternate the activity of different units, which enables work-capacity to be maintained for longer. Explosive strength is manifested by a rapid increase in muscular tension and is determined to a major extent by the nature of the nervous excitation of the muscles. It is chiefly the initial impulse frequency of the motor neurons and their degree of synchronisation that produces faster mobilisation of the motor units.

As discussed earlier (2.2.1), the F(t) curve of explosive effort displays three components and is determined by qualities of the neuromuscular apparatus such as absolute strength, starting-strength and acceleration-strength. The validity of isolating *starting-strength* and *acceleration-strength* has been corroborated by electromyographic research, which reveals differences in their neuromotor patterns, the recruitment of motor-units and the firing frequency of the motoneurons during the production of explosive force (Masalgin, 1980). This confirms the hypothesis that starting strength is to a certain extent determined by the innate qualities of the neuromuscular apparatus, and in particular, the ratio of fast to slow-twitch fibres in the muscles (Vutasalo & Komi, 1978).

Specialisation of the neuromuscular system to develop absolute, starting and acceleration-strength is determined chiefly by the magnitude of the external resistance overcome. Thus, as the moment of inertia of a rotating mass increases and resists movement, the factor structure of explosive strength shows that the roles of starting-strength and speed of movement decrease, while the roles of absolute and acceleration strength increase (Table 3.2). Thus, *the greater the external resistance, the larger the role of absolute strength*. The relationship of the latter to body dimensions and stage of training is also well known.

Table 3.2 Changes in factor structure of speed-strength characteristics of explosive effort (thigh extension) of discus throwers, with increasing torque (factors in percent, Dobrovolsky). (Siff & Verkhoshansky, 1999).

Magnitude of Resistance

Factor Order	Torque = 44 N.m		Torque = 572 N.m		Torque = 1144 N.m	
1	Absolute strength	24.0	Absolute strength	32.1	Absolute strength	34.7
2	Starting strength	15.4	Acceleration strength	17.2	Acceleration strength	16.2
3	Speed of unloaded Movement	13.1	Starting strength	12.6	Hypertrophy	13.5
4	Acceleration strength	12.2	Hypertrophy	10.5	Starting strength	11.3
5	Speed of loaded movement	11.0	Speed of unloaded movemt	9.1	Explosive strength	9.1
6	Hypertrophy	7.5	Explosive strength	7.3	Speed of unloaded movemt	8.4

The functional specialisation of the body over many years of training enhances the efficiency of the metabolic processes which provide the energy for muscular work by maintaining the ATP balance. Thus, in explosive sports or sports where there is relatively brief work of high intensity, energy production by the relevant muscles is improved by raising the power of the metabolic processes, i.e. the speed of energy release and restoration of ATP balance, chiefly by anaerobic means (creatine phosphate reactions). During prolonged work of submaximal power, longer duration metabolic processes are utilised, the basis of which is the anaerobic glycolysis of carbohydrates (see 1.13). This method of resynthesis of ATP is not as powerful as the creatine phosphate reactions, but has a greater capacity. Finally, during prolonged work of moderate intensity, the highest (aerobic) resynthesis of ATP capacity is utilised, where in addition to carbohydrates, lipids can be used.

3.2.2 Strength-Endurance

Strength-endurance is the specific form of strength displayed in activities which require a relatively long duration of muscle tension with minimal decrease in efficiency. For example, an athlete rowing 2000 meters in 6-7 minutes must execute 230-250 strokes (at a rate of 36-45 per minute), with the force of each stroke equivalent to a weight of 40-60 kgf (Samsonov, 1969).

Strength-endurance is an intricate complex of motor abilities which is expressed in two forms: dynamic and static. The type of athletic activity and the way in which muscular tension is displayed provides the distinctions between these two forms of strength-endurance. Thus, based upon the character of muscular tension, strength-endurance may be divided into tension of large or moderate magnitude. Depending upon the type of athletic activity, one may then distinguish between *dynamic strength-endurance*, and *static strength-endurance* as follows:

- *Dynamic strength-endurance* is typically associated with cyclic exercises in which considerable tension is repeated without interruption during each cycle of movement (e.g. in running, swimming and rowing); and also with acyclic exercises which are executed repetitively with different short rest intervals (e.g. repeated jumping or throwing).

- *Static strength-endurance* is associated with activities where it is necessary to exert isometric tension of varying magnitude and duration (e.g. wrestling or sailing) or to hold a certain posture (e.g. shooting or skating). Static strength-endurance is associated with relatively long or short term sustained muscular tension, its duration in each case being determined by its magnitude.

Finally, depending on the number of muscles taking part in the work, it is necessary to classify *strength-endurance* into general and local types:

- *General strength-endurance* associated with activities involving many muscle groups.
- *Local strength-endurance* associated with activities executed by individual muscle groups.

This distinction is very significant, since the means of strength training should influence largely those muscle groups which are responsible for the movement. In several cyclic sports the activity of such muscle groups can be observed with an electromyograph, for example, in rowing (Lazarov, 1967), and indirectly (by correlating strength with sports results) in swimming (Shchavelyev, 1969). The muscles tested in rowing were the quadriceps, gastrocnemius, biceps, triceps, deltoids and latissimus dorsi.

In swimming, the relative involvement of the various muscle groups depends upon the stroke being used. For example, the relative strength of the arm flexors, leg extensors and gastrocnemius muscles are not significantly related to swimming speed of the crawl, back and butterfly strokes, but there is a significant relationship with the breast stroke. On the other hand, the relative strength of the arm extensors is closely connected with the swimming speed of the first three strokes, but not with the breast stroke.

Thus, the forms in which strength-endurance are displayed are extremely diverse, and there is an intricate interdependence between them, as there is with the other strength abilities. For instance, a close connection has been established between strength and static endurance, as well as between strength-endurance and the long-duration endurance of distance runners, swimmers and skiers (Popov, 1968; Trushkin, 1968; Guzhalovski & Fomichenko, 1971). In certain instances these connections are intricate, as can be seen from the correlation model of the special strength preparation of crawl-stroke sprint swimmers (Fig 3.12).

The highest correlations with swimming results are the maximal force of the pull developed over 10 seconds (R = 0.810), and the mean pulling force developed over 40 seconds (R = 0.721). This is closely connected with endurance on dry land and in the water (direct connection), as well as with static-strength of the stroke and general muscular strength (indirect connection).

This is one of only a few studies dealing with the problem of the structure of *strength-endurance*. Unfortunately, recent studies are still rudimentary and theoretically deficient. There is some research into general endurance, but this does not touch at all on the structure of strength-endurance (Nabatnikova, 1972; Volkov, 1975; Mikhailov & Panov, 1975).

Furthermore, as noted earlier, the comparatively small number of studies in this area are distinguished by their great diversity and contradictory conclusions (Zatsiorsky et al, 1965; Verkhoshansky, 1970). For example, one study found a general, positive correlation between strength and endurance, another discovered no such relationship, while a third observed a negative correlation. The reason for these discrepancies is that different endurance abilities usually are measured. Therefore, it has been suggested that endurance be classified into two types, in which the motor abilities refer to qualities such as static strength, absolute strength, acceleration-strength and explosive strength. (Zatsiorsky et al, 1965):

- *Absolute endurance*, the overall result without considering the level of development of the individual motor abilities

- *Partial endurance*, the level of development of specific motor abilities calculated when the influence of other abilities is in some way excluded.

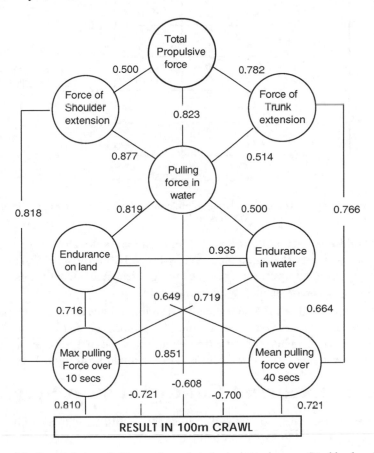

Figure 3.12 Correlation model of special strength fitness of crawl stroke sprint swimmers (Verkhoshansky, 1977).

Thus, to determine partial endurance in strength exercises, a weight which requires exertion of a given percentage of one's maximal strength must be held (static strength-endurance) or moved repetitively to failure (dynamic strength-endurance). A partial index is obtained if there is either no correlation with maximal strength or a negative correlation. In the case where subjects raise the same weight, the assessment of absolute strength-endurance has a high positive correlation with maximal strength (Verkhoshansky, 1997). To distinguish between these subjects, it is then necessary to calculate relative static or dynamic strength-endurance by dividing the load lifted by bodymass or by a bodymass adjustment factor (see 3.3.5). As noted before, the contradictory evaluations of strength-endurance and its relationship to strength may be explained by the fact that some studies examined partial strength-endurance and others examined absolute strength-endurance.

Strength-endurance is as specific as the other characteristics of muscular activity. However, the specificity of strength-endurance is expressed to a lesser degree than, say, the specificity of speed, although its carry-over from one type of activity to another is greater. One should remember that strength-endurance provides a high level of special work capacity that is mainly typical of cyclic types of sport and those involving the repetition of powerful actions (Verkhoshansky, 1997). In acyclic sports and chiefly those where technique and skill are important, the role of strength-endurance, especially the static form, is even more significant (depending upon one's level of sports proficiency).

For example (Fig 3.13), archers experience a steady increase in maximal strength, Fmax, and strength-endurance (judged from tmax, the time taken to reach maximal force). At the same time, the relationship between these indices and sporting results gradually decreases. In this case, it follows that the improvement in the results of highly qualified athletes (archers) is determined not so much by strength-endurance as it is by *the ability to control the muscular contraction* necessary for stretching the bow-string (Farfel et al, 1975).

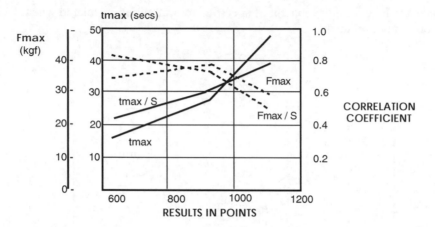

Figure 3.13 The dynamics of strength indices (Fmax) and strength-endurance (tmax) for performance in archery. The dashed lines show the correlation of Fmax and tmax to sports results (S). (Verkhoshansky, 1977).

The hypothesis that special endurance (including strength-endurance) is developed from a preliminary base of general endurance is fairly universally accepted (see review by Nabatnikov, 1972). The best way to develop strength-endurance is to execute the competition exercises under demanding conditions or in a large volume. However, this does not exclude the use of special strength exercises.

In conclusion, it should be pointed out that an objective, reliable means of evaluating strength-endurance in sporting activity has not yet been devised. Specialists frequently use inadequate tests which diminish the value of the studies and produce contradictions. Therefore, the first condition to be met for eliminating deficiencies in the theory of sports training is to devise objective, consistent ways of evaluating strength-endurance.

3.3 Influence of External Conditions on Strength

Muscular force and consequently, the working effect of movement is influenced to a significant extent by external conditions, as well as by physiological and psychological factors.

3.3.1 The Influence of Pre-working State of the Muscles

The working effect of an athletic movement is determined largely by the state of the muscle prior to the production of force: it is important whether it is relaxed, contracted or stretched at the beginning of the action.

Under laboratory conditions, using model movements (e.g. throwing a load upward on a special machine), evaluation of the working effect (the height attained by the load) depends on the pre-working state of the neuromuscular system, as follows:

1. muscles relaxed
2. muscles in isometric tension produced by loading with various weights
3. muscles stretched dynamically, e.g. during the 'wave' phase in swimming
4. muscles stretched by 'shock' loading caused, e.g. by rapid braking of a load which has fallen from a height.

The results of an experiment (Verkhoshansky, 1977), shown graphically in terms of the distance (S_y), velocity (V_y) and acceleration (A_y) of a load, illustrates the growth of the working effect in switching from one thrust variant to another in the sequence shown (Fig 3.14).

In other experiments, the same type of pre-working state of muscle (besides the relaxed state) was reproduced in the take-off for the vertical jump. The subjects executed the vertical jump without arm movement, from a static half-squat position, after a preliminary half-squat and after a depth-jump from 0.5m. The heights attained were, respectively 39.0 ± 6.0 cm; 44.2 ± 5.0 cm and 48.6 ± 7.0 cm. (Verkhoshansky, 1963, 1970).

Thus, the muscle's preliminary state appreciably influences the working effect of the movement. When the muscles are relaxed or in a state of isometric tension, the speed and power of their subsequent contraction is determined primarily by the nervous impulses to the muscles. If the muscles are subjected to a preliminary stretch by an external force, then the work they perform is further aided by some of the elastic energy which they have accumulated. Of considerable significance are the reflexes of the neuromuscular system, which increase the force of muscle contractility as the afferent impulses increase in frequency and intensity.

It is important here to examine the first type of pre-working state of muscle. It is frequently asserted that the muscles must be relaxed in the pre-working state and that this is an important indicator of the athlete's proficiency. However, this recommendation should not be generalised as being appropriate to every sports activity without considering the character of the movements and the situation.

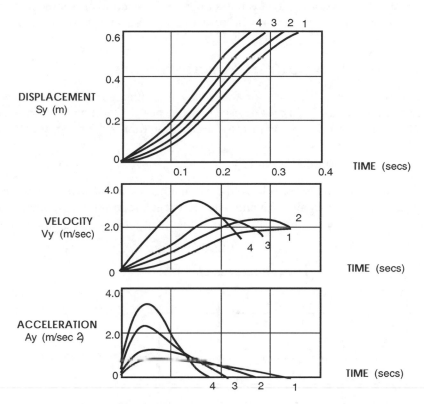

Figure 3.14 The dynamics of a moving load for different pre-working states of muscle (the numbers 1, 2, 3 and 4 refer to the muscle states described in the preceding text). (Verkhoshansky, 1977).

It is known that the working force is preceded by some change in the muscles, particularly in the form of preliminary tension (the 'anticipation tuner' of the neuromuscular system, according to AV Bernstein). Great speed of movement has been noted with the sudden release of muscles from a state of full tetanus (Jewell & Wilkie, 1958). Under conditions of preliminary muscular tension, the subjects executed the movement 4% more rapidly, while the reaction time was seven times faster than in the relaxed state. The fastest reaction time and speed of movement indices correspond in order of effectiveness to the following preliminary muscle conditions: 1. Stretched > 2. Contracted > 3. Relaxed (Smith, 1964). It was also demonstrated that the latent period of a motor reflex reaction is shorter when the muscle is lightly tensed for 10 milliseconds (Person, 1965).

Research indicates that, *when a movement is begun with the muscles relaxed, they are not optimally ready to work*; consequently, they produce a smaller kinetic effect than what they are capable of. Clearly, preliminary muscular tension is not detrimental to performance, as is frequently stated in the literature: it is just the reverse, because an optimal magnitude can increase movement efficiency.

Therefore, *preliminary relaxation should be understood to be relative to the specific movement*. Relaxation, meaning the elimination of excessive or spurious muscular tension, is not directly related to the movement or the working of the muscles engaged in the passive phase of cyclic locomotion, but it is without a doubt an important measure of proficiency in many sports. However, for brief movements, especially if explosive, optimal preliminary tension is appropriate and necessary, although its duration should be limited, because prolonging it can significantly diminish the dynamic functional force. The elimination of spurious muscle tension, i.e. contraction of any muscles which do not contribute to specific mobility or stability during a given sporting action, is always essential for enhancing proficiency (see 3.5.9).

3.3.2 The Effect of Load on Speed of Muscle Contraction

Athletic activities usually require quick and powerful movements and, consequently, depend on the development of explosive strength. Because strength is developed primarily by means of resistance exercises, it is necessary to analyse the relationship between the load and the speed of muscular contraction. Most of the classical work in this field has been done on isolated muscles for single contractions in acyclic activities, hence this section commences with a review of these findings.

The historical importance of this work based on studies of graded isoinertial or isokinetic activities, however, should not overshadow the implications of more recent research into the force-velocity relationships obtained under ballistic conditions (see Section 1.12 and especially Figs 1.25-1.27).

Contraction Speed and Strength in Acyclic Activity

To determine the relationship between the speed of an *isotonic* muscular action (see 1.9) and the resistance overcome, several mathematical formulae have been devised which generally agree with experimental data (Fenn & March, 1935; Hill, 1938; Polissar, 1952; Aubert, 1956). Hill's equation is the most widely used for muscle dynamics:

$$(F + a)(V + b) = (F_o + a) b = \text{constant} \quad \ldots \ldots \ldots \ldots \ldots (3.1)$$

This describes an hyperbola with asymptotes parallel to the two main axes, at a distance from the latter of a and b respectively (graph 1, Fig 3.15). The parameters a and b are constants, representing strength and speed factors, respectively. They can be determined from dynamics experiments or by measuring the heat produced by the muscles (Hill, 1950; Katy, 1939).

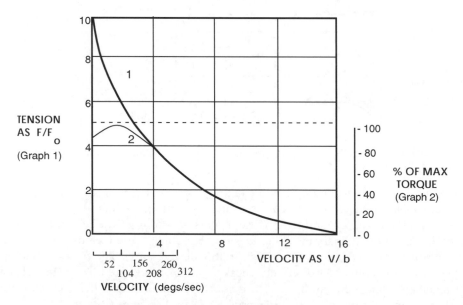

Figure 3.15 Force-velocity relationship of isolated muscle (1) and in vivo human muscles (2) as determined in two separate experiments under similar loading conditions. The hyperbolic curve is based on the work of Hill, while the other curve is obtained from research by Perrine and Edgerton (1978).

This equation establishes the functional connection between the force being exerted (F) and the maximal speed of muscular contraction (V) under 'isotonic' conditions, in which case the speed of muscular contraction diminishes hyperbolically as the load increases. Since any hyperbolic equation can be described by the formula xy = constant, then obviously the speed of muscular contraction is inversely proportional to the load. It is important to point out that it is possible for strength and speed (F and V) produced with different loads to depend on the maximal strength (Fo), as measured isometrically. (*Note*: Fo in this context is not the same as the absolute strength So, defined in Fig 1.1). Note that the force-velocity relation may be highly influenced by muscle fibre composition (Baratta et al, 1995).

The load determines important mechanical characteristics such as the power of muscular work. If muscle contraction is examined, where the changes with load are strength (F) and speed of contraction (V), then the dependence between them will look like that depicted in Figure 3.16. Consequently, muscular power is determined by the product of these changes (P = FV) and reaches a maximum at approximately one-third of the maximal speed of muscular contraction and one-quarter of the maximal strength (Wilkie, 1950). In other words, maximal isotonic muscular power is displayed when the external resistance requires 25% of the maximal force which the muscles are capable of producing.

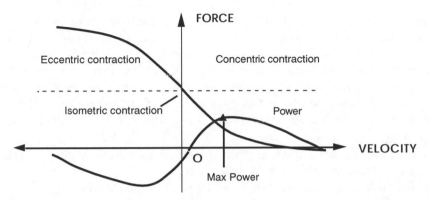

Figure 3.16 Change in muscular power as a function of speed of contraction during forearm flexion and extension. The idealised force-velocity curves for concentric and eccentric contraction are also depicted. Note that power is absorbed at negative velocities, i.e. under eccentric conditions.

It should be noted that the pattern of power production in functional activities can differ significantly from that in the laboratory, just as instantaneous power differs radically from average power over a given range of movement. For example, maximum power in the powerlifting squat is produced with a load of about two-thirds of maximum (Fig 3.17). Power drops to 52% of maximum for a squat with maximal load and the time taken to execute the lift increases by 282%. Power output and speed of execution depend on the load; therefore, selection of the appropriate load is vital for developing the required motor quality (e.g. maximal strength, speed-strength or strength-endurance).

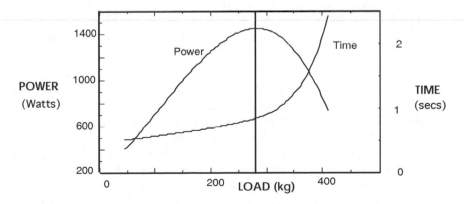

Figure 3.17 The relationship between power, load and movement time for the powerlifting squat for a group of top +125kg lifters whose mean best squat is 407.4kg. If a vertical line is drawn at a given load, the intersection with the graphs gives the corresponding power and the time taken to complete the lift. e.g. the line passing through the maximum power of 1451 watts occurs for a load of 280kg moved over a period of 0.85 sec.

It is interesting to note that the form of Hill's relationship has been modified by more recent research by Perrine and Edgerton (1978). Using *in vivo* methods of studying muscle contraction rather than Hill's *in vitro* approach, these workers discovered that the force-velocity curve is not simply hyperbolic (curve 2 in Fig 3.15). Instead of progressing rapidly towards an asymptote for low velocities, the force displays a more parabolic shape in this region and reaches a peak for low velocities before dropping to a lower value for static contraction (V = 0). In other words, maximum torque or force is not displayed under isometric conditions, but at a certain low velocity. For higher velocities (torque greater than about 200°/sec), Hill's hyperbolic relation still applies.

In general, therefore, the picture which emerges from the equation of muscle dynamics is that of an inverse interplay between the magnitude of the load and the speed of movement, except under isometric and quasi-isometric conditions. Although this interplay is not important for the development of absolute strength, it is important for the problem of speed-strength. The extent to which this problem is solvable at present should become clearer from this text.

Limitations of the Force-Velocity Relation

Although the hyperbolic force-velocity relationship has offered some useful insights into the nature of muscle contraction at different velocities, various authorities have cautioned against its unquestioned application in a wider variety of applications than those for which it was intended. Alongside the force-velocity relationship, the force-length relationship has been used to describe the contractile properties of muscle, but it needs to be remembered that the force-length property describes the maximum isometric force that a muscle can produce as a function of its length.. Herzog (1996) points out that incorporation of the force-length relationship into a model to predict individual muscle force leads to several problems, especially since the force-length relation:

- is unknown for most human muscles
- is plastic and may adapt according to imposed demands, such as those encountered in elite sport
- differs for maximal and submaximal levels of contraction
- differs with the length that is being measured or held constant in an experiment
- is determined by electrical stimulation or voluntary action, each of which leads to different results

Herzog (1996) adds that the force-velocity relationship is used to describe the maximum force that a muscle can produce as a function of its speed of contraction, and characteristically is measured at optimal muscle length. Force is determined once the muscle is under steady state conditions which do not relate to the initial transient behaviour which may be of great importance in many sporting situations. In addition:

- the force-velocity relation of individual muscles in unknown
- the force-velocity relation for maximal and submaximal activation is markedly different
- the force-velocity relation is different for force and for velocity controlled conditions
- the influence of stretch related processes is inadequately understood

The last item above regarding the force-velocity curves associated with different types of jumping or stretch-shortening processes was discussed in section 1.12, which showed no inverse relationship between force and velocity or the typical hyperbolic shaped curve. Work cited in this regard revealed an adaptive effect with plyometric training which allowed the muscles to produce greater force after regular training with depth jumps (Bosco, 1982).

Besides these issues, isometric force production by a muscle depends not only on muscle length and velocity, but also on the history of its contractile conditions. For example, this force after stretch is higher than the corresponding force obtained under strictly isometric conditions and lower after tension release (Abbott & Aubert, 1952; Herzog, 1996). These researchers also found that the steady state reached after stretching or tension release depends on the rate of tension change, with slow stretching leading to a higher steady-state force and slow tension decrease producing a lower steady-state force than their faster counterparts. This type of history-dependent modification of the force-velocity curve are ill understood and, consequently, it does not form a formal aspect of current models of the force-velocity relation.

Determination of the instantaneous contractile conditions in vivo is also fraught with difficulty, because the sarcomeres, the basic contractile elements within the muscle, do not behave linearly in a contracting muscle, so that it is impossible to competently measure the length and change in length of each sarcomere. Assessing the force-velocity and force-length properties by use of overall muscle-tendon length and rate of change of this length also is not possible, since sarcomere length does not depend only on this length, but also on muscle force (Zajac & Gordon, 1989).

Contraction Speed and Strength in Cyclic Activities

The above studies of the relationship between strength and speed were performed in simple single-jointed exercises or on isolated muscles in vitro under conditions which generally excluded the effects of inertia or gravity on the muscle and limb involved. Moreover, research has shown that the velocity-time and velocity-strength relations of elementary motor tasks do not correlate with similar relations for complex, multi-jointed movements. In addition, other studies reveal that *there is a poor transfer of speed-strength abilities developed with single-jointed exercises to multi-jointed activities* carried out under natural conditions involving the forces of gravity and inertia acting on limbs, body and apparatus. Consequently, Kuznetsov & Fiskalov (1985) studied athletes running or walking at different speeds on a treadmill and exerting force against tensiometers. Their results revealed a force-velocity graph which is very different from the hyperbolic graph obtained by Hill (Fig 3.18).

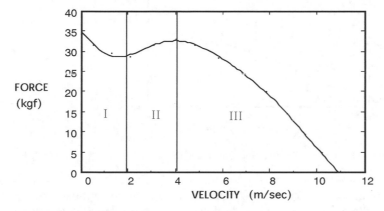

Figure 3.18 Force-velocity relationship for cyclic activity (based on data of Kuznetsov & Fiskalov, 1982).

This graph may be divided into three zones:

- Zone I which shows a correlation similar to that of the classical hyperbolic relationship.

- Zone II in which there is an approximately direct proportionality between force and velocity, i.e. where increase in force is associated with an increase in velocity.

- Zone III in which strength and speed are inversely related, though not in the hyperbolic form found by Hill and others.

The same research programme also found that the maximum force or torque is not necessarily achieved under isometric conditions, a result which agrees with the work of Perrine and Edgerton discussed earlier.

These findings enable one to select speed-strength exercises more precisely for cyclic versus acyclic activities, to design training machines more accurately and to produce force more efficiently under given conditions.

3.3.3 The Effect of Strength on Speed of Muscle Action

Analysis of Hill's equation of muscle dynamics indicates that speed of movement is dependent upon maximum muscular strength, as measured isometrically. It is not difficult to corroborate this. Newton's Second Law of Motion (F = ma or F = m.V/t) shows that velocity (V) generally is directly proportional to force (F) and the time of its action (t), and inversely proportional to the mass (m) of the body, i.e. V = F.t / m.

The physics of this expression is obvious: to increase speed it is necessary to increase the magnitude or duration of the force applied (or both), or decrease the mass of the body. However, for practical purposes, not all of these possibilities can be achieved in human movement. The athlete is unable to decrease the mass of his body or an item of standard athletic apparatus, or increase the duration *t* of a given movement. However, it is possible to increase the time of a movement of limited amplitude only by decreasing its speed, which is nonsense. Consequently, only one recourse remains, namely to increase strength.

This is well known in practice and has been corroborated experimentally. For instance, several researchers have shown that speed of movement increases with muscular strength (Kusinitz & Kecney, 1958; Clarke & Henry, 1961; Hunold, 1961). However, some facts exist which cast doubt on the logic of the above reasoning.

Although there is an increase in muscular strength and speed of movement as a result of training, laboratory experiments have discovered only a moderate correlation between these factors (Clarke & Henry, 1961).

It has been established that *there is essentially no correlation between the absolute speed of unloaded movement and relative strength* (Rach, 1956; Henry, 1960; Henry & Whitely, 1960). In particular, increase in strength has virtually no effect on speed of movement if the external resistance is small. However, the role of strength becomes more important as the load increases. For example, if the speed for raising a weight of 13% of maximum requires 39% of the maximum strength, then a load equal to 51% of maximum requires 71% of maximal strength (Masalgin, 1966). Figure 3.19 illustrates how the correlation between strength and speed of movement increases with load.

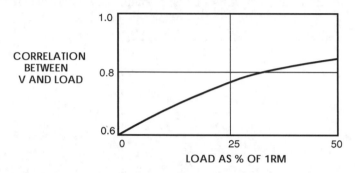

Figure 3.19 Change in correlation coefficient between velocity of movement and resistance, as the resistance increases (Verkhoshansky, 1977).

This same correlation can be seen under other conditions, such as when a movement is executed after a moving load is stopped and is propelled in the opposite direction. In this case, the correlation between muscular strength and speed of movement may remain relatively constant or even decrease (Fig 3.20).

Apart from the magnitude of the load and the type of muscular work, the connection between strength and speed of movement is also determined by differences in the ability to produce strength. An important characteristic governing the relationship between strength and speed is maximum isometric strength F_o (Hill, 1938; Ralston et al, 1949; Wilkie, 1950). If the speed of the load is expressed relative to F_o, and to V_o, the maximal contraction speed without a load, then the ratio (a/F_o) fully determines the character of the load-speed curve. This may be seen if we return to Hill's equation, namely:

$$(F + a)(V + b) = (F_o + a)\, b = constant \quad \ldots\ldots (3.1)$$

And rewrite it thus:

$$F(V + b) + a.V + a.b = b.F_o + a.b$$

i.e.
$$F(V + b) + a.V = b.F_o$$

Dividing both sides of the equation by F_o we obtain the following relationship:

$$(F / F_o)(V + b) + (a / F_o) V = b \quad \text{where } (a / F_o) \text{ is a dimensionless constant} \ldots (3.2)$$

Now, the velocity V reaches a maximum value V_o when the force F = 0

Substituting in equation (3.1): $\qquad\qquad b = a.(V_o/ F_o)$

Substituting for b in equation (3.2): $F/F_o (V + b) = (a/F_o)(V_o - V) \ldots\ldots\ldots\ldots (3.3)$

Masalgin's research has shown that the (a/F_o) ratio is determined largely by the characteristics of the sport (Verkhoshansky, 1977).

Systematic training with a particular type of muscular activity establishes a specific relationship between strength and the speed of muscular contraction. Hill (1950), discussed the broad significance of the velocity constant (b), explaining this by differences measured in the speed of movement of various animals. He also noted a different shape of the load curve in the regions describing the speed of sprinters and distance runners. So, it is obvious that maximum strength is the main factor determining speed of movement, although the role of strength is not the same under different conditions or when different weights are being lifted.

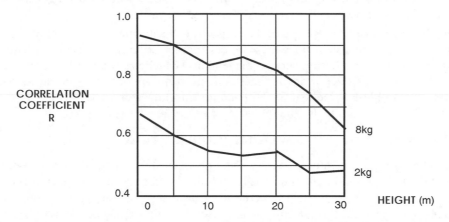

Figure 3.20 Change in correlation coefficient (R) between maximum isometric strength and velocity of movement for throwing 2kg and 8kg weights vertically upwards, relative to the height of the preliminary fall. (Siff & Verkhoshansky, 1999).

The question remains, however, as to why experiments show no correlation between absolute strength and speed of movement, whereas under natural training conditions with an increase in strength, there is a corresponding increase in speed. What is the reason for such a paradox that throws some doubt on the objectivity of the extensive, well-validated research quoted previously? To provide an answer, we must still ascertain which training means, including those for developing strength, enhance the development of speed.

Apparently, something must affect some specific neuromotor mechanism which is essential for enhancing speed of movement. With respect to this, it should be stated that the relationship between speed and strength is related to an earlier conclusion, namely, in selecting a means of strength training, the athlete should be intimately aware of the conditions under which the specific strength quality is to be produced in any movement.

Speed-Strength and Strength-Speed

The classical and revised Hill curves provide a useful means of distinguishing between the different strength-related fitness qualities. It is tempting to refer simply to speed-strength, but this disguises the fact that certain 'speed-strength' sports require a greater emphasis on speed and others on strength. This becomes apparent from the force-velocity curve, which enables us to identify a continuum of strength-related fitness qualities located between the extremes defined by $V = 0$ (static strength) and V very large (explosive strength).

Examination of this force-velocity curve enables us to recognise five different strength-related qualities (as discussed earlier):

- *isometric strength* at zero velocity
- *quasi-isometric strength* at very low velocities
- *strength-speed* at low velocities
- *speed-strength* at intermediate velocities
- *explosive strength* at high velocity.

The distinction between *strength-speed* and *speed-strength* is of particular importance in devising conditioning programmes for specific sports. The former is relevant to training where speed development is vital, but strength is more important, whereas the latter refers to training where speed development against resistance is vital, but strength acquisition is somewhat less important. In the competitive setting, speed-strength and strength-speed sports may be divided into the following categories:

- Cyclical, maximum power, short-duration running, swimming and cycling
- Maximum power output sprint activities with jumping or negotiating obstacles (e.g. hurdles)
- Maximum power output activities against heavy loads (e.g. weightlifting)
- Maximum power output activities involving the throwing of implements (e.g. shotput, javelin)
- Jumping activities
- Jumping activities involving an implement (pole vault).

150

In the language of physics, the terms *speed-strength* and *strength-speed* are synonymous with *power* (the rate of doing work). This quantity is what clearly distinguishes speed-strength and strength-speed activities from all other types of sport: they both produce a very high power output compared with their longer duration, lower intensity counterparts in a given movement.

Finally, in attempting to analyse speed-strength and strength-speed activities, one must not simply confine one's attention to contractile muscle processes, since these types of rapid action frequently involve the release of stored elastic energy from non-contractile tissues such as the tendons (which are stretched by powerful eccentric contraction). The role of the myotatic stretch reflex in facilitating powerful involuntary muscle contraction must also be taken into account. It should be noted that the Hill and Perrine-Edgerton curves do not apply to actions which strongly recruit the stretch reflex or involve the release of stored elastic energy.

The Interrelation between Strength and Other Fitness Factors

Similar work to Hill's has been done to examine the relationship between strength and endurance, and speed and endurance. It emerges that the strength-endurance curve is hyperbolic, but the speed-endurance curve is similar to the Perrine-Edgerton force-velocity curve, namely hyperbolic over most of the range, but more parabolic for endurance where speed is high. Figure 3.21 graphically summarises the interrelation between strength, speed and endurance. Using the same approach as the above section, it enables us to distinguish between the variety of fitness factors involved in all motor activities. If the activities are more cyclic in nature, then the speed-strength curve derived by Kusnetzov and Fiskalov should be applied (Fig 3.18).

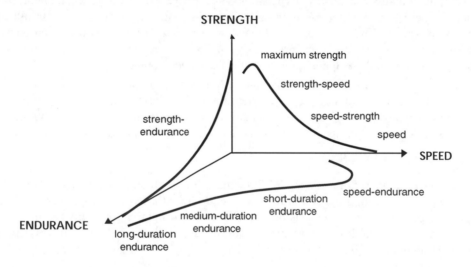

Figure 3.21 The interdependence of the motor qualities of strength, speed and endurance. The curves (not to scale) are based on the separate data of Hill, Perrine and Edgerton, and Gundlach.

3.3.4 The Relationship between Strength and Posture

Of the conditions influencing the displaying of strength, the relative disposition of the body's working links (i.e. posture) has important significance. The joint angles in the working links change with movement; consequently, so does the operating length of the muscles for a given joint and angle of attachment to the bones. Increasing or decreasing the leverage and the moment of the muscular force changes the mechanical conditions of work, which can be advantageous when the force potential of the muscles is used fully and a hindrance when only part of their maximal tension can be used.

3.3.4.1 Strength Variation with Postural Change

Changes in strength which are influenced by posture can produce significant changes in muscle action. For example, the *pectineus* muscle, during extension of the hip joint, externally rotates the thigh; and during flexion of the same joint, rotates the thigh internally (Baeyer, 1922). Depending upon the position of the thigh, the *sartorius* muscle can either flex or extend the hip joint (Ivanntsky, 1956; Donskoi, 1960).

Research on the contribution of the sartorius muscle to flexion and extension of the hip has established that the close correlation between the strength of the sartorius muscle (measured with the thigh at 30° relative to the vertical axis of the body) and the strength of the hip flexors and extensors is greatest at the extreme positions of the latter. The correlation is 0.92 for flexion at a hip angle of 210°, which decreases to 0.41 at 90°, while the reverse is true for extension, i.e. 0.86 at 90° and 0.32 at 210°.

In certain cases a minor change in the position of the links can lead to significant alterations in strength. Thus, pronation of the forearm decreases the strength of the arm in flexion by one-third (Rasch, 1956; Wells, 1960, Tricker, 1967). Slight flexion of the elbows during the barbell clean from the ground decreases the lifting force by 40%, a flexed trunk by 13.3% and lateral tilting of the head by an average of 9% (Sokolov, 1967).

The maximal force displayed at the working points of the system's links during the simultaneous working of muscle groups operating different joints, is dependent largely upon the position of the system's links relative to the proximal joints. For example, the force developed in extension or flexion of the knee joint is determined by the angle at the hip joints (Clarke et al, 1950; Houtz et al, 1957; Lehman, 1962). Thus, maximal force in hip extension in the seated position was found to be at an angle of 160° in the knee joint.

However, in the leg press (lying on the back) no difference in knee extension force was found within a hip angle range of 100°-140° (Lindeburg, 1964). Knee extension strength increases by 10-12% if the torso is inclined 20-25° backwards from the vertical with the subject seated in a rowing position (Dorofeyev, 1965). Thus, to produce maximal force in a movement, one must consider anatomical stability and ensure that at crucial moments posture enables the muscles to develop maximal external force.

3.3.4.2 Strength, Safety and Pelvic Tilt

The pelvis plays a vital role in the ability of the athlete to produce strength efficiently and safely, because it is the major link between the spinal column and the lower extremities. Inappropriate orientation of the pelvis can lead to movements of the spine or hip joint which provide an unstable or weak base for most activities. For instance, pronounced spinal flexion or spinal flexion combined with rotation can impose excessive force on the lumbar spinal discs during lifting movements and produce the so-called 'slipped' (herniated) disc.

Many fitness instructors insist that clients use 'pelvic tilt' to move efficiently and safely because they believe there is only one 'correct' pelvic tilt for all human movement. Therefore, it is necessary to point out that there is a functional difference between *anterior* and *posterior* pelvic tilt and that the type of pelvic tilt used depends on the specific phase of each exercise. The generally recommended posterior pelvic tilt is inappropriate for lifting loads from the ground, as confirmed by video, force plate and EMG analysis of weightlifters and powerlifters. There is a correct *lumbar-pelvic rhythm* in which one form of pelvic tilt synchronously changes to another throughout the lifting process (Cailliet, 1981).

Prescription of any pelvic tilt depends firstly on clear understanding of anatomical terminology. Two systems used to describe the direction of pelvic tilt. One describes tilting of *the top of the pelvis* (or the iliac crest) relative to the neutral pelvic position, the other of *the bottom* (or pubic symphysis) relative to neutral.

Before advising a particular pelvic tilt, it is vital to recall that *the purpose of deliberate pelvic tilting is to maintain the neutral lumbar curvature* as closely as possible, since excessive or prolonged lumbar flexion can be particularly stressful to the lumbar intervertebral joints and the peri-articular soft tissues. However, in this context, one has to question application of the standard definition of neutrality, which refers to the pelvis of a person in the static standing position, with gravity acting longitudinally along the vertical axis of the body. It is obvious that neutrality of pelvic position and the relative degrees of curvature of the three spinal curves will change if the person shifts to a leaning, supine, prone or other asymmetric non-vertical positions. Moreover, neutral pelvic tilt should not be regarded as being synonymous with lowest spinal stress and maximal safety during all static and dynamic activities. The standard definition of neutral pelvic posture should simply serve as a *reference standard* instead of as the most desirable and safest position for all movement. It is in this context that the term 'neutral' is used in the remainder of this section.

Thus, a *neutral pelvic tilt* offers the least stressful position for sitting, standing and walking. It is only when a load (or bodymass) is lifted or resisted that other types of pelvic tilt become necessary. Even then, only sufficient tilt is used to prevent excessive spinal flexion or extension. With reference to the iliac crest convention, the *posterior pelvic tilt* is the appropriate pelvic rotation for sit ups or lifting objects above waist level. Conversely, biomechanical analysis of weightlifters and other athletes reveals that *anterior pelvic tilt* (of the iliac crest) is the correct pelvic rotation for squatting, lifting heavy loads off the floor or toe touching. It is particularly dangerous to commence lifting movements or squatting with a posterior pelvic tilt, since this causes lumbar flexion and exposes the lumbar discs to the possibility of damage.

The anterior-posterior model of pelvic tilting is too restrictive to adequately describe the full 3-dimensional freedom of the pelvis. The pelvis can rotate relative to any of the X, Y and Z axes (Fig 3.22), where rotation about the X-axis is anterior-posterior tilting. The mechanics of the pelvis in all planes of action is highly relevant to safe, efficient use of the lumbar spine and lower limbs, since these systems both interface directly with pelvic structures.

Other types of pelvic rotation occur about the Y and Z axes. Rotation about the Z-axis is associated with the tilting up or down of the left and right iliac crests relative to one another. This characteristic rocking of the pelvis occurs during all normal walking and is natural and safe in walking, but can precipitate injury if it happens during squatting, overhead jerking or pressing, standing calf-raises, alternate dumbbell exercises, seated overhead pressing, deadlifting, upright rowing or any other manoeuvres which require a level or statically stable pelvis.

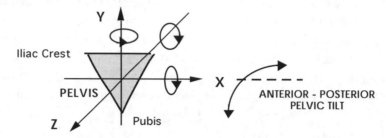

Figure 3.22 The three axes of pelvic rotation

Rotation about the Y-axis also occurs naturally during numerous activities such as walking, running, hitting, throwing and kicking. Excessive range of passive Y rotation, in particular, imposed for long periods or with high intensity by the momentum of heavy objects, sporting opponents or gym machines, can be especially harmful for the lumbar spine. The risks of such activity are exacerbated if Y rotation is accompanied by unskilled rotation about the other axes, thereby producing simultaneous spinal rotation and hyperextension or hyperflexion.

Similar unstable patterns of asymmetric pelvic rotation can occur during most sporting and manual labour actions such as pushing in the rugby scrum, throwing in ball games, kicking, swinging a golfclub, rapid twisting situps, digging, serving in tennis and hurdling in athletics. It is vital to appreciate that there are optimal patterns, principles and timing sequences of pelvic stabilisation and movement. Inappropriate speed, duration or sequences of transitions from one extreme of pelvic rotation to another, and between different phases of stability and mobility can cause many of the lumbar problems seen by physiotherapists today.

Obviously, the concept of pelvic tilt is not as simple as implied by many texts and fitness professionals. It embraces an interrelated series of different types of pelvic rotation, each appropriate to a different phase of human stabilisation and movement in three dimensions.

3.3.4.3 The Effect of Head Position on Strength

The position of the head has a powerful effect on overall posture, particularly during standing and sitting activities. As is well known in gymnastics a dropping of the head forwards initiates the forward somersault, just as the backward throwing of the head initiates the back salto in gymnastics and diving. Flexion of the neck causes a reflex relaxation of the erector muscles of the back, which is potentially dangerous for resisted lifting movements such as squatting, cleaning and deadlifting. Therefore, it is vital to use a definite extension of the neck to facilitate powerful contraction of the postural muscles of the trunk during all lifting movements from the ground. This facilitatory action of the head should not be done so as to cause pronounced hollowing of the back, because this can also load the spinal discs asymmetrically and expose the lumbar spine to damage. Lifting should be done in such a way as to maintain as closely as possible the neutral spinal disposition, with its three natural curvatures. Correct positioning of the head will ensure that the back assumes a posture where trunk stabilisation is shared between the erector muscles and the spinal ligaments. Lumbar hyperextension places a greater load on the muscles, whereas hyperflexion places excessive stress on the ligaments.

Excessive hyperextension or hyperflexion, particularly if combined with rotation, can be very dangerous for the spine. Rotation of the spine can be produced by rotation of the head, so it is vital to ensure that the head is also maintained in a straight forward position. Head rotation not only is inadvisable during lifting, but also during supine loaded movements such as bench pressing or prone movements such as 'good mornings'. If the head is tilted backwards during the bench press to enable the lifter to arch his body from the back of the skull, loaded cervical hyperextension occurs and the fragile structures of the neck can be damaged.

Perfection of many skilled movements such as the snatch or clean-and-jerk depends closely on controlling the head position accurately at each different stage of the lift. For instance, premature throwing back of the head during the pull from the ground can cause the bar to move too far from the body. Tilting of the head backwards during the jerk can cause the lift to be lost forwards, while during the low squat fixation position of the snatch, such tilting to look up at the bar can cause the lifter to fall backwards and lose the lift. Dropping of the head downwards during the squat can be especially dangerous, since this causes the lumbar spine to assume the potentially harmful hyperflexed position.

Action of the eyes is closely related to action of the head, so it is essential to facilitate correct body or limb posture by using the eyes to guide the head into the position which is most appropriate for each stage of a given movement. Generally, the neutral spinal position is maintained most easily if the eyes are looking almost directly ahead and fixed on a distant object. Movement of a coach or fellow athletes in front of a lifter can disrupt patterns of eye fixation, so that care should be taken to avoid this happening in training and competition.

3.3.4.4 Strength, Symmetry and Limb Alignment

The production of strength and the prevention of injury both depend on the alignment of the limbs relative to one another from instant to instant. The stipulation of a single 'correct' technique for executing a given movement creates the impression that efficiency and safety are determined by the repeated reproduction of precisely the same pattern of motion for every individual. Although there is a general model which offers valuable guidelines for every athlete undertaking a particular action, individual differences in factors such as body structure, muscle composition and neuromuscular control decree that it is essential to recognise the existence of a specific model for the individual.

One of the most important facts in this regard is the structural and functional asymmetry of the body and its various components. Any attempt to enforce symmetry of movement simply for the sake of aesthetics or tradition may seriously diminish an athlete's performance, so it is vital to be able to assess when asymmetry is natural and harmless versus when asymmetry is an inefficient and unsafe deviation from a desirable ideal.

For instance, in lifting a weight in any movement, the athlete usually rotates or tilts slightly to one side and the bar fails to travel parallel to the frontal, sagittal or transverse plane. This natural asymmetry must be taken into account when the coach is analysing technique. In doing so, it is necessary to observe and record the trajectory of the bar from both sides of the body and only then compare it with the ideal trajectory for that movement. The importance of experience in observing and analysing sporting movements then becomes obvious.

Reliance on the use of isokinetic or similar technological devices to measure agonist/antagonist and left/right strength ratios in an attempt to correct so-called imbalances, therefore, may be unproductive and ill-advised. The issue of symmetric training is addressed in greater detail in the next chapter (4.2.8)

3.3.5 The Dependence of Strength on Muscle Mass

Strength is related to the cross-sectional area of the muscles and, consequently, indirectly to bodymass. Therefore, the heavier the athlete, the larger the load he can lift. The athlete's bodymass is proportional to the cube of its linear dimensions, whereas a muscle's cross-sectional area is proportional only to its square. From this basic dimensional analysis, the mathematical relationship between maximum strength (F) and bodymass (B) may be expressed as $F = a.B^{2/3}$, where a is a constant, which characterises the athlete's level of strength fitness (Lietzke, 1956). Lietzke found that the most accurate fit to data was obtained for an exponent of 0.6748, which was close to the theoretical value of 0.6667. This equation expresses with modest accuracy the relationship between bodymass and results in the Olympic lifts.

In the practical setting, Hoffman had already appreciated from 1937 the value of the two-thirds power law in comparing the performances of weightlifters of different bodymass and he annexed this equation as the 'Hoffman formula'. Some ten years later, Austin considered the theoretical 2/3 exponent as insufficiently accurate to describe the records of his day, so he produced his 'Austin formula' with an exponent of 3/4. More recently, several researchers persisted with the two-thirds power law, including Karpovich and Sinning (1971), who used current weightlifting records to demonstrate that the exponent is still fairly close to two-thirds. Their equation, however, offered only modest accuracy, with a mean error over all the bodymass classes of 5.2% in interpolation and major inaccuracies in extrapolation for heavier lifters (e.g. the error at 125 kg bodymass was 14.7%).

Numerous attempts have been made since then to derive the closest possible mathematical relationship between the Olympic lifts and bodymass (e.g. by O'Carroll, Vorobyev and Sukhanov), but all equations invariably favoured certain bodymass classes and competitive weightlifters strongly opposed to comparisons of performance based on relative scores using any of the extant formulae.

Consequently, in 1971, Siff and McSorley, an engineering student at the University of Cape Town, South Africa, examined the possibility of fitting different equations to current weightlifting records for all bodymass divisions up to 110 kg. Soon afterwards, McSorley prepared computer-generated parabolic-fit tables to compare performances by weightlifters of different bodymass. In 1972 these tables were adopted by the South African Weightlifting Union and were used for nearly a decade to award trophies and select national teams. In 1976 Sinclair of Canada concluded similarly that a parabolic system offered the best means of comparing the strength of lifters of different bodymasses (Sinclair & Christensen, 1976).

The McSorley and Sinclair parabolic systems were limited in that both were most accurate for bodymasses up to 110 kg and, since they were based on world records of no more than three successive years, the tables became inaccurate whenever world records were broken. To avoid these difficulties, it is preferable to collect a database comprising the mean of the ten best lifts ever achieved in each of the 11 bodymass classes in weightlifting history for bodymasses up to about 165 kg (Siff, 1988). Statistical regression techniques revealed that various sigmoid (S-shaped) curves, such as the logistic, hyperbolic tan and Gompertz functions, and a power law provide highly accurate fits to the data (correlation coefficient $R > 0.998$). The simplest equation for practical application was found to be the following power law equation:

Total lifted $\quad T = a - b.B^{-c}$ $\quad \cdots\cdots\cdots\cdots\cdots\cdots\cdots$ (3.4)

where B = bodymass and a, b and c are numerical constants.

For *weightlifting* data up to 1988, the values of the constants for adult lifters are:

$\quad a = 512.245, b = 146230$ and $c = 1.605$ (R = 0.999)

The same power law equation applies accurately to powerlifting records (Siff, 1988).

For *powerlifting* data up to 1987, the values of the constants are:

Powerlifting Total:	$a = 1270.4,$	$b = 172970,$	$c = 1.3925$	(R = 0.996)
Powerlifting Squat:	$a = 638.01,$	$b = 9517.7,$	$c = 0.7911$	(R = 0.998)
Powerlifting Bench Press:	$a = 408.15,$	$b = 11047,$	$c = 0.9371$	(R = 0.998)
Powerlifting Deadlift:	$a = 433.14,$	$b = 493825,$	$c = 1.9712$	(R = 0.997)

Weightlifting and powerlifting totals calculated from the above power law equations are given in Table 3.3 and may be used to compare performances of lifters of different bodymass.

The database for *juvenile weightlifters* (up to 18 years of age) is considerably smaller and statistical analysis has to be based on single records in each bodymass division rather than on the mean of at least six totals in each division. In this case, the best fit to data is provided by a logistic function of the form:

Juvenile Total $\quad T = a /\left[1 + b.e^{-c.B}\right]$ $\quad \cdots\cdots\cdots\cdots\cdots$ (3.5)

where $a = 329.251$, $b = 35.045$, $c = 0.07906$ (R = 0.9996). Table 3.4 provides actual values of the total, calculated from this equation.

It was found that an exponential law equation provided the best fit to the average of the top 5 *women's weightlifting* totals, as follows (Siff, 1988):

Women's Total $\quad T = c - a.e^{-b.B}$ $\quad \cdots\cdots\cdots\cdots\cdots\cdots$ (3.6)

where $a = 943.063$, $b = 0.05142$ and $c = 257.314$ (R = 0.995). Actual values of the total calculated from this equation appear in Table 3.4.

To compare the performances of lifters of different bodymass, simply substitute each lifter's bodymass in the relevant equations above to calculate the Total (or lift) expected for a top world class lifter. Then divide the each lifter's actual Total by this value and multiply by 100 to obtain the percentage of the world class lift achieved by each lifter. This method is also useful for monitoring the progress of an athlete whose lifts and bodymass increase over a period of time, because it is pointless to do so by referring simply to the increase in absolute mass lifted if the athlete's bodymass has changed significantly.

Table 3.3 The relationship between the mean Total and bodymass for weightlifting and powerlifting for the top ten competitors in history, calculated from the equations in the preceding text. To compare performances by lifters of different bodymass, divide the actual total of lifter A by the total corresponding to his bodymass and multiply by 100. This gives his total as a percentage of mean of the world's top ten totals. Repeat this for other lifters. (WL = weightlifting, PWL = powerlifting; all weights are given in kg).

BMass	WL Total	PWL Total	BMass	WL Total	PWL Total	BMass	WL Total	PWL Total
50	238.0	525.4	80	383.2	883.2	110	434.9	1021.9
51	246.5	545.7	81	385.8	889.9	111	436.0	1025.0
52	254.7	565.0	82	388.3	896.3	112	437.1	1028.1
53	262.5	583.5	83	390.6	902.6	113	438.1	1031.0
54	269.8	601.1	84	393.0	908.6	114	439.2	1034.0
55	276.9	618.0	85	395.2	914.6	115	440.2	1036.8
56	283.6	634.2	86	397.4	920.3	116	441.2	1039.6
57	290.0	649.7	87	399.5	925.9	117	442.2	1042.4
58	296.1	664.5	88	401.5	931.3	118	443.1	1045.0
59	302.0	678.8	89	403.5	936.6	119	444.0	1047.7
60	307.6	692.4	90	405.5	941.8	120	445.0	1050.3
61	312.9	705.6	91	407.3	946.8	121	445.8	1052.8
62	318.0	718.2	92	409.2	951.7	122	446.7	1055.3
63	323.0	730.4	93	410.9	956.5	123	447.6	1057.7
64	327.7	742.1	94	412.7	961.1	124	448.4	1060.1
65	332.2	753.4	95	414.3	965.6	125	449.2	1062.4
66	336.6	764.3	96	416.0	970.0	126	450.0	1064.7
67	340.8	774.8	97	417.6	974.3	127	450.8	1067.0
68	344.8	784.9	98	419.1	978.5	128	451.6	1069.2
69	348.7	794.7	99	420.6	982.6	129	452.3	1071.3
70	352.4	804.1	100	422.1	986.6	130	453.1	1073.5
71	356.0	813.2	101	423.5	990.5	131	453.8	1075.6
72	359.5	822.0	102	424.9	994.3	132	454.5	1077.6
73	362.8	830.6	103	426.3	998.1	133	455.2	1079.6
74	366.1	838.8	104	427.6	1001.7	134	455.9	1081.6
75	369.2	846.8	105	428.9	1005.3	135	456.5	1083.6
76	372.2	854.5	106	430.1	1008.7	136	457.2	1085.5
77	375.1	862.1	107	431.4	1012.1	137	457.8	1087.3
78	377.9	869.3	108	432.6	1015.5	138	458.5	1089.2
79	380.6	876.4	109	433.7	1018.7	139	459.1	1091.0

The connection between a wrestler's absolute strength and his bodymass is expressed by another power law equation: $\log F = \log 1.005 + 0.724 \log B$ (Martirosov et al, 1967). A linear dependence between the strength of certain muscles and bodymass has also been observed in wrestlers.

Quantitative analysis has corroborated the close connection between bodymass and weightlifting achievements (Rasch, 1960; Starodubtsev, 1966; Pismyensky, 1974). However, this dependence is associated only with maximum strength and not the speed with which it is displayed. If speed is considered, then the relationship between bodymass and strength is totally different. The correlation between bodymass and the weight of the barbell decreases as the speed of the lift increases. It is 0.719 for the standing press, 0.706 for the clean-and-jerk and 0.685 for the snatch (Starodubtsev, 1966). A decrease in bodymass has a far smaller effect on the snatch than the press (Vorobyev, 1964; Medvedev & Tumanyan, 1967).

Thus, the highest correlation between muscle mass and strength is observed in those cases when strength is maximal and the speed at which it is displayed is of secondary significance. The correlation between strength and bodymass decreases as the speed at which strength is displayed increases, or to be more precise, a higher correlation is not vital for explosive types of activity, especially jumping exercises (Smith, 1961; Kuras, 1962; Schunke & Peters, 1962).

Table 3.4 The relationship between Total and bodymass for women and juvenile weightlifters, calculated from the equations in the preceding text. Comparison of the performances of lifters of different bodymass is described in Table 3.3 and the text. (All weights given in kg; juvenile lifters are younger than 18 years).

BMass	Women Total	Juv Total	BMass	Women Total	Juv Total	BMass	Women Total	Juv Total
40	136.7	132.6	61	216.4	256.8	82	243.4	312.5
41	142.8	138.9	62	218.4	261.2	83	244.1	313.7
42	148.5	145.3	63	220.4	265.4	84	244.8	314.8
43	154.0	151.7	64	222.2	269.3	85	245.4	315.9
44	159.1	158.2	65	224.0	273.1	86	246.0	316.9
45	164.1	164.7	66	225.6	276.7	87	246.6	317.8
46	168.7	171.2	67	227.2	280.1	88	247.1	318.6
47	173.2	177.7	68	228.7	283.3	89	247.6	319.4
48	177.4	184.1	69	230.2	286.4	90	248.1	320.1
49	181.4	190.5	70	231.5	289.2	91	248.6	320.8
50	185.2	196.8	71	232.8	291.9	92	249.0	321.4
51	188.8	203.0	72	234.1	294.5	93	249.4	322.0
52	192.3	209.1	73	235.2	296.8	94	249.8	322.6
53	195.5	215.1	74	236.3	299.1	95	250.2	323.1
54	198.6	220.9	75	237.4	301.2	96	250.5	323.5
55	201.6	226.6	76	238.4	303.1	97	250.9	323.9
56	204.3	232.1	77	239.3	305.0	98	251.2	324.3
57	207.0	237.4	78	240.2	306.7	99	251.5	324.7
58	209.5	242.6	79	241.1	308.3	100	251.8	325.1
59	211.9	247.5	80	241.9	309.8	101	252.1	325.4
60	214.2	252.3	81	242.7	311.2	102	252.3	325.7

In athletics, especially when comparing athletes of different bodymass and fitness, it is acceptable to consider relative strength. It has been observed that, as bodymass increases, so does absolute strength, while relative strength decreases (Krestovnikov, 1939; Knipst, 1952; Chudinov, 1961; Zatsiorsky, 1966; Martirosov et al, 1967), although just the opposite finding has also been reported (Abramovsky, 1966). Our analysis of the best performances in Olympic weightlifting and powerlifting, however, reveals that relative strength in both of these strength sports reaches a peak for a bodymass of between 60 and 67 kg (Fig 3.23).

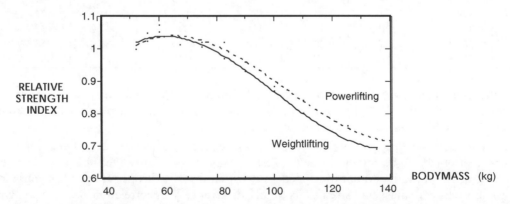

Figure 3.23 The variation of relative strength of elite weightlifters and powerlifters with bodymass (based on the mean of the top 10 performances ever attained in these sports up to 1988). All lifts are normalised with respect to the 52kg bodymass class (i.e. Relative strength index = 1 for 52kg bodymass).

Thus, an increase in muscle mass is accompanied by an increase in strength only in certain cases where the required movement is associated with overcoming a large resistance or moving it at low velocity. Examination of the facts indicates that structural changes in muscles, especially hypertrophy (and even the type of hypertrophy, as discussed in 1.13), influence the character of the strength displayed, as well as the method of its development. These findings lead to the fundamental problem of determining appropriate and effective methods for developing strength fitness, in particular its specificity.

3.3.6 The Relationship between Strength and Height

Analysis of several hundred Russian weightlifters of different levels of mastery (see Ch 2) reveals that strength generally decreases with increasing height for any given bodymass. Table 3.5 summarises the heights of different classes of weightlifters for each bodymass division. The second, third and fourth columns give the height of lifters of different builds for International Master categorisation, i.e. lifters who rank at least at the level of world champion. The last column gives the mean height of Class 1 and 2 lifters, i.e. promising lifters who are at very good Club or national level.

Table 3.5 Relationship between height (in cm) and bodymass of qualified weightlifters.

Bodymass (Kg)	Internat Master Small	Internat Master Medium	Internat Master Large	Class 1 & 2 Medium
52	142.5	145.0	147.5	152.5
56	146.5	149.0	151.5	157.5
60	153.5	156.0	158.5	162.5
67.5	157.5	160.0	162,5	167.5
75	161.5	164.0	166.5	172.5
82.5	165.5	168.0	170.5	177.5
90	169.5	172.0	174.5	180.0
100	172.1	174.6	177.1	180.2
110	174.5	177.0	179.5	180.5

Some of this information is depicted graphically in Figure 3.24.

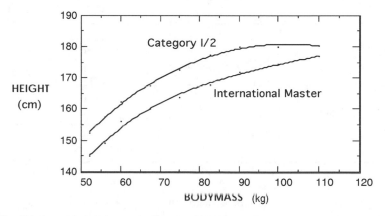

Figure 3.24 The relationship between height and bodymass of different categories (classes) of Olympic weightlifter of medium build (based on performances of the top Russian lifters). In both cases the lifters are of medium build.

The best fit to the data for International Master lifters from Table 3.5 is provided by an exponential equation of the form (Siff, 1988):

Height $\quad$ $H = a - b.e^{-c.B}$ $\quad$ where B is the bodymass of the lifter $\quad$ . . . . (3.7)

The values of the constants are:

Small build $\quad$ a = 180.0, b = 198.8, c = 0.0323 (R = 0.996)
Medium build $\quad$ a = 182.5, b = 198.9, c = 0.0323 (R = 0.996)
Large build $\quad$ a = 185.0, b = 198.9, c = 0.0323 (R = 0.996)

3.3.7 The Relationship between Strength and Age

It is well known that strength varies with age, reaching a peak for men and women between the ages of about 20 and 28 years, before gradually diminishing by approximately 1% per annum. In assessing the dependence of strength on age, we can use two methods: (a) laboratory studies measuring isometric or isokinetic performance, or (b) studies of weightlifting or powerlifting performances in international competitions. Table 3.6 below summarises the data for the two different methods. The laboratory data are based on the work of Hettinger et al

(1961) and MacDougall et al (1982), while the lifting data are derived from juvenile, junior, senior and Master's (veterans over 40 years of age) weightlifting records.

Table 3.6 Variation of strength with age, expressed as a percentage of maximum strength. The laboratory results measured isometric strength with a dynamometer, whereas the lifting results are based on the best Olympic weightlifting performances achieved in age group competitions.

Age	Lab %	Lifting %	Age	Lab %	Lifting %
10	42	59	25	100	100
12	52	62	45	91	79
14	65	66	50	87	70
16	76	75	55	82	64
18	84	83	60	79	59
20	93	97	65	74	49

The laboratory and lifting percentages correspond reasonably well for adolescents, but not for those younger than about 14 or those over 45 years. For prepubescent lifters, the higher than expected scores are probably due to the fact that weight-trained children are much stronger than their untrained peers. For the older lifters, the lower than expected lifting percentages are possibly due to the fact that Olympic weightlifting, unlike isometric testing, requires high levels of agility and strength-speed, necessitating the use of many muscle groups and not just the quadriceps or other limited muscle groups which are usually involved in laboratory studies.

Figure 3.25 depicts graphically the variation of adult strength with age, as derived from laboratory and weightlifting studies. In both cases, a linear regression accurately describes the decrease of strength after the age of 30 years.

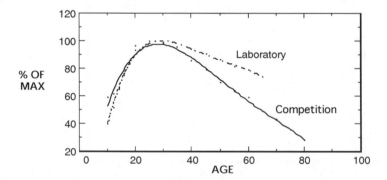

Figure 3.25 The relationship between strength and age based on isometric laboratory measurements with dynamometer and results in age-group weightlifting competitions.

If S is the maximum strength displayed in one's peak years, then the linear equation for untrained laboratory subjects, giving the percentage of this maximum strength which one is capable of producing at any age between 30 and 80 years is:

$$\%S = 120.17 - 0.68865\,A \quad (R = 0.988) \text{ where A is the age in years} \ldots\ldots (3.8)$$

The equation for trained weightlifters, giving the percentage of one's maximum strength which one is capable of producing at any age between 30 and 80 years is:

$$\%S = 140.15 - 1.3853\,A \quad (R = 0.996) \text{ where A is the age in years} \ldots\ldots (3.9)$$

These equations are not merely of academic interest, as they may be used to compare the strength or lifting performances of subjects of different ages. For example, if we wish to compare the relative strength of a young adult lifter A weighing 90kg who lifts a 350kg total with that of a 45 year old lifter B weighing 80kg who lifts 260kg, we would first use equation (3.4) associated with Table 3.3 to adjust for bodymass, then use equation (3.9) to adjust for age. Thus, the bodymass adjustment gives A = 86.3% and B = 67.8%. The age adjustment for 45 years (%S = 77.8%) is divided into B's score to obtain a final score of B = 87.1%. Thus, B has greater relative strength than A.

3.3.8 The Relationship between Strength and Gender

Many studies have shown that the strength of a woman is approximately two-thirds of that of a male of the same bodymass and age, with both male and female reaching peak strength at about the same age. This difference is due largely to the greater percentage of lean muscle mass in the male, because muscle strength in male and female is virtually the same (4 kg per sq cm cross-sectional area).

It is interesting to compare the ratio of female to male weightlifting strength for equivalent bodymass divisions. Table 3.7 is calculated from the mean of the top five weightlifting totals ever achieved for men and women Olympic weightlifters. The interpolation for the men's total at 104.9 kg was determined from regression equation (3.4) described in 3.3.5. It will be noticed that the strength ratio decreases markedly as bodymass increases, indicating that increase in bodymass produces a disproportionately large increase in the strength of males compared with females.

Studies (Hettinger, 1961) have also revealed that there is a different strength ratio for different muscle groups in the male and female (Table 3.8). These ratios are consistent with other research, which reveals that upper body strength in women generally tends to be lower than that of men of equivalent bodymass. They probably reflect the differences in type and intensity of work undertaken by the average man and woman in daily life and it is likely that such differences will decrease or disappear among similarly trained male and female athletes. This table may guide the coach in selecting suitable starting loads for female trainees undertaking specific exercises.

Table 3.7 Ratio of strength of female to male weightlifters, based on competition totals up to 1988

Bodymass (Kg)	Ratio (Female/Male)
52	0.76
56	0.72
60	0.70
67.5	0.67
75	0.64
82.5	0.63
104.9	0.59

Table 3.8 Comparison of strength of different muscles in males and females of the same bodymass

Muscle Groups	Strength Ratio (Female/ Male)
Elbow flexors and extensors	0.55
Trunk extensors and flexors	0.60
Finger flexors and ankle extensors	0.60
Finger adductors and knee extensors	0.65
Deltoids, hand extensors and flexors	0.75
Hip flexors and extensors	0.80
Knee flexors and masticating muscles	0.80

3.3.9 The Increase in Human Strength over Time

The historical progress in athletic records, particularly in weightlifting and powerlifting, show clearly that human strength is gradually increasing with time. The logical way of studying this growth in strength would appear to entail plotting the increase in weightlifting snatch, clean-and-jerk and total over successive years for each bodymass division.

Over the last few decades there have been between 8 and 10 divisions, so that this method would produce as many as 30 graphs, each with a different regression fit to the data. Simultaneous visual comparison of this host of graphs is virtually impossible and impractical. It is more useful to normalise the data by using equation (3.4) in Section 3.3.5 to furnish scores for all bodymass divisions as a percentage of the mean of the ten heaviest weightlifting totals ever achieved.

The result of this analysis appears in Figure 3.26, which shows a very similar trend for the snatch and clean-and-jerk, but a more rapid rate of growth for the press. Unfortunately, the Olympic press was removed from international competition in 1971, so it is not possible to study trends in this lift any further.

A Gompertz regression (commonly used by actuaries and biologists to describe growth or decay processes) offers the best fit to the data from 1950 to 1990, in the following form:

Points $\qquad y = a.e^{-be^{-c.x}} \qquad$ where x = (year - 1950) $\quad$ . . . . (3.10)

The constants for each of the Olympic lifts are given in the following table (R is the correlation coefficient).

Constant	Press	Snatch	Clean-and-Jerk
a	171.305	166.186	176.526
b	1.6118	1.6106	1.4175
c	0.009237	0.006365	0.006658
R	0.994	0.995	0.996

Using similar statistical methods to investigate the cause for the different rate of growth for the press, Siff and Medvedev have both suggested that the discrepancy possibly lies in the widespread use of anabolic substances since the late 1950s, in particular. It is reasonable to expect performance in the press to improve more rapidly than in the more technically demanding other two lifts, because the press is slower and is more dependent on muscle hypertrophy and relative strength. Since anabolic substances have a powerful effect on muscle growth and none on neuromuscular skill, they would be expected to offer greater benefits to slower or more closely quasi-isometric lifts such as the press and the powerlifting squat, bench press and deadlift.

The value of these equations lies in their ability to predict increase both in weightlifting performance and human strength over an extended period of time, not only to determine the trends of world performance, but also to plan the desired improvements for the individual.

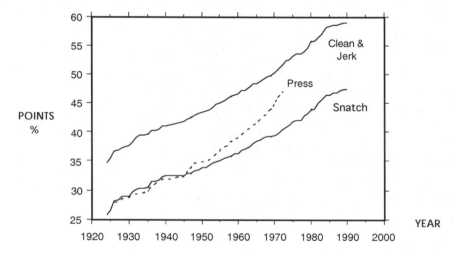

Figure 3.26 The increase in weightlifting performance expressed in points calculated from a power fit to the mean of the top 10 totals ever achieved (see 3.3.5)

3.4 Factors Increasing the Working Effect of Strength

The strength which one can display is not constant and depends strongly on the conditions preceding and accompanying the motor activities. Therefore, in competing with respect to distance, time, rivals and gravity, the greater an athlete's chances for victory, the better he knows how to fully and skillfully use the potential of the nervous and muscular systems.

3.4.1 The Warm-up and Pre-Activity Preparation

The warm-up serves to raise the body to the necessary work capacity. The warm-up comprises two types: general and specific. The purpose of the *general warm-up* is to increase the functional potential of the body as a whole, whereas the purpose of the *specific warm-up* is to establish the optimal relationship between the forthcoming movement and the activities of the central nervous system which are associated with that movement (Ozolin, 1949; Krestovnikov, 1951; Miller, 1951; Blank, 1955). The raising of the work capacity of the body via the warm-up is determined both by central nervous and muscular system changes. In fact, use of the term "warming up" is often highly misleading, because this type of pre-exercise or pre-competition activity may play an even more important role in preparing the nervous system for the major sporting activity which is about to follow. In many cases, little or no general physical "warming up" may be necessary, as is often the case in Olympic lifting or gymnastics, where the athletes rely primarily on the competitive exercises or variations of them to "warm up". Similarly, most or all warming up is unnecessary for endurance athletes, like marathoners, simply because the event offers more than adequate specific warming up. Consequently, the term "warm up" should be replaced by a term such as "pre-activity preparation", which may involve neural 'priming', actual warming up of physical tissues, and psychological readying.

Naturally, the special part of the warm-up preceding all types of strength work is of particular interest (see review by Thompson, 1958; Swegan & Jankosky, 1958; Grose, 1958; Sedgwick & Whalen, 1964).

It is known that a muscle contracts more rapidly and more intensely the higher its temperature within its safe physiological range (Beritov, 1947). The electrical activity of a muscle also increases with rising body temperature (Golenhofen & Goptert, 1958; Book & Golenhofen, 1959), and after stimulation, the period of the active state decreases (Hill, 1951; MacPherson & Wilkie, 1954). Increasing the temperature locally increases strength, as measured on a dynamometer (Robbins, 1942) and by the amount of time over which a muscle is able to maintain a given tension or execute a measured volume of work (Nukada, 1955). A hot shower increases isometric endurance (Nukada, 1955), as well as the speed of muscular contraction and endurance in cyclic work, by 7.5-9.0% (Assmusen & Boje, 1945; Miudo, 1946; Carlisle, 1956; DeVries, 1959).

On the other hand, cooling can decrease strength and lengthen contraction time. Muscles cooled to 18C have a work capacity period that is 2-3 times shorter than normal (Tikhomirova, 1961; Fray & Smith, 1941). It is known that massage has no influence on endurance in cyclic exercises (Karpovich & Hale, 1956; DeVries, 1959), but increases the power of explosive work (Skubic & Hodgkins, 1957; Merlino, 1959).

However, maximal work capacity can be achieved only after a series of muscle contractions, the number and character of which are determined by the functional state of the body and the intensity of the subsequent work. Repetitive work as a form of warm-up increases speed of movement (Swegan & Janosky, 1958), although if this work is of moderate intensity, then it is not beneficial for strength production. An active warm-up which includes intense exercises is an effective means of successfully preparing for speed-strength exercises and explosive exercises, in particular (Hipple, 1956; Michael et al, 1957; Pacheco, 1957).

Thus, it was found that women basketball players increased their jumps by 1.0-4.5 cm (Panaiotov, 1962) and long jumpers by up to 10 cm (Diachkov, 1961). The punching strength of boxers increased an average of 400-700 Newtons, while their striking time decreased by 0.02-0.04 seconds. It is interesting that the rest period between strong, rapid punches shows no significant relationship to punching force (R = 0.40), whereas after a warm-up, there is a moderate correlation (R = 0.62) (Karabanov, 1966). It has often been noticed that a 100 m sprint or a 4x100 m relay sprint enhances subsequent long jumps (Verkhoshansky, 1961).

Therefore, preliminary work which is similar to the subsequent work significantly diminishes the time taken to complete a given motor task. However, it chiefly enables the muscles to withstand a large load without injury and execute powerful, rapid contractions. The movements included in the warm-up should be appropriate for the special exercise, not only in their coordination pattern but also in the intensity of the neuromuscular activity. The latter circumstance is particularly important for speed-strength exercises. In other words, *specificity of warm up*, like specificity of training, is also important (see 1.3).

To examine the necessity for pre-exercise warming up, it is necessary to look at several important issues, including the type of activity, the duration of the activity, age, individual characteristics, injury history and general activity profile. An extensive summary of the literature on warming up was presented by Franks, as follows (Williams, 1983):

- Athletes in high intensity, short duration events such as weightlifting and shotputting can improve performance by warming up

- Vigorous warming up can decrease performance in endurance sports

- Athletes in endurance events or low intensity sports do not benefit much from warming up

- Direct warmups (using activities directly related or similar to that of the sport) of moderate intensity and duration before explosive sports enhances the performance of trained athletes, but not necessarily of untrained athletes

- Indirect warm-ups (using activities not directly related to the sport, such as cycling and stretching) can often enhance performance if kept at an unstressful level

- Almost all studies which show warming up to be detrimental used untrained subjects who apparently cannot tolerate high-intensity warmups

- Strenuous, non-specific warmups can interfere with sports requiring motor skill

- The selection of a suitable warm-up depends on personal experimentation with different methods in training.

3.4.2 The After-Effect of Muscle Activity

It is known that, if a muscle is stimulated by a series of impulses, its activity slows down more after the last one than when it is stimulated by a single impulse. Any stimulus, whether momentary or not, leaves traces in the nervous system. The *traces or after-effect phenomenon* persists for some time after stimulation ceases, which reveals the relative inertness of the nervous system and its great significance for motor activities (Pimenov, 1907, Pavlov, 1929, Orbeli, 1947). In physiology, this specific form of muscular facilitation (see PNF, Ch 7.2) is referred to as *post-tetanic potentiation*, in particular when the preparatory stimulus is produced by maximal or activity or "tetanus" (e.g. Abbate, 2000; Brown & Euler, 1938;. Burke et al, 1970; Grange et al, 1993; Marsden et al, 1971; O'Leary et al, 1997; Palmer & Moore, 1989; Vandervoort, 1983). These phenomena and the processes of adaptation associated with them form the foundation for fitness development. They determine the continuing rise in fitness, despite periodic interruption in the training process (Matveyev, 1964; Mateev 1964; Zimkin, 1965).

Research into the after-effects of muscular activity is contradictory, particularly in Western literature. For instance, a statistically significant increase in the speed of an unloaded movement was found directly after the same movement was executed with a weight (Murray, 1959; Van Huss et al, 1962). Conversely, other research could not detect such an effect, despite subjective claims by the athletes that their movements felt quicker after using loads (Nofsinger, 1963; Nelson & Lamber, 1965). No increase in the vertical jump could be measured shortly after preceding resistive exercises (Stockholm & Nelson, 1965). Shot-put results even deteriorated after preliminary throws with a heavier shot (Bischke & Morehouse, 1950).

The after-effect has been examined in more detail in Russian research. It has been noted that preliminary isometric tension has a positive effect on the subsequent dynamic work. Despite fatigue following isometric tension, the effectiveness of dynamic work increases, usually by up to 20% when compared with work executed without preliminary isometric tension. With the reverse sequence of work, results deteriorate (Shiedin & Kunevich, 1935; Vinogradov & Delov, 1938; Vereshchagin, 1956; Farfel, 1964; Uflyand, 1965).

The after-effect occurs immediately after preliminary isometric tension. The first dynamic contraction still retains some trace of inhibitory influence, but by the second contraction, strength increases sharply compared with its initial level (Leinik, 1951; Vinogradov, 1966). The data indicates that isometric tension under certain conditions can serve as a stimulus for dynamic work and play an important role in developing muscular strength.

Dynamic work with heavy weights (i.e. high tension with relatively few repetitions) also elicits a positive after-effect in the central nervous system (CNS), which produces a general toning influence on the motor apparatus and an improvement in speed and strength (Portnov, 1955; Ratov, 1957; Diachkov, 1961; Muravov & Tkachev, 1964; Letunov, 1965).

In practice, the after-effect phenomenon of strength work is used to exploit its immediate and delayed effects. It should be noted that there is an improvement in performance immediately following strong tension; i.e. this is an immediate after-effect. In addition, intense preliminary strength tension improves results in jumping exercises (Diachkov, 1958; 1961; Verkhoshansky, 1961; Tatian, 1964; Tkachev, 1967), in shotputting (Fritsch, 1961; Ivanova, 1964; Markov, 1966), and in rowing (Ermishkin & Vozniak, 1965; Chuprun, 1966).

For the delayed effects, preliminary stimulation is used to improve the functional state of the neuromuscular apparatus during the athlete's preparation for competition or in training for speed-strength (Diachkov, 1961; Vrzhesnevsky, 1964; Khodykin, 1976). The positive effect is obtained only if this state is promoted at an optimal level of stimulation. Over-excitation of the CNS has a negative effect on the precision and coordination of movements, i.e. on athletic skill (Diachkov, 1961; Yakimova, 1964).

The after-effect phenomenon in the nervous system and its influence on the subsequent work is influenced by many factors, in particular, the strength of the stimulus, fatigue and the time interval separating the preceding activity from the subsequent activity. Thus, after tonic work (with barbell squats) the following changes in the parameters of the force-time curve F(t) of explosive isometric force in a controlled task (leg extension), may be observed (Fig 3.27):

- maximum force increases significantly over the first minute, by 25% of the initial level
- after 4 to 5 minutes the force continues to grow to 65%.

The beginning region of the F(t) curve undergoes less significant change because the magnitude and duration exceed the initial levels by a smaller amount, the closer the beginning force is to the F(t) ordinate. The time required to reach maximum force was reduced by 2.6% immediately after tonic work and by 4.6% after 3-4 minutes (Fig 3.28). Later it began to increase until it exceeded the initial level (Tatian, 1964).

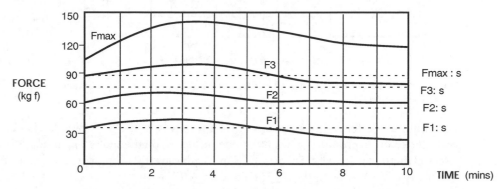

Figure 3.27 The force-time curve of explosive isometric effort achieved for leg extensions with different resistances F1, . . . , Fmax at various times after barbell squatting. The dashed lines indicate the starting values of the force (e.g. Fmax: s refers to the starting value for the curve Fmax and F2 : s is the starting value for curve F2). (Verkhoshansky, 1977).

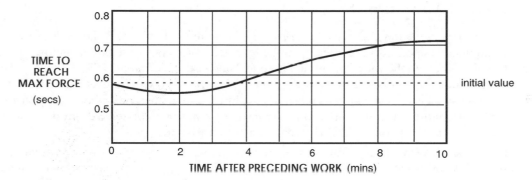

Figure 3.28 Variation in time taken to produce maximum explosive isometric force at different times after preceding tonic work (Verkhoshansky, 1977).

For moderately qualified athletes, the largest increase (90%) in dynamic strength after a static effort corresponds to a load of 50% of 1 repetition maximum (1RM), while the smallest increases corresponded to loads of 25% of 1RM (6.7%) and 100% of 1RM (5.8%). With increase in fitness, the post-work improvement can occur with large loads of up to 100% of maximum (Ilin, 1961). Consequently, with the rise in fitness and the strength of the stimulus, the ability to evoke a subsequent positive effect also rises. However, in principle, the optimal and not the maximal load is necessary for obtaining the greatest post-work improvement.

The strength of the stimulus also determines the time taken to achieve the maximum lifting force and the duration of the after-effect. Therefore, from a practical standpoint, the moment at which subsequent work begins is of some importance. For example, vertical jump height varied in the post-work period, depending on the nature of the tonic work (Fig 3.29). Three to four minutes after barbell squats the height of the jump was 6.8% above initial levels, and 8-10 minutes after depth jumps, it was 8.0% above initial levels (Tatian, 1964).

In experiments with preliminary isometric tension (Ilin, 1961), the maximum was achieved most rapidly with loads of 25% of 1RM (after 12 minutes), and most slowly with 100% of 1RM (after 15.4 minutes) and 50% of 1RM (after 17.2 minutes). Research has determined that the optimal rest interval between sets in weightlifting (during the presence of the after-effect phenomenon in the CNS) is 2-5 minutes, with the rest period increasing with the bodymass of the lifter (Ermolayev, 1937; Krestovnikov, 1952; Budze, 1959; Kazakov, 1961). It has been established that weightlifters who time their rest intervals carefully make 20% fewer failures than those who do not (Klimonov, 1965).

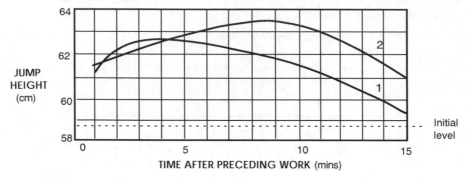

Figure 3.29 Change in height of a vertical jump executed after different types of tonic work (1 = barbell squat; 2 = take-off after a depth jump). (Siff & Verkhoshansky, 1999).

The delayed-effect of strength work depends on the volume and intensity of the preceding loads. For example, a moderate volume of barbell exercises produces a positive tonic influence on the motor apparatus of athletes on the next day or the day after (Diachkov, 1961). The use of depth (plyometric) jumps as a means of stimulation delayed this effect for 5-6 days (Verkhoshansky, 1963; Khodykin, 1976).

The use of the after-effect phenomenon offers some interesting opportunities for increasing the effectiveness of strength preparation via a more limited volume of training work. Athletes and coaches have great potential for creativity, which can significantly enrich the theory and practice of sports training.

3.4.3 Additional Movement

Some experienced coaches judge the mastery of a sprinter by the action of his jaws. If the teeth are clenched and the face has a strained expression during a race, then the level of proficiency is regarded as low. If the jaw is relaxed and the face is calm, then their movements are fluid and unconstrained and the athlete displays the skill for running fast. Although subjective, it is a reasonably accurate evaluation of mastery in cyclic movements when the muscles work in a rapid sequence of tension and relaxation. Clinically, this observation would appear to relate, at least in part, to the TMJ (tempero-mandibular joint) syndrome sometimes treated by physical therapists to relieve muscular stress in various parts of the body which are distant from the jaw.

However, in acyclic movements requiring the display of powerful force, it is not possible to evaluate proficiency in this way. In this case, muscular force is concentrated in a single instantaneous contraction and even the anatomical antagonists may function as synergists. Under these conditions, the so-called *additional movement* contributes to raising the working effect. In physiotherapeutic PNF (see 7.2), this phenomenon is regarded as a consequence of what is termed *overflow* or *irradiation* from stronger to weaker or more fatigued muscles (Knott & Voss, 1968).

Muscular activity (an indicator of electrical excitation) is dependent not only on the processes taking place within the prime movers, but also on the state of the other muscle groups. Both unloaded and loaded movements with large resistance elicit electrical activity in the unexercised musculature of the body (Farfel, 1961; Levin, 1964; Sills & Olson, 1958). Furthermore, the strength and endurance of the arm muscles executing dynamic work increase significantly by including other skeletal muscles in the work (Gorbunova & Khabarova, 1955; Mukhamedova, 1958). Exercising the muscles on one side of the body causes an increase in strength on the unexercised side, i.e., the well-known 'cross training' phenomenon (Wissler & Richardson, 1900; Davis, 1942; Hellebrant et al, 1947; Laun, 1954; Enoka, 1988).

Thus, an additional movement which does not serve to increase the economy of the motor action, has a specific physiological value and its systematic involvement can be very useful.

The combination of two or several muscle groups involved simultaneously or sequentially offers several advantages. Thus, the amount of force developed by the right arm is significantly influenced by the muscles taking part in the additional movement: a momentary contraction of the extensors of the left elbow increases the strength and speed of the flexors of the right elbow to a larger degree than a contraction of the left elbow flexors (Mukhammedova, 1958). If, during rhythmic flexing of the right arm, the extensors of the left are momentarily tensed, then the work capacity of the right arm will increase by 39-42%; if the flexors of the left arm are tensed, it will decrease by 8-22%. Tensing the extensors of the left arm after first fatiguing the flexors of the right, increases the capacity of the latter to do significantly more work. Tensing the flexors of the left arm has no effect in this case (Popov, 1938).

Thus, the change in the work capacity of one muscle group by recruiting others into the work depends on many factors and varies under different circumstances. The athlete's fitness, the type of muscular activity during the additional dynamic or static work, as well as a decrease or increase in the load and work rhythm all influence the working effect (Vinogradov, 1966). Thus, in the above-mentioned experiments by Mukhammedova, a large stimulatory effect is obtained when the additional effort of the left arm reaches 25-33% of that of the right arm.

Finally, results are determined by the functional state of the motor system. Research indicates that, to obtain a definite stimulatory effect, the appropriate motor centre in the brain should be in a state of stable excitation and reactiveness. The excitation of one neurocentre stimulates this process in the other motor centres, if the latter centres become significantly dominant.

Thus, tension in the additional muscle groups increases the excitability of the dominant centre because of the afferent impulses coming from them and enhances the effector process in the fundamental muscle groups. The basis for this dominance phenomenon is obvious: in the initial stages of work when dominance is still only forming, involvement of the other muscle groups will be counter-productive. The effect appears only after some time has passed, when dominance has already been established (Shatenstein & Yordanskaya, 1955).

In athletics there are examples where the motor effect is produced (while using additional movement) by the dominant centre and by clearly mechanical factors. This is observed in exercises involving a take-off from a support using rotary movement (e.g. pole-vaulting). In this case the concentration of muscular excitation, which is crucial for rotational acceleration of the body's links, enhances excitation of the dominant centre, thereby involving the key element of the take-off, namely the action of the extensor muscles. At the same time, reactive force resulting from muscle stretching during the amortisation phase increases the power of the muscles executing the take-off (for example, by an average of 25% in the vertical jump). Thus, additional movement is an example of the body's adaptive capability, playing a useful role when it becomes necessary to produce maximal tension. Clearly, it has a place in strength training.

3.4.4 Preparatory Movement

If one attempts to execute a vertical jump from a half-squat position, it will become immediately obvious that this is very difficult without a preliminary movement. Considerable muscle tension will be needed to restrain the natural preparatory movement which man consciously or unconsciously resorts to each time he is preparing to execute an action requiring the production of significant force.

The preparatory movement is different in each specific case, depending upon the situation and the given motor task. However, the objective is still the same, i.e. to increase the working range and prepare the muscles for a more powerful effort. The latter is accomplished by stretching the muscles, which produces a strong motor impulse via the myotatic reflex and creates additional elastic tension.

The fact that preliminary muscular tension precedes an effort requiring the intense production of strength has been noted in several investigations using EMG analysis (Salchenko, 1960; Kotelnikov, 1966; Popov, 1968; Asmussen & Bonde-Peterson, 1974). Obviously one should not conclude that preliminary muscle tension is always necessary for the execution of exercises. Preliminary tension can be appropriate if it is well timed and immediately precedes the working-effort, or if it is accomplished during the preparatory movement and its magnitude is optimal. Thus, it may be appropriate to use preparatory movements when it is necessary to produce great strength and speed, as well as to enhance the economy of a motor action.

3.4.5 Coordination in Muscular Work

Even with relatively simple movements, the same effect can be produced through many different combinations of the muscles involved. A typical working effect in non-standard muscular work was observed , where the external display of this typical working effect varies with the amplitude, speed and strength of the movement (Fidelius, 1959; Zhukov & Zakhariants, 1960; Zimkin, 1962; Ratov, 1962). Thus, the impulse (F.t) of the vertical jump take-off varies according to the force F and the duration t of its action. The greater the athlete's fitness, the more stable the magnitude of the impulse, and the more stable the distribution of force over time (Verkhoshansky, 1963; Arutyunyan, 1964). Therefore, during a given exercise, the ineffective and weakly effective variants of muscle action which contribute to the movement become distinguished from the more effective combinations (Zimkin, 1962; Korobova, 1964). Well-prepared athletes use only those combinations which enable them to use their motor potential most efficiently.

Changes in the character of muscular activity during the execution of movement can occur in several forms (Averianov, 1963; Moikin, 1964):

- change in the sequence of different muscle groups participating in the movement
- change in the number of muscle groups participating in the movement
- change in the relative degree of participation of different muscles in the movement.

In cyclic movements, the duration of the active and relative rest phases changes (Kuchin, 1960; Ratishvili, 1966), and the maximal contribution shifts from one group of muscles to another (Lazareva, 1966; Absalyamov, 1968).

Movements associated with overcoming large resistance or executed with great speed characteristically switch the activity to the muscles of the proximal links (Ivanitsky, 1956; Lebedev, 1962; Moikin, 1964), as well as produce a differentiation in the activity of different parts of the muscle (Averianov & Shibanov, 1964).

In complex multi-joint movements, the resulting force does not equal the sum of the individual maximum tensions of which each of the contributing muscle groups is capable. For example, the largest summated force which a rower develops is at the beginning of the movement, although at this instant the legs are working at an disadvantageous angle in the knee and hip joints (Table 3.9). However, the percentage utilisation of absolute strength (the sum of the maximum force that the muscles of the arms, torso and legs develop individually) is largest at this moment (Egorov, 1966). Thus, the disadvantageous conditions for the work of one muscle can be compensated for by the more advantageous conditions for another's work through the effective coordination of contributory actions (in this instance, the back muscles).

Table 3.9 Mean strength of rowers (in kgf) and the percentage use of absolute strength at different phases of the stroke (MS = Master of Sport, while III, II and I refer to increasing levels of Sports Mastery). (Siff & Verkhoshansky, 1999).

Level of Sports Mastery

Stroke Phase	Class III	Class II	Class I	MS
Beginning	128	131	134	143
	34%	31%	32%	33%
Middle	119	124	130	128
	27%	26%	27%	29%
End	112	116	118	126
	26%	24%	25%	26%

The most important aspect of muscular coordination in speed-strength exercises is the increase in force at biomechanically crucial stages of the movement. In particular, one of the most typical characteristics of motor skills will be the increase in muscular force where the dynamic emphasis is necessary in a complex motor act to raise its total working effect.

3.4.6 Efficiency of Energy Expenditure

The efficiency with which an athlete executes a given movement has a profound effect on the functional use of strength, speed-strength, strength-endurance and all other components of fitness. Energy expenditure in any individual is affected not only by neuromuscular efficiency, but also by factors such as bodymass and type of exercise.

For instance, after the warm-up, the rate of energy expenditure of Class I-III weightlifters varies from under 8 kjoules/min in the 56 kg division to over 23 kJ/min in the +110kg division, while the mean energy expenditure for Class I-III weightlifters across all bodymass divisions is 14.8 kJ/min (see Table 3.10). Energy expenditure tends to decrease with increasing level of sports proficiency, thereby emphasizing the importance of improving movement skills in physical training. Tables 3.10 and 3.11 show clearly that elite competitors generally use energy more economically than lower ranked athletes. The last column of Table 3.11 reveals that the relative energy expenditure (i.e. energy per unit bodymass) is greater for exercises requiring the use of smaller muscle mass.

Table 3.10 Rate of energy expenditure of weightlifters of different bodymass and levels of qualification in kjoules per minute (based on Vorobyev, 1978). MS = Master of Sport.

Category	56kg	60kg	67.5kg	75kg	82.5kg	90kg	> 90kg
I - III	9.9	11.4	13.0	13.9	15.1	17.2	23.0
MS	7.5	9.8	13.1	12.9	12.2	14.8	19.2

Table 3.11 Relative energy expenditure in calories per kg bodymass for a single repetition of various exercises (based on Vorobyev, 1978). In all exercises except the pulls, the bar was loaded to 80% of the athlete's 1RM; pulls were performed with a load equal to 100% of the snatch and jerk, respectively.

Exercise	Ranked Lifter (cals/kg)	Elite Lifter (cals/kg)	Mean of both groups (cal/kg)	Mean relative to clean & jerk (%)
Snatch pull	83.5	51.0	67.2	117
Snatch	75.3	57.0	66.6	116
Clean pull	78.0	50.4	64.2	112
Power clean	78.0	62.9	70.4	122
Clean-and-jerk	66.5	48.6	57.2	100
Clean-and-press	70.0	49.0	59.9	104
Press from rack	214.0	146.9	180.4	313
Back squat	88.5	68.5	79.0	137
Front squat	126.3	88.0	107.2	186
Bench press	215.0	126.0	170.2	295

For example, the clean-and-jerk, which uses a large number of the muscles in the body, proves to be the most economical exercise relative to bodymass in the above selection, while the press from racks is the most expensive, since the prime movers are mainly the less massive muscles of the arms. However, in terms of absolute energy expenditure, the exercises which involve use of the greatest muscle mass obviously expend the most energy (Table 3.12). A knowledge of the amount of energy expended in executing the major exercises can be useful for planning training sessions and avoiding overtraining.

Table 3.12 Absolute energy expenditure for a 1RM in different exercises by weightlifters of different qualification expressed in kcalories (based on Vorobyev, 1978).

Exercise	Ranked Lifter	Elite Lifter	Mean of both
Snatch Pull	11.0	8.2	9.6
Bench Press	12.2	8.4	10.3
Press off racks	11.1	10.1	10.6
Clean Pull	12.2	9.3	10.8
Back Squat	11.3	11.0	11.1
Power Clean	12.7	11.3	12.0
Snatch	12.7	11.6	12.2
Front Squat	11.8	12.7	12.3
Clean & Press	13.1	11.8	12.5
Clean & Jerk	15.5	13.7	14.6

However, a simplistic calculation of energy expenditure as given in popular athletic training or body weight reduction books can be very misleading, because they usually fail to take into account the effect of rest intervals between exercises or the interaction of successive training sessions. For instance, *we are not justified in equating the effects of two different types of training session just because they may have used virtually identical expenditures of energy.* One of these sessions may have been for bodybuilding purposes using moderate weights for higher repetitions and with short rest periods, whereas the other may have been a pre-contest Olympic weightlifting session using near-maximal weights for few repetitions and with long rest periods between repetitions and sets.

Optimal training versus overtraining is not merely the consequence of calculating the appropriate amount of energy expended, since so many different bodily systems are involved in the production of work. Western research has paid scant attention to the differences in energy consumption among athletes of different levels of expertise and fatigue, yet charts of calorific or energy usage in different sports are applied universally and unquestioningly. The problems are compounded further by the fact that no research has ever managed to quantify the differences between neural, cardiac and muscular fatigue in any activity.

Overtraining is not a single syndrome and generally is regarded as comprising overload (excessive intensity or load) and overuse (excessive work output) types, so it cannot be assessed on the basis of energy expenditure alone. A workout consisting of a few maximal attempts may be elicit an overload type of overtraining far more readily than a much longer workout relying on many sets with moderate weights. Even then, overload may be more a consequence of inappropriate technique that imposes greater stress (force per unit area) on a bodily structure than training with maximal loads. This issue is discussed later in greater depth (Ch 8.7).

The increasing expenditure of energy for the different lifts may be seen more clearly if the information from Table 3.12 is expressed graphically (Fig 3.30).

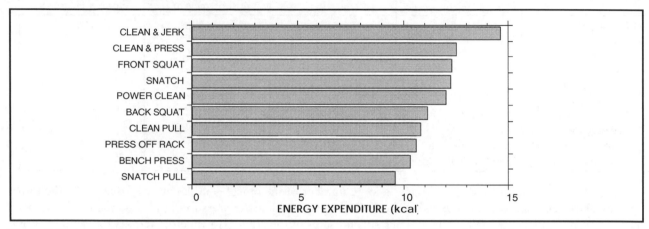

Figure 3.30 Average energy expenditure for 1RM in different lifts by a cross section of lifters of different levels of qualification.

The expenditure of energy in heavy resistance training sessions is characterised by short bursts of intense activity interspersed with longer rest periods. Unless the training is for muscle endurance, continuous loading over prolonged periods is inappropriate and interval training generally is necessary. This is borne out by the fact that, during a strength session lasting 1.5-2.5 hours, actual physical work occupies 5-12 minutes. It is also interesting to note that the specific energy expenditure for an exercise using a series of single repetitions is 35% greater than a continuous set of several repetitions with the same load.

In other words, *interval training with a series of single concentrated efforts places greater demands on the body than continuous training,* as done in traditional bodybuilding or circuit training. Very often, the continuous style of exercising allows one to rely more strongly on momentum and stored elastic energy in the tendons. It also tends to minimise the amount of eccentric, starting-strength and isometric training. This explains why it is far more difficult to execute a set of bench presses or squats if the load is replaced briefly on the racks between each repetition, instead of performing the same number of repetitions continuously.

3.4.7 Emotion and Other Psychological Factors

Muscular activity, including the display of strength, is not isolated from psychological processes but closely related to the individual's motivational level and objective. This objective is the basic reaction of the athlete to the situation in which he executes sporting tasks. Characteristically, it prepares one for undertaking a certain activity and constitutes a major factor in determining the outcome of all sports performance.

Physiological fitness for action is associated with the sensory receptors, which facilitate an adequate perception of stimuli, and via the activation of the motor units, determine muscle action. The motor objective in sport, which prepares the athlete's body for the forthcoming action, is influenced by the situation and the instructions of the coach, and clearly determines the motor task (Ozolin, 1949; Shoikhet, 1966; Eremin, 1968). The formation of such 'tuners' creates the prerequisite for successful performance.

Thus, a preliminary verbal command concerning the heaviness of the load can change the tonus of the working muscles. For example, the words 'heavy load' increase the tension in the working muscles of the arm, whereas the words 'light load' decrease the tonus of the same muscles (Farfel, 1961). Research has also shown that, under certain conditions, hypnosis can increase muscular strength. It can increase strength by 22.5% and lower it by 31.7% (Ikai & Steinhaus, 1961). The correct instructions can have a significant effect on strength if they orient the athlete to execute the movement by emphasizing certain characteristics or improve coordination. This can ensure the optimal combination of force, speed and amplitude of a speed-strength movement to produce the maximum effect for a given functional state.

However, active guidance of the action helps to produce the effective combination more rapidly. Athletes with little experience execute the take-off after a depth jump more slowly or more quickly than usual (Table 3.13), which leads to an increase or a decrease in the height attained, respectively (Verkhoshansky, 1963).

Qualified instruction can ensure the maximal utilisation of force by a more effective distribution of muscular effort. For instance, rowers were informed of the magnitude of the force developed by the sum of the action of all the muscles during the beginning, middle and end phases of the rowing stroke. Then they were told to repeat the effort in these positions by exploiting the force advantages of the relevant muscle groups. All of the subjects increased their strength scores in the rowing phases (Table 3.14), thereby revealing the value of using feedback about this sort of information (Egorov, 1966).

These examples indicate the effectiveness of instructions if they are based on the correct dynamic structure of the movement. These examples also point to the necessity for taking into consideration the qualification of the athlete. Here, it must be noted that the effectiveness of instruction decreases with the increase in qualification, since a Master of Sport to a large degree learns to mobilise his potential to a greater extent.

Instructions should always be given with a precise motor aim in mind and be divided into two types: *heuristic* (what must be done) and *concrete* (how it must be done). In other words, *heuristic* instruction is the precise description of the movement's structure. The athlete is given the task of individually developing his specific technique so as to execute it most effectively. Specific instructions concentrate on the appropriate method of executing the specific details of the action from the coach's point of view. The combined use of these types of instruction by the experienced coach invariably increases the effectiveness of the strength exercises.

Table 3.13 Influence of different motor aims on height of jump (h) and take-off time (t) (Siff & Verkhoshansky, 1999).

	Motor Aim								
Measures	Usual Take-off			Slow Take-off			Fast Take-off		
h (cm) t (sec)	68 0.240	69 0.260	69 0.245	73 0.310	70 0.345	73 0.310	57 0.160	67 0.220	68 0.230

Table 3.14 Mean stroking force (in kgf) by different classes of rowers after instructions to redistribute effort. (Siff & Verkhoshansky, 1999).

	Classification			
Stroke Phase	Class III	Class II	Class I	Master of Sport
Beginning	6.3	10.2	8.8	3.8
Middle	19.4	10.7	12.5	17.5
End	19.3	13.8	21.3	15.0

The force produced is significantly influenced by emotional state. Strong positive emotions can immediately increase the energy of muscular contraction by as much as four times (Vinogradov, 1966). In athletics, observations have shown that group activities produce greater results than individual activities (Gurnee, 1937; Abel, 1938; Weyner & Zeaman, 1956; Beasley, 1958; Cratty, 1965). The presence of spectators also increases the effectiveness of the motor activity (Gates, 1924; Lazaruc et al, 1952; Cratty & Hutten, 1964), with novices demonstrating a significantly higher level of improvement than advanced athletes (Singer, 1965). Thus, carefully directed training creates a specific emotional background which makes strength work more productive.

3.4.8 The Effect of Cold Application

Work ability may be increased by a variety of sensory stimuli, with a significant acute effect being exerted by the application of cold to certain parts of the body. The beneficial effects of warming-up have been discussed earlier, but it is a little known fact that appropriate use of cold may also have a similar influence, although not as a form of pre-exercise preparation.

For instance, in 1957 Michael concluded that cold showers increase work capacity, an effect which is greater among trained athletes than the general public (Vorobyev, 1978). In support of his own experiences with Russian weightlifters, Vorobyev quotes the findings of Happ (1947), Rosen (1952) and O'Rolev (1956) which reveal that cold compresses laid on the abdomen of athletes during intervals between exercises improved their performance. He found similar improvement in performance of weightlifters who were sponged down with cold water in the intervals between lifts in competition. He suggests that the muscle contraction induced by shivering, increased activity of the adrenal glands and a survival-directed central nervous reaction to peripheral excitation contribute to producing this effect.

With reference to the above research, it is apparent that the application of cold was brief in each case; prolonged exposure to cold which may lower muscle temperature or core temperature obviously is contraindicated as an ergogenic aid. The somewhat more prolonged application (5-15 minutes) of cold in the form of ice can be very effective in treating muscle and other soft tissue trauma.

3.4.9 Breathing and Strength Production

Normal breathing is an involuntary act to which little attention is paid by the average person. However, the pattern, duration and rate of breathing are all factors which can have a profound effect on the production of strength in a given situation. For instance, the Valsalva manoeuvre associated with breath-holding plays a vital role in increasing the intra-abdominal pressure to support and stabilise the lumbar spine during heavy lifting. The importance of strong abdominal and oblique muscles in acting as an anatomical corset then becomes obvious. It has been corroborated on many occasions that spinal stress is diminished during any movement against high resistance loading and that exhalation during lifting increases the risk of lumbar injury. Thus, it is unwise to follow the popular medical advice that one should exhale during effort. While this may be appropriate for patients with cardiac disease or hypertension, such action by an athlete during strenuous lifting, squatting or overhead pressing can seriously compromise spinal stability and safety.

Moreover, common sporting actions such as jumping, throwing, pushing against an opponent, striking a ball, standing from a squat or kicking usually elicit involuntary breath-holding, since this serves to enhance performance and accuracy of control in short duration movements. In archery and pistol shooting, stability and accuracy are intimately connected with brief phases of breath-holding. Other research has shown that speed-strength actions are optimally enhanced if the volume of air in the lungs is maintained at about 75% of their maximum capacity (Vorobyev, 1978).

Against this background of information, a study was done to investigate more precisely the relationship between the different phases of weightlifting movements and breathing (Blokhin & Monastirskii, 1985). Using a group of 34 highly qualified weightlifters, bar movement during the clean-and-jerk was recorded biomechanically and breathing patterns were monitored with an electronic spirometer. Each athlete was required to perform several repetitions with lifts of 60-90% of his 1RM and the volume of air inhaled and exhaled was recorded during all the phases of movement. The aggregate of the results was plotted and three major variants of lifting were identified (Fig 3.31). Besides confirming that all lifters held their breath during the pull from the ground and during the jerk, it was found that when breathing occurred during the other stages of the lift the volume of exhalation always exceeded that of inhalation by at least 125 ml.

During breathing with the bar resting on the chest before the jerk, the volume of inhalation was 1620±280 ml and that of exhalation was 1454±301 ml, while the duration of exhalation and inhalation was 1.07±0.09 and 0.86±0.07 seconds, respectively. For variants B and C, the exhalation-inhalation values during the overhead fixation phase were 1263±192 ml and 1138±239 ml, with durations of 0.81±0.07 and 0.74±0.08 seconds, respectively.

The volume of breath held at the end of the fixation phase was 391 ml less than that held at the beginning of the initial pull from the ground. It was concluded that variant B is the optimal one for producing maximal effort, variant A is necessary if corrections of technique have to made during lifting and variant C is characteristic of submaximal lifts which do not tax the athlete to his limits. Similar results were observed in the case of the snatch, and it may be concluded that the same variants occur during many other training lifts.

Consequently, it may be recommended that breath-holding should precede and accompany maximal efforts, which should be followed by brief exhalation-inhalation, unless technical adjustments have to made, in which case breath-holding must persist. Exercise with submaximal loading may be executed with longer phases of normal exhalation-inhalation and shorter phases of breath-holding. Neither rapid, short hyperventilation breathing, nor forced maximal inhalation is desirable for production of maximal effort during any phase of lifting.

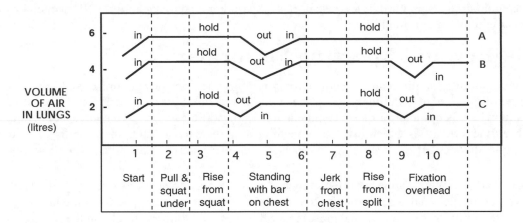

Figure 3.31 Typical relationship between the phases of movement and breathing during the clean-and-jerk. A, B and C are the different major variations of lifting. The vertical axis shows the volume of inspired air in the lungs.

3.4.10 Strength Development and Proprioception

Strength, efficiency and safety of all movement is determined primarily by neuromuscular factors, in particular the sense of kinaesthesis and the underlying proprioceptive mechanisms which inform us about where all the components of our musculoskeletal system are and what they are doing relative to one another in space and time. The integration of information from all the other senses (sight, sound, hearing and touch, in particular), together with this proprioceptive information enables us to execute a given movement in the most appropriate way in terms of pattern, velocity, acceleration and timing. This involves coordination of eye-hand, eye-foot or body-apparatus, processes which receive a great deal of attention in technical training. Inadequate time, however, is generally devoted to specific training of proprioception, even though its importance is central to the physiotherapy rehabilitation system known as PNF (proprioceptive neuromuscular facilitation), which is discussed later in more depth (7.2).

One way of improving proprioceptive efficiency is to diminish or block input from other sensory systems such as the eyes. Thus, training with weights or even executing the Olympic or powerlifting movements blindfolded can be a valuable way of enhancing technical skills and producing strength or power more effectively. Research has shown that blindfolding does not disrupt motor activities; on the contrary, it has been found that exercises are performed with greater precision and stability when the eyes are closed or in darkness (Roman, 1986). The athlete remembers joint angles, the degree of muscular tension, the amplitude of movement and movement patterns best with the eyes closed and reproduces them more easily. Subsequently, when the movements are done with the eyes open, the athlete's enhanced motor sensitivity is preserved and his technical skill improves.

During normal training, the athlete remains largely unaware of his errors and generally feels that the exercise is being done correctly. When the exercises are performed blindfolded, proprioceptive sensitivity is increased and this makes it possible for the athlete to make more accurate internal 'visualisations' of technique, thereby enabling him to correct errors more easily.

In practice, the eyes are covered lightly with a soft, dark material, the eye-covers supplied by many airlines for overnight flights being particularly suitable. The athlete assumes the starting position several times to become familiar with location and balance, with the coach making any necessary tactile and verbal corrections. He then executes the full movement with light weights, with eyes uncovered, then covered, until the action begins to feel natural and stable. The coach offers constant guidance and correction, which diminishes as expertise grows. The athlete progresses to heavier weights, still alternating between movements with eyes uncovered and covered, until the action is mastered with the eyes closed. Finally, when his technique with blindfolding has been perfected, he moves on to heavy weights.

Since the body is in contact with the bar or apparatus throughout all movements in resistance training, it is possible to use this technique for all strength exercises with free weights or machines. With some ingenuity to ensure the safety and confidence of the athlete, many movements (e.g. jumping, track-and-field events, swimming and throwing) may be practised blindfolded to improve proprioception. This technique may also be used successfully for rehabilitation from injury; for instance, a physiotherapist may apply PNF techniques and patterns of movement with the client blindfolded

3.5 Flexibility and Sporting Performance

The functional production of strength in any athletic activity relies on neuromuscular control and joint stability over a specific range of movement. In other words, the strength and flexibility components of overall fitness must interact in a way which is optimal for each movement and each sporting action. To understand the training of strength and other fitness qualities which involve range of movement, such as strength-flexibility, flexibility-speed and flexibility-endurance, it is necessary to analyse the mechanisms which underlie flexibility and stretching.

The concept of flexibility would appear to be clearly and intuitively understood by everyone involved with physical activity, yet, on deeper analysis, it emerges that this is far from being true. Toe-touching has long been regarded as a test of flexibility or suppleness and most physical tests of flexibility still rely on the seated stretch-and-reach-for-the-toes manoeuvre, even though it is well known that flexibility is joint specific. Similarly, the ability to perform the 'splits' has always been extolled as one of the supreme indicators of flexibility. Nevertheless, it is common for toe-touches and splitters to be quite unable to sit on their haunches in a low squat position with heels flat on the ground.

The message here is that the nature of flexibility generally is inadequately appreciated. Flexibility, whatever people mean by that term, differs from joint to joint, displays different properties under dynamic versus static conditions, and concerns not only muscles but all components of the musculoskeletal system, as well as the various types of stretch reflex in the neuromuscular control circuits of the body.

3.5.1 A Definition of Flexibility

Flexibility actually refers to the range of movement (ROM) of a specific joint with respect to a particular degree of freedom. In this respect, each joint exhibits statically or dynamically some or many of the following degrees of freedom:

- flexion-extension
- rotation (internal and external)
- adduction-abduction
- traction-approximation
- protraction-retraction

- inversion-eversion
- varus-valgus
- pronation-supination
- anterior-posterior gliding, rocking (tilting)
- medial-lateral gliding, rocking (tilting)

Some actions, such as flexion, extension, rotation and adduction-abduction are under the active control of the muscles, while movement involving the other degrees of freedom may occur passively as a consequence of forces or torques imposed by external loads or changes in motion associated with active muscular processes. For instance, a sudden stop during running can cause the femoral surface of the knee joint to glide anteriorly relative to its tibial surface. Likewise, impact on the outside of the knee or a rapid swerve may produce lateral-medial gliding and rocking of the same bones of the leg relative to one another.

Flexibility, or range-of-movement, is determined by:

- the structural or architectural limitations of the relevant joint
- the mechanical properties of the muscles and other soft tissues of the joint
- neuromuscular processes that control muscle tension and length
- the level of non-functional muscle tension in the same or other muscles and soft tissues
- the pain threshold of the individual in approaching end of range

In particular, the location of skeletal prominences, the length of ligaments, tendons and muscles, and the sites of attachment and insertion of muscles are all features which affect the ROM of a joint. In this respect two types of flexibility are identifiable: active flexibility and passive flexibility. The former refers to the maximum ROM that can be produced under active muscular control for a particular degree of freedom of any joint, whereas the latter refers to the maximum ROM that can be produced passively by imposition of an external force without causing joint injury.

It should also be remembered that range of movement for any given action (e.g. extension) may be influenced by the presence of any simultaneous movement in another direction (e.g. external rotation). We cannot automatically assume that movement in any given direction is entirely independent of preceding or concurrent movement in other directions, so that laboratory measurements of range of movement may not be as unequivocal as is intimated by research. The muscular system is characterised by the integrated action and interaction of many muscles associated with each joint, so that *limited flexibility in a certain direction may not simply be due to the musculature directly opposing movement in that direction alone*, but also to limitations imposed by other synergistic muscles and other stabilising soft tissues.

The preceding list enables us to consider several methods for increasing range of joint movement, some of which are impractical or impossible. Only the first-named limitation cannot be overcome by training. If restricted movement is due to the skeletal structure of the joint, then it is impossible to remove them by an form of exercise. This leaves three other types of limitation that can be reduced or overcome by appropriate choice of strategy. The success enjoyed by physiotherapeutic PNF (proprioceptive neuromuscular facilitation) 'stretching' manoeuvres emphasizes that the greatest and most rapid gains in ROM may be made by modifying the degree of nervous control of muscle tension and length.

Research and experience reveal the existence of the following practical means of enhancing ROM, given in order of effectiveness:

1. Modifying the neuromuscular processes that control tension and length of tissues in the muscle complex. This increases the ROM most rapidly and most effectively, but the changes tends to be confined to short-term improvements unless the neuromuscular means are used as an ongoing part of all training.

2. Increasing the length and strength of the different soft tissues comprising the muscle complex, especially the collagenous tissues such as the fascia. These changes, although slower to produce, are long-term.

3. Lengthening and strengthening other soft tissues, especially those of the joint capsule and the ligaments. These changes are also long-lasting, but if promoted to the point of joint laxity, joint stability can be severely compromised.

4. Restructuring the articulating surfaces of the joints, a process mediated by many years of regular heavy loading in specific patterns. This should not be regarded as a practical means of increasing ROM, but a natural consequence of loaded movement under full-range functional sporting conditions. More frequently, inappropriate or excessive loading can produce degenerative changes in the articular surfaces that reduce ROM due to structural limitation or to protective pain patterns.

The first three named means will be considered here as the most practical for increasing ROM during sports training and, therefore, the mechanisms underlying their usage will be discussed in some detail in the next few sections.

At this point it is relevant to point out that *stretching and flexibility training are not necessarily synonymous. Some flexibility exercises are not stretching exercises although they increase range of movement*, because they may focus entirely on modifying neuromuscular processes, in particular the stretch and tendon reflexes (see Fig 3.33) that control the functional range of movement. On the other hand, many stretching exercises do not pay any deliberate attention to neuromuscular processes and tend to concentrate on eliciting structural changes in the soft tissues. Thus, static stretches may actually change the length of the muscle complex, but have an inadequate effect on the dynamic range of movement required in a given physical activity. Therefore, it is vitally important to distinguish between the different types stretching and flexibility exercises in order to integrate the most appropriate and effective balance of static and dynamic means of increasing functional ROM into an overall training programme.

For sports participants *active flexibility* is by far the more important, even though passive flexibility provides a protective reserve if a joint is unexpectedly stressed beyond its normal operational limits. The value of active flexibility is emphasized by the fact that sporting prowess (rated in terms of achievement standards in competition) correlates more strongly with active rather than passive flexibility (a correlation coefficient of 0.81 vs 0.69) (Iashvili, 1982). This same Russian study of over 200 adult competitors also concluded that traditional static and passive stretching exercises develop mainly passive flexibility, whereas combined strength and stretching exercises are considerably more effective in developing active flexibility, particularly if strength conditioning is applied in the zone of active muscular inadequacy. This finding will be appreciated more fully when the biomechanics of the soft tissues is analysed later.

The current emphasis on flexibility neglects the equally important mechanical qualities of the tissues comprising the joints, in particular their stiffness and damping ratio. In other words, it is vital that these tissues offer each joint an effective balance between mobility and stability under a wide range of operating conditions. For instance, a joint whose tissues have low stiffness (or high ability to be stretched easily), but a low damping ratio (or poor ability to absorb tensile shocks) will be especially susceptible to overload injuries (Siff, 1986).

Therefore, in analysing flexibility one has to consider the separate and the interrelated effects of the ROM of the joints and the mechanical properties of the tissues comprising them.

3.5.2 The Effects of Stretching

A review of the literature based on research and empirical evidence reveals the following benefits of stretching (Keith, 1977; Weiss, 1976; Holland, 1968; de Vries, 1966, 1966):

- increase in the range of useful movement
- reduction in the incidence of injury
- decrease in the severity of injury
- delay in the onset of muscular fatigue
- prevention and alleviation of muscle soreness after exercise
- increase in the level of skill and muscular efficiency
- prolongation of sporting life

At the same time it needs to be remembered that inappropriate stretching can be detrimental to joint integrity and overall health. For example, tendons and ligaments can be permanently deformed or damaged by over-zealous or prolonged stretching, thereby impairing joint stability. In addition, unskilled application of ballistic stretching can cause muscle soreness and stiffness, while overstretching of components of the cervical or lumbar spine can damage nerves, intervertebral discs and blood vessels, sometimes with serious consequences. This applies especially to passive spinal manipulation manoeuvres in the hands of amateurs, as well as to forceful attempts to assume certain yoga asanas (postures) which involve spinal hyperflexion, hyperextension and rotation.

3.5.3 The Neuromuscular Component of Flexibility

Joint flexibility is determined not only by the above-mentioned factors of musculoskeletal structure and the mechanical properties of their soft tissues, but also by the degree of motor unit activity in the relevant muscles. The result of this activity is muscle contraction with concomitant increase in muscle tension, which thereby tends to counteract any stretching.

Muscle tension involves special reflex processes whose nature has to be clearly understood before stretching can be safely and effectively applied to the muscles and other soft tissues. The muscles and tendons are particularly well endowed with large numbers of two receptors: *muscle spindles* (Fig 3.32), which detect changes in muscle fibre length and rate of change of length, and *Golgi tendon organs*, which monitor the tension in muscle tendon during muscle contraction or stretching. Involuntary reflexes are initiated by the action and interaction of the muscle spindle and the Golgi tendon organ during any movement of the muscles. The function of the muscle spindle is to respond to muscle lengthening by producing 'stretch reflex' contraction of the muscle, whereas the Golgi tendon organ responds with the 'inverse stretch reflex' (4), which tends to relax a contracting muscle if tension becomes excessive (Fig 3.32).

The muscle spindle comprises some 3-10 *intrafusal fibres* which are pointed at their ends and attached to the sheaths of the surrounding *extrafusal fibres* (Fig 3.32). The sensory receptor nerve fibres invest the central region of the spindle which has few or no contractile elements and consist of two different types: *primary receptors* of large type Ia fibres, and *secondary receptors* of smaller type II fibres (Guyton, 1984).

There are also two types of intrafusal fibres: *nuclear bag fibres* and *nuclear chain fibres* (Fig 3.32). The primary receptors innervate both of these fibres, whereas innervation of the secondary receptors is confined almost entirely to the nuclear chain fibres. The primary and secondary receptors produce static and dynamic responses to changes in spindle length. If the spindle is stretched slowly, the number of impulses arising from both receptor types increases almost in direct proportion to the degree of stretch and continues to persist for several minutes. This is known as the static response. The dynamic response is exhibited very powerfully by the primary receptors when they are subjected to a rapid rate of change in length of the spindle. As soon as the increase in length ceases, the impulse rate returns to its original level, except for a small static response still remaining in the signal. The same process occurs when the muscle spindle shortens.

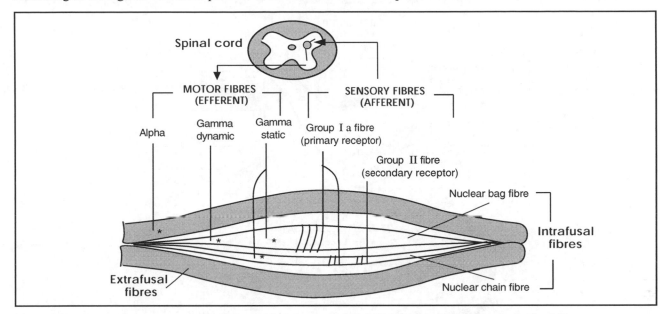

Figure 3.32 Motor and sensory nerve connections with skeletal muscle spindle, showing intrafusal and extrafusal fibres.

Because the primary and secondary receptors both innervate the nuclear chain fibres, it would appear that the latter are responsible for the static response of both the primary and secondary receptors. On the other hand, since the primary receptors alone invest the nuclear bag fibres, these fibres presumably are responsible for the strong dynamic response.

Some authorities consider it appropriate to divide the gamma efferent nerve fibres into two types: *gamma-dynamic* and *gamma-static*, the former exciting mainly the nuclear bag fibres and the latter mainly the nuclear chain fibres. Stimulation of the gamma-dynamic fibres produces a very powerful dynamic response of the muscle spindle, accompanied by minimal static response. Conversely, stimulation of the gamma-static fibres elicits a persistent static response without significant concurrent influence on the dynamic response (Guyton, 1984).

A clear understanding of the static and dynamic mechanisms of afferent and efferent nerve fibres is essential to the efficient and safe utilisation of PNF methods and plyometrics, as discussed elsewhere in this text. For instance, many so-called 'plyometric drills' are too slow to elicit the powerful, dynamic response which is essential for speed-strength development.

This, briefly, describes the structures and mechanisms associated with the various stretch reflexes (Fig 3.33) which act automatically to control muscle length and tension.

The stretch reflex, or myotatic reflex, actually comprises a complex process of interrelated stretch reflexes (Fig 3.33), including the dynamic (phasic) stretch reflex (2), the static (tonic) stretch reflex (3) and the negative stretch reflex (6). The dynamic reflex causes strong reflex contraction of the muscle in response to sudden changes in its length, but this reaction lasts only for a fraction of a second, so the static reflex takes over for as long as tension is being developed in the muscle. This reflex is much weaker, but it can operate for periods up to several hours long. Now, when a muscle is suddenly shortened, an exactly opposite effect takes place. In such a case of rapid tension release, both dynamic and static inhibitory reflex activity, or 'the negative stretch reflex' is elicited so as to oppose muscle shortening in much the same way that the myotatic reflex acts to oppose muscle lengthening.

In brief, it may be seen that the stretch reflex processes tend to maintain the optimum operating range of length in the muscles. However, it should not be forgotten that the stretch reflex system also plays the exceptionally important role of damping or smoothing out excessive oscillation and jerkiness of body movements (Guyton, 1984). As a matter of interest it should also be noted that electromyographic silence may persist in muscles which are being passively stretched, irrespective of whether this is done slowly or rapidly (Basmajian, 1978). It is obvious, therefore, that subjects can relax muscles consciously when normal stretch reflexes would be expected to increase their tension. The implication here is that voluntary mental control or biofeedback techniques can play a useful role in stretching and flexibility procedures.

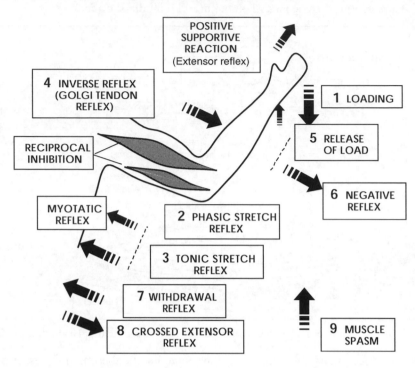

Figure 3.33 A summary of the major neuromuscular reflexes.

As was stated earlier, the Golgi tendon organ produces a reflex which tends to relax a muscle in which the tension is becoming excessive. Whereas the muscle spindle is sensitive to changes in length, the Golgi organ detects changes in muscle tension. Like the primary receptor of the muscle spindle, the Golgi organ responds to phasic (dynamic) and tonic (static) changes during muscle stretching and contracting. When muscle tension increases suddenly, it reacts very intensely (the dynamic response), but very rapidly settles down to a lower level of steady state firing that is approximately directly proportional to the muscle tension (the static response). Formerly it was considered that the Golgi tendon organ plays a solely protective role for the muscle, but it now appears as if it also continuously monitors and regulates muscle tension (Matthews, 1973).

Like most other reflexes, the flexor or *withdrawal reflex* is a protective reflex which tends to remove a limb from an endangering situation (7 in Fig 3.33). Most commonly it is elicited by painful stimuli, such as heat or sharp objects, although stimulation of the touch receptors sometimes can produce a weaker and more prolonged flexor reflex. In other cases, exposure to intense stimulation may necessitate removal of the endangered limb or surface by non-flexor action. Therefore, the flexor and other related types of protective reflex are all known as *withdrawal reflexes*. The pattern of withdrawal depends on the sensory nerves which are stimulated, so that exposure to a painful stimulus may produce complex actions such as concurrent flexion, abduction and external rotation which will result in the most effective removal of the exposed region from danger.

The opposite limbs of the body influence one another automatically during many actions. For example, a flexor reflex in one limb produces an extensor reflex in the contralateral limb approximately 0.2-0.5 second later. This is known as the *crossed extensor reflex* (8 in Fig 3.33). This reflex has an important bearing on activities such as dumbbell training in which the limbs are not used in bilateral symmetrical patterns (e.g. as in squatting or bench pressing). The excitation of one group of muscles is often associated with inhibition of other groups. This is the phenomenon of *reciprocal inhibition*, in which a stretch reflex excites one muscle while it inhibits action in another muscle.

It is relevant to note that the repeated production of involuntary reflex activity, like voluntary effort, results in fatigue. Thus, the level of muscle tension elicited by reflex action, diminishes with repeated stimulation, a fact which is highly relevant to the use of plyometric training (see 5.2.4). Another effect which is closely associated with fatigue is known as *rebound*. This refers to the fact that, after one reflex contraction, stimulation of a second and successive reflexes of the same type becomes progressively more difficult for a certain time afterwards.

Although this inhibits the repetition of near maximal or maximal acyclic exercises, it actually facilitates repetition in cyclic activities. Because of reciprocal inhibition, it becomes easier to activate the antagonist muscles during the period when rebound inhibition of the agonist occurs.

For example, it is more difficult for a few seconds to produce a second flexor reflex in one limb after it has already experienced flexion, but a crossed extensor reflex in the same limb will be strongly enhanced. It is believed that rebound is one of the main mechanisms which facilitate the production of cyclic activities such as locomotion, swimming and cycling (Guyton, 1984).

Finally, it is a little known fact that any form of stretching which exerts pressure on the soles of the feet or palms of the hands will produce strong reflex extension of the limb concerned. This phenomenon is known as the *positive supportive reaction* and it serves to stiffen and stabilise a limb against any externally applied pressure, including the weight of the body or trunk (Guyton, 1984). Toe-touching stretches in the standing and seated positions, therefore, would be seen to be neuromuscularly different procedures. The locus of application of pressure to the surface of the sole of the foot, palm of the hand or other body surface determines the position to which the limb will extend, a process which plays a major role in the use of hand pressure by the physiotherapist to guide the patient to produce a specific pattern in PNF.

Another frequently experienced reflex is local *muscle spasm* (9 in Fig 3.33). Although the underlying mechanism has not been satisfactorily analysed, in many cases the spasm appears to act as a physiological splint to prevent one from using a muscle group which is in danger of being damaged by further strenuous contraction. Sometimes, the spasm will be relieved by utilisation of reciprocal inhibition via voluntary contraction of the agonistic muscle on the opposite side of the limb while the joint is held fixed.

3.5.4 Components of Joint Flexibility

The different soft tissues associated with any joint each contribute to joint flexibility or stiffness to a differing extent. If stretch reflex mechanisms are minimally involved and the muscles are relaxed (which rarely is the case during dynamic functional movement), the relative contributions of the soft tissues to joint stiffness are as follows (Johns & Wright, 1962):

- muscles and their fascial sheaths   41%
- structures of the joint capsule, including ligaments   35%
- skin   11%
- tendons and their sheaths   10%

Since nothing can be done to alter joint structure in order to increase flexibility, it is obvious that appropriate stretching manoeuvres have to be imposed on the soft tissues to achieve this aim. In doing so, it is important to recognize that stretching may result in short-term (elastic), long-term (plastic) or combined short/long term changes in tissue characteristics.

If the average stretching programme is examined it becomes apparent that this distinction is insufficiently emphasized. If one analyses the usual type of pre-event or pre-training warm-up session, it is obvious that it is intended primarily to enhance short-term flexibility for the physical activity which is just about to commence. These brief preparatory sessions are often inadequate to alter long-term flexibility, which requires a specific type of regular conditioning to be built into the overall training programme. The design of such a programme necessitates a fairly thorough understanding of the physiology and biomechanics of the soft tissues involved.

3.5.5 Parameters of Flexibility

Before discussing the theoretical foundations and practical applications of flexibility training, it is relevant to outline those factors which influence flexibility in general:

1. Exercise and Training History

Regular exercise which involves the full range of joint motion generally enhances flexibility. It should be noted, however, that athletes tend to develop patterns of flexibility which are characteristic of their particular sport. Moreover, long-term flexibility may be diminished by sedentary lifestyle, by concentration on activities which rarely involve the joints in full-range movements, by training to develop excessive muscle hypertrophy by the occurrence of soft tissue injuries. Short-term flexibility may be decreased by overtraining-induced muscle soreness, stiffness or injury. In addition, tissue mechanical stiffness remains fairly constant during exercise, although damping ratio invariably increases (Siff, 1986).

2. Age

Flexibility generally tends to decrease with age and hence susceptibility to soft tissue injury increases during intensive exercise. Regular exercise combined with flexibility training, however, can minimise the effect of these physiological changes. At the other age extreme, maximum flexibility is not at a peak in the youngest infants, but seems to be reached between the ages of 10 and 12 years, depending on gender (Beaulieu, 1986).

3. Gender

Females tend to be more flexible than males of the same age with respect to equivalent joints. Moreover, the damping ratio for the soft tissues of the joints in females is greater than that in males, implying that they are intrinsically better equipped to absorb elastic stretch (Siff 1986). Another contributory safety factor lies in the fact that the threshold of pain in response to joint torsion is generally significantly lower in females (Siff, 1986).

4. Temperature

An increase in muscle temperature produced, for instance, by active warming up, passive massage or ultrasound increases flexibility, including improved plastic deformation of collagenous tissues during stretching. An appropriate rhythmic, gentle warm-up is therefore recommended prior to any flexibility training. It should also be noted that the prolonged application of both heat and cold may produce analgesia or modification of the neuromuscular processes associated with the stretch and tendon reflexes, thereby enhancing muscle relaxation and stretching. In addition, cooling of the tissues with ice for the final few minutes of stretching seems to stabilise connective tissues at their new length (Sapega et al, 1981).

5. Type of Joint

Flexibility is specific to each joint, with every person displaying a different relative degree of flexibility from joint to joint. An index of overall flexibility may be determined by averaging the flexibility of a representative number of joints in the body, but what is more relevant is establishing the static and dynamic ranges of movement for the most important joints used by a participant in a particular sport.

6. Type of Movement

The relative degree of flexibility is different for each of the degrees of joint freedom discussed near the beginning of this article, such as flexion, extension, rotation and distraction. It is important to avoid increasing flexibility in any way or direction which may adversely affect the stability of a joint during execution of any specific physical manoeuvre. In this respect it is most important to remember that optimum, and not maximum, static and dynamic flexibility is required for each degree of freedom of every joint. In fact, subjects who are hypermobile in certain joints should avoid increasing flexibility at the expense of stability.

3.5.6 Soft Tissue Biomechanics and Flexibility

Earlier the relative contributions to joint stiffness by the different soft tissues was discussed. To understand and apply the principles of judicious stretching to these various tissues, it is necessary to examine their biomechanical characteristics.

In doing so, it is useful to recall the model of the muscle complex discussed in Chapter 1. It divided the soft tissues into a contractile system, comprising the actin-myosin muscle fibre complex, and a viscoelastic non-contractile system, comprising mainly the connective tissue of tendons, ligaments and capsules. The viscoelastic component of muscle was further analysed in terms of a series elastic component (SEC) and a parallel elastic component (PEC).

An in-depth biomechanical analysis of the different types and methods of stretching is beyond the scope of this text, but is covered elsewhere (Siff, 1987). Most relevant to this text are the following points:

- Different methods are necessary for conditioning muscles, tendons, and other soft tissues
- Slow twitch muscle groups contain a greater proportion of connective tissue than fast twitch muscle groups

- The high stiffness and low strain of slow muscle is most appropriate for muscle function intended for continuous support of posture
- Different brain and spinal cord mechanisms control high speed, low speed, and topological patterns of muscle activity
- All fitness conditioning, including flexibility enhancement, relies predominantly on neuromuscular stimulation
- All conditioning is primarily functional, since functional stimulation precedes structural change (Wolff's Law) - thus, it is erroneous to refer to any exercises as purely 'structural'
- Rapid ballistic stretching of contracted muscle (plyometric loading) should not be avoided by serious athletes, since the ability to use elastic energy is vital to all high level performance
- Static stretching of a relaxed muscle has a more pronounced effect on the PEC than ballistic stretching of a contracted muscle, which has a greater effect on the SEC (essential for any fast activities)
- Static and cyclic stretching, as commonly performed by athletes (up to 90 seconds duration each), increases joint range of motion by increasing stretch tolerance while the viscoelastic characteristics of the muscle remain unaltered (Magnussen et al, 1998)
- Different rates of loading and stretching have different effects on bone, tendon and muscle
- Prolonged slow stretching can cause permanent viscous deformation of connective tissue and high levels of strain in muscle
- Physiotherapeutic PNF shows that rapid or powerful recruitment of the different stretch reflexes can be safely applied to rehabilitate and strengthen - contrary to common belief
- There is generally no such thing as an unsafe stretch or exercise: only an unsafe way of executing any movement for a specific individual at a specific time
- Elastic fibres occur in small concentrations in the intercellular matrix of tendons and most ligaments, and may help restore the crimped collagen fibre configuration after stretching or muscle contraction
- Multi-directional stretching is important, since the structural orientation of the fibres is different for the different collagenous tissues and is specifically suited to the functions of each tissue
- The stress concentration at the insertion of the ligament and tendon into the more rigid bone structure is decreased by the existence of three progressively stiffer transitional composite materials - a system which can be disrupted by ingestion of anabolic steroids
- At slow loading rates, the bony insertion of a ligament or tendon is the weakest component of the bone-soft tissue complex, whereas the soft tissues are the weakest components at very fast loading rates
- Tendons, unlike ligaments, are not simply passive stabilisers of joints - instead, together with strongly contracted muscle fibres (particularly during phases of eccentric contraction), they play a vital role in storing elastic energy during running and other impulsive motor acts, thereby saving energy and increasing the efficiency of muscular activity (Goldspink, 1978).
- No stretching manoeuvres must compromise the strength or ability of the tendons to store elastic energy throughout their range of movement - thus, tendon stretching exercises should be accompanied by strength conditioning against adequate resistance.
- Since tendons and ligaments are viscoelastic, they exhibit sensitivity to loading rate, and undergo stress relaxation, creep and hysteresis.
- Russian and Eastern European scientists discourage the use of cycling by athletes who require large ranges of trunk and hip flexibility, since they have discovered that cycling tends to decrease the functional ROM for these types of athlete. Instead, they encourage intensive sprinting and interval training which tend to use and strengthen the hip and knee joints over a much fuller range of movement. The massive preoccupation of Western gym users with fixed bicycles or treadmill jogging to promote cardiovascular conditioning may then be seen to be potentially detrimental to serious athletes whose joints need to operate over a far more expansive range. These same scientists also discourage conventional pushups and situps because they tend to limit the functional ROM of the shoulder and trunk regions, respectively. Push-ups on floor dipping bars or on parallel bars are preferred, as are backward lying situps over pommel horses or 'Roman chairs'.

- Flexibility and motor skill are also affected by emotion and discomfort or perception of pain, because there are emotion-related and pain-interpreting centres in the cerebrum and the cerebellum that are closely related to the execution of patterned movement. The role of relaxation procedures and breathing regimes that promote relaxation, as taught in yoga, Tai Chi and childbirth, can be valuable in enhancing flexibility training.

Flexibility, Stability and Muscle Activity

Despite the widespread opinion that the muscles act as efficient synergistic stabilisers, it should be remembered that the musculature cannot respond quickly enough to protect a joint against injury if large impacts are applied rapidly, particularly if they are torsional (Pope et al, 1978). It is probably more accurate to state that joint stabilisation takes place in the following manner:

1. The contractile element of muscle activated by the stretch reflex complex, together with the SEC of that muscle, act as primary stabilisers of the joint if the loading rate permits the muscles to respond rapidly enough.

2. If the joint reaches the physical limits of muscle length, strength or endurance, it has to rely on protection by ligaments and the SEC of its muscles. If, at the same time, the inverse stretch reflex signals the muscles to relax at their maximum length, then the PEC of the muscle will also contribute to joint stabilisation. However, it should be noted that receptors resembling Golgi tendon organs have been located on the surface of cruciate ligaments (Schultz et al, 1984) and that muscles will show reflex contraction if ligaments are stretched until pain results (Basmajian, 1978).

3. If the joint is extended to its limits without sufficient muscle contraction becoming possible, primary stabilisation is afforded by the ligaments and the PEC of the muscles. As soon as the initial latency period for muscle excitation is over, the contracting muscles and their SEC will contribute as secondary stabilisers.

4. In certain joints skeletal structure can act as the final stabiliser during movements to the limits of the joint.

Since joint stability involves three-dimensional actions over the many degrees of freedom outlined near the beginning of this section, the necessity for appropriately conditioning all the interacting soft tissues again becomes obvious. These facts are directly relevant to appreciating the difference between static, active, passive and ballistic modes of stretching, with slow and rapid loading rates having different effects on the each of the soft tissues.

3.5.7 The Influence of Exercise on Connective Tissue

Most texts focus more on the effect of different training programmes on muscle than on the collagenous tissues, despite the fact that many animal studies have shown that physical training also strengthens the attachments of tendons and ligaments to bone. Trained ligaments are thicker and heavier, though the increase in mass is not necessarily associated with greater concentration of collagen, a process which is still poorly understood (Booth & Gould, 1975) . In this regard, controlled strain on the soft tissues may increase the formulation of fibres in them, thereby contributing to enhanced elasticity and strength (Holland, 1968).

Regular resistance training produce not only muscle hypertrophy, but also an increase in the collagen content of the ligaments and the connective tissues that surround the muscle fibres (Tipton et al, 1975). At the same time, the activity of an enzyme involved with collagen synthesis is increased by training, an effect which may be stimulated by lactic acid production during exercise (Booth & Gould, 1975). It should be noted, however, that moderate intensity treadmill training of rats produces neither muscle hypertrophy nor increased growth of intra-muscular connective tissue. Prolonged, low intensity training evidently suffices to condition the cardiovascular system significantly, but not the musculoskeletal system. Apparently it is anaerobic, muscle endurance training which has the most pronounced effect on enhancing the concentration and strength of collagenous tissue and its junction zones. Progressive stretching regimes in conjunction with this type of training would then be seen to be especially valuable as a component of all sports preparation.

In contrast to chronic training, single exercise sessions, occasional stretching or sprint training do not produce significant increase in junction strength, although sprinting produces marked increases in ligament mass and concentration (Tipton et al, 1974). Then, just as ligaments become stronger and stiffer when subjected to increased stress, so they become weaker and less stiff with decreased stress, immobilisation and inactivity (Tipton et al, 1970). The similar changes noted with ageing may be due not only to the degenerative process but also to inactivity.

In the light of the above analysis the choice of stretching regime must also take into account the subject's state of training, age and health. Furthermore, alteration in hormonal balance during pregnancy, menstruation and administration of exogenous hormones (such as anabolic steroids and cortisone) can affect the mechanical characteristics of collagenous tissue, so that stretching techniques should be adjusted accordingly (Viidik, 1973).

3.5.8 Stretching Techniques

Practical experience has led to recognition for four fairly traditional categories of stretching, namely: static, ballistic, passive and contract-relax (or PNF - proprioceptive neuromuscular facilitation) stretching. To this list may be added normal, full range of movement exercise, since it also tends to increase both active and passive flexibility. In addition, Olympic Weightlifters are amongst the most supple of all athletes, despite beliefs to the contrary (Siff, 1987). Furthermore, a combination of stretching and weight-training exercises as a supplement to a sprint-training programme produces significantly greater increases in speed over an unsupplemented sprint programme (Siff, 1987). Then, in several of the preceding sections, the role of resistance and muscle endurance training in enhancing tissue strength and flexibility was noted. In other words, suitable full-range resistance training also can improve joint flexibility.

With reference to PNF, it is misleading to regard it or even its contract relax technique as a specialised system used primarily to enhance flexibility. There are at least four distinct types of PNF stretching, anyway. In professional practice, PNF offers a comprehensive form of therapy which conditions neuromuscular processes, isometric and dynamic strength, muscular endurance and functional flexibility more completely than many machine routines (see Ch 7).

In achieving these ends, its various three-dimensional spiral and diagonal patterns and techniques of movement rely on numerous static, active, ballistic and passive manoeuvres. Thus, several of the supposedly distinct types of stretching may be seen to form a subset of the entire discipline of PNF (see Ch 7).

Static stretching normally refers to flexibility exercises which use the weight of the body or its limbs to load the soft tissues. Rarely is this term applied to stretches which are forcibly produced by voluntary muscular contractions, yet this 'cat-stretch' technique is employed successfully in the cat kingdom, by most humans on waking in the morning and by bodybuilders in their posing routines. Obviously the concept of static stretching needs to be expanded.

These facts imply that a more comprehensive categorisation of stretching techniques is necessary. The following integrated model identifies two broad types of stretching, each containing a series of distinct, but related, categories of stretching (Fig 3.34):

1. Static Stretching

- *Free Static Stretching*, which imposes no external loading to increase ROM under conditions of (a) muscle relaxation or (b) isometric muscle contraction (sometimes called Active Static Stretching)

- *Passive Static Stretching*, which imposes external loading on (a) relaxed or (b) isometrically contracted muscles

2. Dynamic Stretching

- *Ballistic Stretching*, which imposes passive momentum to exceed static ROM on (a) the relaxed or (b) the contracted muscle complex. The ballistic action may be done slowly or rapidly, as described later in this section.

- *Active Stretching*, which involves continuous muscle activity to exceed the static ROM, as encountered during normal full-range sporting activities

- *PNF Stretching methods*, which involve intermittent or continuous phases of static or dynamic muscle action, as well as relaxation or passive movement in specific patterns of activation and relaxation

- *Plyometric (Impulsive) Stretching*, which involves rapid termination of eccentric loading followed by a brief isometric phase and an explosive rebound relying on stored elastic energy and powerful reflex muscle contraction. This 'stretch-shortening' action is not intended to increase ROM, but to use specific stretching phenomena to increase speed-strength of movement for a specific sporting purpose (see 5.2.4). It may also be viewed as a form of ballistic stretching done impulsively or explosively.

The specificity of exercise indicates that each one of these categories of stretching may be used effectively and safely for specific subjects at a particular stage of training to achieve optimal stability and mobility. Active and PNF stretching involving progressive muscle contraction in specific patterns of movement against external loading over the full range of movement and beyond the static ROM seem to offer the most effective means of improving full-range functional performance in sport and exercise.

It now becomes possible to use the scheme of Figure 3.34 to describe any of the known modalities of stretching by combining the chosen rate of stretching with the appropriate type of load and state of muscle.

Note that the model depicted in this figure may also be extended to include plyometrics (or plyometric stretching) either as a subset of ballistic stretching or as a specific type of dynamic stretching, namely stretch-shortening or explosive stretching, as described above (see 5.2.4). Its aim is not to increase the range of joint movement, but to enhance the speed and intensity of muscle contraction. This action is usually imposed on a muscle by using a rapid eccentric contraction to recruit the stretch reflex in a specific muscle group so as to produce an explosive concentric rebound contraction. Similar types of conditioning involving activation of the stretch reflex are sometimes used within the spectrum of PNF techniques. This intensive type of neuromuscular training needs to be applied sparingly among advanced, well-prepared athletes by highly experienced coaches if it is not to produce overload injuries.

It should be noted that *stretch-shortening* is not synonymous or commutative with *shortening-stretch*. Stretch-shortening and shortening-stretch cycles are not commutative with respect to the isometric forces following the length changes - i.e., stretch activation before muscle shortening does not produce the same results as muscle shortening before stretch activation. It is well known that prior stretching of the muscle decreases the isometric and maximal force that a muscle can produce. This force depression following muscle shortening is virtually unaffected by previous stretching of the muscle, but force enhancement following stretch-shortening depends in a dose-dependent manner on the amount of muscle shortening which precedes the stretch (Herzog & Leonard, 2000). The history dependence of isometric force following stretch-shortening cycles appears to be independent of the stretch preceding the shortening, except if stretching occurs at very high velocity (i.e. 6-10 times fibre length per second), such as those produced during ballistic movement.

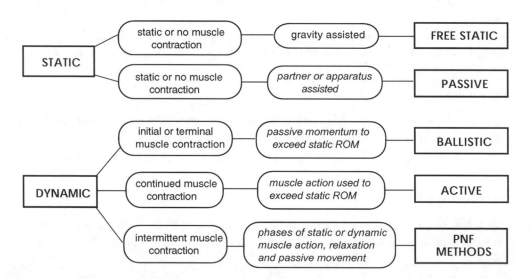

Figure 3.34 Classification of the different means of static and dynamic stretching. Note that plyometric stretching also may be included either as separate form of dynamic stretching or as a subcategory of ballistic stretching.

All the combinations of stretching techniques described by this scheme can be effective for improving different proportions of passive and active flexibility, provided that they are applied with an understanding of personal needs and the properties of the joints and soft tissues involved. Gradually applied static stretches are simple to learn, easy to execute and most suitable for the average person who wishes to improve mainly static flexibility. These are usually done by gradually increasing the duration of each stretch (from a few seconds to 30 or more seconds) before briefly relaxing and increasing the range of stretching slightly for a number of repetitions and sets.

For the competitive athlete or rehabilitating patient, static stretching is insufficient to develop the full range of movement strength, power, mobility and stability required in sport. It must be combined with high intensity static and dynamic activities to condition the collagenous tissues, full-range resistance training to increase muscle strength, and low-intensity cardiovascular and muscle endurance activity to enhance capillarisation and circulatory efficiency.

After all, it is active flexibility of the appropriate degrees of joint freedom which correlates most strongly with sporting proficiency and resistance to injury (Iashvili, 1982). This same study of several Olympic sports revealed some further interesting results:

- The level of joint mobility generally relates strongly to sporting proficiency. The higher the level of sporting proficiency, the greater is passive and active flexibility.

- Static and passive stretching enhance passive flexibility, but only moderately improve active joint mobility, which is by far the most important flexibility quality needed in sport.

- Active flexibility correlates more strongly (R = 0.81) with sporting proficiency than passive flexibility (R = 0.69).

- The pattern and range of joint mobility is sport specific. For example in swimmers, the greatest shoulder and ankle mobility occurs in backstroke and butterfly specialists, whereas breast-stroke swimmers have the lowest flexibility in these joints. Breast-strokers, however, have the greatest range of hip and knee mobility. In track-and-field athletics, throwers, especially javelinists, display the greatest level of shoulder mobility, while the greatest hip flexibility is found among hurdlers.

- The relative relationship between active and passive flexibility depends on the training methods used. If primarily static and passive stretching methods are used, the coefficient of correlation between active and passive flexibility is 0.61-0.73, depending on the joint. The combined use of stretching and strengthening exercises increases this value to 0.91.

- A large difference between active and passive flexibility (a measure which we may call the *flexibility deficit FD)* correlates strongly with the incidence of soft tissue injury.

- The flexibility deficit decreases significantly by means of the concurrent use of stretching and resistance training, particularly if strength exercises are performed in the zone of active flexibility deficiency.

Since active flexibility is a function of soft tissue mechanical stiffness and length (see 1.6.4), as well as the strength of the muscles to move a joint to the limit of its range, any stretching routine should identify which of these factors demands most emphasis in improving active flexibility. Static stretching methods are used where the emphasis needs to be on tissue qualities, whereas dynamic methods are essential for rectifying deficits in full range strength performance. However, it is not only active flexibility, but active functional range of movement in the specific sporting action, that is of central importance to sporting proficiency.

Some scientists have criticised the traditional methods of flexibility measurement, since the examiner usually guides or forces subjects to reach their limits of passive or active movement. A more objective way is to attach a load via a pulley system to the relevant limb and allow the load to pull it in a relaxed state to the limit of range (Tumanyan & Dzhanyan, 1980). Several ranges of flexibility may then be defined:

- maximum passive flexibility (PF_{max}), measured when one reaches the pain threshold of movement

- active flexibility (AF), reached by the non-ballistic action of muscles on the limb

- loaded passive flexibility (PF), measured with a progressively increased load which does not take one to the pain threshold.

This now enables one to calculate three indices of flexibility:

- Maximum active flexibility deficit FD_{max} = $PF_{max} - AF$
- Loaded active flexibility deficit   FD   = $PF - AF$
- Interval of flexibility pain threshold   FPT   = $PF_{max} - PF$

Using these measures, it was found that (Tumanyan & Dzhanyan, 1980) :

- Static and passive stretches increase passive flexibility. Increases in passive and active flexibility are the same and the difference between them remains unchanged.

- Full range strength exercises increase passive flexibility and decrease the difference between active and passive flexibility.

- Concurrent strength and flexibility exercises increase passive and active flexibility and decrease the difference between them.

Thus, dynamic stretching executed while one deliberately concentrates on progressively contracting and relaxing the muscle complex being stretched can prove invaluable in enhancing active flexibility. Although most fitness instructors believe stretching a relaxed muscle to be safer and more effective, the proven PNF techniques using phases of contraction and relaxation can be both safe and very effective (see Ch 7). Application of the PNF principles of spiral and diagonal patterns of movement can also produce superior three-dimensional functional ROM (range of movement) to standard static stretches. In this respect, it is interesting to note that many conventional stretches are executed in only one plane at a time and very few *rotational stretches* about the longitudinal axes of the limbs are ever used. Thus, many of these stretches could be enhanced if they included elements of rotation and twisting, especially if they followed some of the patterns encountered in actual sport.

The use of *quasi-isometric activity* can be especially useful in developing active flexibility (see 1.9). This requires one to exercise a limb through a full range of movement against a resistance which is allowed to stretch a joint gently beyond its limit of static flexibility without producing any sudden movement which may recruit the myotatic reflex. Free weights, pulley and other functional training machines can be particularly versatile in allowing one to execute natural patterns of movement against resistance (see 4.2.7). In addition, longer periods of progressive isometric or quasi-isometric activity in full range movement produce greater gains in active flexibility.

Eccentric quasi-isometrics can be especially useful for enhancing functional range of movement, if one allows the load to force the joint to move slowly and eccentrically beyond its limit of static flexibility. Used as a method of improving flexibility, it does not have to be performed against very heavy loads; one should commence with small loads and use the progressive overload principle to gradually work up to near-maximal loads. In training with light or heavy loads, one should use multiple repetitions, gradually increasing the range of movement with each repetition. Both modes of quasi-isometrics may be used in conjunction with PNF techniques and patterns to improve fitness qualities such as static strength, static flexibility, dynamic flexibility, flexibility-strength and flexibility-endurance (see Ch 7).

Starting-strength is also extremely important to human muscular performance, so the use of injudicious stretching or part-range resistance training which can impair this quality should be discouraged. Conversely, resistance training of gradually increasing intensity in any zones of active muscular inadequacy, particularly in the region of full extension, is to be encouraged. Unfortunately, most isokinetic machines display a small lag in their early phases and therefore are inadequate for developing starting-strength or functional flexibility in this critical joint zone. If the inertia of weights, machines or pulley systems renders them unsuitable for early rehabilitation, progressively sequenced isometric contractions at a variety of joint angles or work against elastic bands (with the fixed end moved to appropriate starting positions) can prove to be especially useful.

"Functional" stretching conditioning also has to enhance the qualities of *flexibility-speed, flexibility-strength* (static and dynamic) and *flexibility-endurance* (static and dynamic) which are required for high level performance in sport. *Flexibility-speed* refers to the ability to produce efficient full ROM at speed; *flexibility-strength* to the ability to produce efficient, powerful static and dynamic movements over a full ROM; and *flexibility-endurance* to the ability to repetitively produce efficient full ROM under static and dynamic conditions. The importance of using a wide variety of carefully sequenced stretching methods of cyclically periodised intensity, duration and complexity then becomes obvious.

The Use of Ballistic Stretching

All too often, it is stated that ballistic stretching generally is harmful and should be avoided at all costs. This well-meaning, but very misleading, statement makes no distinction between the rates at which ballistic stretching is imposed or the different techniques that may be used in applying it. In fact, most forms of ballistic stretching could quite safely be included within the scope of PNF. If gentle bouncing forms of ballistic stretching are used over a gradually increasing range of movement, they will be seen to be a special type of contract-relax or hold-relax PNF activity and therefore may be applied safely and effectively. One may also alternate static stretches with periodic gentle ballistic stretches to enhance the effectiveness of any stretch and one may even carry out ballistic stretches against the resistance offered by stretched elastic bands to provide yet another variant. One may even apply *a principle of progressive gradual stretching increase* to increase safely and effectively the speed and range of ballistic stretching right up to the level of plyometric activity. This approach offers some benefits over static and conventional dynamic stretching because ballistic actions are a frequent component of most sports and other forms of stretching usually do not address this specificity of joint action.

Interestingly, Russian research has shown that ballistic stretching, can be most effectively and safely used if it is performed in 3-5 sets of 8-12 repetitions, with the amplitude of movement gradually increasing with each repetition (Matveyev, 1981). No further repetitions should be performed if the range of movement becomes impaired by fatigue, an approach which may be applied with equal validity to all other forms of stretching.

3.5.9 Low Flexibility versus Non-functional Muscle Tension

Limitations in functional ROM should not automatically be attributed to joint stiffness alone, because this can lead to an unnecessary emphasis on stretching. Limitations to full ROM can also be caused by various forms of *spurious tension* or excessive muscle tension such as *coordination tension*, which may accompany the appropriate muscle tension required by the given movement. This non-functional tension can occur in both phasic and tonic muscles before, during and after the movement.

The level of proficiency of the athlete has a marked influence on the reflex ability of the muscles to contract and relax (Fig 3.35). Rapidity of both contraction and relaxation increases with level of mastery, with a decrease in relaxation time becoming especially evident. The importance of teaching athletes to relax the muscles rapidly and efficiently to enhance the functional range of sporting movement then becomes obvious. It is of little consequence to have highly flexible joints with well conditioned, supple connective tissues and a large range of movement, if action is limited by any spurious muscle tension. Flexibility training, therefore, should always be combined with neuromuscular training to produce efficient, functional ROM.

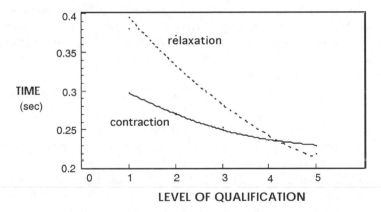

LEVEL OF QUALIFICATION

Figure 3.35 Muscle contraction and relaxation times of athletes of increasing levels of qualification, as measured by electromyography (based on data of Matveyev, 1981). Contraction time is the time from a given signal to the onset of electrical activity in the muscle, while relaxation time is the time taken from the signal to disappearance of electrical activity. Level 1 refers to the novice; Level 2 is a Class 3 athlete; Level 3 is a Class 2 athlete; Level 4 is a Class1 athlete; Level 5 is a Master of Sport.

Some of the ways of improving the ability to relax the muscles are:

• Contract-relax, hold-relax and other PNF methods which use the different stretch reflexes to promote muscle relaxation (see 7.2).

• Sudden unloading, the sudden removal of external resistance imposed under strong isometric or dynamic conditions (e.g. the end of the jerk, completion of a heavy squat or bench press, throwing of a shot or medicine ball, short bursts of strong electromuscular contraction). It has been shown that this means produces the greatest relaxation response of all the means currently used. They become even more effective if the powerful and rapid contraction-relaxation process is related as closely as possible to the given sporting actions.

• The change of muscle groups from a state of tension to relaxation in a controlled, gradual manner or in a series of stages (e.g. Jacobsen's progressive relaxation method).

- Control of spurious tension in the muscles of the face and hands, which tends to reflect general tension fairly well.

- The use of controlled visualisation of the muscles progressing from contraction to relaxation and back.

- The use of autogenic training, progressive relaxation, meditation or massage.

- The use of breathing patterns on the basis that tension is associated with breath inhalation and holding, with breath holding (the Valsalva manoeuvre) being used where maximal force and spinal stabilisation must be produced. Conversely, relaxation is associated with gentle, controlled exhalation. Appropriate techniques of breathing should always be combined with all phases of movement to enhance mobility, stability and relaxation.

- The execution of exercises against a background of exhaustion of selected muscle groups (the so-called pre-exhaustion principle commonly used in bodybuilding for increasing stress on chosen muscle groups), provided that movement technique does not suffer.

- The use of distracting or focusing activities which cause the athlete to concentrate on stimuli other than those associated with the given sporting action (e.g. music, talking to a training partner while running, thinking of something pleasant). These methods may involve internalisation or externalisation of focus, the suitability of any method being determined on an individual basis.

- The gentle use of rhythmic cyclical, swinging, shaking or circling movements of the body and limbs to relax muscles which have just been strongly contracted (e.g. some of the movements of dance, swimming or Tai Chi).

3.6 The Stretching Matrix System

Numerous texts have been written giving prolific illustrations of specific stretches, but it is rare to find one that provides a generalised system for describing all types of stretches and enabling one to create an unlimited repertoire of novel stretches. Such a system may readily be derived from muscle action charts if one remembers that *the reverse of any action to contract a given muscle group becomes a stretch for that same muscle group.* The following series of tables have been constructed on this basis to enable the user to stretch any particular major muscle group which appears at the left of each matrix.

For example, if we refer to Figure 3.36 we can devise stretches for many of the muscles involved with motion of the trunk and neck.

If you wish to stretch *multifidus*, you must flex the trunk forwards and laterally, as well as rotate the trunk, then repeat the same actions to the other side of the trunk. The same actions will stretch the erector spinae and quadratus lumborum (which is stretched without any trunk rotation). *Rectus abdominis* is stretched by backward extension of the trunk, while *psoas* is stretched by extension of the trunk combined with lateral extension. Even though the hip flexors are sometimes referred to as the iliopsoas muscles, iliacus does not attach to the spine or ribs, so it cannot move the trunk and therefore, cannot be stretched by trunk extension.

It should be pointed out that the same muscle is involved in the actions of several joints and is described by more than one of the matrices in this section. For instance, psoas (as part of iliopsoas) also appears in Figure 3.39 as a flexor of the hip and consequently may be stretched by extending the hip joint and rotating it medially. In other words, iliacus can be stretched only by hip extension and medial rotation, whereas psoas is stretched by means of these same actions combined with trunk extension and lateral extension.

To examine an actual stretching manoeuvre, we may refer to the front lunge as done by a fencer. If you lean forward with the trunk inclined forward and almost parallel to the ground, iliacus could be maximally stretched, while psoas would not be fully stretched unless you extended your trunk as far back as possible, while simultaneously extending it laterally to the side of your leading leg. This example of stretching the iliopsoas group of muscles illustrates how these matrices enable you to selectively stretch muscles whose functions may be similar or overlap to a certain extent.

Consider now the *oblique muscles* and *quadratus lumborum*, both of which are involved with lateral flexion of the trunk. The obliques, unlike quadratus lumborum, do not extend the trunk and, therefore, are not stretched by flexion of the trunk. Quadratus lumborum, on the other hand, does not rotate the trunk as do the obliques, so that it is not stretched by trunk rotation. Only lateral extension of the trunk will stretch both quadratus lumborum and the obliques, but will not do so maximally for either muscle unless the other specific actions for stretching those muscles are included simultaneously. Thus, concurrent trunk flexion and lateral extension will maximally stretch quadratus lumborum.

Figure 3.36 Actions for stretching the muscles of the trunk and back

	Actions of Trunk				Actions of Neck			
	Flexion	Extension	Lateral extension	Rotation	Flexion	Extension	Lateral extension	Rotation
Erector spinae	*		*		*		*	*
Semispinalis thoracis	*		*					
Semispinalis cervicis					*		*	*
Semispinalis capitis					*		*	*
Multifidus	*		*	*				
Quadratus lumborum	*		*					
Sternocleidomastoid						*	*	*
Splenius					*		*	*
Scalenus						*	*	
Rectus abdominis		*						
External obliques		*	*	*				
Internal obliques		*	*	*				
Psoas		*	*					

In all the figures given, matrices are given which provide the appropriate end position to be reached in movements for stretching the major muscle groups of the body. In applying them, one should always ascertain from one or more of these matrices *which joints are crossed by a given muscle* and only then decide on the optimal way of stretching all the muscles involved.

As stated before, muscles often cross more than one joint and use of a single matrix may result in a less than maximum stretch. For example, if one consults Figure 3.38 as a guide for stretching the various flexors of the elbow, then one neglects the fact that two of them (biceps brachii and triceps) also cross the shoulder joint. Thus, to stretch the biceps, it is necessary to extend both the shoulder and the elbow joints, while the forearm is simultaneously pronated.

In the case of the triceps, the elbow has to be flexed, while the shoulder joint must be extended both backwards (in the sagittal plane) and abducted (in the frontal plane). It is often helpful to consult the Movement Matrices to ascertain which muscles are responsible for producing a given joint action (see 3.7). In fact, if one employs movement patterns that are similar to those used in one's sport, one can achieve simultaneous strengthening and flexibility. For example in executing a squat or bench press, you can increase your strength-flexibility (see Ch1) by progressively starting from a somewhat deeper position and quasi-isometrically prestretching the relevant muscles before the upward concentric movement begins.

Figure 3.37 Actions for stretching the muscles acting on the upper arm (humerus)

Actions of the shoulder

	Flexion	Extension	Abduction	Adduction	Medial rotation	Lateral rotation
Pectoralis major		✳	✳			✳
Deltoid	✳[2]	✳[1]		✳	✳[2]	✳[1]
Latissimus dorsi	✳		✳			✳
Subscapularis						✳
Supraspinatus				✳	✳	
Infraspinatus			✳		✳	
Teres minor					✳	
Teres major	✳		✳		✳	
Coracobrachialis		✳	✳			
Biceps brachii		✳				✳
Triceps brachii	✳		✳			

1 = anterior fibres
2 = posterior fibres

Figure 3.38 Actions for stretching the muscles acting on the forearm

	Elbow flexion	Elbow extension	Pronation	Supination
Biceps brachii		✳	✳	
Triceps brachii	✳			
Anconeus	✳			
Brachialis		✳		
Brachioradialis		✳		
Pronator teres			✳	
Pronator quadratus			✳	
Supinator			✳	

Figure 3.39 Actions for stretching the muscles acting on the lower extremity

		Actions of the hip						Actions of the knee			
		Flexion	Extension	Abduction	Adduction	Medial rotation	Lateral rotation	Flexion	Extension	Medial rotation	Lateral rotation
Anterior muscles	Rectus femoris		*					*			
	Vastus muscles							*			
	Tensor fasciae latae		*		*		*				
	Iliopsoas		*			*					
	Sartorius		*		*	*			*		*
Medial muscles	Adductor magnus	*4	*3	*		*					
	Adductor longus		*	*		*					
	Adductor brevis		*	*		*					
	Pectineus		*	*		*					
	Gracilis			*					*		*5
Posterior muscles	Gluteus maximus	*		*7	*6	*					
	Gluteus medius	*2	*1		*	*2	*1				
	Gluteus minimus				*		*1				
	Lateral rotators					*					
	Biceps femoris	*				*			*	*	
	Semitendinosus	*							*		*
	Semimembranosus	*							*		*
	Gastrocnemius								*		
	Plantaris								*		
	Popliteus								*		*5

1 = anterior fibres
2 = posterior fibres
3 = adductor portion
4 = hamstring portion
5 = if knee flexed
6 = upper portion
7 = lower portion

Figure 3.40 Actions for stretching the muscles acting on the foot

		Action of the ankle			Action of the toes		
		Plantar-flexion	Dorsi-flexion	Inversion	Eversion	Flexion	Extension
ANTERIOR MUSCLES	Tibialis anterior	✳			✳		
	Extensor digitorum longus	✳		✳		✳	
	Peroneus tertius	✳		✳			
	Extensor hallucis longus	✳			✳	✳ (big toe)	
LATERAL	Peroneus longus						
	Peroneus brevis		✳	✳			
POSTERIOR MUSCLES	Gastrocnemius		✳				
	Soleus		✳				
	Plantaris		✳				
	Flexor digitorum longus		✳		✳		✳
	Flexor hallucis longus		✳		✳		✳ (big toe)
	Tibialis posterior		✳		✳		

The versatility of this stretching matrix system may be appreciated if one realises that many of the actions of the joints concerned may be performed in different basic postures such as standing, lying or sitting. You may use them to analyse the numerous stretches of dance and gymnastics, as well as yoga postures (asanas) and thereby acquire the skills for using the matrices easily and creatively.

These matrices are not intended to exhaustively cover stretches for all the muscle groups; they were presented to introduce the concept of the Stretching Matrix system and to offer basic examples of how to apply it by means of specific exercises. The inventive coach should be able to use the existing series of matrices to devise new stretching manoeuvres and to enhance the effectiveness of stretches which he may already be using.

Since dynamic stretching in functional movement patterns provides the most valuable form of sport specific stretching, the Stretching Matrix concept may be extended to produce a method of full range of movement from a position of full elongation of a muscle to full contraction of the same muscle group and vice versa

Is Stretching Always Necessary?

Possibly the most heretical remark to make about stretching is to suggest that the dedicated use of stretching sessions may not even be necessary, especially since many athletes dispense entirely with special stretching or even warm-up sessions before of after training without suffering injury in training or competition. The prescription of stretching and warm-up or cooling down sessions has become a well-accepted ritual, but that does not imply that this is essential.

While some forms of stretching may be necessary to deform connective tissues to increase range of movement or to re-educate neural facilitatory and inhibitory processes to permit greater "functional" use of a joint, pre-event stretching sessions do not always have to take the form of a discrete component of training. One can use the actual movements from a sport to serve as a highly adequate and effective way of preparing the body for subsequent work. In this case, the athlete simply begins each movement gently and non-ballistically under limited static and dynamic conditions and follows *a principle of gradual progressive stretching and activity increase* by progressively increasing range, speed, complexity, intensity and other aspects of movement until the actual sporting movements themselves are executed under light and ultimately near-competitive conditions.

In weight training situations, you simply begin every exercise with a few preparatory repetitions using a light load and progressively increase the load over a very few sets to reach one's serious training loads until the movement feels unrestricted and fluent. In doing so, you commence with a limited range and speed of movement and place less stress on the tissues and joints, for instance, by taking a narrower than normal grip in the bench press (or other forms of pressing) or a narrower foot spacing during the squat (if one normally uses a medium to wide grip or stance in these exercises).

Concluding Remark

It is unnecessary to devise a host of highly specific individual flexibility manoeuvres to enhance flexibility of the entire body, as this would be time-consuming and inefficient. Instead you may use functional movements that are commonly encountered in the your sport and apply the different stretching techniques discussed earlier. In most cases, a few appropriate dynamic stretches of gradually increasing range, tension and duration using multi-jointed actions encountered in your sport will replace a prolonged session with dozens of single-jointed stretches.

You should always remember that the fundamental purpose of stretching is to enhance performance and reduce the likelihood of injury. Therefore, all stretching routines should increase not only your passive or static range of movement, but also your functional flexibility-strength for all static and dynamic joint actions likely to be needed in your sport, including any necessary ballistic manoeuvres that seem to strike such fear into the hearts of the average fitness instructor.

3.7 The Movement Matrix System

The relationship between joint and muscle actions may be described conveniently by means of a series of *Movement Matrices* . There are two ways of using these matrices:

- reading off the muscles corresponding to a given joint action
- reading off the actions produced by a given muscle group

These matrices will be of special value if the reader needs to analyse or devise exercises according to the scheme of Chapter 8. Examples of these Movement Matrices are given in the next few pages, the only major omission being the matrix corresponding to actions of the wrist and fingers.

It is important to emphasize that it sometimes may be necessary to apply more than one Movement Matrix simultaneously, because some muscles cross more than one joint (even then, it is vital to take consider the complications associated with multiarticular action, as discussed in the closing section of this chapter). For example, if we wish to devise a dynamic stretching pattern for gastrocnemius, which crosses both the knee and the ankle joints, we should consult Figures 3.41 and 3.42 to ascertain which matrix is more appropriate for a given situation (e.g. a single joint exercise) or if both matrices should be used for a multi-joint exercise.

If we wish to devise a suitable exercise for maximally training the biceps brachii, which crosses the elbow and shoulder joints, then we have to consult Figures 3.43 and 3.44. The matrices concerned show that the biceps flex both the shoulder and the elbow, so that both of these joints should be extended if the biceps are to operate from a starting position of full pre-stretch to an end position of full flexion.

This type of situation is the same for any multi-joint actions. Thus, maximal involvement of the rectus femoris, which crosses both hip and knee (Fig 3.41), necessitates beginning from a position of pre-stretching this muscle with hip extension and knee flexion. Gastrocnemius, unlike soleus, is a two-joint muscle which flexes the knee and plantarflexes the ankle (Figs 3.41 and 3.42), so that it can be trained more effectively in any exercises that simultaneously involve both of these actions. This dual action occurs naturally during the *double-knee bend* (or scoop) phase of the weightlifting clean or during what Yessis has called *glute-ham-gastroc raises*, a modified form of prone hyperextensions over a pommel horse with the feet pressed firmly against a vertical plate (Yessis, 1992).

Figure 3.41 Actions of muscles acting on the Lower Extremity

		Hip						Knee			
		Flexion	Extension	Abduction	Adduction	Medial rotation	Lateral rotation	Flexion	Extension	Medial rotation	Lateral rotation
ANTERIOR MUSCLES	Rectus femoris	✲							✲		
	Vastus muscles								✲		
	Tensor fascia latae	✲		✲		✲					
	Iliopsoas	✲ p					✲				
	Sartorius	✲		✲			✲	✲ w		✲	
MEDIAL MUSCLES	Adductor magnus	✲ 3	✲ 4		✲		✲				
	Adductor longus	✲			✲		✲				
	Adductor brevis	✲			✲		✲				
	Pectineus	✲			✲		✲				
	Gracilis				✲			✲		✲ 5	
POSTERIOR MUSCLES	Gluteus maximus		✲ p	✲ 6	✲ 7		✲				
	Gluteus medius	✲ 1	✲ 2	✲		✲ 1	✲ 2				
	Gluteus minimus			✲		✲ 1					
	Lateral rotators						✲				
	Biceps femoris		✲					✲ p			✲
	Semitendinosus		✲					✲ p		✲	
	Semimembranosus		✲					✲ p		✲	
	Gastrocnemius							✲			
	Plantaris							✲			
	Popliteus							✲		✲ 5	

1 = anterior fibres	4 = hamstring portion	7 = lower portion
2 = posterior fibres	5 = if knee flexed	w = weak action
3 = adductor portion	6 = upper portion	p = prime mover

Figure 3.42 Action of the Muscles acting on the Foot

		Ankle				Toes	
		Plantarflexion	Dorsiflexion	Inversion	Eversion	Flexion	Extension
ANTERIOR MUSCLES	Tibialis anterior		✻ p	✻			
	Extensor digitorum longus		✻		✻		✻ p
	Peroneus tertius		✻		✻		
	Extensor hallucis longus		✻	✻			✻ (big toe)
LATERAL	Peroneus longus	✻ w			✻		
	Peroneus brevis	✻ w			✻		
POSTERIOR MUSCLES	Gastrocnemius	✻					
	Soleus	✻					
	Plantaris	✻ w					
	Flexor digitorum longus	✻		✻		✻ p	
	Flexor hallucis longus	✻		✻ p		✻ (big toe)	
	Tibialis posterior	✻		✻			

p = prime mover
w = weak action

These matrices should emphasize that it is preferable to think about joint actions rather than muscle actions when one is analysing which muscles are involved in producing a given movement or if one is trying to ascertain which muscles are trained on a specific machine. The popular practice of identifying only the prime movers, as happens in most popular weight-training or bodybuilding publications, offers a partial and misleading view of the situation, especially as the stabilisers may be contracting far more vigorously than the movers during some exercises. There is no situation in which stabilisers are not also contracting while the movers are carrying out their dynamic role. Thus, in analysing any movement, one should always identify:

- which joints are being moved
- which joints are being stabilised
- which joints are being stabilised and moved concurrently.

Then the relevant muscles involved in any moving and stabilising tasks may be determined by consulting the appropriate Movement Matrices. Even then, this still offers an incomplete view of the mechanics of human movement, because this approach tends to proliferate the popular, but erroneous view that:

- the same movement is always produced by the same muscles
- the same muscles always produce the same movement
- the same muscles are dominant throughout the full range of movement
- muscles only act as active tissues
- muscles only act as movers or stabilisers
- muscles are the only important tissues which control movement

Figure 3.43 Actions of Muscles acting on the Shoulder

		Shoulder						Shoulder girdle					
		Flexion	Extension	Abduction	Adduction	Medial rotation	Lateral rotation	Elevation	Depression	Protraction	Retraction	Upward rotation	Downward rotation
PECTORALS	Pectoralis major (clavicular)	✳p			✳	✳							
	Pectoralis major (sternal & abd)	✳p	✳		✳	✳							
	Pectoralis minor								✳	✳			✳
ROTATOR CUFF	Subscapularis					✳p							
	Supraspinatus			✳			✳						
	Infraspinatus				✳		✳p						
	Teres minor						✳p						
	Teres major		✳		✳	✳							
	Latissimus dorsi		✳p		✳p	✳							
	Biceps brachii	✳		✳1	✳2								
	Triceps brachii (long head)		✳		✳								
	Coracobrachialis	✳			✳								
DELTOIDS	Anterior deltoid	✳		✳		✳							
	Medial deltoid			✳									
	Posterior deltoid		✳	✳			✳						
TRAPEZIUS	Trapezius I							✳					
	Trapezius II							✳			✳	✳	
	Trapezius III										✳		
	Trapezius IV								✳		✳	✳	
	Rhomboids										✳		✳
	Levator scapulae							✳					
	Serratus anterior									✳		✳	
	Subclavius								✳				

p = prime mover   1 = long head of biceps   2 = short head of biceps

Figure 3.44 Actions of Muscles acting on the Arm (Humerus)

	Actions at the shoulder					
	Flexion	Extension	Abduction	Adduction	Medial rotation	Lateral rotation
Pectoralis major	* p			*	*	
Deltoid	* 1 p	* 2 p	*		* 1	* 2
Latissimus dorsi		* p		* p	*	
Subscapularis					* p	
Supraspinatus			*			*
Infraspinatus				*		* p
Teres minor						* p
Teres major		*		*	*	
Coracobrachialis	*			*		
Biceps brachii	*					
Triceps brachii		*		*		

p = prime mover
1 = anterior fibres
2 = posterior fibres

Figure 3.45 Actions of muscles acting on the Forearm

	Elbow flexion	Elbow extension	Pronation	Supination
Biceps brachii	* p			*
Triceps brachii		* p		
Anconeus		*		
Brachialis	* p			
Brachioradialis	*			
Pronator teres			*	
Pronator quadratus			*	
Supinator				*

196

Figure 3.46 Actions of Muscles of the Trunk and Back

	Trunk				Neck			
	Flexion	Extension	Lateral flexion	Rotation	Flexion	Extension	Lateral flexion	Rotation
Erector spinae		✳	✳			✳	✳	✳
Semispinalis thoracis		✳	✳					
Semispinalis cervicis						✳	✳	✳
Semispinalis capitis						✳	✳	✳
Multifidus		✳	✳	✳				
Quadratus lumborum		✳	✳					
Sternocleidomastoid					✳		✳	✳
Splenius						✳	✳	✳
Scalenus					✳		✳	
Rectus abdominis	✳							
External obliques	✳		✳	✳				
Internal obliques	✳		✳	✳				
Psoas	✳		✳					

To identify which muscles are active during any movement, one need not necessarily use an EMG (electromyograph), unless the objective is accurate research. Instead, firm palpation with the fingers over appropriate surface areas of the body will provide a good working knowledge of which muscles or other tissues are involved. These may be checked by referring to any anatomical chart. Though skilled palpation can identify regions of maximum and minimum muscle tension, the more accurate degree to which each muscle group is involved at any given stage of a movement has to be determined by means of an EMG or a myotensiometer, which we used to examine the relationship between joint torque and corresponding changes in muscle tension (Siff, 1986).

This type of testing confirms that it is misleading and inaccurate to refer to muscle isolation exercises, because the degree of isolation (or dominant involvement) of a single muscle group depends on how large the resistance is (Ch 4.2.9). In general, the greater the load, the greater the overflow and the greater the involvement of other muscle groups. A large degree of isolation can be produced by means of electrical stimulation, by concentrated exercise with little or no added load, or by means of loadless training (Ch 2.2.4), but this generally develops more muscle hypertrophy than functional strength, since this is the main aim of 'isolation' training.

Some final remarks are warranted. Lest one be tempted to consider that the muscles alone are responsible for all stabilisation and mobilisation, we must remember that ligaments, fascia and joint capsules play an important role in passively stabilising some joints to enable the body to actively use the muscles to execute other tasks. Although this stabilising role is well known in preventing joint damage when loading threatens to move a joint beyond its active structural limits, these soft tissues also play a vital role during non-emergency situations.

For example, spinal ligament involvement during deadlifting or cleans is invaluable for decreasing the stress on the erector spinae. Spinal flexion during heavy lifts from the ground can damage the intervertebral discs, so competent lifters strive to diminish the flattening of the lumbar spine by actively concentrating on increasing erector spinae tension. If this is overdone, the various spinal ligaments become slack and most of the load is borne by the muscles. Conversely, if the muscles are inadequately contracted, then excessive stress is placed on the ligaments. The skilled lifter is able to optimise the required balance between the spinal muscles and ligaments, thereby enhancing lifting efficiency and diminishing the likelihood of injury. Similar rhythms and patterns of muscular and other soft tissue involvement are essential for all strength training efficiency and safety.

Limitations of Anatomical Movement Analysis

Standard anatomical textbook approaches describing the action of certain muscle groups in controlling isolated joint actions, such as flexion, extension and rotation, frequently are used to identify which muscles should be trained to enhance performance in sport. Virtually every bodybuilding and sports training publication invokes this approach in describing how a given exercise or machine 'works' a given muscle group, as do most of the clinical texts on muscle testing and rehabilitation.

The appropriateness of this tradition, however, recently has been questioned on the basis of biomechanical analysis of multi-articular joint actions (Zajac & Gordon, 1989). This classical method of functional anatomy defines a given muscle, for instance, as a flexor or extensor, on the basis of the torque that it produces around a single joint, but the nature of the body as a linked system of many joints means that muscles which do not span other joints can still produce acceleration about those joints.

The anatomical approach implies that complex multi-articular movement is simply the linear superimposition of the actions of the individual joints which are involved in that movement. However, the mechanical systems of the body are nonlinear and superposition does not apply, since there is no simple relationship between velocity, angle and torque about a single joint in a complex sporting movement. Besides the fact that a single muscle group can simultaneously perform several different stabilising and moving actions about one joint, there is also a fundamental difference between the dynamics of single and multiple joint movements, namely that forces on one segment can be caused by motion of other segments. In the case of uniarticular muscles or even biarticular muscles (like the biceps or triceps), where only one of the joints is constrained to move, the standard approach is acceptable, but not if several joints are free to move concurrently.

Because joint acceleration and individual joint torque are linearly related, Zajac and Gordon (1989) consider it more accurate to rephrase a statement such as "muscle X flexes joint A" as "muscle X acts to accelerate joint A into flexion". Superficially, this may seem a matter of trivial semantics, but the fact that muscles certainly do act to accelerate all joints has profound implications for the analysis of movement. For instance, muscles which cross the ankle joint can extend and flex the knee joint much more than they do the ankle.

Biomechanical analysis reveals that multiarticular muscles may even accelerate a spanned joint in a direction opposite to that of the joint to which it is applying torque.

In the apparently simple action of standing, soleus, usually labelled as an extensor of the ankle, accelerates the knee (which it does not span) into extension (Fig 3.47) twice as much as it acts to accelerate the ankle (which it spans) into extension for positions near upright posture (Zajac & Gordon, 1989).

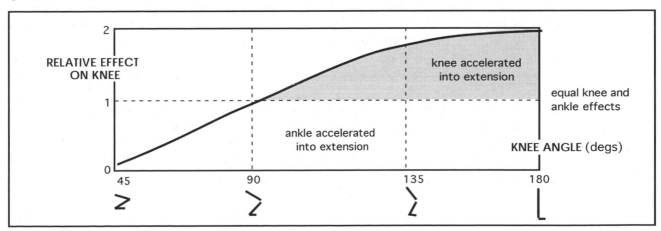

Figure 3.47 Effect of soleus on the angular acceleration of the knee relative to the ankle (based on Zajac & Gordon, 1989).

In work derived from *Lombard's Paradox* ('Antagonist muscles can act in the same contraction mode as their agonists'), Andrews (1985, 1987) found that the rectus femoris of the quadriceps and all the hamstrings act in three different ways during cycling, emphasizing that biarticular muscles are considered enigmatic. This paradox originally became apparent when it was noticed that in actions such as cycling and squatting, extension of the knee and the hip occurs simultaneously, so that the quadriceps and hamstrings are both operating concentrically at the same time. Theoretically, according to the concept of concurrent muscle antagonism, the hamstrings should contract eccentrically while the quadriceps are contracting concentrically, and vice versa, since they are regarded as opposing muscles.

Others have shown that a muscle which is capable of carrying out several different joint actions, does not necessarily do so in every movement (Andrews, 1982, 1985). For instance, gluteus maximus, which can extend and abduct the hip, will not necessarily accelerate the hip simultaneously into extension and abduction, but its extensor torque may even accelerate the hip into adduction (Mansour & Pereira, 1987).

Gastrocnemius, which is generally recognised as a flexor of the knee and an extensor of the ankle, actually can carry out the following complex tasks (see Fig 3.48):

   (a) flex the knee and extend the ankle
   (b) flex the knee and flex the ankle
   (c) extend the knee and extend the ankle

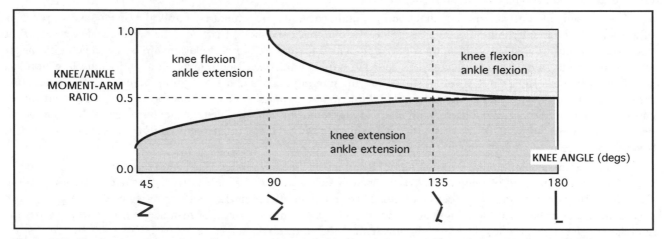

Figure 3.48 The three possible actions of gastrocnemius revealed by the relative moment-arm ratios of the knee and ankle joints (based on Zajac & Gordon, 1989).

During the standing press, which used to be part of Olympic Weightlifting, the back bending action of the trunk is due not only to a Newton III reaction to the overhead pressing action, but also due to acceleration caused by the thrusting backwards of the triceps muscle which crosses the shoulder joint, as well as the elbow joint. This same action of the triceps also occurs during several gymnastic moves on the parallel, horizontal and uneven bars. This back extending action of the triceps is counteracted by the expected trunk flexing action of rectus abdominis and the hip extension action of the hip flexors, accompanied by acceleration of the trunk by the hip flexors.

Appreciation of this frequently ignored type of action by many multiarticular muscles enables us to select and use resistance training exercises far more effectively to meet an athlete's specific sporting needs and to offer superior rehabilitation of the injured athlete.

Because of this multiplicity of actions associated with multiarticular complex movement, Zajac and Gordon stress a point made by Basmajian (1978), namely that it may be more useful to examine muscle action in terms of synergism rather than agonism and antagonism. This is especially important, since a generalised approach to understanding human movement on the basis of breaking down all movement into a series of single joint actions fails to take into account that muscle action is task dependent.

THE MEANS OF SPECIAL STRENGTH TRAINING

Opinion concerning the means and methods of strength training often repeats itself, with the beginning of the modern era identifying more clearly the motor mechanisms of sports technique. This has helped to determine the means of strength training more precisely. However, with the improvement in sporting achievements, the effect of these means became less marked. The volume of the same exercises was increased, but it was found that this approach also has its limitations (Verkhoshansky, 1977). Once again, researchers turned to analysis of sports movements, now equipped with better measuring technology.

This new cycle of research initiated further progress in training methodology. This was the case, for example, when information regarding the significance of strength in sport emerged from the laboratory and coaches looked optimistically to weight training. The next trend was towards specificity, since studies indicated that the strength necessary for the successful execution of one movement has little effect on another movement. Naturally, this specificity of strength turned attention to the principle of selectivity in the means of special preparation.

In general, the progress of strength preparation methods leads logically to examination of the motor mechanisms underlying sports movements. This results in new hypotheses being formulated to replace currently accepted ones, beginning with an understanding of actual sports movements and the specific level of the athlete's physical fitness. Thus, one can understand why it is necessary to devise new means that cannot easily be rejected in favour of fashionable techniques which have become established more on the basis of tradition and emotion than on scientific grounds (Verkhoshansky, 1977).

Thus, the selection of the strength and other training means based on the motor specifics of given sports exercises, is one of the most important tasks in sport. This has marked a turning point in training science, which has identified the progression of all training from a foundation of general physical preparation (GPP) to subsequent specific physical preparation (SPP), guided by an intimate understanding of the specific character of the sports activity. The practice of selecting the means of strength preparation, based upon the specifics of the athlete's movements, leads one to abandon reliance on intuition alone and find a more objective foundation.

This foundation is expressed in the form of the *principle of dynamic correspondence*, which determines how closely the means of special strength preparation corresponds to the functioning of the neuromuscular system in a given sport (Verkhoshansky, 1977).

4.1 The Problem of Training Means

The process of adaptation involves stimulation from the external or internal environment, which leaves certain traces in the body. With repetitive stimulation the traces accumulate, leading to significant modifications which raise the functional capability of the body. A characteristic of every living creature is the relative speed with which it adapts to repetitive stimulation. The same regime of stimulation can rapidly produce habituation and then fail to elicit any further adaptation, only maintaining the existing levels. Another regime can prove excessive and lead to overtraining, which prevents adaptation. An optimum level of stimulation offered in a progressively increasing sequence of carefully chosen means is essential for ensuring adaptation at successively higher levels of performance (see 1.14).

This, in general and simplified terms, is the physiological foundation of training. In reality it is a very intricate process, since systematic exercise as a means of physical conditioning involves a complex of different stimuli which affect all systems of the body. For example, to successfully increase strength, the load, number of repetitions, tempo of execution and workout venue all influence the effectiveness of the training. These variables could be listed at great length, since the development of strength is not the only goal of training. However, besides this, it is likely that the coach will select from the vast number of variations, that combination of means which he considers will produce the greatest success.

4.1.1 Characteristics of Strength Increase

Strength as a specific result of physical adaptation is determined by the intensity and repetitiveness of the stimuli to which the body is exposed during use of the motor apparatus. Only a sufficiently intense level of muscular contraction, which can be achieved in different ways (e.g. using isometric tension or heavy loads at low velocities), will provide an effective training stimulus. Research has shown that the *threshold training stimulus* necessary for increasing muscular strength in the average person should not be less than one-third of the maximal strength (Hettinger & Muller, 1953). As strength increases, the intensity of the stimulus required to produce a training effect should be increased, and reach 80-95% of the athlete's maximum. It may be appropriate that the strength of the training stimulus sometimes equals or even exceeds the level of the competition stimulus of the given exercise (Moroz, 1962; Ratov, 1962; Verkhoshansky, 1963).

Thus, the development of strength requires that the intensity of the stimulus be gradually increased. It was discovered that every stimulus has a specific *strengthening threshold*, the achievement of which fails to elicit any further increase in muscular strength (Muller, 1962). The less trained the muscles, the further the strengthening threshold from the initial state. The rate at which strength increases from the initial level to the *strengthening threshold*, expressed as a percentage of the current maximum strength, is independent of sex, age, muscle group and the level of the strengthening threshold (Muller, 1962). After the strengthening threshold has been reached, strength can be increased only by intensifying the training (e.g. by substituting stronger means, devising more effective combinations or increasing the volume of work).

These early attempts at establishing general principles need to be more precisely applied in terms of the means and methods of strength development, as well as the individual situation. For instance, according to Korobkov (1953), Gerasimov (1953) and Vasiliev (1954), strength increases relatively uniformly during the initial stages of training, independent of how the load is applied in training, whether large or small. Approximately equivalent increases in strength are obtained with loads of 20%, 40%, 60% and 80% of maximum. An increase in the intensity of training in the initial stages (e.g. using a heavier load, faster tempo of movement and shorter intervals between sessions) does not always enhance the effectiveness of strength development, this becoming effective only later, as strength fitness increases.

This principle may be illustrated by referring to the training results of weightlifters. Exercises with 45-60% of 1RM in the first 8 sessions are slightly more effective than exercises with 60-75% and 75-90% of 1RM loads. After 16 sessions, the most effective load was 75-90% of 1RM, whereas the least effective was 45-60% of 1RM (Zimkin, 1961). A noticeable strengthening effect occurs for novices using 30-46% of 1RM, whereas more experienced athletes need to use at least 60% of 1RM (Muller & Hettinger, 1957).

To interpret these factors, one must bear in mind the phasic nature of the response to intense strength loads, characterised by a temporary decrease in strength and speed of movement, and the subsequent increase in strength and speed after the intensity of the resistance has decreased. Therefore, *the effectiveness of heavy weights does not occur immediately, but some time later*. It has been shown that strength increases well after sessions of isometric tension have ceased (Clarke, 1954), while a marked increase in strength and speed of movement from the use of sufficient resistance occurs only after at least 20 training sessions (Chernyavsky, 1966).

An increase averaging 18-25% in speed-strength for a controlled movement was noted after a 10 day rest from intense specialised strength training (Nyeniskin, 1974). It may be assumed that this phenomenon is connected with the well-known *adaptive inertia* of the body and *supercompensatory restoration (adaptive reconstruction)* after strength work.

As strength and level of physical fitness increase, dependence of the increase in strength and its effect on the type of training becomes more apparent (with reference to the given means and methods). In those cases where training is conducted with small loads, there is a concurrent increase in endurance and speed of movement, along with the increase in strength, under loaded and unloaded conditions. If large loads are used in training, strength increases significantly, as does the speed of explosive movement. However, endurance under unloaded conditions begins to diminish and can even drop below initial levels.

The magnitude of strength increase and its specific character are also determined by the combination of the training means used. For instance, the increase in strength and speed of movement after 20 training sessions in which weights of 10% of 1RM and 40% of 1RM were used (in different volumes) were as follows: in the group whose training volume consisted of 20% with the 10% of 1RM load and 80% with the 40% of 1RM load, there was an increase in strength of 44.8% and an increase of 35.2% in the speed of movement from the initial levels. The corresponding figures for the second group doing the reverse combination (20% with 40% of 1RM and 80% with 10% of 1RM) were 31.6% and 18.3% respectively (Chernyavsky, 1966).

The increase in strength also depends upon the athlete's level of initial strength fitness. In principle, the lower the trainee's level of strength, the greater its increase with training. Virtually all training means prove to be beneficial in this case. However, with increase in proficiency, the rate of strength increase diminishes and can be elicited only through sufficiently demanding special means of training.

Developing effective methods of strength training involves maintaining the strength already gained. If the main goal in the preparatory period is strength development, then it is important that as much strength as possible survives into the competition period. In other words, some of the training intensity should be directed at preserving the level of strength attained, which is preferable to restoring strength after it has diminished markedly. Unfortunately, there are few studies in this area. After 1-2 months without systematic strength work, the strength of the extensor muscles decreases by 5-6% and the flexors by 15-20% in skiers. This is especially true of athletes who possess a high level of strength development (Chistyakov, 1965). Muscles can lose up to 30% of their strength after a period of total (bed) rest of only one week (Muller, 1966). The loss of strength caused by complete cessation of resistance training occurs at approximately the same rate as it is increased by training (Hettinger & Muller, 1955; Ravick & Larsen, 1959). Moreover, even if strength level does not decrease, heavy strength training after a lay-off from exercise for a period of as little as 7-10 days may result in pronounced muscle soreness and an inability to maintain training intensity until full recovery has occurred.

The almost total loss of additional strength which was originally produced by 20 sessions of speed-strength exercises was noted 5 months after the special training had ceased (8.8% after the first month, 33.8% after the second, 60.2% after the third, 81.5% after the fourth and 88.8% after the fifth month). The greatest loss was between the second and fourth months (Chenyavsky, 1966). However, according to other data, strength acquired over a period of 40 sessions does not decrease to initial levels even a year after training has ceased (Vasiliev, 1954; McMorris & Eklins, 1954). A significant proportion of the increase in strength achieved as a result of ten electrostimulation sessions was maintained for 5 months (Khvilon, 1974). It has been noted that *an increase in strength is maintained for a longer period of time when it is accompanied by an increase in muscle mass* (DeLorme, 1950; Khrolon, 1974).

Although the above findings give an idea of the general tendencies for the increase and maintenance of muscular strength, there are obvious contradictions. Devising reliable methods of special strength preparation requires the application of scientific methods to:

• Study the training effect of the means used for a given sport at given levels of fitness
• Determine the optimum sequence, interrelation and continuity of training means for the yearly and multi-year training periods for different sports and purposes.

Thus, the combination of teaching efforts and special practice should introduce the quantitative programme via the basic scheme of special strength training depicted in Figure 4.1, where A, B and C are training means of successively greater training effect for a given athlete. In this respect, it should be noted that:

• The contribution of different training means to developing the key motor abilities diminishes with improvement in athletic results
• These means are different in terms of their training effect and the use of each of them is justified only when the athlete's level of fitness is taken into consideration.

In other words, with growth in sporting proficiency, it is necessary to determine the sequence for introducing the chosen means into the training process by calculating the growth and continuity of their training effect. This forms the basis for the progressive increase in special work capacity.

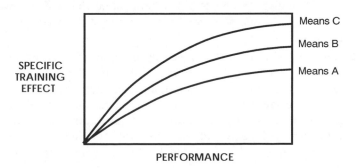

Figure 4.1 The introduction of different means with higher training effect (Verkhoshansky, 1977).

4.1.2 The Effect of the Strength Training Means

In recent years scientific research and years of practical experience have yielded a wealth of findings on which current methods of special strength training are based. However, it is necessary to note that this material is generalised and its analysis is theoretical. Although today's athletes attain a high level of sport proficiency, there is still no basis to state that this is the result of a precise methodology of special strength training. To a great extent they achieve proficiency through a large volume of strength work and a colossal expenditure of energy. Generally, the selection and use of means for organising special strength training has a number of weaknesses.

Despite its apparent diversity, the range of special strength training means is rather limited. In effect, beginners and highly qualified athletes use essentially the same means, the difference being largely in the volume and intensity of their loads.

Firstly, this leads to training monotony and secondly, the body adapts to a repeated stimulus and does not respond with the desired level of adaptation. Qualified athletes therefore spend much time using ineffective means, none of which improves their level of strength fitness. Beginners, on the other hand, often use vigorous overloading methods for which they are not yet prepared and disrupt the natural process of achieving sport mastery.

An essential shortcoming in the organisation of strength training is that athletes pay little attention to the phenomenon of the *qualitative specificity* of the training effect of strength exercises. Therefore, very often they use means whose specific training effect relates only weakly to the demands placed upon the body by the fundamental exercises. For instance, exercises that are selected for strength development often offer only general conditioning.

At the other extreme, there is the attempt to select exercises which are structurally similar to the fundamental exercises. This may be justified under certain circumstances, but it is sometimes carried to absurd lengths and athletes devise such intricate exercises that they are even less effective than traditional general conditioning movements. This reveals that *any system of special training is deficient if it arbitrarily combines general developmental and special strength exercises.*

In order to devise a sound scientific system it is necessary to evaluate objectively the training effect of the strength means. The training effect is result of the influence of a means or complex of means on the body as revealed by the magnitude, quality and stability of the resulting adaptive changes. A number of specific factors which reflect the training effect are examined for selecting the training means and devising a methodical system of special strength preparation.

It is first of all necessary to distinguish (see 6.7.1) between the *acute (immediate) training effect* (ATE) and the *delayed training effect (DTE)*. The body's immediate reaction to the application of a strength means is expressed in a short-term improvement of or deterioration in the athlete's current functional state. Deterioration or improvement depends upon the energy cost of the task, which determines the rest interval prior to execution of the next exercise: it may be increased if the body requires more rest or be optimally shortened if the superimposed after-effect phenomenon is exploited beneficially by the body. The negative reaction of the body is thus removed, as revealed by its relatively stable adaptation, which is substantial only if the volume of the training influence is sufficient.

The particular effect and cumulative effect are the result of the use of one or more unidirectional means or a complex of multi-directional means. In the first case, the adaptation reflects the specificity of the means used in the given regime. In the second case, the adaptation displays an integrated, generalised character. However, this is not simply the sum of the body's functional changes, but a complex of new forms of its motor potential which contains the specific characteristics of the particular training means.

The athlete's success depends largely upon the skill to select a diverse spectrum of exercise means which will produce the required cumulative training effect. One should also take into consideration factors that are characteristic of the training effect, such as absolute and relative strength, muscular endurance, stability and temporal features. It is necessary to evaluate the effectiveness of two or more means in order to select the one which produces the optimal increase in absolute strength. The qualitative and quantitative characteristics of the training effect provide measures of its specific form and the magnitude of improvement in performance. Finally, the stability and temporal characteristics of the training effect are evaluated by the length of time for which it is maintained.

An examination of the specific factors and the characteristics of the training effect of the strength means underlines the complexity of planning the strength training. Although the basis for selecting a strength means by taking into account these indicators and their characteristics is convincing, it still offers a very limited foundation, so the probability that the athlete will attain the desired level of strength preparation is slight.

To eliminate this problem, it is necessary, firstly, to pay serious attention to objectively evaluate the training effect of the strength exercises currently used, and secondly, to conduct scientific research aimed at formulating theoretical and practical solutions to optimise the cumulative effect of a complex of strength means. In this regard, very little has been done, although some generalisations may be made:

1. The training effect of any means diminishes as one's special physical fitness increases

2. The means used should produce the optimal training effect relative to the one's current functional state

3. The after-effect of previous work alters the training effect of any subsequent methods

4. The training effect of a complex of means is determined not only by the sum of the stimuli, but also their combination, order of succession and intervals of separation

5. The content of special strength training should include a complex of specific stimuli and produce the strength fitness required for the given sport, based upon the athlete's level of sports mastery.

With respect to 4 above, application of some mathematical concepts may be useful, as shown below.

Algebraic Relations and Training

Two algebraic laws may be applied to the interaction between different means, methods and techniques in strength (and all sports) training , which are important because they are not generally obeyed in training:

- The Commutative Law $\qquad A*B = B*A$
- The Associative Law $\qquad A*(B*C) = (A*B)*C$

A system may be said to be *commutative* if it does not matter in which order the operations are done in that system, i.e. $A*B = B*A$, where * is some special operation. In sports training, this is not the case, since the order in which one carries out exercises or kinds of exercises can change the outcome, as pointed out in point 3 above. For example, consider a squat and clean sequence: $Clean*Squat \neq Squat*Clean$. Thus, sports training means may be classed as *non-commutative*. For instance, a distance running session shortly before a weights session will invariably decrease one's strength capabilities.

Similarly, over the longer term of successive microcycles or mesocycles in a periodised program, the after-effect phenomenon decrees that the outcome is affected by the order of training means. In the various methods of complex training (combinations of different means in individual sessions or longer cycles), the order of the components of a complex determine the outcome and effectiveness of the system. With hybrid exercises (Ch 7.1), which comprise several movements in one repetition, the order of the individual movements also has a major effect on the execution and effectiveness of the exercise.

The Associative Law is also relevant. A system is said to be *associative* if the operations follow this law: $A*(B*C) = (A*B)*C$. Sports training is *non-associative*, since the use of means A followed by a complex of two means, B and C does not yield the same result as a complex of means A and B, followed by the use of a single means C. Thus, the use of a muscle endurance regime A before a complex of plyometrics B and Olympic lifting C does not yield the same results as the use of a complex of muscle endurance A and plyometrics B, followed by Olympic lifting C on its own.

The non-commutative and non-associative nature of sports training is central to its overall prescription, organisation and management, and should be recalled whenever there is any temptation to design training programmes or periodisation schemes solely on the basis of individual exercises, techniques, volumes, intensities and phases. Every exercise is followed by after-effects, the nature, duration and magnitude of these depending on factors such as intensity, duration and pattern of loading, and these after-effects deem that exercises in different parts of a workout, on different training days and even separated by several days or weeks can interact positively or negatively.

Therefore, it is vital that the context of any training situation in space and time be considered when drawing up a training programme. Remarks such as "plyometric training is dangerous", "power cleans are useless", "periodisation doesn't work", "weight training is supercontraindicated for endurance athletes" and "circuit training is excellent for general preparation" may then be seen to be simplistic and misleading. Virtually any training method may be rendered impotent or harmful if it is administered in an inappropriate manner for a given individual at a given stage of his/her training career. Conversely, methods which may appear to be offer only modest improvements on their own, may in optimal combinations yield results which clearly show that "the whole is greater than the sum of its parts".

Steps Towards Structuring the Training Process

One issue is still very important for devising methods of strength training. A training effect occurs through the frequent and systematic repetition of a complex of different interacting means. The training load is understood to be the sum of all the specific influences on the body, its essential characteristics being:

- its resulting effect (the qualitative and quantitative assessment of the special work capacity of the athlete)
- its composition or contents (the complex of means applied)
- its structure (correlation of means)
- its volume (the quantity of the training work)
- its intensity (the difficulty or quality of the training work).

To assess the effectiveness of the training process, it is appropriate to examine further how the composition, structure, the volume and intensity of the training load relate to the resulting effect. The purpose of managing the training load is to obtain a pronounced and safe training effect through the logical organisation of the composition and structure of the load, by use of an optimal volume and intensity of exercise.

A load will prove effective if its means create an adequate training effect, i.e. evoke specific adaptation in the body. This is especially important for highly qualified athletes, since the means they have used in previous stages of preparation do not elicit an adequate training effect for continued improvement. Therefore, the search for highly effective means and methods of special strength training is always fundamental to scientific sports preparation. During the past few decades, isometric and isokinetic exercises have been used, as well as the plyometric method of developing explosive-strength, the electrostimulation method and others. Although not all of them have been studied sufficiently, and detailed methods for their use have not been determined, they ensure appreciable success, thereby confirming their effectiveness and the research findings in this field.

In recent years the volume of the load has been increased significantly. However, it is impossible to accept the view that increase in training volume is the only or best possibility for enhancing the effectiveness of the athlete's preparation.

Elementary logic and practical experience clearly indicate that it is impossible for sheer quantity of work to compensate for a low training effect of any given means. However, there is also no guarantee that highly effective specialised means, logically organised in a specific training cycle, can produce a high level of special work capacity at a significantly smaller volume of exercise and in a shorter time. Nevertheless, it should be noted that the volume of the load is undoubtedly one of the conditions for raising the special work capacity in many sports (chiefly the cyclic types) during specific stages of preparation.

In order not to create an incorrect impression about the volume of the load we must point out that it resolves two basic tasks in the training process. *Firstly,* it provides a functional base for the further development of specific work capacity. *Secondly,* it is associated with raising the level of special fitness, primarily by developing endurance. If the first task is significant as a universal training principle, then the second is appropriate only for certain types of sport. It should be added that the volume of the training work is an important condition for successful technical preparation. Besides this, research indicates that there is a direct correlation between the volume of the load and the length of time over which a training effect is maintained.

In addition to its volume, *the structure of the training scheme is vitally important in every sport.* From practical experience it is known that no one means or method of special preparation should be considered universal or absolutely effective. Each of them should have its own special place during a particular training stage, depending upon factors including the specificity of the sport, the athlete's level of fitness, the character of the previous training loads, and the specific aims of the current training stage. With respect to this, research has shown clearly that special strength training using a specific system of different means and methods produces a significantly greater effect than the separate random use of different means and methods (see Ch 6), this advantage being achieved even with a smaller volume of work (Verkhoshansky, 1966, 1970; Tatyan, 1974; Khodykin, 1975).

One more feature should be noted. *If the given means do not elicit an adequate training effect, then increase in work capacity becomes more a factor of specialised exercise than training volume and then only if it is executed by training at or near personal maximum levels.* It should be pointed out that the execution of specialised exercises in training at near maximal intensity (as advocated by Bulgarian experts) should be regarded as an advanced strategy, a method which cannot be acknowledged as being universally appropriate. This would imply not only rejecting the principles of the rational structuring of training based on research into training methods, but also a return to the original concepts from which these began.

Thus, the problem of establishing scientifically the means of sport training is far from being solved and the current tendency to increase the volume of the training load should not detract from its significance and turn the attention of specialists away from its in-depth study.

If a logical sequence is to be recommended as a practical solution to the problem of improving the effectiveness of special strength training methods, then it should be laid down as follows:

1. Regime ⟶ 2. Means ⟶ 3. Methods ⟶ 4. System ⟶ 5. Volume

From this scheme it follows that the means of special strength training should be selected on the basis of quantitative descriptions of the motor specificity of the given sport and thereby provide an adequate *regime* of work for the body. The basic criterion for this is a guarantee of a definite training effect for the given level of special fitness.

The next step is to determine a suitable *method* of using the *means* based not only on the specific motor regimes of the given sport, but also on factors such as one's level of fitness and the tasks of the current stage of training. Of great potential for perfecting the methods of special strength training, is the *principle of systematic application of means* to produce the necessary cumulative training effect.

Finally, attaining the necessary level of special strength training depends on the *volume* of the special work, the optimal magnitude of which should be determined by the stage and current tasks of the athlete's preparation, the competition calendar and the intensity of the load.

This scheme emphasizes that, to rely on any one parameter of the load for achieving any given potential is appropriate only after the potential of the previous parameter has been completely exploited. For example, it is unwise to increase training volume without having fully elicited the maximum training effect of the individual strength training means at a particular intensity. This requires dedication and persistence from the specialists, because it requires in-depth investigative effort. Since increasing the training volume is easier than finding a really effective means of special preparation, such a course tends to be a much simpler choice.

4.2 Different Means of Strength Development

The external force generated by muscles is a result of voluntary effort. However, under normal everyday conditions, muscular tension produced by voluntary effort has certain limitations. To increase the external muscular force it is necessary to stimulate them from the outside, for example, by means of mechanical stimulation. Afferent impulses elicited by mechanical stimulation inform the central nervous system about the strength of the external influence evoking the muscular tension. The greater the intensity of the external stimulus, the greater the muscle effector discharge, and the larger the external work produced.

Thus, afferent signals to the neuromuscular system play an important role in determining the qualitative and quantitative characteristics of muscular strength. Therefore, the stimulation of muscular tension for the development of strength is of great significance. So, in all cases the magnitude of working muscular tension is determined by voluntary effort and external mechanical action. The stimulation of working force can be divided into the following basic types:

- Stimulation when muscular tension is produced by voluntary effort against external resistance, and the resistance of the moving load accelerates and regulates the effector impulses to the muscles

- Stimulation by the kinetic energy of a falling object or the body, when the effort is primarily reflexive

- Stimulation caused primarily by voluntary effort, under conditions where additional external mechanical stimulation is absent or limited

- Stimulation of muscle elicited or intensified involuntarily by means of external electrical current.

The first two cases are associated with dynamic work and the third with isometric work. An increase in stimulation is realised in the first case by increasing the velocity of the preliminary fall of the body or load, and by mobilising the athlete's voluntary resources in the third. It should also be pointed out that voluntary effort plays an important role in the magnitude of the effector response of the muscles in the first instance, whereas its influence in the second is insignificant.

The mechanism chiefly responsible for the braking or amortisation work of the muscles causes a protective effector response more rapidly than a voluntary sequence of actions. Therefore, such a reflex stimulus is able to provoke an extraordinary mobilisation of the neuromuscular apparatus, which is impossible where there is reliance on voluntary effort alone. This mechanism forms the foundation of plyometric training (5.2.4).

4.2.1 Electrostimulation

As has already been stated, there is always an ongoing search for novel, highly effective means of special strength training. For example, Russian studies have established that electrostimulation of muscle furnishes an adequate training stimulus for effective development of muscular strength (Kots, 1971; Kots & Khvilon, 1971; Khvilon, 1974). Electrostimulation can be effective for certain purposes in the preparation of highly qualified athletes (mainly in speed-strength sports) and there are a number of advantages associated with this method of developing strength, in particular the reduction of joint loading. It can occupy a specific place in the yearly training cycle, be used in combination with other methods of developing muscular strength and be applied chiefly in the preparation of highly qualified athletes.

Ratov has found that functional electrical stimulation (FENS) can be particularly useful in improving sporting performance. His techniques, developed decades ago from his PhD programme on the interrelation between electrical stimulation and electromyography, has used EMG signals from agonist and antagonist muscles to act as triggers or control mechanisms for electrical stimulation of muscles directly involved in producing functional movements in sport. In his laboratory at the State Central Institute for Sports Science in Moscow he has successfully implemented these neuromuscular stimulation methods in training athletes such as fencers, boxers, rowers, shotputters and weightlifters.

However, it is inappropriate to consider the training applications of electrostimulation in detail here because its methodological fundamentals have still not been determined, especially as it should be applied preferably under suitable conditions by qualified personnel. The next section summarises the effects and applications of electrostimulation as a form of supplementary sports preparation.

4.2.1.1 The Physiological Effects of Electrostimulation

The concept of electrostimulation is not new, and for years has been used by physical therapists in clinical applications such as muscle rehabilitation, relief of muscular spasm, reduction of swelling and pain control. Its possible value in sports training is still considered controversial. In strength conditioning, the applications of electrostimulation fall into the following broad categories:

- Imposition of local physical stress to provoke supercompensation
- Local restoration after exercise or injury
- General central nervous and endocrine restoration after exercise or injury
- Neuromuscular stimulation for pain control or movement patterning

Electrostimulation usually involves feeding the muscles low current electrical impulses via moistened electrode pads placed firmly on the skin. The effectiveness, comfort and depth of excitation depends on factors such as pulse shape, frequency, duration, intensity and modulation pattern. The resulting number of possible stimulation combinations immediately emphasizes how difficult it is to determine the optimum balance of variables and compare the results of different researchers.

The typical clinical machine supplies pulsating direct (galvanic) and/or alternating (faradic) current in the form of brief pulses. The frequency of faradic current is most commonly chosen in the range of about 50-100 Hz, while pulse duration (width) ranges from about 100 microseconds to several hundred milliseconds. This brevity of pulse duration is important to minimise skin irritation and tissue damage. However, the duration at any particular intensity of faradic stimulation should not be too brief Although they may be suitable for decreasing pain, pulses that are too brief will supply insufficient energy to cause full, tetanic muscle contraction.

Machines are designed to apply alternating currents directly at a preset or selected frequency (conventional faradism), or in the form of low frequency currents superimposed on a medium frequency (2000 to 5000 Hz) carrier wave. A variation of the latter method, using two pairs of electrodes each supplying medium frequency waves carrying low frequency waves differing slightly in frequency, forms the basis of what is called interferential stimulation. A major advantage of using a higher frequency carrier wave is that impedance between the electrodes and skin is lowered, enhancing comfort and effectiveness.

American interest in electrostimulation as a training adjunct was aroused in 1971, when Kots in Russia reported increases of more than 20% in muscle strength, speed and power produced by several weeks of electrotraining. Unable to produce comparable results, the Canadians invited him to lecture at Concordia University in 1977. Armed with the new information that Kots employed a sinusoidally modulated 2500 Hz current source applied in a sequence of 10 seconds of contraction followed by 50 seconds of relaxation, they again tried to duplicate Russian claims.

It is noteworthy that this procedure differed significantly from that of top Belgian superheavy weightlifter, Serge Reding, who had close training contact with one of the authors (Siff) while he stayed with him In South Africa in the early 1970s. After training sessions he used 0.5 to 2 second, very high intensity contractions with 10 to 15 second rest periods, for a total of 5 minutes per major muscle group, with agonists and antagonists of each limb alternately stimulated in ipsilateral and contralateral sequences (Siff, 1973). Reding always concluded his sessions with a few repetitions (1-3) of a long duration (10-15 seconds) fairly intense tetanic contraction to serve as a type of deep massage, followed by about 10-15 minutes of microcurrent stimulation (less than 200 microamps) applied across the head and spinal cord with another electrostimulator.

Despite the subsequent success reported by various track coaches in integrating conventional faradic electrostimulation into a carefully periodised training programme (Francis, 1982), researchers continue to disagree on increase in muscle strength.

4.2.1.2 Reasons for Conflicting Research

There are several main reasons for the contradictory research findings:

1. Many studies focus largely on isometric or isokinetic strength changes, which complicates research comparisons. Such research often neglects possible effects of other vital factors such as power, speed, muscular endurance, residual muscle tension, muscle growth and rate of neuromuscular recovery.

2. Much of the research examines injured patients in the process of rehabilitation, untrained individuals, or trained subjects from differing fitness and training backgrounds. It is well known that an increase in strength is proportionately greater in the early stages of a training programme or among untrained subjects. Moreover, increases in strength for novices during the first few weeks of training mainly are due to neuromuscular adaptation and learning, rather than muscle hypertrophy.

3. The effectiveness of electrostimulation is determined by the intensity of the current used and individual tolerance of discomfort caused by stimulation. In addition, no specific waveform has been found to be universally most comfortable. There also can be considerable variation among subjects in their response to different waveforms and stimulation impedances (Delitto & Rose, 1986; Mannheimer & Carlsson, 1979; Moreno-Aranda & Seirig, 1981).

4. The effects of electrostimulation depend on the types and frequency of waveforms used, particularly since there is a distinct difference in the recruitment patterns and functional characteristics of slow-twitch and fast-twitch muscle fibres (Lloyd et al, 1986; Mannheimer & Carlsson, 1979; Pette & Vrbova, 1985). Moreover, the higher the frequency, particularly if a carrier wave is used, the lower the impedance between electrodes and skin, and the greater the degree of comfort.

5. The type, size, number and location of electrodes, as well as the electrode gel, affect the amount of electrical energy transmitted to the muscles, the resultant force of contraction and patient comfort. Many studies do not discuss these details, and therefore, valid comparisons largely are meaningless.

6. Most studies have used commercial electrostimulators which are able to vary only a few of all the possible stimulation parameters. Some of the more extensive studies have varied several of these parameters, as summarised in the thorough review by Lloyd et al (1986). However, because of the enormous number of

stimulation combinations theoretically possible, no single extensive study has been able to examine the effects of varying all the stimulation parameters. This includes frequency, waveform, pulse-width, type of modulation (Frequency Modulation, Amplitude Modulation or pulse-width modulation), impulse interval and electrical energy delivered.

7. The effects of electrostimulation, like plyometric training, may be enhanced by optimal integration into an overall strength and sport specific training programme (e.g. Francis, 1982)

8. Many of the training regimes have been deficiently designed. Usually, the electrostimulator is selected according to the maximum tolerated by subjects, or to a certain percentage of a maximal voluntary isometric or isokinetic contraction as measured on isokinetic or other dynamometers. It should be noted that adaptation to any stimulus occurs, and subjects can withstand greater intensities of electric current from the start to end of any session, and from week to week.

Similarly, studies examining the combined effects of electrostimulation and normal strength training often prescribe weight training with a fixed number of sets and loads at a fixed percentage of single repetition maximum, despite the fact that the latter maximum gradually increases. The accompanying electrical stimulation also is set at a fixed value, which fails to consider that the basic principle of strength and power enhancement is gradual overload. Such a training regime in normal weight training is known to be highly limited in improving physical performance. It would be surprising if it were any different with electrostimulation training.

9. The design and effects of the electrostimulator depend on the choice of physiological model. Most stimulators are designed on the basis of the action-potential model of nerve cell discharge, which considers that cellular communication in the body is mediated by bursts of electrical discharge transmitted along nerve axons. The cell is assumed to be 'on' (discharging electricity) or 'off' (resting), depending on whether the build-up of electrical charge in the cell is large enough to exceed a certain threshold, rendering the cell membrane temporarily more permeable to certain chemical ions. Intermediate subthreshold states are presumed unimportant, although they are central to an understanding of the EEG (brain waves) and other electrical potentials of the central nervous system (Siff, 1981).

Similarly, the numerous glial cells which surround all nerve cells are assumed to play little more than a nutritional or supportive role for the nerves, despite the fact that they display a steady or quasi-steady electric field (Galambos, 1961; Siff, 1981). Some scientists believe that glial cell potentials may have a profound effect on nerve cells by modulating their activity similar to semiconductors such as transistors in electronic circuits (Becker, 1974; Galambos, 1961). In addition, the DC injury potentials measurable on the skin surface after tissue damage are not associated with the action potential system (Becker, 1982).

Moreover, little is known about electrical fields at the subcellular level. The sensitivity of the body to external electric, magnetic and electromagnetic fields cannot satisfactorily be explained in terms of action potentials, which are not directly affected by these fields (Becker, 1965; Cope, 1974). The classical theories also do not explain the mechanisms whereby electric and other fields stimulate processes such as the repair of fractures, the healing of wounds and reduction of thrombosis.

On discovering evidence for semiconduction and the possible existence of superconductivity at room temperature in biological systems, scientists now have postulated that tissue healing, pain mechanisms, cell growth and disease processes may involve biological semiconduction and superconductivity (Becker, 1965; Cope, 1971; Cope, 1974). In addition, Nordenstrom claims to have shown the presence of closed electric circuits in the body, whereby ionic flow concerned with growth and regulatory processes takes place via blood vessels and through or along the capillaries (Nordenstrom, 1983).

All faradic, medium frequency and interferential stimulators (including sports-oriented machines) are designed on the action-potential model for cell operation, which, therefore, do not permit applications relying on the other types of models described above. Such applications involve cell growth, tissue repair and general recuperation, all of which are essential features of physical conditioning. In recent years a few innovative micro-current machines based on these models have been applied clinically with significant success in neuromuscular rehabilitation (Chee & Walton, 1986; Matteson, 1984; Matteson & Eberhardt, 185; Meyer & Nebrensky, 1983; Noto & Grant, 1985).

4.2.1.3 Clinical Applications of Electrostimulation

At this point it is relevant to survey the clinical and research evidence supporting the value of electrostimulation in medical situations. Its major applications or effects are the following:

1. Increase in Muscle Strength

A wide range of low and medium frequencies has been shown to strengthen muscle tissue in the case of subjects who have been incapacitated by injury, illness or childbirth (Eriksson, 1981; Johnson et al, 1977; Laughman et al, 1983; Lloyd et al, 1986; Raitsin, 1974; Romero et al, 1982; Turk et al, 1980). Some studies on the effect of electrostimulation (ES) alone on normal subjects also have revealed strength increases (Currier & Mann, 1983; Laughman et al, 1983: McMiken et al, 1983; Romero et al, 1982; Sekowitz, 1985), although some of these studies showed that ES was not superior to voluntary exercise (Currier & Mann, 1983; Laughmen et al, 1983; McMiken et al, 1983; Sekowitz, 1985). Further studies found minimal or insignificant changes in strength (Massey et al, 1965; Mohr et al, 1985; Singer et al, 1983).

In general, most of these studies indicate that ES unaccompanied by physical training at best produces long-term strength gains which are similar to or smaller than those of voluntary exercise. The greatest strength increases are invariably found in the weakest or most unfit subjects (Fahey et al, 1985; Johnson et al, 1977; Romero et al, 1982). However, in conjunction with periodised exercise programmes, ES appears to increase the strength of competitive athletes in some instances (Francis, 1982; Kots & Chwilon, 1971; Matteson, 1984; Reding, 1973), although these changes may have been the indirect result of some of the other effects of ES discussed below.

2. Re-education of Muscle Action

Some medical disorders or kinesiological habits may produce weak or faulty patterns of muscle action. ES may facilitate more efficient use of the affected muscles. It can be particularly effective in treating chondromalacia patellae, tennis elbow and 'frozen shoulder' (Eriksson, 1981; Godfrey et al, 1979; Johnson et al, 1977; Nirchl & Sobel, 1981).

3. Facilitation of Muscle Contraction

If one is unable to produce a voluntary muscle contraction because of disuse, pain or injury, ES can promote muscle activity and reduce the likelihood of extensive tissue wasting (Eriksson, 1981; Johnson et al, 1977; Turk et al, 1980; Vodovnik et al, 1982).

4. Increase of Muscular and Systemic Endurance

Prolonged application of sub-maximal ES can stimulate the fatiguing conditions encountered in strenuous physical work thereby increasing endurance of the muscles involved (Ikai & Yabe, 1969; Johnson et al, 1977). Russian research reported improvement in cardiovascular efficiency, muscle contractility and rate of general recovery (Dombrovskaya, 1982). Moreover, low frequency (under 15 Hz) ES of long duration (24-hour) continuous stimulation experiments or cross-innervation experiments in animals have been shown to alter fast twitch fibres to become predominantly aerobic and more resistant to fatigue (Jolesz & Sreter, 1981; Pette, 1984; Pette & Vrbova, 1985; Salmons & Vrbova, 1969; Salmons & Henriksson, 1981).

5. Increase of Speed of Muscle Contraction

Long-term higher frequency (more than 40 Hz) ES can improve reaction time and decrease the time to peak tension of fast twitch muscles (Fluery & Lagasse, 1979; Salmons & Vrbova, 1967, 1969).

6. Increase in Local Blood Supply

ES stimulates muscles to contract rhythmically, producing dilatation of the blood vessels, facilitating the transport of nutrients to the tissues, and possibly accelerating healing in tissues which are not extensively injured (Dombrovskaya, 1982; Salmons & Vrbova, 1967 Wadsworth & Chanmugam, 1980). Experiments using different stimulation regimes have measured increases in blood flow ranging from about 20% to more than 200%, both during and after ES, particularly if the frequencies used are below approximately 30 Hz (Currier et al, 1986; Richardson, 1981; Wakim et al, 1948; Wakim, 1953). In general, the higher the frequency of ES, the lower the percentage increase in blood flow (Currier et al, 1986; Wakim, 1953).

7. Provision of Effective Massage

ES increases the pumping action of muscle on the venous and lymphatic systems, which help injured, tense or fatigued areas dissipate fluid and toxin accumulation (Dombrovskaya, 1982; Wadsworth & Chanmugam, 1980). Russian studies using radioactive Xenon ($Xe133$) injected as a tracer confirm that massage accelerates local blood flow and reduces muscle tension, resulting in improved oxygen and nutrient supply to the tissues and faster removal of metabolic waste products (Dubrovsky, 1982).

8. Relief of Pain

ES applied by TENS (Transcutaneous Electrical Nerve Stimulation) devices can relieve painful muscle spasm or tension, as well as diminish acute or chronic pain caused by a wide range of musculoskeletal conditions (Gersh & Wolf, 1985; Jeans, 1979; Lloyd et al, 1986; Mannheim & Carlsson, 1979; Sjolund & Eriksson, 1979; Strauss, 1987; Wadsworth & Chanmugam, 1980). Conventional TENS employs low frequency (50 to 100 Hz) stimulation with no muscle contraction. TENS modes for management of deeper pain may use short, high intensity bursts at frequencies between 1 and 150 Hz with definite muscle contraction.

9. Reduction of Muscle Spasm

Protective spasm can occur in any overloaded, injured, inflamed or painful muscle. The effectiveness of ES in reducing spasm and spasticity has been attributed to one or more of the following mechanisms: promotion of muscular fatigue, disruption of the pain-spasm cycle or restoration of the normal contraction-relaxation process (Alfieri, 1982; Mills et al, 1984; Wadsworth & Chanmugam, 1980).

10. Promotion of Relaxation and Recuperation

Short-term, intense, muscle-contracting ES and mild, non-contracting TENS-type stimulation both can promote local and general relaxation. This effect has been ascribed, in animal and human subjects, to the release in the central nervous system of endorphins and enkephalins, classes of analgesic and tranquiliser which occur naturally in the body (Gersh & Wolf, 1985; Sjolund & Eriksson, 1979). This application is used by Russian athletes in recuperating after strenuous training sessions and in facilitating the onset of sleep, even by applying mild stimulation to the thighs alone (Dombrovskaya, 1982; Kopisov & Nagorniy, 1982).

11. Increase in Range of Movement

In physical therapy, PNF (Proprioceptive Neuromuscular Facilitation) techniques often are used to improve joint mobility caused by inactivity or injury. ES may be used in conjunction with such mobilisation techniques to enhance their effectiveness. In the case of injury, the ES may aid relaxation and mobility by diminishing pain, reducing swelling and improving microcirculation within the tissues (Wadsworth & Chanmugam, 1980).

12. Reduction of Swelling

Swelling (oedema) is the accumulation of excessive extracellular fluid in the region of a joint, arising from leakage of protein and plasma through the capillary walls of soft tissues. It may be caused by inflammation, sprains, strains, tendinitis, rheumatoid arthritis, surgery or disease. Low intensity ES can rapidly reduce swelling of non-infectious origin (Wadsworth & Chanmugam, 1980). Its effectiveness may be due to the pumping action of muscle and/or the creation of an electric gradient across the cell membranes, which triggers the lymphatic system to absorb excess fluid.

13. Reduction of Musculoskeletal Abnormalities

Abnormal spinal curvature has been halted or the progress has slowed in mild to moderate scoliosis, by ES appropriately applied to specific back muscles (Axelgaard et al, 1983; Friedman et al, 1982; Kots & Chwilon, 1971; Schultz et al, 1981).

14. Preferential Recruitment of Different Muscle Fibres

ES tends to recruit the largest diameter axons first (Enoka, 1988), which is the reverse of the natural order of recruitment (see 1.12, especially Fig 1.24). These largest axons are difficult to activate under normal training conditions, so ES may play a useful supplementary role in this respect.

15. Acute Increase in Strength

Several researchers have shown that ES can have a profound effect on strength after a single session (Howard & Enoka, 1987; Alon, 1985). In particular, Alon, in studying a group of 14 subjects, found that one experimental session of ES produced a mean increase in quadriceps strength of about 13%.

16. Improvement in Metabolic Efficiency

Application of ES during exercise can improve the metabolic economy of the movement. Studies carried out by Ratov & Kryazhev (1986) which examined the effect of electrically stimulating the quadriceps during cycling and speed skating showed that oxygen consumption decreased by 10-17% and the time taken to fatigue was extended by 15-20%. Similar research which analysed the effect of ES applied to an athlete running on a treadmill revealed a reduction of some 10% in oxygen consumption. In addition, if work was performed by the muscles which were electrically stimulated shortly before, energy consumption decreased by about 5%.

17. Increase in Muscle Speed

Phasic type of electrical stimulation increases the contractile speed of skeletal muscle. Electrical stimulation, when employed as a technique for subjecting selected muscles to altered use, facilitates precise entrainment of the pattern of functional activity (Karba et al, 1990).

4.2.1.4 Further Research Findings

Recent research and clinical experience have revealed that electric currents as much as 1000 times smaller than that of all the traditional physical therapy modalities can be far more successful than the latter in achieving many of the benefits outlined in the previous section.

Currents as low as 10 microamps (millionths of an amp) pulsating at between 0.1 to 400Hz are too weak to cause muscle contraction, block pain signals or cause local heating, yet their effectiveness and safety is often superior in many applications to that of faradism, interferentialism and conventional TENS (Matteson & Eberhardt, 1985).

The steps to satisfactorily modify the existing paradigm for ES may be sought in the research findings quoted earlier in the section: 'Reasons for conflicting research'. There, it was learned that cellular and subcellular processes not involving cell discharge, propagated electrical impulses, or muscle contraction, appear to be involved with cellular growth and repair.

Some studies have produced findings which offer partial answers to the questions posed by microstimulation. For instance, work by Becker and others suggests that small, steady or slowly varying currents can cause sub-threshold modulation of the electric fields across nerve and glial cells, thereby directly regulating cell growth and communication (Becker, 1974; Becker & Marino, 1982). In this respect, some of Becker's applications included the acceleration of wound healing, partial regeneration of amphibian and rat limbs, and induction of narcosis with transcranial currents. Nordenström maintains that these electric currents can stimulate the flow of ions along the blood vessels and through the cell membranes which constitute the body's closed electric circuits postulated by his theory (Nordenström, 1983).

Pilla (1974) has paid particular attention to electrochemical information transfer across cell membranes. The model in this case hypothesizes that the molecular structure of the cell membrane reflects its current genetic activity. Here, the function of a cell at any instant is determined by feedback between DNA in the cell nucleus and a macromolecule inducer liberated from the membrane by means of a protein (enzyme) regulator derived from messenger RNA activity within the cell. The activity of these membrane-bound proteins is strongly modulated by changes in the concentration of divalent ions (such as calcium Ca^{++}) absorbed on the membrane. ES may elicit these ionic changes and thereby modify cell function.

It has been shown that ES at 5Hz stimulates synthesis of DNA in chick cartilage cells and rat bone by as much as 27%, but not in chick skin fibroblasts or rat spleen lymphocytes (Rodan et al, 1978). Not only does the effect of ES appear to be tissue-specific, but the increase in DNA synthesis occurs 4-6 hours after 15 minutes of ES. The process of membrane depolarisation carried by sodium ions seems to be followed by an increase in intracellular Ca^{++} concentration, thereby triggering DNA synthesis in cells susceptible to the particular stimulus. Further work by Pilla (1981) has confirmed the existence of cellular 'windows' which open most effectively to certain frequencies, pulse widths and pulse amplitudes. To attune the ES signal to these parameters, monitoring of tissue impedances is preferable, a system employed by so-called 'Intelligent TENS' devices.

In addition, Cheng et al (1982) have shown that stimulation with currents from 50-1000 microamps can increase tissue ATP concentrations in rats by 300-500%, and enhances amino acid transport through the cell membrane and consequent protein synthesis by as much as 40%. Interestingly, the same study reported that increasing the current above only one milliamp was sufficient to depress tissue ATP and protein synthesis - and traditional ES usually applies currents exceeding 20 milliamps, at which stage this depression being nearly 50%.

order of these means. However, a still larger effect was obtained by using ES and plyometrics concurrently with heavy resistance exercise, with the ES and plyometric combination having the smallest training effect during periods of complete or partial rest.

In applying the ES, the placement or configuration of electrodes is also very important, since one can use essentially two methods: adjacent or distant attachment. Adjacent or close attachment of the two electrodes tends to localise the muscle contraction and keep it fairly superficial, whereas the distant attachment method (where one electrode is attached to a remote or fairly neutral location from the muscle being stimulated) tends to produce a more extensive, deeper form of muscle contraction. To ensure good and comfortable conduction between electrode and athlete, it is vital to lubricate the area of attachment with a commercial electrode gel or weak saline solution. Any signs of superficial skin irritation or prickliness invariably are the result of the gel drying out. The electrodes may also be used directly over important nerves, but the intensity of the ensuing contraction can be harmful and this method should be restricted to use by experienced physical therapists.

The unified concept of the various ES modalities presented here should enable the scientist or therapist to approach the issue of electrostimulation more systematically. Thus, if additional stress is needed on particular muscle groups to elicit more pronounced supercompensation, the MACS modality should be employed by using faradic or interferential-type devices applied with gradual overload of both training and ES intensity.

Sports Functional Electrostimulation

Little or no mention is made in the West of the application of FES (Functional Electrostimulation) in sports training. In the West, this term or its equivalent FENS (Functional Electroneural Stimulation) invariably applies to the use of electrostimulation to contract the muscles of spinally disabled patients who cannot voluntarily activate their muscles and offer some degree of externally controlled movement. In Russia and other Eastern European countries the terms can also apply to the application of electrostimulation to able-bodied athletes during natural sporting movements to intensify muscle tension at the most appropriate phases of these movements. The innovative Professor Igor Ratov of the State Central Institute of Sports Science in Moscow, has done considerable research in this field with able-bodied and disabled subjects and stresses that this type of functional stimulation is far more consistently successful than the passive methods attributed to Kots by his Western supporters.

Work that I witnessed in his laboratory involved the use of concurrent EMG recordings to phase the FES correctly into specific sporting movements, most specifically to avoid producing spurious muscle tension or uncoordinated movement. Eventually, athletes learn to contract their muscles synchronously with the externally applied electrical field and thereby produce greater strength, power and speed. This method is sometimes called *active electrostimulation*, since the ES is applied to active muscles rather than to relaxed muscles (*passive electrostimulation*), which is the method most commonly used in physical therapy.

The use of highly specific methods like sports FES should not lead us to exclude the possible importance of general methods of ES which intentionally avoid offering any form of functional training. In this respect, the ES training applied to the author by Serge Reding used a *Myogen Parametric* stimulator that was designed to offer external stimulation which in no way simulated the most frequently occurring movements of Olympic lifting. In other words, ES may also be used as a form of GPP (General Physical Preparation). The Reding machine applied brief intense pulses alternately in a flip-flop fashion to opposite sides of the body, though not to paired agonists and antagonists. The intensity of the ES was carefully periodised into the entire training programme alongside other key methods of strength training and training sessions were always terminated with brief, deep ES muscle massage and restorative microstimulation across the brain and along the length of the spinal cord. Reding stressed the importance of different waveforms and regimes of FES for different categories of sport, adding that the method shared by Kots with Canadian coaches was only one of many possibilities.

Overtraining and Restoration

The possibility of overtraining, however, must be considered, especially if ES is being added to an already strenuous training programme. It is generally not advisable to apply more than 5-10 minutes of intense ES per major muscle group, due to the associated tissue necrosis and prolonged soreness that may follow in the days after treatment. The use of biofeedback TENS devices which monitor cellular electrical characteristics and adjust the stimulating parameters automatically, limits the possibility of overstimulation or cell damage.

In general, MICS may be used far more routinely than MACS, since it cannot produce overtraining or injury and since it can accelerate recovery after training. Therefore, it can enable one to train more intensively and recuperate more rapidly between workouts and even between sets, if necessary. For the serious athlete who intends to periodically supplement strenuous weight training with MACS, regular use of MICS as well could prove invaluable in improving performance and minimising the chance of overtraining. It should be remembered, however, that routine or frequent use of accelerated methods of restoration can impair the natural ability of the body to recuperate and adapt; it is sometimes important to allow the body to undergo partial or unaccelerated restoration to facilitate the supercompensatory response (Siff & Yessis, 1992).

Concluding Remarks

The untutored reader is not encouraged to use ES, since it requires considerable theoretical and practical training for its safe and effective application. Those who experiment casually with such devices in training generally note sporadic or short-term progress and discontinue their use after just a few months. Unless applied by experts in their use, these machines are usually a waste of money or disappointing in not living up to their advertised claims.

In several countries (such as the USA), ES devices generally may not be sold to the public or used commercially or therapeutically on any clients by anyone who is not trained in medicine or physiotherapy. Therefore, this section does not present the specific details of application.

4.2.2 Resistance and Strength Training

In principle, the heavier the weight which muscles lift, the greater the tension they develop. The latter is achieved by the effective stimulation and recruitment into the work of a large proportion of the involved muscles. Strength development through the use of resistance activity was demonstrated around 500 BC by the legendary Milo of Crotona. According to legend, he increased his strength enormously by lifting a young bull daily onto his shoulders. As the bull grew in mass, so did Milo's strength.

In our own era Milo's approach is exemplified by the DeLorme method of progressive resistance exercise (DeLorme, 1945; DeLorme & Watkins, 1948, 1951). Essentially, this method consists of developing strength through repetitively lifting a weight which is gradually increased in the workout, as well from workout to workout, as strength increases.

However, when the display of great force was required, the imposition of resistance was a natural means of training, but where speed of movement plays a decisive role, resistance was used initially with great care. At the same time, some researchers noted that strength training makes it possible to improve results in speed type exercises (Dupperon, 1926; Lubimov, 1927; Curie, 1937; Markov, 1938, Ozolin, 1939; Chui, 1950; Gullwer, 1955; Pennybaker, 1961). However, a long period of experimental and practical verification was required before this hypothesis gained acceptance. However, it is correct only relative to the amount of weight, the coordination pattern of the movement, the tempo and the number of repetitions.

When resistance is used for stimulating muscular tension, it is necessary to consider the fact that strength may be displayed in resistance exercises in the form of maximal tension or maximal speed of muscle contraction. One can then refer to *strength exercises* in which force is displayed primarily by increasing the amount of weight, and *speed-strength exercises* in which the display of force is associated with increasing the speed of movement (Farfel, 1940). In the first case, one tries to work with the largest resistance possible and in the second with a resistance whose optimal magnitude is determined by the required speed of movement.

It should be pointed out that the work regimes of strength with primarily slow movements and speed-strength exercises (using inherently fast movements) are essentially different with respect to the physiological mechanisms and the manner in which energy resources are used. Execution of explosive movements invariably requires a high level of excitation of the basic neural processes. In the case of slow movements, the basic role of the nervous system is to produce sufficient excitation and maintain it for a relatively long period (Federov, 1957).

It is useful to examine more closely the dynamics of movements with maximal effort in terms of the magnitude of the resistance displaced and the regime of muscular work. The amount of work obviously increases as the load raised by a weightlifter is increased. However, the changes in the *power output* of the work are not unidirectional. Initially, power output increases, but after the weight of the barbell exceeds 66% of maximum, it begins to decrease (Chikvadze, 1961). A similar result is observed in the jump with a barbell on the shoulders (Fig 4.2). Maximal dynamic force increases as the weight of the apparatus increases during the rapid increase in the movement time, mainly during the active thrust phase. Maximum power output is achieved with weights of 30-40% of the 1RM and a maximal coefficient of reactivity at 30-33% of the 1RM.

The fact that power and the reactivity coefficient increase as movement time increases is due to the additional elastic energy accumulated in the muscles by absorbing the kinetic energy of the body and apparatus during the amortisation phase.

Observations of the movement characteristics of the concentric lifting of progressively heavier weights (20, 40, 60, 80% of maximum) with seated leg extensions (from an initial knee angle of 110°) favour such conclusions (Fig 4.3). It is obvious from the graph that maximum dynamic force and movement time increase with increasing resistance in an analogous way to jumps with a barbell. However, the extra elastic energy is lacking in this case, causing a progressive decrease in power output.

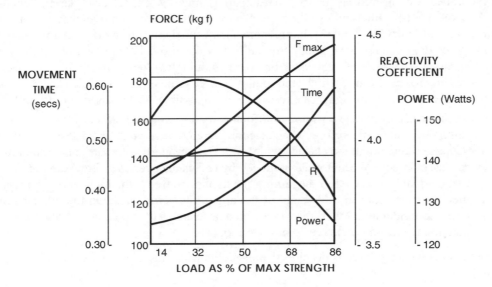

Figure 4.2 Changes in maximal force (Fmax), movement time (t), reactivity coefficient (R) and power of jumping (with a barbell on the shoulders) with increasing load (Siff & Verkhoshansky, 1999).

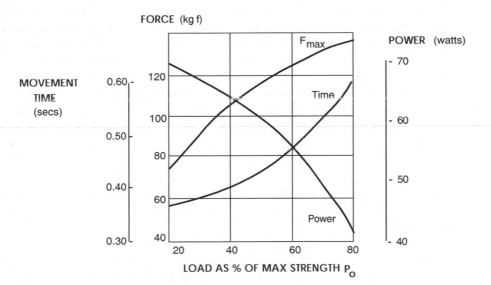

Figure 4.3 Changes in maximal force (Fmax), power and movement time (Time) for the leg-press with respect to increasing resistance (Siff & Verkhoshansky, 1999).

Other factors influence the working effect of a movement against resistance. Variations in the magnitude of the load, the regime of muscular work, the speed and tempo of the movement, the number of repetitions per set and the duration of the rest interval between sets significantly change the biomechanical characteristics of the movement and, consequently, the overall training effect. Therefore, in each case the selection of a particular work regime with resistance must be based upon the specific type of strength displayed in the specialised exercises.

It should also be added that the resistance, its speed of movement and the duration of the work determine how it influences which muscles produce the movement, the coordination of their actions and the instant when the work ceases. The most stable indicator of the coordination of muscular activity during the repetitive lifting of a barbell is the sequential involvement of the same specific muscles which are essential to the given movement.

In an experiment using 60% of 1RM, the muscles taking part in the work remained the same for 82% of the time in all athletes. With 80% of 1RM weights, the degree of consistency was less (thereby showing greater individuality), but was higher for qualified athletes. The coordination of muscular activity was also disrupted by fatigue (Pakhomov, 1967).

In addition, the relative contributions by the participating muscles can change during repetitive work (Lazareva, 1966, Kozlov, 1966). The number of muscle groups involved with a movement can either decrease (Moikin, 1964) or increase (Averyanov, 1963). In movements executed with little effort or low velocity a large part of the work involves the muscles of the body's distal links (Tochilov, 1946; Kosilov, 1948; Vinogradov, 1951). For movements against significant resistance or executed at high velocity, the activity characteristically shifts to the muscles of the proximal links, which tend to play a more tonic or postural role. These findings reveal that muscle isolation under conditions of significant resistance is impossible, as discussed later (4.2.9).

Thus, the factors just discussed have a profound influence on the working effect of the movement and the specificity of the strength developed. Therefore, when selecting strength exercises against resistance, one should consider these factors in accordance with the characteristics of the given sport, with particular attention being paid to the distinctive effects associated with the torque produced by resistance exercises. For example, in the starting position for the squat and squat jumps (before beginning the dynamic effort), the muscles of the legs and torso have already developed tension equal to the weight of the apparatus being held. On the other hand, with the snatch or clean-and-jerk, the fundamental working force which accelerates the apparatus is developed practically from zero. Thus, we can divide resistance exercises into two groups:

- Exercises in which the working force is developed after preliminary muscular tension (equal to the weight of the apparatus)

- Exercises in which force is developed from zero, without appreciable preliminary muscular tension.

The main difference between these groups of exercises is that the exercises in the first group do not appreciably influence the processes connected with physiological changes in the muscles (the excitation-tension link). Consequently, depending upon the amount of weight used, conditions are created chiefly for developing muscular strength or the speed of muscular contraction, but not the speed with which muscles switch from rest to the active state. The conditions of muscular work in the second group of exercises have the simultaneous potential for developing dynamic strength, speed of movement and especially starting strength. This is not simply relevant to understanding movement dynamics, but is very significant for improving strength training methods.

Finally, based upon the conditions under which force is applied, exercises should be distinguished by force directed against the *weight* of a load and by force directed against the *inertia* of a load. In the first case, if one lifts a barbell, for example, the working force of the movement is equal to $F = m(g+a)$, i.e. determined by the mass of the load and the acceleration against gravity. In the second case, the force of the movement is equal to $F = ma$, i.e. dependent only upon the load's force of inertia, moving with a certain acceleration. Examples of such conditions are throwing, sprinting out of the starting blocks and punching, i.e. those situations when strength operates in a direction approximately perpendicular to the gravitational force. The differences in the biomechanics of these types of movements are quite significant.

In the first case (overcoming weight), muscular force initially becomes equal to the amount of weight to be lifted (developed under virtually isometric conditions), then it exceeds it as motion begins, it proceeds to accelerate the load, and then it increases further as it exceeds the weight of the apparatus (see Figs 2.1, 2.13). The preliminary isometric muscular tension causes a large gradient of *acceleration-strength*.

In the second case (overcoming inertia), if friction and the resistance of the surroundings are excluded, then movement of the load begins with insignificant propulsive force. Further changes in the latter are caused wholly by the speed of muscular contraction or, more precisely, the ability of the muscles to move the load by simultaneous production of maximal strength and maximum speed of contraction.

Consequently, under conditions where strength resists the *weight* of the load, primarily the strength component is stimulated. Under conditions where strength is directed against the *inertia* of the load, predominantly the speed of muscular contraction is stimulated.

Thus, in the second case, it is easy to appreciate the possibility for overcoming the opposing tendency between the weight of the load and the speed of muscular contraction. Unfortunately, the necessary specialised equipment for producing muscular work to overcome the inertia of a load is rarely used in training. However, to extend the methods of special strength training, one must consider this concept of *inertial training* more seriously. There are two possible solutions: the application of force (e.g. a thrust) against a horizontal wheel or a suspended load (like a pendulum), or the spinning of a heavy flywheel ergometer by the arms or the legs (e.g. Fig 4.4). In the first example, one can vary the amount of weight and in the second, the moment of inertia of the flywheel to affect speed of contraction. One may use upper body or lower body ergometer flywheel devices in several different ways - accelerating against high inertia, using the heavy wheel to compel one to operate at a certain cadence, and opposing the angular momentum via eccentric muscle action to decelerate the wheel. One may combine all of these methods in short bursts or mixed bursts to offer a varied training regime.

Work with weights should be examined as a special case. Weights are used extensively for increasing the difficulty of movement to develop various motor abilities. Elastic bands are also frequently used as a means of resisting movement, although the character of the force produced depends upon the elastic properties of the material, which limits the effectiveness of these means. Elastic force occurs in accordance with Hooke's Law: $F = k.x$, where k is the spring constant and x is the extension. Thus, elastic force increases with degree of extension, so that resistance begins from zero value and increases with movement range. Therefore, elastic materials should not be used for developing *starting-strength* in ballistic movements or for developing *explosive-strength*.

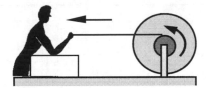

Figure 4.4 Inertial Training by turning a flywheel via the use of elbow flexion (Verkhoshansky, 1977).

It is another matter regarding *strength-endurance* over a selected range. In this case, one can select the length and elasticity of the band so that its resistance will change minimally over the working amplitude of the movement. This method is sometimes used by swimmers for developing strength endurance in pulling movements (Fig 4.5).

Figure 4.5 Elasticised cable exercise for developing strength-endurance in swimming (Verkhoshansky, 1977).

In using elastics in general, the tension always increases with range of movement and this may readily be decreased at 'sticking points' by moving towards the point of attachment of the bands, or conversely, if the tension is still not great enough, one can move away from the point of attachment. Thus, one can tend to overcome the major limitation of elastics, namely their nature to increase tension throughout the range (since tension is proportional to extension, according to Hooke's Law). Resistance can be varied over the full range of movement by accelerating free weights when resistance is decreasing (so-called "Compensatory Acceleration Training') or by using special varying resistance machines, and this method of altering elastic length by postural adjustment also allows one to use elastics to optimise resistance, if required.

The methods of resisted movement are extremely diverse. In each case they are determined by the exercise and the resolution of two tasks: stimulation of muscular contraction and facilitation of transfer to the natural conditions of the movement (for example, putting a regulation shot after training with an overweight one). Movements can be made more difficult with small weights, thereby insignificantly increasing the mass of the body or its links. This may be accomplished with belts, weights, cuffs, sandbags, boots and other apparatus.

This effect can also be obtained by exercising in water, in deep snow, up a hill, on the beach, or rowing against a rowing ergometer. Exercises with weights are not necessarily adequate for developing speed of movement (e.g. using the speed of unloaded movement or movement against a relatively small external resistance), especially for highly qualified athletes.

Careful analysis of experimental and empirical data indicates that increasing the speed of movement through resistance exercises (i.e. to develop absolute muscular strength) is primarily for novice athletes. This is completely justified for augmenting muscular strength, and from a physiological standpoint promotes quicker execution of movement. However, this factor quickly exhausts its value. Initially a positive influence, it becomes negative, because resistance exercises not only can enhance the physiological processes essential for facilitating rapid movement, but can also have a detrimental effect on them.

If one is referring to speed-strength movements (characterised by explosive force) associated with overcoming significant resistance, then resistance exercises are definitely useful, but only in those cases when they are executed in certain types of muscular work, at a reasonable volume, at specific stages of training, in a way which is specific to the given sport.

4.2.3 Kinetic Energy and Strength Processes

Consider the case where a training device, such as a barbell, possesses some velocity attained by falling from some height, and the athlete's task consists of first actively stopping it, then quickly thrusting it upwards (Fig 4.6).

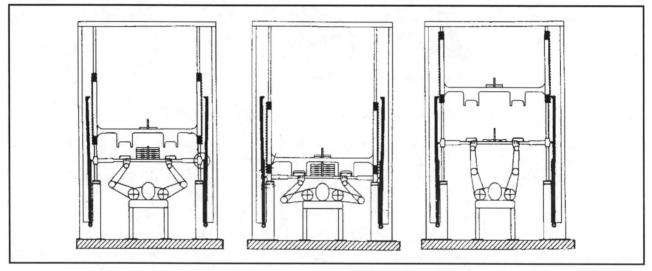

Figure 4.6 Thrusting a load upwards after it has fallen from a given height. This plyometric bench press device was designed by R Adcock, A Chantler, H Glyn-Jones and T Rademeyer, students in the School of Mechanical Engineering at the University of the Witwatersrand as part of a senior biomechanics project (1992).

Under similar circumstances the total muscular working force developed by eccentric amortisation followed by active concentric work may be calculated from $F = m(g+a)$, where the acceleration $a = V^2/2.s$, from the equation $V^2 = u^2 + 2a.s$:

$$F = m (V_1^2/2S_1 + g) + m (V_2^2/2S_2 + g).$$

where V_1, V_2 refer to the velocity of the barbell at displacements S_1 and S_2 respectively, m is the mass of the barbell, and g is the acceleration due to gravity.

A characteristic of such a movement is that much of the kinetic energy of the apparatus is transformed during the amortisation phase into elastic energy, which is then used in the subsequent concentric work. If energy losses by processes such as heat generation and viscous damping in the muscle complex are excluded as a first approximation, this elastic energy is equal to the kinetic energy of the apparatus at the end of its fall (KE = mgh where m = mass, h = the height of the fall and g = acceleration due to gravity). The muscular force developed at the instant of switching from eccentric to concentric work will be greater for a shorter amortisation phase and a shorter braking time. This applies strictly to those conditions when the action as a whole is aimed at thrusting the apparatus with maximum speed immediately after it has been stopped.

Thus, what we are referring to is completely different from the traditional production of muscular tension. The external mechanical stimulus is not so much the weight (and its force of inertia) as the energy accumulated after its free-fall.

If one considers the dynamics of muscular work with variations of the take-off in the vertical jump for example (Fig 4.7), it may be seen that such a means of stimulating muscular tension offers significant advantages, namely:

1. It develops maximal dynamic force very rapidly
2. The magnitude of this maximum is significantly larger than that produced by other methods
3. A large maximal force is achieved without the use of additional resistance
4. Change from eccentric to concentric work occurs far more rapidly than with other methods
5. The significant elastic energy accumulated (without additional resistance) during the amortisation phase produces muscular work of greater power in the thrust phase and faster muscular contraction, which may be inferred from the greater height attained by the body during the subsequent upward drive.

Thus, stimulation of muscular tension by absorption of the energy of the athlete's falling body or a training apparatus can produce a large force of muscular contraction without using weights (which is impossible with other means of mechanical stimulation). This is achieved not only without decreasing the speed of muscular contraction, but even increasing it in comparison with the usual resistance methods.

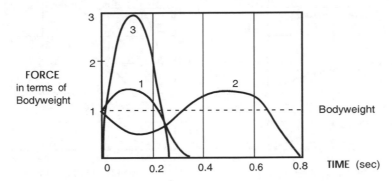

Figure 4.7 The development of force for various vertical jumps: (1) jumping from rest from a low squat (2) the usual jump with a dip or amortisation phase (3) after a depth-jump from 0.4 metre. The jump heights reached were 0.67m, 0.74m and 0.80m respectively. (Verkhoshansky, 1977).

The first experimental steps taken to study this principle of muscular stimulation revealed its particular effectiveness in developing explosive strength and starting strength. The potential for developing starting strength generally is limited because it depends upon one's ability to concentrate intensively on a specific voluntary effort.

This strength is acquired very slowly in training because particularly stressful conditions are required, namely a stimulus of such intensity that it provokes the appropriate adaptive reaction. Even the wide variety of popular resistance strength exercises usually do not fulfill these requirements, despite the fact that they usually require force to be developed from rest.

Several studies suggest that such exercises can have a place if, for example, muscular tension is achieved by means of an abrupt stretch at the instant when a falling body or object is stopped (Ramsey, 1944; Hill, 1955; Tweit et al, 1963). It should be emphasized that significant and almost instantaneous development of muscular tension in this case is due to the mechanical stimulation of proprioceptors in the neuromuscular system, which creates the conditions for developing starting strength and explosiveness of muscular action.

Thus, we have a specific work regime which no heavy resistance exercise can imitate, because stimulation of muscular activity with significant extra resistance slows down the transition from eccentric to concentric work. The utilisation of energy of a falling body or object for mechanical stimulation requires the muscles to initially develop significant elastic tension, use it in overcoming the inertia of a relatively small weight, then quickly switch to concentric work and produce a high speed of muscle contraction.

The role of kinetic energy in stimulating explosive muscle action warrants detailed analysis. To do this in the laboratory a special experimental stand was constructed to measure the height attained by a load when a subject threw it upward after it had first fallen from some height (from 0.5 to 3.0 metres). The kinetic energy used for muscle stimulation changed according to the weight (3.3, 6.6, 9.9 and 13.3% of the maximum isometric strength) and the height of the fall (Verkhoshansky, 1977). The experiment showed that an increase in kinetic energy caused by an increase in the mass of the load decreases the height to which a load is thrown, but an increase in the distance through which a load falls increases the height to which it is thrown (Fig 4.8a).

A similar picture emerges from research on reactive ability (Fig 4.8b). This tendency, in general, is displayed by movements executed under other conditions, although these have their own peculiarities (Figs 4.9, 4.10). These examples show clearly that it is not beneficial to increase kinetic energy by use of heavier loads. It is therefore necessary to examine a better means of increasing the thrust height. The depth jump which has immediate practical significance for developing jumping ability is given in the example illustrated in Figure 4.10. Here maximal force (Fmax) increases up to a height of 1.15 metres, then diminishes sharply, while movement time begins by changing insignificantly, then increasing sharply. Maximum power and reactivity are achieved using a drop height of approximately 0.75 metres.

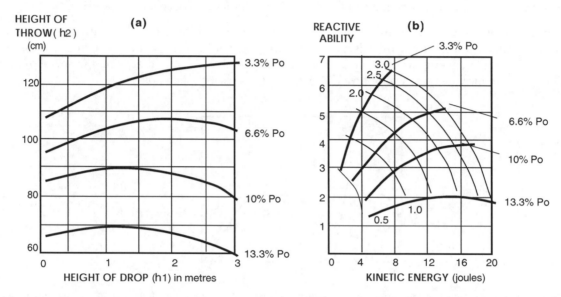

Figure 4.8 (a) Changes in height (h2) of thrown loads of different mass (in terms of maximum isometric strength Po), after having fallen from different heights (h1) **(b)** Changes in reactivity coefficient (RC) with respect to the kinetic energy of the falling load. (Verkhoshansky, 1977).

Thus, the optimal range of depth jumping for the stimulation of muscular activity is 0.75-1.15 metres, because at the lower end of this range the muscles are working at maximal power and at the upper end they are working at maximal dynamic force. This finding forms the basis for the recommendations for using depth jumps in the training of advanced jumpers (Verkhoshansky 1963, 1964, 1966), though it is preferable to err on the conservative side of using considerably lower jump heights with anyone who is unused to this type of training and to strictly limit the volume of this type of 'shock' training.

Further increases in the height of the depth jump significantly decrease the magnitude of the dynamic parameters of the take-off. The support time increases quickly, primarily because the phase of switching from eccentric to concentric work is lengthened. In addition, the maximum dynamic force of take-off and the speed of muscular contraction stabilise and do not increase any further.

The take-off comprises two distinct actions: *amortisation* (where the kinetic energy of the fall is absorbed), and the *thrust* proper. The amortisation is characterised by the increasing depth of the resulting knee flexion, and the thrust proper by a fairly constant speed of muscle contraction. Thus, the positive effect of muscle stimulation by absorption of kinetic energy from a fall can be used successfully only under certain conditions by taking into consideration the optimal height of the fall, bodymass, additional load, and any other factors which may facilitate a quick take-off.

However, the state of the neuromuscular system during the amortisation phase of the falling body also can play an independent training role. Tension developed reflexively during this phase enhances the ability of the muscles to switch quickly to the active state. Experience indicates that this is not detrimental to speed-strength preparation and the musculoskeletal support apparatus, although further research is required in order to make definitive practical recommendations in this area.

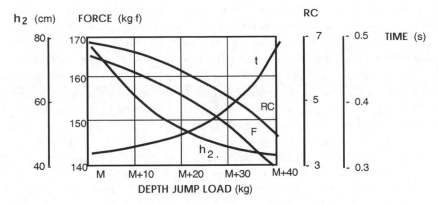

Figure 4.9 Take-off characteristics after an unloaded depth-jump (M = mass of athlete) and with an extra 10, 20, 30 and 40 kg load. RC is the reactivity coefficient, t is the time, F is the force and h_2 is the height of the subsequent jump. (Verkhoshansky, 1977).

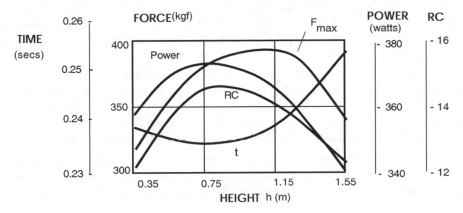

Figure 4.10 Take-off characteristics after depth jumping from gradually greater heights (h). RC is the reactivity coefficient, Fmax is the maximal force and t is the ground contact time. (Verkhoshansky, 1977).

Therefore, muscle stimulation by the absorption of energy of a falling body can be a very effective method of loading, the basis of which lies in the ability of the muscles to contract more powerfully after a sharp preliminary stretch. This mechanism enables one to successfully overcome the force of body inertia in emergency situations, which proves to be of particular value in sport.

Preliminary muscle stretching has a place in a number of strength exercises such as squats and jumps with a barbell on the shoulders. However, these exercises are not as intensely impulsive as exercises which brake the velocity of a preliminary fall and display a sharp, shock-like character.

Therefore, the method of muscle stimulation by means of absorbing the kinetic energy of a fall, now known as plyometrics, was originally called the 'shock method' (Verkhoshansky 1966, 1968). Research by Verkhoshansky (1958, 1976) took the first serious steps in studying and formulating this method and much subsequent research has corroborated its effectiveness in specific applications (Kuznetsov, 1966; Papysheva, 1966; Chudinov, 1966; Chernesheva, 1967; Semenov, 1967; Tatian, 1974; Khodykin, 1975). However, more work is needed in the laboratory and under training conditions before its full scope is covered.

4.2.4 Isometric Training

In athletics, isometric exercises were very popular in the mid-1950s as a result of the search for economical and effective methods of developing strength. Hettinger and Muller (1953, 1955) established that one daily effort of two-thirds of one's maximum exerted for six seconds at a time for 10 weeks will increase strength about 5% per week, while Clark et al (1954) found that static strength continues to increase even after the conclusion of a four-week programme of isometric exercises.

The success of isometric training provoked considerable research, much of it being concerned with the question of its effectiveness compared with dynamic training. This research produced rather contradictory data (see review by Verkhoshansky, 1970). However, research produced the general conclusion that isometric training can be more effective than dynamic exercises in those cases where the specific exercise requires muscle contraction of large magnitude at a certain stage of a movement or during the early stages of injury rehabilitation.

If the specific exercise involves high-speed movement, then sustained isometric training is less effective. Research indicates that there are distinct differences between the training effects of static and dynamic exercises. It is important that muscular tension should be increased slowly and be held for a relatively long time when executing isometric exercises, because the usual purpose of isometric training is to develop *absolute strength*. Prolonged maintenance of muscular tension requires an energy expenditure which stimulates adequate adaptation in the neuromuscular system, thereby determining its strength potential. The increase in strength can be more significant than that produced by transient dynamic tension. If one notes the fact that some researchers have not discovered an essential difference in the growth of strength produced by muscle tension of various intensities, then it is obvious that the fundamental conditioning factor is not so much the magnitude of the isometric tension as its duration.

A technique which may be referred to as *oscillatory isometrics* may also be useful in producing powerful contractions over a small range of movement. This is corroborated by research which showed the maximum tension that can be produced voluntarily during sinusoidally pulsed brief isometric jerks at 5 Hz is the same as the maximum sustained tension (Soechting & Roberts, 1975). Basmajian (1978) commented that this emphasizes the importance of muscle fibre recruitment in the gradation of tension and synchronisation of motor unit activity during the short bursts of loading.

In other applications, short periods of low frequency mechanical vibration (10-35 Hz) on the body have been shown to induce faster recovery, have a positive effect on different body systems, modulate muscle activity, elicit a higher stable state of strength and power, lower arterial pressure, and enhance oxidative processes (Kopysov, 1978; Lebedev & Peliakov, 1991). More recently, it has been found that powerful whole body vibrations imposed at 26 Hz through the lower extremities produces marked increases in jumping power (Bosco et al, 1998).

These findings may relate to a similar impulsive loading process which is associated with the training effects of plyometrics, thereby adding further fuel to the debate (Ingen Schenau et al, 1997) about which of the following effects may predominate during plyometrics: elastic energy storage/utilisation in the soft tissues, neural facilitation or intrinsic muscle changes.

At this point it must be stressed that isometric training is not simply a matter of holding a static muscle contraction for a given time. Isometric contraction requires a muscle to increase its tension from rest to a maximum or sub-maximal value over a certain time (rise or 'attack' time), to sustain this tension for another period (the resistance phase) and to decrease this tension to rest or a lower value (decay time). Consequently, one may distinguish between *explosive isometrics*, which have a very brief rise time, and *slow isometrics*, with a much longer rise time (Fig 4.12). The isometric contraction may be produced by voluntary contraction or involuntarily by the reflex response of the muscle between the eccentric and concentric phases of plyometric activities such as the depth jump or weightlifting clean-and-jerk. The different types of isometric contraction are categorised in Figure 4.11.

Each class of isometric training produces its own distinct training effects. If isometric exercises are executed with the accent on the speed of developing force, then they can be as effective for developing explosive strength as dynamic exercises. The steepness of the force-time curve (Fig 3.3) and the greater magnitude of maximum isometric than dynamic maximum force for equivalent joint angles is the basis for this assertion. Therefore, *it is doubtful whether it is always productive to maintain a rigid distinction between dynamic and isometric exercise*. In general, the harder the muscles work in overcoming large resistance, the more closely the work becomes isometric, as may be seen from the force-velocity curves of muscle action (Figs 3.15 & 3.16). In other words, *isometric work is really the limiting case of dynamic work as the velocity of movement tends to zero*. Furthermore, because the inhibitory effects usually associated with voluntary muscle action are not encountered in reflexive isometric contraction, even greater explosive force can be displayed isometrically than dynamically.

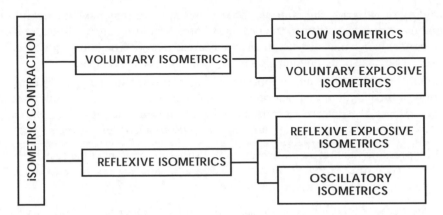

Figure 4.11 Categorisation of the different types of isometric muscle contraction.

In connection with this, it makes sense to distinguish *isometric training for developing absolute strength* and *isometric training for developing explosive strength* and to use one or the other in the appropriate circumstances. However, this still requires detailed experimental corroboration. Nevertheless, isometrics should not be neglected as a means of strength development, so that negative evaluations of this method are premature.

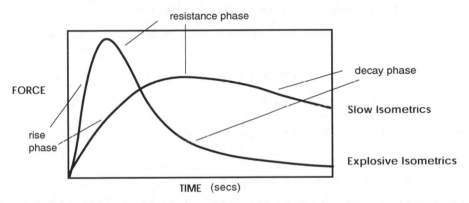

Figure 4.12 Comparison of slow and explosive isometric action, distinguished by their force-time characteristics. The slope of the rise phase is even greater and the duration of the resistance phase is much shorter during reflexive explosive isometric action.

It is necessary to bear in mind the following advantages of isometric training, as emphasized by its proponents:

1. It requires very simple apparatus.

2. It can locally exercise any muscle group at a specific joint angle. During dynamic work the display of maximal effort at the necessary joint angle can be achieved only for a fraction of a second. In some cases, this is generally not possible since the movement's inertia quickly moves the apparatus through that position at which the muscular tension would yield the greatest effect. Such a joint angle can be fixed precisely during isometric training.

3. The training is very productive, if the time expended is considered. Each 6-second isometric contraction is equivalent in its effect to many dynamic contractions (of the ballistic type) in which maximal force lasts no more than 0.1 second. From a practical standpoint this means that 10 minutes of isometric tension in specially selected exercises can replace a fatiguing hour of training with weights.

4. There is an insignificant increase in muscle mass and bodymass in comparison with dynamic strength work, particularly with pressing exercises.

5. There is usually a far smaller expenditure of time and energy than with dynamic weight training. It is possible to preserve a high level of speed-strength in the period of crucial competitions.

6. It offers a greater potential than dynamic exercises for using visual and kinaesthetic cues to hold any given position. This gives isometrics a distinct advantage for studying and correcting errors.

Isometrics have the following drawbacks: they fatigue the nervous system, may have a harmful effect on the cardiovascular system in some individuals (due to the prolonged breath-holding and consequent elevated blood pressure), disturb coordination, enhance muscle performance only close to a specific joint angle, decrease speed of movement, and diminish soft tissue elasticity and functional range of dynamic movement.

However, with proper uniform breathing, an appropriate sequence of work and rest pauses between exercises for relaxation, and limitation of the length of contraction to no more than 6 seconds (some authors recommend 10 seconds), the harmful after-effects of isometric exercises can be minimised (see Figs 5.2, 5.3). The following methods of execution are recommended for developing *absolute strength* with isometric exercises:

1. Tension is produced by pressing against an immovable solid structure or against the resistance of a partner. The shortcoming of this type of exercise is that the increase in tension resulting from training can be estimated only subjectively, unless a dynamometer is used.

2. Tension is produced by using a load which is raised and held for a specified period. A variation of this method involves shifting the load slowly over a wide working range with stops at different joint angles (quasi-isometrics). This enables one to work the muscle's entire range and assess the growth of strength by the increase in training weight.

3. Tension is produced by pushing a weight from a lower support to reach and press against an upper stop (e.g. on a so-called 'power rack'). This method begins with a short dynamic phase and gives the athlete a specific idea of the magnitude of the tension. He can lift the weight several times between the stops then execute an isometric contraction for the necessary duration against the upper stop.

4. Tension is produced by using a dynamometer or other resistance device to control and display the magnitude of muscular tension.

In all cases using non-explosive isometrics it is necessary to:

*   apply force gradually to the immovable object
*   hold the maximal tension for no longer than 8 seconds (see Fig 5.2)
*   perform the maximal contractions for 6 repetitions (Fig 5.3)
*   use a 5-10 second rest between repetitions (see 5.2.1)
*   limit the total duration of isometric training to 10 minutes per session
*   finish the training session with relaxation exercises.

If the purpose is to develop *explosive strength*, then the isometric tension should be generated with the maximum speed possible to a magnitude of 70-80% of one's maximum strength. The reflexive explosive isometric action produced by plyometric movements can be extremely effective in this respect.

Isometric exercises can be very diverse, depending upon the reasons for their use, so that is very difficult to recommend specific exercises in each case. Athletes who understand the basic rules of isometric training can choose the necessary exercises, provided that this selection is based on the principle of dynamic correspondence and personal inventiveness.

Isometric Training and Angular Specificity

Many studies have reported that isometric training produces maximum strength gains at or very close to the angle at which the isometric contractions are used (e.g. see 1.3), with the result that athletes often avoid using any form of isometric training. This observation of angular specificity must be viewed more critically, in that other studies have shown that isometric training also produces significant strength increase over a range of up to as much as 15 degrees on either side of the training angle. Moreover, as with all strength measurements, there is a specific force or torque versus joint angle curve for each type of muscle contraction (see 2.1.2), so that it is highly unlikely that strength increase would be confined to a very precise angle and nowhere else in the range. As discussed in Section 1.3, it is more accurate to refer to *regional specificity*, rather than angular specificity (or muscle length specificity).

Recent work has revealed that this regional specificity of isometric training tends to be exhibited most strongly when the muscle is most shortened and least when the muscle is most lengthened (Thepault-Mathieu et al, 1988). In this study, a group of males training isometrically (for 5 weeks with 5 sets of 5 repetitions held for 5 seconds three times a week) at an angle of elbow flexion of 25 degrees (full extension = 0°) showed a strength increase of 54% at the training angle and an average increase of about 25% over the remainder of range. A second group training at an elbow angle of 80° increased their strength by 30% at the training angle and about 25% over the rest of the range. Finally, a third group training at 120° increased their strength by 25% at the training angle, but only by about 7% over the remainder of range.

In other words, isometric training of muscles in a relatively lengthened state can produce substantial strength increase not only near the region of training, but also throughout the range of movement. This finding, however, should not be interpreted to mean that isometric training can replace other forms of strength training, because the production of a specific type of static or dynamic strength depends on neuromuscular factors which govern the pattern and manner in which muscular force is to be exerted in a given situation.

Isometric Endurance

Isometric endurance with resistance exceeding 10-15 percent of a muscle's maximal strength is very short compared with that of dynamic exercise, because of metabolic demands and the impairment in blood flow to the exercising muscles by the intense muscle contraction (Petrofsky & Phillips, 1986). Exercise involving less than this level of muscle tension are considered to be non-fatiguing, since the intramuscular pressure is low and readily exceeded by the mean arterial pressure rising in the capillaries (Fig 4.13).

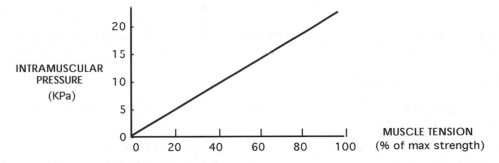

Figure 4.13 Mean intramuscular pressure in soleus and gastrocnemius of a cat measured during electrical stimulation at different muscle tensions (based on Petrofsky & Hendershot, 1984)

As muscle tension increases, intramuscular pressure also increases and metabolism is unable to meet the physiological demands of the exercise, resulting in a hyperbolic drop in performance and marked increase in fatigue (Fig 4.14). This curve was originally derived by Monod and Sherrer (1967) and later by Rohmert (1968), then becoming known as a Rohmert curve. As can be seen from Figure 4.14, there is a marked difference in endurance between the muscles of males and females, with the latter being able to sustain the same tension for longer periods than the former at any level of tension, a finding which has not been adequately explained yet.

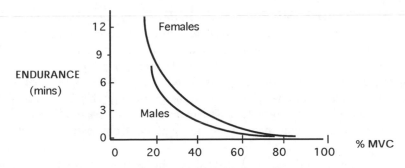

Figure 4.14 Rohmert curve: Isometric endurance of finger flexors for males and females (based on Petrofsky, 1980). MVC is the Maximum Voluntary Contraction.

Isometric endurance is also profoundly affected by muscle temperature, with hot packs reducing endurance and icing prior to exercise increasing endurance. Research by Clarke et al (1958) discovered that there is an optimum core muscle temperature above and below which isometric muscle endurance fairly rapidly decreases (Fig 4.14), with others later showing that this optimal temperature lies around 27-28 Celsius (Petrofsky & Phillips, 1986). It was also found that the greater the percentage of bodyfat on an individual, the lower the isometric endurance in most situations, because of the higher resting muscle temperature. Temperature also exerts different effects for the different types of muscle action, with dynamic exercise taking place more efficiently at higher temperatures, apparently because of reduced environmental tissue viscosity at these temperatures. In the case of isometric contraction, muscle fibres do not move during the contractions, viscosity of the medium would appear to play an insignificant role compared with that of muscle metabolism (Petrofsky & Phillips, 1986).

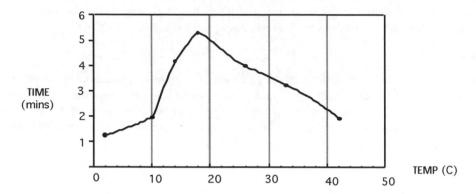

Figure 4.15 Mean variation in isometric endurance measured in human subjects after 30 minutes of forearm immersion in water baths at increasing temperature (based on Clarke et al, 1958).

Recovery after Isometric Activity

Recovery from isometric contraction is different from that of dynamic muscle action. It appears to take place in three phases (Petrofsky & Phillips, 1986):

- Rapid recovery of about 50% of endurance during the first 3 minutes after exercise
- A slower recovery lasting about 20 minutes during which recovery reaches about 90% of initial endurance
- A complete recovery within at least 24 hours.

Interestingly, recovery from low tension isometric contraction is slower during the first phases of recovery.

Other Aspects of Isometric Activity

Isometric contraction is always distinguished from the dynamic forms of muscle contraction (concentric and eccentric), as if it is due to an entirely different process. *Irrespective of whether a muscle contraction produces or does not produce external movement of a joint, the process of contraction remains the same.* Nervous impulses reaching the muscle fibres produce a sliding of myosin and actin filaments relative to one another until fatigue sets in and relaxation occurs.

The difference between static and dynamic muscle contraction lies not in the muscle, but in the nervous system which controls the intensity, speed, duration, type and pattern of contraction. It is the nervous system which recruits a specific group and number of muscle fibres at a particular rate, time and sequence. It activates prime movers, antagonists, assistant movers, emergency muscles and other groups of muscles to produce the necessary controlled movement of a given joint or series of joints. What needs to be appreciated is the fact that the concept of isometrics is far broader than is intimated by most texts on training. Little is said about how the isometric contractions are initiated, controlled or terminated. The main focus appears to be on the intensity and duration of the contraction rather than on the overall pattern of muscle action from resting state back to resting state after activity.

As discussed earlier, isometric contraction always takes place automatically during some stage of the transition between concentric and eccentric muscle action. Under voluntary control, isometric contraction may be initiated or terminated slowly or rapidly, and maintained for a certain duration at a specific percentage of one's maximal strength for one repetition (for a particular joint action).

Maintenance of a maximal isometric contraction, however, depends ultimately on autonomic responses produced by muscle fatigue or protective reflexes elicited in the muscles or connective tissues. Motivation may overcome the negative feedback from these tissues for somewhat longer, but voluntary activation of the muscles eventually becomes impossible and rest becomes necessary.

4.2.1.5 An Integrated Theory of Electrostimulation

Therefore, it appears as if macroelectric cellular stimulation (MACS - currents exceeding one milliamp) acts as a physiological stressor, which in the short term causes the typical alarm response described by Selye (1975). This is supported by the work of Eriksson et al (1981), who found that the acute effects of traditional ES are similar to those found for intense voluntary exercise. Furthermore, Gambke et al (1985) have found in animal studies that long-term MACS causes some muscle fibres to degenerate and be replaced by newly formed fibres from satellite cell proliferation. This fibre necrosis occurs a few days after application of ES and seems to affect mainly the FT fibres. The fact that the various muscle fibres do not transform at the same time may be due to different thresholds of each fibre to the stimulus that elicits the transformation. Possibly, the earlier changes might induce subsequent ones.

Thus, if Selye's General Adaptation Syndrome model (see 1.16) is applied to MACS-type stimulation, the body would have to draw on its superficial adaptation energy stores and adapt to the ES-imposed stress by increasing strength or endurance, or by initiating transformation of muscle fibre types. If the ES is too intense, too prolonged or inappropriately used to augment a weight training programme, adaptation might not occur or it might increase the proportion of slow twitch fibres and thereby reduce strength. This could explain some of the negative research findings discussed earlier.

Furthermore, excessively demanding MACS conceivably might cause the body to draw on its deep adaptation energy and lead to permanent tissue damage. Consequently, any athlete who may derive definite performance benefits from MACS should not assume that increased dosage will lead to further improvement. The contrary may well prove to be true.

Microelectric cellular stimulation (MICS - currents below one milliamp), on the other hand, would not act as a stressor. Instead, the evidence implies that it elicits biochemical changes associated with enhanced adaptation, growth and repair. Since MICS appears to operate more on the basis of resonant attunement of the stimulus to cellular and subcellular processes, the specific therapeutic effects are determined by how efficiently the stimulation parameters match the electrical characteristic of the different cells, in particular, their impedance at different frequencies.   MICS may be applied in several ways to facilitate restoration:

*   locally over specific soft tissues
*   transcranially via electrodes on the earlobes or on sites on the surface of the skull
*   at acupuncture points on the body, hands or ears.

It is generally entirely safe to apply MICS anywhere on the body, because the current and energy transmitted is too low to produce any thermal or electrolytic effects on vital tissues. Under no circumstances should MACS be applied across the brain, as it can cause serious harm. It is generally not advisable to apply any form of ES to epileptics, pregnant women, cardiac patients or persons with heart pacemakers.

4.2.1.6 The Use of Electrostimulation in Training

The summary of successful applications of ES in numerous situations which are relevant to all athletes makes it unfortunate that its value has been assessed largely in terms of its direct and often contradictory effects on isometric or isokinetic strength. Enhanced recuperation, improved endurance, diminished residual muscle tension, pain relief, efficient massage, modification of muscle fibre type, increase in mobility, increased speed of muscle contraction and reduction of certain musculoskeletal abnormalities together supply an impressive variety of possible aids to any training programme. Coupled with this is the observation that some ES procedures integrated into carefully periodised training schedules may significantly increase strength, muscular endurance and power.

The Integrated Use of Electrostimulation

Electrostimulation can provide a valuable additional means of restoration and is generally of greater importance than as a means of stressing the muscles. This type of restoration (Siff & Yessis, 1992) may be applied *locally* to specific muscle groups, other soft tissues or joints, or *generally* across the central nervous system (transcranially, on specific acupuncture points or between the brain and the lumbar spine), using very low current devices at low frequencies (characteristically between 0.5-8 Hz).

Several researchers (Purvin, Deniskin, Khodykin) studied the integration of ES into other regimes of training. They found that the use of ES first, followed by plyometrics produces a greater training effect than the reverse

Isometric contractions may be submaximal or maximal, short or long duration (depending on the length and frequency of rest intervals), continuous or intermittent, sequenced over a series of different joint angles, alternated between agonist and antagonist (or adductor and abductor, or medial and lateral rotators), and alternated between different intensities. One can voluntarily oscillate isometric contractions between high and low levels of intensity, thereby prolonging the period of its application. Isometrics performed very slowly over a given range of joint action have been referred to earlier as *quasi-isometrics* (see 1.10).

We have already learned that the stretch reflex may also be recruited impulsively following an eccentric contraction, forming the basis of the training method known as *plyometrics*. What is often overlooked is the fact that termination of the eccentric amortisation phase is followed by a brief isometric contraction (reflexive explosive isometric action) augmenting the force produced by the elastic recoil of the stretched connective tissue (such as the tendons).

One criticism of traditional training is that coaches erroneously believe that muscle action is most efficient if initiated from a completely relaxed state. Their justification is that initial tension hinders subsequent action and produces a slower or less controlled movement. As pointed out earlier, isometric contraction released explosively can decrease the reaction response time by as much as 7%, particularly if associated with a strong pre-stretch. Verkhoshansky stresses that, *when a movement is produced from a state of complete relaxation, the subsequent action is usually slower and less forceful.*

In the pioneering days of DeLorme, Hettinger and Müller, much emphasis was placed on the importance of isometric effort, but with the advent of gymnasium machines and the demise of Charles Atlas' dynamic tension mail-order programmes, isometrics has all but fallen into oblivion as a training modality. Nevertheless, its role continues to be recognised by physical therapists in the early stages of injury rehabilitation and by Russian coaches who often prescribe the 75% concentrics, 15% eccentrics, 10% isometrics strength training regime advocated by their scientists for the average athlete.

Sometimes the isometric holding of a heavy load at certain 'sticking points' in an exercise can decrease any deficiencies in that region or prime the nervous system to cope with greater levels of loading which will eventually be encountered during the process of gradual progressive overload. For example, the mere supporting of a supramaximal load (e.g. 120-150% of one's 1RM) on the shoulders or quasi-isometric movement over the first few degrees of knee flexion of a squat can accustom the body neuromuscularly and favourably enhance one's mental perception to undertake future squats which are going to be only slightly heavier than one's current 1RM.

An appreciation of its value and breadth of application should restore isometrics to a place of importance in all training programmes. Since one of the basic principles of PNF is that mobility, or dynamic contraction, is more primitive than stability or isometric contraction, then stability is at a higher level of muscular learning(see 7.2). Correct understanding and the use of the isometric state needs to become a vital tool in the repertoire of the scientific coach.

We may distinguish between what may be termed *external isometrics* and *internal isometrics*. The former refers to isometric contraction exerted against an external load, whereas the latter refers to contraction exerted against opposing muscles within the body, much like the muscle posing actions performed by bodybuilders. The role of this type of training, is sometimes called *loadless training*.

Loadless Training

A great deal is written about resistance training with weights, machines and other modalities, but little is ever said about a method which is used almost exclusively by bodybuilders. This is 'posing' training, a workout executed by bodybuilders, usually in front of mirrors, to perfect the appearance and sequence of their competition posing routines.

Although this method is not done by bodybuilders as a form of resistance training, Russian scientists have for many years been describing its value as a specific training variation (Vorobyev, 1978). In the early 1900s Anokhin and Proshek already proposed developing strength by the motivated tensing of one's agonists and antagonists for every joint, which is precisely what bodybuilders do in tensing their muscles before the judges in contests.

Despite these early suggestions, this technique was not studied scientifically until after 1965. In particular, Kovalik (1978) carried out a doctoral thesis on what he called *voluntary loadless muscle tensing* or what the Russians usually term *loadless training*. One of his aims was to develop a supplementary system of training which would impose less stress on the joints than weight training, particularly with the younger lifter whose skeletal system has not yet reached maturity. His subjects were told to perform all the Olympic and supplementary lifts (e.g. snatch pull and front squat) with a broomstick while trying to generate maximum muscle tension, as if they were overcoming a maximal weight. He found that this method produced definite muscle strengthening and improvement in technical skill, but concluded that it must be used cautiously in Olympic weightlifting, because it might disrupt the optimal extensor-flexor strength ratios.

Loadless training is especially useful if one has no access to training facilities or if one is recuperating from musculoskeletal injuries. Combined with pushups and free-standing squats, loadless training can be used to good effect on trips away from home. Loadless training may be performed isometrically, with a joint held at a specific angle; quasi-isometrically, with the joint moved powerfully through a full range of movement; or dynamically by imitating any given weight training movement with unloaded muscle tension against a broomstick.

Research indicates that consecutive sets (Kovalik recommended 5 sets of each exercise) should be separated by between 3-10 seconds of rest. During quasi-isometric loadless training, there should be no long periods of intense breath-holding: instead, one should breathe out slowly in synchrony with the slow tensing of each movement. Moreover, each movement should involve strong tension in simultaneously contracted agonists and antagonists, with all movements starting from full extension and ending with stretching beyond full extension and back again over a period of 10-15 seconds. The holding phase at the end of each movement (e.g. the overhead jerk position) should be held with maximal muscle tension for 6-8 seconds. Rotation of the joints in different planes and movements of the limbs in various diagonal and spiral patterns will obey some of the basic principles of physiotherapeutic PNF (proprioceptive neuromuscular facilitation) and enhance the effectiveness of the loadless training as a form of supplementary strengthening (Ch 6). The value of this type of training is corroborated by research which has revealed that dynamic stretching against resistance may strengthen muscle and connective tissue.

One can even tense several muscles groups simultaneously and imitate actual sporting movements with clear visualisations of these actions in your mind. This type of active visualisation, as opposed to the passive, relaxed visualisation recommended by many sports psychologists, can be useful adjunct to skills training, provided it does not alter the dynamic structure of normal competitive patterns.

4.2.5 Eccentric Training

Eccentric contraction refers to muscle action in which the muscle force succumbs to the imposed load and the muscle complex lengthens (see 1.10). Not only is it metabolically much more efficient than concentric contraction, but it is also capable of generating higher forces (Kaneko et al, 1984; Komi, 1973; Rodgers & Berger, 1974). In addition, this difference between concentric and eccentric contractions has been found to depend on the velocity of contraction (Komi, 1973). As the velocity of contraction increases, so the maximum eccentric force increases, whereas the maximum concentric force decreases (Fig 3.16), even though the corresponding EMG for the given muscle group remains reasonably constant.

Investigations into the change in strength elicited by concentric and eccentric work are often contradictory. Johnson et al (1976) found that there were no significant differences between the two methods of training. Komi and Buskirk (1972), using an isokinetic dynamometer, found that eccentric training produced greater eccentric, concentric and isometric strength increases than concentric training. The concentric training increased only concentric and eccentric strength. Friden et al (1983b) found that eccentric training to failure produces marked increases in *eccentric strength-endurance*, but minimal changes in concentric strength-endurance.

The high speed, large acceleration SMART (Seated Movement Aerobic and Resistive Training) or *Supersitting* system created by Lisa Ericson (1992) for work with the disabled, however, tends to increase both concentric and eccentric strength-endurance. Other workers have reported adaptation differences relating to training velocity, measurement velocity and particular muscle groups, while very few studies exist which compare functional strength and power changes with free weights, auxotonic activities or natural sporting manoeuvres. The central role played by the specificity principle clearly has a profound effect on the experimental analysis.

The ability of a muscle to produce greater eccentric than concentric force may be a result of the tension-generating capacity of the connective tissues rather than the contractile elements of the muscle. Therefore, the superior strengthening observed for high velocity (over 180° per second) *isokinetic eccentric training* may be due to selective increase in the tensile strength of the tendon and other series elastic components of the muscle complex. The training and rehabilitation implication is that high velocity eccentric exercise, applied in a progressive overload manner, may enable the connective tissue, especially that of the musculotendinous junction, to resist high impact forces associated with running, jumping and other impulsive actions.

Since lengthening of the muscle complex occurs with eccentric contraction, the stretching SEC (series elastic component) is exposed to greater strain than under concentric conditions and the potential for injury increases. Thus, it is not surprising to learn that most muscle strains and ruptures occur during the eccentric phase of movement (Garrett, 1986).

It is often been shown that a single session of intense eccentric exercise causes pronounced DOMS (delayed onset muscle soreness) which peaks between 24-72 hours after exercise and disappears several days later (Friden et al, 1983a). This soreness is accompanied by reduced dynamic strength and damage to the myofibrils and connective tissue elements such as the Z bands, which are a component of the SEC. Friden et al (1983b) also examined the effects of longer periods of eccentric exercise (3 sessions a week over a total of 8 weeks) and discovered that post-exercise soreness not only did not occur after 2-3 weeks, but the ability to perform eccentric work even increased by 375%. At the same time, biopsies revealed that Z band damage had not taken place, suggesting that adaptation to eccentric exercise had occurred. This research was corroborated by Schwane and Armstrong (1983), who found that downhill running in rats produced a superior training effect to level or uphill training and prevented injury more effectively.

It is known that that eccentric exercise tends to produce greater and more rapid increases in muscle strength and hypertrophy than concentric exercise (Hortobagyi et al, 2000), and it is sometimes suggested that this may be the result of greater tissue damage being produced under eccentric conditions. Recent work, however, has discovered that the increase in myofibral cross-sectional area is much the same in unchanged muscle fibres following concentric exercise as that following eccentric exercise, which is more damaging (Komulainen et al, 2000). These results do not support the hypothesis that fibre hypertrophy depends on the extent of the fibre damage in exercised muscles.

4.2.6 Isokinetic and Other Training Means

It has already been stated that the interest in studying the characteristics of muscular work in sport is associated with determining those regimes which ensure that the athlete's motor potential will be realised to the fullest and that the training conditions will yield the greatest effect from the special strength training. In the latter case, research has been done in basically two directions:

- determination of the most effective strength training regime
- determination of the most effective combination of the various regimes of muscular work or complex of training means within a specified period.

It should be stated, however, that these types of research project are not very numerous and have a number of deficiencies. Firstly, they are carried out with athletes of low qualification; secondly, in many cases there is a tendency to deliberately favour that method which is fashionable, such as eccentrics, 'cross training' or circuit training. Therefore, to speak of anything definitive in terms of the effectiveness of any regime or combination of regimes is premature. One can only closely examine the state of this problem and draw preliminary conclusions. From the more recent regimes of muscular work used for strength development, two of them should be considered: *isokinetic* and *static-dynamic*.

4.2.6.1 The Isokinetic Training Method

The isokinetic method was very popular in the latter part of the 1960's and early 1970's, particularly in the USA (see 1.10). Essentially this method involves the use of a special device (such as a centrifugal clutch, or hydraulic system) which automatically adjusts the resistance to the movement, controls its speed and ensures a maximum load on the muscles throughout the entire working amplitude. In other words, the limiting factor is the speed with which the exercise is executed, not the magnitude of the resistance as it is for weightlifting exercises. The resistance increases as the speed increases.

In *isokinetics*, the resistance is a function of the force applied. Depending on the apparatus, it may be offered in the form of *concentric isokinetics* or *eccentric isokinetics*, although most commercial machines at present offer only the concentric mode. The isokinetic device controls the velocity of the movement so that the athlete can fully use the working amplitude of the movement to produce muscular tension. The device is constructed so as to offer resistance whose magnitude can be varied from the force of finger pressure to hundreds of Newtons. The athlete attempts to apply maximum force and the device automatically varies the resistance. Because muscular force and work capacity change during the specific movement, the resistance automatically accommodates to the muscles' capability at each angle throughout the working range. The isokinetic device provides the muscles with a near-maximal load on each repetition of the exercise, independent of mechanical advantage. This accommodating resistance spontaneously adjusts to the specific work capacity of the muscles, provided that the athlete is able to maintain sufficient motivation to produce sustained strength output against the machine.

The basic advantage of the isokinetic method over others, claimed by one of the pioneers who popularised it for training athletes, Counsilman (1971, 1972), is that this method forces the muscles to work with maximal effort all the time and produces a larger, faster increase in strength for particular actions, even for very strong athletes. This contention, however, is incorrect, since *isokinetic force is usually less than isometric force* throughout the range of all joint movements, and maximal strength production is not possible under isokinetic conditions (see 1.10 and Figs 2.8, 2.9). Even allowing for commercial claims, it is noteworthy that some of the reputed benefits of isokinetics have been corroborated in certain sports (e.g. in swimming and rowing) by considerable research (Chu & Smith, 1971; Rosentsweig & Hinson, 1972; Hinson & Rosentsweig, 1972; Wilson, 1972). These studies promote the following advantages of the isokinetic method of strength training:

1. The isokinetic device accommodates to the athlete's capabilities throughout the range of motion, instead of the athlete accommodating to the resistance. This prevents the athlete from doing more than he is capable of under these conditions. The individual automatically accommodates his effort in response to muscular fatigue or pain, as well as to the increase in strength resulting from the training. Such a method minimises the possibility of injury.

2. The necessity for prolonged warming up is largely eliminated with isokinetics, and in five minutes one can have a very demanding workout. Despite the fact that athletes may train as a team and have different strength capabilities, it is unnecessary to adjust the device to suit each athlete, thereby saving time.

3. By using resistance which automatically accommodates to the applied force, significant strength can be achieved with fewer repetitions per exercise, since each repetition loads the muscle intensively throughout the entire range of motion.

4. The athlete is able to see his results displayed on a computer monitor or on a graph while exercising and thus is able to compete against himself or other athletes.

5. The elimination of eccentric activity by most isokinetic machines diminishes the incidence of post-exercise soreness.

In interpreting some of these advantages, one must remember that these studies on which these comments are based were not done with top level international athletes, nor was the precise phase of the training programme specified (e.g. general vs specific preparation).

Several studies have compared isometric, dynamic and isokinetic regimes for effectiveness of strength development (Thistle et al, 1967; Rosentsweig & Hinson, 1972). These established that isokinetic exercise for the average person produces greater electrical activity in the given muscles, the largest muscle hypertrophy, and highly effective maintenance of muscular strength for specific muscle groups. Laboratory studies show that more significant gains in muscular strength in a shorter period, as well as shorter training sessions, are possible with isokinetic training. The transfer of this effect to multi-dimensional functional sporting activity or its effectiveness with athletes of different qualification, however, has not been proved. Isokinetic training also ensures a limited degree of speed specificity of trained strength over some ranges of sporting movement because the trainer can control the speed of joint action, although it is unable to mimic the force-time curves associated with specific sports movements.

In interpreting these findings, it is vital to remember the specificity principle (see Ch 1), especially since functional strength in a given movement involves skilled neuromuscular coordination of many participating muscle groups. For example, increase in isokinetic strength of the quadriceps does not result in a comparable increase in squatting strength. Moreover, few, if any, of the studies examined the effect of isokinetic training on starting-strength, acceleration-strength, explosive strength, eccentric strength, strength deficit (see Fig 1.1), or neuromuscular skill in producing functional sporting progress, motor qualities that are vital in most sports. In addition, these studies did not examine the effect of prolonged isokinetic training on different categories of athlete, especially the elite competitor.

4.2.6.2 Limitations of the Isokinetic Method

A great deal of muscle testing and rehabilitation after injury is based on the use of isokinetic dynamometers such as Cybex™ and Orthotron™. Inadequate performance and injuries are attributed to differences in strength between interacting muscle groups as determined isokinetically. Athletes are claimed to be training scientifically if they are tested regularly under isokinetic conditions. Research evaluating the effectiveness of training regimes is almost invariably based on isokinetic measurement and often the reputation of their authors means that the validity of this work is rarely doubted. This section examines if this extensive reliance on isokinetic measurement and rehabilitation is warranted.

Fundamental Biomechanics of Isokinetic Devices

The faulty basic assumption is that isokinetic dynamometers are accurately constant angular velocity devices. The laws of physics deem it impossible to construct any machine which offers purely isokinetic resistance from beginning to end of motion. When a body is at rest, it has to be accelerated to reach a certain terminal velocity that can be maintained for a given period of time before it has to be decelerated to return to rest once more. This means that there is always a period of positive or negative acceleration associated with all movement, isokinetic or otherwise. The best that manufacturers of isokinetic devices can do is to minimise the duration of these phases, although they can never entirely eliminate them. To produce entirely isokinetic conditions from beginning to end of motion would necessitate the production of infinite acceleration, which contradicts the laws of science.

Justifiably, it might be asked if the existence of non-isokinetic measuring phases on these machines is important. This fact is vitally important, because most injuries occur during these transition phases when a limb is changing its velocity or tension is changing in the musculotendinous system and isokinetic testing can reveal no useful information about what is happening to the muscles then. A most serious problem is that isokinetic testing can give no information on the major contribution played by the storage and release of elastic energy in the soft tissues during dynamic, natural actions such as walking, running, jumping or throwing. Stated simply, isokinetic testing or training is non-functional, except possibly for swimmers whose movements are approximately isokinetic over part of their range.

Biomechanical analysis of the force-time and rate of force development (RFD) curves for resisted free movement confirm the existence of vital muscular performance qualities such as maximal strength, starting strength (at the beginning of a movement), acceleration strength (while the movement is speeding up to maximum velocity) and explosive strength (see Fig 2.13). The curves obtained isokinetically are so radically different from their free movement equivalents that they are of minimal value either for functional analysis or specific neuromuscular conditioning.

Recommended Strength Ratios

It is often claimed that the optimal ratio of quadriceps to hamstring strength is 60:40, but Russian scientists have found that this ratio depends on the specific type of sport (Vorobyev, 1978). For example, they have determined that this ratio (measured when knee extension torque is greatest) should be nearer 80:20 for weightlifters and jumpers. Moreover, if the ratio is measured during movement on a treadmill, the ratio for runners is approximately 50:50. Despite these findings, the traditional 60:40 recommendation is widely accepted and much rehabilitation is based on restoring this ratio. Another popular belief is that injuries are far more common if the difference in strength between left and right lower extremities is more than 10%.

Recent research, however, has shown that neither of these recommendations is supported by scientifically controlled experiments which correct torque outputs for the effect of gravity and avoid stretching the hamstrings (Stephens & Reid, 1988). In addition, the recommendation of a specific flexor/extensor ratio is vague, because this ratio varies throughout the range of joint motion, as may be seen in Figure 4.16.

For example, the ratio for the knee at 80° is about 75:25 at 36 degs/sec, whereas it is 68:32 at 180 degs/ sec. The only stage at which the ratio is 60:40 occurs at an angle of approximately 50°. Not only does the ratio change with joint angle, but it also changes with velocity of measurement, so it is meaningless to prescribe an optimal ratio for any joint. It would be more relevant to refer to a characteristic curve over a full range of movement for a given angular velocity.

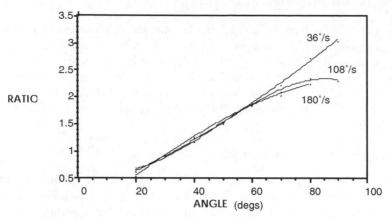

Figure 4.16 Ratio of isokinetic torque of knee extensors to flexors at 36 degs/sec, 108 degs/sec and 180 degs/sec. The knee extension data measured on a Cybex™ dynamometer were divided by the knee flexion data for the equivalent joint angle in each case. Joint angle varies between partial knee flexion in the seated position to full extension at 90 degrees.

Functional Anatomy

Another confounding factor is the influence of the angle of nearby joints on the torque that is produced by given muscles about the joint in question. For instance, knee extension torque increases with hip angle, a phenomenon that is of immense practical importance to weightlifters, jumpers and sprinters, in particular. These athletes are well aware of operating over optimal ranges of relative knee and hip angle. Measurement of the relative disposition of these angles forms the basis of the cyclogram used by biomechanists to study gait efficiency. Therapists attempt to solve this problem by immobilising the seated athlete's hips by using strong inextensible straps across the upper thighs. This immediately creates non-functional conditions for evaluating the biomechanics of knee extension/flexion in free space. The seated posture produces highly constrained and accurate conditions for measuring torque that is specific to the seated posture and not to the posture exhibited during any actual sporting action.

Furthermore, seated isokinetic evaluation of knee motion is usually imprecisely controlled, since it is rarely combined with electromyography or myotonometry (muscle tension measurement) to ascertain the relative contributions made to joint torque by the different muscles comprising the quadriceps and hamstrings. Prescription of any exercise regime without knowing precisely which muscles are involved is just as haphazard with or without the aid of costly isokinetic devices. What complicates matters further is that the degree of lateral or medial rotation of the lower extremity has a significant effect on the relative involvement of vastus medialis and lateralis, so that this variable also needs to be more accurately controlled if isokinetic testing is to become scientifically rigorous. Open-chain testing of the lower extremity with the sole of the foot not in contact with the ground alters the way in which popliteus initiates knee flexion or gastrocnemius contributes to knee flexion, two actions that are of great importance in running, lifting or jumping.

In addition, seated testing does not take into consideration medial rotation of the knee by sartorius, gracilis, semimembranosus or semitendinosus, or lateral rotation by biceps femoris. The role of these muscles in performance may be largely ignored for the average client, but certainly not in the case of competitive athletes, who place maximal demands on their bodies.

The entire system of PNF is based on the importance of specific patterns of joint action and muscle recruitment in determining movement efficiency and safety, yet therapists with an extensive knowledge of PNF unquestioningly accept results produced under the highly unnatural conditions imposed by isokinetic machines. They are fully aware that training in a given way produces specific neural changes which become part of the central nervous programme that determines all movement efficiency; they meticulously apply the precise kinesiological patterns prescribed by Knott and Voss (1977), but they are compelled to ignore this knowledge when using isokinetic machines.

Muscle Physiology

Some of the implications of muscle physiology are also relevant to understanding the limitations of isokinetic testing:

- The initial muscular state preceding many sporting actions is intense isometric contraction or explosive isometric contraction accompanied by storage of elastic energy in the tendons (see 1.6.2). This state has a profound influence on explosive strength, metabolic efficiency and safety, yet all isokinetic testing or training involves insignificant initial levels of isometric contraction.

- The myotatic stretch reflex has great significance for increasing the working effect of concentric muscle action, with the greater the rate of stretch, the stronger this reflex. Most explosive movements in running, jumping, lifting and throwing rely on intense recruitment of this reflex, which is not possible under isokinetic conditions. In fact, the production of powerful, skillful movements in all sports relies on the establishment of precise neuromuscular patterns through integration of many different reflexes. The elimination of most of these reflex actions by isokinetic apparatus ensures that isokinetic testing and training is only of value during the early general conditioning or rehabilitation phase, but of no real significance during the specific preparation or competitive phases of sports training.

- Muscles generally interact to produce two kinds of action: cocontraction or ballistic movement (see 1.8). In cocontraction, agonists and antagonists contract simultaneously, with dominance of the former producing the external motion. Ballistic movement comprises bursts of agonist activity followed by phases of relaxation during which the motion continues due to stored limb momentum. Skilled, rapid ballistic and fast continuous movements are preprogrammed in the central nervous system (CNS) and rarely involve feedback during the action, whereas slower, discontinuous movements involve cocontraction and ongoing feedback to the CNS from the muscles and joints. Isokinetic conditions do not permit the production of ballistic or discontinuous cocontractive actions, so that they address only a few of the needs of sports testing and preparation.

- Some authorities maintain that strength is best developed if muscle tension is kept at a maximum throughout the movement by the use of isokinetics (Thistle et al, 1967). This proposition is neither proved nor is it universally accepted with reference to all types of strength. Moreover, torque produced under isokinetic conditions is usually much lower than that produced isometrically at the same joint angle (Figs 2.8, 2.9).

- If contraction of the agonists is preceded immediately by maximal contraction of the antagonists, the force produced by the agonists is increased, a phenomenon often called reciprocal inhibition and regularly used in PNF. Most isokinetic devices do not permit this type of motion, which commonly occurs during plyometric rebounding activity.

- The patterns of force production are different for bilateral (simultaneous use of both limbs) and unilateral (alternate use of each limb) sports, so that isokinetic comparisons of relative limb strength can be very misleading. Furthermore, each person has a dominant limb, so that functional asymmetry is perfectly normal. This does not imply that the dominant limb has superior strength; it often displays superiority in skill, especially in kicking, jumping and throwing sports. Yet, it is common to find therapists trying to strengthen the weaker kicking limb of a footballer isokinetically, although the support leg is meant to produce greater stabilising strength.

The Importance of Specificity

Indiscriminate use of isokinetics neglects the proven principle of specificity (discussed in detail in 1.3) with respect to:

- Type of Muscle Contraction
- Movement Pattern
- Region of Movement
- Velocity of Movement
- Force of Contraction

- Muscle Fibre Recruitment
- Metabolism
- Biochemical Adaptation
- Flexibility
- Fatigue

Therefore, it is vital to understand the limitations of using isokinetics to test or train the athlete and appreciate that sport specific conditioning has little to do with isokinetic performance. As has been stressed by Sale and McDougall (1981), increased strength is apparent only when measured during the same type of movement used in training. The importance of training specificity is underlined further by the considerable research of Verkhoshansky, which culminated in his formulating the *principle of dynamic correspondence* (see 4.3) This principle emphasizes that the means of strength training for all sports should enhance the required motor qualities in terms of factors such as amplitude and direction of movement, and the rate and time of maximal force production.

On this basis, as well, isokinetic training and measurement are seen to be so functionally different from normal sporting movement as to be relatively useless for giving any information that is accurately applicable to the competitive athlete.

Concluding Remarks

Although technological measurement is invaluable and highly desirable in sport and rehabilitation, oversimplification of any highly complex situation can lead to serious errors and hinder scientific progress. The simplistic central sun and planetary electron model of the atom was a valuable tool for early 20th century physicists, but its replacement by more sophisticated quantum models has advanced our understanding of the universe enormously. Unqualified reliance on a single isokinetic model to assess muscular strength and endurance is tantamount to permanently accepting the early model of the atom, just because it is easy to work with.

The fact is that human motion involving static and dynamic multiple link components is extremely complicated and isokinetic testing can offer only a very simplistic way of obtaining information on a limited number of variables. Isokinetic machines are useful for measuring isokinetic actions and changes in two dimensions, just as isometric dynamometry is useful for measuring isometric strength at a given joint angle. Extrapolation of results obtained under these conditions to sporting actions involving other types of muscle contraction and patterns of movement is scientifically unacceptable and misleading. Human mobility and stability are the integrated result of the appropriate phases of isometric and non-isokinetic muscle contraction occurring with a specific timing in three-dimensional space over specific ranges of joint angle. Multi-faceted human movement demands the use of far more versatile and complex technological means, a type of kinesiological polygraph which integrates information yielded by concurrent use of devices such as high speed video, EMG, myotensiometers, accelerometers and force plates.

The ultimate measure of successful testing and training is unequivocal improvement in the athlete's performance, so that sporting movements should still be regarded as the final test of any training or rehabilitation regime. In addition, an inexpensive and highly effective alternative to isokinetics is the APRE system based on the original work of DeLorme (see 5.2.2). The convenience of isokinetic testing should be weighed against its high cost, limited application and the unsupported claims of manufacturers. The detailed review of the strengths and weaknesses of isokinetic methods given by Osternig (1986) provides further useful information in this regard.

4.2.6.3 Static-Dynamic Methods

The *static-dynamic method* of developing muscular strength involves the sequential combination in one exercise of isometric and dynamic (auxotonic) muscular activity, each of which can provide its own distinct quantitative characteristics. For example, the following variations of static-dynamic exercise have been shown to be effective:

- a 2-3 second isometric contraction (at 80% of one's maximum) is held, followed by explosive concentric dynamic work with a load of 30% of maximum

- with both the isometric and dynamic components, a constant load of 75-80% of maximum is used.

In the latter case, for instance, the athlete sinks into the half-squat position with a barbell on his shoulders, holds this position for 2 seconds, then with maximal acceleration, jumps upward. After careful landing he repeats the exercise.

It has been established experimentally that the first variant of static-dynamic exercise is better than dynamic exercise alone for developing speed-strength. The second variant has an equivalent affect on the improvement of speed-strength and absolute strength (Dobrovolsky, 1972, 1973).

4.2.6.4 Choice of Muscle Training Regimes

One may now ask the question: Of all these regimes, which is the most effective? It is difficult to give a categorical answer for several reasons:

1. Comprehensive research to evaluate the effectiveness of all the regimes has not been conducted. An attempt, for example, to study the effectiveness of eccentric, concentric, isometric and combined regimes revealed

some advantages of the concentric over the eccentric and isometric method, but the main method using combined regimes showed a clear advantage (Pletnev, 1975).

2. Similar comparative research is difficult with respect to controlling the training loads of the different regimes.

3. It is inappropriate to raise the question of the absolute effectiveness of any specific regime. Each of them can be the most effective, depending upon factors such as the situation, stage of the annual cycle, level of the athlete, the primary regime of muscular work in the special exercise, and the specificity of the strength ability acquired as a result of training.

Today it can be ascertained with reasonable certainty that the most rational means of enhancing the effectiveness of special strength preparation is to combine the various regimes of muscular work. This has been corroborated by several studies (Vorobyev, 1966; Andrianov & Vorobyev, 1969; Kuznetsov, 1970; Verkhoshansky, 1970, 1972; Slobodyan, 1972; Tatyan, 1974; Pletnev 1975; Khodykin, 1975; Savin, 1974). Such a training combination is selected by taking into consideration its cumulative effect and its correspondence to the specific conditions of the sport.

4.2.7 The Use of Training Machines

Recently, training machines for strength development have become very popular in most modern gymnasia. However, before machines are used in training, it is important to understand that there are essentially two distinct classes of machine:

- *Functional resistance machines*, whose purpose is to offer resistance in sport specific patterns
- *Non-functional resistance machines*, whose sole purpose is to offer general resistance in non-sport specific patterns

An appreciation of this distinction is vital for many coaches and athletes in the West, because the impressive fitness centres in which they often train are usually entirely equipped with non-functional resistance (NFR) machines. In fact, the machine training syndrome has become so popular among the average population that it is frequently difficult to find adequate free weights or functional resistance (FR) machines in these 'state-of-the-art' centres. While the use of NFR machines may be adequate for the casual fitness client, it can be profoundly counterproductive for sport specific trainees if used in place of FR machines or free weights. Current commercialised emphasis on circuit and cross training has proliferated the use of NFR machines, so the serious athlete should become aware of their limitations in sport and rehabilitation, particularly regarding the detrimental effects they can have on the specificity of fitness, proprioceptive efficiency, central nervous programming and sporting skills. The remarks of Zatsiorsky (1995) on this issue are highly relevant:

The important limitation of many strength training machines is that they are designed to train muscles, not movement. Because of this, they are not the most important training tool for athletes.

4.2.7.1 Functional Resistance Machines

Functional strength (FR) machines are devised to provide resistance to various movements encountered in sport. Depending on the setting, sport-specific resistance devices are supposed to imitate or train certain elements of an athletic exercise in order to provide the necessary specific loads in the different regimes of muscular work (Ratov, 1976). Research on the use of FR training devices in athletics has shown them to be very effective for aspects of special strength training of many types of athlete (Semenov, 1970; Petrova & Gorbunov, 1970; Verkhoshansky, 1970; Deniskin & Kuznetsov, 1972; Dobrovolski, 1972, 1973; Kuznetsov & Aiunts, 1974; Savin, 1974).

This can be explained by the fact that they permit the strict regulation of the load and the spatial characteristics of the movement in order to use extensively the appropriate regimes of muscular work and to programme the characteristics of the force over time. They reproduce stereotypical training movements and are economical for the athlete in terms of time and energy.

One of the simplest, cheapest and most versatile of all FR devices is the pulley machine, which used to be widely used in gymnasia until supplanted by the more commercially persuasive chromium-plated 'modern' machines. The 'hi-lo' pulley machine permits one to use the pulleys in high or low positions for all varieties of movement in space and time. Since the handles are attached to ropes unlike the fixed bars and pivots of most NFR machines, they can be used to exercise in sport specific patterns of great complexity, if so desired.

With appropriate choice and layout of hand grips, bars, pulleys and benches, it is possible to perform dozens of different exercises for every body part on a single pulley machine. A fixture of only 4 pulley machines can actually provide a circuit training facility which cannot be equalled by fewer than 40 'state of the art' machines. A circuit comprising 10 pulley machines, a few benches, a few jumping boards, a few bars, a few mats, gymnastic wall-bars and a few racks can provide more clients with a larger range of exercises than 100 specialised machines - at less than 15% of the cost. Even then, the NFR machine-only facility would provide inferior multi-dimensional conditioning of the body.

A major advantage of sport-specific FR training devices lies in the fact that it is possible to obtain crucial visual and computerised feedback about the qualitative and quantitative characteristics of the movement, as well as to control the athlete's special strength training. All of these advantages create significant potential for perfecting the athlete's special strength training programme. Therefore, the design, introduction of various types of FR training device becomes a very important task.

In using any machine, however, it is vital to note that simulation of any sporting movement against heavy loads can alter the force-time characteristics of the action significantly and disrupt the neuromuscular programmes responsible for the movement. The magnitude of the load, the pattern of movement and the principle of dynamic correspondence have to be considered carefully if one intends to use machines to simulate actual sporting movements in any way. Most important is the fact that functionality is not the automatic consequence of a specific exercise, but of the functional objectives associated with using any exercise, irrespective of its similarity to any sports action and integrating it effectively into the long-term conditioning programme.

4.2.7.2 Non-Functional Resistance Machines

Non-functional resistance (NFR) machines can play a useful supplementary role to free weight and functional machine training, but in general they are unable to provide the same degree of multi-dimensional, full range neuromuscular and musculoskeletal training as free weights and 'functional' machines.

Very often, NFR machines compel the user to sit or lie, thereby minimising the training effect on the major stabilising muscles of the body and involving fewer of the joints in fewer degrees of freedom of movement. While this may be valuable in the earlier stages of rehabilitating certain injuries, it is an incomplete way of regularly training the body for functional development. One of their major deficiencies for the competitive athlete or average person is the limitation they impose on proprioceptive processes and the kinaesthetic sense in functional strength development. Since machines usually stabilise major regions of the body and limit the number of joints which move, they diminish one's ability to exercise freely in three dimensional space and thereby do not adequately train balance, coordination and other components of proprioception. The dangers of regular supplementary circuit training as a form of 'cross training' for sporting preparation should then become obvious.

NFR machines may be useful in concentrating more on the development of certain muscle groups for supplementing overall bodybuilding training or the primary stages of injury rehabilitation, but they are unsuitable for providing all-round conditioning of entire muscle groups, interacting agonist/antagonist muscles and motor systems. For instance, there is no single machine that can rival the training effect of a barbell squat, a barbell or dumbbell curl, a barbell bench press, a power clean, a standing press, lateral raises with dumbbells or a barbell deadlift. On the other hand, one machine, namely the 'lat pulley' machine, is generally more suitable and safer for training the latissimus dorsi than the free weights equivalent of bent-over rowing.

It is important to note that, if a machine compels a user to use fewer joints and muscles than an equivalent free weights or pulley exercise, then the stress on all of those structures will be increased proportionately. For example, the free standing squat involves three joints (hip, knee and ankle), whereas the seated knee extension machine constrains the body to use only one joint (the knee) in exercising the quadriceps, so that, in producing a comparable level of exercise over the same range of movement, this machine increases the shearing force across the knee. Moreover, the squat also offers the added advantages of exercising the thigh adductors, the spinal erectors and several other stabilising muscles, besides enhancing general balance and bone density (due to longitudinal compressive loading of the skeleton).

It is not often appreciated that seated exercise always imposes a greater load on the lumbar spinal discs than equivalent standing exercises. Even without an added load, sitting with the back maintaining its neutral curvatures increases the lumbar disc pressure by about 40% (Chaffin & Andersson, 1984). If the back is allowed to flex forwards, this stress can increase by as much as 90%. An ergonomically designed backrest which adequately supports the lumbar region lowers the stress, but even then the lumbar disc pressure can be some 75% greater than during standing. The increase in stress becomes far greater against resistance, particularly if jerky movements are used to initiate or terminate the movement. The dangers are exacerbated by sitting, because one is unable to absorb any shock loading by flexing the knees, hips or ankles, as is the case when standing.

In the vast majority of cases, NFR machines provide an inferior, incomplete and less efficient way of training the musculoskeletal system. This is particularly true regarding the conditioning of the neuromuscular system in rapid or explosive movements, as well as the elastic qualities of the tendons and other connective tissues which are essential in all sports involving running, jumping, throwing, catching or any other ballistic actions. Isokinetic machines can be especially deficient in this regard, so that their appropriateness of use must be clearly understood if they are to prove beneficial in sport specific training (see 4.2.6). Nevertheless, some machines may be used productively as an occasional form of General Physical Training, rehabilitation or restoration.

4.2.7.3 Machines and the Variable Resistance Philosophy

As discussed elsewhere in this text, the torque produced by a muscle in a particular movement varies with joint angle. Many machine manufacturers have used this fact to justify the design of machines whose resistance varies in an attempt to match the torque curves of natural joint movement. They maintain that variable resistance machines offer superior strength training to free weights and other resistance devices. What they fail to point out is that regular training on any machine, whether variable resistance or not, provides inadequate functional proprioceptive training and thereby can reduce one's level of motor efficiency, stability and safety.

Their claims are based on the faulty premise that the resistance offered to the muscles by a free weight always remains the same. So, for example, if you perform a biceps curl with 50 kg, then it is implied that you are exerting a force of 50 kg weight (about 490 Newtons) from beginning to end of movement. Machine manufacturers stress that their bicep curl machine offers some form of automatically adjusting resistance to account for the variation of strength with joint angle, apparently something that never happens with free weights.

A simple application of Newton's Second Law of Motion (force is proportional to the acceleration of the object) reveals that the resistance offered by a free weight changes with acceleration from rest and during any other time when the trainee speeds up or slows down the movement when the weight feels lighter or heavier respectively. The force exerted by any weight which begins from and returns to rest is always varying, anyway, as can easily be demonstrated by force plate, cable tensiometer or high speed video analysis. The skilled trainee is able to rely on his proprioceptive apparatus to perceive any changes in force or pattern of movement so as to statically and dynamically vary the resistance and its direction more efficiently than any current machines.

4.2.7.4 The Training Safety of Machines

It is often claimed that the NFR machines found in most fitness centres are much safer to use than free weights. Injuries to the back and knees (on leg press, hack-squat and hip-sled machines), the shoulders and chest (on bench press and pec-deck machines), the elbow joint (bicep curl machines), the back (back extension machines) and other joints are just as common with machines as with free weights. In fact, many machines, such as the 'pec-deck', bench-press, leg press, calf-raise and seated press machines force the user to commence the movement from the biomechanically least efficient and potentially most harmful position for the relevant joint. Partners to 'spot' machine users are just as necessary as spotters for free weights users. Faulty technique is equally dangerous with machines or free weights.

Some machines such as leg extension, lat pulley and seated bicep curl machines are certainly safer if an individual is suffering from back weakness or injury. They can be very helpful in the early stages of rehabilitation, but are not helpful in the long-term, since continual avoidance of stress to the regions involved eventually leads to their progressive weakening. There is a definite supplementary place in a gymnasium for certain NFR machines, but they should not replace free weights, pulley machines and other FR devices. A more detailed analysis of the safety of training with specific machines is covered later (Ch 8.8).

4.2.7.5 The Efficiency of Machine Training

Contrary to what the equipment manufacturers state, it takes far longer for NFR machines to provide a similar multi-faceted training effect to the equivalent free weights or FR machines. For instance, it requires at least twelve NFR machines to approximately equal the training effect of the clean-and-push press, at least four machines to rival the training effect of the free standing squat, more than three machines to equal the training effect of the standing dumbbell curl, and at least five machines to rival the effectiveness of the flexed-knee deadlift.

In other words, more than 24 NFR machines are required to challenge the effectiveness of a circuit comprising only four free weights exercises: the clean-and-push press, the squat, deadlift, and biceps curl. In this case, the combined cost of these machines is about forty times greater than the combined cost of several sets of free weights and the necessary racks. Moreover, the maintenance cost of most NFR machines is considerably higher than that of virtually indestructible free weights and the breakdown of machines is a regular occurrence in a well-used gymnasium.

4.2.8 The Concept of Symmetric Training

Asymmetry in leg length, muscle strength, stride length and several other features of human structure and function has been blamed as one of the causes of inefficient movement and injury. Likewise, imbalances in muscle strength between agonists and antagonists, left and right limbs, and in isokinetic muscle endurance, as measured on isokinetic devices have been singled out as leading causes of muscle injury (see 4.2.6).

Research, however, has revealed that isokinetically-measured discrepancies as large as 10% between left/right leg strength and agonist/antagonist strength of the right and left legs do not statistically correlate with a major increase in muscular injuries.

The body and its muscles, tendons and bones are characteristically asymmetric and any attempts to produce greater anthropomorphic and kinesiological symmetry could exacerbate the existing problem or cause new injuries. One has to ascertain the degree of asymmetry not only by static measurements of *structural* features such as leg length and spinal curvature, but also by dynamic biomechanical analysis of *functional* features such as force distribution, movement patterns, ground reaction force, electrical activity of postural (tonic) and phasic muscle groups, and the timing of the different phases of movement.

Differences in *structural* characteristics including muscle and tendon length, the sites of tendon and ligament attachments to bone, and bone size and mass are quite natural in all humans. It is only when these *structural* differences lead to serious *functional* imbalances in movement patterns that surgical or orthotic means may have to be implemented to solve the problem. Even then, one has to ensure that the excessive functional asymmetry is due primarily to structural and not neuromuscular or central nervous processes. It may be that the centrally stored nervous patterns are producing the troublesome kinesiological imperfections, so that the answer lies in paying attention to modifying the *motor skills* required for the specific sport.

It is important to appreciate that there is no perfect way of executing any movement: everyone has an individualised version of the supposedly 'ideal' model of every skill. Some sports coaches and aerobic instructors place an unnecessarily restrictive emphasis on what they consider to be 'correct' exercise technique and allow inadequate latitude for individual interpretation (i.e. *style*, as opposed to *skill*). One simply has to examine the drastically different walking and running styles of world class athletes to realise that there is no such thing as perfect style. There is only an optimal style for each individual, where style refers to the individual expression of a motor skill. This style has to be developed on the basis of observing and experimenting with the 'ideal' model until the person produces a central nervous programme which suits his or her body.

Recent research by Yushkevich (1989) supports these points. He analysed the symmetry of leg strength in sprinters and concluded that striving for full leg symmetry is inappropriate. He found that the extensors of all the joints of the push-off leg generally were significantly stronger than those of the swing-leg, whereas there was no definite difference between the flexor strengths of either leg. There were distinct differences in the patterns of asymmetry between novice, Class 3, Class 2, Class 1 and more highly qualified athletes. For instance, novices displayed greater strength of the hip flexors of the *push-off leg* than of the swing-leg. The knee flexors of novices, Class 3 and Class 2 were stronger in the *swing-leg*, whereas those of Class 1, Master and other more highly qualified athletes were stronger in the *push-off* leg. Dorsiflexion was stronger in the push-off leg of all athletes except novices.

Interestingly, leg strength asymmetry was found to increase as sprinters increase in proficiency, reaching a peak among Class 2 athletes, then diminishing again as level of sports mastery increased. Furthermore, Yushkevich found that *good sprint times correlated more closely with swing-leg strength than push-off leg strength*.

This study concluded that, not only are attempts to produce symmetrical muscle strength ill-advised, but that it can be beneficial to perform *asymmetric exercises* by running or jumping on sloping or inclined tracks, by running around curves in both directions, running and jumping in shoes with soles of different thickness, or running with leg weights of different mass. Yushkevich (1989) stressed this type of training thus: *'Asymmetric exercises destabilise the space-time characteristics of motor acts, thereby helping athletes break speed barriers'*.

There is an ancient injunction that the weavers of Eastern carpet must include at least one flaw in their work to recognise that perfection is reserved for the Divine and not for humans. The above findings imply that similar asymmetry or lack of perfection may be desirable for all human physical performance and training.

4.2.9 The Concept of Muscle Isolation

Generations of muscle magazine authors have extolled the virtues of special ways of training to isolate specific muscle groups. They have advocated certain machines, ways of fixating the joints, precise placement of the limbs and numerous other ingenious manoeuvres to ensure that one muscle is maximally recruited while others remain largely dormant.

EMG studies reveal that isolation of minute muscle groups is indeed possible under low intensities of loading (e.g. Basmajian, 1978). Intuitively, we are aware that low intensity actions such as eye-blinking, piano-playing or relaxed speaking are due to the precise action of specific muscle groups, a fact which the EMG clearly corroborates.

However, if large loads are imposed on a given muscle group by intense resistance, isolation becomes virtually impossible. Immediately the load is applied, stabilising muscles become involved to ensure that the body or specific joints remain stable, while the prime movers attempt to cope with the load. If the nervous system signals that the prime movers are inadequate to execute the desired joint action, assistant movers, shunt muscles, emergency muscles and neutralisers may all be recruited to augment the action of the prime movers.

Physiotherapists relying on PNF techniques sometimes impose maximal loading on a joint to elicit compensatory or overflow activity of muscles other than the 'prime movers.' This is not possible if the resistance imposed is inadequate to overload the 'prime movers.' Similarly, the weight trainer who wishes to increase hypertrophy or strength of a given muscle selects a weight which forces it to operate at high intensity. The higher the intensity or the greater the duration of the exercise, the less likely is isolation of the prime mover, even if certain joints are restrained as on an isokinetic test machine.

In many cases the tension developed in the stabilisers or assistant stabilisers will equal or exceed that of the prime movers. For example, during heavy standing tricep press-downs with cable machines, the abdominal muscles, latissimus dorsi and erector spinae of the back may be as strongly contracted as the triceps, even though this is supposedly an isolation exercise for the triceps. Analysis of many seated or reclining isolation exercises on machines reveals that isolation simply does not occur with heavy loads.

This is not to negate the value of so-called isolation exercises. Not only can they be useful during the early stages of injury rehabilitation, but overflow to other muscle groups may be very desirable (if the exercise is performed safely), since it simultaneously offers isometric and dynamic training to many other muscle groups. It is necessary, however, to clarify the popular misconceptions surrounding the misleading concept of muscle isolation still proliferated by numerous instructors and in many training texts.

4.3 Dynamic Correspondence as a Means of Strength Training

Devising methods of special strength training is associated firstly with the selection of the means and methods for developing muscular strength. All sporting movement is specific and goal-directed. Therefore, the strength displayed in the execution of each movement is also specific and goal-directed. One should not refer to strength in general, but only in the context of the given task. In other words, the means and methods of strength training should provide an adequate conditioning regime for the motor system in the special exercises and thereby ensure continued improvement in sporting performance.

The foundation of this assertion lies in *the principle of dynamic correspondence*, which emphasizes that the means and methods of strength training for specific sports should be chosen to enhance the required motor qualities in terms of :

- The amplitude and direction of movement
- The accentuated region of force production
- The dynamics of the effort
- The rate and time of maximum force production
- The regime of muscular work

4.3.1 The Amplitude and Direction of Movement

The criterion of correspondence with respect to the *amplitude* and *direction* originates from the patterns of the movement relative to the adjacent body part. It determines which muscles are involved in the work and allows for anatomical peculiarities and the external conditions of work. Thus, the movement of the shoulder girdle of a rower or shot putter is about the same in amplitude, but the direction of the working force is different (Fig 4.17). In the first case the pulling of the oars involves shoulder extension, whereas in the second case it involves shoulder flexion acting in opposition to the force of inertia of the shot.

The importance of the correspondence of muscular work, in terms of the relevant criteria may be illustrated by the following example. In track-and-field training, jumpers and sprinters sometimes do exercises to develop the hip flexor muscles in a standing position on a hip flexor machine which offers resistance by means of a pad pressing against the front of the thigh.

However, the amplitude of thigh movement in running and jumping (when moving the legs forward) is significantly greater than the amplitude of this exercise, and begins at an angle of about 210° in the hip joint, relative to the torso. Therefore, the execution of this exercise in the standing position does not duplicate the mechanism of the movement in the sport specific exercise (e.g. jumping or sprinting).

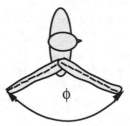

Figure 4.17 Working amplitude of shoulder movement of a rower and a shotputter (Siff & Verkhoshansky, 1999).

If the athlete's position changes (Fig 4.18), the criterion of the correspondence is met, not only with respect to the amplitude of the movement, but also to the sporting movement, because the resistance imitates the inertial resistance of the mass of the leg rotating about the hip joint in the special exercise. By altering the load, the number of repetitions and the tempo of movement, the task of developing the strength to produce the required force and strength-endurance, will be solved. Thus, to fulfill the criteria of correspondence with respect to the amplitude and direction of movement, it is advisable to select the exact starting position and posture of the athlete, as well as to calculate the direction of action of the forces associated with the working links of the system and the additional load.

The line of action of the applied external resistance and of the loaded movement as a whole must also be taken into account. For example, in middle-distance running, skiing and skating, a knapsack full of sand or a weight belt are sometimes used as resistance. However, the muscles which bear the load are those which resist the weight of the body. This can increase the ability to cope with vertical loading and develop general strength-endurance, but does not strengthen those muscles which propel the body horizontally.

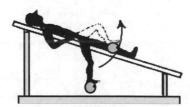

Figure 4.18 Exercise for developing hip flexion strength based on consideration for the accentuated part of the working amplitude and the resistance to the force of muscle contraction (Siff & Verkhoshansky, 1999).

Similarly, a skater may execute jumps on one leg on the floor or from a bench. These exercises strengthen the leg muscles supporting the body and the static-endurance of the back muscles, but do not fully imitate the working of the muscles for the push-off, where the force is directed backward.

Skaters should use another method of resisted movement by changing the direction in which the force of resistance is acting (Fig 4.19). These methods to a large extent match the training exercise to the dynamics of the sport specific actions.

Figure 4.19 Training means for increasing resistance during skating (Verkhoshansky, 1977).

In sport, the working force is developed by the simultaneous coordinated tension of the muscle groups which move the various segments of the body. The most characteristic example of such cooperation of the working muscles is the simultaneous flexion and extension at the two hip joints (e.g. in running, jumping, fencing, figure skating, basketball or tennis), where the angular movement of one leg enhances the push-off movement of the other. It is useful to imitate this combination with special strength exercises which take into account the working amplitude of the movement and the direction of the opposing force (as in Fig 4.20). On the other hand, it is usually inappropriate to perform the actual sporting movements with significantly large added loads in an attempt to provide exact simulation, since the added loading invariably alters the centres of gravity and rotation of the limbs and body, thereby altering the underlying motor patterns and dispositions of joints relative to one another.

Figure 4.20 Complex exercise for simultaneous strengthening of the hip flexors and extensors, and knee extensors (Verkhoshansky, 1977).

Parachute Resistance Training

Sometimes, small parachutes of different size (to offer different degrees of resistance) may be attached with a quick-release harness to the trunk of the athlete to offer a low-inertia form of resistance (Popov, 1966). Although there have been claims that these parachutes were developed secretly in Moscow in 1988 (Brunner & Tabachnik *Soviet Training and Recovery Methods* 1990), this reference shows that Popov and others were researching their use more than 20 years earlier.

The quick release may be used to decrease the resistance rapidly while the athlete is running and thereby offer the benefits of *contrast training*, such as acceleration strength (see 7.1). Due largely to the efforts of émigré Russians such as Dr Ben Tabachnik, a former soviet track coach now living in the USA, these running parachutes have become a popular training aid in the West, where they generally have been applied fairly randomly with little knowledge of periodising them optimally into overall training programmes. Appropriateness of use depends on an understanding of which strength qualities are required by the athlete at a given stage of training.

In particular, parachute training plays no role in the development of starting strength, which is produced under isometric conditions. They, however, offer a safer alternative to the use of weights added to the extremities or body, or dragged behind the athlete (e.g. a car tyre or sled), because they do not increase the vertical reaction forces acting on the body. The fact that the parachutes offer aerodynamic resistance which increases rapidly with velocity (actually the square of the velocity) allows us to use these devices more knowledgeably. Thus, smaller parachutes are more suited for speed development, medium parachutes for speed-endurance and large parachutes for speed-strength and acceleration-strength. Naturally, running speed determines the degree of drag resistance, so that optimal development of these fitness or motor qualities depends on attempts to run at maximum speed for as long as possible and implementation of various fartlek or interval methods. The drag force characteristically varies between 5 - 200 Newtons for running speeds of 6 -10 metres per second, depending on the size of the parachute (Zatsiorsky, 1995).

Quick release of the parachute at maximum velocity can be helpful as a special contrast method in enhancing speed and stride frequency. Training distances commonly vary between 30m and 150m, with smaller parachutes being used for the longer distances. If the basic principles of its application are clearly understood, parachute training can be used successfully by distance runners, as well as sprint or distance cyclists and swimmers. As with other resistance training, this method must be applied carefully so as not to disrupt motor skill and coordination. In particular, it should be noted that parachutes offer the same degree of resistance during both the support and non-support phases of running, thereby disrupting speed and acceleration of limb and body movement during flight. In addition, parachutes alter the relative position of the joints during landing, especially during hurdling and jumping. All of this can adversely affect several aspects of the degree of dynamic correspondence of the training means to the actual sporting movements (as discussed throughut Ch 4.3).

In using parachutes, the principle of gradual progressive overloading should be applied, with larger parachutes being used over a period of weeks. In doing so, it is essential to periodically decrease the loading in any given workout or microcycle and to apply the sudden release contrast method to enhance the training effect (see 1.16.3). In any workout, it is common to progress rapidly after the warm-up to the use of large resistance parachutes, then conclude with a few repetitions using smaller parachutes.

To ensure that this aerodynamic resistance training does not leave after-effects which disturb one's normal neuromuscular skills, it is advisable to precede and follow all parachute sessions with the same exercises performed without parachutes. During the preparatory weekly microcycles, parachute sessions typically are performed two or three times a week on alternate days between other types of training session. They are used more frequently nearer the later stage of the preparatory phase immediately preceding the competitive season.

4.3.2 The Accentuated Region of Force Production

Muscular effort changes during the course of every movement and maximum force is developed at the most appropriate instant for a given action. In ballistic movements this instant corresponds to the beginning part of the working amplitude and in movements of mixed regimes of muscular work, this takes place at the instant of switching from one regime to another (Verkhoshansky, 1977). Thus, the working amplitude always has an accentuated region where the maximum dynamic force occurs close to a specific joint angle. Based on this, the criterion of correspondence includes the need to produce the required force at a specific joint angle.

In the previous example it should be noted that the accentuated region of the working amplitude of the leg movement is near the beginning, as discussed earlier and as shown in the graph of hip flexion torque in the air (Fig 4.21).

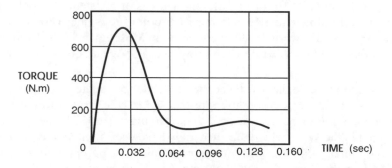

Figure 4.21 Change in the moment of the force during repetitive flexion-extension of the leg during the take-off for the triple jump (Siff & Verkhoshansky, 1999).

Consequently, the athletes referred to earlier who run with loads or use hip flexor machines regularly not only do not reproduce the required full amplitude of the movement, but also lose the ability to train the muscles to generate the necessary force at the appropriate hip joint angle. This clearly illustrates the importance of the starting position for executing the special strength exercises that have a local effect on the motor system. The strength exercise should not only reproduce the full amplitude of the movement but also the specific direction of resistance to the pull of the muscles.

Following these requirements can sometimes lead to such initial positions using weights or pulley machines which are incongruous and artificial (Fig 4.22). However, this occurs only when an exercise is attempted which fails to take into consideration the appropriate criteria. In example illustrated, the partner seated on the athlete's shoulders simulates the vertical loading which sprinting normally imposes, while the partner pulling the back leg offers resistance intended to strengthen the power of the hip flexors. While this exercise may be appropriate if applied carefully, incorrect positioning or imposition of resistance can reduce its effectiveness markedly.

Figure 4.22 A special strength exercise intended to simulate the flexion-extension action of the hip during sports activities, where the accentuated regions of force production can be incorrectly resisted and posture can be inappropriately held (Siff & Verkhoshansky, 1999).

It is possible to develop force at the required joint angles with isometric exercises, because they can have a particular value in this respect (see 4.2.4). With isometrics or quasi-isometrics over a given range of movement one can locally influence certain muscle groups by paying particular attention to the accentuated regions of the movements where they are involved. Therefore, the selection of these exercises should be based on the joint angle at which maximal torque is developed in the special exercise.

4.3.3 The Dynamics of the Effort

The criterion of dynamic effort is the quantitative correspondence of the dynamics of the training means to the specific sports movement. This criterion states that the intensity of the training stimulus should not be less than that encountered in the given exercise at the corresponding level of sports proficiency and should even exceed it. In other words, the effort exerted in training should not be less than the effort generated in the specific sports movement. One must now ask whether the maximum value or the mean value should be considered as the criterion of correspondence of strength.

Depending upon external conditions, a person can display maximal strength in two forms: in the movement of heavy loads or light loads. The maximum force can actually be larger in the second case than in the first, since the lighter load can be rapidly accelerated (remembering that $\mathbf{F} = m\mathbf{a}$). However, it is unnecessary to exercise only with light loads, even if the maximum achieved corresponds closely to the dynamics of the special exercise. It is important to consider first the duration and character of the effort.

The fact is that the external force displayed in these two cases is qualitatively different: in the first, maximum force is determined by the *absolute strength* of the muscles, and in the second by the *speed of contraction*. Therefore, the strength and training effects of the respective movements are also different.

From this it follows that, in striving to generate maximal effort in training, the athlete should become clearly acquainted with the type of strength which is needed and satisfy the criteria of correspondence according to the amount of effort and the movement time for the specific exercise. In other words, correspondence with respect to the maximum and mean magnitude of strength can be determined only by calculating the speed of movement. If the athlete finds the means for achieving this, he can be confident that he is on the right track in organising his special strength training.

The following examples serve to clarify the issue. If the special exercise requires the athlete to overcome a large resistance at a relatively low speed, then training should be aimed primarily at developing maximal strength. Conversely, if the athlete has to deal with a small resistance in the special exercise and execute the movement at maximal speed, then, according to the criterion of correspondence, he should apply a moderate amount of effort and pay particular attention to the duration of the movement.

4.3.4 The Rate and Time of Force Production

The criterion of correspondence regarding the rate of developing maximum force (see 2.2.1) complements the criterion of dynamic effort and is particularly important in those sporting activities requiring *explosive strength*. We have already stated that the strength displayed in training should be examined by taking into account its rate of production, which is equivalent to measuring the time taken to execute the movement. The production of explosive strength implicates a brief-acting moderate force whose characteristics may be described in terms of features such as the *power* and the *impulse* ($\mathbf{F}.\Delta t$) of the force, where $\mathbf{s}$ is the displacement and Δt is the brief time interval over which the force $\mathbf{F}$ acts (see 5.1). The following factors are relevant in this context:

Power $\qquad\qquad P = \dfrac{dW}{dt}$ $\qquad$ i.e. The rate of doing work at any instant

Here W refers to the work and may be defined in its integral form as $W = \int F(t).ds$ where $\mathbf{s}$ is the displacement produced by the force $\mathbf{F}$. Thus, if F is constant over the interval concerned, we obtain:

$$P = \frac{d}{dt}\int F(t).ds \;\;\ldots\ldots\ldots\; (4.1) \qquad or \qquad P = F.\frac{d}{dt}\int ds$$

The right hand side of this equation quite simply reduces to the familiar basic expression for power:

Power $\qquad\qquad P = F.V$ $\qquad$ ..... where V is the velocity of the object

Unfortunately, *this basic definition is applied without qualification in many strength training texts and can lead to serious misunderstanding of training theory and methods*. If the force is not constant over the time period being analysed, then we have to rely on a more precise form such as equation (4.1) which reminds us to consider how the force and velocity (as functions of time) vary over the time interval concerned. This can be done most conveniently by examining graphs of F versus V (e.g. Figs 3.15 - 3.18), F versus time and V versus time (e.g. Figs 2.13, 3.3, 3.4, 3.14, 3.27, 4.7).

It is especially important to be aware of how the force-time (i.e. the RFD or Rate of Force Development) curve changes with time (i.e., the slope of the F-t curve, shown in Fig 2.13). It is inadequate to refer to average or peak force alone. *The ability to increase power or explosive strength also depends on specifically training the RFD factor* (which was introduced in 2.2.1 as the factor that best defines explosive strength). This conclusion is vital to the design of strength training programmes to improve performance in any sport which involves explosive actions. The emergence of plyometric training as an adjunct method of special strength training is one of the practical consequences of understanding the implications of the preceding analysis of power as a motor ability.

In all plyometric actions, the force changes very rapidly as a complicated transient spike function and cannot be regarded as a constant throughout the rebound phase. In such cases it is better to rely on a force plate or high speed video methods to analyse the movement than to attempt to apply elementary biomechanical calculations that will inevitably produce grave errors.

The other factor used to analyse explosive strength, the *Reactivity Coefficient*, was defined earlier (2.2.1) as the RFD relative to one's bodyweight (or the weight of any object being moved rapidly):

Reactivity Coefficient $\qquad RC = F_{max} / t_{max}.mg \;=\; RFD_{max} / W$

where F_{max} is the maximum force exerted, t_{max} is the time taken to reach this maximum, the mass is m and g is the acceleration due to gravity $= 9.8 m/s^2$.

The above equations may be used to evaluate explosive strength, although the significance of each of them can be different, depending on conditions. Thus, evaluation using calculations of the impulse of the force is acceptable only when it is not necessary to compare different movements. If such a need arises, then the evaluation is valid only if the time taken is identical for each movement, a situation that does not occur in human movement. Therefore, in this particular case, determination of the impulse of the force is irrelevant.

In those cases where the working effort is displayed over a brief time interval, a necessary condition of the movement's effectiveness is the speed with which maximum effort is developed. In other words, if it is necessary for the athlete to produce a large force within some time limit, he must do it quickly and use a high RFD. Such a necessity is dictated by the conditions of the activity and by the biomechanical characteristics of the musculoskeletal system, especially the working amplitude of the movement.

Thus, the RFD, or rate with which the required maximum force is developed (determined from the slope of the force-time curve), is an important criterion of correspondence for resolving the task of special strength training (see 2.2.1), which relates directly to the characteristics of the neuromuscular system. This again emphasizes the fact that *all training is primarily neuromuscular* and that training based entirely on variables such as exercise choice, load, sets and repetitions is highly inadequate for producing sport specific fitness.

It should be stressed that fulfillment of the criterion of correspondence regarding strength and the speed with which it achieves a maximum creates its own unique problem, the successful resolution of which depends upon the efficiency of the neuromuscular training process.

4.3.5 The Regime of Muscular Work

The criterion of correspondence regarding the sports regime relies on determining the character of the muscular work involved. In particular, the regime of muscular work should be taken into consideration for selecting the means and methods of special strength training. The fact is that, depending upon the character of its execution, the same means can solve different tasks. For example, boxers and shot putters need to execute the same exercise (e.g. performing a thrusting arm movement against the resistance of a pulley machine) with different weights, tempos, number of sets and repetitions, because boxing requires primarily a quick, unresisted movement and the ability to repeat it many times without significant decrease in force, whereas shotputting involves rapid single movements against a specific resistance.

The selection of a regime of muscular work is difficult where a specific motor action is concerned. However, it is even more difficult in all-round sports like decathlon, gymnastics and modern pentathlon. Therefore, the problem of selecting a regime of muscular work involves two obvious tasks:

- selection of the regime for a specific motor action (e.g. the key elements in an exercise)
- selection of the main regime which will best develop all of the diverse muscular activities in all-round training.

The latter issue is still far from being resolved, although the evolution of training methods in sport indicates that it should be more thoroughly understood in the near future.

Almost one hundred years of experience in training all-round track athletes indicates that their fundamental training regime is speed-cyclic with dynamic tension, primarily of the explosive type. This was corroborated by using statistical analysis to identify the key exercises in the 'all-round' complex (Zatsiorsky, 1966; Lukauskas, 1967; Mamdzhanyan, 1976). To corroborate this idea one should examine the preparation of gymnasts. For a long time they adhered to primarily static training, with many of them including some dynamic exercises such as jumping. The progress of competitive standards and the necessity to master complex elements such as jumping with extensive longitudinal rotation compelled them to examine the value of the cyclic work regime and reconsider it in favour of dynamic muscular tension.

Thus, it may be concluded that cyclic and phasic-tonic regimes probably should be regarded as the most important in all-round training. It is also necessary to add other regimes, determined by the motor skills required by the specific sport. However, this conclusion needs rigorous experimental substantiation.

In conjunction with perfecting motor skills in a specific activity, one should consider the importance of changing from one activity to another in those exercises where this is necessary. Thus, an athlete's results in the long jump are determined mainly by the ability to switch from the cyclic regime of muscular work in running, to explosive effort in the take-off. For instance, good gymnasts are capable of switching rapidly from dynamic explosive effort to isometric tension. The methodology underlying the development of these complex capabilities is the aim of technical training in all sport. Its resolution is the goal of special strength training.

4.3.6 Correspondence of Training Means to the Sports Movements

The scientific understanding of the character of muscular work and motor strength is derived from analysis of the athlete's movements, i.e. the entire complex of interacting motor actions which resolve the motor tasks most effectively. The most convenient way of doing this is to use a high speed video system to record and analyse each movement at intervals separated by fractions of a second.

The kinematic structure characterises the interrelation of the separate movements in space and time and helps to identify those actions which play either a fundamental or supportive role in determining motor skill. From here it is easy to take one further step to determine the means of perfecting the movements and especially the means and methods of developing functional strength. Naturally, knowledge of the movement will be more precise if it is based on quantitative information which can be obtained only from computerised video analysis.

The analysis of the kinematics of a motor action to model its mechanisms can be based on scrutiny of the phasic structure of the movement (according to Donskoi). The act as a whole or its elements can always be divided into separate phases in which the direction of movement, the application of force and the character of muscular work are distinguished. The interrelation between separate phases enables one to gain some idea of the muscle actions and the movement as a whole, particularly during critical phases of the task. Such a representation will be more complete if forces are simultaneously recorded along with the video images (e.g. using a force plate or cable tensiometer), thereby permitting the total interaction of the person with the external objects to be analysed.

As has already been stated, full reproduction of the complex interaction of the different types of fitness strength is not always possible in training. It becomes necessary to exercise locally the interacting muscle groups that are crucial for controlling specific movements in a sporting task, which suggests that the training load be increased. Such exercise should be based on the characteristics for forming and developing the kinesiological structure of the motor action (see 2.1.2, 2.1.3). It has been established that, in the course of mastering a motor act, the elements of the kinesiological structure develop in a particular pattern of heterochronicity, depending on their origin and manner of interdependence (see 2.2.3).

The development of some elements is determined by their direct interaction with external objects, whereas others are determined by indirect interaction with these objects, so that they develop at a slower rate. An indispensable condition for forming and developing the biodynamic structure is the relatively harmonious development of its elements. This task can be successfully undertaken only by means of an organised system of special strength training.

Thus, it must be emphasized again that success in selecting the means of special strength training is determined by a thorough knowledge of the biomechanics of the movements.

4.4 Strength Training and General Endurance

The scientifically corroborated concepts concerning energy production for muscular work play an important role in solving the practical problems of training. Analysis of the functional specialisation of the body solely at the level of the cardiovascular-respiratory and motor systems is inadequate, especially if the physiology of endurance is considered with respect to the respiratory functions and maximum oxygen consumption (VO_2 max) alone. Since existing regimes of endurance training are still based on such ideas, improvement of modern methods of endurance development is now particularly urgent. This question is examined in detail below:

1. Athletes who have equivalent VO_2 max levels show different results, and conversely, athletes with different levels of aerobic efficiency demonstrate the same results. For example, top middle-distance runners of the 1940s had the same VO_2 max as today's athletes, yet there are major differences in performance (Faulkner, 1968). There are no statistically reliable differences between athletes of different qualification regarding the development of aerobic potential, although there are significant differences with respect to anaerobic efficiency (Nabotnikova, 1972; Serafimova, 1974; Rusko, 1976).

2. The VO_2 max levels in highly-qualified athletes stabilises, but results continue to improve. For example, over a 4-5 year period the VO_2 max levels of the best Soviet and Swedish skaters stabilised, but their results still improved from year to year (Orlov & Sharova, 1977). VO_2 max levels remained practically unchanged in qualified road cyclists over many years of training, yet their performances improved (Melenberg et al, 1972).

3. A significant decrease in VO_2 max levels has been observed during the competition period, especially in cyclists (Bakhvalov, 1974; Zatsiorsky et al, 1974), swimmers (Serafimov, 1974; Volkov et al, 1974; Naumenko, 1978), skiers (Vasiliev & Trunin, 1974; Zima et al, 1975), skaters (Stenin, 1973; Vavilov, 1977), middle-distance runners (Loktyev, 1978, Borisov, 1979; Sirenko, 1981) and hockey players (Koloskov, 1976). There is a decreasing correlation between VO_2 max and improving sport results. The correlation

coefficient is R = 0.7 during the preparation period, whereas it is 0.4 during the competitive period (Vasiliev & Trunin, 1974; Melenberg, 1981).

This data indicates that V02 max on its own is no guarantee of outstanding performance. It is now recognised that, apart from aerobic power, other factors play a role, such as the ability to perform work for a prolonged period at a level of oxygen consumption close to the VO2 max, and the ability to effectively utilise available energy under competitive conditions. This concerns the decrease in V02 max during the competition period, a phenomenon possibly explained by the decreasing trainability of aerobic processes or by an inherent antagonism between aerobic and anaerobic processes (Zatsiorsky et al, 1974; Volkov, 1975).

Oxidative Capacity and Muscular Endurance

Practical improvement of the metabolic processes in endurance sports is associated with increasing the potential to utilise aerobic sources of energy by raising the Onset of Blood Lactate Accumulation (OBLA), i.e. that level of oxygen consumption at which the anaerobic processes begin to be prominently activated. Anaerobic work is approximately 50% more effective than aerobic work in raising this lactate threshold, therefore it is to the athlete's advantage to execute prolonged, intense work without the preliminary accumulation of lactate and include anaerobic energy production (Christensen & Hogberg, 1950).

Since OBLA depends on V02 max, it is considered useful to strive to raise V02 max, and in particular, to create some reserve of aerobic power by the end of the preparatory period to avoid a decrease in V02 max during the competition period, which may lower the specific work-capacity. Considering that a significant amount of the energy production of intense muscular work is achieved by recruiting the glycolytic mechanism of ATP resynthesis, it is advisable to execute a specific part of the training load with a high blood lactate concentration.

However, recent research indicates that an increase in endurance is associated more with enhancing the ability of the muscles to utilise a higher percentage of the oxygen already in the blood than with increasing the amount of oxygen in the bloodstream and improving the oxygen supply to the working muscles (Ekblom, 1969; Rowell, 1971; Saltin, 1974). Consequently, it is not simply the magnitude of V02 max that determines endurance, but intramuscular factors which facilitate adaptation of the muscles to prolonged intense work. A rise in intramuscular energy potential, the power of the oxidative processes and the contractile (strength) qualities of the muscles decrease the rate of glycolysis (Newshalme & Randle, 1964; Saltin & Karlsson, 1971; Paul et al, 1966; Grimby et al, 1967). At the same time, there is a significant drop in the end products of metabolism, including the speed of oxidation of lactate in the working muscles (Jorfeldt, 1970). It is in the skeletal muscles and not in the liver and myocardium, as has always been believed, where there is a drop in lactate during and after work (Jorfeldt, 1970; Knutten, 1971; Gollnick & Hermansen, 1973).

Thus, *the development of endurance is associated with functional specialisation of the skeletal muscles, particularly the enhancement of their strength and oxidative qualities, rather than improvement of cardiorespiratory ability.* Consequently, the fundamental emphasis in developing endurance should be to decrease the proportion of glycolysis in supplying the energy for work and improve the ability of the muscles to oxidise lactate during work, and not simply to improve accommodation to high concentrations of blood lactate. In other words, in addition to utilising the aerobic pathway of energy production with maximum efficiency, the development of endurance should be aimed chiefly at eliminating the disparity between the anaerobic and aerobic abilities of the muscles, which is the main reason for a high lactate concentration. Recently, haemodynamic factors have been shown to play an important role in the functional specialisation of the body during endurance work (Vasiliev, 1970, 1974; Ozolin & Partsik, 1970; Danilov, 1980; Kurbanov, 1977; Rowell, 1971; Kaijser, 1970; Karlsson, 1971; Gollnick et al, 1975). *The redistribution of blood and an increase in circulation to the working muscles contributes to satisfying the oxygen requirements of the muscles and the removal of anaerobic metabolites.*

Differentiation of the vesicular reaction providing effective redistribution of blood flow and an optimal blood supply to the working muscles takes place during the competition period as a result of the extensive aerobic loading executed during the preparatory period. For example, research has shown that improvement in cycling performance (in 25 km road racing) is accompanied by a decrease in V02 max during the competition period, while peak blood flow to the lower extremities increases. At the same time, cardiac output decreases during the competition period, a measure which reflects the efficiency of the cardiovascular system (Stepochkin et al, 1970). The very same conditions which create economy of aerobic energy production decrease the involvement of glycolytic processes and, consequently, lessen dependence on V02 max. In this way, it is possible to eliminate the basic cause of the decrease in V02 max during the competition period. If this is so, then the assumption concerning antagonism in endurance sport between the development of the aerobic and anaerobic mechanisms must be questioned (Mellenberg & Khvan, 1982).

One should consider the fact that OBLA (lactate threshold) and V02 max levels can change independently of each other. It is interesting to note that, while there is some decrease in V02 max during the competition period, OBLA can rise (Zatsiorsky et al, 1974; Sirenko, 1979; Nurmekivan, 1974). Research indicates that blood lactate concentration can increase by some 6% as a result of training, while the V02 max level increases by only 7% (Williams et al, 1967). It has also been shown, that the mean change in V02 max of qualified skaters is 5-10% in the competition period, while local blood flow is increased much more significantly (50-250%) (Mellenberg, 1981). This also corroborates the finding that effectiveness of training does not lie in raising V02 max, but in enhancing the haemodynamic efficiency of oxygen transport, which thereby can meet the oxygen requirements of the tissues by decreasing reliance on the contribution of anaerobic metabolism.

Consequently, together with the rise in strength and oxidative qualities of the muscles, *the redistribution of blood flow and improved local vesicular reaction are important conditions for developing local muscle endurance.* Sports exercises are performed by specific muscle groups and if metabolic processes in these muscles are especially intense, then the products of anaerobic metabolism accumulate, resulting in fatigue and decreased work capacity. Therefore, adaptation of the muscles to anaerobic work is clearly local in nature. For example, if one trains different muscle groups, then it is possible to achieve approximately equivalent functional effect at the level of the cardiovascular-respiratory systems. However, it is displayed only in specific situations, i.e. while using those same muscle groups (Clausen et al, 1970; Holmer & Astrand, 1972). With skiers, running and imitation skiing without poles raises the general functional level during the preparatory period, including V02 max, but does not develop the specific physical preparedness necessary for speed of movement on skis. On the other hand, imitation skiing and indoor skiing on rollers with poles enhances local muscular endurance and vesicular reactions in the muscles of the upper extremities, which leads to the efficient redistribution of blood flow and an increase in specific work-capacity for skiing (Yevstratov et al, 1975).

Local muscular endurance is the athlete's ability to produce the strength component of movement for a prolonged period without significant fatigue. For example, this may be seen in 400m sprinting, especially regarding the changes in stride length and tempo with increase in sport mastery (Fig 4.23). It is clear that stride length is maintained with some decrease in tempo at the high-mastery level by means of local strength-endurance. In the fatigued state, athletes of different sex and level of qualification all display a greater decrease in stride length than tempo, but the decrease in speed is associated exclusively with the strength factor.

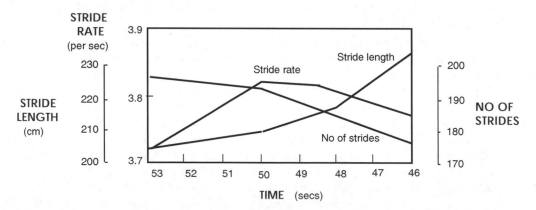

Figure 4.23 Change in stride length accompanying increase in the speed of running 400m (Popov, 1972).

Thus, the importance of local muscle endurance in sports requiring prolonged maintenance of a specific work output, is obvious. However, practical ways of developing local muscular endurance still need serious research. Clearly, one should find ways to intensify muscular work in those regimes characterising the given sport and utilise special strength exercises for this purpose (Verkhoshansky, 1977).

Strength Training and General Endurance

With respect to what has just been discussed, one should examine the research showing that strength training leads to a greater rise in haemoglobin content (Petrov & Lapchenkov, 1978) and myoglobin (Pattengale & Holloszy, 1967; Hemmingsen, 1963) than endurance training; and that strength training, even in the beginning stages of training, contributes more to the largest improvements in distance sports than aerobic training (Neminushchii & Filin, 1972; Gavrilenko & Mikhailov, 1981). Several decades ago, scientists pointed out the importance of local (strength) endurance for cyclic types of sport (Reindel, 1962; Fetz, 1965; Nett, 1964; Asmussen, 1969; Cook & Byrnston, 1973; Simri, 1974; Nurmekivi, 1974), but in our time, it has not been given serious attention. Methods of endurance development were aimed chiefly at improving the cardiovascular-respiratory functions (mainly by distance training), which are a major factor in determining progress in cyclic sports, especially in longer distance running.

Furthermore, the above data justify the importance of solving the problem of enhancing endurance, where it is considered to be a complex resultant of motor abilities (Reindel, 1962; Roskamm et al, 1952; Brogli & Antonov, 1969; Larson & Yocom, 1952; Posker & Steblo, 1967; Wilt, 1970). In accordance with this, general endurance is defined in terms of the cardiovascular-respiratory functions which provide the necessary oxygen and the appropriate state of the neuromuscular system. From this standpoint, the development of endurance should be carried out in the form of a scheme of training complexes based on the interaction between the cardiovascular-respiratory and motor systems.

These characteristics of endurance agree with the concepts of the motor-visceral reflexes (Mogendovich, 1962) and the energetics of muscle contraction (Arshavsky, 1967). In accordance with these concepts, the efficiency of muscular work is determined by the interdependence of motor activity, topography, sequentiality and the work regime of the muscles involved, and the respiratory, circulatory and metabolic processes in the body.

With respect to the interdependence of the cardiovascular-respiratory and motor processes, the latter plays the key role insofar as functioning of the motor apparatus determines the training of the cardiovascular-respiratory systems. It should be noted that the cooperation between the cardiovascular-respiratory and motor systems is important for improving work-capacity, not only in endurance sports, but in all sports. Therefore, it is a serious error to draw a line between them, as is quite common in the methodology of special physical training.

The Process of Functional Specialisation

If we focus on the process of functional specialisation over many years of training, its most general features may be represented in an ascending flowchart (Fig 4.24). We are endowed with an enormous ability to execute any motor task and perfect this ability. We have flexible mechanisms of coordination, regulation and energy production for motor function, and the ability to produce movements which require the display of speed, strength, or endurance. These mechanisms ensure the success of human activities in daily life and offer extensive possibilities for adaptation (Level 1). Changes in environmental conditions imposed by sport activities in training and competition stimulate the motor function, which coordinates all muscular activity (Level 2). The motor function specialises chiefly by developing the ability to display explosive force and specific endurance independent of the type of sport (Level 3).

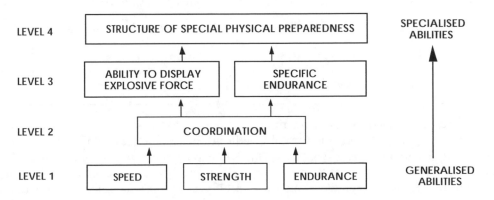

Figure 4.24 The general sequence of the body's functional specialisation over many years of training (Siff & Verkhoshansky, 1999).

It should be noted that specific endurance may be predominantly cardiovascular or local muscular in nature. In addition, explosive force relates closely to the motor qualities of starting strength, acceleration-strength and absolute strength (see 3.2.1). The intensive stage of functional specialisation follows which, along with further improving its survival capability, forms the structure of special physical preparedness (Level 4). The latter displays its own form with respect to interaction of the cardiovascular-respiratory and motor systems, which secure the athlete's high work-capacity.

Within the confines of such structures, the functional systems interact in cooperative and subordinate relationships. In the first case (cooperation) their relationship is characterised by the effective interaction of all the systems responsible for producing the working capabilities of the body, whereas in the second case (subordination) the productivity of one system is enhanced by the functional potentials of the others. The structure of special physical preparedness is determined by the specific training regime, and does not relate to conditions imposed by other sporting activities. This fact should be noted by anyone who may be contemplating the use of generalised cross training with various sports.

Factor Analysis

Methodical study of the structure of special physical preparedness may be achieved via statistical analysis of the characteristics which describe the various aspects of the athlete's work-capacity. Results of factor analysis are especially informative in those cases where one of the composite schemes describes the preparedness of athletes of different qualification or the same athlete at different stages of training.

This type of information, gathered from results in many sports, indicates that *there are distinct changes in the structure of an athlete's physical preparedness with increasing sports proficiency*, with marked differences being observed between athletes of high and low qualification.

The data in Table 4.1 show that athletes (high jumpers, Class 1-MS), concurrently with increase in proficiency, develop the specific ability to generate powerful force during the take-off in jumping exercises (factor I) and perfect the ability to powerfully extend the body with the dynamic participation of the knee and back extensor muscles (factor III).

The ability of the extensor muscles of the take-off leg to display explosive force under isometric conditions (factor II) assumes major significance (see more details on explosive isometrics in 4.2.4). This ability serves as the foundation of factors IV and V which is characteristic of the structure of Class 2 and 3 athletes. At the same time, indicators which characterise the explosive capabilities of the plantar flexors shift from factor II (Class 2 and 3 athletes) to factor IV (Class 1 athletes and MS), the contribution of which diminishes significantly. On the whole, the role of special physical preparedness of jumpers increases with level of qualification.

Table 4.1 The factor structure (in %) of Special Physical Preparedness of high jumpers, in terms of the major factors displayed by a large sample of competitors of different levels of qualification (Nikitin, 1983)

Factor Order	Class 2-3 Athletes		Class 1 - MS	
I	General athletic preparedness	29.6	Specific athletic preparedness	27.4
II	Power of plantarflexors	19.6	Power of knee extension isometrically	23.4
III	Power of knee extension in dynamic regime	13.0	Power of knee extension dynamically	18.5
IV	Isometric strength of knee extensors	10.5	Power of plantarflexors	11.8
V	Explosive-strength of knee extensors (isometric)	6.5		

As an important practical consequence emanating from the data in Table 4.1, one needs to note that the contribution of isometric strength in the formation of the specific ability to generate explosive force in the take-off assumes great significance for highly qualified athletes. This is due to the large loading of the muscles during the take-off, where the support (take-off) leg acts as a lever, and converts into vertical lift the angular velocity acquired during the run-up. Furthermore, the plantarflexors play a diminishing role, because under intense overloading the muscles of the support leg are already unable to make a significant contribution to the dynamics of the take-off.

The nature of the changes in an athlete's structure of special fitness in cyclic sports is presented in Table 4.2. One should note the sharp rise in the role of energetic efficiency of special work and multifaceted technical preparedness, factors which make an increasing contribution to general development. One should also point out that the first two factors (power and aerobic capacity) of Class 1 athletes may be combined as one factor (i.e.

aerobic efficiency) whose role at Master of Sport level decreases in the general structure of special fitness. At the same time the significance of anaerobic power increases slightly (factor III).

Table 4.2 The factor structure (in %) of special fitness of skaters in terms of the major factors displayed by a large sample of competitors of different levels of qualification (Shchirkovyets & Rosovtsyev, 1977).

Factor Order	Class 1 Athletes		Master of Sport	
I	Aerobic Power	35.9	Energetic efficiency of executing specific work	36.5
II	Aerobic Capacity	23.3	Multi-faceted technical preparedness	21.9
III	Power of anaerobic processes	16.8	Power of anaerobic processes	19.8
IV	Energetic efficiency of executing specific work	2.7	Aerobic efficiency	10.9
V	Multi-faceted technical preparedness	8.9		

These results indicate that a high level of aerobic potential still does not ensure top-level performance in skating. To efficiently generate a high level of aerobic power, it necessary to have excellent movement technique and a high level of anaerobic (non-oxidative glycolytic) productivity, thereby expanding the athlete's motor capabilities.

Thus, factor research offers a useful statistical model of the structure of the athlete's special physical preparedness (SPP). This structure can have different forms which are determined by the motor qualities characteristic of the individual and the organisation of training. Therefore, when programming training it is necessary to take into consideration the general trends of change in the factor structure of special physical preparedness with increase in proficiency, as well as the individual peculiarities of a specific athlete and all changes in the level of and the interrelation between the main functional characteristics.

THE METHODS OF SPECIAL STRENGTH TRAINING

The optimal selection of the means for developing strength is based upon the criterion of correspondence of the special exercise to the actual sporting activities (discussed in Ch 4), a step which already increases the likelihood of successful training. However, this is only part of the process. The final task in complying with the principle of dynamic correspondence is determination of the specific means and methods of strength development.

Unfortunately, the problem of the methods of strength development is far from being solved, despite significant scientific and practical advances. The higher the curtain to this uncharted territory is raised, the greater the horizon that confronts researchers. Newer findings emerge which conflict with well-established and influential theories and methods. The threat to earlier work has to be handled objectively and carefully, because tradition dies hard and innovative research is often rejected by those who are committed to existing dogma. A combination of exhaustive creative study and practice is necessary in order to re-examine current hypotheses and analyse the field of strength training more thoroughly, and thereby formulate a more scientific basis for the methods of strength development (Verkhoshansky, 1977).

5.1 The Problem of Methods

Firstly, a number of methodological errors must be pointed out that result from attempts to devise methods of developing muscular strength, because they can misdirect one's thinking. Training methods must be based on a clear understanding of the processes underlying all sporting movement. At a *physiological level*, muscular contraction controlled by nervous processes is the source of all voluntary movement, determining, in particular, its speed and the working effect as a whole. At a *biomechanical level*, the force-time curve for human movement may be regarded as the starting point for analysing all types of strength production. Thus, it is vital to gain a good working knowledge of the most important features of both neuromuscular control and movement biomechanics.

The significance of *physiological processes* was discussed in depth in the preceding chapters; therefore, it is the objective of this section to offer further background on the fundamental biomechanical features of training. The *biomechanical foundations* of the major motor qualities of strength, including maximum strength, explosive strength, acceleration strength and starting strength, were covered in Section 2.2, where the importance of the Force-Time and Rate of Force Development curves was stressed. Force-Time, Force-Velocity and other graphs describing isometric, dynamic and ballistic movements, as well as Hill's classic mathematical relationship between muscular force and velocity of movement (3.3.2) were discussed in Chapter 3. The characteristics of power production were covered in Section 4.3.4. It remains the task here to understand the implications for strength training of the basic laws of dynamics, particularly Newton's 2nd Law of Motion.

Some Implications of the Laws of Dynamics

If the Force-Time curve is to be regarded as the graphical starting point for sport biomechanics, then Newton's 2nd Law of Motion must logically serve as the corresponding mathematical starting point.

In its original form, Newton II stated that *Force is proportional to the rate of change of momentum* of the mass concerned, where momentum (the tendency of a body to keep in motion) = m.v. Thus, if the appropriate units of measurement are used, Newton II may be written in calculus form as:

$$\mathbf{F} = \frac{d(m.\mathbf{v})}{dt} = m.\frac{d\mathbf{v}}{dt} + \mathbf{v}.\frac{dm}{dt} \qquad \ldots\ldots\ldots (5.1)$$

$$\mathbf{F} = m.\mathbf{a} + \mathbf{v}.\frac{dm}{dt}$$

$$\mathbf{F} = m.\mathbf{a} \qquad \text{if the mass of the system is not changing with time}$$

In other words, force **F** equals mass m times acceleration **a**. This is the familiar basic form of Newton II that is applied in most sporting situations, since ongoing loss of mass (like the expulsion of exhaust gases derived from a given mass m of fuel used to propel jet aircraft) does not occur in sport. It should be noted that acceleration and velocity are vector quantities, so that any change in direction, and not only magnitude, will also be associated with a change in force.

The manner in which the force is generated was discussed earlier (2.2.1), by examining the rate of change of force. The maximum value of this term, (dF/dt) or Rate of Force Development (RFD), was used to define an index of explosive strength IES.

It is essential now to distinguish between force that is generated ballistically or impulsively versus force that is produced more slowly. In the latter case, it is useful to refer to the *momentum* m.**v** of the body, but with respect to brief transient force development, it is conventional to talk about the *impulse* I of the force. In this case, equation (5.1) is used to define the concept of impulse. The impulse I is obtained by taking the integral of both sides of this equation. Here the brief-acting force is very large and the time interval during the impulsive phase is ΔT. The final velocity reached at the end of this phase is Δ**V**.

$$I = \int_0^{\Delta T} \mathbf{F}.dt = \int_0^{\Delta V} m.d\mathbf{v} \qquad \text{or:}$$

$$I = \mathbf{F}.\Delta T = m.\Delta V$$

Even if neither F nor ΔT is known, the impulse may be calculated from the change in momentum, m.Δ**V**.

In Ch 2.2.2 we used this information to compare the performances of two different athletes in executing the same exercise, but it is relevant to repeat it here. Both athletes were instructed to perform a single maximal repetition of this exercise as rapidly as possible and to hold the load until fatigue forced them to stop. Their resulting force-time curves (Fig 5.1) show that athlete B exerts a greater maximal force and continues to produce force for longer than athlete A. However, at any instant T_1 between 0 and time T_2, athlete A is able to exert greater force than athlete B. If the sport concerned requires rapid RFD, then athlete A will have the advantage.

This quality is essential in any sports which involve jumping, striking or throwing, such as basketball, martial arts and track-and-field. In this case, any training aimed at increasing B's maximal strength or bulk will be misdirected, because he needs to concentrate on explosive strength (RFD) training. If the sport requires a high maximal force or a large amount of momentum to be exerted irrespective of time, then athlete B will prove to be superior. Athlete A will not improve unless he trains to increase maximal strength.

The area under the curve (i.e. the momentum) describing athlete B's performance is greater than the corresponding area for athlete A, like the total duration of his curve (i.e. reflecting muscle endurance), so that B has a distinct advantage in any activity that requires great momentum or great muscle endurance during a single heavy effort. This situation occurs in events such as wrestling, powerlifting and scrummaging in rugby.

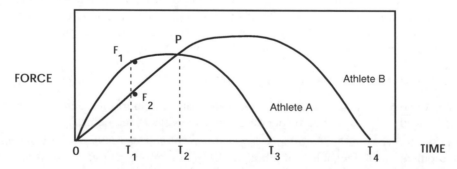

Figure 5.1 Force curves F1 and F2, produced by different athletes in reaching and attempting to maintain their respective maximum forces for as long as possible in a given exercise.

Mechanical position during movement is preserved only within a known range, since the shape of the force-time curve is determined by the characteristics of the neuromuscular system, imparting to it the ability to develop muscular force with the speed necessary to produce the required motor effect. This ability to control muscular activity and movement in space and time is a specific property of the neuromuscular system and requires specialised means of training. A lack of effective neuromuscular training leads to errors and can cost the athlete years of hard and fruitless work.

All subsequent training and performance errors are caused by inappropriate neuromuscular programming. The above-mentioned motor qualities (force and velocity) of the neuromuscular system at a high level of development are inversely proportional to one another (see Ch 4). Excessive development of both is not required in athletics because they are not achieved in isolation, but are interrelated aspects of characteristics associated with all motor activity. Depending upon the character and the objective of the movement, one of these qualities achieves greater development but generally displays approximately the same pattern.

Thus, *speed-strength, strength-endurance* and *speed-endurance* are not simply derivatives of strength, speed and endurance, but are totally independent qualities. This is emphasized by the fact that an increase in absolute strength does not necessarily enhance any of these three qualities. They should be placed alongside the latter in a group, each with its own particular means and methods of development (Verkhoshansky, 1963). However, the first attempts to devise methods for developing these newly-recognised qualities were based mainly on an approach which led to a solution based on the *analytical-synthetic method,* as follows: the qualities should be developed separately with the appropriate means and then they should be integrated into the special exercises. In this context, *analysis* refers to breaking down a process into its components, whereas *synthesis* means combining separate components into an integrated whole which is different from each of its components.

Regarding the analytical-synthetic method, it may be appropriate for gymnasts and weightlifters to do sprints and other track-and-field exercises for developing speed, while barbell exercises may be recommended for the strength training of track athletes (Verkhoshansky, 1977). Furthermore, cross-country running, swimming, cross-country skiing and other cyclic exercises may be considered beneficial for developing general endurance. Although it is extremely difficult to deny the value of these ostensibly logical recommendations, they are appropriate only for the initial stages of training and it would be a serious error for highly-qualified athletes to use them casually. A practical consequence of this last comment is to conclude that *multi-faceted preparation* in athletics should be the leading training principle. However, such an assertion is partly true and only under certain circumstances. The suitability of multi-faceted preparation is based purely on observation of unifactorial adaptation of the body rather than on quantitative analysis of the interrelation among all the factors involved.

However, some recent studies indicate that *unifactorial adaptation* (separately to various different stimuli) does not imply the different training stimuli are all interrelated. This concerns the synthesis of motor qualities and their transference from one movement to another, as well as the fact that such a phenomenon occurs to a certain degree, primarily in the initial stages of developing sports fitness (Yakovlev, 1968; Zimkin, 1965; Zatsiorsky, 1965). This, however, does not constitute evidence for considering multi-faceted preparation to be the main training principle. With the improvement in sporting performance, multi-faceted preparation inevitably opposes the law of gradual development (in the sports training process, STP) and can hinder the body's specialised adaptation (Verkhoshansky, 1977).

These comments are of particular relevance in the West today because of the growing popularity of so-called *cross training,* which is one form of multi-faceted training (see 5.5). The concurrent use of a variety of different training means or roughly similar sports over the same period to prevent stagnation can be counterproductive and valuable only during particular transitional stages of long-term training. Even then, *it is important to combine different training means or sports according to the most appropriate sequentiality, simultaneity or scheme of superposition at each stage of preparation.*

As stated before, there is also the danger of an excessive passion for making the strength training means correspond structurally to the special exercises, so that an inadequate understanding of the *principle of dynamic correspondence* can limit the scope of training means. The misinterpretation of this principle lies in literally copying the special exercise in training movements, instead of selecting a specific arsenal of means corresponding to the most important *motor characteristics* of the given sport and controlling their growth by creating conditions under which they will develop steadily. In other words, it is inappropriate to try to simulate sports specific movements with supplementary training activities. Not only does this not accurately develop the necessary fitness and motor abilities, but it can also alter the neuromuscular programmes which control the motor actions. Rather, it is important to focus on developing the *specific type of fitness* and *motor characteristics* of the sport.

5.2 General Principles of Special Strength Training

Systematising the methods of strength training necessitates classifying the means of developing muscular strength. The basic prerequisite for classification is associated firstly with the general characteristics of the motor regimes underlying the various sporting actions. Four categories of sports may be identified according to these characteristics. Physical conditioning, especially strength training methods, should be examined in the context of these groups, namely (Diachkov, 1961):

1. Sports characterised by the production of maximal strength
2. Sports characterised by the display of endurance with optimal efforts of various intensities
3. Sports characterised by a high level of skill
4. Sports characterised by the complex display of several motor abilities at different levels of development.

This grouping of exercises identifies the primary emphasis of the strength training, which determines the choice of suitable methods. The necessity for developing *explosive strength*, *strength-endurance*, *strength-skill* (Diachkov, 1961; Kuznetsov, 1970), *relative strength*, *absolute strength*, and *strength-endurance* (Chudinov, 1961) arises from this grouping (see 1.16.4). The preceding classification can also act as the basis for deriving principles which involve the following:

- The magnitude of the main load (Diachkov, 1961; Zatsiorsky, 1966; Vorobyev, 1971)
- The specific need to change the training load (DeLorme, 1945, 1946; Zinovieff, 1951)
- The method of incorporating into a training scheme the means for exploiting the after-effect of previous work (Verkhoshansky, 1970).

A distinction between *maximal tension*, *speed-strength* and *strength-endurance* loads must be made (Letunov & Motylyanskaya, 1955; Nabatnikova, 1972; Platonov, 1974; Mikhailov & Panov, 1975). The production of maximal tension (via repetitively lifting a certain weight to the point of failure, or lifting a maximal weight at maximal velocity in a given situation) implies that three ways of developing strength may be distinguished, i.e. *repetitive*, *maximal* and *dynamic* effort (Zatsiorsky, 1966).

It is useful to systematise the methods of developing special-strength according to the specific type of strength they develop and to divide these into several basic groups of conditioning methods, namely *absolute strength*, *speed-strength*, *explosive strength*, *reactive ability* and *strength-endurance*. Within each group it is possible and necessary to differentiate methods regarding the particular type of muscular contraction in the given sports exercises (see 3.1). These methods are discussed in the subsections which follow.

5.2.1 The Development of Maximum Strength

Maximum strength, in the context of this chapter, is the maximal force that a person can develop voluntarily, as measured on a dynamometer or in terms of the heaviest weight that can be lifted (see Fig 1.1). In other words, maximum strength is the maximal force displayed under isometric conditions or in a very slow movement against a maximal load. There are two basic methods of developing maximum (and absolute) strength: the *method of repetitive effort* and the *method of brief maximal tension*. Whichever method is used, it is important to note that *maximum strength produced by training is retained for longer if it is founded first upon a base of increased muscle hypertrophy*. It declines more rapidly if it is enhanced primarily on the basis of improved neuromuscular efficiency.

The Repetitive Effort Method

The method of repetitive effort consists of repetitively lifting a weight whose magnitude is increased as muscular strength grows. The effect that this type of training produces depends upon the proprioceptive feedback which accompanies the slow lifting of weights. The corresponding adaptation which occurs is a result of the strong excitation of the neural pathways from the cortex to the muscles and the increase in the number of motor units recruited (Kabat, 1947; Hellebrant & Houtz, 1956).

A variable method of repetitive effort is the *progressive resistance method*. Initially, the weight which can be lifted ten times is determined: it is designated the 10RM (10 repetition maximum). The weights corresponding to the 5RM and the 10RM are, for any muscles, are about 89% and 74% of the 1RM weights respectively (see Fig 1.9). Training sessions consist typically of three sets of 10 slowly executed repetitions, using a heavier load with successive sets. With the classical *DeLorme method*, a weight of 50% of the 10RM is lifted 10 times for the first set, 75% of the 10RM for the second set and the 10RM weight for the third set (Hettinger, 1961). Progressively increasing the resistance over an extended period is useful for developing strength and endurance (Faulkner, 1950; Lindervold, 1952; Montgomery, 1954).

Other modifications of the DeLorme method involve decreasing the number of repetitions, increasing the amount of weight and varying other features such as the number of sets and the sequence of weights in the training cycle (Hoog, 1946; Houtz et al, 1946; Zinovieff, 1951; Watkins, 1952; McGovern & Luscombe, 1953; McQueen, 1954). Thus, execution of the exercise in the reverse order (i.e. after a warmup, moving to a maximum and then working downwards to lighter weights with more repetitions) is sometimes called the *Oxford* or *Zinovieff Method* (Zinovieff, 1951), and the 50% of 10RM, 10RM, 75% of 10RM sequence is referred to as the *McCloy Method* (McCloy, 1954).

Comparison of these modifications indicates they add nothing new to the DeLorme method, although the level of strength developed is slightly different, with the DeLorme system producing a larger increase in strength than the McCloy system (154% versus 142%). However, the McCloy system increases endurance more (212.8% versus 186%) than the DeLorme system (Faulkner, 1950). Training first with heavy weights then with lighter weights elicits a larger increase in muscle size (5.5%) compared with training first with light weights, then switching to heavier weights. The statistical reliability of these differences, however, has not yet been corroborated, particularly with advanced athletes (McMorris & Elks, 1954).

Training with a weight equal to 25% of the 5RM in set 1, 50% in set 2 and 75% for set 3 (5 repetitions per set) is just as effective for increasing strength as training with the 5RM for the set 1, 125% of the 5RM in set 2 and 150% of the 5RM in set 3 (Krusen, 1949).

Vorobyev (1971) showed that the major portion of the training load of modern weightlifters is with weights of 70% of 1RM and higher. The portion of the load devoted to lighter weights is about 10% of the entire load. Other studies have shown that most weightlifting training is done with 1-3 repetitions for advanced weightlifters, thereby emphasizing the importance of 1RM, 2RM and 3RM loads for enhancing competitive strength, especially where strength-skill is involved.

It is natural that, in perfecting the methods for developing maximum strength, consideration be given to questions such as the number of sets with a given weight, the number of repetitions per set and the tempo of movement. Thus, an experiment was conducted on the training effect of nine different programmes with the bench press. It was discovered that 3 sets of 6 repetitions (with the 6RM weight) was the most effective (Berger, 1962), corroborating earlier work by Keipen (1956), who had demonstrated the effectiveness of three sets with a 5RM.

Later, Berger (1963) investigated why 6 repetitions per set are more effective than either 2 or 10 repetitions in developing maximum strength. He concluded that training with a heavy weight does not permit the optimal number of repetitions necessary for increasing strength. He also found the reverse result, namely that training with light weights and many repetitions offers too weak a stimulus to significantly improve maximum strength. A significant difference in strength increase was not found between training regimes using 2RM, 5RM or 10RM, with maximal weights (10RM for one set three times per week), or with submaximal weights (90% of 10RM twice a week and the 10RM three times). There was also no major difference between the effectiveness of 2 or 3 training sessions per week.

It is known that, in all cases, training with a rest interval of two days between sessions is significantly more effective than with a rest interval of one day (Vasiliev, 1954). Five training programmes were compared. They were distinguished from each other primarily by the maximum weight used in one set:

1. 2/3 of 1RM twice a week and the 1RM for the third workout
2. 2/3 of 1RM twice a week and 80% of 1RM for the third workout
3. 2/3 of the 1RM twice a week and 90% of the 1RM the third time
4. 1RM once a week
5. 2/3 of 1RM three times a week.

The only programme which did not produce an increase in strength was the fifth one. The increases in strength from the other programmes were approximately the same (Berger, 1965). Thus, the following conclusions may be drawn:

1. Training with submaximal weights (2/3 and more of 1RM) twice a week and with maximal weights once a week is as effective for developing strength as training with maximal weights three times per week.

2. The increase in strength resulting from training with 2/3 of 1RM twice a week and with the 1RM in the third workout is due mainly to training with the 1RM.

3. To obtain the optimal increase in strength with three workouts per week, the load per set should be between the 3RM and the 10RM.

257

4. Training once a week with the 1RM for 1 set increases strength significantly for up to 6 weeks.

5. Training twice a week with 3 sets of the 10RM is as effective as training with 3 sets of 10RM three times a week.

6. If the 10RM is used for one set, subsequent lifts with lighter loads have no training value.

It should be emphasized that *these conclusions were based on research with untrained subjects or subjects with very little training experience* prior to the experiments. Significant increases in strength have been observed in novices training once a week, as well as five times per week. It should be noted that the recuperative powers of the body deteriorate under the influence of a large number of workouts per week. Since the optimal number of training sessions per week depends upon the body's capacity to recuperate, no precise rules regarding the number of sets and repetitions can be made, and no single programme can be ideal for everyone (Berger, 1962, 1963).

According to Vorobyev (1978), between 1-6 repetitions is the optimum number for training highly qualified weightlifters and an increase in this number hinders strength development. The movement tempo of resistance exercises also has great significance for the development of muscular strength (Vorobyev, 1978). Recently it has been shown that the largest increases in muscular strength are obtained by executing resistance movements at a moderate tempo. Under these conditions, strength continues to increase over a period of 30 training sessions, whereas it increases only over a period of 15 sessions with other tempos. It has been established that the most effective variant is a combination of different movement tempos. Thus, the increase in strength with this type of training over a period of 10 weeks was 22.6 ± 0.6 kg; and 16.3 ± 0.5 kg for the execution of movements at a moderate tempo for both concentric and eccentric actions (Lelikov, 1975).

It is interesting that, under certain conditions, the amount of strength developed by the repetition method is not determined by the magnitude of the load, but the quantity of work done. Thus, according to Vasiliev (1954), after 40 training sessions of equivalent work (in joules) with all loads (20%, 40%, 60%, 80% of 1RM) at a tempo of 45 lifts per minute and with different muscle groups, the results obtained were virtually indistinguishable. The 80% of 1RM load produced a slightly larger training effect, but not for all of the muscle groups exercised. Similar training at a maximal tempo became less effective as the load was increased. A high tempo of movement was not very effective for developing strength. Only with a load of 20% of 1RM in some muscle groups was the increase in strength approximately the same as it was when training at a tempo of 45 lifts per minute.

Experiments with frogs and observations using ergonometric methods have revealed that, up to the onset of fatigue, muscles execute the same number of contractions with a load of constant magnitude as when the load is increased gradually to this level. Since the larger the load, the faster the onset of fatigue, it is sensible to shorten the period of gradual increase in weight so as to reach optimal loads early and work with them throughout the training session (Narikashvili et al, 1960).

The Brief Maximal Tension Method

If the rapid display of maximum strength is required, then the *brief maximal tension method* is given priority in training. It is distinguished from the progressive resistance method in that heavy weights (85-95% of 1RM, i.e. 3-5RM) are primarily used and are combined with the lifting of lighter weights (in one training session) and maximal weights (one repetition once or twice a week). However, the number of sets should be increased to more than three (Berger, 1962). Thus, it is recommended that weightlifters execute 5-6 exercises for 6-10 sets of 1-3 repetitions in one training session (Medvedev, 1967; Vorobyev, 1971).

The *brief maximal tension method* develops the ability to concentrate neuromuscular effort and yields a larger training effect than the progressive resistance method for developing maximum strength and the ability to display it quickly (Diachkov, 1961; Chudinov, 1961). It increases strength without increasing muscle mass, which is important for sports which require primarily the development of relative strength (Chudinov, 1961). The brief maximal tension method has another important feature. Lifting maximal and near-maximal weights enhances the ability to accelerate heavy loads and increases special work capacity, as expressed by the skill to develop a brief concentrated effort of great power.

Isometrics can be useful to develop maximum strength which does not require the rapid production of force, although it has not been adequately established whether dynamic training or static training renders the quicker or most consistent increases in strength. Isometric training consisting of 2-15 contractions in one minute executed four times a week does not increase strength significantly more than lifting weights dynamically with the same frequency (Salter, 1955).

The same is the case with *static flexibility-isometric* routines using 5-10 stretches and 6-second isometric contractions (Denison et al, 1961). Similar conclusions were obtained in other studies (Asmussen, 1949; Darcus, 1955; Rose et al, 1951; Berger, 1962). It has been shown that dynamic work executed for 3 sets of 5 or 6 repetitions is more effective than the corresponding amount of isometric work (Rasch & Morehouse, 1957; Berger, 1962). Comparison with explosive isometrics, however, has not yet been done (see 4.2.4).

There has been considerable interest in studying the potential of eccentric exercise with weights for developing strength (Verkhoshansky, 1961; Semyonov & Chudinov, 1963; Ivanov, 1966; Semyonov, 1968). The first positive results in this direction were supported by various specialists and served as the basis for their recommendations on using eccentric work to develop strength (Medvedev & Vorobyev, 1967). However, until more reliable results are obtained, comment on the general effectiveness of eccentric training ('negatives' in bodybuilding jargon) should be guarded (see 4.2.5).

A 3-month experiment comparing the effectiveness of concentric, eccentric and isometric work showed that the largest increase in a 1RM squat occurred with eccentric work (average 15 kg), and the smallest with isometric tension (9.2 kg). Not unexpectedly, the largest increase in isometric strength was obtained with isometric tension (30.2 kg), and the smallest increase with concentric work (14.6 kg). Vertical jump increased only with the concentric training regime (3.7 cm). The vertical jump heights decreased by 1.6 cm for the eccentric regime and by 5.4 cm for isometric tension (Ivanov, 1966). Thus, this research does not support the effectiveness of eccentric work as much as it corroborates the principle of the neuromuscular specificity of strength, which dictates the method of its development.

Similar significant increases in maximum strength can be obtained by the repetitive effort and brief maximal tension methods, as well as with isometric tension. However, the strength acquired from each of these methods has its own neuromuscular specificity.

The repetitive effort method is appropriate in the initial stages of strength development and when strength and its speed of production are not important. Repetitive work with moderate weights (50-60% of 1RM) and a fairly large number of repetitions (8-12) increases muscle mass. Strength increases more rapidly with heavy weights (90-95% of 1RM) and fewer repetitions (3-6), this being accompanied by a smaller increase in muscle mass. The training effect is enhanced by increasing the magnitude of the load and the volume of work.

The brief maximal tension method increases maximum strength without appreciably increasing muscle mass and simultaneously improves the ability to display strength quickly. It is appropriate to use this method when the repetitive effort method has become ineffective for strength development and when it is necessary to increase strength quickly in a relatively short period with a small volume of work. The brief maximal tension method is effective for maintaining the existing level of strength, the general tonus of the neuromuscular system and sporting form. The strength training effect is enhanced by increasing the maximal weight, increasing the average weight lifted per session and reducing the number of sets and repetitions.

Isometric tension (with gradual increase in effort) is useful for developing maximum strength without an accompanying increase in muscle mass and for enhancing the general tonus of the neuromuscular system. This method can be used to maintain the existing level of strength development in cases where speed of movement is not important, during the preparatory training of athletes and during the early stages of musculoskeletal rehabilitation, when movement might be restricted. An increase in the training effect is achieved primarily through the use of maximal tension which is progressively increased by means of heavier loads as muscular strength increases. It should be remembered that isometric tension may be applied slowly or explosively (see 4.2.4), the choice of method depending on the athlete's condition and goal of training.

5.2.2 Autoregulating Progressive Resistance Exercise

Another variant of the DeLorme system has been used successfully in physiotherapy by Knight (1979). Known as the DAPRE (Daily Adjustable Progressive Resistance Exercise) method, it offers a combination of training and testing for the recovering patient. It requires four sets of exercises to be performed per given muscle group, beginning with a set of 10 repetitions with 50% of one's anticipated 6RM. Set 2 consists of 6 repetitions with 75% of the anticipated 6RM, while set 3 with the anticipated 6RM is performed to failure. The number of strict, full repetitions with this weight is used to determine the appropriate load for set 4, according to an adjustment table. Finally, the number of repetitions completed with this set is used to calculate the starting weight for the following workout.

If the exercise weight is ideal, the individual will be able to execute 6 repetitions when working to failure. If he can perform more than 6 repetitions, the weight is too light and must be increased. Conversely, if fewer than 6 repetitions can be completed strictly, the weight is too heavy and must be decreased. In both cases, adjustments are made according to a table of guidelines, as given below.

The DAPRE version of the DeLorme system, however, needs to be expanded somewhat to meet different training needs and to conform more closely to the principles of supercompensation and functional fitness. This is advisable because daily training of the same muscle groups using the same resistance regime is neither necessary nor recommended if the body is to adapt efficiently to the imposed demands. Consequently a modified system, which may be termed APRE (Autoregulating Progressive Resistance Exercise), is given here. APRE employs 3RM (strength/power), 6RM (strength/ hypertrophy) and 10RM (hypertrophy) regimes of conditioning, as detailed below.

Pre-Testing Phase

Before testing for a 6RM or any other goal of performance, a skills/learning phase of about two weeks is advisable. A rough guide is a warm-up without weights, leading to 2-3 sets comprising 8-10 repetitions with approximately 20% of bodymass for males and 10% of bodymass for females, using somewhat heavier loads for the large muscle groups (e.g. quadriceps, pectorals and erector spinae) and lighter loads for the smaller muscle groups of the extremities. During the second week of this phase, these percentages might easily be doubled. On the last day of this phase, the individual should be tested for a 6RM.

Testing Phase

A pyramid system, beginning with 10 repetitions with approximately 40% of bodymass for males and 20% for females, depending on the specific muscle group, is used to determine the 6RM of the athlete. Thus, if set 1 with 10 repetitions is successfully completed, more weight is added and the athlete attempts to perform 8 repetitions. If this attempt is successful, further weight is added and the athlete tries to execute 6 repetitions. If more repetitions are completed, more weight must be added; if fewer are completed, weight must be removed. This process is continued until the athlete can just manage to complete the sixth repetition.

Method of Execution

The subject should execute the concentric and eccentric phases of movement at a fairly constant, slow rate (about 3-4 seconds per phase), without any sudden changes of speed or direction. If possible, full range movements should be done in the same pattern and same manner for each repetition.

In the injured person, limbs may be exercised separately, whereas in the athlete, limbs should be exercised separately and together, so as to measure any significant imbalances or deficiencies. A prolonged eccentric phase (about double the normal time for lowering the load) may be used to assess the strength deficit between eccentric and isometric activity, a measure which is very important to the speed-strength athlete who often has to produce numerous explosive actions (see Ch 1).

Training Phase

The training phase begins with a suitable warmup of the relevant muscle through the entire pain-free range of movement. This is followed by four sets of the given exercise, with 2-4 minutes of rest (preferably mild active rest with unloaded movements) between sets, organised according to the methods of Table 5.1 below.

Table 5.1 Methods of applying Autoregulating Progressive Resistance Exercise (APRE)

Set	6RM Routine	10RM Routine	3RM Routine
0	Warmup	Warmup	Warmup
1	10 reps/ 50% of 6RM	12 reps/ 50% of 10RM	6 reps/ 50% of 3RM
2	6 reps/ 75% of 6RM	10 reps/ 75% of 10RM	3 reps/ 75% of 3RM
3	reps to failure/ 6RM *	reps to failure/ 10RM *	reps to failure/ 3RM *
4	adjusted reps to failure *	adjusted reps to failure *	adjusted reps to failure *

* The asterisk indicates that the training load must be adjusted according to Table 5.2.

Table 5.2 Adjustment table for the different APRE methods

Adjustments: 6RM routine		Adjustments: 10RM routine		Adjustments: 3 RM routine	
Repetitions	Set 4	Repetitions	Set 4	Repetitions	Set 4
0 - 2	decr 2.5 -5 kg	4 - 6	decr 2.5-5 kg	1 - 2	decr 2.5-5 kg
3 - 4	decr 0-2.5 kg	7 - 8	decr 0-2.5 kg	3 - 4	leave same
5 - 7	leave same	9 - 11	leave same	5 - 6	incr 2.5-5 kg
8 - 12	incr 2.5-5 kg	12 - 16	incr 2.5-5 kg	7 -	incr 5-10 kg
13 -	incr 5-7.5 kg	17 -	incr 5-7.5 kg		

Programme for Subsequent Days

Set 4 is used to determine the next session's 6RM (10RM or 3RM), according to the adjustment table above. Generally, the 6RM routine should be followed for 6-8 weeks, before the 3RM routine is introduced. The 10RM may be introduced at any stage to improve general muscle endurance and hypertrophy.

The method of execution may also be altered, as the fitness of the athlete increases. For instance, the repetitions may be done more rapidly and a brief ballistic action may be used near the end of the movement, in order to recruit the phasic stretch reflex more powerfully and to prepare the musculoskeletal system more effectively for the more rapid transitions phases of functional exercise.

Isometric APRE

This system may also be applied with an isometric training regime and may be especially valuable during the earliest stages of muscular rehabilitation, when dynamic activities may be inadvisable.

Studies of strength increases produced by isometric training of different intensities, durations and repetitions have revealed that the optimal combination of these variables is 6 repetitions of 100% of one's 1RM held for 6-8 seconds per repetition (Figs 5.2, 5.3).

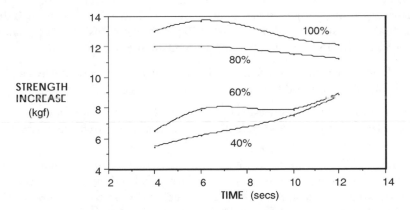

Figure 5.2 Isometric strength increase produced by isometric training with different percentages of maximal contraction held for different periods of time (based on data of Ivenov).

Thus, in isometric APRE, the athlete is required to hold a certain weight with an isometric contraction for a 6SM (6 second maximum) at a specified joint angle (beginning at or near full extension in most cases), with a 5-10 second rest between repetitions. Set 1 is with 50% of the 6SM weight, Set 2 is with 75% of the 6SM and Set 3 is performed until the weight cannot be held for the full 6 seconds. The weight for Set 4 is adjusted according to the same adjustment guide given in Table 5.2 for the 6RM routine. In each case a suitable weight is one which can be held for the full 6 seconds with every repetition. Since isometric training is highly angle specific, especially for small joint angles (see 4.2.4), it is a good idea to exercise and test the relevant joint at a series of angles between full extension and full flexion.

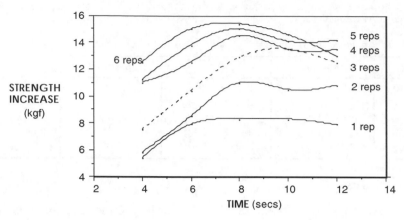

Figure 5.3 Isometric strength increase produced by isometric training with different numbers of repetitions held for different periods of time (based on data of Ivenov).

Muscle Testing with APRE

This system can often provide an effective alternative to the extremely costly isokinetic measuring systems relied upon by many physiotherapists and exercise scientists to test the strength of muscles, left/right strength ratios and agonist/antagonist strength ratios. If the APRE training and testing is done in sport specific or PNF (proprioceptive neuromuscular facilitation) patterns, it can offer a distinct advantage over the traditional isokinetic testing methods. Testing of the average person may be done quite effectively with the 6RM method, whereas the 3RM method is more useful for testing the near-maximal strength performance of serious athletes. The 10RM method relates more to muscle hypertrophy and moderate local muscle endurance. The degree of hypertrophy may be assessed in combination with girth and skinfold thickness measures of the relevant limb regions.

5.2.3 The Development of Speed-Strength

The concept of *speed-strength* is highly generalised and context-dependent. Moreover, one must appreciate the subtle difference between *speed-strength* and *strength-speed* as discussed in Chapter 2. The strength displayed in quick movements has many qualitative subtleties and it is rather difficult to distinguish between them, although movements requiring *speed-strength* can be divided roughly into two fundamental groups:

• Movements in which speed of movement plays a fundamental role in overcoming a relatively small resistance
• Movements in which effort is rapidly developed to overcome large resistance.

Maximum strength is generally unimportant for the first type of movement, but it plays a decisive role in the second type of movement. In the first group one can identify movements which involve a rapid reaction to external stimuli with brief contractions or with frequent repetitive contractions.

In the second group it is logical to divide the movements according to the type of muscular tension (see 3.1): *explosive-isometric* tension (associated with overcoming a relatively large load and rapidly developing maximum force); *explosive-ballistic* tension (the rapid overcoming of low resistance) and *explosive reactive-ballistic* tension (where the working effect is produced immediately after a preliminary muscular stretch).

It is necessary to deal with hitherto unanswered questions concerning the development of starting strength and reactive ability. Therefore, it is appropriate that this method receives further attention in a separate section (5.2.4).

Thus it may be seen that the production of *speed-strength* is extremely diverse. By nature it has a high degree of specificity, its transference from one movement to another being relatively poor and being developed relatively slowly. The methods of perfecting *speed-strength* are very specific and theoretically are far from being thoroughly understood. The methods of developing *speed-strength* are applicable to the types of movements mentioned above and have their own characteristics.

Practice and research indicate that the development of *speed-strength* is more effective the more speed loading there is in training and the shorter the time spent using slow movements (Yakovlev et al, 1960). Exercise with small loads (with approximately 20% of 1RM) is the principal method of developing *speed-strength* (Korobkov, 1953; Vasiliev, 1954; Gerasimov, Yakhontov, 1954; Zimkin, 1956; Agdgomelashvili, 1964; Butenko,

1967). With this method, speed of movement increases with and without loads, and experiments have shown that the general increase in speed can reach 146% of the initial level. Movements should be executed with maximal effort and the apparatus should be accelerated as rapidly as possible.

To promote muscle recruitment in the active state, exercises with light and heavier weights (up to 40% of 1RM) should be combined (the variable method) and the load should be lifted with the emphasis on acceleration at the beginning of the movement. Plyometric exercises (see 5.2.4), as well as exercises where isometric tension is generated quickly using 60-80% of 1RM, should also be included. The optimal combination of the volume of exercises with light weights and relatively heavy weights should be in a ratio of 5:1. Regarding sequencing, it has been found that the alternation of exercises is most effective for the ranked athlete.

To develop *speed-strength* in acyclic movements, plyometric or throwing exercises should be selected on the basis of their relevance to the sports activity. For example, to develop strength for the waterpolo throw, better results are obtained by throwing a medicine ball of 2 kg weight rather than one of 4 kg, the increases in throwing distance being 13.6% and 8.9%, respectively. Moreover, throwing a 4 kg ball is detrimental to technique (Rogener, 1961).

Training with a light (57 grams) and a heavy (184 gm) baseball for throwing ability results in improvements with both of them, where the mass of a regulation ball is about 148 gm. However, the transfer of specific fitness is not uniform: throwing the light ball improves precision for throwing the heavier ball, but the reverse effect does not occur (Egstrom et al, 1960). The optimal weight for javelin training which does not disrupt technique is 3 kg (Matveyev, 1967).

The progressive development of *speed-strength* is the result of combining means for exploiting the *after-effect phenomenon* of preceding work to increase the effectiveness of subsequent work. In devising training means and methods for perfecting sporting performance, modelling is of central importance, where *sports modelling* refers to the formulation of descriptive models of sporting activities on the basis of biomechanical, kinesiological, physiological and other scientific measures.

Exercise modelling experiments show that the working effect of an explosive movement, as measured by the height to which a load was thrown (Fig 5.4), increases by an average of 38-40% after execution of barbell presses for 3 sets of 3 repetitions with 80% of the 1RM (with a rest interval of 10 minutes between the pressing and the throwing). Movement time decreases, there is an increase in the length of the working path, the average speed, the driving force and power output (Table 5.3). Thus, the repetition of the same stimulus evokes a more pronounced reaction by the body and greater development of strength and speed.

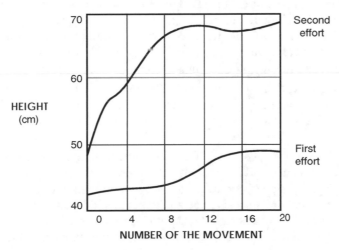

Figure 5.4 The after-effect of prior tonic work on the height of a thrown object (Siff & Verkhoshansky, 1999).

Research shows that speed of movement increases significantly by use of the *variation method:* for example, by putting the shot directly after muscular contraction has been produced by putting a lighter object. In one experiment, lighter and heavier shots differing in mass by 250 grams were thrown at different velocities. A statistically significant difference was not found in the mean results of alternately putting standard shots of different mass. However, distances close to the mean were obtained with a difference in mass of 250 grams, whereas this closeness to the average was not achieved with a difference of 500 grams (Ivanova, 1964; Vasiliev, 1975).

Table 5.3 Arm movement characteristics for throwing a weight before and after tonic work (Verkhoshansky, 1977).

Arm Movement Characteristic	First Effort	Second Effort	Difference (%)
Height of throw (cm)	44.0	61.0	+38.8
Movement time (sec)	0.266	0.250	-6.8
Working path (cm)	62.0	65.0	+4.8
Average speed of movement (m/sec)	2.330	2.600	+11.7
Average driving force (kgf)	5.550	7.430	+33.8
Power (kg.m/s)	1.310	1.930	+47.3

Thus, the transference of throwing speeds from a lighter to a heavier mass (i.e. the normal mass) apparently is possible only by alternating the throwing of shots of different mass. The effectiveness of the variable method of developing speed of movement was confirmed in the training of hockey players who successively hit a normal and a heavier puck. The optimal mass of the heavier puck was found to be between 0.6-0.8 kg. However, it is necessary to select the mass for each player individually, based on the athlete's ability to hit the heavier puck efficiently (Savin, 1974).

It should be pointed out that certain Eastern European and Chinese athletes train with heavier implements in their own sports and maintain that this method contributes to their impressive results. For instance, some table tennis competitors will eventually train with as much as 2kg bats, which is considerably heavier than typical bats of about 100 grams mass. Their coaches stress that this type of training is done only with carefully balanced bats by elite athletes about once a week before the competition phase, with less advanced competitors gradually increasing the weight of their bats over a prolonged period. This method should not be emulated by less experienced coaches, as the untutored use of this extraordinary approach can lead to overload injuries and altered neural control patterns.

Attempts must be made to resolve the conflict between the magnitude of the load and speed of movement in developing *speed-strength*. In this instance, this may be achieved if strength is used to oppose not the weight (gravitational force), but its inertia (acceleration force). Unfortunately this method is very seldom used in practice and its potential for enhancing strength is largely unexplored (see Fig 4.4), so that it is difficult to give specific recommendations for its application.

The next issue is the rest interval between sets of exercises. This interval is determined by level of fitness, the level of special endurance to repeatedly produce maximal tension and the degree of strength exerted. Experiments show that, with an optimal pause of 0.5-1 minute, speed-strength output can be maintained at a high level for a fairly long period without serious deterioration. The possible gradual decrease of speed-strength with exhausting, monotonous work can be largely eliminated by creating a favourable emotional state.

Speed-strength as displayed in rapid cyclical movements is characterised by repetitive contractions separated by relaxation phases. Depending on the special exercise, the effect of speed-strength can be determined by the ability of the neuromuscular apparatus to maintain the strength output for a long period at a specific work rate.

Thus, the movement tempo and the duration of work are of great significance in the development of speed-strength in speed-cyclic exercises. The resistance and the movement tempo are inversely proportional to one another. In other words, an increase in the resistance decreases the movement tempo and promotes the rapid onset of fatigue. Therefore, the optimal combination of resistance and tempo should be selected in each specific case, based on the kinesiological structure of the given exercise. It should be remembered that speed of movement decreases over a long period of training done at a slow tempo and increases through training at the optimal speed (Korobkov, 1953; Monogarov, 1958).

The ability to correctly execute the full movement cycle, including the appropriate phases of tension and muscular relaxation, should serve as a criterion. The movement tempo should gradually approach the tempo of the special exercise and even exceed it, while the working time should lengthen (Diachkov, 1961).

All that has been stated concerning the development of speed-strength is related primarily to exercising functionally the relevant muscle groups by means of the special exercise. However, good results are achieved by making the special exercise more demanding. Thus, the use of water resistance in rowing or very small loads on the limbs of track-and-field athletes and gymnasts can enhance speed-strength under conditions that are very close to those of the special exercise.

In certain cases, power can be increased without using additional loads. For example, with jumps from one leg to the other, the push-off displays values of power which are greater than in running. Therefore, these jumps are excellent for the special strength training of sprinters. It is only necessary to execute them correctly by not accentuating the push-off of the body (which does not happen in sprinting), but by active gathering-in of the planted leg (i.e. via hip flexion). These jumps should be executed repetitively over distances of 50-100 meters as fast as possible. The addition of small cuffs weighing from 100-150 grams on each thigh can makes such exercises more effective in experienced athletes (based on Verkhoshansky's experience with top Russian sprinters, such as Zubov).

Thus, to develop *speed-strength* one should use exercises, primarily with small resistance (20% of 1RM) and, for acyclic activities of brief duration, a combination of these exercises with weights up to 40% of 1RM in a ratio of 5 to 1. The work regime should correspond to the special exercise (cyclic or acyclic) and take into account the initial conditions from which force is developed (i.e. with the muscles relaxed, in a state of preliminary tension or stretched).

Perfecting the methods of developing speed-strength is a result of the search for a specific combination of means that exploit:

- the positive after-effect of preceding work on the subsequent activity
- the use of exercises in which muscular force opposes the inertia of the load and not its weight.

Fatigue must be avoided when one is trying to develop speed-strength for acyclic movements. However, fatigue is a necessary component of training for speed-strength in cyclic movements which require speed-endurance. Precise implementation of these findings is possible only under specific training conditions so, for the present, one has to rely on empirical methods.

5.2.4 Development of Explosive Strength and Reactive Ability

The development of effective methods to develop explosive strength and reactive ability logically begins with an analysis of the speed-strength methods traditionally used for this purpose. For instance, athletes often attempt to develop *explosive strength* in the legs by using heavy barbell squats. In this case the muscles work very slowly (quasi-isometrically) with a relatively constant tension produced by the load. Consequently, the muscles primarily develop isometric strength, but this does not mean that it is impossible for them to execute fast dynamic contractions. It should be added that increase in the weight of the barbell, which is frequently considered a basic indicator of special strength fitness, places a large and generally unnecessary load on the spine.

However, to solve the task of *speed-strength* preparation, athletes use smaller loads. For example, doing squat thrusts with a 60kg barbell on the shoulders produces a large dynamic maximum force. Therefore, exercises with heavy weights tend to increase the strength potential of the muscles, while fast exercises with light weights improve speed. Nevertheless, these means are not the only way of developing explosive strength.

Explosive strength is a motor quality requiring specific movements and training means. The above-mentioned means of strength training do not adequately enhance specific components of explosive movements such as the rapid excitation of muscles and the rapid changing from eccentric to concentric work.

These and allied skills require a specific training regime which is impossible to imitate with only one resistance exercise. Indeed, stimulation of muscular activity with slow resistance movements, and lifting a barbell in preparation for squatting or jumping with it, removes the possibility of controlling the mechanisms which are crucial to the rapid switching of muscles to the active state. At the same time, a decrease in the resistance diminishes the dynamic effort required and creates a vicious cycle from which there is no apparent escape.

Thus, if the athlete successfully develops a high level of explosive strength, then it may be attributed to certain means in his training. Consequently, the problem amounts to singling out those means and organising them so as to systematise the special strength training.

The Plyometric Method

Prolonged research in the direction discussed above led to the development of the so-called 'shock' (plyometric) method of developing explosive strength and reactive ability (see 1.5). Basically it consists of stimulating the muscles by means of a sudden stretch preceding any voluntary effort (see 4.2.3). Kinetic energy and not heavy weights should be used for this, where the kinetic energy may be accumulated by means of the body or loads dropping from a certain height (see 4.2.3). Depth jumps and medicine ball rebounding are two of the exercise regimes commonly used in plyometrics.

The increase in popularity of plyometrics in the West deems it necessary that the concept be more rigorously defined. Plyometrics or the 'shock method' means precisely that - a method of mechanical shock stimulation to force the muscle to produce as much tension as possible. This method is characterised by impulsive action of minimal duration between the end of the eccentric braking phase and initiation of the concentric acceleration phase. It relies on the production of a very brief explosive-isometric and eccentric-isometric phase which precedes the release of the elastic energy stored in the tendons and other components of the series elastic component of the muscle complex during the eccentric deceleration phase (see 1.9, 3.1 and Fig 4.11). If the transition phase (or, coupling phase) is prolonged by more than about 0.15 second, the action may be considered to constitute ordinary jumping and not classical *training plyometrics*. A useful visualisation is to imagine that the surface being touched by the hands or the feet during the plyometric contact phase is red hot, so that any prolonged contact would be dangerous.

It is important to note that the activity is not accurately plyometric if the athlete relies upon ongoing feedback processes to control the isometric and concentric actions instead of upon feedforward programmes established before any movement begins (see 1.8 and 1.12). True plyometric training usually involves ballistic rather than cocontraction processes, a concept discussed earlier (see 1.8).

Plyometrics as a Discrete Training System

A thorough discussion of what is meant by the term *plyometrics* is essential, because one must distinguish clearly between *plyometric actions*, which occur as part of many running, jumping, hurdling, striking and other rebounding movements in sport, and *plyometric training*, which applies plyometric actions as a distinct training modality according to a definite methodology.

The fairly recent adoption of plyometrics by Western coaches as a so-called 'Russian training secret' has created an unwarranted mystique about a method that has been used extensively in Russia since its scientific formalisation in the early 1960s as a discrete training system by Verkhoshansky. In recognising that plyometric actions are widespread in most sport, Verkhoshansky has always consistently favoured the use of the term 'shock method' instead of 'plyometrics' to distinguish between naturally occurring plyometric actions in sport and the formal discipline he devised as a discrete training system to develop speed-strength in particular. This is why the term *powermetrics* has been suggested elsewhere in this text to refer to plyometric training, as opposed to plyometric actions which occur quite naturally in many natural ballistic movements. The earliest published use of the word *plyometrics* seems to have been in a Soviet publication (Zanon, 1966).

Popular adoption of the term 'plyometrics' in the place of 'shock method' has produced this confusion, just as popular use of the term 'aerobics' has caused widespread confusion between aerobic (cardiovascular) conditioning and aerobics as a form of exercise to music. Consequently, it is probably better to refer to plyometric action as *stretch-shortening action*, as has been done in much of the scientific literature, and to redefine 'plyometrics' as a specific training system in its own right, or, *powermetrics*.

Possibly the easiest way of showing that the shock method can indeed be regarded as a separate, goal-directed training system is to examine the concept of resistance training. Resistance to movement is encountered in all sport, so the critics of plyometrics as a definite training method should then agree that it is equally logical to conclude that resistance training must not be regarded as a distinct training system. On this basis one might also conclude that distance running or cycling are resistance training methods, because the athlete certainly experiences resistance and produces high levels of muscular tension in these sports.

One might extend this argument further and conclude that all human movement is really resistance training. After all, it is somewhat artificial to refer to weight training as resistance training and to ignore other sports that also involve work against significant resistance, simply because the loads superficially appear to be heavier in weight training. Basic biomechanical analysis of the forces and tensions involved show clearly that the high levels of resistance and muscle tension involved in sports such as gymnastics, swimming, rowing and wrestling easily justify any objections to regarding resistance training as a separate training system.

Just as resistance training has adopted means, methods and apparatus from other sports and physical activities to create a discrete training discipline, so has plyometric training or *powermetrics* (as distinct from plyometric action) done the same to create its own methodology.

Plyometric Training and Safety

Plyometric training (*powermetrics)* is not without its vociferous opponents, all of whom believe that high impact loading of the joints in jumping or other impulsive activities is harmful to the joints and unproven in enhancing explosive performance. As yet, the opinion that plyometric drills on their own are dangerous and useless has not been proved experimentally or clinically, especially since it is very difficult to design an experiment which isolates plyometric effects from the accompanying effects of other activities associated with a given sport and which includes control groups who are exposed to comparable overall intensity, duration and complexity of loading. Thusfar, the dangers of plyometrics are inferred from the magnitude of the impulsive peak forces which have been measured via force plate research during jumping activities, in particular. The opponents of plyometrics who use this research or theoretical calculations of force from Newton's Second Law to proclaim an unqualified condemnation of all plyometric training (*powermetrics*) or any other types of ballistic training, for that matter, seem to overlook the obvious fact that running, jumping and other ballistic activities are an integral part of most sports. In other words, they are implying that these activities in the context of normal sport are perfectly safe, but in the context of special plyometric drills are dangerous.

They also are implementing the unproved hypothesis that impulsive loading is far more dangerous for the joints than any other forms of less stressful loading. Moreover, they seem to be assuming that the joints do not follow the principle of Specific Adaptation to Imposed Demands (SAID) and that they can do little else than deteriorate in response to impulsive and ballistic loading.

In this regard it is relevant to point out that joints subjected to heavy impact are relatively free from osteoarthritis in old age and that those subjected to much lower loading experience a greater incidence of osteoarthritis and cartilage fibrillation (Bullough et al, 1973; Kempson et al, 1975; Seedhom & Swann, 1985; Seedhom & Wright, 1988; Seedhom et al, 1977). Siff's former colleague, Dr Mark Swanepoel, at the University of the Witwatersrand in South Africa, pointed out that, as one progresses up the lower extremity from the ankle, to the knee, the hip and finally to the lumbar spine, so the extent of fibrillation increases at any given age.

It appears that the cartilages of joints subjected to regular impulsive loading with relatively high contact stresses is mechanically much stiffer and better adapted to withstand the exceptional loading of running and jumping than the softer cartilage associated with low loading. Thus, joint cartilage subjected to regular repetitive loading remains healthy and copes very well with impulsive loads, whereas cartilage that is heavily loaded infrequently softens due to decrease in proteoglycan production, the collagen network loses its cohesion and the cartilage deteriorates (Swanepoel, 1998).

This discussion does not dismiss the risks posed by inappropriate or excessive use of plyometric training (*powermetrics*), but it stresses that it is not the inherent nature of plyometrics which may produce injury, but the manner in which it is used, as is the case with all forms of training. In the case of plyometrics, the zealous way in which this so-called Russian training secret has been modified, extended and implemented in the West certainly does warrant a great deal of the criticism that has been levelled at it. Virtually every Western book or article on the subject presents encyclopaedic compilations of drills offered in extended, isolated and highly repetitive forms which often create the impression that quantity is more important than quality. Complexity of drills and apparatus often seems to replace optimal simplicity, technical correctness and elegance. Many repetitions of plyometric drills frequently are prescribed for some sports because of assumptions that this sort of training will improve fatigue resistance in repeated actions such as rebounding in basketball, yet research has shown this to be untrue (Nicol et al, 1997).

Often, plyometric drills are prescribed without adequate attention being paid to the entire context of training, including the interaction with other physical activities, loading imposed by other work or play, the psychological modification of reflexes or the use of formal restoration. More often than not, plyometric enthusiasts do not consider the possibility that the athlete's sport alone may offer all or most of the plyometric training that is necessary and that adding more of this type of loading may be excessive or unwarranted. All exercise has to be offered in a way which is concordant with its advantages, disadvantages, scope and limitations - and plyometrics are no exception.

Thus, any lack of safety in plyometric training has more to do with inappropriate and ineffective prescription than this mode of exercise itself, with overtraining being a major contributory factor (see 8.8). In this regard, overtraining comprises two distinct components: overload (the imposition of too great a force at any given time) and overuse (the imposition of too great a volume of exercise). Thus, the prescription of an individually appropriate volume and intensity (e.g. via choice of drop height) of plyometric exercises according to the principle of gradual progressive overload integrated periodically into an overall training programme with adequate restoration regimes need pose no greater risks than the naturally occurring plyometric actions found in running and jumping. Finally, in designing a training programme, it might be preferable to avoid use of the popular term plyometric *drills*, because drills tend to be associated with militarism and authoritarianism rather than with individual flow, sensitivity, flair and nuances of personal interpretation.

The Fundamental Theory of Plyometrics

Plyometric activity is characterised by the following phases of action between initiation and termination of the sequence of events (Fig 5.5):

1. *An initial momentum phase* during which the body or part of the body is moving because of kinetic energy (KE) it has accumulated from a preceding action.

2. *An electromechanical delay phase* which occurs when some event such as contact with a surface prevents a limb from moving further and provokes the muscles to contract. This delay refers to the time elapsing between the onset of the action potential in the motor nerves and the onset of the muscle contraction. Some workers define this phase to include the lengthening of the SEC (Series Elastic Component) of the muscle complex, but the name *electromechanical* was coined to mean the start of the electrical signal to the start of the mechanical contraction in a muscle, which does not include the passive stretching of connective tissue.

3. *An amortisation phase* when the KE produces a powerful myotatic stretch reflex which leads to eccentric muscle contraction accompanied by explosive isometric contraction (see Fig 3.33) and stretching of the SEC (Series Elastic Component, e.g. tendons) of the muscle complex (see Figs 1.14, 1.18). The explosive isometric phase between the end of the eccentric action and the beginning of the concentric action lasts for a period known as the *coupling time* (Fig 5.5), which will be discussed shortly in greater detail.

4. *A rebound phase* involving the release of elastic energy from the SEC, together with the involuntary concentric muscle contraction evoked by the myotatic stretch reflex, as well as possible local change in the muscle fibre mechanics. This phase may include the contribution added by voluntary concentric contraction.

5. *A final momentum phase* which occurs after the concentric contraction is complete and the body or limb concerned continues to move by means of the kinetic energy imparted by concentric contraction and the release of elastic energy from the SEC.

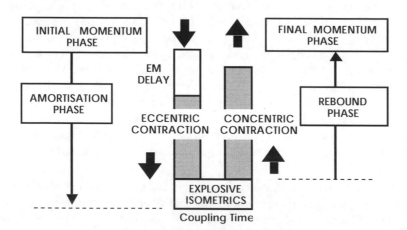

Figure 5.5 The different phases of a plyometric action. EM delay = Electromechanical delay between signal to terminate initial momentum phase and instant when eccentric contraction begins.

Discussion of the coupling time is of great importance because it has a fundamental bearing on whether or not any action may be accurately classified as classical plyometrics. Earlier it was stated that classical plyometrics are characterised by a delay of no more than approximately 0.15 second between the eccentric and subsequent concentric contractions, a statement which requires some qualification. For instance, research by Wilson et al (1990) examining different delay times in the bench press showed that the benefits of prior stretch may endure for as long as 4 seconds, at which stage it is suggested that all stored elastic energy is lost (see Fig 5.6).

Chapman and Caldwell (1985), on the other hand, found that the benefits of prior stretching during forearm movement were dissipated within 0.25 second, a figure which agrees with Siff's analysis of explosive rebound elbow flexion without additional loading (Fig 5.7). Other work by Wilson et al (1991) examining rebound action of the chest/arms concluded that no benefits of prior stretching are evident after 0.37 second.

This research seems to suggest that delays of as long as a second or two can still produce significant augmentation of the subsequent concentric phase for some activities, but delays as short as 0.2 second are sufficient to dissipate the benefits of prior stretch during other activities. Research by Bosco et al (1982a) offers a partial solution to this apparent contradiction. They proposed that individuals with a high percentage of FT fibres in the leg muscles exhibit a maximum plyometric effect when the eccentric phase is short, movement range is small and coupling time is brief. On the other hand, subjects with a high percentage of ST fibres apparently produce their best jumping performance when the eccentric phase is longer, movement range is greater and the coupling time is longer, since the actin-myosin cross-bridging attachment time is of greater duration.

It is also tempting to attribute these major differences in coupling times to the existence of specific maximum delays for each joint action. While this probably is true for different simple and complex joint actions, it is also important to note that the human body exhibits many different reflexes, each of which acts under different conditions and at different rates (see 3.5.3).

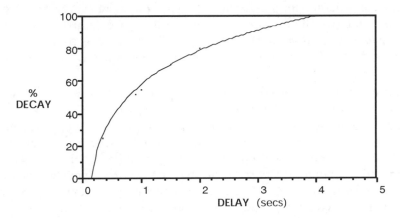

Figure 5.6 The effect of a time delay on the additional force produced by a preliminary stretch in a bench press (based on the data of Wilson et al, 1991).

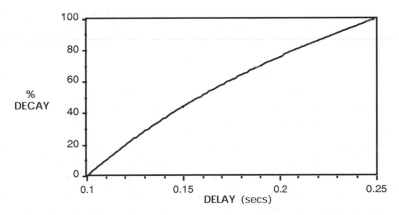

Figure 5.7 The effect of a time delay on the additional force produced by a preliminary stretch in unloaded elbow flexion.

In particular, there are tonic (static) and phasic (dynamic) stretch reflexes and very rapid receptors such as pacinian corpuscles in joint capsules that detect the rates of movement and *allow the nervous system to predict where the extremities will be at any precise moment*, thereby facilitating anticipatory modifications in limb position to ensure effective control and stability (Guyton, 1984). Loss of this predictive function apparently makes it virtually impossible for one to run, jump, throw or catch. Other receptors such as the Ruffini endings and receptors in the ligaments like the Golgi tendon organs are strongly stimulated when a joint is suddenly moved and after a slight initial adaptation, they transmit a steady response.

In addition, weightlifters and sometimes bodybuilders use the so-called *pre-stretch principle* to produce a more powerful concentric muscle contraction to enable them to lift heavier loads. In doing so, they begin a movement from a starting position which imposes an intense stretch on the relevant muscles, hold it for a couple of seconds and then thrust as strongly as possible from that position. It would seem that this longer delay would implicate the more tonic type of reflex with a characteristically greater coupling time. The action could certainly not be called plyometric, despite the fact that prior stretch had contributed to the subsequent concentric action. Conversely, phasic reflex activity would more likely be implicated in the explosive movements which typify classical plyometrics and the type of activity described graphically in Figure 5.7.

This explanation also serves to further distinguish between plyometric action and plyometric training, an issue discussed earlier in this section. One cannot simply distinguish between plyometric and non-plyometric solely on the basis of coupling times, otherwise one would have to classify jogging or even brisk walking as classical plyometrics, because the time taken for the ground reaction force to reach a maximum can be less than 0.15 second. One also has to take the force-time pattern and the rate of force development (RFD) into account (see Fig 2.13).

On this scientific basis, the argument as to whether a given action is classically plyometric or not becomes complex and academic, with no real benefit to the prescription of plyometric training. It is better to recognise the existence of different types of plyometric training (*powermetrics*). At the outset, a distinction should be made between *maximal plyometrics training* and *sub-maximal plyometric training*. In doing so, it is valuable to apply *a powermetrics intensity scale* similar to that used in weightlifting, where exercises are ranked in terms of percentages of one's 1RM.

The concept of 1RMs is meaningless in plyometric training, so one must rely on estimates of muscle tension produced by a given drill or on estimates of the impulse (see 5.1) produced during the contact phase of body with the ground or projectile. Impulse is equivalent to the change of momentum ($m.\Delta V$) during the amortisation phase, so that its magnitude for a falling body depends on the height from which the body drops. Thus, the momentum just before contact (estimated from height of the drop jump or distance fallen by the object) may serve as a measure of intensity. At one end of the scale lies maximal plyometrics (the equivalent of the emotionally demanding competitive maximum, CFmax) and at the other end lies preparatory non-impact plyometrics (see Fig 5.8). Maximal, submaximal and non-plyometrics are depicted in the same box in this diagram as a reminder that there is really a continuum of intensities, rather than an abrupt difference between each type of plyometric training.

Maximal plyometrics essentially are low-repetition activities where the intensity of the depth jump or rebound exercise is such that maximal or near-maximal rebound tension is produced in the relevant muscles. Just like maximal strength training with weights, these powerful impulses are not meant to be imposed on the musculature every workout, nor are multiple repetitions even possible or advisable. Moreover, a rest interval of 2-4 minutes is recommended between successive repetitions and as much as 10-12 minutes between sets.

Sub-maximal plyometrics involve mechanical impulses which do not produce maximal muscular tension, although they are still performed with a minimally long contact phase with the floor or projected object. For example, lower box heights are used for depth jumps and the athlete does not strive to reach maximal rebound height. Rapid double-footed bouncing or low skipping on the spot are other typical sub-maximal exercises.

Two broad classes of plyometric training may be recognised: *impact plyometrics* and *non-impact plyometrics* (Fig 5.8). During *impact plyometrics* the rebound is stimulated by contact with a surface or object, whereas the recoil in *non-impact plyometrics* is mediated by explosive eccentric action of the muscles that produce a movement not terminated by contact with a surface. Depth jumps are a typical example of impact plyometrics, while snap kicks or rapidly-retracted blows in boxing or the martial arts exemplify non-impact plyometrics. Depending on the power of the movements, non-impact plyometrics may also be maximal or submaximal.

Plyometric training, in turn, involves several distinct categories of activities: classical plyometric exercises, supplementary plyometrics and preparatory drills for plyometrics (Fig 5.8). Classical plyometric exercises are either functional or non-functional, the former referring to activities which are matched as closely as possible to the specific explosive actions of the particular sport with respect to movement pattern, muscle involvement, timing and direction of motion. Non-functional plyometrics are exercises intended to offer general training of the explosive qualities required by the sport. For example, functional plyometrics in long jump would use forward bounding, shotputting would involve backward rebounds, all forms of jumping would sometimes use one-legged hopping forwards, and basketball would involve both short and relatively long amortisation phases in vertical rebounds to emulate the different ways of jumping for the basket.

The preparatory or supplementary drills consist of weight training exercises to develop sufficient muscular strength (especially eccentric strength) and connective tissue strength and elasticity, as well as varieties of jumping, swinging, throwing and catching drills with longer duration transition phases. Most of the drills described in popular books on plyometrics in the West are actually supplementary exercises for plyometrics. In some cases, it is appropriate to refer to some drills as *pseudo-plyometric*. These activities appear to be or are incorrectly labelled as plyometric because they include a sudden stop or some form of jump. Examples of pseudo-plyometrics are the so-called 'power moves' (involving quick landings and delayed jumps in a semi-squat position) and many 'water plyos' (involving jumps in water) in commercial aerobics classes. Because of their frequent lack of an explosive rebound phase with a short coupling time, these exercises generally serve as a form of preparatory non-plyometrics.

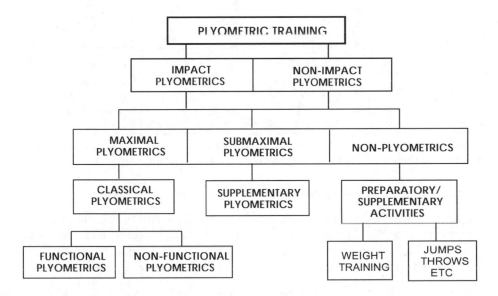

Figure 5.8 Categorisation scheme of the different classes of plyometric (powermetric) training.

Plyometrics may be better understood by applying Newton's Second Law in its simplest form: $F = ma$. In normal resistance training, the *mass* is increased, whereas the *acceleration* is increased in plyometrics. Plyometrics is a system of explosive training using relatively low inertial loading, but weight training usually relies on high inertia loading. One may produce the same force by moving a heavy load with low acceleration or a light load with a large acceleration, but the training effect is very different. Explosive, low inertia training targets involuntary, neuromuscular and central nervous processes more strongly than high inertia training, which has a greater effect on static strength development and muscle hypertrophy.

To ascertain whether an athlete needs plyometric or heavy resistance training depends on measuring the *strength deficit*, or the difference between the absolute (involuntary) strength maximum and the voluntary strength maximum (see Ch 1). Without such testing, prescription of plyometric training tends to remain hit-and-miss. The opposition to plyometric training by some experts is largely the result of this type of guesswork training, which can hinder performance and increase the risk of injury.

Correct breathing is important during plyometric training. It is vital that the athlete holds the breath during the amortisation and early propulsion phase to stabilise the body, offer pneumatic shock absorption and to increase the rebound force. Forced exhalation may accompany the remainder of the propulsion phase. Footwear or the floor covering should not be very soft or excessively shock absorbent, since this may impair ankle stability, diminish the storage of elastic energy in the SEC (e.g. tendons) and delay the triggering of the positive supportive reaction of the foot (see 6.1.2) when contacting the floor.

The Prescription of Plyometric Exercise

Practical application of the plyometric method to different muscle groups is illustrated in the following exercises (Fig 5.9). The range of motion should be somewhat greater than the required coordination range of the exercise in order to enhance shock absorption by the soft tissues and thereby avoid impact injury. With the examples presented as a guideline, an athlete of any specialisation requiring explosive strength can select the necessary complex of exercises personally.

Figure 5.9 Plyometric exercises for strength development, using resistance and other apparatus (Verkhoshansky, 1977).

It is necessary to take into account the following guidelines for using plyometric exercises:

1. The magnitude of the impulsive load is determined by the weight and the height of its free-fall. The optimal combination is determined empirically in each specific case; however, preference should be given to a large height over a heavy weight. Since the resulting force is governed by Newton's Second Law (F = m.a), a force plate may be used to determine the height of drop to produce the required force.

2. The amortisation phase should be of minimal duration, but sufficient to create impulsive contraction of the muscles. Therefore, the initial posture with respect to the joint angles should correspond to the same position in which the working movement begins in the sporting exercise.

3. The plyometric training should be preceded by a good warmup of the intensively involved muscles.

4. As an initial guideline, the dosage of plyometric exercises should not exceed 5-8 repetitions in one set. A more precise way to determine this is to calculate the force involved (from bodymass and the drop height) and the athlete's level of special *speed-strength*.

5. One should aim to increase the speed and acceleration of movement before increasing the drop height or take-off height.

6. Rest periods are crucial for the effective and safe use of plyometrics. The rest interval between sets of maximal plyometric exercises should be about 10 minutes for power development (strength-speed and speed-strength) and much shorter intervals with submaximal plyometrics to develop explosive-strength endurance.

In those cases where the plyometric method is used for developing jumping power (i.e. explosive strength and the reactive ability of the extensors of the torso and legs), one can work without an additional load and utilise only falling bodymass for providing the impulsive stimulation. For example, one may energetically jump upwards, or upward and forwards, after a depth-jump from some height (Fig 5.10). The optimal depth of the jump is determined by the athlete's strength fitness, while the athlete should ensure that significant dynamic force is developed without slowing down the transition from eccentric to concentric work by the muscles involved.

One should land with the legs slightly flexed, muscles mildly tensed and on the balls of the feet in order to avoid an excessive shock. The depth of amortisation should not be great and the subsequent take-off needs to be executed very quickly with an energetic throwing upwards of the arms. To stimulate a powerful take-off it is necessary to strive with the hands or head to reach some height indicated by some marker if the take-off is executed upward, or to land at some point if it is directed upward and forward. An increase in height or distance of the jump clearly indicates improvement in special fitness, which always has a positive effect on the athlete's emotional state.

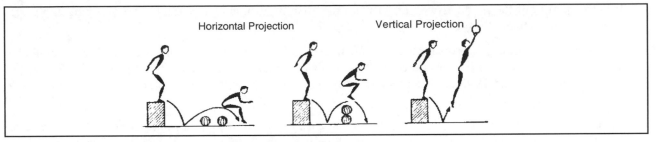

Figure 5.10 Different types of depth jumping (Verkhoshansky, 1977).

Prolific experience with depth-jumps for developing jumping power produces the following recommendations:

1. Depth-jumps require special preliminary preparation such as a significant volume of barbell exercises and traditional jumping, short sprints and skipping over a period of several months. One should begin at a relatively low height and increase it gradually to the optimal height. It makes sense to begin by jumping upward and forward and only after sufficient training, to jump strictly upward. Good results are obtained with depth-jumps using a complex of vertical jumps (Fig 5.11). Each exercise is executed in sets of 10 repetitions, with 1-15 minutes of rest between sets. Muscle or tendon fatigue, pain or soreness, as well as incompletely healed injuries, are contra-indications to depth jumping.

2. The optimal dosage of depth-jumps with an energetic vertical take-off in one training session should not exceed 4 sets of 10 jumps for well-conditioned athletes and 2-3 sets of 5-8 jumps for lesser conditioned athletes. Easy running and relaxation exercises for a period of 10-15 minutes should be done between sets.

3. Depth-jumps executed in the volume indicated should be done once or twice a week in training sessions devoted to special strength training. Besides including depth-jumps, these sessions can include localised exercises for other muscle groups and general developmental exercises executed with a small volume. Well-conditioned athletes can execute depth-jumps 3 times per week for 2 sets of 10 jumps at the completion of technical training in the particular sport.

4. Depth-jumps strongly excite the nervous system. Therefore, they should be used not less than 3-4 days before a technique training session. Sessions devoted to general physical preparation with a small volume of work should be done after depth-jump workouts.

5. Depth-jumps occupy a fundamental place in the second half of the preparatory period of the yearly cycle. However, they can function as a means of maintaining the achieved level of special strength fitness in the competition period. During the competition period they should be included once every 10-14 days, but no later than 10 days before a competition.

6. A useful initial sub-maximal plyometric drill is hopping on the spot at a frequency which feels most comfortable for the athlete, using a few sets of about 25 repetitions. This enables the athlete to develop a sensitivity to timing, optimal depth of joint flexion and rebound coordination. These small vertical hops may then be replaced by small forward hops, backward hops, sideward hops, forward-backward hops and zig-zag hops. Next the athlete should try to execute the small vertical hops as rapidly as possible, again using a few sets of about 20 repetitions.

7. Skipping in different patterns, on one or both legs, with a rope can serve as a useful preparatory activity for depth-jump plyometrics. It should be remembered that the aim is not to improve endurance, but speed and speed-strength, so that long periods of skipping are not the appropriate form of preparatory drill.

8. The optimal height of a depth jump does not result in a landing where the heel is forced to the ground by momentum.

9. Head posture and direction of gaze play important roles in controlling all aspects of depth jumping. Flexing the head downward to look at the floor before take-off may result in spurious muscle contraction or altered timing. Similarly if the head is not thrust upwards during the take-off, maximal height will not be reached.

10. Depth-jumping necessitates falling in a relaxed state, but not jumping, off the box.

11. It is the quality of the plyometric exercises, not the quantity, which is important for developing explosive strength and reactive ability.

12. Inappropriate breathing patterns reduce the effectiveness of the exercises. In particular, the breath should be held and never released during the contact phase or any phase where maximal effort is to be produced. Exhalation during any landing phase reduces overall stability and increases the loading on the spine during depth-jumping.

13. Before athletes attempt depth-jumping, they must learn the techniques of normal jumping. It is important that they acquire competence in use of the correct lumbar-pelvic rhythm, as is also used during clean pulls or power cleans from the ground. In this respect, these weightlifting manoeuvres can be helpful in teaching efficient use of the knees, hips and spine.

14. Great caution must be exercised in performing any form of depth-jumps which involve one-legged thrusts, changes of direction or complex variations, since the injury risk is significantly higher. The skills of any such movements must be learned at progressively higher levels of complexity and intensity before maximal attempts are used.

15. The successful integration of depth-jumps into a training programme depends on not disrupting the delayed training effect of prior strength work. It should be noted that the use of depth-jumps as a means of stimulation can delay this effect for 5-6 days.

Figure 5.11 Jumping exercises for developing reactive ability (Verkhoshansky, 1977).

It must be stressed that depth-jumping is not a basic type of training to be indulged in lightly by athletes who are relatively unused to explosive or strongly resisted movements. For anyone who is not accustomed to movements such as weightlifting cleans, jerks, squats or hurdling, it is highly advisable that a preparatory programme using submaximal plyometrics, non-impact and non-plyometrics be followed before the above recommendations are implemented (see Fig 5.8). A preparatory programme may be based on a clear understanding of the nature of true plyometric methods, as follows:

- Because plyometric actions involve a powerful eccentric amortisation phase terminating in an explosive isometric contraction, *a primary requirement for anyone contemplating the use of classical plyometrics is a high level of eccentric strength and explosive isometric strength.* Herein lies the value of small-range squats, power cleans, power snatches, cleans from the hang, snatches from the hang, push presses or jerks, push presses or jerks from racks, and the descent of flights of stairs. Both front and back squats should be used, since they each model different types of jump (directly upwards versus forwards and upwards). Slow quasi-isometric squats over a moderate range with heavy weights should later lead to more rapid dips over a shallower range with lighter weights.

- Since plyometric actions involve a powerful concentric phase assisted by activation of the muscles by the stretch reflex, it is initially useful to improve jumping ability from a static start, without exposing oneself to the greater musculotendinous stress of a dynamic start. Standing broad and vertical jumps, with regular attempts to increase the distance or height achieved without a preliminary dynamic dip, can be useful in this regard. The usual vertical jump test may be used as one of the exercises, progressing from a static flexed knee start to a dynamic dip start with arms flung vigorously upwards. To gain an idea of individual progress, the power developed may be calculated from the Lewis nomogram or from the formula: Power P $= (21.693) \text{ B}\sqrt{\text{H}}$ watts, where B = bodymass in kg and H = height jumped in metres.

As eccentric, isometric and concentric strength increases in individual exercises over the range commonly used for the plyometric activities, the athlete may progress to actions which more rapidly integrate all three aspects of plyometric movement. Although lower body plyometric actions have been referred to above in the form of depth-jumps, the same principles may be applied to upper body impulsive methods with medicine ball catching and throwing, plyometric press-ups, plyometric bench-presses and similar actions using loaded swings or other specialised apparatus.

The training effect of depth-jumps or shock-loading for developing explosive strength is very large, having little equal when compared with the other means of strength training, especially when combined in a complex with other forms of intensive strength training. This has been corroborated by a number of studies (Semyenov, 1971; Tatyan, 1974; Dobrovolsky, 1972; Savin, 1974; Khodykin, 1974; Deniskin, 1976), the results of which are discussed further in several articles (Papysheva, 1967; Kharabuga, 1967; Cheryeshneva, 1967; Kuznetsov, 1970; Burla, 1973; Press, 1974). The plyometric method of developing explosive strength already occupies a firm place in athletics and is used by many distinguished athletes.

It is interesting to note that *depth landings* (i.e. depth jumps without the rebound after landing) alone can also have a significant effect on concentric and eccentric strength. This was shown by Dursenev and Raevsky (1978) who investigated the effect of depth landings from heights of 2m or more onto soft gymnastic mats. Under these conditions, the subjects acquired the ability to display brief muscle tension (over periods of between 0.028-0.061 secs) of magnitude 1500-3500 kgf, i.e. over 20 times bodyweight for heights of up to 3.2 metres. The rationale for using this method was that weight training or other similar methods of resistance training cannot produce this intensity of voluntary effort.

It was found that the maximum possible height which the athletes could contemplate using produced the greatest increase in strength, although they often hesitated to attempt these extremely stressful jumps. It should be pointed out that the drop heights studied were for experimental purposes alone and it would be most inadvisable to use drops of 3.2 metres for training. It appeared that the main consideration for enhancing strength is not the type of muscle contraction, but the intensity and speed of contraction elicited by the exercise. The high risk of overload injury associated with falling from great heights should always be borne in mind, so it is important to increase the drop height gradually from fairly low levels, to limit the number of drops per session, to land on suitably firm shock-absorbing surfaces and to pay careful attention to landing technique.

The plyometric method of developing explosive strength and reactive ability solves to a significant degree the problem of economising training, since it ensures that a high level of special conditioning is attained in the minimum time. Thus, a comparative experiment revealed that a group of track-and-field jumpers executing primarily depth-jumps (all of them did 475 jumps) over a 12 week period in the preparation phase showed greater improvement in reactive ability than the group which trained with traditional methods and executed 1472 general push-offs (squats, jumping and hopping with a barbell weighing 90-95%, 70-80% and 30-40% of 1RM) and lifted a total volume of 93 tons! Carefully periodised training programmes which combine resistance exercises with plyometrics can develop explosive strength even more effectively than plyometrics alone, provided the resistance movements precede the plyometric activities in individual sessions.

The use of many repetitions and sets of plyometric drills in an attempt to facilitate adaptation to cope with exhaustive bouts of stretch-shortening activities such as rebounding in basketball is not supported by research (Nicol et al, 1997). Instead any improvement in such situations is better mediated by the use of training to enhance movement efficiency. This is a very important point which concerns all explosive and ballistic activities:

it is futile to rely predominantly on plyometric drills to enhance sport specific explosive strength and power, because efficiency of motor control is fundamental to all skilled sporting performance.

Thus, research and practical experience provide strong evidence that plyometric methods should occupy a prominent place in training to develop explosive strength and reactive ability. However, it is necessary to construct the method of developing explosive strength as a whole by taking into account the athlete's level of fitness, the stage in the yearly and multi-yearly training cycle and to stipulate the specific combination, as well as the sequence and continuity of the means and methods used. Although it should form an integral part of the training programme, plyometrics should not be combined in the beginning stages with resistance exercises such as the *brief maximal tension* method .

In those cases where explosive force is associated with the overcoming of large resistance, preference should be given to the brief maximal tension method, as used commonly in Olympic weightlifting. In situations where the resistance is small and the working effect depends upon the reactive ability of the muscles, plyometric methods should be given preference. In subsequent stages, plyometrics should be the main method in the training of highly qualified athletes for developing explosive strength and reactive ability.

Means for developing the ability to quickly develop significant force from rest, as well as to switch from eccentric to concentric work under conditions of great dynamic effort warrant a place in texts on the development of explosive strength. Thus, effective use of the concentric regime to develop explosive strength involves exercises with maximum effort and mixed regimes using weights equal to 40% of 1RM, or 30% of 1RM (Verkhoshansky, 1963; Papysheva, 1966). Explosive-isometric tension up to 80% of maximum should be used in conjunction with this routine.

Besides depth jumps, many common day activities may be used for powermetric training, such as the simple children's swing placed near a wall or some rigid upright structure against which the athlete's feet can push after he/she has swung from a suitable height. One may commence with a very small swing and apply the gradual progressive overload principle by increasing the height of the backward swing over a period of time. It should, of course, be noted that suitable striking uprights may be placed before the swing to enable the athlete to do upper body powermetric rebounds as well. The length of the ropes supporting the seat determines the overall time taken to complete a single oscillation, so if a slower rate of repetition is required, the longer the ropes have to be.

The surface on which the plyometric training (*powermetrics*) takes place can also have a significant effect on the outcome of the exercise, as alluded to earlier in comments made about the alterations in motor skill and proprioceptive sensitivity associated with the use of soft-soled shoes and very resilient jumping surfaces. A little known finding is that plyometric and jumping drills performed according to carefully planned progressive patterns in sand can significantly enhance jumping skills in a short period, even as short as 5 days in duration (Montagni & Cardinale, 1996). The value of beach volleyball and beach handball (an Italian innovation which is currently being seriously researched by Cardinale and Bosco) thus becomes apparent. The low cost of providing a suitable sand pit for this type of powermetrics means that this type of training could be used very extensively.

Another toy which was used many years ago and which seems to have been totally forgotten is the so-called 'Pogo-Stick' or spring-loaded bouncing stick upon which one would balance to execute repeated hops in various patterns on the ground. This can still serve as a useful powermetric training tool, with the intensity of loading being determined by the height of rebound, which, in turn, depends on the amount of muscular effort put into compressing the spring. Similarly, skipping manoeuvres and skills commonly used by boxers can also provide a useful source of powermetric training.

Asymmetric Plyometrics

Many articles on plyometrics describe exercises such as depth jumps and medicine ball drills as suitable supplementary speed-strength exercises for all sports. This approach, however, fails to distinguish adequately between the different sports, because some sports require symmetry of joint action and rhythms, while others display asymmetry and unilateral emphasis. Depth jumps and medicine ball drills using both limbs simultaneously and symmetrically may be valuable for sports which require this type of limb action, but are far less beneficial for sports which involve alternate action of the limbs in different patterns of movement.

Therefore, before selecting plyometric drills, it is important to categorize sporting movements as cyclic, acyclic, unilateral, bilateral, symmetric, asymmetric or as various combinations of the preceding actions. One also needs to distinguish between dominant and non-dominant limbs, as well as driving leg and swing leg in running, since the efficiency of movement depends primarily on central nervous factors and not merely indiscriminate muscular development. Furthermore, it is important to remember that all activity of the legs in sport is related in specific spatio-temporal patterns to motion in the arms.

It is also little appreciated that the body exhibits clockwise or anti-clockwise rotational dominance about its longitudinal axis, as determined by one's dominance of hand. For example, a right-handed baseballer, golfer or shotputter displays anti-clockwise rotational dominance, whereas the left-hander displays clockwise rotational dominance. Clearly, this has a distinct influence on upper body catching and throwing drills with medicine ball plyometrics. Yet, it is rare to find any textbook that comments on how jumping, bounding, catching and other drills should be used to take functional asymmetries and dominances into account in improving neuromuscular efficiency in given sporting movements.

Research has shown that the transfer of strength developed in bilateral training (e.g. using squats or power cleans) offers specific improvement in performance in bilateral events such as the squat clean and snatch in weightlifting, while unilateral training (e.g. with dumbbells or split cleans) enhances performances more effectively in unilateral activity such as running, jumping or karate. Similarly, it should be appreciated that speed-strength development is influenced by the type of plyometric drill chosen for regular training. That this point is not sufficiently understood in the West is emphasized by the fact that the chapters on so-called 'sport specific' plyometrics in the best-known texts make no mention of specificity of explosive exercises with respect to limb or rotational dominance. Yet, even a rudimentary working knowledge of the principles of neuro-developmental training and PNF reveals that motor performance is determined by how competently one programs the central nervous computer of the body, taking functional asymmetry into careful consideration when doing so.

One method of strength training is referred to as the *alternate-asymmetric method* in Russia, since it requires the athlete to execute strength and jumping exercises alternately with each leg, rather than with both legs simultaneously. In addition, synchronisation of each leg with the opposite arm or with both arms, depending on the given activity (e.g. sprinting vs volleyball, basketball or trampolining), may be referred to as the *limb-synchronisation method*.

This information has emerged from research by the author in the biomechanics laboratory in the School of Mechanical Engineering at University of the Witwatersrand to investigate the role of asymmetry and dominance factors in plyometric training (*powermetrics*). In one of the studies, measures such as the time taken to execute a specific plyometric (jumping, bounding or throwing) drill, the peak force, rate of force development and distance covered in a given interval, executed from a start with the dominant versus the non-dominant limb, reveal that it may be relevant to individualise plyometric drills to match the functional asymmetry and limb dominance characteristics of the athlete in specific sporting situations.

It is fast becoming apparent that plyometric training is not simply a special type of high speed rebounding activity that may be applied in a fairly general fashion to every sport. In the light of the above findings, the old saying 'putting the right foot forward' then begins to take on new relevance in sports training.

Non-Impact Plyometrics

In the West, plyometrics (*powermetrics*) have become synonymous with depth jumps and medicine ball throwing, in other words, with activities involving impulsive contact between the extremities of the body and the ground or some object. Even in Russia, the birthplace of scientific plyometrics, the emphasis has been almost entirely on actions which exert some form of impact loading on the body. It may also be stated that all running, jumping and other ballistic actions involve a phase of plyometric activity, so that shock contact of parts of the body with some surface would appear to be the common denominator underlying all plyometrics.

However, this is not the only way of producing plyometric action. As discussed earlier, all plyometric drills so far used in the athletic world are of the impact variety. The existence of the non-impact variety was recognised when the author used a force plate to analyse biomechanically martial arts movements and the seated fitness system (*Supersitting*) developed by his wife, Lisa Ericson of Denver, Colorado. She attracted worldwide attention for her 'seated aerobics' classes, which she developed after becoming paralysed. A former professional ice-skater who was determined to explore and expand the range of possibilities for physical activity by spinal cord patients, she developed a system of exercise rehabilitation which can produce very significant improvements in motor control, strength and hypertrophy without the use of weights or any other resistance apparatus.

After years of experimentation with different training methods, she has managed to gain recognition for her work and for several years has been teaching her seated fitness class to spinal patients at the renowned Craig Rehabilitation Hospital in Denver, as well as to regular aerobics clients at other athletic clubs in that city.

What distinguishes her exercise routines from normal aerobics is that she often uses very rapid wide-range movements choreographed at rates exceeding 240 beats per minute, interspersed with rhythmic transitional PNF-type patterns, offered over a session which characteristically lasts for 60 minutes. After an extended warm-up to ensure that the arms are adequately prepared for the main, high-intensity phase, the subsequent movements are initiated and terminated explosively in sets of uninterrupted sequences which regularly change their form and direction to avoid excessive fatigue, habituation or injury.

This system recruits the myotatic stretch reflex dynamically and powerfully in agonistic and antagonistic muscles over as large a range of movement as possible. The use of patterns, deliberately deviating in space and timing from those recommended by PNF and Pilates practitioners, cause pronounced overflow to adjacent muscles and speed up the rehabilitation of spinal patients, a phenomenon that has attracted the attention of medical specialists.

Ericson's system may best be categorised as *non-impact plyometrics*, (*non-impact powermetrics*) because it obeys all the requirements of plyometrics as originally conceived by Russian scientists. True plyometric activity involves a ballistic action which is rapidly terminated by eccentric and explosive isometric muscle contraction, followed immediately by a powerful concentric recoil mediated by recruitment of the myotatic stretch reflex and augmented by the release of elastic energy stored in the connective tissues of the muscle-tendon complex.

The system developed by Ericson is reminiscent in many ways of some of the training methods used in *karate* which involve explosive snap punches, blows and kicks, or some *boxing* training drills such as shadow boxing or speed ball. In karate, the limbs are thrust powerfully outwards and then drawn back in a whip-like action, ready for the next repetition. In the martial arts, the number of repetitions are relatively few in number and separated by very brief intervals between them, whereas the Ericson system uses many repetitions without pause. The karate punch is rarely whipped back immediately, but makes contact with its target for a very short period, which is sufficient to dissipate much of the elastic energy stored in the connective tissues. The transition phase between eccentric and concentric phases in the Ericson system is usually shorter than that in karate and, therefore, maintains high levels of muscle tension for prolonged periods. The shorter transition phase and the greater number of continuous repetitions in the Ericson system probably explains the differences in functional and structural development produced by it compared with the karate system.

The implications of the Ericson *Supersitting* system for sports training are great. Traditional plyometric drills have often been criticised because they all involve high impact forces produced during explosive contact of parts of the body with some surface or object. The Ericson system eliminates the need for impulsive contact with a hard surface and drastically diminishes the intensity of shock waves transmitted to the joints and entire musculoskeletal system by explosive two-way movements.

Most of the Ericson movements offered in the average fitness class more accurately would be classed as submaximal plyometrics, just like the more usual repetitive rebounding drills over obstacles or with medicine balls. Performed in the form of all-out single movements, they become maximal non-impact plyometrics. Since depth-jumps involve the projection of the entire mass of the body, maximal impact plyometrics will generally increase muscle tension to a greater extent than the equivalent non-impact movements for the leg and hip extensors (e.g. the karate thrust-kick).

Nevertheless, maximal non-impact plyometrics, like submaximal impact plyometrics can serve as a preparatory tool for maximal impact plyometrics, for enhancing other functional and structural qualities or for selectively offering plyometric training to certain muscle groups instead of unnecessarily stressing the entire musculature. These qualities may include strength, muscle hypertrophy, muscle endurance and speed-strength endurance. To date, research into plyometrics has devoted most of its attention to increases in speed-strength (power), rather than these other qualities, so that preliminary studies executed in 1995 by University of Pretoria physiotherapy students supervised by Siff and Ericson warrant more detailed expansion.

Meanwhile, the significant increases in strength, speed-strength endurance and hypertrophy (which are not simply a result of propelling their wheelchairs) achieved by Ericson and her wheelchair athletes emphasize that there is still much more to be discovered about the methods and consequences of the different types of resistance training. Up till now, it has been considered fairly accurate to state that strength and power are best achieved by few repetitions of high-intensity exercises, whereas hypertrophy is best produced by medium numbers of repetitions with 65-85% of one's 1RM. Plyometric exercise traditionally fits into this scheme as a means of enhancing speed-strength.

From the changes observed in Ericson's students, it would appear that even plyometrics should be examined in the context of the nature, duration and pattern of sets and repetitions, since it may be used to enhance fitness qualities other than speed-strength alone. Her system of non-impact plyometrics offers a safe addition to the fields of sports plyometrics and popular aerobics. It is potentially beneficial to any athletes who require high levels of upper body power and endurance, and vastly expands the somewhat uninspiring repertoire of arm rehabilitation techniques generally offered to injured clients or spinal damaged patients in conventional physiotherapy. The aerobics world has erroneously labelled some rapid landing and jumping movements as aerobic plyometrics, but the latter, unlike the Ericson movements, in no way comply with the definition of classical plyometrics. It is apparent that the aerobics community, as well as strength conditioning coaches, have a great deal to learn from an innovative non-impact plyometric system developed by a creative athlete in a wheelchair.

Non-Impact Plyometrics in Sports Training

Although sports involving explosive non-impact plyometric actions are commonplace in international sport, these actions had not been used systematically as plyometric training drills prior to the fundamental research conducted in this field by the author in 1994 (Fig 5.7 was derived from some of this work on upper-body non-impact plyometrics). Every Western training book on plyometrics to date seems to have been devoted exclusively to impact plyometrics using high inertia systems such as the human body, weighted medicine balls or other heavy objects. This is entirely a consequence of the West, in its quest for 'Russian training secrets', simply applying the pioneering scientific work carried out by Verkhoshansky to devise an ever expanding repertoire of 'plyometric drills' and market various high inertia systems for explosive training.

In this endeavour, a vast encyclopaedia of non-impact actions from boxing and the martial arts, in particular, lay largely unutilised. To this we may now add many of the movements developed by Ericson in her SMART seated fitness system. *Low impact plyometric* methods using very light objects for activities such as throwing or kicking may also be included in this low inertia approach to plyometrics. Interestingly, many of the movements derived from all of these systems share a common denominator in PNF (Proprioceptive Neuromuscular Facilitation), in that they naturally follow spiral and diagonal paths which move both ways across the midline of the body. Deliberate deviation from the classical PNF patterns is also encouraged in applying non-impact plyometrics, since this develops a wider range of more demanding functional motor abilities that typify sport.

Thus, from the realm of martial arts alone, one may borrow thrust punches, rising blocks, downward blocks, knife-hand thrusts, palm-heel strikes, front kicks, side snap kicks, side thrust kicks, front kicks and many other standard forms in a wide variety of full or limited range movements to offer non-impact plyometric drills. These actions may be performed solo in a static stance with some of the classical pre-stretching techniques, with explosive punches terminating in a brief isometrically-held end position or with rapid recoil actions which snap the extremities back to their starting positions.

The same movements may be done in fixed routines between opponents standing facing one another, in the form of kata (prescribed sequences of movements) or in freestyle sparring (no body contact). These offer a repertoire, not only of non-impact plyometric drills, but also of many other methods for enhancing explosive strength, movement speed, quickness, rapid decision-making skill, reaction time, kinaesthetic awareness and other qualities which are important in sports demanding rapidity of action. The use of martial arts, boxing and Ericson's SMART methods in explosive sports training was described and demonstrated at the 1994 NSCA (National Strength & Conditioning Association) Conference by Siff and Ericson (*Myths and Facts of Speed-Strength, Explosive Power and Plyometric Training* June 1994). The advisability of integrating such methods into a periodised weight training scheme was emphasized to enhance acquisition of the necessary explosive qualities and minimise the possibility of injury, as was the role of cognitive plyometric processes and asymmetric plyometric training in ensuring that sport specific motor qualities are developed.

Resisted and Water Plyometric Training

Plyometric drills may be offered with some form of resistance being imposed during the amortisation phase, concentric rebound phase or both of these phases. Thus, one may jump and land with light weights or against resistance offered by elastic cords attached to a harness located near the waist or hips. Although both of these methods increase the landing impact and ostensibly increase the strength of reflex muscle contraction, they also increase the risk of impact and overload injuries and should be applied occasionally with great caution. Even normal running or hurdling with very light weights constitutes a form of loaded plyometric training. No resistance methods should not use heavy weights or stiff elastic cords during depth jumps, since this increases the coupling time and imposes unnecessarily large loads on the spine and the tendons of the lower extremities, especially during the landing or contact phase.

A far safer resisted alternative is water or *aqua plyometrics*, a method used for many decades to decrease the landing force and increase the resistance during the recoil phase. Although this variant does not offer maximal or shock method plyometrics, it can serve as a usual form of preparatory or submaximal plyometrics, especially for one-legged drills. The depth of water determines the level of resistance, with chest or shoulder high water offering greater resistance during the landing and take-off phases, less intense eccentric muscle activity, smaller impact forces and enhanced safety. Repeated aqua jumps for developing rebound explosive muscle endurance with one or both legs are considerably safer than their land-based equivalents, though they should not completely replace the latter, since they do not adequately develop the specific neuromuscular patterns or functional needs of explosive sports. Upper body aqua plyometrics may be offered in varying depths of water by performing suitable non-impact plyometric actions derived from the martial arts or SMART fitness systems, as discussed above.

Popular Information on Plyometrics

Most of the popular plyometric textbooks in the West (e.g. Chu, 1992; Radcliffe & Farantinos, 1985) present an interesting array of jumping and rebound activities, many of which do not constitute true plyometric training as originally conceived by Russian scientists. Such exercises are often supplementary or preparatory movements which lead up to or accompany plyometric training, but they are not really 'shock method' plyometric drills. Most books classify extended range swinging, passing or catching of medicine balls or other objects as 'plyometric', although the amortisation phase is too long to produce classical plyometrics. This is not to say that these exercises are not useful: they can play a useful role in enhancing qualities such as eye-hand coordination, eccentric strength and starting strength, but they are not strictly plyometric.

Although some of these books, often advertised to be the most complete ever written on plyometrics, claim to dispel the myths and misinformation about plyometrics, the contents do not confirm these sentiments, for they often fail to reveal an thorough understanding of the scientific model upon which the original Russian shock method ("udarniye metod") is based.

This method was refined by identifying many different strength qualities such as strength-speed, speed-strength, explosive strength, acceleration strength, maximal strength, absolute strength and starting strength. In particular, it relies on the production of a very brief explosive-isometric and eccentric-isometric phase which precedes the release of the elastic energy stored in the tendons and other components of the series elastic component of the muscle complex during the eccentric deceleration phase. Although most books pay detailed attention to the myotatic reflex, which comprises a *tonic*, longer duration reflex and a *phasic*, rapid reflex, they do not discuss their relationship to the different types of plyometric drill. The relevance of positive supportive reaction, the crossed extensor reflex and other important reflexes is also not covered. The role of correctly phased breathing, which is vital to maximal plyometrics and efficient stabilisation of the body, is not mentioned in any book.

Distinction is seldom made between maximal and submaximal plyometrics (and how they are produced), nor is the concurrent and sequential prescription of plyometric and other forms of training discussed in any depth. For example, several books advocate sessions with over 100 repetitions of plyometric movements, sometimes combined with resistance training. This volume of *maximal plyometrics* (unlike sub-maximal plyometrics) is neither productive nor safe for any athlete. Maximal plyometrics, like maximal weight lifting, involves single all-out repetitions separated by a few minutes of rest. It is extremely demanding on the central nervous system and imposes great mechanical strain on the tendons, in particular.

To ascertain whether an athlete needs plyometric or heavy resistance training depends on measuring the *strength deficit* (see Ch 1), prescription of plyometric training remains haphazard, yet plyometric books rarely mention this concept. The opposition to plyometric training (*powermetrics*) by some experts is often the result of this type of guesswork training, which can hinder performance and increase the risk of injury.

Some authors rightly criticize the recommendation sometimes put forward that athletes should be able to squat 1.5 - 2 times bodymass in order to use certain plyometric drills, since they consider that this criterion is not based on research evidence and does not apply to all plyometric exercises. This recommendation is a safety measure based on force plate analysis of *maximal plyometrics* in the form of depth jumps, where the ground reaction force on the lower extremity can easily exceed 6 times bodyweight. *This guideline was never intended to apply religiously to submaximal plyometrics* using small drops, skipping drills or less demanding actions. This misunderstanding of Russian guidelines is largely a result of an incomplete grasp of the scientific principles on which the original shock method was based.

Coaches would appreciate more what plyometrics really is if they were introduced to some of the facilitation techniques used in physiotherapeutic PNF (see 7.2). The physical therapist sometimes imposes a short, sharp jerk on an eccentrically or isometrically contracting muscle to produce strong muscle contraction in a weakened muscle. Relatively prolonged movements such as many of the drills recommended in most books are used for other purposes, including the reduction of spasm or increasing functional range of movement. These principles have preceded sporting plyometrics by several decades, so it is surprising that so much confusion still abounds over plyometrics. Certainly, the so-called plyometric drills in current Western texts are known to enhance performance, but it is not predominantly due to plyometric training, but more to *the increased loading of eccentric contraction, the conditioning of connective tissue, the improvement of voluntary starting strength from the quasi-isometric state, the use of prestretch, and enhancement of acceleration strength* by increasing the velocity of projectiles such as medicine balls.

Plyometrics and the Brain

Recent brain research reveals that plyometric action is not simply a phenomenon that can be adequately explained on the basis of stored elastic energy and the stretch shortening cycle. The phenomenon of *plyometrics involves far more intricate processes than reflexive muscle activities* that operate at the level of the spinal column and bypass the brain. Many of the subtleties and complexities of plyometrics can be missed if one is preoccupied with the prescription of so-called plyometric drills or with laboratory measurement of the stretch-shortening cycle as a local musculotendinous phenomenon. In both cases, it is easy to overlook the possibility that activities such as depth-jumping or medicine ball throwing may involve non-local events, particularly the enormously complicated computer programs in the brain.

While it is accurate to state that plyometric actions are extremely rapid and therefore occur at the level of specific spinal nerves without involving conscious thought processes, it must be remembered that the preparatory period prior to the plyometric action can involve higher order mental processing of exceptional intricacy (see Fig 3.11). In fact, the period prior to execution of any skilled movement involves running mental programmes that have been stored and refined by repeated rehearsal in the brain of the well-trained athlete.

One can distinguish further between a plyometric action produced under conditions in which the athlete anticipates a particular course of action (*cognitive plyometrics*) and a plyometric action produced as a purely reflexive response under unexpected circumstances (*non-cognitive plyometrics*). The latter type of plyometrics occur primarily under survival or self-preservation conditions intended to protect a person from injury or death. The rapidity of the event does not permit any forethought or planning, but relies on primitive reflexes that generally tend to bypass the brain by acting at the more spontaneous level of the spinal cord. Cognitive plyometrics, though also a very rapid phenomenon, is preceded by a phase of thinking that prepares the person for a specific course of action to achieve a definite goal.

One should not conclude simplistically that non-cognitive plyometrics are purely instinctive or automatic actions which involve no cognitive or learning processes. It should never be forgotten that efficient execution of plyometric actions and drills only takes place after a considerable amount of practice using cognitive processes. In fact, most athletes do not manage to perfect plyometric skills even after many weeks of practice. The use of numerous sequential repetitions to imprint these skills may constitute the inappropriate strategy because classical plyometrics are 1RM movements which require as much as several minutes of rest before recovery is complete. Submaximal plyometrics and pseudo-plyometrics may be performed in a state of advancing fatigue, unlike classical 'shock method' plyometrics. The neural and reflexive processes are quite different in each case.

Even then, what appears to be quite reflexive still involves a certain degree of cognitive preparation and control. The lack of adequate mention of the importance of cognitive and learning processes in plyometrics by all popular texts on the subject constitutes a major deficit in the field. Reflexes are casually referred to as entirely robotic actions that elicit or inhibit muscle contraction, but little is mentioned of the fact that reflexes can be trained and modified, something that the renowned Russian physiologist, Pavlov, had proved some 70 years ago in the form of his 'conditioned reflexes'. Later, Skinner (1938) distinguished between two types of conditioning: which he called *respondent conditioning*, in which the response is modified by a preceding stimulus, and *operant conditioning*, in which the response is strengthened or weakened by events that follow the response.

In the plyometric situation, this implies that a stimulus such as an emotion (e.g. fear, excitement) or a mental image (or visualisation) one entertains before an action like a depth jump can shape the subsequent neuromuscular reflexes. Likewise, any event (such as the jarring of the body, post-exercise fatigue or an injury) following a plyometric action can modify these reflexes. In fact, it is common for plyometric activity to be associated with both respondent and operant conditioning.

It has also been shown that if the reflex learning process is carried out with the subject in a particular physiological or psychological state, then the conditioned reflexes are exhibited only when the same state is present, but not when the state is different. This phenomenon is known as *state-dependent learning*. Its existence implies that plyometric proficiency or deficiency learned in a specific training situation may not be reproduced under competitive circumstances which differ from those of the learning situation.

What the preceding few paragraphs imply is that it is only partially correct to regard plyometrics as a process in which basic reflexes automatically produce a powerful muscle contraction which is accompanied by elastic energy released after the muscle has been stretched eccentrically. It is vital to note that the entire plyometric process involves complex state-dependent learning events which modify the pattern of reflex activity according to how the given plyometric drills are executed. This may be one of the reasons why some researchers have carried out experiments which apparently have shown plyometric training to produce little or no improvement in speed-strength or sporting performance. One cannot ignore the neural factors involved in studying the effects of any neuromuscular phenomena: study of muscular output alone is incomplete and lack of control over essential neural factors affecting the experiment can easily distort the results.

It should be more obvious now that plyometric training is not simply a matter of dropping from a height or throwing an object for a given number of repetitions to improve fitness qualities such as strength-speed or explosive strength. Sport usually involves the reproduction of a wide variety of technical skills under expected and unexpected conditions, so that feedforward training and other 'visualisation' (mental and kinaesthetic imaging) techniques must be used to enable the athlete not only to increase explosive strength and strength-speed, but also to efficiently manage any plyometric actions under real sporting conditions.

Lest the connection between visualization and movement be oversimplified by sports psychologists, neuroscientist, Dr Kensall Wise of the University of Michigan, points out that the part of the brain which can visualise a given action is totally separate from those parts which initiate the muscle contractions to carry out the action (*Scientific American*, Oct 1988: 23). Although fairly modern research has identified some of the connections between some regions of the brain and functions such as sight, hearing and motor output, researchers still have only a vague idea of how the nervous system initiates and manages any given actions.

The importance of ballistic activity to humankind recently has been shown to extend far beyond the realms of sport. Neurophysiologist, William Calvin, has proposed the fascinating hypothesis that the brain's planning of ballistic movements may have played a major role in the development of language, music and intelligence over the ages (*Scientific American*, Oct 1994). He makes this proposal, since ballistic movements and language processes involve some of the same regions of the brain, in particular those associated with sequencing and planning. In reaching this conclusion, he emphasizes that ballistic movements, unlike cocontractive slower movements, require a great amount of planning and problem solving. Slow movements may be corrected readily by ongoing feedback information, but ballistic movements require the brain to determine every detail of the action in advance by mentally planning the exact sequence of neural activation for numerous individual muscles.

Apparently, parts of the language cortex of the brain serve a far more generalised function than previously suspected. It is implicated in the production of novel sequences of sensations and movements for both the hands and mouth, so that ballistic arm actions may play a role in mental development. Calvin adds that improvements in language skills might improve dexterity and vice versa. The emphasis placed by Russian coaches on athletes being able to accurately describe, draw and visualise sporting movements would appear to correlate with this proposal. Instead of simply executing entertaining plyometric drills like biological robots, athletes would be well advised to integrate cognitive processes more actively into the training programme.

Various Shock Methods

Plyometrics should not be thought of as the only type of 'shock training', even though the term 'shock method' was the preferred name given to the plyometric method by Verkhoshansky when he first formalised this category of impulsive training. Training plyometrics may be regarded as one of several shock methods that may be used in special strength training to provide intense stimulation to compel the body to attain a higher level of functional adaptation. The principle of gradual progressive overloading may, after a prolonged period of unvaried use, sometimes fail to improve strength or performance, as is commonly the case among elite athletes. In this situation, it may be necessary to disrupt the persistent state of stagnation by use of one of the following shock methods (see 7.1):

- plyometrics
- supramaximal methods
- repeated single 1RM training
- contrast methods
- forced repetitions
- electrical stimulation (macrostimulation)
- restricted range maxima
- maximal eccentrics

The appropriate method, its timing and the duration of its use must be chosen with great care, since lack of progress may be due to overtraining rather than long-term stagnation. The use of any shock method under such circumstances is potentially harmful and definitely detrimental to performance. These methods are generally unsuitable for novices and should only be employed by experienced athletes with a solid background of special strength training.

5.2.5 The Development of Strength-Endurance

Strength-endurance involves the production of muscular tension without a decrease in efficiency over a long period. *Strength-endurance*, like explosive strength, has several forms, depending upon the motor pattern of the athletic activity, in particular the categories of dynamic and static endurance.

Dynamic strength-endurance is typical of exercises involving repetitive and significant muscular tension at a relatively slow speed of movement, as well as repeated cyclic or acyclic exercises requiring speed-strength. In the latter case we are referring to the specific endurance to execute special speed-strength and explosive work without a decrease in efficiency over a relatively long period. *Static strength-endurance* is typical of activities associated with the maintenance of maximal and near-maximal tension, as well as the moderate tension necessary for holding a specific posture (for example, in shooting or speed-skating).

The development of *strength-endurance* is an inherent characteristic and a fundamental principle of training for developing general endurance. Training for *strength-endurance* is determined predominantly by:

1. The magnitude of the load
2. The tempo of movement
3. The duration of each movement and each phase of the movements
4. The rest interval between training sessions
5. The length of the training period
6. The initial levels of strength-endurance of the athlete
7. The kinesiological structure of the movement
8. The relative involvement of static and dynamic strength-endurance.

Repetition work with weights 25-50% of 1RM at a moderate tempo (from 60-120 repetitions/minute) is used for developing *strength-endurance*. The effectiveness of *strength-endurance* development, using equivalent weights and movement tempos, will be higher if the work is executed to complete fatigue, although work of shorter duration (60% of the maximal work capacity time) also will yield satisfactory results (Agolinsky, 1953; Korobkov, 1953; Monogarov, 1958; Diachkov, 1961).

Strength-endurance, like the other characteristics of muscular activity, is specific. However, the specificity of strength-endurance is expressed to a lesser degree than the specificity of speed, for example, while its carry-over from one activity to another is greater. When the activity involves repetitively overcoming significant resistance (exceeding 75-80% of 1RM), one cannot enhance endurance, since one becomes constrained to developing strength predominantly (Zatsiorsky, 1966).

This study by Zatsiorsky showed that i*sometric endurance* increased 84% as a result of exercising 10 times a day for 5 weeks with the elbow flexors holding a 60% maximal contraction for as long as possible. *Dynamic endurance* increased by 93% as a result of performing these arm curls with a weight of 60% of 1RM at a rate of 28 repetitions per minute until it was impossible to increase the tempo further. At the same time, the ability to execute repetitive isometric contractions (60% of maximal strength for 5 seconds of tension and 2 seconds of rest) to failure increased by 219%. A similar experiment with 10 dynamic movements executed daily with maximal resistance for 5 weeks resulted in increases in both dynamic and static strength, but dynamic and static endurance remained almost unchanged (Hansen, 1963). This indicates that it is necessary to optimise the volume of work required to develop *strength-endurance*.

It has been established that an increase in *strength-endurance* contributes to improving endurance in distance runners, skiers and skaters (Popov, 1968; Nabatnikova, 1972; Mikhailov & Panov, 1975). However, it must be emphasized that the magnitude of the strength load used is different if, on the one hand, the key quality required is *general endurance* and, on the other hand, it is *strength-endurance*.

It should be noted that certain popular strength exercises such as running with a sack of sand weighing 25% of the subject's bodyweight, barbell pressing, squats, 'good mornings', and twisting with a barbell not only do not enhance, but to a certain degree, will even hinder the development of endurance in cyclic type exercises (Maisuradze, 1960). It some instances the increase in strength is associated with excessive muscle hypertrophy, which is a by-product of strength training. Endurance and hypertrophy do not increase simultaneously and there is no correlation between them (Maison & Broeker, 1941; McMorris & Elkins, 1954).

The lack of a definite correlation between special strength and muscle mass in different sports where the key quality is endurance has been observed by several authors (Chistyakov, 1965; Chernyaev, 1965; Nabatnikova, 1972). This concerns primarily cyclic sports (middle distance running, skating and skiing). In other cases, for example, with gymnasts, a positive linear correlation (R = 0.77) is noticed between *strength-endurance* and *relative strength* (Zhalei, 1964). Therefore, in those cases where endurance is associated with the display of significant strength, some muscular hypertrophy does not negatively influence training results.

The general principles concerning the development of *strength-endurance*, which were discussed earlier, are applied differently in each specific case, depending on the characteristics of the sport, for example:

- During the preparatory period, skiers should exercise with weights which are up to 65% of 1RM, in combination with simulation exercises on a flat surface, as well as with movements on roller-skis (Chistyakov, 1965).

- Middle and long distance runners obtain good results from lifting a barbell of 55-60% of bodymass up to head level 8-10 times rhythmically, clean-and-jerks with various weights (60-85% of bodymass); jumps with kettlebells from a squat position (using about one-third of bodymass for 18-20 repetitions) and squats with 55-60% of bodymass until complete fatigue (Likachyevskaya & Kovalchuk, 1963). Exercises with weights of 60-80% of 1RM for multiple repetitions, jumping and hard running are also recommended (Popov, 1966).

- Exercises with heavy weights (80-85% of 1RM), as well as medium and small weights are recommended for developing *strength-endurance* in skaters. Exercises with heavy loads are executed for several sets at a moderate tempo for 4-12 repetitions per set until the point of complete fatigue, with 2-4 minutes of rest between sets. Exercises with light and moderate weights are executed as rapidly as possible for 15-25 repetitions per set, for 3-5 sets with rest intervals of 5-8 minutes (Mikhailov & Panov, 1975).

- Male rowers obtain good results with weights of 50-80% of 1RM and female rowers with loads of 30-40% of 1RM (Ulrich et al, 1966). Significant improvement (up to 40% from initial levels) in *strength-endurance* has been noted in women rowers working with light weights (18-20kg) for many repetitions (Chumakova, 1964). Improvement is greater with these weights than with larger loads (35-50 kg) executed in sets of 2-3 repetitions, and it is even greater (by 28%) than that produced by a combination of both methods.

It is necessary to increase the amount of weight and the number of repetitions as *strength-endurance* increases. The following method is recommended for skaters to develop *strength-endurance* in the legs: increasing the number of barbell squats by 20-30 each week (beginning with 50 squats per set and over a period of 2-3 months increasing this to 200-300 repetitions), then increasing the amount of weight and starting a new cycle of strength training, but beginning with a smaller number of squats (Mikhailov & Panov, 1975).

For developing *strength-endurance* it is always appropriate to strive to execute the work under demanding conditions, though with movements whose coordination and structure in space and time are close to those of the special exercise. For instance, a runner may run with a small parachute resisting him or pull a loaded sled in the preparatory phases (Popov, 1966). Similarly, gymnasts may use a heavy belt and vest (Zhilei, 1964) and rowers a special water-resistance device attached to the hull of the boat (Chuprun, 1966). In the case of the rowers, *strength-endurance* as measured by the number of pull-ups, the number of arm flexions in the prone position and the number of barbell presses in 30 seconds increased by 57.1%, 27.8% and 9.1%, respectively.

Thus, multiple repetition exercises with various weights should be considered the fundamental method for developing *strength-endurance*, with the load being determined by the dynamics of the given exercise. In cases requiring intense effort, an optimally heavy weight should be used together with light weights or with exercises simulating the given sport activity. If the special exercise is associated with the prolonged production of moderate force, then it is useful to work with light weights in repeated sets to the point of fatigue or failure.

Strength training should not result in increased muscle mass in those types of sport where the key quality is endurance of moderate work output. If *strength-endurance* is required, especially in those cases where it is necessary to overcome a large resistance, a small increase in muscle mass is permissible. In no cases, should the training ever produce a decrease in relative strength of any muscle groups in the body.

5.3 Application of Special Strength Training Means

The value of systematic application of the training means has been investigated repeatedly, but the preliminary conclusions still need to be extended. Consequently, there have been attempts to devise a rational combination of strength, speed and endurance exercises to:

- raise the body's general work capacity (Zimkin, Yakovlev, Korobkov, Zatsiorsky)
- investigate the effectiveness of sequential and concurrent (parallel or complex) use of the means for developing endurance and *speed-strength* (Ozolin, Diachkov, Mikhailov, Volkov et al)
- study the effect of the sequential use of aerobic and anaerobic exercise on the development of endurance (Volkov et al, Gordon et al)
- investigate the sequential use of *strength* and *speed-strength* exercises as one of the schemes for systematically developing explosive strength (Ozolin, Diachkov, Vorobyev, Filin, Verkhoshansky).

However, research in the area of the systematic use of means is limited and no definitive practical recommendations have yet emerged.

The systematic use of means of special strength training over a given period produces a cumulative effect which is significantly greater than the separate non-sequential application of these same means. In principle, there arc two possible variants for thc systematic application of means: sequential and concurrent, as mentioned above:

1. *The first variant (sequential means)* involves the strictly determined, successive introduction of different means, each with a higher training effect, into the annual or multi-annual cycle. The theoretical basis for this variant is based upon two observations:

- the training effect of any means diminishes as the body adapts to its influence
- the training effect must be maintained by using a complex of means to steadily increase the body's special work capacity.

In addition, experience and research indicate that the training regime designed to develop a particular motor ability is determined largely by the degree of continuity in sequentially changing means with different training effects. Because of this, functional changes produced by earlier means should create favourable conditions for achieving the training effect of subsequent means. To devise a systematic sequence of the means of special strength training, one must:

- assess the quantitative and qualitative components of the training effect
- categorise the means relative to the level of the athlete's special fitness.

This, in effect, is the subject of research aimed at identifying the principles for devising logical systems for applying the different means of special strength training effectively. As an example, the sequential development of endurance begins by training aerobic (cardiorespiratory) processes, then non-oxidative glycolysis and finally high energy phosphagen processes. This sequential introduction of 'anaerobic' work creates favourable conditions for the training effect of 'aerobic' work (Ozolin, 1959, 1970; Volkov, 1963; Yakovlev, 1957; Borisov, 1979).

2. *The second variant (concurrent means)* involves the parallel use of means (over an extended period) that are close to the body's work regime, but which produce a largely different training effect. This method is based on experimental evidence that adaptation elicited by the separate components of the complex of training work is not simply a summation of the separate effects, but the synergistic result of the interaction of the effects at each stage of training. This interaction produces a new physical state with a significantly greater work potential than would

have resulted from the separate non-systematic use of these same means, even at increased volume. Experimental assessment of the cumulative effects of different variations of the combination of means is necessary for applying the complex system of special strength training means.

A number of researchers, including Purvin, Khodykin, Deniskin, Tatian and Chernousov have studied the systematic use of special strength means in *speed-strength* sports. They have established that the sequence of means in the preparatory period (beginning with *strength*, then *speed-strength* means, or vice-versa) has no real significance for novices. Consequently, the same effect can be obtained by using these means in any order.

A relatively larger effect than produced by the above-mentioned variants (with the same volume of training load) occurred in groups who used *strength* and *speed-strength* means concurrently by alternating them in mixed training sessions. This alternation sequence creates the optimal conditions for functional adaptation. This does not ignore the fact that this training regime, with a rest interval between sessions on the same day, also produces a positive response of the after-effect phenomenon by use of the *strength* and *speed-strength* exercises. On the whole, this elicited more intense and more stable adaptation. It should be noted that the contrasting of stimuli in mixed workouts by alternating training means which are primarily of a *strength* and *speed-strength* character undoubtedly has a positive effect.

In another experiment one group of novice athletes used weights exercises in the first stage of training and plyometric depth jumps in the next stage. A second group did the same exercises in reverse order and a third group did these same exercises together in both stages, although not in the same workout. It was established that the first variant was more effective for developing *speed-strength*. The concurrent use of exercises (the third variant) caused significant improvement in *speed-strength* in the first stage, but the rate of improvement in *speed-strength* decreased noticeably in the second stage, due to monotonous repetition. The second variant (reversed use of these same means) produced significant improvement after the first stage due to the larger training effect of the plyometric method. However, the acquired *speed-strength* qualities were lowest at the end of the second stage.

Another experiment studied the question of whether the execution of *speed-strength* exercises in one workout against the background of the positive after-effect produced by previous tonic strength work influences the effectiveness of *speed-strength* preparation of novices. One group of athletes executed exercises in this sequence (i.e. strength, then speed-strength work) during the fundamental stage of their workouts, while another group did the reverse. The pauses between exercises were increased slightly to minimise the influence of the positive after-effect of the preceding work on the subsequent work. A third group executed depth jumps. The presence of this group in the experiment served two purposes: firstly, to study the effectiveness of plyometrics and secondly, to compare this effect with the results obtained with a complex of less effective means. There was no statistically significant difference in *speed-strength* of the subjects in the first two groups. The largest increase in all the parameters of the control movement was discovered in the third group.

Thus, an increase in the training effect of *speed-strength* exercises performed against the background of the positive after-effect of *strength* work has not been corroborated in the training of novices. In this experiment, the means with a higher training effect (i.e. depth-jumps) produced significantly larger improvement in *speed-strength* fitness for a smaller volume of training. In explaining these results, one should take into account that any training influence will leave significant traces in an untrained person. The body is unable to react selectively to a chiefly *strength* or *speed-strength* means in one workout. In addition, the period over which the traces of the training stimulus are maintained is apparently longer than the duration of the after-effect of prior tonic work. Within one workout, the traces of all the training tasks are summed, which results in the same effect, despite these tasks being done in succession.

These findings should not be considered to disprove in general the appropriateness of using a complex of means in training, which exploits the positive after-effect of preceding strength work to enhance the training effect of the subsequent *speed-strength* and *speed* work. Since the experiment was conducted on a group of novice athletes, it is very likely that their lower level of special fitness excluded the possibility for exploiting this phenomenon adequately. A well-trained athlete can expect the preceding strength work to have a positive effect on the training effect of *speed-strength* and *speed* work in a training programme. However, the validity of this hypothesis can be established conclusively only by careful experimentation.

In an experiment with junior class sprinters the specific effect of short jumping exercises and the systematic use of combinations of these exercises was investigated. The jumping exercises involved variations of repeated jumps on one and two legs, as well as variations of triple and quintuple standing broad jumps and long jumping exercises (multiple jumps on one leg or from leg to leg over distances of 30-100m). One group of sprinters executed mainly short jumps, a second group did mainly long jumping exercises and a third group did both for a period of eight months (see Fig 5.12). The short jumping exercises developed primarily length and speed of the running stride, whereas the long jumping exercises largely increased maximum running *speed* and *speed-strength endurance*. The combination of short and long jumping exercises led to a summation of their separate training effects and the development of *speed-strength* abilities which are specific to sprinters.

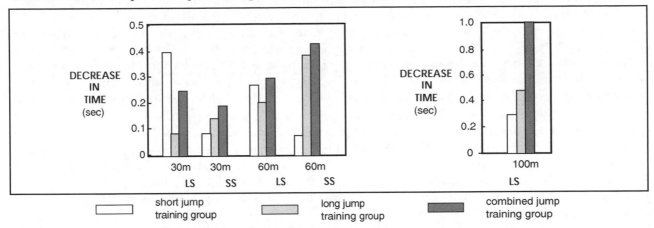

Figure 5.12 Decrease in sprint times for three groups of athletes over various distances after 8 months of training. LS = low start, SS = standing start. (Siff & Verkhoshansky, 1999).

Under natural training conditions, three equivalent groups of jumpers of average qualification were used to compare the effectiveness of different systems of strength training (Fig 5.13). All of the groups used special jumping exercises in the first stage of the preparation period. Groups 2 and 3 switched to barbell exercises in the second stage, while group 1 continued to do the jumping exercises. Group 3 began to use depth-jumps in the third stage while group 1 continued to do the jumping exercises and group 2 did the barbell exercises.

The special strength training indicators displayed a clear tendency to stabilise in groups 1 and 2 after the first and second stages respectively, and in group 1, even to decrease during the third stage. Thus, the sequential use of means with higher, specific training effects clearly produces a positive result. At the same time, the use of the same means, even with an increase in volume, not only does not produce a positive change, but decreases the existing level of special strength fitness (Verkhoshansky & Aganin, 1970).

Research with novices and athletes of average qualification leads us to make the following conclusions about the effectiveness of the variants studied for these athletes:

• The best results are obtained by consistently using those combinations or complexes of means which produce the optimal training effect (e.g. as shown in Fig 5.13)

• A slightly smaller effect is obtained by the concurrent use of *strength* and *speed-strength* means in one training session or their sequential use in successive sessions

• Least effective is the sequence of *strength* followed by *speed-strength* means during the same session.

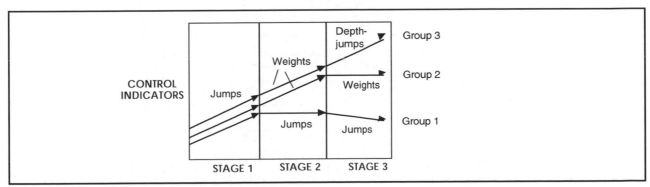

Figure 5.13 Dynamics of the control indicators for the three groups using different combinations of training methods (see the text). (Siff & Verkhoshansky, 1999).

The following principles for the sequential use of training means over a given period emerge:

287

- *Strength* exercises should be done after *speed-strength* exercises in training
- Strong-acting *plyometric* methods should be done after *strength* exercises, but not before.

In another study (Fig 5.14), qualified athletes modelled different variants of weightlifting pre-competition training under laboratory conditions (Deniskin, 1976). A leg extension movement involving the lifting of a 1RM was used as a model, starting with an initial knee angle of 90°. The training effect of the plyometric method (with depth-jumps) was investigated after a first stage of intensive work with resistance, the purpose of which was to increase explosive strength. Only depth-jumps were used during the second and third stages. The necessity for having two such stages was dictated by the results of a preliminary investigation which showed that the rise in functional state achieved after one stage is unstable. The fourth stage served as a control and served only to test performance. The subjects were given a complete rest between stages to enhance supercompensation.

The experiment showed that the plyometric method produces an additional, significant increase in the level of explosive strength that was first attained with resistance training. This demonstrates the use of these means in two appropriate stages: the first stage, which improves explosive strength, and the second stage, which stabilises the level of special fitness. There was a significant increase in all the control indicators after a period of complete rest following the first and second stages. This emphasizes that rest may be used as a training means. This is not a paradox, because growth and maintenance processes take place predominantly during sleep and other forms of passive or active rest.

Several researchers have studied the systematic use of special strength training by highly qualified athletes under various training conditions (Purvin, Deniskin, Khodykin). It was established that using electromuscular stimulation (ES) first, followed by plyometrics yielded a larger training effect than the use of these means in the reverse order. However, a significantly larger training effect was obtained by using them together during the same stage, when, for example, ES and plyometrics are applied concurrently with heavy resistance exercises. When the training is not chiefly for strength, ES and plyometrics were observed to have the lowest effect during periods of complete or partial rest.

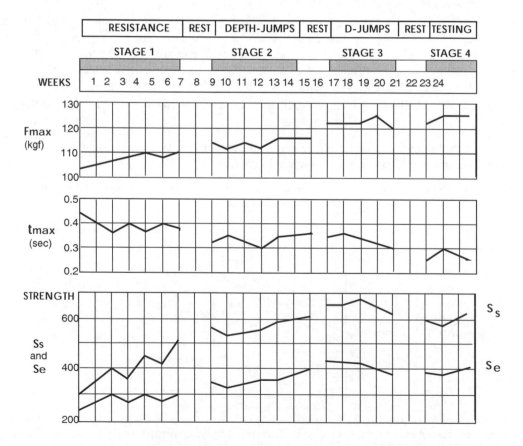

Figure 5.14 Results of an experiment showing changes in performance indicators with different combinations of training, as explained in the accompanying text. Ss = starting strength, Se = explosive strength, Fmax = maximum force, and tmax = time taken to reach maximum force Fmax. D-Jumps refers to Depth Jumps. (Deniskin, 1976)

5.3.1 Interaction between Different Training Means

Special attention must be paid to the prescription of general heavy resistance exercises. They enable the athlete to reach the necessary level of absolute strength, to provide general physical conditioning and to train the neuromuscular system non-specifically. However, it is undesirable to use them extensively during specialised training phases, since they can diminish speed and explosiveness. High volume strength loads used after a phase of specialised jump training can substantially reduce the existing level of explosive strength (by as much as 30%).

Kotz has shown that prolonged, heavy workloads slow the contraction speed of trained muscles. More specifically, Filinov has established that excessively heavy strength loads diminish the force and speed of boxers' punches, while Deniskin (1976) has found that prolonged use of high volume strength loads diminishes the power and speed of weightlifters, high jumpers and triple jumpers.

Thus, *speed-strength* and *strength-speed* cease to increase after a certain volume of heavy strength training has been executed. Deniskin observed this phenomenon after 18 weeks (54 workouts) of strength training. Other studies have also noted the same phenomenon after 50-60 training sessions or approximately 12 weeks of training. This research shows that there are certain volumes and durations of strength training that are essential for achieving an optimum training effect. Exceeding these optimal values renders any further increase in training volume not only unproductive, but detrimental to the athlete's preparation.

The rising standards of performance in sport has led to a general increase in the volume of strength training and technical preparation, especially in speed-strength sports. Throwers have sharply increased their quota of maximum distance throws and throws with heavier-than-normal implements, while jumpers have increased the number of jumps with a full approach run and jumps for maximum height. For example, discus throwers may execute as many as 100 throws in one workout and high jumpers perform as many as 80 jumps.

The demands on time caused by this increase in training volume usually compels one to prescribe physical conditioning and technical training concurrently. From the point of view of the theoretically valid principles of *coupled effects*, *unity of skills and fitness qualities* and *unity of physical and technical training*, this approach would appear to be fully warranted. These principles, in their most general form, express the interactive nature of the training process. In this sense this is correct.

However, in the context of the yearly training cycle or the training of highly qualified athletes, then a literal interpretation of this concept of unified training by the concurrent prescription of physical and technical training leads to serious error. Such a solution immediately contradicts the well-known need for the athlete to practise technical skills when he is fresh.

For instance, research by Verkhoshansky and colleagues has established that *excessive maximum strength training can impair speed-strength and technical skill* in boxers (Verkhoshansky, 1977). It can also lead to a deterioration of several months' duration in the technique of weightlifters and javelin throwers. Other studies have shown that heavy training loads reduce one's ability to control movements, primarily of their most complex technical phases. The negative influence of heavy strength training on sports technique may be due substantially to deterioration of the speed-strength qualities of the neuromuscular system.

With the widespread, almost mandatory use of supplementary strength training in most sports, it is surprising that research such as that quoted above has not stimulated more extensive work to investigate the practical application of strength training in sport. In this regard, it is disturbing to note the minimally varying composition of popular training means and the rubber-stamp way in which they are applied in short-term and long-term training. Virtually the only factors that change are the load and overall volume. This highlights the need for developing a clearer methodology for structuring sport-specific strength training programmes and applying existing research findings more competently. In general, an effective system of using the means of special strength training may be devised in the way discussed in the following sections of this chapter and in Chapter 6.

5.3.2 A Sequential System of Training Means

The development of specific motor abilities from the level of performance of the average healthy person to a high degree of proficiency occurs in a specific pattern. Because of this pattern, it is necessary to sequentially improve the functioning of those systems and physiological mechanisms which are crucial for developing a specific motor ability.

Progressive functional changes in some systems act as prerequisites for improving the performance of other systems which limit development of the required motor abilities. It is easy to understand that the given response is produced only if the conditioning process is organised so as to produce suitable conditions which efficiently integrate the use of all means with different training effects.

It is known that, in order to steadily increase the body's special work capacity, the means used should elicit a definite training effect, but its magnitude should correspond to the body's current level of specific fitness and increase in conjunction with the latter. Despite the logic of this principle, it is nevertheless not always practical to achieve. Very often the means are selected on the spur of the moment without considering their precise training effect and often on the basis of what is currently fashionable or subjectively preferred. For instance, means which are highly effective during more advanced stages of training may be used inappropriately during the early stages of the yearly cycle or in the beginning stages of multi-year training.

The repertoire of means is usually extremely limited and is repeated in much the same way from year to year. This is not a general trend but a fairly typical occurrence, which reveals that even well-known and theoretical principles of major significance are consciously or unconsciously ignored. Hence, the necessity becomes obvious for devising a scheme for sequentially introducing means of gradually greater training effect into training.

Specificity becomes more relevant to one's state of fitness as sports proficiency increases. At the same time, the role of the means used to develop trainability grows. Introduction of the means should be carefully timed and the contents of future training should be based entirely on the preceding stages. These means should be novel, so as to promote a greater training effect by compelling the adaptive processes to transcend any performance plateau.

Research has investigated changing the special training means only once or twice during the period of study. However, suitable variations for the systematic use of means with greater training effects involve multiple changes. Consequently, the logical organisation of training loads, as exemplified by the *conjugate sequence system* of special strength training needs to be examined. This is done in the next section.

5.3.3 The Conjugate Sequence System of Training Means

In the training of highly qualified athletes it always becomes necessary to raise the developmental level of any of the basic qualities of the motor system which may be limiting improvement of the specific motor abilities. A logical solution would appear to be the introduction of a particular means capable of eliminating this insufficiency. However, this measure, which displays a very low probability of transferring specific motor abilities to the given sporting activity, is not very effective. If a specially sequenced system, known as the *conjugate sequence system*, is regularly used in training, then the likelihood that such situations will arise is minimised and the situation will rapidly improve (Verkhoshansky, 1978).

There are essentially two main systems of organising long term training: the *concurrent system* and the *conjugate sequence system*. The *concurrent system* involves the parallel training of several motor abilities, such as strength, speed and endurance, over the same period, with the intention of producing multi-faceted development of physical fitness. Although research has corroborated the effectiveness of this system, the subjects used in these studies were generally conducted on athletes of lower qualification. While the negative influence of the complex system is not apparent with less advanced athletes, it becomes very noticeable with elite athletes, in whom it produces only average results. To evoke a more powerful training effect in athletes who have already accommodated to high levels of stimulation, it becomes necessary to impose intense phases of uni-directional loading on the body. This is precisely the purpose of the conjugate sequence system.

The *conjugate sequence system* (sometimes translated from the Russian as the *coupled successive system*) involves successively introducing into the training programme separate, specific means, each of which has a progressively stronger training effect, and coupling them sequentially to create favourable conditions for eliciting the cumulative effect of all the training loads. The *conjugate sequence* use of unidirectional means, integrated by separately developing individual, specific motor abilities (e.g. strength, speed and strength-endurance), can be an invaluable method of organising special strength training for more advanced athletes. Usually, it involves training a carefully chosen sequence of specific motor abilities, each of which is confined largely to a given period, a scheme that saves time and energy. It is appropriate to use concentrated loading primarily for enhancing the effectiveness of the SPP (Special Physical Preparation) phase, and for this, one may use loading of any primary emphasis.

As is known, the 'degree of contrast' in training (i.e. the alternation of means with different beneficial training effects over certain optimal periods) is a factor which enhances the functional responsiveness of the body. With the conjugate sequence scheme, this factor optimally enhances the effectiveness of the special strength training.

One should take into account some of the characteristics for systematically prescribing special strength training to yield a sufficiently large training effect. Therefore, it is appropriate to devise training chiefly on the basis of a sequential system of means:

- to create favourable conditions for systematically developing specific motor abilities
- to enhance the effectiveness of the special strength training by systematic, periodic revision of the training means.

During each stage, one should use exercises with different training effects, specifying the order and timing of all the means. It is appropriate for qualified athletes (who are at a high level of special strength fitness) to use primarily a complex system of means for:

- producing the specific training effect of the complex of means
- preserving the magnitude of the training effect.

The latter should be realised by the sequential replacement of one complex combination of means with another. It should be emphasized that the long-term use of the same means, even if the volume is increased, not only will not increase one's level of special fitness but will also decrease the existing level of *speed-strength* and especially, maximum strength.

A scheme of loading organisation, based on the conjugate sequence system is presented in Figure 5.15. The scheme depicts an appropriate sequence of loads with different primary emphasis, which takes into account their positive interaction and the increase in specific training potential over time. To develop *speed-endurance*, the following sequence of stages is recommended:

1. Aerobic
2. Mixed anaerobic (ATP-CP and anaerobic glycolysis)
3. High energy phosphagens (ATP-CP)
4. Anaerobic glycolysis.

The block of specialised strength work is concentrated in stage 2, speed work is concentrated mainly in stage 3 and is executed against a background of the long-term delayed training effect of the strength block, and stage 4 is devoted to improving speed-endurance while the general volume of loading is decreased significantly.

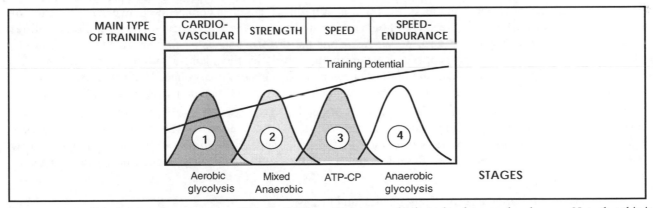

Figure 5.15 Conjugate sequence organisation of loads of different training emphasis to develop speed-endurance. Note that this is solely a descriptive scheme, which does not give quantitative details of intensity, volume or timing of loading. (Siff & Verkhoshansky, 1999). Note that there may be a certain amount of overlap of all training stages 1-4 over any given period.

A typical sequence for *speed-strength* and *complex-technique* types of sport is as follows:

1. General development work,
2. Concentrated strength loading,
3. In-depth perfecting of technique against a background of the delayed training effect of the strength block
4. Further perfecting of technique under competitive conditions.

Unidirectional emphasis on qualities such as strength or endurance may be used not only in individual workouts, but also during each microcycle (Kudelin, 1980; Budokho et al, 1978; Mironenko, 1980). Research has shown that unidirectional training over periods as long as 4-12 weeks can be very effective, especially if the intensity is gradually increased for each form of loading in the given cycle. Moreover, the effectiveness of the conjugate sequence system with advanced athletes is such that the training volume over a macrocycle can be reduced by as much as 20%, a phenomenon referred to as the *acceleration of specific adaptation* (see 5.4.2).

However, it must be noted that unidirectional loading is effective only if one uses a diverse complex of means with a single primary emphasis, together with a variety of training methods (Fedorova et al, 1975; Platonov & Monograov, 1977; Verkhoshansky, 1977). Furthermore, an important condition for implementing concentrated loading is the relatively low intensity of the means, since the frequent use of these means already intensifies the training. In this context, the loading may be considered concentrated if its volume in the month in which it is applied constitutes 23-25% of the general volume for the year.

The system is not without its dangers, since concentrated loading is very stressful and, besides increasing the potential for overtraining, it can decrease motor qualities such as speed-strength. After a phase of emphasis on heavy strength training, there may be an increase in muscle stiffness and a loss of explosive strength, sporting skill or speed. Since the conjugate sequence system is based on exploitation of the delayed training effect, *a diminished loading and restorative period has to be observed after a given concentrated loading phase to allow the body to supercompensate to the desired level of preparedness.* The gains elicited, for instance, by 4-8 week concentrated blocks of strength, speed-strength or speed training, may occur most commonly after a latency period of 1-3 weeks, so it is essential for the athlete not to lose patience and hasten into the next concentrated phase without adequate restoration. Not only does premature imposition of concentrated loading suppress the delayed training effect of the previous stage, but it also lowers the effectiveness of future training.

5.4 The Principal Aims of Special Strength Training

During the initial stages of training the body reacts to any stimulus with all of its survival mechanisms and motor abilities. As a result of this general adaptation response, the specific training effects which enhance working potential are not produced. Characteristically, there is a relatively high correlation between the various motor abilities and the development of even those abilities which are not directly implicated. The transfer of fitness is very distinct here.

As sporting proficiency grows, so the adaptation response becomes more selective. Functional adaptation is confined primarily to those systems which are the most active and develops in those directions which are determined by the specific components of the training stimulus. The close connection between separate motor abilities tends to diminish during the stage of high sports proficiency, the rate of development of motor abilities which are not the direct object of training slows down, and the *transfer phenomenon* is not displayed as sharply as before. Thus, the direction of progress is determined entirely by the specific components of the training stimulus. Since sport achievements at the high levels of sports proficiency are produced by a complex of specific motor abilities, the regime of the means used should contain an optimal combination of specific training means.

It is now appropriate to formulate a set of general principles for organising special strength training, based on the specific characteristics of physical training and the long-term dynamics of the STS (Sports Training Process). In general, they express the chief ways of exploiting these characteristics and form the foundation of a new system of sport training, although they do not exclude all of the traditional principles and rules. These principles are:

- Converging the partial effects of strength training means
- Accelerating specific adaptation
- Specific correspondence of the training effect
- Maintaining the strength training effect.

5.4.1 Converging the Partial Effects of Strength Training Means

The principle of *converging the partial effects of strength training means* is fundamental to the long-term organisation of strength training. It is achieved by the convergence of all the different partial training effects, i.e. the gradual convergence of their cumulative training effect to those important specific characteristics which are essential to the functioning of the body in a particular sport.

During the initial stages of the sports training process (STP) the tasks which determine the diversity of the training means are far apart. They are loosely connected only by the long-term plan of the STP and implied by that training programme which takes into account the characteristics of producing a specific type of fitness for a given sport.

In particular, this occurs by adaptation to the motor regime required by the sport, i.e. its specialisation is firstly according to *ability* (but not to the *physiological system*) and is not related to the motor pattern (see 2.2.3). At the same time, training of the body to improve performance involves enhancing its functional abilities and raising its working potential.

As the STP advances, the training effects of the means begin to converge according to their specificity. In this respect, the functional characteristics demanded by the sport determine the requirements of the special strength training, while the level of special fitness determines the progress of the STP as a whole.

Thus, at the high level of sports mastery the special strength training converges towards the specific character of the motor regime of the given exercise and its specific motor pattern. However, the criterion of successful convergence is the closeness of correspondence of the training effect to the performance characteristics of the given sport. As training progresses, the effect of the specific training means exceeds the required degree of closeness, while the general training means more strongly reflect the specifics of the special exercise. At this stage, there is a close interrelation between all components which constitute the STP. The correspondence between each of the components is reflected in the growth of sporting proficiency, the latter being determined by the body's level of special fitness and the athlete's ability to attain his full motor potential.

This process is illustrated in Figure 5.16. During the STP the characteristics of the key motor ability M gradually move closer to the working pattern of the motor apparatus in sport A. At the same time the complex of individual motor abilities determining the key motor ability (i.e. M1, M2, M3) correspond more closely to the specifics of the key motor ability.

This concept has already been studied regarding early specialisation by youngsters (Verkhoshansky, 1963, 1972). Since this question is directly connected with the initial stages of the STP, particular consideration was given to the advisability of early specialisation, not in the specific type of sport, but in the specific motor regime involved. In other words, orientation of the child to the sport and physical training with the sports means does not begin with specialised exercise to achieve competitive performance standards (which can easily lead to forced training). Instead, it begins with systematic management of the functional perfecting of the body.

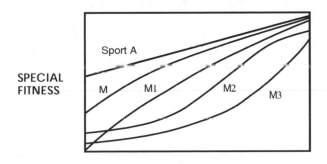

Figure 5.16 The aim of converging the partial effects of different strength-training means. Details of this process is explained in the accompanying text. STP is the Sports Training Process or PASM (Process of Achieving Sports Mastery). M1, M2 and M3 refer to the different motor abilities, while M is the key motor ability. (Siff & Verkhoshansky, 1999).

This means that, in physical education and competition, the child may display a predisposition to a particular form of athletic activity (e.g. quick reactions, speed of movement, a capacity for *speed-strength* activities or motor dexterity). Thus, the child will begin training in a group specialising in the appropriate motor regime (*the first stage* of a children's sport school in Russia). The goal of such training is to enhance the body's functional abilities using a diversity of elementary motor forms which do not involve specialisation in some specific sport.

Competitions, primarily in team sports, are indispensable elements of such training because they involve those same elementary motor forms. During the course of training, which imposes a gradual increase in the demands on the body, the teacher will determine the child's predisposition to a specific sport and transfer him to the appropriate sport school for specialised training (*the second stage* of a children's sports school in Russia).

Even in countries whose schools do not offer this type of sporting education, the same approach can be adopted successfully if these two stages of early sporting preparation are applied systematically in a single school or club.

5.4.2 Acceleration of Specific Adaptation

The principle of accelerating specific adaptation emphasizes the key role of special strength training as the foundation for developing sports proficiency, with particular reference to its organisation over a long period. The idea is that specific adaptation should be accelerated by advancing the stage when maximum sports proficiency is expected to be produced by the current training regime. In practice this means that the task of functional specialisation should be based on accurate modelling of all aspects of the motor activity. The requirements of this specialisation are then presented to the body in a specific sequence during the STP (Sports Training Process) in order to accelerate adaptation.

Thus, the successful acceleration of specific adaptation depends on anticipating any conditions which may delay the subsequent course of the STP. This ensures the steady progress of the STP, except when physical fitness lags due to unforeseen circumstances such as adaptational idiosyncrasies, illness or injury. Even then, a contingency plan should always be available to maintain the fitness level of those systems which can still be exercised.

The achievement of accelerated adaptation necessitates using statistical data which reflect the basic trends in the dynamics of the athlete's specific motor abilities in the given sport (see 2.2.3), where the athlete's existing level of special physical fitness is carefully taken into account. This accelerated adaptation may be achieved by controlling the post-training supercompensatory phases by using the conjugate sequence method of training, by the heterochronicity principle of superimposed cycles of training the different components of fitness, by converging the partial effects of the training means, or by correctly periodised full or partial restoration after training (see 8.5).

Specialised means of strength training selected to take into account the specific movements of the given sport and the participant's existing level of fitness produce a timely and substantial increase in relative and starting strength, significantly exceeding the average indices typical of the training of that type of athlete. It should also be pointed out that the use of complex, novel means of strength training enable highly qualified athletes to avoid the typically slow rate of increase in starting strength.

5.4.3 Specific Correspondence of the Training Effect

The principle of specific correspondence points to the need for correspondence between the general effect of the strength work and the specific character of the motor regime of the given sport. This is achieved on the basis of systematically organising means so that the resulting cumulative effect fully establishes the special strength fitness required at the current stage of the sports training process.

The practical realisation of this aim should be based upon the following scheme of the functional specialisation of the body in the sports training process (Fig 5.17). Along with the body's general adaptation response, it selectively reacts to the dominant motor regime and movement pattern.

This causes local, functional improvement in the fitness qualities of the kinematic chain's motor system (*specialisation of systems*) and develops qualities which are appropriate to the motor skills of the sport (*specialisation of ability*), as was discussed earlier (2.2.4). Subsequently, a definitive, more precise structure of the key muscle groups and the structure of their functional integration occurs, as well as the efficient development of the necessary specific motor abilities. Thus, specific correspondence of the training effect is based on the following tasks:

- Timeous development of the required level of special strength fitness
- Elimination, where necessary, of heterochronological stages which were initially suitable for the intense functional specialisation of the key muscle groups
- Elimination of any lag in the development of strength fitness of individual muscle groups
- Intensifying the development of the essential strength abilities during the stage of advanced sports mastery.

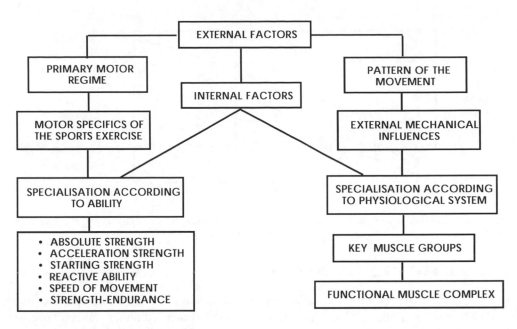

Figure 5.17 Principal scheme of the functional specialisation of the body in the sports training process (Siff & Verkhoshansky, 1999).

5.4.4 Maintaining the Strength Training Effect

Preservation of the training effect means that the load should always produce a training effect by the systematic, timely introduction of more effective training means based on logical continuity. This provides the basic condition for developing the sports training process, i.e. uninterrupted growth in special work capacity to avoid the states of stagnation and deterioration described in Chapter 1 (see Fig 1.32). Achievement of correspondence between special work capacity and the steady growth of physical demands produces the conditions under which the special exercises are executed.

Practical application of this principle is associated with the sequential introduction of more effective training means, based upon the *conjugate sequence method* (5.3). The plan of this method is as follows (Fig 4.1): as the training effect of some means decreases, so more effective, newer means are introduced which, in turn, are replaced by even more effective means. For practical use of this method, experimental assessment of the training effect and categorisation of the specific complex of means is necessary. An example of the categorisation of means for developing explosive leg strength in the preparation period of a jumper is given in Figure 5.18 (Verkhoshansky, 1969, 1970).

The long term use of the *conjugate sequence method* involves implementing a repetitive, cyclical system of sequentially applied means, each of increasing intensity. With this method it is possible and advisable to revise the complex of means (Fig 5.19), successively replacing those which played an earlier progressive role in increasing the athlete's fitness (means A and B) with newer, more effective means (C and D), and finally with still other means (E).

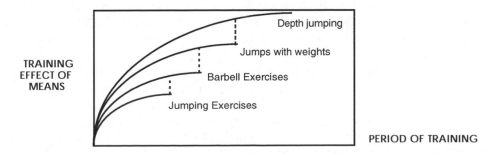

Figure 5.18 The conjugate sequence method of organising speed-strength loads for developing explosive strength of jumpers. The dashed lines indicate when one type of training means is changed to the next training means

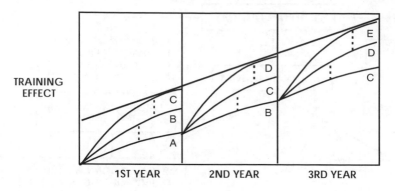

Figure 5.19 Application of the conjugate sequence method of organising speed-strength loads in multi-year training. A, B, C, D and E are the training means that constitute the complex sequence (based on Verkhoshansky, 1977).

5.5 Cross Training in Sport

In the West, the term *cross training* refers to using relevant *secondary sports* to augment the training effect produced in an athlete's *primary sport*.   It has been applied for some years to training which involves performing several sports daily or weekly within the same training programme. Thus, a supplementary fitness programme which incorporates gymnasium exercises, aerobics, cycling and swimming is popularly called 'cross training'. Typically, some exercises or sports are done on one day, others on another day.

In planning this type of training, it is important to recall the two basic ways of combining training: *concurrent* and *sequential* (see 5.3). Thus, cross training may involve supplementary activities being prescribed concurrently with the athlete's main sport on the same day or during the same training phase or in a definite sequence where one supplementary activity gives way to another and finally to the main sport over a given period. The design of any cross-training programme, therefore, necessitates applying a thorough knowledge of factors such as the interaction between activities of different primary emphasis, the influence of short- and long-term after-effects of training, supercompensation, the specificity of training, periodisation and restoration, topics which are covered elsewhere in this text.

In Russia and Eastern Europe, the prescription of adjunct means of physical preparation does not simply focus primarily on the type of sport used, but rather on the relationship between the motor and fitness qualities in the supplementary activities and the primary sport. This involves the qualitative and quantitative modelling of each sport involved so as to ensure that the supplementary sports do not impair performance in the primary sport (see Ch 6). It is inadequate, for example, to state that track-and-field athletics, rugby or American football require the development of strength, so that heavy weight training must constitute appropriate cross training. Earlier in this text, we have stressed the importance of defining the different types of strength and their development, so it should be obvious that this simplistic approach can offer little more than short term progress.

For many years the Russians and Eastern Europeans have supplemented the training of their competitive athletes with systematic supplementary training in other sports. For instance, Olympic weightlifters and field athletes have included volleyball or basketball in their overall training regimens. In the West, however, 'cross training' generally has not advanced scientifically much beyond the way in which it was used several decades ago, and the choice of combinations, durations, intensities and periodisation systems is often guesswork. Combinational training of complementary sports or exercises can be valuable if prescribed scientifically, but detrimental if done randomly.

Certain sports are used in Russia and allied countries during the off-season, some during the early preparation phases, others during the competitive season, and still others as a means of recuperation or enhancing certain qualities such as fine motor control or explosiveness. These sports have not been chosen simply to add random variety to stagnating athletes; they have been periodised carefully into closely monitored long-term training programmes. Part of this supplementary training has even included phases of specialised electrical stimulation of the muscles or the central nervous system.

The Russians have consistently identified the most important fitness factors required by specific sports, then divided the sports training programme into a periodised model aimed at using supplementary activities

(General Physical Preparation) to assist in the transfer of skills in the Specific Physical Preparation phase which precedes the Competition phase (Ch 6).

The concept of cross training is sound under certain circumstances, provided the tendency to overtrain is resisted. Variety usually adds interest, ensures novelty of neuromuscular stimulation and can reduce the likelihood of stagnation, but the enthusiasm it engenders can cause the recent convert to raise the intensity or volume of training to inappropriately high levels and produce overtraining.

As discussed previously, combinations of predominantly cardiovascular activities such as regular distance running, cycling or swimming with weightlifting, rugby, or other strength sports may be counterproductive, since muscular endurance and cardiovascular fitness may be enhanced at the expense of strength, muscle mass and power. Some sports can actually interfere with the fitness components and neuromuscular patterns acquired in other sports. The maxim of regular variation in training has to be applied with intelligent circumspection.

Similarly, inappropriate weight training using largely bodybuilding techniques might be detrimental to the marathoner or endurance athlete, especially if it fails to increase functional relative strength. The shortage of adequately trained strength specialists in local gyms renders incorrect use of supplementary resistance training a real possibility for serious athletes.

The term *cross training* has actually been used for many years by physiologists to describe the phenomenon whereby training one limb can produce a training effect in the opposite limb. The training effect elicited in one (ipsilateral) limb by active exercise or even passive manipulation is transmitted by central nervous pathways to the opposite (contralateral) limb. Though the strengthening effect is not as great as in the actively trained limb, this 'cross training' effect can occur and usefully be applied in cases where an individual cannot use one limb due to injury (Enoka, 1988).

In the interests of etymology (the study of word origins) and scientific exactitude, it would be preferable that the term *cross training* be applied as intended originally and that a term such as *combinational training* or *complementary training* be used to describe physical conditioning via several sports in a single programme. At present, confusion exists in employing the same term for defining two different concepts in exercise prescription.

Some authors have been swift to categorise certain sports as beneficial and others as detrimental as 'cross training' activities for specific sports. This restricted view, however, fails to take into account the fact that every sports training programme consists of distinct overlapping phases, each concentrating on developing and integrating different fitness qualities. For example, it is erroneous to label cross-country running as totally unsuitable for rugby or American football players. Although prolonged aerobic activity generally is inadvisable for use during the competitive season, it can have a place during the early off-season period, since it can improve peripheral vascularisation and recuperation after intense exercise. Similarly, weight training should not be dismissed from the training schedule of a distance runner, when it may be useful in strengthening certain muscles or enhancing local muscle endurance.

To employ cross training efficiently and appropriately, it is essential to understand *sports modelling* and some of the different models of periodisation devised by Matveyev, Vorobyev, Verkhoshansky, Bogdanov, Kuzwecov and others, each of whom has worked in the Russia or Eastern Europe with different types of athlete. Most of these models comprise a General Preparation Phase, a Specific Preparation Phase, Transition Phases, Stabilisation Phases, a Competition Phase, Conversion Phases, Maintenance Phases and Reconstruction Phases (Ch 6). Once these principles are understood, it becomes possible to select different secondary sports and activities to augment each different phase of training for the primary sport. In order to do so, one must understand precisely which fitness qualities (static strength, dynamic strength, power, dynamic flexibility, muscle endurance and so forth) are developed by the primary and the secondary supplementary sports.

In this respect, it is important to recall that sporting prowess involves specialisation by physiological system and specialisation by ability or skill (see 2.2.3 and 5.4.3). Therefore, any cross training programme must ensure that it enhances and does not compromise either of these processes.

Some of the secondary activities may be used either *to enhance the training effects* of the primary sports or *to assist in recuperation and relaxation* after specific training for the primary sport. In doing so, it is vital to recognise that attention has to be paid not only to the *physical*, but also the *psychological*, effects of the secondary activities.

For example, learning to push against maximal loads during the late off-season and early season can enhance the overall motivation of a rugby or football player in coping with high levels of physical and mental stress. Swimming can teach an athlete a great deal about breathing patterns, dancing and gymnastics about coordination and balance, and karate or boxing about reaction time training, as can basketball and hurdling about explosive leg power. Even some computer games may assist in improving motor skills and reactivity.

Since some form of weight or circuit training is very popular as a cross training activity, it is vital to point out that most machines used in fitness centres constrain one to move along fixed, two-dimensional paths and, if used regularly, can interfere with the three-dimensional neuromuscular patterns characteristic of all sport, under-utilise the postural muscles or create muscular imbalances between agonists and antagonists. Similarly, isokinetic rehabilitation machines do not develop the three-dimensional, eccentric, concentric and explosive muscle activation patterns needed in competitive sport. They should be used only for limited, specific applications during the earlier stages of general physical preparation or rehabilitation.

In planning any type of cross training activity, it is always relevant to ask the questions: *Will this activity be directly beneficial to my sport ?, Will this activity be indirectly beneficial to my sport?, When will other activities be beneficial or detrimental to my sport?* and *Would the time be better spent training with sport specific exercises?*

Cross training is currently highly attractive and popular among journalists and coaches, but its successful use is by no means as simple as implied by many personal trainers. As one of the more sophisticated concepts in sports preparation, it requires an extensive theoretical knowledge of all aspects of physical conditioning, years of practical experience in working with different athletes, and close collaboration with experts in different sports.

5.6 Circuit Training

Circuit training has once again surged into prominence as a training modality in commercial gymnasia, largely because of the fads promoted in the USA in response to the regularly changing appetites of the average non-competitive fitness client. Both instructors and pupils are becoming bored with traditional aerobics classes, aerobic dance is often too complicated for the fast-fitness client or uncoordinated male, weight training is still struggling against public confusion of it with overdeveloped bodybuilding physiques, so circuit training is stepping in as the so-called 'new' method of fitness conditioning.

Circuit training is by no means a new concept. As it is defined today, it seems to have been formalised by R Morgan and G Adamson in 1953 at the University of Leeds in England as a system which would train several of the components of fitness simultaneously, rather than strength or cardiovascular endurance separately.

Actually, circuit training is really an extended form of 'supersetting', which has been used by the bodybuilding fraternity for decades (see Ch 7). It is defined as a routine which requires one to alternate sets between two (or a small number of) different exercises. For instance, a typical superset might require you to do set 1 of a bench press, then set 1 of a squat, back to set 2 of the bench press, then set 2 of the squat, and so on until the specified number of sets has been completed for both exercises. A circuit simply extends the superset from two or a few exercises to a sequence of many exercises .

The term 'circuit' now refers to a collection of 'stations', each station being an area or specific machine or weight at which a chosen exercise has to be performed for a certain time or number of repetitions. Successive stations characteristically require one to use a prescribed resistance machine, bicycle, mini-trampoline, skipping rope, barbell or free exercises such as pushups, situps or jumps.

The typical modern circuit requires one to move rapidly in a stipulated order from station to station through the circuit and repeat it for a set number of times, the intention being to develop strength, cardiovascular stamina, muscular endurance and flexibility. Frequently a timing system with an audible alarm is used to signal participants when they should hasten to the next station. In other systems, a certain number of repetitions is prescribed for each station. A much publicised feature is its claimed ability to develop all these fitness factors, while lowering percentage bodyfat and improving shape.

What is not widely appreciated is the fact that most instructors rely on the circuit training systems developed and advertised by the manufacturers of expensive specialised machines. Equipment salesmen, for obvious reasons, do not promote the fact that highly successful circuits can be set up without apparatus or with very cheap apparatus. Circuits can even be set up on sports fields, in parks, in corridors, in the aerobics class or in the swimming pool .

The Aims of Circuit Training

As recounted earlier, circuit training has been advertised as a highly successful system for developing all-round fitness. However, this claim is not accurate for the average commercial circuit, since research has shown that only a moderate compromise of the reputed cardiovascular and strength conditioning benefits can be achieved by traditional circuit training.

It has been shown that CWT using combinations of gymnasium apparatus with fixed bicycles or mini-trampolines cannot produce cardiovascular conditioning which rivals that of running, cycling and other traditional forms of cardiovascular conditioning. Furthermore, because CWT generally relies on the use of light weights and high repetitions, increase in strength and power is also very limited. A literature review reveals that CWT has not been adequately studied in terms of simultaneously developed dynamic strength, muscular endurance, flexibility and cardiovascular fitness. Virtually the only significant benefits of the average commercial circuit are a modest development of local muscular endurance, moderate decrease in percentage bodyfat and a mild improvement in cardiovascular fitness.

Alternation of conventional weight training on one day and endurance training on another day produces superior results to traditional circuit training in terms of improvements in strength, and cardiovascular stamina. Training is highly specific and if one wishes to enhance strength, one has to do high intensity strength training with a minimum of prolonged aerobic training, since the latter tends to decrease strength. Similarly, aerobic performance is enhanced by specific aerobic training of long duration. Aerobic running training does not even cause greatly enhanced performance in distance cycling or swimming.

Periodically alternated and modified circuits for achieving a specific type of conditioning are preferable to the typical chrome-and-carpet arrangements which cater for the average up-market individual who indulges in one current fashion after another. To these clients, any exercise is acceptable, provided they are pampered, entertained, making some improvement, and are seen to be doing something fashionable.

The principle of specificity (see 1.3) does not allow us to produce simultaneous maximum conditioning of strength, flexibility, cardiovascular endurance and the other fitness components. Only a certain compromise is feasible, as dictated by individual capabilities, needs and wants. This is not to state that circuit training is of little value. On the contrary, a circuit training programme tailored to meet the characteristics of the individual can serve as an effective form of conditioning during certain stages of the conditioning programme. Like every form of training, it has certain strengths and weaknesses, so it has to be administered on the basis of a sound knowledge of exercise and strength science.

An informed instructor will realise that each station may be used in a different way to meet the individual needs of clients. The circuit may be the same for all clients, but the way in which they perform their particular programmes may differ regarding muscle contraction, acceleration and velocity of movement, posture, joint angle, hand spacing, foot spacing, and so forth.

Circuit training can achieve far more than the benefits advertised by equipment manufacturers if it is realised that the traditional circuit training impose unnecessary limitations on its more extensive utilisation. For instance, a circuit may be done entirely in water or done partly on land and partly in water, involving devices such as bicycles, waterpolo balls, medicine balls, canoes, dinghies or flippers. Even an element of airborne exercise can be incorporated by use of a trampoline or diving springboard as one of the stations. The scope of circuit training is then limited solely by the imagination of the instructor and participants.

Differences between Circuit and Conventional Resistance Training

In understanding the nature of circuit training, whether it involves apparatus or not, it is important that one appreciates how its definition causes it to differ from conventional resistance training, in general. Those who train exclusively with weights, in effect, also move from apparatus to apparatus in a chosen sequence for a specific number of sets and repetitions, so why is conventional resistance training not regarded as a form of circuit training?

The basic differences lie in the fact that circuit training operates on the assumption that it can simultaneously condition you aerobically and anaerobically. Now, it is well known that any rest intervals will tend to prevent the body from operating in the aerobic conditioning zone, so that circuit training does not permit rest periods other than the brief time it takes from one station to the next. The athlete has to keep moving and try to complete a circuit as rapidly as possible within the limits imposed by his current level of fitness.

Conventional resistance training, on the other hand, is characterised by a specific number of exercises performed with a selected resistance (usually progressively increasing) for a chosen number of repetitions and sets, with a rest interval between every set. The duration of this rest period depends on how strenuous a particular set is, with intervals of 2-4 minutes being common for few repetitions (1-3) with loads close to one's

1RM (single repetition maximum) or a fairly large number of repetitions (10-15) with over 80% of one's 1RM. Research has also shown that heavier individuals require longer recovery periods than their lighter colleagues. Thus, in the average resistance training workout, the actual training time could easily constitute less than 20% of the total time spent in the gymnasium. On this basis, the critics of resistance training considered this to be an inefficient way of training, especially as far as the cardiovascular system is concerned. So, circuit training was developed specifically to eliminate rest periods and introduce some element of aerobic training into the gymnasium setting.

As stated earlier, this aim is not satisfactorily achieved and circuit training on its own is unable to produce all-round conditioning. Paradoxically, its major limitations are imposed by its very attempt to introduce aerobic conditioning into conventional weight training by eliminating rest intervals. The absence of rest periods prevents one from using heavy weights and developing strength, from holding static or resistance-assisted stretches to enhance flexibility, and from performing intensive explosive movements to improve speed. Only if the rest intervals are re-incorporated into circuit training can more effective all-round conditioning become possible.

Extending the Scope of Circuit Training

The evaluation of circuit training (CT) up to this point would imply that it is a system of limited worth and simply another product of successful marketing by the manufacturers of gymnasium apparatus. This is generally true if the traditional concept of CT is adhered to.

However, if rest intervals are re-introduced into the system, CT can be extended enormously to produce a far more versatile training modality. The idea of stations can certainly be retained and the concept of circuit training may be expanded by including what may be called Interval Circuit Training (ICT). This results in a system of known benefits, familiar to all runners in the form of interval training and fartlek ('speed-play', or 'jog-sprint-walk'). In the gym situation, the earlier-mentioned training method known as 'supersetting' is similar in that it involves one in executing set 1 of exercise 1, then set 1 of exercise 2, then set 1 of exercise 3, before executing set 2 of exercise 1, and so on for as many exercises as are included in the sequence. For consistency of terminology, the term 'super circuit' should then be reserved for the type of ICT system which supersets a series of resistance exercises. At this point it is helpful to subdivide Circuit Training into several categories, so as to cater for many training possibilities. Circuit Training (CT) then consists of two primary categories and one mixed category:

A. *Continuous Circuit Training (CCT)*, which in turn comprises:

- Unresisted Continuous Circuit Training (UNRECCT)
- Resisted Continuous Circuit Training (RECCT)
- Combined (Unresisted & Resisted) Continuous Circuit Training (CCCT)

B. *Interval Circuit Training (ICT)*, which comprises:

- Unresisted Interval Circuit Training (UNRICT)
- Resisted Interval Circuit Training (RICT)
- Combined (Unresisted & Resisted) Interval Circuit Training (CICT)

C. *Mixed Circuit Training (MCT)*, which comprises combinations of the preceding forms of Circuit Training

The element of aerobic conditioning can readily be introduced into any type of circuit by including a 15 minute period of cycling, jogging or skipping, preferably at the end of the session. Similarly, stretching stations could form part of an ICT course to provide flexibility conditioning or the first round through a circuit can be done in a warmup and stretching manner to achieve functional flexibility in a wide variety of manoeuvres. A special 10 - 15 minute warming-up and flexibility circuit could also be designed to precede the main conditioning circuit. Full-range movement against adequate resistance is particularly effective in enhancing functional flexibility and it should form part of all training programmes.

A 5-10 minute type of cooling-down circuit, which could even be the original circuit executed with light resistance through a full range of joint movement or at a leisurely pace, could conclude the training session.

Types of Circuit

The above extension of the concept of CT now permits one to devise a wide variety of different circuits to achieve specific purposes for each individual or team. For instance, the scope offered by all the classes of CCT, ICT and MCT can produce, inter alia, the following circuits:

- Cardiovascular Circuits
- Aerobic Class Circuits
- Rehabilitation Circuits
- Strength Circuits
- Plyometric Circuits
- Speed Circuits
- Yoga Circuits
- Agility Circuits
- Restoration Circuits
- Warming-up and Cooling-down Circuit

- Power Circuits
- Martial Arts Circuits
- Muscle Endurance Circuits
- Boxing (Equipment) Circuits
- Muscle Bulking Circuits
- Flexibility Circuits
- Upper Body Circuits
- Lower Body Circuits
- Isometric Circuits
- Mixed Circuits

These circuits may be designed as discrete units or aspects of each may be incorporated into a single circuit, as it is impossible to have a facility large enough to cater for such a variety of separate circuits. A single set of stations may be used to offer many of the above circuits, if the instructor understands how to vary the way in which each circuit must be executed.

Circuits and Apparatus

The above categorisation of the extensive range of possible circuits immediately reveals a repertoire of hundreds of different exercises both with and without the aid of apparatus for inclusion in any circuit. For instance, the following types of apparatus or methods are typical of those which may be used:

- Free Weights
- Pulley Systems
- Non-variable Resistance Machines
- Variable Resistance Machines
- Elastic Bands or Springs
- Punch bags/balls
- Isokinetic Machines
- Climbing ropes

- Olympic gymnastics apparatus
- Batons/broomsticks/clubs
- Ergometers - cycle and rowing types
- Skipping ropes
- Mini-trampolines or Jogging Boards
- Strap-on weights (wrist, ankle, waist)
- Floating jackets and flippers (for aquacircuits)
- Medicine balls and other throwing objects

In selecting the particular type of apparatus for a specific training purpose, it is important for the coach to be aware of the advantages and disadvantages of the most frequently used devices or methods. For instance, if cost (capital outlay and maintenance) is of prime concern, as it would be for small gymnasia, schools and minor clubs, then specialised variable and non-variable multi-purpose machines have to be regarded as the lowest priority. In such cases, a few inexpensive 'hi-lo' pulley machines would be a more than adequate substitute. In fact, the latter offer a level of three-dimensional variety that other machines cannot emulate.

A well chosen collection of free weights, benches, racks and pulley machines, wedded with a skipping surface, padded aerobics area, bouncing boards and a few basic fixed cycles, offers virtually everything that the most impressive multi-station machines offer at a fraction of the price. Differences in safety are minimal in that some free weight exercises are more dangerous than certain machine exercises, and vice versa. Similarly, space savings are inconsequential, as optimal utilisation of floor area is more a matter of efficient planning and layout than of choice of machines alone.

Free weights are generally far more effective than any variable and non-variable 'isotonic' and isokinetic machines in developing strength and power, in offering greater versatility in training most muscles of the body, in facilitating full-range three-dimensional conditioning of the proprioceptive mechanisms, in economy of space usage and in terms of relatively low cost.

The main advantage of most machines is that the load can be changed more rapidly than on a barbell, a feature which is particularly valuable if a large group of trainees of very different individual strengths have to move against the clock through a circuit. In this respect, lower priced pulley machines offer this same feature, plus the additional ability to provide resistance in three dimensions over an extremely wide range of movements.

The major disadvantages of most resistance machines, besides high cost, are that they are designed to match the 'average' body and constrain each limb to move in set two-dimensional patterns which do not stimulate development of balance, positioning and movement in three-dimensional space (see Ch 7). This fact means that a very wide range of specialised machines is necessary if each joint and muscle group is to be adequately conditioned. For example, it would require at least seven different machines to train the muscles involved in the basic movement of cleaning a barbell from the ground to the shoulders. It requires at least three machines to offer the training benefits of the basic squat.

Moreover, many of these machines compel one to begin the required movement in the most vulnerable and biomechanically weakest joint position with little possibility for pre-stretching before starting strength is exerted. In this regard, most bench press, seated press, seated leg press, leg extension and 'pec deck' machines are particularly bad offenders. This is why it is highly advisable that a training partner hand you the grips of the machine in your strongest position or stabilise you before you begin to move, particularly if you are having to rush against the clock through a circuit. Contrary to what manufacturers may state, one needs a 'spotter' or training partner to guide you safely and efficiently through any circuit.

Factors such as the above have to be taken into serious consideration in the designing any circuit, but ultimately it is even more important to understand the strengths, weaknesses and danger aspects of every device in a specific circuit. In continuous circuit training (CCT), possibly more than in traditional weight training, is it important to constantly monitor client technique. This is because the aim of CCT is ostensibly to focus on cardiovascular conditioning, which constrains participants to work rapidly against the clock, thereby producing fatigue, carelessness and deterioration of motor skills. On the other hand, the rest periods and heavier loading characteristic of interval circuit training (ICT) causes one to employ a more technically correct style of execution.

Differences between Aerobic and Anaerobic Circuits

Another fundamental consideration in the setting up of a circuit is whether the latter is to impose aerobic or anaerobic demands on the participants. As discussed earlier, cardiovascular circuits all fall under the category of CCT (continuous circuit training), although traditional circuit weight training (CWT) has been shown to be only mildly effective in producing cardiovascular conditioning. A true aerobic circuit would involve the predominant use of very low resistance devices or prolonged rhythmic movements such as jogging, skipping, cycling and swimming. In contrast to aerobic circuits, anaerobic circuits may be either CCT (continuous) or ICT (interval), with the former resulting largely in muscle endurance, and variations of the latter developing strength, power, muscle endurance, speed or flexibility.

Some rough guidelines for the use of different types of circuit are given below, but it should be remembered that a considerable degree of individuality is involved and no precise figures can be quoted to be universally appropriate for everyone (see Table 1.1 for further information).

Cardiovascular (aerobic) circuits are generally characterised by:

- Continuous activity or very brief intervals taken in moving from one station to the next.
- Alternation of distinctly aerobic activity (such as cycling, jogging on the spot and skipping) between resistance stations.
- A fairly high number of repetitions at each resistance station (20-40)
- Relatively low resistance at resistance stations (usually not more than 30% of 1RM)
- Many excursions around the circuit (5-10).

Anaerobic circuits, on the other hand, are characterised by:

- Rest intervals between stations to permit some recovery (1-4 minutes)
- Fewer aerobic stations and more resistance stations
- Lower number of repetitions at resistance stations (3-8)
- Fewer number of excursions around the circuit (3-5)
- Higher resistance at each resistance station (usually more than 70% of 1RM).

If an anaerobic circuit is meant primarily for development of dynamic muscle endurance, then resistance should be nearer 50% of 1RM, repetitions should be nearer 50, number of excursions should be near 4 and rest intervals should be shorter. However, if strength and power are the essential considerations, then resistance should exceed 75% of 1RM, repetitions should not exceed 5, rest intervals should be nearer 2 minutes and there should be no more than 3 excursions around the circuit. Development of power generally requires the smallest number of repetitions. Flexibility circuits may require static stretches to be held for 20-30 seconds, and rest intervals are irrelevant, unless pulley-assisted or dynamic stretches are included.

Since their aim is neuromuscular coordination, agility circuits (which rely minimally on machines and heavily on specific free movements with or without hand-held apparatus) necessitate many repetitions to imprint the correct movement patterns in the central nervous tissue. Restoration circuits are intended for relaxation and lowering of physiological and psychological stress after exercise, so they have to be of low intensity, moderate duration and low complexity. Rhythmic, relaxed, carefully sequenced patterns of spiral and diagonal forms such as those used in physiotherapeutic PNF or Tai Chi are eminently suited to this purpose. Focus is on relaxed breathing and mental visualisation.

Practical Design of Circuits

It is now appropriate to examine the structure of the various different types of circuit which may be constructed for specific purposes. In doing so, it needs to be stressed that there is no such entity as the best circuit, only the most appropriate and effective circuit for achieving specific fitness aims in a particular person at a particular stage of training. There are only certain recommendations and precautions based on whether a continuous or interval circuit approach is to be used to produce specific aerobic or anaerobic conditioning effects.

Once it has been decided which specific type of circuit is necessary for the group (e.g. cardiovascular, strength, muscle endurance or flexibility), it is advisable to organise each circuit programme to cater for individual levels of fitness, as follows:

- beginner circuit
- intermediate circuit
- advanced circuit

The well-known lighthearted maxim of KISS (Keep It Simple, Simon) offers sound advice for those preparing circuit training systems. Circuits should always progress from simple to complex, light to strenuous, short to long, and low resistance to high resistance. Thus, beginner circuits may be modified to become intermediate or advanced circuits by:

- addition of more stations
- increase in resistance (especially in strength circuits)
- increase in number of repetitions at each station (depending on the type of circuit)
- increase in number of excursions around the circuit
- inclusion of hybrid exercises (see 7.1) at some stations
- substitution of more demanding stations for the easier stations
- changing the type of muscle contraction (concentric, isometric or eccentric) at each station
- increase in working rate, assessed by heart rate or Rating of Perceived Exertion (Ch 1).

In general, circuits should be increased in duration up to a maximum of about 1 hour for CCT aerobic circuits and increased in resistance for ICT strength circuits (as discussed above). In the case of the latter, increases in resistance necessitate decreases in the number of repetitions and increases in duration of the rest intervals between successive stations. There are essentially two ways of prescribing the training loads to be used in a resistance or circuit training programme:

- a certain percentage of one's 1RM, 6RM or 10RM (Russian system)
- a certain number of kilograms below one's 1RM, 6RM or 10RM (Bulgarian system).

Both systems have their respective merits and deficiencies, although the trainee generally tends to think in terms of actual weights and percentages, so that the second method would appear to be more intuitive and generally easier to calculate mentally.

Both have the disadvantage of being based on testing the trainee with a maximal effort for 1, 6 or more repetitions. Maximal stress testing with treadmills, ergometers, machines or free weights is not generally advisable for the novice. There should be a pre-testing phase to teach the novice the necessary skills of using the test apparatus and of adapting to the specific nature of the new physical stresses in his life. It is preferable to start with very light loads that the trainee can complete without undue strain and to prescribe programmes in terms of adding 5kg, 10kg and so forth to one's starting load. After completion of about three weeks of this pre-testing phase, the trainee may then attempt a 6RM or 10RM. After some three months, it should be safe for the novice to attempt a 1RM, if necessary.

As mentioned earlier, a popular method for increasing the level of aerobic circuits involves prescription of a certain target heart rate as follows:

- 40-50% of maximal recommended heart rate (i.e.: 220 - Age) for beginner circuits
- 50-65% of (220 - Age) for intermediate circuits
- 65-80% of (220 - Age) for advanced circuits.

Another system is sometimes used for selecting the load to be applied in anaerobic circuits. The client first becomes familiar with the exercises by executing them for a few weeks outside the circuit situation before being tested for a 10RM, 5RM or 1RM. He then moves onto the circuit, using loads selected according to the following scheme, which is applicable to the average programme designed to moderately enhance muscle endurance and cardiovascular performance:

- 40-50% of 10RM for beginners
- 40-50% of 5RM for intermediate trainees
- 40-50% of 1RM for advanced trainees.

For elite athletes or strength circuits, as much as 80% of the 1RM may be used.

The use of the above types of exercise prescription guide is valuable, but individual variations should always be taken into account, and after-exercise condition should be monitored regularly (in terms of tiredness, muscle soreness and other factors discussed in 8.4).

Fundamental Circuits

There are endless possibilities for designing each of the different types of cardiovascular, strength, endurance, flexibility and other circuits. This section serves to illustrate just a few of the ways in which circuits may be established for various purposes.

For instance, a single circuit can cater simultaneously for the needs of beginner, intermediate and advanced participants (Fig 5.20). Here the total beginner can work twice through the circuit from A to B; after a week or two, he may go 3 times through this portion of the circuit: and finally, he can increase the number of excursions to as many as 6, depending on the number of stations involved. At the intermediate level, a few more stations may be added, so that participants have to work 3-6 times through the circuit A to C. Similarly, yet further stations may be added to the advanced circuit so that participants have to perform 3-5 excursions through circuit A to D, depending on the total number of stations. Progression may be built into each circuit by increasing load, repetitions, duration and so on.

It is unnecessary to confine circuits to the gymnasium or sports field alone: some stations could be on land around a swimming pool, while other stations could be in the water, involving swimming different strokes, using legs or arms alone, or standing in the water and performing movements against water resistance (Fig 5.21). Combined water-land or *aqualand circuits* are appropriate if the water temperature and cleanliness are acceptable for athletes. Unfortunately, random analyses reveal that the urine content of health centre pools increases rapidly when they are used daily for aquarobics sessions. Regular changing of the pool water then becomes essential.

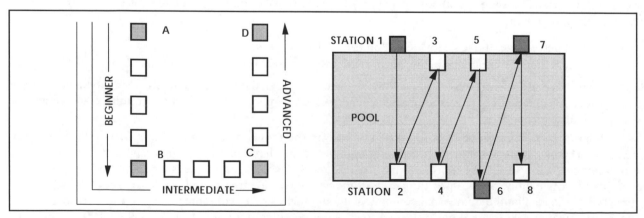

Figure 5.20 A basic multi-level circuit   **Figure 5.21** Basic layout of an aqualand circuit

One of the advantages of exercise in water is that the resistance offered by water increases with the velocity of movement (actually, the square of the velocity). Since the resistance to movement is also directly proportional to the area of the limb pushing against the water, resistance may simply be increased by closing the fingers or wearing paddles on the hands or feet. In addition, the buoyancy furnished by the water minimises the effects of gravity and, consequently, the production of jarring, high impact movements, or the occurrence of accidental falls. Figures 5.21 and 5.22 give the general layout of typical aqualand circuits, while Figure 5.23 gives a specific layout of a typical aqualand circuit.

Land stations may consist of free weights, machines or aerobics exercises, while water stations may comprise different swimming strokes, treading water, jumping, walking, running, various aqua-aerobics movements or synchronised swimming actions. Appropriate music, buzzers or verbal commands (as tape recordings to a musical background) may be used to complete the professionalism of the circuit. It should be remembered that, just as a logical and safe sequence is used for resistance training in a gymnasium, combined aqualand circuits should also follow similar guidelines. Moreover, it is sometimes impractical for athletes to move from water to land stations because it is inadvisable to have water dripping from wet athletes on the floor and onto indoor apparatus.

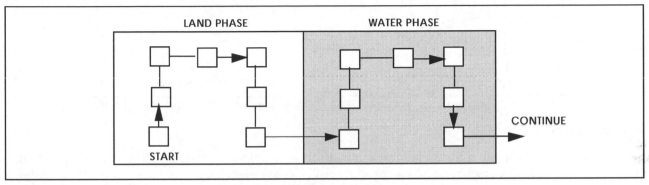

Figure 5. 22 An example of an aqualand circuit with separate land and water phases

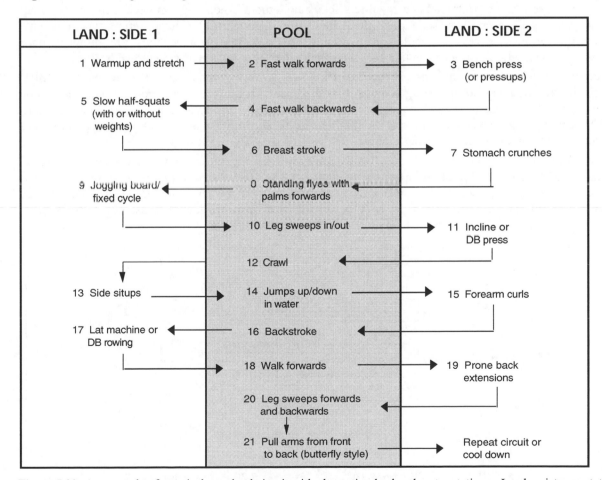

Figure 5.23 An example of a typical aqualand circuit with alternating land and water stations. Land resistance stations may be replaced by free-standing exercises, if desired.

Agility circuits may be constructed by setting up small beacons or cones in specific patterns which constrain participants to execute prescribed skillful manoeuvres such as running, hopping, bounding, turning, running, touching, and ball bouncing (with hand or bat) or kicking (Fig 5.24a, 5.24b). Free exercises such as pushups, free-standing half-squats and situps may be added at each beacon to produce a combined agility-endurance circuit. The layout of beacons and distance between successive beacons is a matter of personal preference and depends on space, training goals and participants.

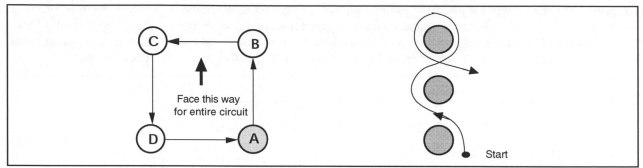

Figure 5.24 (a) Square agility circuit   **Figure 5.24 (b)** Linear zig-zag circuit

Layout of Stations

There are literally thousands of possible circuit layouts, with the number of possibilities increasing with the number of barbells, pulley machines and other resistance devices available in a particular facility. Even without machines, one can devise hundreds of circuit layouts by choosing exercises from physical fitness and aerobics classes. No circuit layout stands out head and shoulders above any others, whether the most expensive machines are included or not. As has been discussed earlier, there are essential guidelines for the selection, type, intensity and duration of the various exercises, depending on the training effects desired. Provided these are followed, there is no reason why a imaginative instructor cannot assemble many interesting, effective and enjoyable circuits .

The effectiveness of any circuit may be enhanced by taking cognizance of the Setchinov phenomenon, which encourages restoration by means of diverting activity performed between exercises. For example, this may entail exercise of upper body muscles alternating with exercise of unfatigued muscles of the legs. In applying this principle to circuit training, upper body stations should then alternately exercise upper and lower body muscles, back and front muscles, or agonistic and antagonistic muscles.

Figures 5.25 to 5.28 give examples of some basic circuit layouts. Aerobic stations such as fixed cycles or skipping (AS1, AS2, . . .) can alternate with resistance stations (RS1, RS2,...), as in Figure 5.25, with the latter alternating between upper and lower body movements. Other circuits, with a focus more on muscle endurance or strength, can begin with an aerobics station, then progress through a succession of resistance stations, also preferably sequenced in accordance with the Setchinov principle.

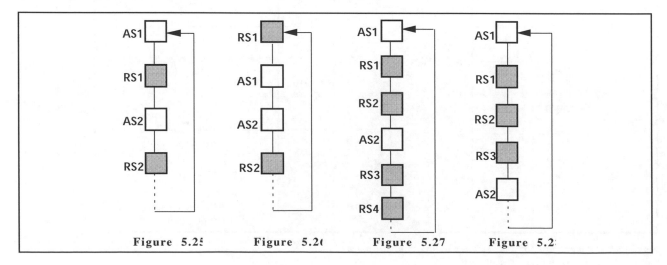

Figure 5.25   **Figure 5.26**   **Figure 5.27**   **Figure 5.28**

Another balanced sequence is depicted in Figure 5.27, in which one aerobic station is followed by two resistance stations, the latter again alternately exercising the upper and lower (or front/back, left/right, etc.) parts of the body. Another layout may have each aerobic station followed by three resistance stations (Fig 5.28); others may include free-standing stations using exercises like pushups, situps or dips between parallel bars - the list is virtually endless.

Systems Classification of Circuits

Most commercial circuits involve a traditional, largely unoriginal linear or circular method of moving through a circuit for a fixed number of sets.

If a systems approach adapted from applied mathematics is applied to circuit training, many variations of any specific layout of stations become possible. The traditional approach requires one to proceed from starting station to terminal station for a certain number of sets, without backtracking, omitting stations or diverting to extra equipment not in the circuit. The more generalised approach includes the possibility of backtracking, omitting stations, altering the sequence of stations, diverting to other equipment, using different speeds of movement or time periods on each station, changing the exercise pattern at each station, and changing the types of muscle contraction at each station.

Classification and design of advanced circuits may best be understood by examining the similarities between supersets and circuits. Suppose we have two exercises A and B: conventional training requires you to complete a specific number of sets of exercise A before proceeding to do the same for exercise B. Supersetting requires you to do set 1 of exercise A, then set 1 of exercise B, set 2 of A, set 2 of B, and so on for the required number of sets. A circuit with two exercises would require the identical procedure. Thus a circuit with two stations is exactly the same as a superset with two exercises (Fig 5.29).

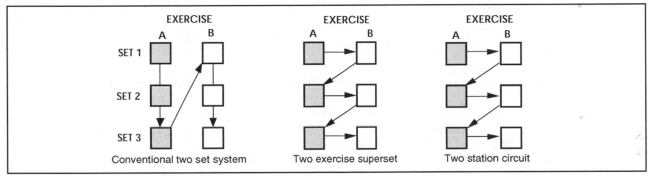

Figure 5.29 Comparison of conventional, superset and circuit training

If one or more exercises are added, the number of possibilities increases. Not only can we have the conventional series of sets and circuits, but we can backtrack by one station for every two stations completed, thereby producing a variation which may be called a retrophase circuit (Fig 5.30). One may backtrack for two or more stations, but the complexity may cause confusion if there is a large group of athletes trying to move efficiently around the circuit. With a smaller number of more advanced clients, many original and challenging retrophase circuits may be offered, thereby diminishing the likelihood of stagnation and boredom.

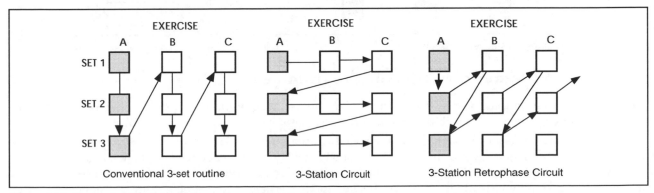

Figure 5.30 Conventional training routine and variations of circuit training

Numerous other variations become possible if one discards the traditional definition of a circuit as a simple clockwise progression of exercises done via a linear arrangement of exercise stations. One may complete two sets at each station before moving to the next station, then backtrack to complete the remaining two sets, and so on to execute the entire circuit (Fig 5.31b). One may also perform a series of discrete supersets within each circuit by supersetting exercises A and B before going on to superset exercises C and D, and so on (Fig 5.31a).

Variations in the arrangement of stations can also enhance their versatility. For instance, a staggered or zig-zag circuit may be arranged to enable clients to progress through portions of a circuit easily without obstructing others doing other portions of the same circuit (Fig 5.32). In the example shown, some clients may execute the inner circuit, while others perform the outer circuit. At other times, more advanced clients may zigzag through the entire circuit. The aerobic stations may even be situated in the middle of the floor as a linear circuit to be entered at any stage by clients executing either the inner or the outer circuit.

Detour circuits may be arranged by directing clients to exit at a particular point to perform a sub-circuit of free weights, aerobic activities, skill activities, flexibility manoeuvres, track running, step climbing, plyometric movements or water exercises set out elsewhere in the training facility (Fig 5.33).

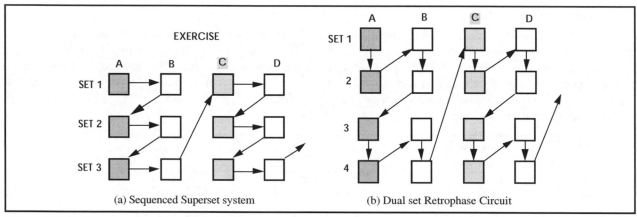

Figure 5.31 Further examples of advanced circuits.

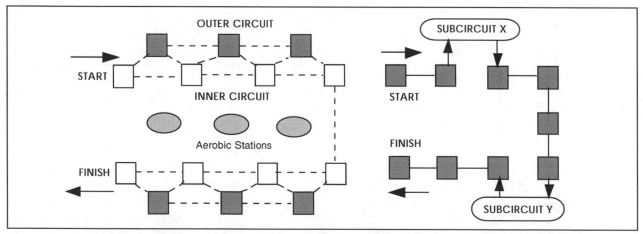

Figure 5.32 An example of a staggered circuit.   Figure 5.33 Example of a typical detour circuit.

Examples of Elementary Circuit Programmes

So far, the general principles of circuit training have been discussed: it might be helpful now to present basic examples of exercise sequences which can be used in the gymnasium by the average client (Table 5.4).

This first sequence is a continuous circuit intended to offer training which focuses largely on cardiovascular fitness and muscle endurance, while the second one may be used as an interval circuit relying on higher resistance with longer rest intervals between stations to emphasize production of strength or muscle endurance. Note that Circuits A and B employ virtually the same resistance exercises arranged so that, in general, the upper and lower body muscles are trained alternately.

Table 5.4 Examples of two basic circuits using essentially the same exercises.

Circuit A	Circuit B
1 Fixed cycle (12 mins)	1 Fixed cycle (4 mins)
2 Standing DB press	2 Standing DB press
3 Jogging on mat	3 Half squats
4 Leg extensions	4 Bench press
5 Fixed cycle	5 Leg curls
6 Bench press	6 Arm curls
7 Jogging on mat	7 Leg extensions
8 Leg curls	8 Upright rowing
9 Arm curls	9 Trunk extensions
10 Fixed cycle	10 Lat pulldowns
11 Upright rowing	11 Situps
12 Situps	
13 Fixed cycle	
14 Lat pulldowns	

Other Circuit Possibilities

One can expand the scope of circuit training by borrowing techniques traditionally used by bodybuilders and weightlifters. For instance, the method of 'burning reps' or 'repetitions to failure' may be incorporated into a circuit, by stipulating that every resistance exercise should be performed not for a prescribed period, but to the point of failure with a certain percentage of one's 1RM, 6RM or 10RM.

The method of pyramiding (Ch 7) may be used to create *pyramid circuits* which would require each resistance exercise to be increased in load (from 40-80% of 1RM) and decreased in the number of repetitions (e.g. from 10 to 4) with each excursion around the circuit.

For schools and other organisations run on smaller budgets, it is possible to organise entire *dumbbell circuits* or *pulley machine circuits*. In conjunction with a few benches, racks and floor mats, these low-cost circuits may be set up indoors or outdoors, on land or in water to offer a more than adequate circuit training facility for those who otherwise would be unable to afford them. This is of particular relevance in the so-called Third World countries whose populations rarely can afford one machine, let alone a series of them at schools or clubs.

All circuits may be executed in a way which significantly enhances muscle endurance and muscular definition by using the *continuous progressive unloading* technique referred to by bodybuilders as 'stripping'. This method requires the trainee to work in a way similar to a routine comprising upward pyramiding followed by downward pyramiding to and from a few repetition maximum (see 7.1).

For example, you would perform a stripping bench press by pyramiding from 10 repetitions with 60kg up to 6 repetitions with 100kg (see 7.1). You then replace the bar on the racks for a moment to enable your training partner to strip off two 5kg weights to decrease the load to 90kg. Without pausing, you continue to failure with this load, replace the bar again while your partner strips the load to 80kg. Once more you continue with this load to failure. Your partner lowers the load to 70kg, and so forth until you have completed the prescribed number of sets. Obviously, the stripping may be done more rapidly if you are using machines with selectable weight stacks or compressed air resistance. You could even execute stripping sets on your own, but the fact that you are working to failure makes it highly advisable that you have a 'spotting' partner nearby.

A 'stripping circuit' means that you move around the circuit by pyramiding upwards to, say, a 6RM or 10RM on each station, then progressively strip the load down so that you can work to failure at each station until you have completed the prescribed number of circuits. Depending on the exercise, you would generally strip off about 10kg each time.

Furthermore, *variable repetition* or *variable interval* sets are possible in a circuit. Here different numbers of repetitions are executed in each set, not only with different loads but also with the same load, or the timing devices are adjusted to change the period spent at each station. If the timing is controlled by computer, it is simple to programme different times for each station, different rest periods and decreasing or increasing times for each excursion around a circuit.

One can even establish an *aerobics class circuit* without the need for fixed stations spread around a gymnasium. The instructor can then structure the class so that each person does a sequence of free-standing exercises or movements using strap-on ankle/wrist weights according to the structure of a circuit such as any one of those depicted in Figures 5.21 to 5.24. Instead of following the traditional approach of doing every exercise to completion for several dozen repetitions, one executes a set sequence of, say, ten exercises for a fixed number of excursions through the circuit. The aerobics class may easily consist of two or three discrete circuits to be performed in the same session, depending on the level of fitness of the participants. In such a case, circuit 1 may be a flexibility circuit; circuit 2 may be a muscle endurance circuit; and the final circuit may be an aerobic circuit.

Concluding Comments

The above information was presented to evaluate the merits and limitations of traditional circuits in order that a far more extensive and useful concept of continuous and interval circuit training could be developed. It by no means exhausts the full repertoire of available theory and practical applications, but it furnishes necessary and sufficient material to enable the instructor to create effective, appropriate, safe and entertaining circuit training programmes.

A final word of advice is probably necessary for the instructor. *The design of any circuit training programme is incomplete if attention is paid to the single session alone.* A long-term plan has to be drawn up in which the type, duration, intensity and complexity of each circuit is changed to facilitate the development of the necessary fitness factors. In particular, the principles of supercompensation and periodisation have to be applied to ensure that progress is optimised and injury is minimised. For example, it would be advisable to ensure that light and heavy circuits alternate, with provision being made for adequate restoration by means of active and passive rest periods or days.

If this type of scientific planning is observed, the instructor should be able to ensure that this extended circuit training system will be of definite benefit to all participants during all stages of their fitness programmes. It should always be remembered that *all forms of circuit training are largely suited to the average non-athlete or competitive athlete during the early preparatory phase of training.* The constant progression in a circuit from one exercise to another without completing all sets with one exercise to a prescribed maximum number of repetitions before moving to the next exercise does not permit one to adequately develop the different types of sport specific strength. Even with interval circuit training on machines, it is not possible to train with the medium heavy, near maximal or explosive loading which is necessary to develop qualities such as muscle hypertrophy, speed-strength, strength-speed, static strength, flexibility-strength, explosive strength and acceleration strength. The length of the interval between successive sets of the same exercise depends on the number of stations in the circuit, so the larger the circuit, the less its ability to significantly develop any of the major sport-specific strength-related qualities.

PROGRAMMING AND ORGANISATION OF TRAINING

6.1 The Development of Training Organisation

The organisation of the training process is fundamental to all highly competitive sports today, being responsible for the exceptional performances produced by modern athletes. The need for proper organisation for physical fitness is not new; it was an essential part of preparation for warfare in many ancient cultures such as China, Greece and Rome, since their ability to survive depended largely on the military capabilities of their armies (see Ch 1). In the formalised sports setting, the Greeks of more than two thousand years ago prepared for the Olympic Games by allocating a preparatory training period of at least 10 months a year.

The organisation of training into phases of different types of exercise done at varying intensity and volume, however, is a much more recent development which gained a great deal of impetus near the beginning of the 20th century when researchers began to probe human physiology and psychology with an enthusiasm which has not yet abated. Scientists such as Pavlov studied how the body adapts to environmental stimuli and the idea of conditioning soon became an integral part of understanding adaptation.

The foundations of modern training organisation and periodisation were laid in the Soviet Union at about the time of the Russian revolution. One of the earliest texts on this subject was written by Kotov (*Olympic Sport*, 1917), who considered it appropriate to divide training into general, preparatory and specific stages. The general stage was aimed at developing the vegetative (cardiovascular-respiratory) and muscular systems, while preparatory training of about two months' duration was devoted to improving strength and muscle endurance. The specific stage was used to prepare the athlete for a given sporting event in two parts: initial and main training, both of about four months' duration, but there was still no overall methodology of periodisation in the form of definite cycles of different types of training.

The preliminary steps towards establishing this methodology appeared a few years later in two books: *Scientific Foundations of Training* by Gorinewsky (1922) and *The Basis of Training* by Birsin (1925). Some of the first practical applications of early periodisation were made in track-and-field by Vsorov (*Basic Principles of Training Athletes*, Moscow, 1938), in skiing by Bergman (*Training programmes and Periods of Training in Skiing*, Moscow, 1938), in gymnastics by Korijakovsky (*Gymnastics*, Moscow, 1938), in boxing by Gradopolov (*Manual of Boxing*, Moscow, 1938) and in water sports by Shuvalov (*Swimming, Waterpolo, Diving*, Moscow, 1940).

In Finland, Pikhala had already published his treatise called *Athletism* (1930), which drew up a series of basic principles, especially the prevention of overtraining by using an undulating rhythm of training which alternates periods of work and rest. Like many other authors at the time, his planning was founded upon the traditional importance of climatic seasons, rather than quantitatively determined phases of loading.

At about the same time, research findings and the practical experience of athletes were assembled by Grantyn in an article 'Contents and General Foundations of Training Preparation' (*Teoriya i Praktika Fizischeskoi Kultury,* Moscow, 1939: 7). In it, he divided the annual training cycle into three periods: preparatory, main and transitional, with the transitional period comprising two stages, namely a gradual detraining to rest, followed by active rest using methods of general physical preparation at reduced intensity. Other sports such as gymnastics and jogging were recommended as suitable for the transition period, thereby already suggesting the role of 'combinational training' as a form of restoration and predating the commercialised idea of 'cross training' by many decades.

The importance of considering the competitive calendar and climatic factors in periodising training was stressed by Ozolin in his important text *Training the Athlete* (Moscow, 1949). In it he also emphasized that active rest should form an integral part of the transition phase to maintain and improve preparedness. This view was supported by the research of Hettinger and Müller in 1955, who found that lowest trainability occurred during the winter months and highest trainability took place in summer and autumn, with a sharp drop in trainability at the onset of winter (Hettinger, 1961). This work suggested that the changes seemed to coincide with changes in the levels of ultraviolet radiation, especially since exposure of athletes to artificial ultraviolet light during the winter eliminated the observed changes in trainability. In fact, the book by Hettinger which quoted these studies (*The Physiology of Strength*), like some of the early work by DeLorme, still remains one of the best pioneering texts on popularised scientific strength training, with the team of Hettinger and Muller undertaking many studies which were often well ahead of their time.

Another useful contribution was made by Letunov, who wrote an article 'Reflections on the Systematic Formulation of Training' (*Sovietsky Sport*, 1950: 125) which strongly criticised the formulation of training regimes on the basis of the competition calendar alone. He felt that the stages of training were a consequence of biological processes, although he failed to appreciate that these processes, in turn, were modified by the training loads.

In England, Dyson was one of the first Westerners to popularise periodisation by using his knowledge of Eastern and Western training methods to write a textbook *A New System of Training* (1946), which delineated a five-phase system of periodisation for athletics:

1. Non-competitive preparation period (5 months) with activities like gym training and cross-country running
2. Pre-competitive period, the beginning of specific preparation (1 month).
3. Initial competitive period (6 weeks).
4. Main competitive period (6 weeks).
5. Post-competitive period (6 weeks).

Ways of Organising Training

The above summary of the emergence of periodisation as a means of organising training may create the impression that periodisation is the only type of organisation or that it is synonymous with the organisation or scheduling of training. This is far from the truth, since there are numerous ways of preparing an athlete for competition and classical methods of periodisation may not necessarily offer the best approach to training organisation. Training for all sport may be carried out in terms of two broad general categories:

- Use of the sport alone to develop fitness for the given sport
- Use of the sport and supplementary activities to develop fitness for the given sport.

In the first case, training uses both the sport as a entire entity and the various aspects of the sport to enhance fitness, such as selected movements and portions of the play. In the latter case, supplementary activities such as resistance training, running and jumping may be used to develop the most important fitness qualities (e.g. speed, speed-strength or muscular endurance) demanded by the sport. Today, the idea of 'cross training' with other sports is also popular for achieving this aim. Most of the supplementary training is usually carried out before the competitive season begins, with intermittent use of such training in small doses to maintain the specific fitness qualities. Both of these categories of training require some or other form of organisation, one of the approaches being to rely strictly on periodisation.

Whichever system of organisation is chosen, *the underlying principle to be applied is that of optimal stress and restoration* (see 1.16). This entails designing a physical training programme which stresses the body in such a way as to cause the appropriate form of supercompensatory adaptation, facilitated by regular use of restorative means to optimise the process and by regular enhancement of motor skills through nervous stimulation. To summarise what was covered in detail in 1.16, each training stimulus acts as a stressor which causes an acute (short-term) and a delayed response. If the stressor is of suitable intensity and duration, the restorative measures are adequate and subsequent stimuli (in the workout, microcycle or mesocycle) are applied at the most advantageous time of the stress recovery curve, then supercompensation and adaptation at a higher level of performance will follow. With special regard to strength training, Hettinger (1961) pointed out the following features of training which stimulate supercompensation. It is interesting to note that, although these points have been modified and extended by more recent research, they still offer useful information for the general strength training world today:

1. Production of adequate muscle tension is central to all muscle training
2. The maximum training benefits are derived by using muscle tension of no less than 40-50% of one's 1RM
3. Maximum training effect does not require prolonging muscle tension to the point of fatigue
4. One single maximal strength effort per day is sufficient to maintain progress

Division of the sporting year into preparatory and competitive phases emerged logically from the experience of coaches and athletes, a distinction which creates *the false impression that no preparation occurs during the competitive phase and no competition occurs during the preparatory phase.* In team sports or track-and-field, the season is often so prolonged that this distinction cannot always be applied with such purity. Competitions may serve as a form of testing, controlled training or specific preparation; moreover, there are regular transition phases between preparatory stages and competitions over a prolonged season.

It can also be misleading to state categorically that there is a generalised training model for each sport. As in all scientific disciplines, several models may be possible, depending on many factors, including the situation, the individual, the variables and the period. Effective modern programming is a science and art which involves creativity, flexibility, individuality and understanding. Contingency plans should also be available to cope with unexpected or unplanned situations such as injury, loss of motivation, premature stagnation, changes in the rules, changes in the competitive roster, and personal trauma.

Implementation of the principle of specificity (see 1.3) is vital to the success of training, with high intensity sport-specific training under competitive circumstances (known as *event-specific training*) during both the preparatory and competition phases being an integral part of the programme. It is inadequate to train conservatively throughout the preparatory stage and the early competitive phase, deliberately avoiding stressful competitive situations in an attempt to produce maximal supercompensation with minimum injury by a specific date. Part of sport specific preparation is training under conditions which simulate those of the actual event so that one can cope efficiently with the demands of competition.

The precise balance between *event-specific*, *sport-specific* and *general training* is determined by the type of sport and the individual. For example, supplementary training (sport-specific and general training) for speed-strength and strength sports should constitute about 50-60% of the total work, whereas in distance endurance events, this type of training should constitute no more than about 20-30% of the work load.

Considerable research and experience has shown that the system of using the sport alone to develop proficiency generally is less effective than the integrated system of sport and supplementary training, although there seem to be notable exceptions in certain sports such as gymnastics. However, this is not necessarily an indictment of the use of strength training in some situations; more often than not it reflects a lack of adequate information and experience in this regard. The main ways in which an adjunct strength training system may be applied are as follows:

- Non-quantitative supplementary training consisting of general preparatory exercises precedes the competitive period, during which predominantly event-specific training is done. No calculations of training intensity or volume are made for prescribing the stages of training, although sports results or 1RMs may be used to modify the programme.

- Non-quantitative supplementary training comprising a general preparatory phase and a special preparatory phase precedes the competitive phase, during which predominantly event-specific training is done. No calculations of training intensity or volume are made for prescribing and monitoring the various stages of training, although sports results or 1RMs may be used to modify the programme.

- Some form of long-term periodisation is applied. Calculations of training intensity and volume are made to ensure that certain performance goals are attained at given stages of the long-term programme.

Before any serious discussion on periodisation begins, it is relevant to deal with the contention by some authorities that this cycled method of training organisation is unnecessary. It is quite true that many athletes have excelled with other methods, but this is not to say that all variants of periodisation need to be dismissed out of hand. On the contrary, some Western research which regards periodisation as a special version of the progressive overload principle is now beginning to corroborate the findings of Russian workers. The alternation of heavy, medium and light days and phases alone would appear to facilitate recovery and adaptation to heavy loading more effectively than the use of monotonic increasing loading from phase to phase. Here, the heavy training days would strongly activate the relevant muscles, while the alternate lower intensity days would minimise the chance of overtraining or impaired restoration (Fry et al, 1994a; Fry et al, 1994b). Other research has shown the importance of periodising variations in training, especially as the latter becomes more demanding (Kraemer & Koziris 1992, Kraemer & Koziris 1994, Häkinnen 1989, Häkinnen & Komi 1986, Häkinnen & Pakarinen 1993a, Häkinnen & Pakarinen 1993b).

6.2 Periodisation as a Form of Organisation

As defined briefly in earlier chapters, the overall long-term cyclic structuring of training and practice to maximise performance to coincide with important competitions is known as *periodisation* (see 1.14, 5.3 and 5.4).

Definitions and Fundamental Concepts

It is interesting to note that at least one Biblical quotation contains in colloquial terms some of the most fundamental concepts of periodisation or cycled training, namely Ecclesiastes 3:

> *"There is a time for everything and a season for every activity under heaven . . .*
> *A time to tear down and a time to build . . .*
> *A time to search and a time to give up . . .*
> *A time to keep and a time to throw away,*
> *A time to tear and a time to mend . . ."*

The periodisation approach organises all training in terms of several basic structural units, namely the training session (the fundamental unit), the training day, the microcycle, the mesocycle, the macrocycle, the Olympic (or quadrennial) cycle and the multi-year cycle.

The *microcycle* refers to a number of training sessions which form a recurrent unit with a period of several days. Its minimum content is two different types of workout. The training day comprises one or more interrelated training sessions, with Bulgarian weightlifters commonly using in excess of 5 sessions per day, six days a week, each session comprising a few key exercises. The *mesocycle* refers to a number of microcycles which serve as a recurring unit over a period of several weeks or months, while a *macrocycle* (which refers to a single competitive season) comprises a number of mesocycles occupying a period of many months. It should be noted that earlier Russian literature, in contravention of the meaning of the prefixes *meso-* (middle) and *macro-* (large), used the term macrocycle to refer to what is now known as a mesocycle and vice versa. Any reader who may concurrently be referring to older Russian material should bear in mind that the above linguistically corrected meanings for the various training cycles are used in this text. The *multi-year plan* usually refers to a period exceeding that of the Olympic cycle.

More quantitatively, the microcycle typically has a duration of about 5-10 days; the mesocycle, a duration of 1-4 months; and the macrocycle, 10-12 months. The term *'large macrocycle'* sometimes is also used and may refer, for instance, to the training period of four years between successive Olympic Games or the several years taken to raise the level of qualification of an athlete from one Class to the next highest. Multi-year planning can include the latter type of macrocycle, but more characteristically, this term refers to the long-term organisation of an athlete's career as a junior or senior competitor or of the athlete's entire competitive lifespan. Three major phases of all training are recognised conventionally: preparation, competition and post-competition.

The contents and characteristics of each cycle are determined by the specific goals or results desired at the end of the cycle concerned. One has to be extremely carefully not to devise training units or programmes which try to develop any motor abilities or types of fitness which interfere with one another, as has been discussed earlier. Sometimes the coach may also attempt to develop too many or all types of fitness required by a given sport, thereby contravening the heterochronicity principle of development of the different motor abilities (see 2.2.3 and later 6.10).

Various *transition phases* are often recognised between each of the major phases, with the post-competition phase often being regarded as the main transition phase, being used mainly for restoration. Some authorities consider that one of the transition phases should be recognised as a *conversion phase* during which specialised training converts maximum strength either into speed-strength or strength-endurance. Although this terminology superficially seems attractive and descriptive, it is scientifically inaccurate, since one type of strength or motor ability cannot change into another, as has been shown by considerable research into the specificity of adaptation. It is more accurate to state that a prior stage of maximal strength training may serve as the *foundation* upon which later training for speed-strength or endurance is based, a sequence which is fundamental to some systems of training, e.g. the conjugate sequence system (see 5.3).

Similarly, different types of microcycle are sometimes identified, such as *ordinary* (the usual scheme of uniformly increasing loading), *introductory* (bringing the athlete up to the competition stage), *restorative* (after heavy loading), *competitive* (immediately before and including the competition), and *shock* or stress (stimulating the athlete out of a state of stagnation) microcycles (Matveyev, 1981). Shock microcycles typically are used if the current programme is not eliciting adequate strength gains. Generally, the microcycle following a shock microcycle is of low intensity, although, some elite athletes may employ two sequential shock microcycles (*a double shock microcycle*). It is inadvisable to use more than 3-4 shock microcycles a year or more than one double shock microcycle a year because of the serious risk of overtraining or injury. It must be stressed that, if any shock cycles are used, the application of formal restoration becomes even more important (Ch 8.6). Using these concepts, typical mesocycles may be constructed logically from these microcycles, as follows:

- ordinary > ordinary > shock > restorative
- ordinary > introductory > competitive > restorative
- shock > ordinary > shock > restorative
- restorative > ordinary > ordinary > restorative.

Mesocycles may also be defined similarly, including *introductory* (beginning the preparatory period), *base* (the main types for increasing specific functional abilities), *control-preparatory* (transitional between base and competitive types), *pre-competitive* (immediate preparation for competition), *competitive,* and *intermediate* (restorative) mesocycles (Matveyev, 1981). The intermediate mesocycles, sometimes further broken down into *restorative-preparatory* and *restorative-maintenance* mesocycles, usually offer systematic active rest to help the athlete recover after heavy loading. Sometimes, the restorative-maintenance mesocycle is simply referred to as a maintenance phase used to stabilise the high level of preparedness achieved during preceding phases. Several experts recognise *large mesocycles,* which comprise a closely integrated system of smaller mesocycles each of which has specific training goals. Later in this text, the concept of *concentrated loading mesocycles* is covered in detail because of its special training potential for advanced athletes.

Each phase of periodisation may be described in terms of sequences of these mesocycles. For example, a preparatory phase for *long-duration endurance sports* may use the following scheme:

- Introductory > base (general preparatory, developing) > base (stabilising) > base (special preparatory, developing) > control-preparatory > base > pre-competitive.

Speed-strength sports may have a preparatory phase structured in various other ways, for example:

- Introductory > base (developing > control-preparatory) > base (with pre-competitive elements).
- Introductory > base (general preparatory) > base (special preparatory) > pre-competitive.

Preparatory Phases of Training

As implied by the above discussion on mesocycles, the preparatory phase may be broken down further into GPP (General Physical Preparation) and SPP (Specialised Physical Preparation). However, it should always be remembered that the GPP and SPP always form an interconnected unit. In some cases, the GPP and SPP may even be concurrent or the GPP may be largely indistinguishable from the SPP (Bondarchuk, 1979).

The GPP is intended to provide balanced physical conditioning in endurance, strength, speed, flexibility and other basic factors of fitness, whereas the SPP concentrates on exercises which are more specific to the particular sport. Characteristically, the GPP may include participation in a variety of different physical activities which provide low intensity, all-round conditioning, with little emphasis on specific sporting skills. Participation in activities such as jogging, swimming, cycling, tennis or volleyball may be appropriate in this phase for some sports. If the player needs to gain muscle or lose excess fat, this is regarded as the appropriate period to do so. Sometimes an *hypertrophy phase* may be included in the GPP if there is a need for gaining functional muscle bulk. The decision to utilise this type of phase should be based on an assessment of the strength deficit discussed previously (Ch 1 and Fig 1.1).

Sometimes it is important to include very specific *SPP-type exercises during the GPP* either to rehabilitate any existing injuries or to eliminate any structural or functional deficiencies or imbalances in physique, posture and neuromuscular skill. It may also be relevant to curtail or eliminate standard types of GPP from the training programme of anyone who is an advanced athlete or has trained regularly for a prolonged period at increasing levels of proficiency. Similarly, the use of GPP-type exercises may be appropriate for brief periods during the SPP to facilitate recovery or prevent stagnation. Moreover, the methods of GPP training are unsuitable for adequately or timeously stimulating improvements in performance among advanced athletes, whose trainability has already waned considerably over years of competition and whose continued growth depends on more specific or demanding methods.

Some transition phases, especially those following the end of a training season, may display many of the characteristics of a typical GPP. However, one should be careful not to allow prolonged GPP type training during any transition phases to diminish the sport specific fitness of the athlete.

According to the more traditional schemes of periodisation, the volume of loading should be high during GPP and its intensity low, then a gradual transition to SPP should occur, during which the exercise volume should decrease and its intensity should increase (Fig 6.1). At the same time, increasing emphasis should be laid on developing the sport specific fitness factors such as speed-strength, flexibility-strength, static endurance and dynamic flexibility, as well as the specific skills required by the particular player. Appropriate variations should be introduced during this phase to ensure progress and motivation.

Further Phases and Principles

Near the beginning of the competitive season, a *stabilisation phase* may be commenced to ensure that the various fitness qualities developed in the off-season are maintained throughout the season. It is important to remember that the average athlete usually has little desire to spend hours in a gymnasium or undertaking 'cross training'. Consequently, it is often recommended that stabilisation training generally needs to occupy a short period before or during practice or preferably twice a week for no more than 30 minutes in a gymnasium, using a limited number of major multi-joint exercises. Some of the basic strengthening and flexibility exercises may be integrated into normal practice sessions, using partners to offer resistance, if necessary.

The *gradual overload principle*, with periodic underloading days or microcycles, is constantly adhered to through all training cycles to ensure that an adequate, but not excessive, training stimulus is imposed on the body. A preliminary recommendation is that individual workouts should generally be alternated in terms of light, medium and heavy loading to guard against overtraining and to ensure optimal training and competitive efficiency. This variation in training load on a daily, microcyclic and mesocyclic basis is essential for avoiding stagnation. In this respect, it is common to observe the well-known empirical *Rule of Sixty Percent,* which states that the training volume of any stage (day or microcycle) with light loading should be approximately 60% of the volume of a stage with heavy (maximal or near-maximal) loading.

Acquisition and Stabilisation of Technical Skills

Even the most meticulous computation and prescription of load intensity, volume and sequencing that optimally develops work capacity is of little consequence to performance if changes in technical mastery are not constantly monitored. Laboratory tests may reveal excellent maximal strength, VO_2 max, muscle endurance, reaction times and so forth, but they simply identify the potential offered by the athlete's work capacity and not functional preparedness, which relies on the mastery of specific motor skills to produce top-level performance.

Thus, it is essential to quantitatively monitor progressive changes in technical skill. One way of doing this is to record the athlete's *reliability of technique* by keeping a record of the percentages of successes experienced in executing the same specific skills during training and competition. Reliability often changes under different conditions, so that it is valuable to keep a record of *competitive reliability* versus *training reliability.* A low competitive reliability relative to training reliability indicates that the athlete probably has difficulty in performing under conditions of high emotional excitement and needs to simulate those conditions during training. The term 'gym lifters' has been applied for many years to lifters who can lift much more in training than on the platform. In this case it is apparent that emotional stress during competition exerts a negative effect, not on the obviously adequate levels of strength or power, but on the technical skills required.

Progression to more difficult skills should not occur until the reliability at the preceding level of complexity or intensity has stabilised at a level of at least 70-80%, where zones of intensity or complexity are formally laid down for each aspect of a given sport. This method is sometimes called the *zone-by-zone mastering of intensity* (Matveyev, 1977). It stresses the importance of:

- eliminating any factors from training which disrupt learning of technique
- the premature introduction of skills for an athlete of a certain qualification
- the ability to master mental control and attitudes towards complex, demanding or fearful tasks

Consequently, it is vital to monitor reliability of technique at all stages of short- and long-term planning and organisation. Sometimes, loss of form is prematurely attributed to overtraining or deficient training, but in many cases, the problem may lie in inadequate attention being paid to the regular monitoring and cyclical variation of skills training. A carefully periodised curve to depict emphasis on technical training cannot be highly prescriptive, since it can fluctuate rapidly, so the prescription of intensity and volume of technical training must guided by two methods:

- *Feedforward method* - the quantitatively planned long-term scheme to coincide with volume and intensity of the general training
- *Feedback method* - the ad hoc daily approach used to modify training at any stage.

6.2.1 Types of Periodisation

The proliferation of Western texts on generalised periodisation has tended to create the impression that there is solely one model of periodisation, which is most usually the well-known variant shown in Figure 6.1, namely the scheme that increases training intensity and decreases volume smoothly as the year progresses (Matveyev, 1964). The aim in this case is to produce maximum intensity shortly before the main competition or series of competitions of the season.

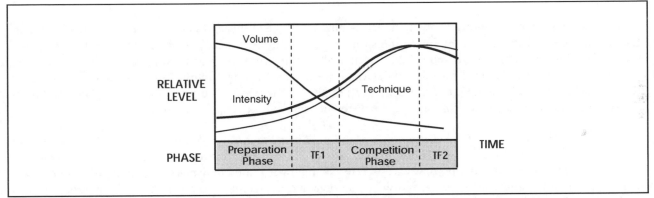

Figure 6.1 Wave-like basic periodisation scheme (Matveyev, 1964). TF1 = first transition phase, during which intensive loading replaces extensive loading. TF2 = second transition phase for restoration after competition (off-season restoration)

It is important to realise that this type of model is suitable for certain sports for less qualified athletes, but it is neither the only periodisation scheme nor the most applicable in all situations. Even if these limitations are accepted, a fairly cursory examination of the above version of the Matveyev model reveals some noteworthy weaknesses and problems in training logic, many of which have more to do with limited Western access to the author's original material than with the model itself. Before unquestioningly applying the modified Matveyev model as it stands, with minimal analysis of the implications of the graphs and their underlying assumptions, it can be very instructional to list some of these:

1. The model makes the important point that volume and intensity of load generally are or should be inversely proportional to one another, but the absence of Matveyev's original text means that other details are not deducible, such as which exercises should be included in the computation of volume and intensity. Moreover, maintenance of volume at a certain fixed value while the intensity is increased does not necessarily lead to overtraining or injury - on the contrary, Medvedev (1986) has found that this can provide one of the most favourable ways of enhancing performance once the athlete has attained a certain level of performance.

2. The smooth undulating shape of the graphs indicates an unpunctuated, subtle merging of all training sessions and stages with one another, which generally is highly suitable for novices, but requires modification to suit the individual cases of more advanced athletes.

3. This general model appears to imply that all of the means of training (e.g. running, weight training and muscle endurance regimes) may be described by this set of three graphs. Even though its proponents may make it clear that this model applies simply to the strength training component of the overall programme, it is unrealistic to assume that any one component of a programme functions in isolation of all the others. For example, if a middle distance runner is concurrently doing running training and weight training, the stress imposed by demanding distance work or sprints can seriously impair one's capabilities in many strength exercises.

4. Initially high volumes of training, even at low intensity, may not necessarily be the most efficient way of introducing a novice to a training programme, because this is also likely to cause post-exercise soreness, impaired adaptation and reduced motivation.

5. The graphs give no information on the content or components of the loading, such as the specific involvement of the different fitness qualities such as strength, cardiovascular endurance, speed-strength and strength-endurance. The conjugate sequence model proposed by Verkhoshansky discussed later addresses the sequential overlapping and management of such components.

6. The graphs tell us nothing about the possible influence of the order of exercises and their interaction. They suggest that the effects of a given volume and intensity at any given time are independent of the structure and content of the training session.

7. The graphs imply that the athlete is preparing to attain peak performance only once in the season. This is rarely the case, especially in team sports or some individual tournaments (as in tennis, track & field and cycling tours) which may require production of the highest level of performance in possibly several events within several days or weeks.

8. The gradual increase in emphasis on technical training implies that this aspect of training is far less important in the early stages of training. A minimal time spent initially with novices to a given programme, followed by a gradually increasing emphasis on much more technical training runs counter to what is needed in practice. Beginners characteristically need far more emphasis on technical training and elite athletes far less. Later, we will see that Bondarchuk points out that skill and strength training need to be integrated, partly because higher levels of performance and greater stresses require different technical skills in many cases.

Even Matveyev (1964) himself discussed some of the limitations and scope of his model, details of which are essential to read if one wishes to appreciate the nuances of his scheme (Matveyev, 1981). In his textbook, for instance, he quotes a periodised plan that was used by the renowned middle distance runner, Jim Ryun, to show how this remarkable athlete planned the individual aerobic and non-aerobic components of the microcycles and mesocycles which lead to achieving several world records in the same period (Fig 6.2).

The value of this example is that it partially answers some of the issues raised above, but Matveyev's accompanying commentary on the Ryun programme also emphasizes the importance of what he calls an *intermediate mesocycle*. In doing so, he states that it is similar to or even a special type of transition cycle, though he considers that it is not at all transitional in nature, but very important as a special mesocycle in its own right, since it plays a vital role in between a series of demanding competitions. As such, the intermediate mesocycle goes further than being a mere maintenance phase, by also providing relative unloading and restoration in the form of specific active rest and even stimulating further development of some fitness qualities.

He adds that monotonous, highly deterministic routines are not advisable during these transition phases, but should not be rigidly organised around the same gym or sports field settings. They should allow the athlete wide freedom of personal choice of activities and encourage a positive emotional atmosphere. He even mentions the possible application of GPP (General Physical Preparation) methods during these and other cycles which many coaches think are rigidly fixed under standardised names like GPP, SPP, competitive phase, maintenance phase, hypertrophy phase and so forth.

Matveyev, in addressing other issues concerning so-called transition mesocycles, posed the intriguing question: "Why not retain sporting form permanently as a state which is optimal for the athlete?" This would obviate the need for detraining after a competitive phase or including transition phases which are commonly part of the 'off-season' in the West. In asking this question, he is clearly re-examining the entire rationale behind his model, thereby suggesting that one must be very circumspect before taking any training model at face value.

He answers his own question by stating that retention of the same sporting form ignores the fact that the same training stressors which contribute positively to an athlete's fitness over a certain period can become negative stressors if used for too long, since adaptation is a characteristic of all life and variety ensures growth. Moreover, the sporting form needed for reaching another level of performance requires further different adaptive reconstruction of all systems of the body, since sporting form which may be optimal for a given stage of performance is not optimal for the next stage of performance. Thus, he is clearly pointing out the need for regular updating of any periodisation or organisational training model or even changing to another one which may differ radically from that of a previous stage in an athlete's career.

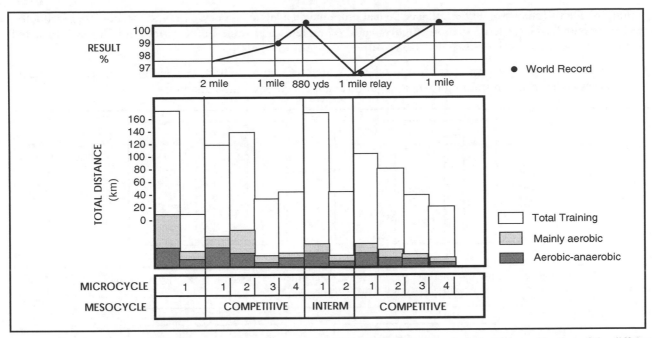

Figure 6.2 An example of a series of competitive mesocycles in middle-distance running, depicting the combination of the different types of training used by Jim Ryun to achieve several world track records in the same season. Also shown is an intermediate restoration-preparatory mesocycle (based on Matveyev, 1978).

Despite any apparent weaknesses revealed by the above analysis of the modified Matveyev model, it served the invaluable purpose of creating a greater awareness of the many aspects and complexities of the long-term training process, especially when viewed in the light of Matveyev's own observations, which are very rarely noted in the West. This immediately leads us to appreciate that there is not simply one grand unified model of periodisation, but several broad periodisation schemes, each with its own variations for different sports and different levels of athlete qualification, including the following:

1. *Smooth wave-like variations of the load over definite phases* (Matveyev, 1977; Ozolin, 1970; Sholikh, 1966). Research indicates that the load volume during the competitive phase should be about 10-15% lower than the maximum that is reached during the preparatory phase, as illustrated in Figure 6.1 (Matveyev, 1964).

2. *Discontinuous step-like alternation of loads of different intensity* (light, medium, heavy) over the short term and long term. This may be applied in a monotonic increasing fashion (such as 75-75%, 85-85%, 90-90%, 100-100%, 105-105%), where each of these percentages refers to percentage of 1RM, or in fluctuating fashion (e.g. 85-85%, 90-90%, 100-100%, 95-95%. . .). At the short-term level, the training load is varied sharply from session to session, and in the weekly and monthly cycles (see Figs 6.2-6.6). Its success has been corroborated by the research of several workers (Yakovlev, 1971; Grokin, 1951; Vorobyev, 1972; Ermakov, 1974). This method is described in detail in Vorobyev's *Textbook on Weightlifting* (1978).

3. *Equal distribution of training loads comprising strength and technical skills* work (Komarova, 1984). This form of loading, applied during the preparatory and competitive phases, was successfully used in preparing the Soviet track-and-field team for the 1980 Olympics (Bondarchuk, 1976, 1979). In one variant, large volume technique training is executed during the preparatory phase, with greater volume of strength work taking place near the end of the preparatory phase and at the beginning of the competitive phase. The development of skill enables the athlete to utilise the increasing strength, which is the reason why technical skills training is necessary in the preparatory phase. Increase in strength without concurrent improvement in sport-specific skills training is considered inefficient.

4. *Asymmetric pyramid-like variation* of loading (e.g. Reding, 1971). Here the load increases and decreases in pyramid fashion, displaying an overall upward trend over time. For example: 80-90-95-100-95-90-100-105% , etc.

5. *The wave-like concentration of loading* with a given primary emphasis for about 5-8 weeks at a time (Verkhoshansky, 1978, 1979). Each concentrated load with one emphasis acts as the foundation for the next

load with a different primary emphasis, so that pronounced adaptation occurs in time for major competitions. This method is intended for more highly qualified athletes and must be prescribed intelligently to avoid overtraining during any given phase (see 6.10).

6. *The pendulum approach* (of Arosiev and others), which uses smooth, uniform, rhythmical alternation of the different components of training (e.g. strength, strength-speed, strength-endurance).

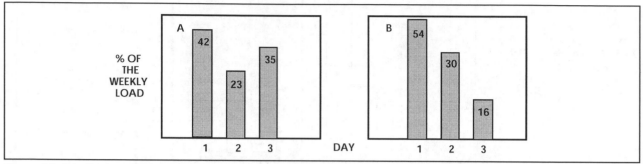

Figure 6.2 Distribution of the daily training load for a qualified weightlifter over a week. A = Scheme for the average week a few months before competitions. B = Scheme for the week directly before a contest.

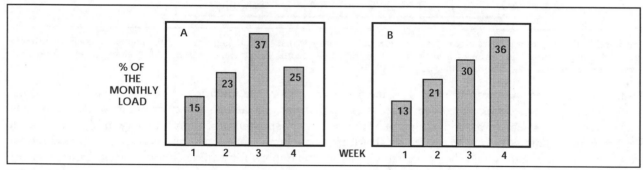

Figure 6.3 The distribution of weekly training volumes over a month for weightlifting. A = Scheme for highly qualified lifter in the month before a contest. B = Scheme if the previous month volume of loading was high (Vorobyev, 1978).

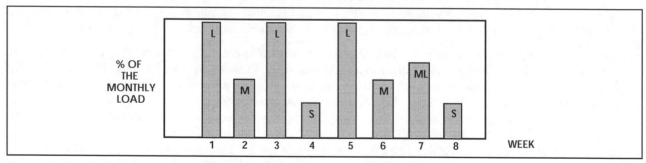

Figure 6.4 The distribution of weekly training volumes over two months for qualified weightlifters. This scheme has been shown to be more effective than traditional schemes which gradually increase, then decrease the loading volume (Ermakov, 1974).

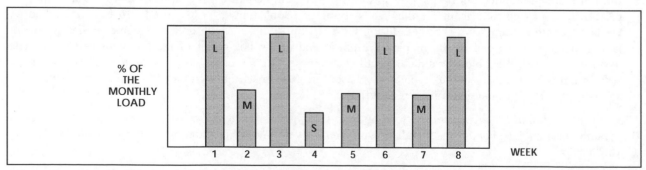

Figure 6.5 The distribution of weekly training volumes over two months for elite weightlifters. This scheme has been shown to be more effective than that of Figure 6.3, since world-class competitors can tolerate significantly larger loads (Vorobyev, 1978).

The largest emphasis of this chapter will be on system 4, since the other more familiar systems have been discussed in depth in the references cited in each case.

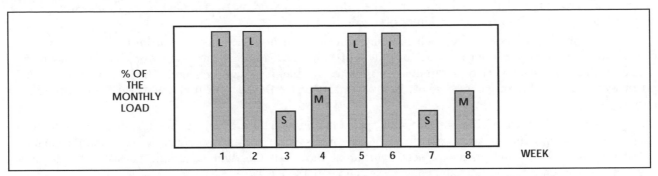

Figure 6.6 The distribution of weekly training volumes over two months for well trained weightlifters who can tolerate two successive weeks of heavy loading (Vorobyev, 1978).

6.2.2 Calculation of the Parameters of Periodisation

The effective prescription and organisation of training depends on calculating the most important parameters of loading. Conventionally, the most frequently computed parameters are the volume and intensity of the load, where volume is intended to provide some measure of the total work done over a given period and intensity is a measure of the average force exerted. The precise methods of physics are not applied, because of their greater complexity for the average coach or competitor; instead, approximate measures which correlate closely with the physically computed values are used.

Thus, *volume* of any exercise is calculated (in kilograms) by multiplying the weight lifted by the number of repetitions at that weight. The total volume for a workout is the sum of the volumes calculated for all the major exercises. Some authorities (Chernyak, 1978) stipulate that only weights of greater than 40% of 1RM should be taken into account when performing these calculations, since the strengthening effects of lighter weights than this is minimal.

Often, the quantity of lifts is calculated by adding together the total number of lifts done. The intensity of a given exercise is calculated by dividing the volume of that exercise by the number of repetitions executed for that exercise. The *intensity* of a workout is the total volume of all the major exercises divided by the total number of lifts in the workout, i.e. it is the average weight lifted in a given workout or period. Generally, except for beginners, warmup sets with loads of less than about 70% of 1RM are not included in the calculations. The following example shows how these parameters are calculated for Exercise A done for four sets (the first figure is the load; the second figure, the number of repetitions):

Exercise A: 60kg x 10, 80kg x 8, 100kg x 4, 110kg x 2   Maximum (1RM) = 120kg

The first set with 60kg (i.e. 50% of 1RM) is ignored, since it constitutes a warmup. Thus:

Volume V_A = 640 + 400 + 220 = 1260kg   Total reps R_A = 14
Intensity I_A = V_A / R_A = 1260/14 = 90kg

This intensity may be expressed as a percentage of the 1RM to yield the *relative intensity*, which is usually more meaningful. In this case, we obtain:

Relative intensity I_{rel} = (90/120) x 100 = 75%

This same procedure may be followed for an entire workout comprising several different exercises. However, the use of overall averages can be very misleading in prescribing training, since they give no indication of the range of loads used. For instance, the relative intensity of the four sets of Exercise A (75%) is below what may be classed as a heavy workout, even though the heaviest load used was 110kg (92% of 1RM). The same relative intensity could be achieved by executing 3 identical sets each with 75kg for 3 repetitions. Obviously this would be far less demanding than the former regime. Thus, the overall demands of training must always be examined simultaneously in terms of intensity and volume.

For the same reason, it is preferable to determine the distribution of loading in different intensity zones. In strength sports, nine intensity zones are usually defined, although it is adequate to use the following five zones: 50%+ (50-59%), 60%+ (between 60-69%), 70%+ (70-79%), 80%+ (80-89%), 90%+ (90-100%).   The number of lifts (or percentage of the total number of the lifts in each workout) performed in each intensity zone is recorded, together with the volume and intensity, as defined above.

The distribution of volume in each intensity zone may also be depicted in the form of a histogram or distribution graph to give a clear visual overview of how the loading is imposed. For example, Figure 6.7 illustrates the three basic types of distribution of volume over the five intensity zones. The normal distribution is given by A, a distribution skewed towards lower intensity by B and a distribution skewed towards higher intensity by C.

The above approach enables one to construct a far more informative training log than the usual card consisting of a simple list of exercises, the weight, repetitions and sets. The training diary is organised so that the left hand page records the exercises, sets, repetitions and load; the right hand side consists of a table of calculations derived from the left hand page (see example in Table 6.1).

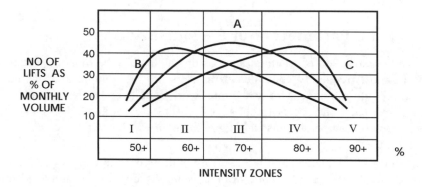

Figure 6.7 The distribution of monthly volume into different intensity zones (based on Matveyev, 1977).

If a specific volume, average intensity and distribution of loads in the different intensity zones are required, they are filled in here and used to adjust the training regime accordingly. If the athlete misses an attempt, but only by a small margin, the attempt is included in the calculations; e.g. if a weightlifter manages to raise a snatch or jerk above the head, but fails to complete the lift, then the attempt is counted. The mistake should not be made of assuming that higher intensities (mean loads) or a greater number of lifts in the higher intensity zones will produce superior results. At any given time, there is an optimal load and load distribution for athletes of different bodymass and level of qualification, as well as individual responses to different loading regimes. It is vital that the volume, intensity and distribution of volume in each intensity zone is recorded at the level of the individual session, the week or microcycle, the month, the mesocycle and the macrocycle.

Table 6.1 Example of the recording of loading parameters in a training programme. Vol = volume of each lift, NL = number of lifts, Iav = average weight, Irel = relative average weight = 100.Iav / 1RM. The number of lifts (or their percentage of the total workout volume for each row) is inserted in each column from I to V.

INTENSITY ZONE

EXERCISE	I	II	III	IV	V	CALCULATIONS				
	60%-	60%+	70%+	80%+	90%+	Vol	NL	Iav	1RM	Irel
Exercise A										
Exercise B										
Exercise C										
Total Lifts										
Total Lifts (%)										

There are three alternative ways of writing up the lifts in the exercise chart itself, namely:

• *Exercise A* : 60 x 10, 70 x 8, 80 x 6, 80 x 6

- *Exercise A* : $10(60)^1$, $8(70)^1$, $6(80)^2$
- *Exercise A* : $\dfrac{60}{10}.1, \dfrac{70}{8}.1, \dfrac{80}{6}.2$

Hybrid exercises, which consist of several different movements within the same exercise (see 7.1), are best expressed in terms of the last-mentioned format. For example, if a single exercise with 100kg consists of a power clean (for 2 reps), a front squat (3 reps) and a push press (1 rep), it would be written as follows:

Exercise B: $\dfrac{100}{2+3+1}$

The volume in this case is : (100) x (2+3+1) = 100 x 6 = 600kg

If a weight of 100kg is cleaned 3 times and jerked once, it is recorded thus: C&J : $\dfrac{100}{3+1}$

If the same weight is cleaned once and jerked 3 times, it is recorded thus: C&J : $\dfrac{100}{1+3}$

If a quantitative record of technical training is to be kept for weightlifters or powerlifters, then the calculations for the competition lifts and the supplementary lifts are separated. If some exercises are performed without weights, they are still recorded in a similar way. For instance, if jumps are done as part of explosive training, the height (or length) of the jumps and their number of repetitions is written down in a special section of the training log.

It should be noted that some coaching scientists, such as Medvedev (1989), who often prefer to record volume in terms of number of lifts (NL), because of ease of calculation and the lack of necessity to compute average loads (in which a few sets of lighter loads can swamp the effect of a small number of maximal efforts). They consider that programmes expressed in terms of number of lifts with a given load or number of lifts in certain intensity zones (% of 1RM) give perfectly adequate information for devising any training regimes.

With respect to training intensity, it is interesting to examine the recommendations made for Olympic weightlifters, based on research and experience with Russian lifters (Vorobyev, 1985). There is an optimal mean training weight in each bodymass division for each level of qualification (Table 6.2). Obviously, as human strength increases with time, so these recommended intensities will also increase; the necessary adjustments may be made by using the formula presented in Section 3.3.9. Although this table does not reflect the distribution of loading over the different intensity zones, it furnishes upper limits of the mean intensity which the speed-strength athlete should not exceed over any cycle of training.

Special recommendations for training loads have also been made for junior lifters, based on Dvorkin's research (1980) using the maximum and recovery heart rate method described later. Thus, the fundamental training weights for 13-14 year olds are considered to be 50-70%, 60-90% for 15-16 year olds and 80-90% for 17-20 year olds, the most suitable value depending on individual responses to the loading (Medvedev, 1986).

Table 6.2 Mean training load (intensity) in kg for Olympic weightlifters of different levels of qualification. CMS = Candidate for Master of Sport, MS = Master of Sport.

BMass (kg)	Class III	Class II	Class I	CMS	MS
52	51.0	63.5	70.0	78.0	80.0
56	57.0	73.4	81.0	89.0	90.0
60	61.0	76.5	85.5	95.0	96.0
67.5	66.0	85.0	93.0	103.0	107.0
75	70.0	92.0	99.0	111.0	116.0
82.5	75.0	94.0	105.0	115.0	118.0
90	78.0	98.0	110.0	119.0	127.0
100	82.0	101.0	113.0	125.0	132.0
110	83.0	105.0	118.0	127.0	139.0
+110	86.0	109.0	120.0	130.0	147.0

Drawing up the Periodisation Scheme

Conventionally, drawing up any periodisation scheme involves the filling in of a series of arrays (or spreadsheets) and graphs of all the contents and quantities of the training means and methods in the successive microcycles, mesocycle and macrocycles.

Since computations are based on the percentages of a 1RM (Russian approach) or number of kilograms above or below one's 1RM (Bulgarian approach), one of the important early steps is the determination of one's 1RM. Since it is usually excessively demanding on a complete novice to strength training to be subjected to 1RM efforts at the beginning of any training cycle, it is preferable to regard the first few weeks as a pre-testing, initial transitional phase of adaptation to the process of resistance methods. If some estimate of one's 1RM is required, then it is more rational to obtain such an estimation from one's 5RM or 6RM, using extrapolation tables or graphs such as those given earlier (Ch 1.3).

Once this 1RM has been determined, it is most usual to plan the training programme from the overall macrocyclic or annual picture, using a type of graphic overview such as the fundamental one depicted in the Matveyev model (Fig 6.1). To do this, the foundation for the entire training program may be expressed in the form of a divided horizontal bar graph showing all major phases involved in the annual macrocycle (Fig 6.8). Here, the introductory phase is a transition phase which comprises activity which familiarises the athlete with the exercises and prepares the body for any physical testing which may be necessary.

INTRODUCTORY PHASE	GENERAL PHYSICAL PREPARATION	TP	SPECIAL PHYSICAL PREPARATION	TP	COMPETITIVE PHASE	TP

Figure 6.8 Overall view of a typical macrocycle, showing commonly used phases. The lengths of each phase do not represent the relative durations of each, but merely indicate a sequence. TP = Transition Phases

This divided bar graph is used now to produce a sort of graphic calendar, which then acts as the foundation for computation of the various sub-phases and components of training, right down to the level of the microcycle (commonly a week long) and the individual session (Fig 6.9). Once the major and other competitions are filled in, you work backwards from each one of them to identify the most appropriate mesocycles and sketch in the approximate graphs with the desired trends in intensity and volume. Then, after the actual computations have been made at the more detailed sub-levels, the exact graphs are drawn in.

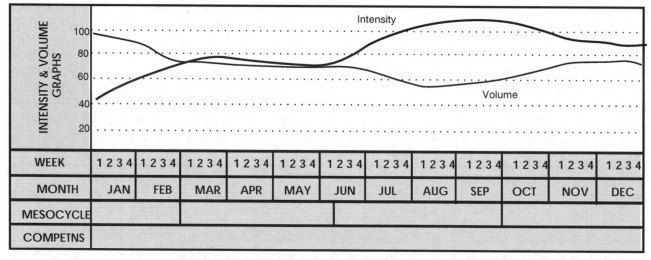

Figure 6.9 Macrocyclic plan, showing the various sub-cycles and sample graphs. Note that the graphs depicted are entirely hypothetical and do not relate to any specific training programme; moreover, curves of other training parameters may be added.

Sometimes, the relative levels of all of the different types of training may be included in the form of vertical bars, as was done in Figure 6.2 in summarising the training programme used by Ryun, resulting in the scheme shown below (Fig 6.10). It is unnecessary to depict all the information shown in this diagram; the final form is determined by one's individual needs and preferences, with certain features either being excluded or included.

Using this long-term plan, we now draw up a mesocyclic plan of all the different components of training, including strength training, sport specific training and any other additional training means (Table 6.3). This process is repeated for all of the successive mesocycles that were devised for the annual macrocycle, according to the above scheme. This table is then used as an organisational guide for working out exactly what the content, volume, intensity, duration and structure are for each different training means at the level of the microcycle and individual workout.

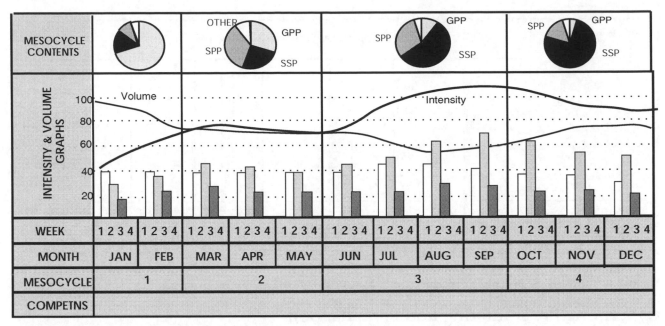

Figure 6.10 Macrocyclic plan, showing the various sub-cycles and sample graphs. The shaded bars depict components of training, such as strength, speed and cardiovascular endurance, while the pie charts show how the contents of each mesocycle (SSP = Special Sports Preparation). Note that the graphs depicted are entirely hypothetical and do not relate to any specific training programme.

Table 6.3 Mesocyclic plan of the training content (here only a portion of the plan is shown for the purposes of illustration)

TRAINING MEANS	M	T	W	T	F	S	S	M	T	W	T	F	S	S	M	T	W	T	F	S	S	M
Strength Training	•		•		•			•		•					•		•		•			•
Running (middle)																						
Running (Fartlek)				•		•					•		•			•						
Running (sprints)	•							•													•	
Sport								•		•		•					•	•				
Plyometrics						•					•					•						
Swimming			•					•							•				•	•		•
Recreational		•			•		•					•					•		•			
Other																						

The next step involves the drawing up of the appropriate volumes and intensities of the microcycle plan, which most usually lasts for a week and comprises several or no training sessions per day, depending on the specific needs of the athlete, the sport and the phase (Fig 6.11). Although many plans do not always include a specific row to indicate the presence of restoration or rest periods, as discussed in more detail in Chapter 8, it is important to remember that properly prescribed restoration sessions are an essential part of any training regime.

Finally, the details of the individual training sessions are devised for all the training means used in the athlete's preparation. In the case of the strength training component, the suitable loads, sets and repetitions are filled into an intensity zone table like the one depicted in Table 6.1 or into a simpler one which dispenses with the use of such zones and simply records the loads, sets and repetitions (as in Table 6.4, with or without the columns for the various ratings and loading calculations).

In devising any periodisation plans, it is important to note that these still remain guidelines, not scientific computations that will ensure a precisely predetermined outcome. It is also relevant to appreciate that any training programme may comprise several workouts per day. In fact, the subdivision of any daily routine into a series of interrelated *training modules* comprising only a very few exercises at a time can be a highly effective way of optimising adaptation, since this can enable one to work at a higher intensity with more adequate restoration. This modular approach can be extremely effective for both aerobic and anaerobic types of sport.

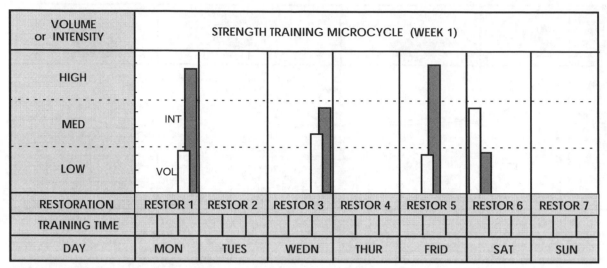

Figure 6.11 Microcyclic plan, showing the intensity and volume for the different daily training sessions

Cybernetic Programming and Periodisation

The use of numerical computations as the sole descriptor of loading often overlooks the fact that apparently objective measures like this do not take into account the athlete's *subjective perception of the intensity and overall effects of the loading*. This issue was of great concern to Bulgarian weightlifting and led to implementation of their successful training method, which required athletes always to train at a perceived maximum load. Consequently, it can be very helpful to add another column (RPE or Rating of Perceived Effort) in which you assign a value to your perception of how strenuous a particular exercise, set or session feels, using a scale as coarse as a three-point one from 1 to 3 (light, medium, heavy), as fine tuned as an extended scale from 1-10 (where 10 is maximum) or as the most popular scale from 1 to 5. You do not record an RPE for every repetition or exercise, but note it mentally in each set and use it to guide you in your next set. At the end of the workout, you then record only the RPE for the heaviest or most demanding sets which you executed in the major exercises.

Alongside the numerical calculations for the same set, this method enables one to deduce a more accurate picture of the training schedule on a short and long term basis (Table 6.4). After all, the athlete responds to any exercise in terms of how the load feels at any given moment or period, rather than mechanically according to some numerical computation. In applying this RPE of the loading, it is advisable that it usually be used to identify any decrease rather than an increase in actual load.

Table 6.4 Training programme for one session, showing Rating of Perceived Exertion (RPE) and Rating of Technique (RT). The calculations column may include computations such as number of Lifts (NL), Volume (V) and other factors given in Table 6.1

	SET 1 (loadx reps)	SET 2 (loadx reps)	SET 3 (loadx reps)	SET N (loadx reps)	RPE	RT	CALCULATIONS V	NL
Exercise A								
Exercise B								
Exercise C								
Exercise D								

For long-term assessment of the effectiveness of the training program, it can be very helpful to plot graphically on the same set of axes the calculations of intensities, volumes, actual training performances and RPEs over an extended period. As discussed earlier under the heading 'Acquisition and Stabilisation of Technical Skills', it is often pertinent to include a rating of the athlete's reliability of technique for the most important exercises, by having a coach award points for the most demanding efforts on a *Rating of Technique* scale (Table 6.4). If greater validity of technical analysis is required, then it can be very helpful to use a video recorder regularly.

Over-reliance on numerical computations in preparing a periodisation chart is a major reason why some coaches tend to dismiss their relevance; hence the value of using this combined objective-subjective system.

This modified form of periodisation may be known as *cybernetic periodisation,* since the original preplanned periodisation scheme is regularly modified by subjective and objective feedback obtained from the lifter's current performance state. The term *cybernetic* was coined from the Greek 'kybernetes' (steersman) by the renowned scientist, Norbert Wiener, to describe the new science of control and communication which he founded (Wiener, 1948). In his new science, the role of feedback from the output of any system was used to modify dynamically and regularly the input to the system. Traditional periodisation can often prove to be as limited as non-periodised training, since all loading is based upon a fixed original input; hence the value of introducing a method of enhancing overall control and efficiency of performance (or, output).

In essence, cybernetic programming or periodisation is a quantified extension of what may be termed intuitive training, an approach which probably is as old as the history of physical training. Although the Bulgarians did not write down specific RPEs, they relied heavily on how the heaviest lifts felt to them in a given set and used that perception to guide them in their choice of loading for the next repetition or set. For instance, if the maximum lift attempted felt very demanding, the lifter might decrease the load by 10kg and perform a few sets of no more than 2 repetitions with it, and then follow this with an increase of 5kg for another few single attempts at this weight. They termed this type of training, the *method of maximum effort,* though they could not claim any originality for this concept, since it has been used by individual lifters in many countries since the beginning of the 20th century.

Another problem is inherent in the use of calculations in all periodisation schemes, since it is not always clear whether or not one should calculate intensities and volumes for every exercise, especially those which involve smaller muscle groups. Generally, one excludes the effect of these apparently minor exercises, but it may be necessary to carry them out periodically in case they may help explain why an apparently well-planned schedule is not producing the results that it should. For example, exclusion of exercises such as calf-raises, elbow curls or lat pulldowns from the calculations might disguise the fact that they are fatiguing some muscle groups that are vital to the powerful execution of the major exercises. For this reason, it is valuable to avoid the random placement of such supplementary exercises before the major exercises or technical lifts.

It is also relevant to take into account the effect of any heavy loading imposed by the athlete's normal daily job by applying an RPE and Rating of Technique at strategic points in the workout to modify any exercise, its load or volume, wherever necessary. This issue can be most significant in the case of heavy manual labourers.

Training Intensity, Heart Rate and Other Tests

It can sometimes also be useful to monitor acute and chronic changes in heart rate associated with training. If the heart rate increases noticeably prior to the heavier or heaviest training loads in any session, it indicates the presence of significant levels of emotional arousal and a more demanding level of training intensity, even though the periodisation computations might indicate otherwise. The use of heart rate solely as an indicator of identifying or prescribing cardiovascular training in certain target heart rate zones and so forth understates its value in assessing other changes of state. Measurement of heart rate immediately before an exercise, directly afterwards and at 1 minutes intervals for 4 minutes (recovery heart rate) after an exercise can yield useful information on how strenuous the exercise is at that point, how emotionally aroused the athlete is and what her level of preparedness is during that workout. However, in the case of resistance training, because of the effects such as local muscle ischaemia during intense muscle contraction, it is preferable to avoid the standard methods of assessing cardiac recovery rates on a treadmill or similar cardiovascular devices and to measure these recovery heart rates after more specific lifting exercises such as repetition squats, cleans and bench press.

For instance, the squat has been used by Russian scientists to monitor the work capacity of Olympic weightlifters (Novik et al, 1980). Based on their studies, they recommended applying their test as follows: At the beginning of a training cycle (when first beginning training, preparing for competition etc.), the lifter determines his 1RM squat. Then, with 85-90% of this 1RM, the lifter performs one set of 3 repetitions of squats, immediately after which his heart rate is measured for a period lasting one minute. This process is continued throughout the training cycle to provide ongoing information on the lifter's work capacity. If the immediate post-squatting and the post-one minute heart rates decrease, then work capacity has increased and loading may be increased. Chapter 8.7 also contains important tests of cardiovascular function in strength athletes.

Another test computes the adapted PWC-170 (*Physical Work Capacity*, 170 beats per minute heart rate) test. This test is common in the world of cardiovascular performance, but Russian research enables one to produce a version which may be applied to weight training situations (Karpman et al, 1982; Dvorkin, 1988). Although this test may be administered according to other protocols, one popular version requires the athlete to be tested with his 10RM load for a given exercise. He then rests for about 5 minutes, then performs 5 repetitions with this load, immediately after which his heart rate is measured. He rests for another 5 minutes, then repeats the same lift for 8-10 repetitions. His post-exercise heart rate is measured again and his PWC-170 is computed from the following equation, where it should be noted that the squat is far more commonly used than the other lifts:

$$\text{PWC-170} = N_1 + (N_2 - N_1).(170 - F_1) / (F_2 - F_1)$$

where: F_1 = heart rate immediately after R_1 repetitions with weight W (in kg)

and: F_2 = heart rate immediately after R_2 repetitions with weight W (in kg)

Work done in 1st effort N_1 = (9.8) W. R_1.(D)

Work done in 2nd effort N_2 = (9.8) W. R_2.(D)

where D is the distance (in metres) through which the load is moved by the lifter. Its magnitude is given below as a fraction of the height of the lifter (Table 6.5). This distance in the Olympic lifts generally decreases with the level of proficiency of the lifter, but it does not differ by more than a small percentage from the mean values given here, so that the latter may be used to a most acceptable degree of accuracy for general testing. What is of more concern is that this version of the PWC protocol computes only the concentric muscle work for all lifts. So, for greater validity, the contribution of any eccentric muscle action in each case has been estimated to add 70% more work in each case where there is significant eccentric action and this value has been added to the concentric value to yield an estimated equivalent D for the total work done.

Table 6.5 The magnitude of distance D through which the load is lifted for different exercises, where D is expressed as a fraction of the lifter's height H in metres (based on Dvorkin, 1988).

EXERCISE	D FOR CONCENTRIC WORK	EQUIVALENT D FOR TOTAL WORK
Full back squat	0.35 H	0.60 H
Half (powerlifting) squat	0.22 H	0.37 H
Bench press	0.28 H	0.56 H
Squat clean	0.67 H	1.26 H
Split clean	0.55 H	0.77 H
Clean pull	0.50 H	0.50 H
Snatch pull	0.59 H	0.59 H
Power clean	0.65 H	0.69 H
Good mornings (deep)	0.35 H	0.52 H
Jerk (from chest)	0.54 H	0.60 H
Split snatch	0.67 H	0.89 H

Heart rate (HR) monitoring is valuable not only in endurance sports (*Cardiovascular HR Monitoring*), but also in explosive and other non-oxidative activities to estimate levels of both physical and mental stress. For instance, maintaining a heart rate of at least 80% of maximum is sometimes advocated during rowing training for Olympic rowers for developing muscle endurance (*Muscle Endurance HR Monitoring*). Overall preparedness is also assessed by measuring the difference between resting HR and HR immediately after and for a few minutes after suddenly jumping up from a supine position (*Postural HR Monitoring*). Similar measurements are taken before, during and after breath holding for maximal duration as a guide to anoxic capability during intensive breath-holding sports such as weightlifting and wrestling (*Apnoeic HR Monitoring*). *Medical HR Monitoring* is used, of course, to diagnose the existence of illness or pathology in the athlete.

Some authorities also measure *blood pressure* (BP) daily to offer some insights into the overall effect of training. They use graphical plots of the athlete's BP (taken soon after rising in the morning) to identify the possibility of overtraining, with erratic changes or unexpected increases in diastolic or systolic BP being regarded as relevant indicators of excessive loading at any given time.

A far less familiar battery of psychodiagnostic tests of neurological changes (Shishkin, 1989) involves the regular measuring of electrodermal resistance (with skin impedance apparatus which is similar to those often used in the West to calculate bodyfat) and the *quasi-stationary electrical potential* (Siff, 1977) of key areas of the cerebral cortex of the brain (using specialised electroencephalographic or EEG apparatus to measure very slow varying currents below the slowest delta rhythms normally monitored by conventional EEG machines). These tests are used to give information on acute physiological and psychological changes which reflect on performance in the next 5-6 hours. The apparatus and tests involved were developed (in collaboration with various Austrian scientists) originally to improve the performance of pilots, cosmonauts, air controllers, military personnel and workers in highly skilled industries, particularly since the standard blood pressure, reaction time, cardiac, medico-physical, biochemical and other tests failed to give sufficient relevant information to improve work efficiency and reduce accident rate or stress-related problems (Shishkin, 1989).

A test which can be of special value in sports involving racing over a distance (such as running, swimming, rowing and cycling) involves calculation of the coefficient of effectiveness, which is defined as follows:

Coefficient of Effectiveness $C_{eff} = V. (60)/ HR$

where V is the mean velocity (in metres per second) over a given distance (in metres) and HR is the heart rate immediately after the activity. This coefficient reflects the distance in metres covered by the athlete in one heartbeat and has been used very successfully for assessing the change in the functional state of athletes and the effectiveness of various methods of restoration (Spiridonova & Kuznetsova, 1986). Any decrease in C_{eff} indicates a decrease in functional state, since such a change is produced by a decrease in velocity, an increase in heart rate or both of those negative changes together.

Other methods of testing relate to the interaction between the athletes and the interaction between the coach and athletes. Some of this work being done at the psychodiagnostic complex at the State Central Institute of Sports Science in Moscow was shown by Professor Albert Rodionov to the authors of this book to illustrate how stress between individuals, which can have a profound effect on sporting performance, may be detected and quantitatively measured by special computer programs. This work is a highly specialised graphical extension of the applications of fairly well-known communication theories involving the study of proxemics (interpersonal physical closeness) and kinesics (movements in the interpersonal space). Although this type of testing does not relate directly to the physiological tests which predominate in the assessment of athletic preparation, it should not be neglected, because the impact of psychological and sociological factors on individual capabilities in serious competition can spell the difference between success and failure.

Less commonly used, yet also sometimes useful in identifying local overtraining, is the application of physiotherapy-based *palpation* (finger pressure) tests of soreness or pain of certain key soft tissues. Firm pressure is applied (usually with the thumb) to the selected soft tissues and the athlete is asked to rate on a scale of 1 to 5 or 1 to 10 (the highest figure relating to unbearable pain). Important tissues to be palpated are the muscles, tendons and ligaments, such as the mid quadriceps, hamstrings, erector spinae, patellar ligament, Achilles tendon, gastrocnemius, outer pectorals, and the soft tissues over the shins, the relative importance depending on the given sport. Persistent or increasing levels of soreness (with or without palpation) often indicates inflammation, impaired adaptation or minor tissue damage which may lead to more serious trauma or injury.

Non Technological Testing

The ongoing application of scientific testing on a day to day basis is rarely, if ever, possible in the normal training situation, so that the observations of a coach and the perceptions of the athlete, as mentioned earlier in this section, always play a vital role in the control of the training process. In this regard, the value of formalised subjective observation and perception in the form of *Perceived Ratings of Effort* and *Ratings of Technique* was stressed, especially when this information is methodically collected in the form of a well-organised organisational or periodisation chart.

Analysis of this information may be enhanced if some of the same formal principles used in scientific research are used as guidelines to assess the value of a given training scheme. There are two distinct methods used for deriving information from experimental results or observations, namely *order analysis* and *causal analysis* (Siff, 1990):

1. *Order Analysis* compares similarities and dissimilarities between items. Therefore, if we compare a given training system whose effects are not well known, we may compare it with another training system whose effects have been well established by experiment or by practice, and assess if features in the known system can guide us towards using the novel system more competently. This method might also involve attempts to organise some of the important training variables within a given training system into a table that allows one to deduce relationships or missing links in that system. Classic examples of order analysis include the Periodic Table of elements as devised by the Russian chemist Medeleev in 1869 and the organisation of all living forms into a grand scheme of species and sub-species in biology and botany.

2. *Causal Analysis* typically involves the following methods:

• *The method of agreement*. If the conditions governing the outcome of an training scheme all have one factor in common, then that factor may be the cause of that outcome. It is usually difficult to ascertain that this is the only common cause.

• *The method of difference*. Conditions governing the outcome of two otherwise identical training schemes differ in only one factor. If the scheme containing that factor leads to the observed outcome, and the other does not, then that factor may be considered the cause of the outcome. The problem is that it is impossible to implement two identical training schemes.

• *The method of concomitant variation*. If a variation in the magnitude of one training factor results in a parallel variation (covariation) in the outcome of the entire training scheme, then this factor may be the cause of the change in outcome. Here a causal relationship, but not a proof, is indicated. The change in outcome may be positive or negative, linear or non-linear, direct or inverse, small or large, depending on the given scheme, situation and individual.

• *The method of residues*. If all known causes and their corresponding effects are eliminated during analysis of a given training scheme, then any residue of the process is the effect of the remaining variable. Thus, if we notice that a change in training is not explainable by a change in training variable X or Y, then it may be due to change in yet another variable Z. This method of elimination faces the problem of handling isolated factors which may not be strictly independent.

Application of one or more of these methods may make your task somewhat easier if you are confronted with the problem of trying to assess the merits of one of the many training exercises and regimes which are offered in textbooks, popular training magazines or seminars by various coaches.

6.2.3 The Relationship between Intensity and Volume

Studies have shown that, in the annual macrocycle, the weekly levels of volume and intensity coincide fairly closely in sports requiring strength (Chernyak et al, 1979). Generally, the largest number of weeks involve medium volume and medium intensity, as well as weeks with high volume and high intensity. Chernyak's research produced the following recommendations for strength-speed sports:

1. It is inadvisable always to combine low volume with low intensity, medium volume with medium intensity and large volume with high intensity.

2. Training is most effective and least injurious if:
   • medium volume, medium intensity loading is used most frequently (about 12-15 weeks per year)
   • medium or high volume, low intensity loading is used next most frequently (9-10 weeks per year)
   • low volume, medium intensity loading is then most commonly applied (6-7 weeks per year).

3. Other combinations should be applied even less frequently, such as:
   • large volume, medium intensity (3-4 weeks)
   • large volume, high intensity (2-3 weeks)
   • low volume, high intensity (3-4 weeks)
   • low volume, low intensity (1-2 weeks).

However, it should be remembered that the overall volume and intensity of any load tell us little about the loading imposed in different intensity zones or at the level of individual muscle groups. Nor does it say anything about the individual's perceived response to loading, as discussed earlier. Therefore, it is always to pay attention to these details, as well as the level of mastery of the athlete, in devising an effective training programme.

6.3 The Periodisation Controversy

The widespread Western use of classical periodisation along the lines originally pioneered by Matveyev may create the impression that it should be regarded as the pre-eminent and most appropriate method of organising long term training. However, even among Russian researchers and scientists, this approach to training has attracted some fierce criticism.

Some of this criticism is warranted, such as the belief that periodisation is an exact science in which all training may be prescribed via the use of computerised programmes based upon exact calculations of intensity and volume of every training session, microcycle and longer term cycle. The body is not an exactly controlled, deterministic system, but its subsystems are attracted to and deviate from approximate states of balance which show continual variation to ensure long term efficiency and health, as is being confirmed by more and more research into the nature of fractal, chaotic or fuzzy processes in biology (see Ch 8). The organisation of training is as much a matter of art, trial-and-error, and intuition, as it is of science, so that periodisation schemes should serve as approximate guidelines to be followed and modified by ongoing analysis of various physiological and psychological markers of progress.   Some of the methods, such as ratings of perceived effort, which may be used to provide fine tuning of periodisation schemes were discussed in the sections immediately preceding this one.

Verkhoshansky (1997), in particular, has roundly criticised texts which extol so-called 'periodisation breakthroughs', stating that the material being offered as an exact science is setting back the progress of training organisation to the era of the 1950s. He stresses that periodisation is not a suitable model for training for elite sportsmen and should be rejected or modified according to trends in the very full calendars of world sports which involve far more competition at higher levels than when the concept of periodisation was first formulated. Thus, at best, separate forms of periodisation should be used by novice and young athletes.

He points out that the typical mechanical division of annual training into periods and mesocycles has been based on the short-term experience of preparation of athletes during the early stage of formulating the Soviet system of training (of the 1950s) and mainly on the example of three sports, namely swimming, weightlifting, track and field athletics, and therefore cannot be universally applied in its basic form. It is emphasized, that any system of training should be based not so much on logic and empirical experience, but much more on physiology.

Verkhoshansky (1997) considers that Russian experts in cyclic sports, guided by periodisation, have applied outdated training methods which for many years have retarded sporting progress. He states that such a procedure is insufficiently scientifically substantiated and is not capable of providing accurate long-term preparation of athletes. Plans to produce high results should not be based on training to achieve what he terms "notorious peaks of sports form", but should meet the ongoing demands of events distributed throughout a competitive season and not simply to produce performance peaks for a very few events.

In his critique, Verkhoshansky (1997) makes specific reference to distance running. He emphasizes that the very successful African athletes, especially the Kenyans, train in mountainous terrain and have certain genetic and cultural predispositions, as confirmed by Soviet experts, and that they have never implemented periodisation in their training.   He adds that African and European athletes should not imitate one another, even if impressive results may tempt athletes to do so. He also refers to articles by Horwill (1992, 1995) on the same topic which condemn "the slavish worship of the theory of periodisation as used by some runners in different countries". He stresses that Soviet runners did not improve world records in running middle distances and the British runners who used the Russian concept of periodisation did not gain gold medals on Olympic games over the last 30 years, but produced great achievements before they used such concepts. British runners started to use Matveyev's block scheme of periodisation widely after 1980 and from then on their results showed a disturbing tendency to decline.

Verkhoshansky cites the work of Tschiene (1991, 1992) who has analysed a number of present training concepts to conclude that periodisation has not changed from the moment of Matveyev's first formalisation of the topic in 1965.   Although the nature of major sports and scientific achievements have progressed greatly since those early days, Tschiene observes that many coach's doctrines have not advanced or given way to other more progressive approaches.

Several critics of classical periodisation stress the artificiality and clumsiness of classifying the various microcycles and mesocycles in the form of an exact number of days or weeks, as well as the dubious linear stringing together of fairly arbitrary, non-linear, non-discrete building blocks of subjectively chosen exercises.

For instance, the use of an unloading microcycle in a given mesocycle while the body of the athlete is in a state of supercompensation does not take into account the sometimes random and unpredictable effects of average and small waves of loads on the body. As a result, it needs to be stressed that organising training according to the classical model of Matveyev can be used only by athletes of low qualification for certain phases of the programme. This is a major reason why this textbook introduced the use of methods based upon ongoing subjective and objective assessment of the athlete's condition.

Verkhoshansky (1997) is especially critical of any periodisation texts which confuse the meaning of "law", "principles", "fundamentals" and so forth, because of the lack of adequate scientific research to support such notions. He feels that much of the terminology represents a thinly veiled attempt to create a greater aura of authenticity to the host of periodisation schemes that flow from the pens of many authors and coaches, especially in the West, without their being able to scientifically validate their creations. He stresses that with respect to advanced physical training, there are no 'laws' in the rigorous sense of this word. Similarly, he dismisses as word play the use of terms such as 'undulating models and 'wave models' as meaningless attempts to disguise periodisation in different language, without changing the status quo in the least.

He makes the interesting observation that many Westerners seem to be oblivious of the fact that the general paradigm of periodisation was based heavily upon the philosophies and methodologies of communism. The cyclical nature of periodisation was strongly influenced by the 'five year plans' and other cycles of productivity in the soviet system, while the precise calculation of training quantities reflected attempts to minimise the unscientific factors of subjectivity and emotiveness.

An issue that is also of real concern is the fact that classical computation of periodisation training schemes generally utilises only two factors in regulating the training of the athlete, namely the volume and intensity of the training load. This is one reason why this book paid special attention to Matveyev's attempt to include technical skill training as one of the factors involved in periodisation, as well as to models such as that of Bondarchuk, who stressed the interdependence of technique and load throughout the training process. Mention was also made earlier of the value of prescribing training in terms of zones of intensity and various perceived ratings of technique, effort and fatigue to overcome the limits of classical periodisation (see the section on Cybernetic Periodisation).

Some of Verkhoshansky's criticism have been countered by the Bulgarian scientist, Zheljazkov (1998), who considers that the concept of periodisation, however empirical and simplistic it may have been for much of its history, still managed to be utilised very effectively for many years in training numerous elite soviet and Eastern European athletes in many sports. He comments that it is erroneous for anyone, including Verkhoshansky, to consider Matveyev's concept of periodisation as being the complete theory of sports training in the preparation, because this was not the aim of its author. He does not accept the judgement that it has played a negative role in the field of elite sports preparation. because he feels that the outstanding achievements of athletes of the former Soviet Union vigorously disprove this point of view. He considers that Verkhoshansky's emotional conclusions that the theory of periodization is constructed on 'primitive methodology' and 'scholastic demagogy' constitute a unprofessional personal attack on Matveyev. He disagrees that the crisis in cyclic sports and loss of progress by athletes in certain countries in running and track and field athletics are due to the 'ill-starred' classical theory of periodization by Matveyev, because all sports in all nations naturally undergo periods of ascendancy and decline. He agrees that models of society such as communism indeed have a profound impact on the nature of sports training, but that this happens in all countries and should not necessarily be taken to mean that this interaction between sport and society is always negative.

Zheljazkov (1998) considers that the classical application of periodisation, in describing the varying, phasic nature of progress in sporting form, has not lost its fundamental importance, although in the technology of its modelling, application and management it exhibits certain serious qualitative limitations, which may be modified in the light of modern research and sporting experience. These modifications depend on the effective socialisation of sport in any country, the effect of commercialisation and professionalism, the integration of all relevant scientific research into training, the development of strong psychological attributes, in athletes, the attachment of status to sporting achievement and the application of a more expansive systems theoretical model of the training process.

With respect to a systems approach, Zheljazkov (1998) stresses the importance of using scientific research to learn more about the processes of exhaustion, adaptation and restoration so that the methods of training can be integrated closely with methods for enhancing adaptation, regeneration and growth under a wide variety of sporting conditions. This may then be used to modify classical periodisation. He adds that a better knowledge of the process of adaptation is very necessary because the dynamics of regeneration, regardless of kind, display a nonlinear and heterochronical character, i.e., restoration and supercompensation of the various metabolic, neural and motor functions of the body do not proceed concurrently and linearly.

He maintains that progress in this regard will overcome the serious limitations imposed by simplistic application of classical principles of loading, especially that of progressive gradual overload. He considers that relevant scientific technology to monitor, analyse, offer biofeedback, refine and restore physical and mental functioning should play a major role in directing the training process, especially in enabling the athlete to cope with greater intensities and volumes of loading, while simultaneously being able to recover more rapidly. He concludes that this type of applied sports science does not at all replace the entire concept of periodisation, but enriches it to become a far more productive training approach.

Chronobiology and Periodisation

Future corroboration of the principles of periodisation may rely on some of the advances being made in the field of chronobiology which is examining the role played by biological clocks or pacemakers. Daily rhythms of structural and function change occur widely in biology, with most behavioral and physiological systems in mammals displaying at least some evidence of a 24 hour temporal structure. Although some of these daily rhythms may represent reactions to cyclic changes in light, temperature or other environmental stimuli, most reflect an innate timing program controlled by internal 24 hour biological clocks. The existence of such an endogenous 24 hour biological clock is the observation that daily rhythms of wakefulness and sleep can persist indefinitely in environments which exclude time cues such as natural light.

In such environments (e.g. underground caves), daily rhythms assume a regular periodicity that is approximately a day long ('circadian') rather than precisely 24 hours. Organisms, thus, have evolved mechanisms by which cyclic environmental stimuli can adjust the circadian clock each day to ensure that their rhythms remained synchronized to local time. The brain structures regulating the generation of rhythms and their entrainment by cyclic stimuli are collectively known as the 'circadian system'.

Biological clocks provide at least two basic functions, namely awareness of local change (like a sundial) and measurement of the passage of time (like an hourglass). This allows the organism to maintain an internal temporal order and to anticipate change in order to enhance adaptation and survival. At the molecular level, a biological clock comprises a system of oscillating levels of proteins, controlled by transcription factors, which are proteins that switch specific genes on or off. In a series of three papers, Young's group analysed the molecular workings of a major clock in drosophila flies, consisting of two proteins that initiate and control oscillation (Myers et al, 1995; Gekakis et al, 1995; Sehgal et al, 1995).

Since oscillatory processes lie at the heart of chronobiology, research is concentrating on how the endogenous oscillator works, how it synchronises with external cues and how time information is given by the oscillator to the rest of the cell, as well the overall interrelationship between environmental input, the oscillating mechanism, and the body's response.

In 1972, scientists identified the brain's seat of circadian cycling in rats, the suprachiasmatic nuclei (SCN) (Moore & Eichler, 1972; Stephan & Zucker, 1972) and thereby narrowed down the search for the neural origins of the biological clock. The clock mechanism appears to reside in individual neurons in the SCN, but the mechanisms by which these neurons are coupled to form a stable oscillating ensemble have not yet been fully elucidated

From research to date, we then note that the circadian system in mammals comprises at least one master circadian pacemaker, a structure in the hypothalamus known as the suprachiasmatic nucleus that is entrained to the cycle of day and night by nervous input from the retina. Damage to this pacemaker disrupts or eliminates daily rhythms in animals. This pacemaker can also be shifted or entrained by other stimuli, such as an appropriately timed bouts of exercise, and certain hormones, neurotransmitters and drugs. The suprachiasmatic nucleus receives information from a limited number of brain structures, and these appear to be responsible for entraining the clock to periodic stimuli. The retinal input governs entrainment to the day-night cycle, whereas two other inputs (one from the thalamic intergeniculate structure, and another from the midbrain raphe nuclei) appear to play an important role in entraining or shifting rhythms by means of exercise and emotional arousal.

The possible link to periodisation of physical training then becomes apparent. Other pacemakers may also exist in mammals. For example, there is phenomenological evidence for a second pacemaker in humans that regulates the daily temperature cycle and other associated rhythms, although the interpretation of that data is contentious. The physical location of other possible pacemakers is unknown. There are numerous other texts which cover some of the advances in chronobiology and the nature of circadian rhythms, which are worthy of some study fort those who may be interested in investigating this field more thoroughly (e.g., Klein et al, 1991; Moore-Ede et al, 1992; Nagai, 1992; Chadwick & Ackrill, 1996; Redfern & Lemmer, 1997).

6.4 Training as a Problem in Management

Programming and organisation of training require in-depth and comprehensive knowledge of the principles of training. It is appropriate, therefore, to examine programming as a problem in management.

The essence of management may be expressed in terms of the changes of state of the relevant systems produced by given tasks, while the criterion of effectiveness lies in its functioning or development. Consequently, for practical implementation of management, it is necessary firstly to establish concepts about the structure of the managed system and the characteristics of raising it from one state to another.

Let us examine a logical scheme of training organisation for describing the components of management in sports training (Fig 6.12). Training is organised in accordance with specific tasks which result in a definite improvement in sports results, so that the degree of improvement in sporting performance is the criterion of the effectiveness of training. Sports results are the observable product of the organisation of the athlete's external interactions. In other words, this is the result of the organisation of the athlete's movements which make effective use of strength and motor potential for executing specific motor tasks.

The patterning of the external influences and an increase in the relative contribution of those forces which directly contribute to the execution of the motor tasks are important conditions for improving sporting proficiency. Therefore, one has to identify the major components of management in sports training, as follows:

1. The complex of the *athlete's external influences* encountered in competition. The greater the athlete's motor potential, the more effectively the complex of external interactions can be organised. Therefore, in multi-year training, athletes train to increase their motor potential and specific work-capacity.

2. In this regard, the *athlete's fitness state*, as a characteristic of motor potential, should be classified as the second component of management in the system of sports training. In this context, *fitness state* refers to the athlete's structural-functional qualities which determine the athlete's potential to produce sporting prowess (Zatsiorsky, 1979). The complex of external interactions and the athlete's fitness state are established effectively as a result of the systematic specialisation of the motor activities. The latter provides a number of specific training influences organised to produce the required changes in the complex comprising the external influences and the athlete's fitness state.

3. Consequently, specialised motor activities, i.e. the *training load* is the third component of management in the system of sport training (see 6.12).

Thus, the preceding components together represent an hierarchically organised complex which undergoes goal-directed changes during sports training. In training, the ordered influences address all three components of the management process simultaneously. However, the basis for changes of fitness state during training lies in a specific, cyclic sequence of events. The dosage of the training load is prescribed to promote changes in the athlete's fitness state which, in turn, entails changes in the complex of external interactions of the athlete and a corresponding improvement in sporting results.

When the planned results are achieved, the programme and the organisation of the loading are determined for the next stage of training, and the sequence of the preceding conditions is repeated at higher levels. The cyclicity of this process in accordance with sport specific periodisation determines the contents of the athlete's training programme.

Completion of the tasks, executed as separate components of the complex system of management process, gives rise to an intricate dynamic complex of cause-effect relations between them, which may be considered as the structure of the managed system. Thus, the aggregate of the components of this complex system, with its characteristic cause-effect connections, represents the overall managed system.

Thus, management involves all the tasks of training, motivation, the athlete's personality and social factors which express and integrate the interests of the athlete, coach and team, as well as the practical experience and theory of training construction. In orienting the course of training in a specific direction, model characteristics are quantitatively assigned which relate to the training load, the athlete's fitness state and his external interactions (see Fig 6.12).

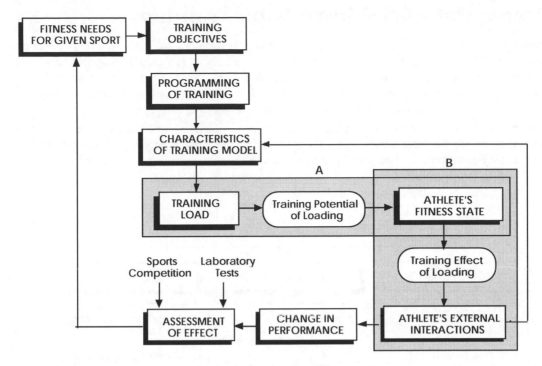

Figure 6.12 A logical scheme for organising sports training (Siff & Verkhoshansky, 1999).

The main idea of managing training consists of raising the fitness state of the body to a higher functional level. Control of this process is accomplished by assessing the effect at primarily two levels of management, namely at the level of the athlete's fitness state (control of the effect of the loading on fitness) and at the level of external interactions of the athlete (control of the change in their characteristics as a result of changes in fitness). Based on a comparison of different effects achieved at the levels indicated by the given model characteristics, suitable solutions are implemented in order to manage the later course of training. Analysis of the contents and organisation of training may now be summarised as follows:

1. Firstly, the interaction between the components of the managed system is determined by the *training potential* and the *training effect* of the loading (Fig 6.12). Here, the *training potential of the loading* is understood to mean its potential for promoting adaptation of the body and corresponding changes in its fitness state and, consequently, in its external interactions. The training potential of the loading is a relative concept which should be examined and assessed in accordance with the athlete's current fitness state. *Assessment of the training effect* of the loading means measuring the performance change that the loading produces in each case under competitive and laboratory conditions.

    The training effect is achieved with relatively stable adaptation within the body, by use of any logical training programme. The basis for the training effect is the accumulation of adaptive traces within the body produced by the entire complex of training influences. The substantive meaning of training, encompassing the concepts of *training potential* and *training effect* of the loading has central significance for programming training and will be examined later in more detail.

2. The connection between the beginning and end points of training management is highly complex. The extent of this connection is determined primarily by the effectiveness of the operations of two interdependent subsystems of regulation (see Fig 6.12): {*Training Load - Training Potential of Loading - Athlete's Fitness State*} (subsystem A) and {*Training Effect of Loading - Athlete's Fitness State - Athlete's External Interactions*} (subsystem B). Assessment of the predictive reliability and the probability of success of regulation at the level of each subsystem shows one can be certain that the lower the measures for the first one (A), the weaker the link in the entire management system.

3. The necessity for effective management arises when there is a problem in selecting a training regime. In such situations success depends on the degree of accuracy in choosing the optimal from the multitude of possible solutions.

6.5 Prerequisites for Organising Training

A successful solution to the problem of programming and organising training cannot be obtained only by assembling the results of individual fragments of research. Intensive research is required to formulate usable concepts concerning the training process and identifying those conditions which determine its efficient development. A preliminary examination of this problem already enables one to determine the goal of the task, the fundamental direction of research, and the specific information required (Fig 6.13).

The scheme need not be described in much detail, because its meaning and contents are sufficiently clear and their analysis is a matter for later discussion. Formulating a generalised theory of training requires a complex approach to the organisation of research, without repeating those experimental errors which were proliferated during the preceding few decades.

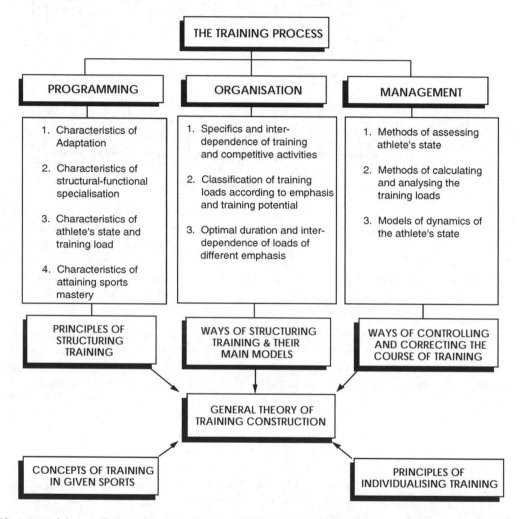

Figure 6.13 A general theory of structuring sports training (Siff & Verkhoshansky, 1999).

In sport physiology especially, a divergence of the professional interests of specialists leads to the human body being regarded as two fairly distinct systems. Some specialists limit their study primarily to the neuromuscular system and its regulation by the CNS, applying their work largely to speed-strength and complex-technical types of sport. Others focus their interest on the cardiovascular-respiratory systems and metabolic processes which determine success in primarily cyclic types of sport.

Such specialisation is quite convenient for science, but is effective and applicable only on the basis of close integration between theory and practice. All too often, studies are based on the effect of a single factor on performance; very rarely does research focus on the interactive effects of concurrent or sequential complexes of training methods.

In particular, understanding of the scientific and practical fundamentals of the development of general endurance suffers. Attention is centred on the mechanism of energy production, which ignores the specialisation of the muscular apparatus as the direct executor of work, and general endurance is considered exclusively to be a function of respiratory potential. Therefore, physiologists were perplexed when information was revealed about the decrease in VO2max during the competition period and the unexpectedly low VO2max levels among many athletes in cyclic sports. However, this should not have been unexpected if they had concurrently examined the contractile and metabolic characteristics of the muscles of athletes who specialise in general endurance sports.

Sport training theory also abounds with misdirected efforts. Here there is a similar division in the interests of specialists who give preference primarily to speed-strength or cyclic sports and tend to minimise the role of general endurance training. This professional specialisation cannot be condemned if they limit their theoretical and practical generalisations to 'their' types of sport. It is when they attempt to apply the same principles and methods to other types of sport that this single-minded approach becomes misleading.

A definite weakness in modern sports training theory is the result of underestimating the importance of information obtained from physiological and biochemical research in sport, as well as from the limited amount of definitive scientific information which forms the basis for establishing training principles. Until recently, generalised practical experience was usually regarded as the only valid way of establishing effective training principles and methods, thereby neglecting the important contributions of scientific research. At the same time, scientists disdained this attitude and coaches regarded scientists as impractical theoreticians, with the result that their individual bodies of information were not shared and training methodology suffered. The advancement of sport now depends strongly on close cooperation between scientists, coaches and athletes.

6.6 Basic Management Theory

In most interactions in the work, social or recreational setting, leaders or managers emerge or are appointed to control, coordinate and guide their fellow humans to carry out certain tasks or achieve specific goals or fulfill a prescribed purpose.

The terms *leadership* and *management* are often used interchangeably, but there are distinct differences between the two, depending on the situation. Small, ephemeral groups may have leaders or elected chairpersons, but usually not managers. The chairman of the board of a company does not play the managerial role of the executive director, who in turn does not function like the sales manager, who also may act as the highly motivating leader of a sales team. Sports teams have captains, who are special types of leader, but they also have managers who have no leadership function whatsoever on the field of play. Similarly, captains usually have no prescribed leadership role off the field. Military officers often have to fill roles of leadership and management. What is common to both leadership and management is the task of marshalling together the abilities and efforts of groups of individuals to reach specific goals, whether social, economic, military, sporting or otherwise. What is also common to both is that communication is essential to the entire process.

Tellier states that management roles are determined by position in an organisation and are characterised by three basic elements: *responsibility, authority* and *accountability*. Leadership, on the other hand, implies power to influence others, which relies on factors such as expertise, personality and charisma.

Management and leadership both require an understanding of human behaviour in terms of needs, wants and drives, hence the next section introduces you to theories of human behaviour and motivation.

6.6.1 Human Needs and Motivation

Although many models have been formulated to explain human needs, only a few have been selected here to enable you to appreciate the strengths and weaknesses of each and be able to select a suitable model for a given situation (Siff, 1990). The motivation process involved in human drive may be summarized in the following way (Fig 6.14):

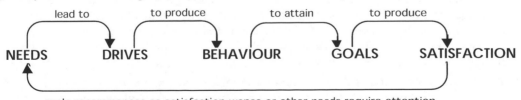

Figure 6.14 The motivational process associated with human drives and behaviour

At this point it is relevant to discuss the relationship between performance and motivation or. arousal. Higher levels of arousal do not necessarily lead to increased performance. on the contrary, excessive arousal may lead to a drop in performance, lowered productivity and an increase in the incidence of mistakes and accidents. There appears to be an optimum level of arousal for any person performing a specific task at a specific time, as was revealed by the work of Yerkes and Dodson (see Fig 6.15).

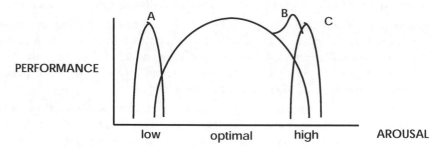

Figure 6.15 The relationship between performance and arousal

The exact shape of the curve depends on individual characteristics such as level of introversion/extroversion, level of exhaustion, standard of health, and task complexity. There is no easy formula to determine the characteristic curve for any individual; instead it depends on the effort of a manager, leader or coach to become adequately informed of the personal attributes, performance and characteristics of each worker or athlete. What is relevant is that the manager or coach appreciates that all motivational techniques are not universally applicable to everyone. Instead, they are to be applied with a thorough understanding of the individual and the situation.

Caution must be exercised when applying the Yerkes-Dodson (Y-D) model, since it implies that there is just one discrete peak for a specific optimal level of arousal or stress. The existence of the 'second wind' phenomenon (curve B) and the effect of task complexity on curve shape are two of several reasons why the original curve must be applied to restoration and stress management with circumspection.

It also implies that very low and very high levels of arousal invariably lead to diminished performance. While this may be generally true, it is well known that both sensory underload and overload may lead to phases of enhanced performance (curves A, C). The consequences of low arousal levels is not necessarily sleep or coma. On the contrary, meditation and similar altered states of consciousness may enhance performance in certain situations (curve A).

Moreover, sleep, reverie, day-dreaming and relaxed visualisation should not be viewed always as unproductive and disconnected, since research and experience reveal that problem-solving, creativity and physiological repair may occur strongly in these altered, though perfectly normal, states. The occurrence of nightmares and vigorous muscular activity also suggests that high stress levels may persist even in sleep.

Notions of optimising one's stress level thus may be seen to be based on a limited mechanistic model of human behaviour. Altered states of consciousness are a normal part of life and are not adequately described by the Y-D or Selye curves. In fact, the most efficient use and channeling of 'stress energy' may be mediated during periodic altered states which the Y-D model describes as inadequately stressful to produce meaningful performance (curve A). Therefore, both optimisation and transcendental stress management strategies are necessary if effective use is to be made of stress.

Furthermore, regular exposure to a stressor may produce either *habituation* or *oversensitisation*, so that the same level of stress may not produce the same response at a later stage. In either event, timely use of restoration measures is of central importance.

Personality can have a significant effect on the shape of the Y-D curve. For instance, the introvert appears to have a lower optimal arousal zone, unlike the extrovert who requires greater stimulation and can cope better with high levels of stress. This difference in the effect of high levels of training and competitive stress has important implications for the prescription of restorative procedures, with the introvert probably requiring early restoration and the extrovert requiring careful monitoring to prevent overtraining caused by a desire for greater stimulation.

Task structure also modifies the shape of the Y-D curve. Complex tasks require low levels of arousal to reach optimal performance over very limited periods (e.g. in golf, gymnastics and pole vaulting), whereas simple sports tasks may be executed over a longer period at higher levels of arousal. Excessive exposure of an athlete to complex training tasks can lead rapidly to 'overstress', while simple tasks may be insufficiently challenging to produce continued supercompensation. A balance between complexity, simplicity, intensity and volume of load is necessary to ensure growth and to minimise overtraining.

Maslow's Hierarchy of Needs

One of the best known, though simplistic, models of human needs is that of psychologist, Abraham Maslow. He devised an hierarchy of needs ranging from the most basic, which have to be satisfied first before subsequent needs will begin to exert a significant influence on a person. This hierarchy may be arranged in the form of a triangle with the most basic physiological, concrete needs at its base and the highest level, abstract need for self-actualization (the need to achieve one's highest potential in a specific situation) at its apex. It may also be arranged to explain the needs of the individual in both a private or a professional capacity (see Fig 6.16).

Occasionally, this model may include a state beyond self-actualisation, called transcendence which is associated with states of profoundly altered consciousness such as religious reverie or trance meditation. However, this state is not simply the preserve of the ascetic or mystic, because many athletes have reported achieving world class performances in similar altered states (Murphy & White, 1978)

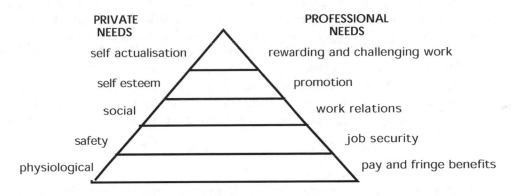

Figure 6.16 Maslow's hierarchy of needs in the private and professional settings

Other Theories of Needs

Alderfer identified the following categories of needs:

- *Existence* needs, which concern our physiological and material desires, such as those for hunger and shelter
- *Relatedness* needs, which concern relationships between people
- *Growth* needs, which concern personal development, change, evolution and creativity.

McClelland, like the neurophysiologist, James Olds, however, maintained that there are only two human needs ~ the need for pleasure and the need to avoid pain. All other needs or motives are learned. On this basis, McClelland then categorized these acquired needs as follows:

- *Achievement*. There is a strong need among some people to excel. They have a high achievement need and want to do a task well for its own sake, rather than for its material rewards.
- *Power*. This refers to the desire to influence, regulate and control the actions and behaviour of other people.
- *Affiliation* This refers to the need for positive relationships with other people and probably is described best by the word 'friendship'. A major aspect of the affiliation need is the need for communication.

Alderfer's model differs significantly from Maslow's in that it recognizes that satisfied needs may still continue to be influential, particularly if they can substitute for an unsatisfied need. Research by Alderfer also reveals that higher order (growth) needs can arise or exist simultaneously with the lower order needs. It also emerges that certain needs become even more intensified if they are more satisfied than others. It is obvious then that Maslow's hierarchy, like all theory, has to be applied with circumspection.

Expectancy Theory of Motivation

All the above theories overlap in some respects or have strong similarities. They are usefully augmented or replaced in the analysis of management interactions by Vroom's *Expectancy Theory of Motivation*, which can be particularly valuable to apply in the workplace or advertising realm. This theory posits that it is not merely a specific goal, but the individual perception of that goal which motivates people. Vroom stated that *Motivational Force* depends on two factors (Tellier, 1978):

- the *perceived attractiveness* (valence V) of the goal or outcome
- the *perceived probability of achieving* that goal or outcome (one's personal belief, B, that success is likely)

He then combined these two factors so that the Motivational Force F depends on their arithmetic product $F = V \times B$. In other words, if a goal is highly attractive and you believe strongly that it is within your reach, the Motivational Force driving you will be very strong. However, if a goal is extremely attractive, but you believe it to be far outside your reach, you will experience a small Motivational Force and put in minimal effort to attain that goal. Under such circumstances, it is desirable to break down a large or distant goal into smaller goals to be achieved over a period or at a rate which you perceive to be more matched to your capabilities or experience.

Vroom's detailed theory involves allocating numerical values to the contributing factors. Perceived attractiveness is rated from -5 (extremely undesirable) to +5 (extremely desirable), while belief in success is rated on a scale from 0 (total disbelief) to 1 (total belief). The overall Motivational Force is the sum of the motivational forces calculated from the products of perceived attractiveness and perceived belief for all the important goals or outcomes associated with carrying out the task.

Detailed examples of this theory are outside the scope of this book, so it is sufficient to note that a manager or leader can motivate athletes strongly if he appreciates that motivation depends on perceptions of goal attractiveness and attainability. He can improve performance either by modifying the task accordingly or by altering the athlete's perceptions of the task and its outcomes.

6.6.2 Management Models

Management implies the existence of authority. Oncken identifies four types of authority: authority of position or power, authority of personality, authority of competence, and authority of integrity.

The Traditional Model

Tradition decreed that workers were of secondary importance to productivity, that they were possessions, slaves or hired slaves. This linear approach to management may be summarized in the form of the following diagram (Fig 6.17). All too often this model continues to be applied by managers, leaders and coaches steeped in the traditional ways.

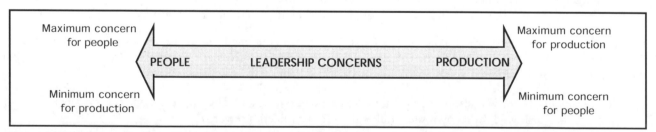

Figure 6.17 The linear, single continuum model of traditional management

The Managerial Grid

Experience and subsequent research have revealed that productivity is enhanced if an appropriate balance is established between concern for people and production. This led Blake and Mouton to devise the Ohio State University model, which emphasizes the relationship between productivity and people concern (Fig 6.18).

All management styles may be identified by selecting suitable coordinates from the grid. For instance, the autocrat would have a rating of (9,1), whereas the laissez faire leader would have a rating of (1,9). Coordinates (1,1) characterize impoverished leadership, while (9,9) refers to ideal management. The middle-of-the-road manager is located at (5,5).

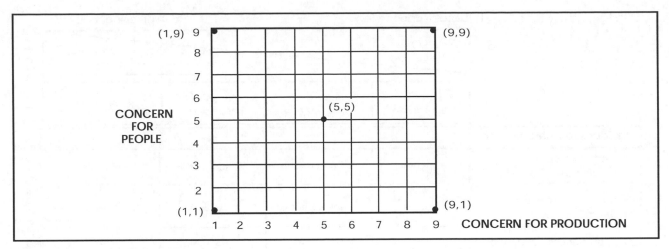

Figure 6.18 The Blake-Mouton managerial grid

Situational Leadership

Hersey and Blanchard stated that leadership style ought to be implemented according to each situation which arises. Their model illustrates how leadership style may be adapted to a given situation according to the 'maturity' (education, experience, responsibility, self-motivation, degree of self-actualization) of the worker or follower (Fig 6.19).

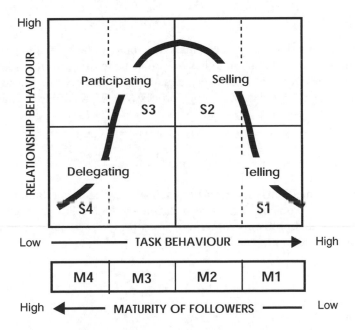

Figure 6.19 The Situational Leadership Model (Hersey and Blanchard)

To use this system, the coach in playing a role as leader rates the maturity of the follower as low, moderate or high (M1, M2, M3 or M4), then reads off the appropriate leadership style (S1, S2, S3 or S4) in the relevant box above. Relationship behaviour includes the amount of time and effort put into interaction with followers. One spends more time in Selling or Participatory situations than in Telling or Delegating situations, hence the shape of the curve.

The Leadership Continuum

Tannenbaum and Schmidt devised a leadership continuum extending between the extremes of Leader-centredness and Worker-centredness. It relates well to the leadership characteristics of Likert's four management styles, as follows (Fig 6.20).

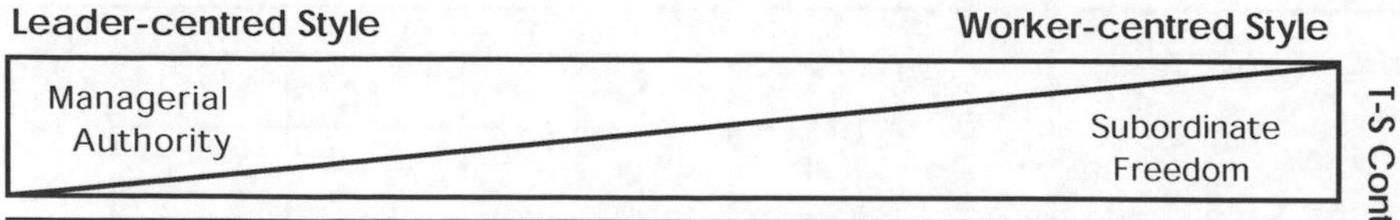

	Leader-centred Style			Worker-centred Style	

	Managerial Authority			Subordinate Freedom	T-S Continuum

System	exploitative autocratic	benevolent autocratic	consultative participation	democratic	
Leadership Characteristic	**1**	**2**	**3**	**4**	
Superior's trust in subordinates	none	condescending	substantial	complete	
Subordinate's trust in superiors	none	subservient	substantial	complete	Likert Management Styles
Supportiveness of superiors to subordinates	never	in a few situations	in most situations	in all situations	
Freedom of subordinates to discuss job with superiors	none	very little	substantial	complete	
Extent of subordinate participating in decision making	seldom	sometimes	usually	always	

Figure 6.20   The Tannenbaum-Schmidt leadership continuum and its relation to Likert's management style

Decision Making and Problem Solving

Decision-making is a vital part of all management situations, so it is essential that some of the formal theory of this process be covered. Often, managers or committees are called upon to handle problems in order of importance. The word 'Importance' is far too unspecific to be of any real value in every situation; it is relative to the individual perceptions of all concerned in the problem solving or decision-making process. It is preferable to rate every problem in terms of:

- Seriousness or size
- Urgency
- Growth potential or growth rate

In using such a system, one allocates H (high), M (medium) or L (low) to each of these factors relating to all the problems to be considered in a particular situation. Problems identified by triple or double H's are then handled before those with fewer or no H's, with triple L's rated problems receiving lowest priority. In attempting to solve any problem, it is useful to recognize the main six steps in problem-solving:

1. Identification and definition of problem
2. Generation of alternative solutions
3. Evaluation of the alternative solutions
4. Decision -making: selection of solution
5. Implementation of decision
6. Testing of solution.

Should the final step verify the value of the chosen solution, the process will terminate. If not, one may return to steps 1, 2 or 3 and repeat the process until a suitable solution emerges. Limitations involving factors such as time, information, expertise, money and materials may hinder or halt this process. Consequently, one might make inappropriate or ill-considered decisions. A better understanding of the nature of problem-solving and decision-making then becomes advisable.

Maier (1963) identified two fundamental factors in the decision-making process: the objective *quality* of the decision, and the *acceptance* of that decision by those concerned, which involves their subjective feelings. Depending on one's individual decision-making style, he will tend to focus separately on quality or acceptance, regardless of the problem situation. Roskin, therefore, developed a decision-making inventory to make one more aware that personal decision-making style should be more flexible and guided by the situation concerned (Maier,

1963). In this system, you have to identify the problem type in terms of its relative quality and acceptance, than decide on one of four decision-making styles (Fig 6.21). It is essential to remember that implementation of all styles depends on the *time available* for managing the different phases of the problem.

Figure 6.21 Roskin's decision-making guide

Concluding Remarks

This section was included to enable you to apply some of the vast field of management and leadership theory in the major communication situations you will encounter as a professional. It does not pretend to offer any completeness. Not only is thorough coverage of the topic outside the scope of this book, but management is a dynamic and rapidly expanding discipline, with nuances and expertise being added regularly by innovative managers and scientists.

For instance, the close interaction of manager and worker, logic and emotion, science and intuition are being closely examined. Researchers have produced the 7-S Framework to define the scope of management more clearly. It stresses that management must take account of the following factors in any organization: *structure, staff, systems, strategy, skills, style* and *shared values* (Peters & Waterman, 1983). It is up to interested readers to expand their knowledge by reading some of the standard management texts and professional journals.

6.7 Classification of Sports

Establishing the principles and rules of programming training necessitates determining clearly the limits of generality and specificity in individual sports or groups of related sports. To do this it is necessary to classify sports scientifically to establish programming criteria.

Sport is associated first of all, with the spatio-temporal organisation of the athlete's movements, which is determined by the rules and conditions of competition and by the effective use of motor potential for executing the required motor tasks. In all cases, this requires perfecting the central nervous processes which control movement, as well as raising the functional potential of the muscles and metabolic systems. Classification of sports into individual, team, ball or water sports, for example, is not scientifically useful; it is more appropriate to classify sports on the basis of the particular organisation of the sporting movements and characteristics of the physical systems used to produce their working effect.

The more prolonged and the lower the intensity of muscular work, the greater the role of aerobic processes and the greater the functional specialisation of the muscles to utilise oxygen more fully. The role of the glycolytic mechanisms of energy production grows as the duration of work decreases and the power of muscular work increases. The muscles adapt to working conditions of an inadequate supply of oxygen and the rapid removal of lactate during the exercise.

The loading of the motor apparatus and the power of explosive effort increase significantly during brief acyclic work. Under conditions of heavy dynamic overload, athletes must overcome significant external resistance which they must accomplish in a very short time (tenths and even hundredths of a second). This complicates movement coordination significantly and requires the development of an effective and reliable biodynamic structure (see 2.1.3). Under these conditions, the neuromuscular apparatus improves intramuscular regulation and increases the power of anaerobic energy production. This preamble shows that sports may be divided into two broad groups, namely *acyclic* and *cyclic* sports:

- *Acyclic sports* characterised by the complex organisation of motor actions and an intense concentration of working effort, displayed briefly under competition conditions. Such sports have an inherently stable biodynamic movement structure and definite structural-functional specialisation of the neuromuscular apparatus which recruits its abilities to display powerful explosive effort and anaerobic power; primarily through ATP-CP energy processes.

- *Cyclic sports* characterised by prolonged repetition of stereotyped work cycles of relatively simple organisation which do not require maximal muscular tension. The energy acquired for such work comes primarily from stored glycogen or free fatty acids metabolised in the presence of oxygen during the exercise. One of the most important conditions for improving performance in this group of sports is the structural and functional specialisation of the muscles to improve their ability to oxidise metabolites, as well as to increase the capacity of the metabolic processes and the economy of using the energy substrates during exercise.

One should further subdivide the sports in each of these broad groups in terms of specific characteristics of movement organisation and energy production. Thus, the acyclic group embraces sports that require powerful, brief, explosive efforts and others which involve fine motor control and spatially precise movement. In the cyclical group there are some sports where the work is executed under conditions of extensive oxygen utilisation and others where the muscles have an inadequate oxygen supply.

Finally, one should identify a third group of sports, characterised by varying competition demands and the need to maintain a high work output under conditions of fatigue. These types of sports combine characteristics of the preceding two groups. They involve constant changes in intensity of the competition activities, as well as bursts of high power movements with periodic rest pauses, so that energy production is of a mixed aerobic-anaerobic character, with the greater part being derived from glycolytic reactions. Thus we may classify sports into three groups, as already outlined by Farfel (1969):

- *Acyclic sports*, in which perfecting of the neuromuscular system for precise regulation of movements and the ability to produce great power play the dominant roles

- *Cyclic sports* (usually of submaximal and of moderate power), associated primarily with the production of muscular work through aerobic processes

- *Complex (combined) sports*, where characteristically there is a high variability of motor actions under conditions of advancing fatigue and varying intensity of work, typified by team sports and one-on-one events (e.g. boxing and fencing).

In classifying sports, it is necessary to consider competitive, as well as training activities. This is important, because in some cases the training exercises are very different from competitive actions, often due to the necessity for repeated reproduction of the competitive movements in training. In practice, we refer to special endurance (e.g. speed-, jumping-, and strength-endurance) in such cases. For example, the shortest sprint distance in track-and-field (100 metres) is covered in approximately 10 seconds. The effort expended to achieve this does not depend on oxidative efficiency. However, in order for a sprinter to prepare himself to effectively display such effort, he should execute training loads that develop his aerobic and anaerobic potential, in particular the latter. The general principles of programming training for each of the above groups of sport will be examined later.

6.8 Characteristics of the Training Process

Formulation of theories and practical methods of programming training, as stated before, is possible only through understanding the training process. Therefore, it is relevant to return to the scheme presented in Figure 6.8 to examine the characteristics of the long-term adaptation to intense muscular work. We will then examine the characteristics of the structural and functional specialisation of the body as a specific external expression of long-term adaptation to intense muscular work. Finally, we will investigate some of the characteristics of developing technical proficiency in different sports to understand how the athlete masters the skill to use motor potential efficiently in competition.

6.8.1 Adaptation to Intense Muscular Work

Extensive experimental data has been collected concerning the restorative processes and the body's reaction after brief training stimuli in sport (the *immediate training effect*). It has been shown that the after-effect of large loading does not simply restore the expended energy but leads to super-restoration which exceeds the initial level (see 1.14). This phenomenon (Weigert's law of supercompensation) was first formally described by Folbrot (1941, 1952, 1958), while its relation to exhaustion-restoration processes under different types of loading has been studied by several other specialists (Yakovlev, 1955, 1975; Gorkin et al, 1973; Volkov, 1975; Monogarov & Platonov, 1975; Sergeyev, 1981). Application of the these findings on the nature of adaptation and supercompensation led to rapid acceptance of the following practical recommendations:

- It is necessary for the athlete to maintain a state of adaptation during training, so that it is possible to execute the fundamental sporting actions effectively over an extended period
- Repetition of training loads when the body is in a state of insufficient restoration is generally undesirable, although this is permissible in certain instances
- Special work capacity should rise steadily during the course of training; any decrease at given stages of training would indicate that the training is incorrectly organised.

Undoubtedly, all of these premises were progressive in their time and to a certain extent are still valid today. However, modern sporting requirements reveal the necessity to alter the main approach to structuring training and obey common sense, which indicates that the fundamental unit of training should be the mesocycle and not the microcycle. An extensive study of the characteristics of long-term adaptation is required for this. The practical value of this study will be appreciated only if one can observe the specific effect of given training loads on the dynamics of the athlete's state and determine the quantitative characteristics of the adaptation process.

The initial results of this research already have convincingly demonstrated its scientific and practical value, especially in the case of sports which require explosive effort. General concepts about the development of long-term adaptation are the result of observing the dynamics of an athlete's special physical preparedness indicators over many years of training. Extensive research allows us to reach the following conclusions:

1. The absolute and mean level of special strength preparedness increases annually.

2. The initial level of speed-strength in each annual cycle is lower than the level at the end of the preceding year's, but higher than at its beginning.

3. The rise in speed-strength from year to year is larger for athletes of medium qualification than for highly qualified athletes.

4. There is a definite trend in the dynamics of special strength preparedness in the annual cycle, which is determined by the traditional periodisation of training for the given sport and competition calendar. One can clearly trace a twin peak in the dynamics of speed-strength with two competition stages, because the level of special strength preparedness is higher in the second competition stage than in the first. In types of sports with one competition season, speed-strength rises regularly and uniformly.

Drawing such conclusions about some of the characteristics of long-term adaptation to intense muscular work in sport has important practical significance for programming training.

The performance results of the adaptation process, expressed by the dynamics of special work capacity, may be presented schematically in the form of several concurrent graphs (Fig 6.22). Graphs B and C reflect the dynamics of the athlete's special work capacity in annual cycles (for bi-cyclic and mono-cyclic periodisation, respectively). Graph A depicts the dynamics of relatively stable, long-term adaptation over many years.

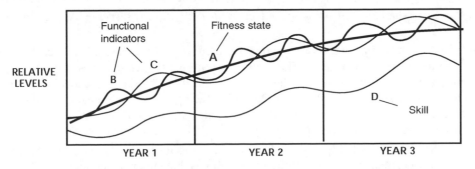

Figure 6.22 The dynamics of adaptation in sports training over several years (Siff & Verkhoshansky, 1999).

The changes in the functional indicators (graphs B and C) during the annual cycle are temporary, unstable and to a certain extent, reversible. The basis for these changes are the so-called compensatory mechanisms, i.e. reactions designed to maintain the necessary level of functioning for brief periods under demanding conditions which ultimately lead to stable adaptation. The compensatory mechanisms are dynamic physiological means of repairing the body during extreme conditions and gradually fade as adaptation takes place. Insofar as these mechanisms precede adaptation, they should be designated *pre-adaptation phenomena* (Kuznyetsov, 1979).

Thus, compensatory adaptation is a prerequisite condition for the development of long-term, stable adaptation (graph A). The latter can progressively increase if the functional reconstruction during the course of compensatory adaptation is sufficient to produce a noticeable effect on the external interactions of the body and increase its special work capacity. It should be stressed that adaptation in sport consists not only of increased motor potential, but also the improvement of the athlete's skills to more effectively utilise this potential for coping with specific motor tasks (graph D).

In the light of scientific research, *adaptation cannot be considered an equilibrium process. Adaptation is the dynamic maintenance of a definite level of imbalance between the body and the environment at a given time,* which is the fundamental reason for the origin and development of accommodative reconstruction (Bauer, 1935; Bernstein, 1966).

Figure 6.22 illustrates the gross changes in special preparedness with time and, therefore, reflects only the general aspects of long-term adaptation. In reality, changes in special work capacity are produced by an extensive complex of adaptive processes which involve all of the body's survival systems. The rate of improving the performance of these systems and the stages of accelerated physical development can be different. This heterochronicity is determined by:

• the action of particular physiological systems in establishing long-term adaptation of a specific emphasis
• differences in their reactiveness (or adaptive inertia)
• changes in the role of these systems at different stages of long-term adaptation.

A clear picture of the development of long-term adaptation in endurance sports has not been observed as it has been in explosive-strength sports. In this case, it is not a matter of some specific differences in the adaptation process, but in the ability to observe it in the factors used for analysis. The measures of aerobic and anaerobic output reflect the general level of special work capacity (i.e. endurance), but they do not express the internal changes associated with adaptation to intense cyclic or acyclic work. A great deal of work still has to be done in understanding adaptation as the result of the summation of physiological responses to different training stresses, in particular regarding the endocrine system, neurohormonal processes, the neuromuscular system and the entire nervous system. The research done by Folbrot (1941), Selye (see 1.16) and others has to be taken much further in its application to the development of sporting mastery, especially in endurance sports. Until then one can assume that long-term adaptation to endurance work is developed by the same, above-mentioned chief mechanisms, although at another level of the physiological systems.

Long-term compensatory adaptation cannot continue indefinitely. The effect of compensatory adaptation on special work capacity diminishes with each repetition; with the adaptation being described by a parabola whose peak is eventually reached with time (Fig 6.22, graph A). This indicates that an athlete's general adaptation reserves have a limit that is genetically predetermined. One can judge the limits of compensatory adaptation by the presence of waves in the dynamics of special work capacity (graphs B and C). One of the reasons for the appearance of these waves is the use of traditional periodisation of training (mono- or bi-cyclic periodisation), but a more important reason is the exhaustion of the so-called *current adaptation reserves* (CAR) of the body (see 1.16).

At any instant, the body has a definite reserve potential, i.e. a capability of responding to adapt to external influences and raise itself to a new functional level. The capacity of these adaptive reserves is limited by definite physiological mechanisms which determine the absolute level of the body's adaptive capability. Hence, the intensity, volume and duration of the training influences determine the optimal development of the body's CAR. If the magnitude of these are below certain thresholds, the body will not fully utilise its CAR, whereas, if they exceed it, exhaustion of reserve potential will occur and the training effect will be low or negative.

The adaptation process has been divided by different researchers into three phases, based on observations of physiological changes and the corresponding dynamics of sporting achievements, namely: (a) the growth of trainability, (b) sporting form, (c) loss of trainability (Letunov, 1952), or as the similar scheme: (a) adaptation, (b) the highest sport work-capacity, (c) re-adaptation (Prokor, 1959). In the latter case, re-adaptation refers to the decrease in work capacity as the limits of adaptability are exceeded, i.e. the adaptation energy is lowered. Subsequent workers have designated these phases simply as *acquisition, preservation* and *brief loss* of sporting form (Matveyev, 1964).

Thus, one can consider training organisation to be effective when it produces the maximum growth of the body's CAR by means of the appropriate volume of loading. Hence, useful ways of programming and organising training emerge if we devise means of assessing the body's CAR in each case, together with criteria for determining the contents and volume of the training loads that are necessary for building up the CAR. The possibility of devising a quantitative approach to determine the body's reserve capacity has already been discussed in the literature for several decades. It is based, in particular, on assessments of a number of bio-chemical indicators of energy exchange processes (Beckman et al, 1961; Yakovlev, 1977).

Two forms of compensatory adaptation, associated with enhancing the CAR by systematic training, which differ in volume and organisation of the training loads, have been identified and studied in explosive sports (Fig 6.23). The first form of adaptation, produced by *distributed loading* (A), is characterised by a gradual increase in the functional indicators and is associated with a moderate volume of continuous loading. In this case, periodic brief disturbances of the body's homeostasis occur and the current expenditure of energy resources is compensated during training. This form of compensatory adaptation follows traditional concepts for developing trainability and is typical for athletes of medium classification under contemporary training conditions.

The second form of compensatory adaptation, produced by *concentrated loading* (B), is associated with the use of a large, concentrated volume of special physical preparation means, concentrated in the first half of the training phase. These large volumes provoke a profound and prolonged disturbance of the body's homeostasis, which is reflected by decrease of the functional indicators. Then, after the volume of loading is decreased, their increase accelerates and exceeds the level achieved with the first form of adaptation. This way of organising loading in the preparatory mesocycles was devised for highly qualified athletes and has been shown by research to be effective for all types of sport (Verkhoshansky, 1977).

The practical aspects of utilising this form of compensatory adaptation in actual training conditions will be dealt with later. It is relevant here to dwell on the results of research which studied compensatory adaptation and methods of maximally enhancing the body's CAR during the training mesocycle.

Firstly, the optimal duration of the training influences was determined, since this is vital for maximal enhancement of the body's CAR. It was learned that the appropriate duration of continuous training is 5-6 weeks, and with concentrated loading, the duration is 3-4 weeks, after which a recuperation period is necessary for activating the compensatory processes.

It was also revealed that the trained athlete is able to tolerate three such sequential blocks of loading, separated by short recuperation pauses (7-10 days). After this, a longer recuperation period is necessary to facilitate stabilisation at the new level of adaptation. Thus, the time interval necessary for exhausting the body's CAR is between 18-22 weeks (see Fig 6.23). This period coincides with observations of highly qualified athletes training in different sports, including cyclic types (Zhikharevich, 1976; Sirenko, 1980).

In order to apply this information, it is necessary to appreciate that the body cannot indefinitely continue to adapt successively to training loads. There are definite time limits during which the body is able to react positively to continuous training loads of large volume. and these must be taken into account when programming training. Whatever training regime is devised, it must always be remembered that it is inappropriate to subject the body to extreme exhaustion of its energy reserves. This requires a longer recuperation period and has a negative effect on the subsequent stages of adaptation.

The preceding cautionary remarks apparently have not been fully appreciated by the critics (such as Komarova, 1984) of the concentrated loading system. Komarova correctly recognises that premature or prolonged application of concentrated loading can lead to overtraining, stagnation or injury, as has been emphasized regularly in this textbook. However, he errs in extrapolating this analysis to completely dismiss the periodic use of concentrated loading by qualified athletes. This underlines how important it is for the coach to be able to select the appropriate form of periodisation to suit the athlete during every stage of the training process.

Research aimed at revealing effective ways of maximally developing the body's CAR, has revealed one of the most important features of adaptation associated with the extensive disturbance of the body's homeostasis (Verkhoshansky, 1977). It was found that the more extensive and longer the exhaustion of the body's energy resources by concentrated loading during specific mesocycles of training (obviously within reasonable limits), the higher their subsequent super-restoration and the longer the new functional level is maintained. The key issue, of course, is determining the optimal duration of concentrated loading, so as to avoid exhaustion and diminished performance.

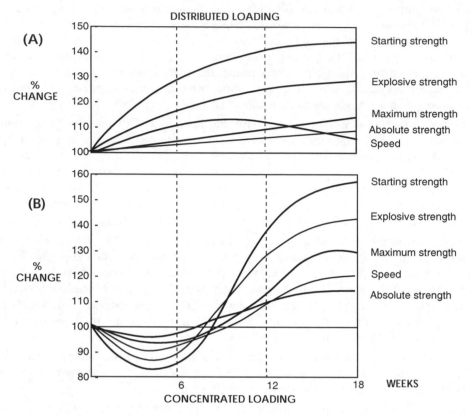

Figure 6.23 Two forms of compensatory adaptation during the large preparation phase (Siff & Verkhoshansky, 1999).

It is interesting to note the results of a study done by Bondarchuk (1982) which analysed the effect of different volumes of an identical training programme on a group of hammer-throwers. He found that a 50% increase in volume of loading had no significant effect on the duration of maintenance of the training effect and sporting performance. Although Bondarchuk stresses that this finding applies strictly to a particular group of athletes, it tends to confirm that major changes in intensity have a more profound effect on athletic state than comparable changes in volume. It also implies that calculations of volume are not as critical as those of intensity, thus corroborating *the importance of paying careful attention to zones of loading intensity*, as emphasized earlier in 6.2.2 (see also Table 6.1).

Training organisation which elicits extensive and relatively prolonged disturbance of homeostasis necessitates the inclusion of suitable restorative stages for triggering a compensatory reaction, thereby eliminating inappropriately phased peaking of the various functional indicators and stabilising the body at the new functional level. The general volume of the load should be decreased at this time and General Physical Preparation means should be introduced into training so as to intensify the compensatory reaction. The more extensive and prolonged the disturbance of homeostasis, the longer the restorative stage should be. The concept of CAR and the characteristics of compensatory adaptation have great significance for programming training and especially for effective annual periodisation.

6.8.2 Structural-Functional Specialisation in Training

Structural-functional specialisation refers to those stable, adaptive changes that are produced by the specific form of conditioning imposed by a given sport. All of the survival systems of the body undergo adaptive reconstruction in response to external stressors. However, it is not difficult to observe that those systems which are of major importance for success in sport undergo an accelerated rate of functional growth.

It has been noted already that the specifics of adaptation are determined primarily by two factors, namely the work regime in sports, and the gradual, but steady increase in complexity of the body's external interactions associated with the growth of sporting proficiency.

For example, improvement of the triple jump requires developing the ability of the motor apparatus to produce great power. Increase in jumping distance, which is accomplished primarily by increasing running speed, is associated with a significant increase in complexity of the interaction of the feet with the support at each take-off, a situation that requires significant improvement in reactive ability.

Cyclic locomotion, to a great extent, necessitates increasing the power and the capacity of the body's systems which are crucial for energy production of muscular work. Energy expenditure increases greatly with increase in movement speed. For example, oxygen requirements increase considerably with running speed, energy expenditure being almost proportional to the fourth power of running speed (Sargent, 1926). This rising cost of running speed is associated with a greater reliance being placed on anaerobic processes for generating the necessary energy of work (Henry, 1951; Margaria, 1963).

As discussed previously (see 2.2.3, 5.4.3). two forms of functional perfecting of the body may be distinguished in the training process, namely, *specialisation by physiological system* and *specialisation by motor ability* (Verkhoshansky, 1971). The most obvious evidence of specialisation appears when comparing the functional development of the body in different sports. If we refer to the classification scheme of 6.5, *specialisation by physiological system* means that acyclic sports rely predominantly on anaerobic processes and functional hypertrophy of the motor apparatus, whereas cyclic sports place major reliance on aerobic processes. In complex (combined) sports, there is an intense functional development of both the motor apparatus and the energy production systems. *Specialisation by motor ability* refers to the exact programme of neuromuscular control that is developed by repetitive execution of the motor skills required in a given sport (see 2.2.3).

However, it is important to emphasize that specialisation in the first two cases does not imply that development is either strictly aerobic or anaerobic, but rather that there is a particular primary emphasis of functional specialisation. One can successfully develop a high level of explosive strength in acyclic locomotion only when one possesses sufficiently high aerobic efficiency. At the same time, improving the efficiency of the energy producing systems in cyclic locomotion should be based on highly developed muscular strength and local muscular endurance.

The kinesiological patterns of motor activity in various types of sports are approximately equivalent, although there are some qualitative and quantitative differences associated with specific types of sports. Thus, sprint swimmers have higher rates and developmental levels of anaerobic productivity than distance swimmers, whereas aerobic productivity is superior for distance swimmers. This is determined by the emphasis of the training.

In the multi-year training of sprinters, up to Class I-CMS (Class I - Candidate for Master of Sport), the chief emphasis is on developing general (aerobic) endurance and speed, whereas at MS-MSIC (Master of Sport - Master of Sport, International Class) level the emphasis is on developing speed (anaerobic) endurance. In the training of distance athletes of all qualification levels, the chief emphasis is on developing aerobic productivity, while at the MS-MSIC level, the emphasis is on enhancing anaerobic productivity (Vankov, 1978).

In cyclic sports, strength preparedness, mainly in the form of strength-endurance, plays an important role. Research shows that, with a relatively moderate increase in muscular strength, together with a rise in the athlete's qualification, the qualities of dynamic strength-endurance and power accelerate the increase in functional strength (Zhurbinoi, 1978).

The process of functional specialisation is characterised by the fact that there is a definite sequence (known as heterochronicity, as detailed in 2.2.3) in the development of adaptation. This means that the body adapts to external influences only when they become necessary for the further growth of sporting proficiency, and this involves only those systems whose functions satisfy all the necessary requirements for enhancing sport specific fitness.

The multi-year functional specialisation of the body is closely connected with its corresponding physical adaptation. This adaptation leaves traces of the training influences on the body for long periods and serves as the foundation for its functional perfecting. These traces have been studied extensively in general terms at the level of muscle tissue, cardiac muscle, skeletal structure, cardiovascular mechanisms and other systems. Further study of the multi-year characteristics of structural-functional specialisation in particular types of sport is important in formulating the principles of programming training.

6.8.3 The Structure of Special Physical Preparedness

The above-mentioned characteristics of functional specialisation in multi-year training are associated with specific adaptive changes in the cardiovascular-respiratory and neuromuscular systems, as well as in the efficiency of the central nervous mechanisms that regulate their activities. For many years, it was not appreciated that each type of sport requires not only a distinct type of motor skill, but also a different type of physiological fitness. Even today, the role and nature of supplementary training is not clearly understood. For example, much the same sort of resistance training may be prescribed for many different athletes in various sports, simply because the sports seem to be superficially similar.   It must be realised that supplementary or 'cross' training cannot simply be used in a very general way in the belief that strength, speed or endurance acquired in one situation will be of direct benefit to performance in another situation.

For example, muscle endurance gained through supplementary running training does not mean that it will directly improve the performance of a competitive rower or cyclist. Special physical preparedness (SPP) depends on developing the necessary physiological qualities with the same muscles and neuromuscular mechanisms that are encountered in the given sport. Therefore, training for special physical preparedness must be based on a thorough understanding of the different types of specificity discussed in 1.3 and the characteristics of the interaction between the various organs and the neuromuscular system, which determines the change in special work capacity.

It was also assumed that one could develop each fitness quality separately with some or other form of general training, then assemble all of them to produce the necessary sport specific fitness from them. The emergence of specificity from an array of non-specific fitness qualities, however, is not supported by current physiological and biochemical research, so it is clear that the management of training must take into consideration the effects of concurrent and sequential training means. Therefore, the problem of programming training was examined from several different positions in earlier chapters (see especially 3.2.1 regarding speed and quickness, and 4.4 regarding general endurance).

6.9 Preparedness and the Training Load

The connection between the athlete's fitness state and a given loading regime is the central issue in the theory and practice of programming training (see 6.3). It is also the weakest link in the management of training, which requires the special attention of scientists and coaches. Before examining the practical aspects of the connection between loading and the athlete's fitness state, the concepts of training load and training effect must be defined more thoroughly (see Fig 6.12).

Strictly speaking, the training load does not exist as an independent entity. Terminologically, it must be distinguished from the load used in weight training, which refers to the resistance or force imposed on the body by a weight or machine. Training load is related to the muscular work which the body must produce to carry out a given regime of exercise in training or competition. More precisely, muscular work is that training potential which elicits an appropriate training effect from the body. Thus, the training potential of muscular work, and consequently its training effect is to a large extent determined by the athlete's current fitness state.

It should be clear that the interrelation between the athlete's fitness state and the training load is extremely complex, dependent upon many factors and determined by numerous variables (see Fig 6.12). Unfortunately, research concerning this connection is limited and often contradictory. Therefore, this chapter attempts to systematise and examine the connection between the athlete's fitness state and the training load, drawing largely upon the results of extensive research by Verkhoshansky and his co-workers.

6.9.1 The Training Load and its Effect

The training load refers to the quantitative calculation of the training work performed. It is customary to recognise the concepts of external, internal and psychological loading, i.e. the quantity of work done, its effect on the body and the psychologically perceived effect on the athlete, respectively (Matveyev, 1964; Volkov, 1969; Ozolin, 1970; Tumanyan, 1974). Volume and intensity are used as the most general characteristics of the training load, as defined in 6.2.2 (Ozolin, 1949; Matveyev, 1956; Khomenkov, 1970; Nabatnikova, 1972).

There are other classifications of the training load based on the motor characteristics of the sport, the power of muscular work, the pedagogical tasks of the training, the effect on restoration, the effect on subsequent work, the interaction of work regimes of different emphasis (e.g. the interaction of primarily strength work and speed-strength work) and other criteria (Farfel, 1958; Volkov, 1969, 1974; Zimkin, 1963; Monogarov & Platonov, 1975; Suslov, 1978; Scherrer, 1962, 1969).

However, each of these classifications, applied separately, are not quite suitable for resolving the task of the programming of training. A somewhat different approach is required here, which provides special requirements for the preliminary assessment of the loading and takes into account the above classification criteria.

The concept of loading suggests firstly a physiological measure of the effect of specialised muscular work on the body, reflected in the form of specific functional reactions. Consequently the necessity arose, in developing the concepts of external and internal loading, for introducing the concepts of the *training potential* of the loading and its *training effect* to enable one to more precisely describe the relationship between cause and effect (see 6.3, especially Fig 6.12).

The influence of the loading is expressed by its training effect (TE), assessed, first of all, by the magnitude of the change in the athlete's fitness state. Research concerning the forms in which the TE occurs is very contradictory, generally amounting to the following representation of events in the training process (Zatsiorsky, 1964; Volkov, 1966; Matveyev, 1977):

Acute TE > Delayed TE > Cumulative TE.

The first two forms are associated with the single training session: the *acute TE* is the body's current reaction to the physical loading, while the *delayed TE* is the alteration in the athlete's state observed some time after the workout. The *cumulative TE* is the result of the subsequent accumulation of all the TEs that were elicited during training.

However, the above scheme is one-sided and does not take into account the qualitative changes in the TE when they are produced by training loads of different primary emphasis (e.g. on strength, speed-strength or muscle endurance). The fact is that the accumulation of training effects is not simply a summation of separate effects, but a synergistic whole (i.e. the sum of the parts is greater than the whole).

The mechanism of generalised adaptation as a universal quality of a biological system establishing a balance between its state and external conditions, is determined primarily by the automatic selection of an accommodative strategy which is most appropriate in that situation. This involves selective response to the training influences of different primary emphasis and their stable integration into a well-adapted system. As has already been mentioned, the cumulative TE itself can have a different quantitative and qualitative expression, depending on factors including the current state of fitness, the order in which training regimes of different emphasis follow each other, the after-effects of preceding loading, and the duration of given training means (Verkhoshansky, 1970).

For example, it has long been known that the result of a workout depends on the sequence of exercises (e.g. with primary emphasis on speed, strength or endurance). Considerable research has shown clearly the effect of a particular sequence of training loads of different emphasis during long term training on the body, e.g 'aerobic' and 'anaerobic' glycolytic loading for developing special endurance (Nabatnikova, 1972; Volkov, 1975; Platonov, 1980) or strength and jumping exercises for explosive strength (Tatyan, 1975; Khodykin, 1976; Chernousov, 1978; Levchenko, 1980).

Based on similar research, it has been suggested that a distinction be made between the concepts of *partial TE* (the result of the effect of loading of one primary emphasis or means) and *cumulative TE* (the result of the generalised effect on the body of loading of different primary emphasis, applied concurrently or sequentially). In the latter case there are both quantitative and qualitative aspects to the TE. The distinction between these concepts can best be explained by examples.

In one experiment (Fig 6.24), group 1 began by using barbell exercises, followed by depth-jumps (a plyometric method of developing explosive strength). Group 2 used the reverse sequence of means. Each group of means were used for three months each. Group 3 used the barbell exercises and the depth-jumps concurrently throughout both 3-month stages. The overall volume of the loading was equivalent in all groups.

The results of the studies enabled us first of all to compare the partial TE of utilising only barbell exercises and depth-jumps (the first stage for groups 1 and 2), as well as the cumulative TE obtained as a result of two different ways of organising the loading: concurrent (group 3) and sequential (the second stage of groups 1 and 2). The following conclusions were derived from this experiment:

1. The partial TE of the depth-jumping is greater than that of the barbell exercises.

2. The final effect of the training is altered substantially by re-arrangement of the loading of different primary emphasis. The sequence of using barbell exercises followed by depth-jumps (group 1) produced a higher level of speed-strength preparedness (a positive cumulative TE), than the reverse sequence (group 2). In group 2 the TE was essentially lower at the end of the second stage than after the first (a negative cumulative TE).

3. The concurrent use of the above means in the first stage (group 3) yielded a larger cumulative effect than in groups 1 and 2. However, the TE noticeably decreased for group 3 during the second stage because the lengthy use of a single means decreases the training potential of the loading.

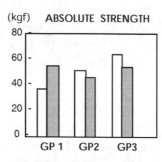 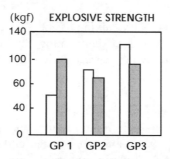 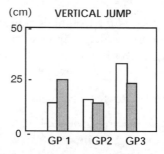

Figure 6.24 The training effect of different sequences of speed-strength means for high jumpers of medium qualification. Graph 1 shows the increase in absolute strength of the plantarflexors; graph 2, the increase in maximal explosive effort in a vertical jump; graph 3, the increase in height after a depth jump. All values in % increase over initial values. White bars = first 3 months; shaded bars = next 3 months of training. (Siff & Verkhoshansky, 1999).

In another experiment (Fig 6.25), over a 7-week period, group 1 used weights exercises with 30-50% of 1RM; group 2 used 70-90% of 1RM and group 3 used weights of 30-90% of 1RM concurrently (i.e. using the 30-50% and 70-90% regimes together). The general loading in all groups was equivalent in terms of the metabolic cost of the work. Again it is easy to see the partial TE of using different weights (groups 1 and 2) and the cumulative TE from the concurrent use of those and other forms of resisted forms of loading (group 3).

One should pay special attention to how the cumulative phenomenon appears as a result of combination work with weights of 30-90% of 1RM regarding the power achieved in group 3, and how much higher it is relative to the partial TE obtained with means of single emphasis (groups 1 and 2). At the same time it should be noted that the greatest increase in speed was produced by training with loads of 30-50% of 1RM (Group 1, graph 2).

The data shows clearly how much the athlete's special preparedness depends on the organisation of training loads, what must be emphasized when organising training, what type of TE is required in each case and what one needs to do to achieve it.

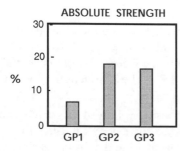 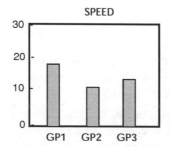 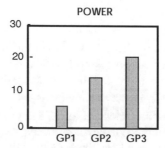

Figure 6.25 The training effect (in % increase) of different loading schemes on highly qualified jumpers for the extensor muscles of both legs (Nedobyvailov). Details are given in the text. (Siff & Verkhoshansky, 1999).

From a practical standpoint, it is expedient to assess the TE with respect to two criteria: the temporal (acute and delayed) and the qualitative (partial and cumulative). The acute TE is the effect observed immediately during or directly after a training session, while the delayed TE appears a relatively short time after the loading, for example, in a number of mixed sessions or over a short period (the short-term TE), or preserved for a longer time after the loading imposed over prolonged training stages (the long-term TE). The latter of these is analysed more thoroughly later (see 6.8).

A number of qualitative forms of the cumulative TE (acute or delayed) are distinguished, depending on the organisation of the training loads (Fig 6.26). Thus, the accumulation can be *transient* (the body's immediate reaction to a complex of training influences of different emphasis, imposed in one or mixed workouts, as well as the prolonged, parallel use of loading of different emphasis), *accumulated* (the stratification of traces of the training loads of different emphasis, following in a certain order in prolonged training stages), and finally, *positive or negative* (if the traces of some loads create or, conversely, do not create favourable conditions for adaptation to other loading).

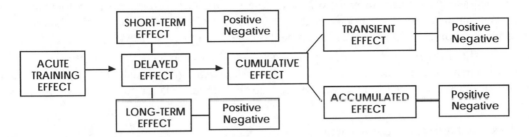

Figure 6.26 The relationship between the different types of training effect. (Siff & Verkhoshansky, 1999).

At first glance, this classification of the TE may appear to be somewhat tedious. However, its basis is the dependence of the athlete's state of fitness on the training loads under actual sporting conditions and it is impossible not to take its complexity into account when programming training.

The physiological nature of the TE is so complex and the forms in which it occurs so diverse that exhaustive analysis of its characteristics is possible only on the basis of the criteria identified earlier. This has great practical significance, since the programming of training loads should be based primarily on the objective of achieving a definite TE. Therefore, a clear understanding of the required TE and the conditions necessary for its achievement is essential for determining the contents and organisation of training.

6.9.2 Factors determining the Training Effect

In order to select the optimal training loads from the many possible variations, it is necessary to undertake a preliminary assessment of their effectiveness. To do this, it is useful to analyse the physical effects of the loading in terms of characteristics such as its contents, volume and organisation (Fig 6.27). The degree of reliability providing the effect generated by each of these characteristics has great significance for the success of the training.

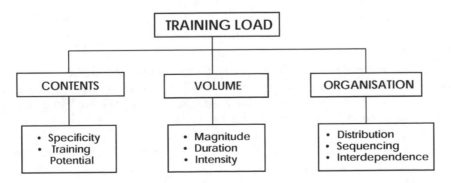

Figure 6.27 Factors concerned with producing the training effect. (Siff & Verkhoshansky, 1999).

We will examine in more detail the basis for a particular selection associated with each characteristic. In doing so, we will focus our attention on loading intended to develop explosive-strength and specific endurance.

6.9.3 The Contents of the Loading

The programming of training begins with the determination of its contents, i.e. the composition of the means, selected on the basis of preliminary assessments using two criteria, namely the *specificity* of the training load and the *training potential* (see Fig 6.27).

Specificity of the Load

The specificity of the training means refers to their similarity to competition activities regarding motor structure (including movement patterns), regime of work and mechanism of energy production. This particular criterion is used to distinguish between means of special and general physical preparedness (SPP and GPP). The SPP means primarily are for increasing the specific work capacity, whereas the GPP means are used for general physical development, for activating restorative processes after prolonged or intense loading, or for facilitating changes from one type of work to another (Ozolin, 1949; Khomenkov, 1957; Matveyev, 1964).

The SPP means should correspond as closely as possible to the dynamics and regime of work of the sports activity. This requirement is the *principle of dynamic correspondence* (discussed in 4.3) which stipulates the importance of the similarity between the training means and the fundamental sport exercises with respect to the following indicators (see 4.3):

- The amplitude and direction of movement
- The accentuated region of force production
- The dynamics of the effort (including maximum force)
- The rate and time of maximum force production
- The regime of muscular work.

One should, however, take into account that in practice the external similarity of the training means to the fundamental sport exercise is often overemphasized, whereas the importance of the similarity of the means to the *regime of muscular work* and to the *mechanism of its energy production* is underemphasized. It should be noted that literal similarity of the training means to the fundamental sports activities in motor structure is appropriate only if it directly improves the athlete's level of physical and technical preparedness (Dyachkov, 1968, 1975).

However, for SPP to be effective, it is not so important that the training means precisely mimic the spatial characteristics of the given exercise. The main criterion of conformity in this case is the regime of muscular work as a whole. For example, strength exercises such as barbell squats bear little resemblance to the athlete's movement in running, throwing or playing basketball. However, the use of squats is justified because they actively contribute to raising the athlete's special work capacity of the appropriate muscles in these sports.

An adequate number of SPP means which conform to the fundamental actions is available for training in every sport. However, it is important to point out that the need to preserve the training potential of the loading (especially for highly qualified athletes) requires using means that not only conform to, but exceed, competition conditions, with regard to maximum force, time of maximum force development and the power of the metabolic processes which determine work-capacity. On this basis, it is easy to conclude that satisfaction of this requirement should be associated with improving the strength component of the movement. This emphasis on strength or, more precisely, the use of specialised strength exercises in the regime of SPP means makes it necessary to examine this question in more detail.

First of all, one must emphasize that the role of strength exercises in sports training is not limited to enhancing strength alone, as is sometimes thought. *It is undoubtedly important to increase strength, but this is not the fundamental and sole task of strength training.* By itself, the value of maximal strength, in particular, dwindles and may not sufficiently be utilised in practice for enhancing the effect and specificity of the loading under actual sporting conditions. However, its role in speed-strength sports is obvious and achieved successfully, but in many other types of sport (in particular, those requiring endurance), it is still not adequately understood.

The development of endurance is associated primarily with using long duration or distance training to improve aerobic capacity. However, the importance of muscular adaptation to intense and prolonged work invariably is underestimated. It also appears to be forgotten that specialisation of the muscles, as the direct executor of the work, is of greater significance than development of the cardiovascular-respiratory component of endurance. A more intense stimulus is necessary for promoting adaptation of the muscles to endurance work than for producing cardiovascular and respiratory conditioning. Therefore, when one uses only the long duration method for developing endurance, a definite imbalance can arise between the functional level of the cardiovascular-respiratory systems and the working potential of the muscles. In this case, the anticipated sporting proficiency will not result.

This situation is very typical of the preparation of middle-distance runners. Elementary logic decrees that in order to run 800m in 1:45:0, it is necessary to be able to achieve a time of 10.6-10.7 seconds in the 100m. One needs to possess great strength potential to do this, e.g. the ability to execute three consecutive standing long jumps covering a total distance of at least 9m, or ten consecutive standing long jumps totalling 33-34m, for which middle-distance runners usually do not have the strength. Elimination of this insufficiency is possible only through specialised strength and jump training which exerts a stronger influence on the muscles than distance training, thereby intensifying their adaptation to endurance work and activating the relevant functional reserves of the body. As a result, the power and the capacity of the metabolic processes are enhanced, including 'anaerobic' energy production, which provides a high level of local muscular endurance and complements the body's already-acquired 'aerobic' ability. At the same time, it is possible to reduce the volume of exhausting endurance work in the 'anaerobic' glycolytic zone (Zhdanovich, 1980; Verkhoshansky & Sirenko, 1982).

Methods of executing specialised strength and jumping exercises in endurance sports should firstly increase strength up to a definite optimum, and secondly, exploit the specific energy processes crucial for producing repeated motor actions. The characteristics of the sport, practical experience and experimentation should determine the optimal regimes of specialised strength training in each case. The main thing is to overcome the archaic viewpoint which regards strength training as a means of increasing absolute strength alone.

The GPP means play no less an important role in the organisation of training. Besides improving traditional multi-faceted motor coordination and creating a foundation for subsequent specialised motor skill training, some GPP means can activate the restorative processes. This has special significance in those sports in which there are few supplementary training means and training is inherently monotonous, i.e. where the competition exercises are the basic training means (gymnastics, weightlifting and cyclic sports).

For example, research showed that the sole and systematic use of swimming restoration procedures during the execution of voluminous loading produced an increase of 24.2% in absolute strength and 18.9% in strength-endurance, whereas swimmers who did not use the restorative procedures increased these indicators by only 7.7% and 4.9% respectively. At the same time, the volume of the training load was increased by an average of 15% (Kuchnyev, 1977; Platonov, 1980). In the pre-competition preparation of highly qualified middle-distance runners, the complex use of low frequency vibromassage and psycho-regulatory training contributed to an increase in the speed of training distances by 2-4% and to an increase of 12-20% in training volume, executed at competition speed (Potapchenko, 1979).

Thus, the organised combination of training loads and restorative procedures is an important prerequisite for intensifying and increasing the effectiveness of training. However, it must be emphasized that restoration after work is a natural process which occurs in a definite sequence over a certain period. This process occurs through adaptation of interacting physiological systems to stress generated by systematic loading (Yakovlev, 1971). Artificially accelerating the restoration process as a routine can disturb the natural course of the body's long-term adaptation to intense muscular activity and therefore can be justified only in clear cases of over-exertion (Siff & Yessis, 1992).

Frequent and regular application of non-specific means of restoration may hinder the adaptation process, especially when large training loads are used. Increasing the volume and intensity of the loading disturbs homeostasis as a basic condition for promoting adaptation to loading and enhancement of the restoration processes. At the same time, premature intervention during the course of restoration can hinder the body's supercompensatory ability to enhance this process by natural means (Yevgenyev et al, 1975). The interconnected process of loading-restoration within the general scheme of sports training should be strictly regulated on the basis of scientific assessment of the athlete's fitness state.

Training Potential of the Loading

The training potential associated with the loading characterises the extent of its influence on the athlete's fitness. The higher the training potential relative to the current fitness state, the greater the probability of raising the athlete's special work capacity. The training potential of the means employed decreases as the special work capacity increases; therefore, it is important to preserve it by introducing more effective means into the training. This important principle of organising training is presented in Figure 6.28 (see also 5.4.4). The graph depicts the practical possibility of altering the athlete's state by using means with different training potential (A, B, C). However, it is inappropriate to use highly stimulating means prematurely, because the body is functionally unprepared for them, a situation that can cause excessive intensification of training and disturbance of the natural course of adaptation.

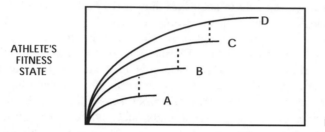

Figure 6.28 The effect of a sequence of training means with different training effects. The dashed lines show where one training means is replaced by a successive one with different training potential.

The means of SPP are introduced into training in a definite sequence, the so-called *conjugate sequence method* discussed earlier (see 5.3.3 and 5.4.4). The absolute intensity of the training influences on the body is gradually increased and a logical continuity is observed, so that the preceding means provide favourable conditions for utilising the subsequent means. Figure 5.15 gave a practical example of such a system of special strength training means in track-and-field sport. We will examine in more detail the practical issues associated with the application of this system.

6.9.4 The Volume of the Training Load

The volume of the training load refers primarily to the quantitative aspects of training and plays an important role in the long-term adaptation of the body to intense muscular work.

The function of the volume of the load consists chiefly of the systematic and prolonged disturbance of the body's homeostasis, which stimulates the mobilisation of its energy resources and plastic reserves. This is the fundamental condition for switching from the acute (specific) reaction provoked by individual components of the training, to the general (non-specific) adaptive reaction, and then to the development of long-term adaptation of the body. Therefore, in each successive annual cycle athletes should execute larger volumes of loading (within optimal limits) to raise and maintain the special work-capacity.

In types of sports requiring brief, highly concentrated efforts, the volume of loading has yet another important significance. As discussed earlier, *the mechanical integrity of the ligamentous-joint apparatus can become the limiting factor to the progress of sporting performance* (see 1.6 and 1.7.2). If these connective tissues are not prepared by extensive work of moderate intensity, then the great dynamic overloading encountered at the level of peak performance can lead to severe joint injury. This occurs frequently in gymnastics, weightlifting, high jumping and triple jumping.

The volume on its own does not determine the specificity of the training influence of the loading on the body and the characteristics of the body's adaptive reactions. Therefore, when programming training, the influence of the volume can be determined correctly only if one also takes into consideration the magnitude of the loading, its duration and intensity. The magnitude of the volume is the quantitative measure of the actual or planned training load of a certain primary emphasis calculated during each specific microcycle, stage or annual cycle as a whole (see 6.2.2).

The magnitude of the volume is determined, first of all, on the basis of the athlete's qualification. The higher the qualification, the larger the volume of loading over the year and each stage of preparation. As the athlete's qualification rises (also within a four-year cycle), so the magnitude, and consequently, the ratio of the loading volume of different primary emphasis shifts towards an increase in the portion devoted to specialised loading (Panov, 1975; Zhikharevich, 1976; Vankov, 1977; Matveyev, 1977; Gilyazova, 1978).

The magnitude of the annual loading volume is established individually by examining the characteristics of the athlete's preparation during the preceding stages of training. A more serious task of programming training is the calculation of the optimal volume of loading in distinct time segments (month, stage or phase). This magnitude should be determined on the basis of the goals of training during each stage of the annual cycle and according to the principles of effective organisation of training loads of different primary emphasis, as discussed in this chapter.

The intensity of the loading determines the strength and specificity of its effect on the body or the difficulty of the training. The intensity regulates the training potential of the given means, the frequency of their use and the intervals between repeated means or training sessions with large training potential, as well as the ratio of the volume of the loading divided by the time taken to reach the maximum load in a given stage. The latter measure has especially important significance for programming training over prolonged periods, since it takes into account the loading concentration relative to time. Intensification of loading is permitted during specific stages in the annual cycle and only after preliminary preparation with extensive low intensity loading (see Fig 6.1).

The duration of the training load is a vital measure of the volume and must be discussed in more detail, since it has a significant effect on the dynamics of the athlete's fitness state and can easily be miscalculated by the average coach.

It has already been mentioned that the length of time over which systematic training regimes are employed (the general volume of loading) has a definite maximum limit, depending on the current adaptation reserves (CAR) of the body (see 1.16). At the same time, considerable research has established that there is also an upper limit to the duration of using any specialised training means with a primary emphasis, the exceeding of which is detrimental to the development of maximum and explosive strength, as well as to the growth of aerobic and anaerobic capacity. Exceeding this limit does not enhance fitness and wastes the athlete's time and energy. In programming training, it is important to determine the optimal duration of loading of any primary emphasis, as well as a suitable rate of increase of the relevant performance indicators.

Unfortunately there is no special research directed at determining the optimal length of time for applying loading of a specific primary emphasis. However, indirect data has been gathered which sheds some light on this problem. Thus, there is a linear increase in absolute strength in response to a given regime of loading, which slows down as the limit of this optimal time-span of training is reached, a point which defines exhaustion of the body's current adaptation energy (see 1.16). Observation of highly qualified athletes indicates that absolute strength increases with little variation, rising continuously during the year's training.

When explosive strength is the purpose of special training, there is a clear tendency for the rise in explosive strength to slow down; the sharper its growth, the earlier it plateaus. When one is emphasizing the development of explosive strength exclusively, the plateau appears within 3-4 months. In those cases where explosive strength is not the key ability (e.g. in a mono-cycle of periodisation in the annual training of decathletes), the increase in explosive strength can continue (with some fluctuation) for up to 10 months.

Loading that is primarily aerobic will produce significant increases in aerobic efficiency even within one month of training (Borisov, 1979; Sirenko, 1980). The dynamics of the level of aerobic fitness and the indicators of aerobic loading executed within the aerobic zone (at a HR of 120-170 beats/minute) parallel one another. Their rate of increase is approximately the same and is linear over a 2-3 months period. Despite increased loading volume, the aerobic fitness indicators do not increase significantly later on, but fluctuate around the maximum level achieved (Zatsiorsky et al, 1974; Skorodymova, 1974; Suslov, 1977; Ustkachkintsev, 1979; Sirenko, 1980).

About 4 months are necessary to achieve the highest results in anaerobic-glycolytic productivity (Zatsiorsky et al, 1974; Serafimova, 1974; Doroshchenko, 1976; Ustkachkintsev, 1979). Increasing the volume of anaerobic work produces a positive effect only if it precedes a significant volume of aerobic work, thereby stimulating the aerobic reaction (Serafimova, 1974; Naumenko, 1978).

Note that the above data applies to the natural conditions of an athlete's preparation, where development of a given motor ability is achieved together with the execution of other tasks and loading of other primary emphasis. They conform to those actual loading volumes that highly qualified athletes use according to contemporary principles of organising training. Since these principles are being constantly refined, the duration of loading quoted above is not definitive. However, they offer a preliminary guide for the programming of training.

6.9.5   The Organisation of Training Loads

The organisation of training refers to its regulation over a definite period to ensure attainment of the planned level of SPP and physical fitness. The basis of such regulation should be the achievement of the positive cumulative training effect of the loading of different primary emphasis (see Fig 6.26). Here, it is necessary to observe the chief requirement of maintaining the training potential of the loading. The basic organisational principles of special strength training, which are discussed in the following sections, are:

• The specificity of muscular work

- The concentration of loading over time
- The separation of strength load, speed development and perfection of technique
- Utilisation of the Long-term Training Effect

The organisation of loading is defined by two criteria, namely the nature of its distribution over time and the interrelation between the loads of different primary emphasis.

The distribution of the training load over time refers to the way in which it is organised in separate stages, cycles and phases of the annual cycle. The distribution of the general volume of loading and its dynamics in the annual cycle are determined by the traditional periodisation of training and the characteristics of the body's long-term adaptation to training. If one speaks of loading of one primary emphasis, then one must distinguish between two ways of organising it, namely *distributed loading* and *concentrated loading* (see 6.6.1 and Fig 6.23). The first assumes a relatively uniform distribution of means during an annual cycle; the second, the concentration of means over definite training stages.

The effectiveness of the distribution and concentration methods of organising training loads should be based on the athlete's level of qualification. Research indicates that both methods are successful in training athletes of medium qualification. The concentrated loading method is appropriate for the training of highly qualified athletes. In this regard, it has been shown that *distribution of glycolytic work over the annual cycle of highly qualified sprinters raises the loading volume, but does not increase the effectiveness of the loading.* However, by concentrating the volume of glycolytic work at certain stages, the work can be executed at a smaller volume but with a more significant improvement in speed-endurance (Kornelyuk, 1980). Similar results have been obtained by concentrating the volume of special strength work of sprinters (Levchenko, 1986), middle-distance runners (Sirenko & Zhdanovich, 1982), boxers (Filimonov, 1979) and jumpers (Mironenko & Antonova, 1981).

The above research has shown that *concentration of the volume of uni-directional loading produces more extensive functional changes and greater improvement* in the athlete's physical fitness. The regular use of training with distributed loading which is dispersed over a prolonged period evokes only a transient functional reaction which does not enhance the development of long-term adaptation. Distributed loading initially can yield some rise in functional level but its training potential soon drops because of rapid adaptation of the body to the training stimuli.

The use of loads of different primary emphasis produces the required cumulative training effect, provided that they are combined logically over time, since *the cumulative loading with means of different primary emphasis can have positive or negative effects.* Thus, to develop explosive strength, a positive cumulative effect on the body may be achieved by use of the following brief combinations of training means:

- short and long jumping exercises
- barbell exercises and jumping exercises
- barbell exercises with 30% and 90% of maximum
- barbell exercises and the plyometric method of developing explosive-strength
- leaping with kettle-bells and jumping exercises
- barbell exercises and leaping with kettle-bells.

In a single training session the order of the above means, combined in a systematic complex is fairly unimportant, since the length of time for which the body maintains the after-effect of training stress exceeds the duration of the workout. During this session and the subsequent restoration period, a generalised summation of the after-effects of the entire complex of training influences of different primary emphasis occurs, which produces the same cumulative effect, generally regardless of their sequence. However, it is still sensible to apply the recommended scheme of Figure 1.7 to minimise the risk of reducing skill and safety.

Thus, *concerning the development of explosive strength, the order of the means is not fundamentally as important as the volume of the loading and the degree of contrast between the different training means.* Nevertheless, one should still preserve the above order of combining means in each case, since this provides the favourable effect of a brief rise in fitness state, which the first exercise produces as the second one is executed (see Ch 5.3). The best way of using the above combination of special strength exercises is to employ them sequentially with active rest between each series. When repeating such a series, it is desirable to vary the exercises to avoid monotony and to maintain the optimal rest interval for facilitating recovery.

One cannot speak with similar certainty about the effect of the interaction of loading of different primary emphasis on the development of endurance. Research findings are inadequate and are often so contradictory that it is very difficult to discern definite trends. It is believed that the main reason for this situation is the unsuccessful attempt at definitive analysis of less popular concepts concerning the mechanisms of energy production for intense muscular work (Margaria et al, 1964). Current models classify training loads as aerobic (oxidative glycolysis), alactic-anaerobic (ATP-CP processes), anaerobic-glycolytic (oxygen-independent glycolysis), mixed and so forth. Since the definitions of these categories are so conditional that they permit very broad interpretation, they cannot be strictly applied analysing the primary emphasis of different loads and consequently, to the objective assessment of their training effect.

It should be noted that little research has investigated the precise contribution of the different energy processes during the short duration activity of strength, strength-speed and strength-endurance sports. Moreover, no research has analysed the energy processes occurring while the general activity is undoubtedly aerobic, but the postural muscles are strongly contracted, a situation which suggests that aerobic processes can be strongly active at a general level while anaerobic processes can also be strongly evident at a local level. This obviously poses a major problem for the prescription of sport specific training.

It is to be hoped that in the near future the negative consequences of such interpretations will be eliminated, but until then it should be noted that current experimental data indicates that a positive interaction of endurance loading occurs when:

- aerobic exercises are done after ATP-CP training
- aerobic exercises are done after glycolytic-anaerobic training (in small volume)
- glycolytic-anaerobic exercises are done after ATP-CP training.

Under these conditions the previous loading creates favourable conditions for executing the subsequent loading and raises the effect of the training session as a whole.

There is a negative interaction when (Volkov, 1975):

- ATP-CP exercises are done after a large amount of any glycolytic work
- glycolytic-anaerobic exercises follow large volumes of aerobic work.

It has been established that restoration of energy resources and disturbance of endocrine equilibrium within the body is prolonged by 2-3 days after a large volume of aerobic work. During this period it is appropriate to employ a small volume of anaerobic loading which will not negatively influence the restoration of aerobic capacity and will stimulate the development of anaerobic capacity.

Restoration after moderate volumes of anaerobic loading usually takes 3-8 hours. However, very large volumes of anaerobic loading will delay restoration. The training effect of ATP-CP workouts deteriorates if the sessions are done without allowing full restoration from the preceding loading (Nabatnikova, 1972; Volkov, 1975; Platonov, 1980).

Sequential accumulation of the training effect of loading of different primary emphasis has a place in long-term preparation and is achieved by the action of preceding work on subsequent work. In this case, if the preceding work creates favourable circumstances for the subsequent work, there is a positive accumulation of their training effects.

For the development of explosive strength, positive accumulation is achieved by means of a sequence which applies extensive (i.e. high volume) training with submaximal resistance first, followed by explosive training. In this case the positive accumulation is achieved by the first loading regime producing a rise in the general energy potential of the neuromuscular system. This creates favourable conditions for further adaptation, facilitated by the subsequent loading and emphasis on developing the athlete's ability to display great explosive power. The reverse sequence of this loading scheme leads to a negative cumulative effect.

The mechanism of sequential accumulation is appropriate only if the training effect of the previous work has become relatively stable, which takes at least 4-6 weeks. When the strength means of different emphasis are changed over shorter time intervals, for example after 2 weeks, the body cannot differentiate between the specifics of their individual influence and the body's adaptive reaction as mediated by the *transient accumulation* process. Thus, a change after 2-week stages of use in the order of loading of different emphasis minimally alters the resulting training effect.

With the development of special endurance (i.e. the main aim of cyclic sports), the sequential accumulation of the training effect of loading of different primary emphasis displays a more complex character than the development of explosive strength, which leads to the following conclusions:

- It is permissible and customary to develop explosive abilities with supplementary means that sometimes deviate far from the motor structure of the fundamental sport exercise; however, the fundamental sport activity is traditionally the chief means of developing special endurance in cyclic sports. Here the development of special endurance depends on the optimal selection of the relative volumes of work of different intensity and duration.

- *Endurance training* causes more profound changes than explosive training within the body and requires more time for restoration. Therefore, selection of subsequent training is very important. Since it is appropriate to do work of a different type, which in particular intensifies restoration or improves other abilities, this complicates the maintenance of the main emphasis of the training regime and leads to use of concurrent training means, which may not always be appropriate for highly qualified athletes (Platonov, 1980).

The methods of developing endurance were established long ago and there are still two opposing viewpoints. One of these is based on the value of concurrent development of general and special endurance (Matveyev, 1970; Ogoltsov, 1971; Nabatnikova, 1972). This variant introduces special endurance loading right from the beginning of the preparatory period, during which one is also developing general endurance. It is assumed that this training will be more specialised, creating more favourable conditions for specific adaptation to competitive activities. This point of view has been corroborated experimentally, much of the research having been done with athletes who had not yet reached the highest levels of sports mastery, in particular with junior middle-distance runners (Baranov, 1969), swimmers (Kuzovenkov, 1969) and skiers (Malikov, 1974).

The viewpoint emphasizes the sequential development of endurance, where one begins by enhancing cardiovascular capability, followed by anaerobic-glycolytic endurance, and finally, short-term endurance (the creatine phosphate process). The introduction of aerobic work in this sequence promotes the training-effect of anaerobic work (Ozolin, 1959, 1970; Volkov, 1963; Yakovlev, 1957; Borisov, 1979; Loktev, 1978). A gradual increase in the duration of cardiovascular loading leads to an accumulation of energy substrates and an increase in the body's energy potential (Yakovlev, et al, 1960). Here, the intensity of loading, rather than its volume is of principal significance (Astrand & Rodahl, 1970). When one's cardiovascular ability is insufficient, an excessive increase in the volume of anaerobic means causes a decrease in sporting performance (Naumenko, 1978; Vavilov, 1977; Serafimova, 1974; Morzhevikov, 1980).

A third viewpoint on endurance development has been formulated and experimentally verified. Basically, it involves the increase in volume of concurrent aerobic and anaerobic training means, but with a sequential change in emphasis from general to special endurance. The effectiveness of this type of training construction in the annual cycle has been demonstrated, in particular, for highly qualified middle-distance runners (Doroshchenko, 1976; Loktev, 1978; Borisov, 1979), as well as for multi-year training (Linyets, 1979). One can assume that this system represents a compromise which combines the benefits of concurrent and sequential special endurance training.

The organisation of loading is closely associated with selecting the *optimal rest interval* between repetitions in a single training session and between successive sessions. It is vital to remember that the essence of training consists not only of muscular work, but also of the effect of the adaptive reaction elicited by it. Therefore, *the rest pause is actually a training means which is just as important as muscular work*, so that it should be employed skillfully. It has been emphasized repeatedly that the art of training management consists of the systematic combination of specific and non-specific loading, together with careful regulation of work and rest stages (Hippenreitor, 1955; Petrovsky, 1969; Ozolin, 1949, 1966). The rest interval is one of the most important components of training methodology. Devising the optimal pause between repetitions and other stages of training work requires extensive methodological competence and practical skill in utilising this pause effectively.

These findings highlight the extremely complex connection between the athlete's state and the training load, and coupled with this, the difficulty of selecting the optimal method of training organisation to achieve the desired special work capacity. Nevertheless, despite the paucity of data, which does not allow one to prescribe exact recommendations for each sport, some principal guidelines for organising annual training loads may be identified, as given in various sections of this text.

6.10 The Long-Term Delayed Training Effect

The particular connection between the dynamics of the athlete's state and the loading regime in long-term training will now be examined in detail.

Considerable research (Nikitin, 1977; Mironenko, 1979; Antonova, 1982; Levchenko, 1982) has revealed a steady decrease in speed-strength preparedness during individual training stages of different length (from 5-12 weeks). This decrease is the result of voluminous strength loading (Figure 6.29, shaded rectangle), after which speed-strength returns to its initial level and significantly exceeds it. Since this phenomenon does not agree with established ideas which stipulate a continuous rise in special physical preparedness as an essential condition for effective organisation of training, and since it is not accompanied by marked signs of overtraining, it has become a subject of special study. The results of this study occupy the remainder of this section.

The volume of the training load has a definite optimum level for each athlete, above or below which the body reacts with diminished response. There is a characteristically simple connection between the quantity of work and the dynamics of the athlete's fitness state.

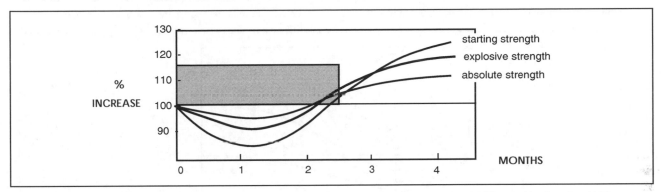

Figure 6.29 The effect of concentrated strength loading on speed-strength indicators of sprinters (Siff & Verkhoshansky, 1999).

An increase in volume of loading raises the athlete's special work-capacity, whereas a decrease lowers it. If the volume of loading is lower than the optimum level, special work-capacity decreases after some initial rise. If the volume of loading significantly exceeds this level, a steady decrease in special work-capacity occurs which, however, rises intensely during the carefully-timed reduction in the volume. This intense rise in special work-capacity is the phenomenon known as the *long-term delayed training effect* (LDTE) which accompanies one of the forms of adaptation to volume of loading.

This phenomenon has been known for some time in practice, where it has been observed as an increase in performance in several sports after a decrease in the volume of the training load during the pre-competition stage (Ozolin, 1949, 1967; Dyachkov, 1953; Matveyev, 1970; Charyev, 1975). However, this reflects only the external evidence of this type of adaptation, and the physiological conditions, mechanisms and characteristics of the LDTE until recently have not been a subject of much research. Essentially, no one expected that the existence of the LDTE offered any great promise for systematising training, especially for highly qualified athletes.

The LDTE phenomenon of concentrated strength loading has also been observed in several cyclic sports, including middle-distance running (Zhdanovich, 1980), swimming (Rudokene, 1981) and ice-skating (Kabachkova et al, 1982). Thus, a steady increase in the strength-endurance of middle-distance runners was verified, being reflected in increased stride length and improved results in ten standing long jumps (Fig 6.30) following a block of concentrated strength loading. It is interesting that there is an increase in the ability of these runners to produce a single explosive effort (e.g. in vertical jumping) during the concentrated strength loading stage, but this ability decreases during the competition stage. One may assume that the reason for this phenomenon is the increase in volume of intense distance work, which impairs the ability to produce explosive strength, because the latter plays a non-specific role in cyclic sports. Based on research and experience, the LDTE phenomenon may be characterised as follows (see Fig 6.31):

1. Concentration of the volume of strength loading (A) over a limited period exerts an extensive, unidirectional training influence on the body. Concentration of strength loading is the basic condition for the beginning of the LDTE.

2. The lower the speed-strength levels fall (within an optimal range) during the concentration of strength loading stage, the higher they rise in the subsequent LDTE phase (graphs of F1 and F2). Excessive concentration of strength loading leads to a more significant drop in speed-strength and disruption of adaptation (graph F3).

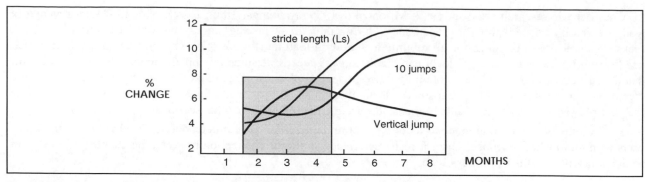

Figure 6.30 An example of the LDTE of concentrated block of strength loading for middle-distance runners (Zhdanovich, 1980).

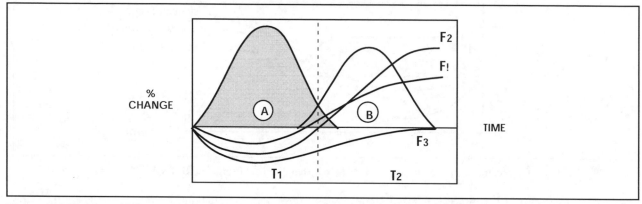

Figure 6.31 The general scheme of the LDTE of concentrated strength loading (Siff & Verkhoshansky, 1999).

3. When concentrated strength loading is used to elicit a LDTE, the selected means should not be intensive. Concentration of unidirectional loading already intensifies the training process, and one should not intensify it further with high intensity means.

4. A subsequent moderate volume of general developmental work, combined with special work of gradually increasing intensity contributes to eliciting the LDTE initiated by the concentrated strength loading (B).

5. The length of time for which the LDTE is displayed is determined by the volume and duration of the concentrated strength loading. In principle, the duration of the LDTE (T2) is approximately equal to the duration of the strength training stage (T1). Under the actual training conditions of highly qualified athletes, the LDTE was observed to last from 4-12 weeks during the long-term stages of strength preparation. However, one should bear in mind that appearance of the LDTE is individualised and to a large degree depends on the athlete's volume of loading and individual recuperative ability. An equivalent volume of loading for two athletes of the same qualification can yield significantly different effects.

There are a number of important circumstances associated with the production and use of the LDTE of strength loading during the annual cycle. Athletes invariably do not allow or do not have sufficient time for recuperation after extensive strength loading. Consequently, they minimise the possibility of stimulating a LDTE of strength loading and thereby maintain conditions which are extremely stressful for the body. Besides this, the body is regularly forced to unjustifiably deplete its current adaptation energy and sometimes draw upon its deep adaptation energy to restore its energy potential. Consequently, the effectiveness of preparation is fairly low under such conditions and special work-capacity is not very high during the competition stage.

During the period of emergence of the LDTE of extensive strength loading, it is relatively easy and painless for the body to change to *intensive* loading, but it will react negatively to *extensive* work. This is manifested in the slowed or even decreased growth of speed-strength. The volume of training work, therefore, should not be increased during the period of emergence of the LDTE. One should be especially cautious with strength loading during the competition period. At this time, intensive and short-term strength work can be used in a small volume to tone the neuromuscular system during competition preparation, as well as to maintain the achieved level of speed-strength preparedness if the length of the competition period exceeds the duration of the LDTE of strength loading.

At this point it is relevant to comment on the relationship between strength training and technical training, especially since it has often been stressed that there seems to be no logical connection between these types of training. It should be noted that *the competitive action executed with maximal physical exertion represents the most specific of all the special training means*. Therefore, this special means of training should be viewed simultaneously as a highly intense means of strength training and should occupy a place of central importance in the training programme. In other words, a strength training programme should first be constructed in accordance with the principle of gradual increase in intensity and secondly, be combined with technique training so as to peak concurrently with the competitive act, performed with maximal effort.

At the highest level of sports mastery, improvement in performance is determined primarily by increasing the athlete's special work capacity, which is essential for improving proficiency in any competitive event. Technical mastery is the ability to effectively realise one's motor potential under competitive conditions. Increasing the level of special work capacity, in particular one's strength potential, in turn, promotes improvement in technique. This is largely a result of the athlete becoming able to concentrate his effort more effectively, increase range of movement, decrease the time of execution of movements, improve his stability, improve the strength of muscular control over all movements and increase his resistance to fatigue. Thus, special physical preparation and technical training are closely linked and interdependent. However, the dominant role in this interaction is played by special physical preparation, both in the yearly cycle and in long-term training.

It should never be forgotten that high-volume strength loads are detrimental to one's current level of speed-strength fitness and, consequently, to technical preparation. To avoid this, it is advisable in training high level athletes to structure the programme so that strength work precedes and does not interfere with technical training. Technical training should take place in the presence of the delayed training effect of the concentrated volume of strength work, i.e. when there is recovery of work capacity and an increase in the level of speed-strength. Technique rapidly adjusts to the athlete's higher level of specialised work capacity and there is much less likelihood of reinforcing errors which may arise in connection with the body's lowered functional state, caused by high-volume loads. This type of programming, especially as part of the conjugate system of training, successively introduces different modes of loading into the training rather than separating them in time, so that each mode tends to gradually replace its predecessor.

The Delayed Training Effect and Long Duration Work

With respect to aerobic and anaerobic productivity, there is no experimental data that clearly documents occurrence of the LDTE phenomenon in cyclic distance training. The exceptions are cases of intense training under the lowered oxygen conditions of high altitude. Here, characteristics of the LDTE phenomenon have been observed in swimmers, with significant increases being measured in maximum aerobic capacity, the total volume of work which can be executed at the critical level of power, VO_2 max and the onset of blood lactate accumulation (Vaitsekhovsky et al, 1974). These changes persisted for more than 4 weeks after 3 weeks of training at an altitude of 1700m above sea level, with a peak response taking place about 1 week after the altitude training. All of the athletes in the study improved their results immediately after training at altitude.

Similar results were obtained with skaters who were first tested with 4 minutes on a cycle ergometer every week for 3 weeks at an altitude of 2250m, then with the same test for the next 3 weeks at sea level (Ivanov, 1977). At altitude, there was a decrease in mechanical efficiency and an increase in oxygen consumption, energy expenditure and lactate accumulation. After a return to sea level, it was found that the functional efficiency of the work exceeded the pre-experimental levels as a result of more economical metabolism and a significantly diminished amount of anaerobically produced ATP.

The stay at low-oxygen (hypobaric) conditions common to both experiments provided a very demanding training influence which provoked persistent disturbance of the body's homeostasis and subsequent activation of its adaptive processes.

As already emphasized, the LDTE phenomenon is not observed by using traditional ways of investigating the cardiovascular-respiratory systems under normal barometric conditions. However, if it originates from the general biological processes of adaptation to external influences, the prolonged disturbance of homeostasis which is essential for producing the LDTE will occur at the level of more subtle physiological systems and changes in its dynamics will not be detectable by methods used for assessing the more gross aerobic and anaerobic processes

(Verkhoshansky, 1977). In this case, adaptation apparently occurs at deeper cellular and molecular levels (e.g. in the mitochondria and endocrine system), as indicated by considerable biochemical research (Yakovlev, 1957, 1974; Viru, 1969, 1981; Finogenov, 1979). However, disturbance of homeostasis can be detected in the dynamics of a number of psycho-physiological indicators which reflect the functional state of the central nervous and neuromuscular systems.

Another study showed that the use of large training loads decreases the motor capabilities of swimmers, revealed by the slowing of complex motor reactions, diminished precision in producing movement patterns and deterioration of precision in tracking a moving object (Susman, 1978). At the same time there was a noticeable decrease in work capacity, in the functional state of the cardiovascular system (assessed from ECG data), in muscle tonus, and in hormonal levels in the adrenal cortex. After the training loads were reduced and the intensity of the swimming workouts was altered, there was a rise in the psycho-physiological indicators as the supercompensation (adaptive reconstruction) phase emerged. Simultaneously, the work capacity of the swimmers increased, the functional state of the cardiovascular system improved and muscle tonus increased.

Concluding Comments

It is hoped that research in this area in the near future will enable us to characterise more completely the LDTE phenomenon of extensive specific loading in long-duration cyclic sports and make a significant contribution to the science of programming training. The characteristics of the LDTE phenomenon should be considered an important foundation for devising programmes for training highly qualified athletes over the annual cycle, because the creation of conditions for evoking and exploiting the LDTE significantly increases the possibility for enhancing the effectiveness of training for all sports.

It is necessary to emphasize that *one must differentiate between maintenance of the training effect and the LDTE of loading*. In the first case, the key issue is the retention of functional adaptation for a given period after training has ceased, whereas in the second case, the vital issue is the relatively prolonged increase in the functional indicators as a result of specially organised, concentrated volumes of loading.

6.11 The Dynamics of Training in the Annual Cycle

As has already been emphasized, knowledge of the characteristics of the interdependence between the dynamics of the athlete's fitness state and the training loads is of central importance in programming training. However, in practice, there is very little research concerning the dynamics of the athlete's state over the annual cycle. Research assessing the athlete's state 3 to 4 times a year is not very informative, since the most interesting changes in state occur between each of these stages.

There is considerable research on the changes in the functional indicators of untrained subjects exercising under laboratory conditions for periods of 3-4 months (Pollock, 1973). These studies are undoubtedly of interest for studying the mechanism of the body's short-term adaptation to muscular work, but are of little use in programming the training of highly qualified athletes. Therefore, Verkhoshansky and his colleagues undertook research of exercise dynamics and experiments under the natural conditions of training athletes of various levels of qualification, recording functional indicators twice a month and correlating all changes with calculations of the training loads and volumes (the results of which are given throughout Chapter 5 and this chapter).

Research has established that in sports requiring explosive force, random increases in speed-strength are observed in *athletes of medium qualification*, together with insignificant changes in speed-strength during the annual cycle. Furthermore, these fluctuations often do not conform to the periodisation schemes of training or the competition calendar. The reason for this lies in the use of complex training (i.e. the concurrent use of loading regimes of different primary emphasis) and the monotonous monthly distribution of the general volume of loading over the annual cycle.

Accompanying the growth of proficiency of non-elite athletes, the fitness state shows a trend towards regularity which reflects the type of training periodisation used during the annual cycle. During monocyclic periodisation (e.g. in the decathlon) the level of special-strength preparedness generally increases without any significant fluctuations throughout the year. In bi-cyclic periodisation, two large waves are clearly planned which conform to two mesocycles of preparation, one ending in the winter and the other in the summer competition.

However, in the case of *highly qualified athletes*, the dynamics of speed-strength over the annual cycle cannot be regulated in such a manner. Research reveals a pronounced diversity in the dynamics of the fitness state of these athletes. Large fluctuations in speed-strength preparedness can be of different duration and magnitude, can occur at different stages of the annual cycle and often show neither a logical correlation with traditional periodisation of training (for the given sport) nor the competition calendar.

A phenomenon which has great significance for regulating the influence of loading was first discovered by observing the dynamics of the functional state over the annual cycle. It was found that *the speed-strength of thigh extension, knee extension and plantarflexion can show different trends of change at certain training stages*. The dynamics of the explosive strength of triple jumpers serves as an example (Verkhoshansky, 1988). This phenomenon is associated with the relatively unequal emphasis of the training influences on the functioning of the muscles which are responsible for movement of the lower extremities. The concurrent use of jumping and barbell exercises exerts a more intense local influence on the plantarflexors than other muscles of the lower extremity and, consequently, depresses their functional state. However, the loading is not as intense on the thigh extensors, so that their functional indicators reflect a high value. In this case, the athlete notices that movement coordination is difficult although, on the whole, he feels perfectly fit.

Thus, when one attempts to determine the composition and the means of special strength training without taking into account the differences in their primary emphasis on the specific muscle groups producing a sporting movement, the result can be that the functional state of the muscles involved does not conform to that required by the sport. This, in turn, exerts a negative effect on the quality of the athlete's technical preparation and his preparedness for competition. Consequently, in this case, it is necessary to regulate the emphasis of the loading on the plantarflexors, and periodically decrease the loading on them, especially during the technical and immediate pre-competition training stages.

The athlete's fitness state, as characterised by his aerobic and anaerobic capabilities, depends on the contents and organisation of the training loads. One study which corroborated this finding examined the results of two groups of middle-distance runners training with different training programmes over an annual cycle (Sirenko, 1980). Each group followed a training programme with the same volume and distribution of running means, but Group 1 used a traditional single-peak distribution of strength-means, whereas Group 2 used a double-peaked distribution of means with the emphasis concentrated in December and March-April.

Group 2 proved superior in all tests of functional ability, including aerobic efficiency, 'anaerobic threshold' (onset of blood lactate accumulation) and the results of control runs of 400m and 1200m, as well as in their sporting performances. During the summer competition stage Group 2 improved the 800m time by an average of 4.8 seconds and the 1500m run by 6.3 seconds, whereas in Group 1, the improvements were 3.4 and 4.6 seconds, respectively.

This and other studies of the influence of training loads on functional indicators show that three levels of change in an athlete's fitness state during training may be identified:

1. *A long-term level* characterised by the steady rise in the athlete's special work capacity. This level is associated with prolonged training periods of one or more years and its basis lies in long-term adaptation, promoted chiefly by the volume of loading.

2. *A medium-term level* characterised by less stable and readily reversible functional changes, the basis for which is compensatory adaptation. These changes are associated with lengthy training stages of up to 5-6 months and, together with the volume of the load, are produced by the characteristics of its contents, in particular, the proportion of intensive means in the total volume of loading.

3. *A short-term level* characterised by brief, but not precisely measurable, changes in the functional indicators, i.e. changes representing the body's acute reaction to the training load. These changes concern the microcycle and are elicited by the magnitude of the load, the intensity of loading, the individual ability of the athlete to endure the loading and his restorative capabilities. At this level, the dynamics of the functional indicators are largely random and at times unpredictable. This level is not determined by the adaptation of the first two levels and is important only for organisation of the microcycle and achievement of the immediate effect of the current loading.

One practical conclusion that can be drawn from these findings is that the dynamics of the athlete's fitness state during the annual cycle are controllable. The dependence of the dynamics of fitness on the contents, volume and organisation of the loading is determined by definite adaptive processes. Consequently, training should be structured by first of all taking into account the dynamics of the athlete's special physical preparedness (SPP) and controlling the degree of conformity of the training to the actual sporting dynamics required at each stage.

Mastering the ability to effectively programme the contents of training and regulate the dynamics of the athlete's fitness state during training involves eliminating all weak links in the system of managing training and thereby significantly increasing the probability of achieving the intended level of sporting performance.

The art of controlling the dynamics of the athlete's fitness state consists, firstly, of achieving the necessary level of conditioning and, secondly, achieving it at the required time, as dictated by the competition calendar. Research shows that achievement of the second requirement is not especially complex. However, the probability of successfully achieving the first requirement is much smaller.

6.12 Principles of Programming and Organising Training

The basis of programming is the programme-objective approach, in accordance with which the contents, volume and organisation of training loads are determined by the *objectives* of the preparation (see Fig 6.8). The objectives consist of three main components:

- the desired improvement in performance
- the appropriate changes in technical-tactical, psychological and competition preparedness
- the necessary modification of special physical preparedness.

In practice, the selection of a programming strategy is performed by means of a logical 'if-then' approach, which is understood in the following way: if one sets a specific and quantitatively defined goal, then the precise work and methods necessary to accomplish this goal constitute the appropriate strategy.

6.12.1 Forms of Constructing Training

Construction of training involves regulating its contents to provide the effective use of loading of different primary emphasis, i.e. the organisation of the contents over time, so that the required training effect occurs with a minimal expenditure of energy.

Consequently, time and organisation are two closely interdependent variables in the planning of training. The contents and organisation of training are dictated by the training objectives and the characteristics of adaptation to the intense muscular work deemed to be necessary for the given period. The time limitation imposed by the competition calendar and the duration of the energy supply from the current adaptation reserves affects the selection of the contents and organisation of training. Actual conditions do not always satisfy the optimal values of these variables. Therefore, programming of training requires creative flexibility based on the skill to anticipate the effect of any form of training and select its optimal variant.

It is appropriate now to examine the different forms of training against a background of research into the characteristics of adaptation to intense exercise and the principal trends produced by the given loading in the dynamics of the athlete's exercise state. Two categories of training construction may be identified: one based on structural organisation and the other on time management. With respect to organisation, one has to consider the ways of combining loading of different primary emphasis as a basic condition for achieving a large training effect. With respect to time, one has to consider ways of regulating the loading within definite cycles and stages, as determined by the periodisation of training and the competition calendar.

6.12.2 Organisational Aspects of Structuring Training

There are essentially two basic different ways of organising training, namely the complex and the concentrated loading methods. Complex loading involves prescription of multi-faceted training regimes to achieve several different fitness objectives over the same period, whereas the concentrated loading method concentrates for a given period on producing a single major specific fitness quality via the use of a unidirectional regime of training.

Complex training refers to the concurrent use of different training means in the same workout, microcycle or mesocycle. For instance, a complex workout might comprise resistance training, plyometrics and sprinting; a complex microcycle (typically a week) might employ those same training means on different days or during different sessions on the same day.   If complex means are to be utilised, it is essential to understand fully how the different means and exercises interact with one another, as determined by the acute and delayed after-effects of each (discussed earlier in this chapter). In addition, the prescription of complex means depends on the individual, the level of proficiency of the athlete, the specific objective, and the stage of the training programme, especially the proximity to important competitions

Complex Training

Complex training, which involves concurrent (during one workout or microcycle) and parallel (prolonged stages of training, up to a year) use of several training tasks and loads of different primary emphasis, is usually regarded as the most effective form of training construction. This is a direct result of considerable early research that supported the principle of complex organisation of training. The results showed that the athlete achieves balanced and multi-faceted physical fitness, that development of one motor ability contributes to the development of others and that multifaceted loading improves strength, speed of movement and endurance to a greater extent than unidirectional exercise (Krestovnikov, 1951; Letunov et al., 1954; Zimkin, 1956; Korobkov et al, 1960).

Consequently, arguments were propounded for unifying the GPP and SPP, and combining personal qualities to determine training methods, independent of the athlete's level of qualification. Complex training became preferred over the unidirectional approach, with its inherently monotonous workouts that tend to diminish conditioning effectiveness and promote one-sided physical preparation.

Prolonged unidirectional work (focused on developing factors such as strength or speed) apparently causes the body to adapt to loading with the dominant involvement of only some of the physiological mechanisms and does not create conditions for specific adaptation to competition activities. Parallel loading of different emphasis was shown to simultaneously improve different physiological functions in the necessary balance for various sports (Matveyev, 1970).

All of these concepts are indisputable in principle and are important as the most general guidelines, serving as the fundamentals of physical education and sport training. However, the research supporting these ideas was done many years ago and utilised athletes of low qualification. Had advanced athletes taken part in these studies, then their achievements would have been only average with respect to modern criteria. Besides this, the form of loading in those days was different. Therefore, under modern conditions this loading would be applicable only to beginners or athletes of average qualification.

According to Verkhoshansky (1977), there generally appears to be little advantage for high-level athletes to utilise the complex system of training, although one should not dismiss their possible value at different stages of training with certain individuals in specific cases. Arguments in favour of another approach may be based on more progressive sports practice, involving the search to overcome the major deficiencies of the complex system of training, in particular the following:

1. Highly qualified athletes have a very high level of special physical preparedness. To raise this significantly to improve sports proficiency, one must use strong and relatively prolonged training influences of appropriate emphasis. Complex training does not achieve this. In complex training, the distribution of the volume of special loading (see 6.7.4) is not able to provoke extensive adaptation of the necessary emphasis.

2. There is a definite specificity in the structure of the physical preparedness of high-level athletes. Complex training, with its multifaceted influence on the body, cannot create the conditions necessary for producing highly specific physical preparedness. Besides this, complex training at high volume accentuates the need to establish specific relationships between the processes which develop separate systems of the body, as well as between the training effects of loading of different primary emphasis.

3. Highly qualified athletes have to execute the competition activities expertly and with precise control. Extensive complex loading to simultaneously perfect sport technique and special physical preparedness inevitably leads to general fatigue and deterioration of this control.

Unidirectional Training

The above deficiencies of complex training are not as noticeable in athletes of average qualification and are much more obvious at the level of high proficiency where the general volume and intensity of loading is high. If one does not prescribe measures to eliminate these deficiencies, they can significantly diminish the success of training.

Consequently, it is important to determine such measures for systematically applying loading of some single training emphasis in separate workouts and during stages of different duration. For example, research has shown that the use of unidirectional loading in separate workouts makes it possible to achieve training objectives more effectively. Because of this, the level of adaptation in the body is more marked than when one is trying to achieve several simultaneous training objectives with means of different primary influence (Handelsman & Stetsenko, 1980).

It has also been shown that individual workouts devoted solely to perfecting sport technique are appropriate. Even when a wide variety of means and regimes of work and rest are used, these types of training session are very effective in improving technical skill (Struchkov, 1980; Mironenko, 1981; Petrovsky, 1977). It has been shown that training sessions with the primary emphasis on developing a single motor ability (under conditions of a wide variety of means and methods) exert a more profound effect on special preparedness compared with training sessions where several objectives are pursued concurrently (Urzhensnevsky, 1969; Gorkin et al, 1973; Monogradov & Platonov, 1975; Fedorova et al, 1975; Chepelyev, 1980).

In addition to its value during separate workouts, unidirectional loading is also appropriate during microcycles (Kudelin, 1980; Mikhailova & Sokolova, 1980; Budokho et al, 1978; Mironenko, 1981). For example, it has been established that microcycles of a single primary emphasis (in particular, to increase speed or various types of endurance) powerfully stimulate the trainability of swimmers (Kudelin, 1980). Similarly, it has been shown that microcycles of a primarily strength emphasis significantly raise the special physical preparedness of track-and-field jumpers (Mironenko, 1981).

However, research shows that unidirectional loading is effective only if it forms part of a complex of several means of a single primary emphasis involving a variety of methods (Fedorova et al, 1975; Platonov & Monogradov, 1977; Verkhoshansky, 1977).

Considerable work has revealed that the primary use of unidirectional training for prolonged stages (4-12 weeks) of training can be very effective. Use of a variety of means, especially when applied with a gradual increase in intensity, has been shown to be particularly appropriate for enhancing sporting technique, speed-strength, and the capacity and power of the ATP-CP and glycolytic-anaerobic energy processes (Mironenko, 1981; Antonova, 1980; Deniskin, 1976; Levchenko, 1981; Kornelyuk, 1980).

Concentrated Loading

Thus, the method of concentrated training loads was devised for preparing highly qualified athletes, with the loading being concentrated during specific stages of preparation (Verkhoshansky, 1977). The main novelty of this method consists of exerting a concentrated training influence on the body with a high volume of unidirectional loading for a limited period (of up to 2 months). This concentrated influence produces a brief, fairly stable state of incomplete restoration which is associated with the persistent and relatively prolonged disturbance of homeostasis. This triggers extensive functional changes which are prerequisites for subsequent supercompensation and the raising of the body to a higher level of special preparedness. An important condition for the using concentrated loading is the relatively low intensity of the means, since the frequent use of these means already intensifies the training. The loading may be defined as concentrated if its volume in the month in which it is concentrated is 23-25% of the general annual volume.

It is appropriate to use concentrated loading primarily for increasing the effectiveness of SPP, and for this purpose one can use loading of any primary emphasis. However, the concentration of specialised strength loading is of particular significance, not only for raising the athlete's physical fitness, but also for regulating the entire complex of loading over the annual cycle in all sports.

Concentrated strength loading constitutes a relatively independent part or block of training to create a functional foundation for the subsequent enhancement of technical skill or those motor abilities which chiefly determine success in a given sport. Hence:

- The composition of means and their organisation in strength blocks, as well as their logical connection with other loading, should be determined by taking into account the training specifics of that type of sport.

- The strength block should have a specific place in the annual cycle, and consequently, have a beneficial effect on the sequence of loading and the organisation of loading of other primary emphasis over time.

Here the concept of a block has a definite meaning, arising from the programming of technique. To achieve the principal aims of organising loading in the annual cycle, the coach must select a certain strength block or substitute one block for another, depending on the situation and the individual. Obviously, in order to do this, he needs to prepare a detailed selection of appropriate strength blocks in advance.

The effectiveness of concentrated strength loading has been confirmed by many coaches and special research in a number of speed-strength, cyclic and team sports (Varakin, 1979; Zhdanovich, 1980; Rudokene, 1981; Naraliev, 1981; Ptushkin, 1981; Verkhoshanskaya, 1982; Kabachkova et al, 1982). In particular, it has been established that this system is most appropriate for highly qualified athletes. Moreover, the use of concentrated strength loading enables the general annual volume of strength loading to be reduced (by 13-15%), when compared with the conventional approach (Mironenko, 1981; Antonova, 1982).

Problems with Concentrated Loading

Concentrated strength loading does have its deficiencies along with its obvious advantages. For instance, it leads to a brief but consistent decrease in speed-strength, which diminishes the athlete's special work-capacity and complicates the task of improving technical skills and speed of movement.

The connection between the organisation and the volume of training loads, the changes in the force-time characteristics of the take-off in jumping, the sport results and the explosive strength of women long jumpers was also analysed (Antonova, 1982). It was found that in the months with the largest training volumes, there was a noticeable decrease in the special-strength preparedness and sporting results. However, these same qualities rose during the subsequent months of reduced loading.

Another study examined the interdependence between the dynamics of the volume of special strength-training means, the elasticity of the muscles and the control results of the standing triple-jump of highly qualified sprinters during the spring-summer stage (15 weeks) of training (Levchenko, 1980). Here, it was also found that an increase in the volume of special strength-training means results in increased muscle stiffness and decreased explosive force. Unfavourable conditions were thus created for improving technique and running speed and the likelihood of injury increased significantly.

Thus, it is apparent that voluminous strength loading creates adverse conditions for improving skill and speed. Considerable research has established that voluminous strength loading is detrimental to the technique of the weightlifting movements (Khlystov, 1976; Vorobyev et al, 1978), javelin throwing (Ruvinsky, 1980) and punching speed in boxing (Filimonov, 1979). Rather than negating the value of concentrated loading, these findings stress the importance of knowing when this method may be appropriate to use. It is important to remember, too, that if concentrated loading is used, then *cybernetic periodisation* or programming based on Perceived Ratings of Effort and Ratings of Technique, as well as formal testing, can assist greatly in preventing overtraining (see 6.2.2).

The Use of Concentrated Loading

In more advanced stages, the concentrated unidirectional method of loading is the most effective way of further increasing the high level of physical fitness which athletes achieve with multi-year training. In order to employ it, one should find ways of overcoming the above disadvantages. One way is to periodically devise regimes of concentrated loading which definitely do not produce negative training effects (Verkhoshansky, 1977).

For example, the scheme in Figure 6.32(a) presents the block-loading of concentrated strength means (shaded area) and the work associated with improving technique in speed-strength and complex-technical types of sports. It must be emphasized that the block-loading method should not be taken literally as being strictly limited to strength and technique training. *Although there is a primary emphasis on a specific motor quality at different stages of training, this does not mean that technique work is totally omitted during the stage of concentrated strength loading.* It is necessary to examine some features of technical preparation in order to determine the correct methodological approach.

One must work on improving technique daily, especially in speed-strength and complex-technical types of sports, with 'freshness' of the body being an important prerequisite for development of technique (Dyachkov, 1966; Ozolin, 1970; Ratov, 1979). Separate tasks of technical training which do not require maximum intensity of effort can be performed with the body in a lowered functional state, but the execution of other tasks under such conditions is unacceptable. For instance, the most important aspect of technical preparation during the competition stage is associated with executing the fundamental sports exercise at high intensity under conditions that are close to those encountered in competition. This type of work should be done when the body is at its highest functional level and should begin in the preparatory period, since it would be too late were it to commence in the competitive period.

Thus, one may recognise two successive stages of technical training in the preparatory period. During the first stage, one perfects those *components of technique* which need improvement and during the second, the emphasis is on executing *the sport exercise as a whole* with high intensity of effort.

Improvement in technical skill involves a multi-year, continuous learning process. The basis for this is the athlete's constant striving to master the skill by continuously raising his motor abilities to a higher level of special physical preparedness in successive cycles. Each cycle consists of the preliminary development of the motor qualities which the athlete needs to reproduce in the near future, accompanied by the immediate accommodation of technique to that level. Completion of this process marks the point where a new cycle needs to begin, so that two stages may be recognised for inclusion into the idealised annual cycle of training. With the use of such a system, the athlete will not be unduly concerned about technique and his achievements will not stagnate.

The above concepts may be explained more thoroughly by referring to Figure 6.32(a). During the stage of concentrated strength loading, one should primarily emphasize motor learning, i.e. mastering the more precise variants of technique, oriented to that specific level of speed-strength preparedness which will be provided by the concentrated loading. Noting that one's functional state will be lowered during this stage, this task is carried out at low intensity. This will be done chiefly by means of special supplementary exercises, by imitation of the rhythmic pattern (but not the tempo) and its related individual elements, and by execution of the whole sports exercise, not at full strength, but under less demanding conditions (including accentuation of individual elements, as discussed in 4.3). The effort is gradually intensified during execution of the whole sports exercise.

During the LDTE stage of strength loading, the athlete begins perfecting technique and adapting it to his increasing speed-strength preparedness. This is where one models competition conditions in training to stabilise the perfected technique of the competition exercise at the necessary high intensity of effort. Since perfecting of technique is timed for the LDTE stage of the strength loading, it is appropriate to examine this phenomenon and add further information to the recommendations made earlier (see 6.11).

A relatively prolonged stage of reduction in the volume of training is necessary to promote the LDTE. However, in practice, coaches usually aim to achieve large volumes of accumulated loading and do not always emphasize the role of restoration. Although they provide recuperation pauses within the microcycle and the so-called overload microcycles to provide some rest, they still do not effectively utilise prolonged reduction of loading after large volumes. However, such methods are necessary, not only for restoration, but also for the development and optimal use of those physiological processes which underlie adaptation. These processes occur relatively slowly and an extended period is necessary for their completion, which is far longer than the 1-2 weeks usually allocated for reduction of loading.

By overestimating the loading required for developing special preparedness, athletes frequently not only undertake an excessive volume of work, but also execute this volume when it is clearly contraindicated, namely when restoration is vital. Therefore, additional volumes of loading not only do not offer increased training benefits, but also become a major barrier to stimulating the restoration which is sorely needed by the body.

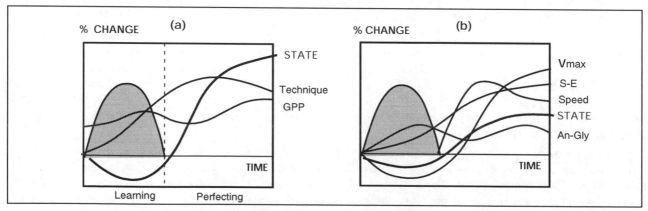

Figure 6.32 (a) Organisation of loading for speed-strength and complex-technical types of sport (b) Organisation of loading for speed sports with a cyclical movement structure. The shaded areas refer to concentrated strength loading, S-E = strength-endurance, An-Gly = anaerobic-glycolytic, Vmax = maximum velocity. In both graphs, the % change over time for all factors relative to their initial values is depicted. 'State' refers to the overall fitness state of the athlete at any time. (Siff & Verkhoshansky, 1999).

A training scheme which emphasizes the development of speed is presented in Figure 6.32(b). It is distinguished from speed-strength sports (Fig 6.32a) in that it provides a sharper separation between concentrated strength loading (shaded area) and work on improving speed. Speed work is excluded totally from the concentrated strength loading stage. However, it is possible during this stage to perfect the athlete's motor skill, which directly determines high speed of movement.

This motor proficiency requires efficient intermuscular coordination, when there should be no tension in the muscle groups which do not directly take part in executing the motor tasks. This involves a specific sequence of tension and relaxation of the working muscle groups to perfect the general coordination structure of the given exercise. This type of work is quite compatible with the athlete's decreased functional state, provided it is executed in the optimal range of intensity of effort and frequency of movement.

Speed work begins only at the beginning of the LDTE of strength loading (when the 'State' curve rises above the time axis), together with the necessary gradual rise in the training intensity. At this time, both the frequency and the speed of movement also rise.

High speed of movement under competition conditions is determined largely by specific speed-endurance, which is produced at a definite level of power and capacity of the anaerobic-glycolytic energy processes. The necessary type of anaerobic-glycolytic loading exhibits two peaks (see Fig 6.32b):

- The first peak is timed to end near the conclusion of the stage of concentrated strength loading. Specialised strength means are employed and the objective is to develop special strength-endurance which is primarily of a local nature.

- The second peak follows the period during which volume of speed work reaches a peak. Distance methods (in cyclic sports) or specialised means and methods (in one-on-one events and team sports) are employed, where the objective is to develop specific speed-endurance. To ensure that it does not produce a negative effect, this type of work should be done in segments of small volume and combined with speed work.

It should be taken into account that, along with the rise in strength-endurance, explosive strength tends to decrease when the second peak of the anaerobic-glycolytic loading occurs. Therefore, in those sports where explosive strength is of great importance, it is necessary to include a sufficiently intensive, small volume of maintenance loading.

The above forms of loading organisation of different primary emphasis illustrate the departure from the traditional complex training principle, which consists of the parallel execution of several tasks. However, these forms by no means negate the value of complex preparation. They only show that the latter method is limited as a general principle for training all athletes at all stages of development and highlights the necessity for devising more effective ways of training highly qualified athletes.

Use of the Conjugate Sequence System

Recent research shows that it is appropriate to employ the *conjugate sequence system* of loading for highly qualified athletes (discussed in 5.3.3). *The conjugate sequence system does not reject the complex (concurrent) method as the most general principle of training, but only extends it so that it meets the requirements of conditioning highly qualified athletes.* Complexity should be understood in terms of its evolution over time, not its contents and structure at a given instant. As stated before, the chief mechanism of the training effect of such a method consists of the summation of positive, accumulated after-effects of preceding loading of different primary emphasis. Thus, the conjugate sequence system not only preserves the advantage of the complex method of training, but it also accentuates the specific training effect of the loading of a given emphasis. On the whole, the positive accumulation of preceding training effects of this form results in a more unidirectional elevation of the body to a higher and more stable special work capacity.

The advantage of the conjugate sequence system consists not only in providing a high and stable cumulative effect of loading of different primary emphasis, but also in achieving a high degree of functional effectiveness. In this case, the entire volume of the unidirectional loading contributes to enhancing motor potential and perfecting technical skill. At the same time, superfluous work is excluded, because it does not enhance trainability, but often hinders achievement of the planned cumulative training effect.

The conjugate sequence system should be used in the annual training cycle for organising loading of different primary emphasis and during separate stages for organising loading of a single primary emphasis. Furthermore, it should be distinguished in terms of the power and specificity of the training influence of the means and methods used.

6.12.3 Constructing Training by Functional Indicators

Assessment of functional indicators furnishes an effective way of organising training over a given period influenced by factors such as external conditions, the competition calendar, type of periodisation, work demands or educational studies. Three fundamental units of training construction need to be distinguished: the annual cycle (which is a particular macrocycle), the mesocycle and the microcycle. Training will be effective if it has been constructed optimally with respect to organisational structure and relevant functional indicators.

In this chapter, *the term 'mesocycle' is reserved for what in Russian is called 'the large stage' or large mesocycle*, which extends over several months to produce a specific adaptive effect. In most other applications, the term 'mesocycle' is used fairly loosely to refer to a period of several weeks or months consisting of a certain number of microcycles. The large mesocycle, in fact, may comprise a few conventional mesocycles and also be referred to as a phase. Thus, a preparatory large mesocycle may be called a preparatory phase in other texts.

Research into the time variable of training organisation has traditionally concentrated on two of its units: the *annual cycle* (regarding systematic periodisation and coordination with the competition calendar) and the *microcycle* (devising models for different periods and stages of the annual cycle). Although the annual cycle is usually divided into separate mesocyclic stages, the principles governing their construction are given little attention. These stages are often calculated arbitrarily and intuitively, as dictated by the competition calendar and the current training objectives. The length and sometimes the quantity of the stages changes from year to year, current circumstances often determining what happens next. The need to establish some systematic principles which unify the contents of training used over separate stages into functionally integrated forms frequently does not arise. The exception to this is the pre-competition training stage lasting 4-6 weeks, to which considerable research has been devoted (Ozolin, 1953, 1966, 1970; Arosyev, 1969; Matveyev, 1977).

Practice has identified the requirements of the preparatory period through empirically established ways of constructing separate stages from combinations of microcycles of different emphasis. The literature reveals that three and four week stages are the most frequently used, where the last one week serves as a restoration week. There are combinations of two weeks with heavy loading and two weeks with moderate loading, or an alternation of weeks with high and moderate loading. One can find many variations of such combinations in practice, and all of them, depending on circumstances, can produce good results. It is very difficult to establish which of these is the most effective, since the criteria are extremely diverse.

Therefore, it was decided to examine several possible ways of organising the mesocycle as a discrete and relatively independent part of the annual training cycle. The differentiation of such a stage is based on the characteristics of adaptation to intense muscular activity, in particular the optimal periods of drawing energy from the current adaptation reserves.

Based on a knowledge of the different forms of adaptation, various forms of training organisation in the mesocycle were examined (Fig 6.33). It may be seen that the one form of adaptation (A) displays a smooth increase in the functional indicators until it reaches a distinct plateau; the other (B), begins with a steady decline which is followed by a sharp increase in the functional indicators up to a level which significantly exceeds the maximum of the first variant. Variant A is a traditional form of training organisation and requires little explanation. However, the loading scheme of Variant B warrants deeper analysis.

1. Two micro-stages may be distinguished within the mesocycle of variant B. There is a concentration of loading during the first micro-stage, focused primarily on achieving special physical preparation (Fig 6.33c). Since the means of SPP require increased expenditure of energy, they cause extensive adaptation, which produces a steady decrease in the functional indicators (Fig 6.33a). Specialised loading which includes competition loading is done at a lower volume in the second stage. This loading is designed primarily to improve technique or speed so as to stimulate supercompensation of energy resources and increase special work-capacity. The stabilisation of the body at a new functional level signifies an increase in adaptive reserves and, consequently, its readiness to accommodate positively to further training influences.

2. The traditional volume and intensity ratio is preserved during the mesocycle for Variant B, but it is achieved in a somewhat different form (see Fig 6.33c). The volume increases and decreases more steeply than in the traditional scheme, while there is a slight rise in the intensity of loading. The need for interdependence between the volume and intensity of the loading is explained by the fact that the concentrated volume of intense loading can seriously overstrain the body and disrupt adaptation. In other words, one can achieve the necessary volume of work only with a relatively low intensity of loading.

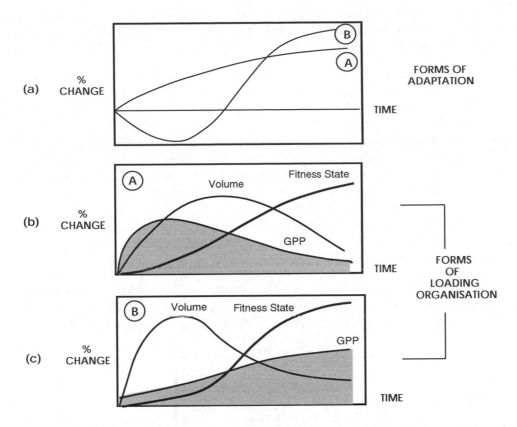

Figure 6.33 Two forms of loading organisation at the mesocycle level of training. (a) illustrates the forms of adaptation for the different training regimes A and B. (b) depicts the characteristics of training regime A and its effect on the athlete's fitness state. (c) gives the same information for regime B. GPP = General Physical Preparation. (Siff & Verkhoshansky, 1999).

3. The above ways of constructing the training mesocycle eliminate the contradictions that arise when one attempts to achieve the objectives of training and competition by exhausting the motor potential. If this method were to be used, then the athlete's results would decrease with each competition. However, this does not occur with correct organisation of training. On the contrary, variant B leads to an increase in the athlete's special work capacity and achievements during the competition phase.

   Training and competition loading differ in the magnitude and the specificity of their effects on the body. The forms of preparation in a mesocycle are associated with a very definite sequence and continuity. The first stage provides the necessary prerequisites for further increase in the athlete's work-capacity. If not excessively demanding, the second stage intensifies those physiological processes which form the basis for raising this level of work capacity. Therefore, the success of the training as a whole depends on a proper understanding of the objectives, roles and ratios of the loading in the mesocycle.

4. Variant B provides extensive and unidirectional utilisation of the GPP means and rational combination of them with the special work. The basic purpose of this GPP is to facilitate the transition to activities which differ from the special work and thereby promote restoration. The GPP means solve the problem of restoring work-capacity during extensive concentrated loading and during appearance of the LDTE, being used for restoration, especially after high intensity technique and speed work. On the whole, the GPP means are executed at low intensity. However, to prepare the body to switch to training to develop speed and technical skill during the stage of reduced concentrated loading, the intensity of the GPP means is increased slightly.

5. Variant A is appropriate for athletes of medium qualification, as well as for qualified athletes needing to devote much time to perfecting technical skill. Variant B can be used best by qualified athletes who possess a high special physical work-capacity, can endure voluminous loading and display excellent sports technique.

6. The tasks and forms of mesocycle organisation should have a specific emphasis aimed at systematically achieving the special objectives of the year's training, in particular raising the body to a new level of

competitive preparedness. The necessary contents, volume and organisation of training and competition loading are determined on the basis of this training emphasis. The central trait of the mesocycle is the execution of all the intermediate tasks associated with special physical, technical and competition preparation.

Thus, the large mesocycle is a relatively independent part of the annual cycle which integrates the fundamental forms and skills of training prescribed for all the microcycles. The duration of the large mesocycle can vary (usually 3-5 months), since its calculation depends on the competition calendar and especially on the dates of the most important competitions.

Research shows that it is appropriate to use two large mesocycles in the annual cycle to promote supercompensation of the current adaptation reserves (Figure 6.34). In this case, the athlete's state displays two large peaks, with the second one producing the higher special work-capacity (i.e. fitness state). This further corroborates the value of this form of bi-cyclic organisation of annual preparation which was empirically worked out and applied successfully long ago in several sports.

Consequently, unquestioning adherence to monocyclic periodisation in a number of sports is not justified, and it is advisable that coaches re-examine this tradition carefully. Bi-cyclic periodisation may also be applied in several different types of sport which traditionally employ other forms of periodisation, in particular monocyclic forms in skiing (Ogoltsov, 1979) and middle-distance running (Turin, 1980; Sirenko, 1980), as well as tri-cyclical forms in boxing (Nikiforov & Viktorov, 1978) and swimming (Vaitsekhovsky, 1981). In a number of team sports and one-on-one events, tri-cyclic periodisation may have to be used, as dictated by the competition calendar, whereas in long-duration endurance sports, monocyclic periodisation is usually recommended.

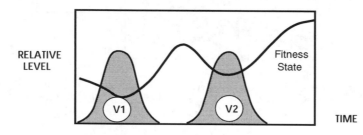

Figure 6.34 Organisation of annual training with two mesocycles of strength loading (Siff & Verkhoshansky, 1999).

The principles of programming and organising training in the annual cycle will be discussed later, but it is relevant now to examine the microcycle more carefully.

In planning large mesocycles, the problem of fitting in the necessary volume of work arises, which complicates the structuring the microcycle. In this respect, all traditional schemes of constructing a microcycle with complex training to achieve several simultaneous training objectives and increase specific work capacity at the beginning of a new microcycle do not satisfy these requirements. It is necessary to seek new forms of constructing microcycles which permit the use of high volumes of loading, including unidirectional regimes. It is important to note that microcycles are the basic units of training construction, whose function is to utilise those parts of the volume which help them to comply with the objectives and general strategy of the mesocycle.

It is relevant now to examine the currently scant experimental findings which suggest ways of solving these problems. It has been established that large unidirectional loading sharply reduces the capability of displaying those qualities and abilities which facilitate the effective and safe execution of training programmes. At the same time, athletes who exhibit a high work capacity generally achieve it by means of other training systems (Monogarov & Platonov, 1975; Fedorova et al, 1975; Chepelyev, 1980; Platonov, 1980).

For example, a week's cycle was devised (Fig 6.35), which took into account the length of restoration periods needed by highly qualified swimmers after high volume unidirectional workouts. The scheme was intended to achieve a generally high volume of loading using a systematic combination of workouts of different magnitude and emphasis which took into account the duration of the accompanying restoration processes.

It should be noted that, despite the uni-directional character of individual workouts, the microcycle as the whole typifies the complex (multi-faceted) form of training organisation. The body cannot simultaneously differentiate between and accumulate specific reactions to every type of daily loading and respond to them with generalised reactions which contain separate proportions of adaptation to each of the different training influences. Therefore, this form of microcycle construction enables one to achieve a large volume of loading, but the absence of any marked supercompensation (as revealed by the trend of restoration curve) shows that it fails to produce a definite increase in speed, aerobic or anaerobic productivity.

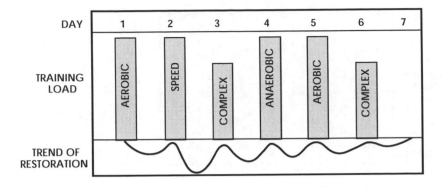

Figure 6.35 Structure of a week's microcycle for swimming, illustrating the trend of restoration processes on a daily basis. The graph of restoration combines the separate effects on restoration for the aerobic, anaerobic and speed components of fitness (Siff & Verkhoshansky, 1999).

Figure 6.36(a) gives examples of the unidirectional organisation of week-cycles for highly qualified swimmers, which includes three workouts with loading of either aerobic or anaerobic emphasis, combined with workouts emphasizing complex, speed-strength and speed-endurance training. Observations of the acute (immediate) delayed training effect (ADTE) showed (Fig 6.36b), that in the first instance there was a significant depression of aerobic potential (VO2 max), the restoration of which was observed over a 72 hour period. At the same time, anaerobic potential, assessed by a swimming test of 4 x 50m, restored quickly and exceeded its initial level. In the second case, restoration of anaerobic productivity took longer and exceeded its initial level after 72 hours. It is interesting that, during this time, aerobic potential rose over a 12 hour span and then diminished.

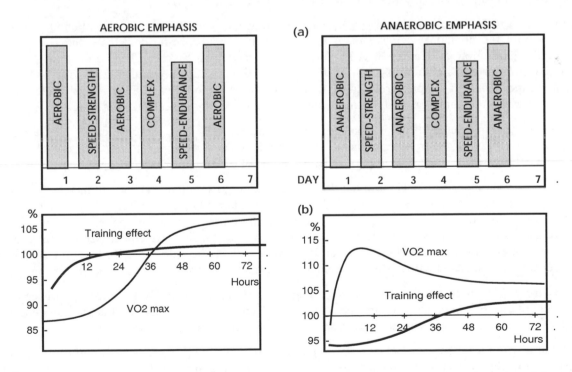

Figures 6.36 (a) The unidirectional organisation of a weekly microcycle in swimming. (b) The dynamics of the corresponding restoration processes after this microcycle (Kubelin, 1980).

Figure 6.37 illustrates another way of organising a weekly microcycle which emphasizes chiefly special-strength training for speed-strength and complex-technical types of sport. In addition to comprising workouts with large and moderate volumes of strength loading, these microcycles include workouts with an emphasis on technical and complex training.

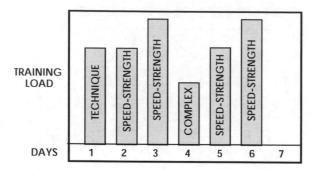

Figure 6.37 Unidirectional organisation of weekly microcycles for speed-strength sports (Mironenko, 1979).

Due to the modern demands of preparing skilled athletes, the microcycles used years ago have become the weakest link in the programming of training. Naturally, the preceding examples still do not eliminate those insufficiencies, although they point the way in which scientific research should be directed.

6.13 Primary Aims in Programming Training

The above findings may be expressed as a number of general aims to form the basis for devising effective sports training programmes. The primary aims comprise a separate category of methodological concepts and rules, especially regarding the general principles of physical education and sport training. They develop these principles, which are applicable to the training of highly qualified athletes under modern conditions, and become the definitive rules of programming. These aims are summarised below:

1. Exploiting the current adaptation reserves of the body based on the characteristics of adaptation to specialised training. Within the annual cycle, one plans the mesocycles, their specific objectives and the contents, volume and organisation of loading necessary to achieve these objectives. The mesocycles should be incorporated into the year's training system so that the special work capacity peaks at the time of the most important competitions. It is appropriate to fit at least two large mesocycles into the annual cycle, even in sports which traditionally have one main competitive period and use monocyclic periodisation.

2. Preserving the training potential of the loading, which is associated with systematically increasing the intensity and specificity of the training influence, according to the rise in work capacity. This is achieved by applying the conjugate sequence system of organising loading of different primary emphasis (see 5.3.3).

3. Concentrated use of extensive, specialised uni-directional loading to stimulate the body to increase its special physical preparedness. In order to promote steady, functional adaptation, the training influence should be of optimal intensity, frequency and duration. The method of concentration may be applied to loading of any primary emphasis. It is particularly effective for special strength loading, which can serve as a relatively independent block in the annual training scheme. Its purpose is to create a functional base for the subsequent special preparation associated with perfecting technical skills and developing speed or special endurance.

4. Exploiting the LDTE of concentrated strength loading primarily to determine systematic ways of regulating the general volume of loading in the annual cycle and effectively use specialised strength work to create favourable conditions for improving technique, speed and competitive preparedness.

5. Block-loading with means of different primary emphasis, which are mainly to effectively utilise intrinsically incompatible loading regimes (e.g. emphasizing strength, technique or speed), eliminate or minimise negative interaction between loads of different primary emphasis, and devise combinations which provide sequential accumulation of the partial training effects of different loads.

6. Transcending the emphasis of SPP, which stresses the key role of this training in improving the performance of skilled athletes. This aim is associated with training where SPP precedes in-depth technique or speed work.

7. Modelling competition activities associated with reproducing training work that typifies competitive conditions, especially regarding execution of sporting actions at the high intensity which is encountered in competition. This is a very effective form of special training, improving the athlete's physical, psychological, technical-tactical and competitive preparedness.

These aims form the foundation for devising general strategies for organising training and establishing a definitive method of programming training quantitatively. However, adherence to these aims will lead to success only if all the preceding preparation has been systematic and the athlete has achieved well-balanced technical and special physical preparedness. To achieve these aims, one must institute measures that take into account actual conditions, the individual characteristics of the athlete and the specifics of the sport.

6.14 Models for Structuring Annual Training

The development of principles regarding the contents and organisation of training on the basis of scientific research leads to the concept of *sports modelling* and ways of applying it. Modelling makes it possible to manage the organisational complexity of sports activities and devise a practical scheme for describing and controlling the training process. With respect to the theory of sport training, there are two classes of model which are essential to the design of training programmes, namely the *descriptive model* and the *prescriptive model*.

The *descriptive model* furnishes qualitative details of the motor qualities and fitness factors needed for proficiency in a given sport, as well as desirable quantitative kinanthropometric, kinesiological, physiological and biomechanical details which characterise movement at all stages of that sport. This model describes the sport and participants in terms of the optimal values of factors such as movement patterns, velocities and accelerations at different joint angles or stages of an event, reaction time, 'lactate threshold' (OBLA), relative muscle strength, body proportions, agonist/antagonist muscle strength ratios and timing of segments of important movements. The Multifactorial Fitness Profile (MFP) discussed later may also form part of this model (Ch 7). Overall modelling describes the construction of training over time, as well as defining the methodological concepts involved.

The prescriptive model represents a simplified analogue of the actual training process, omitting some details, but preserving the essential information concerning its composition and structure. It describes the dynamics of the athlete's fitness state and the systems of organising annual training.

A model of the dynamics of the athlete's state diagramatically expresses the optimal changes in the most important indicators of special work capacity over time. It determines the specific periods when one should plan to achieve peak levels of the functional indicators and serves as the initial prerequisite for programming training. The prescriptive model draws strongly on the data furnished by the descriptive model of the sport.

Two types of model are distinguished: *qualitative* and *quantitative*. The qualitative model describes the dynamics of the athlete's state (the functional indicators), the most important parameters of the contents (such as strength, endurance and speed-strength training) and the interconnections between the components of training (e.g. concentrated loads, preparatory phases, microcycles and mesocycles). The quantitative model contains all numerical aspects of the training in microcycles, mesocycles and macrocycles, such as calculation of volume, intensity, duration of stages and loading distribution in different intensity zones (see 6.2.2). Before specific models are analysed, it is useful to present some of the general information concerning them:

1. Since the models concern summer and winter sports, the specific months of the year are not designated. Each model consists of about 11 months, since, on average, one month is allotted for the final transition period.

2. Models of systems of training construction include two components for each sport group: a model of the dynamics of the athlete's state (the functional indicators, e.g. as shown in upper diagram of Fig 6.39) and a model of the programme of loading (e.g. lower diagram in Fig 6.39). The scheme of training construction in each sport group is based on that periodisation regime of annual training which best characterises it.

3. The model of the dynamics of the athlete's fitness state includes the most important functional indicators of special work capacity. One can use any method that enables one to measure the values of these indicators.

4. All models in this chapter use the principle of concentrated special strength loading, which elicits the LDTE. The strength loading is represented by blocks which are timed to occupy specific stages of the annual cycle.

5. By describing the qualitative features of training organisation, the models present the most desirable trend in the distribution of the volume of loading of different emphasis over the annual cycle and the variation of

this loading over time. However, for the sake of simplicity, this variation is not illustrated precisely. *The use of rectangular blocks should not create the impression that the concentrated loads are applied suddenly at peak intensity* according to some step function; the actual loading follows a concentrated wave pattern which gradually reaches a peak, then subsides in volume (as in Fig 6.38).

6. The boundaries of the stages and dates of the major competitions in the given models are based on the most typical schemes of events in each sport. However, if the actual calendar is taken into account, they can vary somewhat so as to fulfill the general principles of loading organisation.

Examples of Descriptive Modelling

It would require a large separate volume for each sport to present the most important qualitative and quantitative factors which constitute a thorough descriptive model in every case. However, it is useful to select a few examples of the types of information that feature in such a model.

For instance, kinanthropometric data in weightlifting would include the bodymass-height, strength-bodymass and strength-age relationships discussed in Section 3.3. Other useful information may be obtained from lean muscle mass or bodyfat ratios, and physical work capacity (PWC170) measurements (Table 6.6).

Many years of Russian research have produced models for every type of sport which offer information not only on the sport specific movements, but also on any supplementary exercises or tests that are of importance in a given sport. These norms enable the coach to identify any weaknesses in the state of the athlete and thereby modify the training programme to improve results.

It is of little value to identify which energy systems, types of fitness or movement patterns are involved in a sport unless accurate numerical determinations are regularly made of each of these factors. Even then, we have to remember that the body is not simply a machine in which input and output are deterministically related, but an organism whose behaviour displays non-linearity and fairly random deviations form what one may expect on the basis of quantitative measurements. Nevertheless, without this information, long-term programming becomes imprecise with little hope of producing consistent, reasonably predictable growth of results. It is useful to study some track-and-field models to understand the characteristics which the Russians typically have used to construct sports models or devise tests for controlling the athlete's progress and prescribing efficient and safe training (Tables 6.6 - 6.12).

Table 6.6 Muscle and fat proportions, and physical work capacity PWC-170 of highly qualified Russian weightlifters (Stepanova et al, 1983). Column 5 gives the absolute value of work capacity in kg-metres per minute, while column 6 gives the relative work capacity per unit bodymass in kg-m per min per kg bodymass.

Division	% Muscle	% Fat	Muscle/Fat	PWC170 kgm/min	PWC170 kgm/min/kg
52	53.64	7.75	7.07	855	15.2
56	54.95	8.33	6.68	1142	18.4
60	56.11	7.99	6.89	1196	18.3
67.5	55.74	8.93	6.25	1167	16.5
75	56.73	8.94	6.53	1304	16.8
82.5	57.26	8.99	6.58	1380	16.5
90	57.69	9.26	6.61	1566	17.4
100	56.09	11.01	5.47	1474	14.8
110	55.55	12.29	4.91	1634	14.8
110+	53.51	16.23	3.69	2009	14.6
MEAN	55.73	9.97	6.07	1373	16.3

None of these examples should not be regarded as all-embracing models. Several other factors may also be added to enhance the specificity of each scheme. For instance, the model for javelin throwing may include measures of supplementary throwing activities (Table 6.11) or the model for middle-distance runners may present the average of all strength tests stated in Table 6.8 in the form of a single indicator (Table 6.7), as well as offering tests for flexibility and general endurance.

Table 6.7 Model characteristics for middle distance runners of different levels of qualification. The strength tests represent the mean of the strength of the extensors and flexors of the hip, knee and ankle joints relative to bodymass. The different splits describe the flexibility in striding during running. Special endurance is assessed by measuring the time taken for 2 series of 4 x 400m, with 2 mins rest between each 400m and 8-10 mins rest between each series (Maximenko, 1979).

Control Tests	Class III	Class II	Class I
800m run	2:11:07	2:02:04	1:56:02
1500m run	4:31:05	4:16:01	4:01:08
30m from running start (sec)	3.48	3.35	3.23
Relative mean strength of 5 muscle groups (kg)	5.72	5.87	6.11
Standing triple jump (m)	6.98	7.28	7.99
Stride splits (degrees)	111.5	116.8	131.5
Straddle splits (degrees)	105.3	106.1	107.5
Running 2 x (4 x 400m) total (special endurance)	9:22:08	8:52:06	8:18:07
5000m run (i.e. general endurance)	18:03:02	17:10:03	15:52:04

Table 6.8 Model characteristics of 100m sprinters for use in special physical preparation to achieve a time of 10.0 secs and 11.0 secs for men and women, respectively (Tabachnik, 1979).

Model Characteristics	Men 10.0 secs	Women 11.0 secs
General data		
Initial 100m time (secs)	11.62	13.0
Age of beginning sprinting (years)	14.6	14.1
Years of sprinting	8.4	8.3
Speed Indicators		
Simple motor reaction time	0.110	0.121
Starting reaction time	0.136	0.149
Total starting time (sec)	0.37	0.40
5m run from low start	1.18	1.32
30m run from low start	3.80	4.25
50m run from a low start	5.70	6.15
Time for last 50m of 100m sprint (sec)	4.45	5.00
Relative muscular strength (relative to bodymass)		
Trunk extension	2.00	2.60
Trunk flexion	1.20	1.15
Knee extension	2.20	2.00
Knee flexion	1.10	1.05
Hip extension	3.10	2.80
Hip flexion	1.20	1.05
Ankle plantarflexion	3.00	2.80
Speed-strength Indicators		
Standing long jump (m)	3.20	2.80
Standing triple jump (m)	10.0	8.40
Ten-step jump from standing start (m)	36.0	32.0

Table 6.9 Model of time characteristics for 100m sprinters (Tabachnik, 1979).

Time of section in seconds

Goal (sec)	15m	30m	1st 50m	2nd 50m	Last 10m
10.0	1.16 - 1.18	3.70 - 3.80	5.60 - 5.70	4.30 - 4.40	0.900
10.2	1.18 - 1.20	3.80 - 3.90	5.70 - 5.80	4.40 - 4.50	0.925
10.5	1.26 - 1.28	4.00 - 4.10	5.80 - 5.90	4.60 - 4.70	0.952
10.7	1.28 - 1.30	4.10 - 4.20	5.90 - 6.00	4.70 - 4.80	0.970
10.9	1.30 - 1.32	4.20 - 4.30	6.00 - 6.10	4.80 - 4.90	0.990

Table 6.10 Model characteristics of highly qualified 800m and 1500m runners (Maximenko, 1979).

Control Tests	800m runners CMS	800m runners MS	1500m runners CMS	1500m runners MS
800m run	1:51:02	1:47:08	1:53:07	1:49:07
1500m run	3:54:00	3:48:04	3:48:04	3:40:03
30m from running start (sec)	3.00	2.80	3.18	3.03
Relative mean strength of 5 muscle groups (kg)	6.19	6.39	6.21	6.33
Standing triple jump (m)	8.38	8.63	8.19	8.49
Stride splits (degrees)	107.3	115.7	122.4	118.0
Straddle splits (degrees)	103.0	107.8	107.2	104.6
Running 2 x (4 x 400m) total (special endurance)	7:56:08	7:35:03	7:34:01	7:24:00
5000m run (general endurance)	15:32:08	15:03:01	14:33:01	14:11:03

Table 6.11 Model characteristics of international class javelin throwers (Konstantinov, 1978).

Model Characteristics	Men	Women
Anthropometric data		
Height (cm)	185 - 195	170 - 180
Bodymass (kg)	95 - 105	70 - 80
Arm span (cm)	195 - 205	175 - 180
% Muscle	53 - 55	48 - 50
% Fat	10 -12	16 - 18
Physical Preparation data		
30m from running start (sec)	2.90	3.20
100m from running start (sec)	10.20	11.50
Standing broad jump (m)	3.20	2.80
Standing triple jump (m)	10.20	7.80
Long jump from 8-step approach (m)	6.40	5.40
Vertical jump (cm)	95.0	70.0
Throwing shot backward over head (m)	19.50	17.50
Throwing shot forward from behind head (m)	26.0	19.0
Snatch (kg)	Bmass + 15kg	Bmass+10kg
Back squats (kg)	2 x Bmass	1.5 x Bmass
Throwing assistance objects or javelin with average intensity	170 times	140 times
Throwing javelin with above average intensity	35 times	30 times
Technical Preparation data		
Javelin throw from standing (m)	70.0	46.0
Javelin throw from 3 throwing strides (m)	76.0	54.0
Full javelin throw (mean of 3 best out of 6 attempts)	86.0	62.0

Table 6.12 Control tests and norms for juvenile sprinters (based on Alabin & Yushkevitch, 1978)

Age (years)	11	12	13	14	15	16
Height (cm)	148.5	153.8	160.3	168.2	172.8	176.7
Bodymass (kg)	37.9	41.4	47.0	55.6	60.7	65.6
60m sprint (sec)	9.83	9.35	8.81	8.08	7.75	7.21
100m sprint (sec)	15.9	15.0	13.9	12.9	12.3	11.9
300m run (sec)	58.4	54.2	49.9	46.2	42.8	40.4
20m (running start)	2.96	2.76	2.58	2.31	2.22	2.15
Standing long jump (cm)	179.8	190.9	209.7	233.4	249.2	261.2
Standing quintuple jump (cm)	9.25	9.84	10.74	12.00	12.75	13.70
Dynamometer back strength (kgf)	73.5	87.6	112.2	135.6	148.7	147.6

The Composition of the Concentrated Loading Volume

As mentioned earlier, the rectangular blocks used in the diagrams of the training models to depict stages of concentrated loading are not intended to show their precise form or contents. Each block represents concentrated loading of a primary emphasis, which does not necessarily utilise only one means of training. For instance, a concentrated block intended to increase speed-strength may consist of several different resistance and jumping means and methods introduced in a specific conjugate sequence.

In Figure 6.38, methods with a successively greater training effect are sequenced within the concentrated loading stage, thus: Jumping > Weights exercises > Plyometrics. These exercises are not sharply separated by time intervals, but substituted continuously for one another, ensuring that intensity and functional indicators are monitored carefully to avoid overtraining.

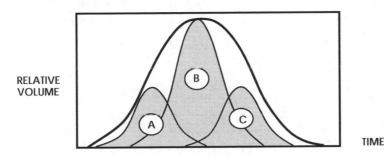

Figure 6.38 Structure and contents of exercises within a typical concentrated loading volume for speed-strength sports. A = jumps, B= weights exercises, C = plyometric depth jumps. (Verkhoshansky, 1977).

It is now appropriate to examine principal prescriptive models of the systems of constructing training in the annual cycle for a number of sport groups.

6.14.1 A Model for Sports requiring Explosive Strength

This model involves bi-cyclic periodisation of training and includes two mesocycles aimed at optimally developing the body's current adaptation reserves and achieving the planned level of special-strength preparedness at the most important competitions (Fig 6.39). The model of the dynamics of the athlete's fitness state (upper diagram) shows the optimal trend in the changes of the absolute, explosive and starting strength indicators, the highest values of which are achieved at the end of each mesocycle.

The organisation of loading provides for exploiting the LDTE of the block of strength work in each mesocycle against a background of the fundamental speed and technical training. The basic principle is block loading with means of different primary emphasis, which creates favourable conditions for in-depth improvement of technique and uni-directional preparation for competition. As stated before, technique work is not excluded during the strength loading block. However, such work is included at reduced intensity using the separate elements and their links (see 2.1.2), as well as the rhythmic patterns of individual phases.

The second strength block imposes a smaller volume, although the general loading intensity is higher than in the first block. Since the second block is executed against a background of the adaptation occurring in the first mesocycle, the LDTE will be preserved during the second competitive stage. It is unnecessary at this time to further increase the volume of strength work, which can be used exclusively for preparing the neuromuscular system before the subsequent training that emphasizes technique or competitive readiness. The contents and the organisation of the strength loading blocks are based on the principle of preserving the training potential of the loading by means of the conjugate sequence system (5.3.3).

The means of GPP have a specific purpose. Within each block, they offer variety and aid restoration after high volume strength loading, while at the LDTE stage, the GPP assists restoration after intense specialised loading. It should always be remembered that this procedure constitutes part of pedagogical restoration, which facilitates recovery alongside other methods such as sports massage (see 8.5). The largest relative volume of GPP means occurs during the competitive periods.

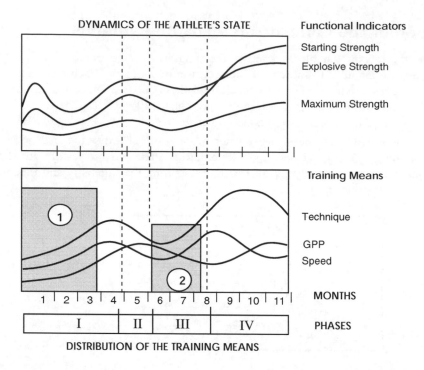

DISTRIBUTION OF THE TRAINING MEANS

Figure 6.39 A model of constructing the training for sports requiring explosive effort. I = the 1st preparation phase, II = the 1st competition phase, III = the 2nd preparation phase, IV = the 2nd competition phase. The shaded blocks represent the stages of concentrated special strength loading to promote the subsequent LDTE. (Siff & Verkhoshansky, 1999).

6.14.2 A Model for Medium Duration Endurance Sports

The model is based on bi-cyclic periodisation and consists of two mesocycles designed for optimally developing the current adaptation reserves (Fig 6.40). There are two competition stages in the annual cycle and one need not compete at the fundamental distance during the first stage. Here, it is important to maintain the trend towards intensifying the training, in order to increase the current adaptation reserves. One can achieve this by competing at other distances in competition, which will simultaneously serve as control estimates of the athlete's level of aerobic and anaerobic capacity.

The model of the dynamics of the athlete's state promotes twin-peaked changes in aerobic and anaerobic capacity. The dynamics of the special strength preparedness are expressed in the form of an accelerated increase in general strength-endurance and special endurance for repetitive production of explosive force (i.e. explosive strength-endurance) during the second competitive stage, as well as by the planned rise in maximum strength.

Explosive strength peaks at the beginning of the second competition stage, after which it decreases, together with the rise in the volume of intense (anaerobic-glycolytic) cyclic work. The fundamental functional indicators, namely anaerobic capacity and strength-endurance, reach their highest levels during the most important competitive stage (10th - 11th months).

This organisation of loading combines two strength blocks concurrently with special aerobic-anaerobic work, where the ratio of aerobic to anaerobic work changes over the annual cycle. There is a predominance of aerobic loading during the first preparatory stage; during the second stage the work is chiefly at the OBLA (onset of blood lactate accumulation) level. There is an increase in the volume of aerobic loading again during the second competition stage, its role being to promote restoration. Speed work (primarily in the ATP-CP zone) and the development of speed-endurance (chiefly in the anaerobic-glycolytic zone) are timed for the stage where one realises the LDTE of the strength loading, i.e. the development of speed precedes that of speed-endurance.

Thus, the general strategy of loading organisation in the annual cycle is based on the following sequence of enhancing special work capacity: General endurance > Speed > Speed-endurance, the orientation of the training process being towards the systematic development of strength and speed-endurance during the stage when there are important competitions.

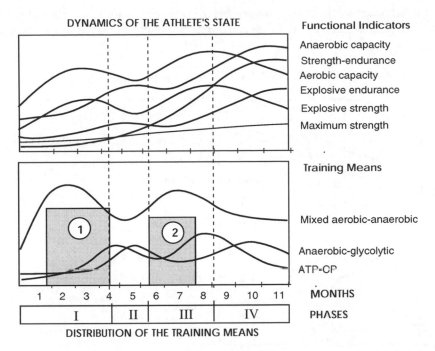

DISTRIBUTION OF THE TRAINING MEANS

Figure 6.40 A model of the training for sports which require special endurance (medium duration). Details are discussed in the accompanying text. I = the 1st preparation phase, II = the 1st competition phase, III = the 2nd preparation phase, IV = the 2nd competition phase. The shaded blocks represent the stages of concentrated special strength loading to promote the subsequent LDTE.

The contents of the strength-training blocks are selected by taking into account their conformity to the specific work regime of the sports activity (see 3.2). The first block emphasizes the development of explosive strength and local muscular endurance, while the second emphasizes mainly local muscular endurance.

6.14.3 A Model for Long Duration Endurance Sports

This model provides monocyclic periodisation with one competitive stage (Fig 6.41). Practice shows that competition in long duration events requires a long preparatory period (up to 6 months) for creating stable adaptation to preserve the special work-capacity for some 4-5 months during the competitive period. Therefore, in the given case, with reference to the predominance of low intensity work (relative to other groups of sports), the optimal date for increasing the current adaptation reserves is deferred, a detail which is taken into account in the model.

The model has yet another distinguishing feature. With monocyclic periodisation, stable sport results are achieved in the competitive phase if the increase in loading during the preparatory period occurs gradually (a mean monthly increase of 7-14%), if there is not a sharp drop in the volume of loading during the competitive period, and if the portion of loading in the zone of anaerobic energy production is not increased (Gilyazova, 1978). It has been established that the prolonged reduction in the volume of loading during the competition period (with monocyclic periodisation) leads to re-adaptation at a lower level, which is reflected in the drop of non-specific trainability. Competition and special supplementary loading (with limited volumes) cannot stimulate further development or even maintain special work-capacity. Thus, it is appropriate to periodically increase the volume of competition and special assistance loading (Baranovsky, 1969; Kryazh, 1969; Muzis, 1970; Zhikharevich, 1976).

Therefore, one feature of the given model is that within a monocycle of periodisation, it provides a two-stage organisation of strength and speed training. Against a background of the traditional distribution of aerobic, mixed and anaerobic (chiefly glycolytic) loading, two blocks of special-strength and speed (chiefly ATP-CP) training are included. The first block contains general conditioning strength work, while the second block emphasizes the development of local muscular endurance. This provides for an increase in special work-capacity and its stabilisation during the competitive period, right up to the important competitions in the 10th and 11th months.

This model provides for achievement of maximum aerobic productivity at the beginning of the competition period, and some decrease. There is a gradual rise in special strength-endurance and absolute strength up to the stage of important competitions.

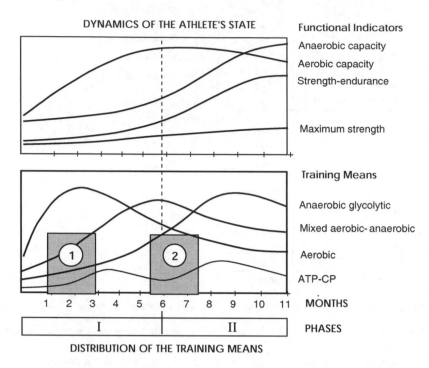

Figure 6.41 A model of the training for long-duration endurance sports. I = preparatory phase, II = competitive phase. The shaded blocks represent the stages of concentrated special strength loading to promote the subsequent LDTE. (Siff & Verkhoshansky, 1999).

6.14.4 A Model for Sports requiring Tricyclic Periodisation

The tri-cyclic model is intended primarily for individual and one-on-one sports (Fig 6.42). It comprises three mesocycles, with preparatory and competitive micro-stages. The first stage is oriented chiefly towards special physical preparation; the second, to perfecting technical mastery, and the third, to readiness for the major competitions. Depending on the competition calendar and the characteristics of the training objectives in the annual cycle, the length of the third stage can be increased by shortening the duration of the second stage. In certain cases a bi-cyclic model of training can be employed with this group of sports.

The model of the athlete's state provides for the achievement of maximum aerobic productivity during the second stage, followed by some decrease. Maximum strength rises uniformly, while strength-endurance accelerates more during the third stage. Explosive strength reaches a maximum at the beginning of the second and at the end of the third stages.

The loading includes three strength blocks. The objectives of the first are to develop maximum and explosive strength; the second, to develop strength-endurance; the third, chiefly to increase explosive strength and create conditions for exploiting the LDTE of the strength loading during the fundamental competition phase.

The first and third blocks of strength work are executed in combination with special work in the mixed (aerobic-anaerobic) zone of energy production, while the second is combined with work in the anaerobic (ATP-CP and anaerobic-glycolytic) zone. The fundamental volume of speed and technical-tactical preparation is executed against a background of the LDTE elicited by the blocks of strength work.

More Advanced Use of Concentrated Loading

The preceding models of bi-cyclic and tri-cyclic periodisation involved successive blocks of concentrated loading separated by several weeks from one another, a scheme which may be modified in certain situations. For example, in speed-strength sports, the magnitude of the delayed training effect (LDTE) may be enhanced further if the concentrated loading is followed by specialised work of moderate volume, which includes higher power or more explosive muscle contraction regimes, such as jumps, plyometrics and maximal attempts.

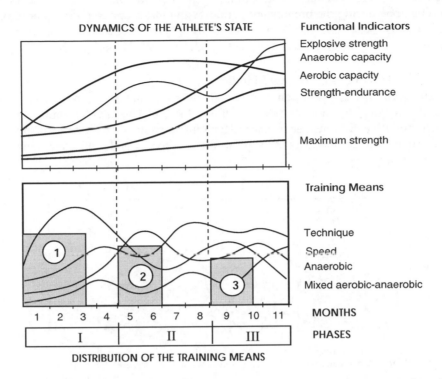

Figure 6.42 A model of tri-cyclic periodisation. The shaded blocks represent the stages of concentrated special strength loading to promote the subsequent LDTE (Siff & Verkhoshansky, 1999).

There is an overlapping of the different training volumes, which peak smoothly in each case to ensure optimal increase in the LDTE. The cases of monocyclic and bi-cyclic periodisation, respectively, are shown in Figures 6.43 and 6.44. In Figure 6.44, stages A and C refer to concentrated periods of high volume, low intensity work and stages B and D to moderate volumes of specialised, higher intensity speed-strength work. This scheme has been recommended to ensure continuous increase in special strength over a long period (Verkhoshansky, 1978).

The shape of the curves drawn in the diagram does not depict the precise nature of the training. For instance, stage B does not necessarily begin where shown, but may commence far earlier, while stage A may tail off right near the end of phase B. This emphasizes what Matveyev stated about the non-discreteness of the preparatory and competitive phases in his fundamental model, namely that it is sometimes perfectly appropriate to have elements of each intermingled in various 'doses'. Naturally, as with all systems of training organisation, the inclusion of regular passive and active restoration periods between stages of greater loading is important to facilitate development of the LDTE.

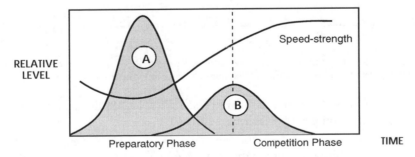

Figure 6.43 Enhancement of the delayed training effect (LDTE) and a typical functional indicator (speed-strength) by moderate volume of loading (B) following concentrated volume of loading (A). A monocyclic periodisation model for a large mesocycle is illustrated. (Siff & Verkhoshansky, 1999).

Since large volumes of strength and technique training generally are incompatible, the greatest quantity of strength work should be done during the preparatory period, with more emphasis being placed on technique work during the competitive phase when the LDTE rises markedly. This is particularly important because technical mastery can be acquired only through practice with high intensity loading which simulates competition conditions.

Proficiency gained under conditions of low stimulation and intensity do not usually transfer successfully to the maximal effort situations of top-level competition. This is relevant to the use of visualisation to perfect sporting movements; this technique is not very successful if it does not offer mental simulation of the movements, the feelings and the competitive circumstances under which the movements have to be displayed. Practice only makes perfect if one practises all components of the performance process under the conditions which mimic those of the sporting event as closely as possible.

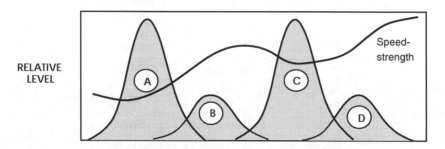

Figure 6.44 Increase in a typical functional indicator (speed-strength) by the systematic sequencing of overlapping loads of concentrated and moderate volume. A bi-cyclic periodisation model is shown. (Siff & Verkhoshansky, 1999).

This information may now be applied to formulate actual training models for different types of sport, integrating strength, aerobic and other forms of training into an effective periodised scheme (Verkhoshansky, 1978). For example, to prepare high level athletes in speed-strength sports, the concentrated strength loading block occupies the first half of the large mesocycle, following the groundwork laid by general physical preparation (GPP) and the peak amount of aerobic work (Fig 6.45). Technique and speed training occupies the second half of the large mesocycle, and as the athlete's fitness state rises, the training intensity gradually increases, especially as a consequence of participation in competition.

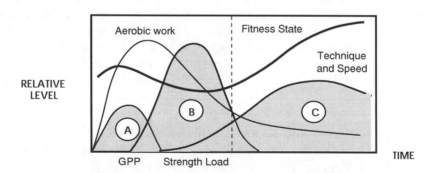

Figure 6.45 A model for constructing training over a large mesocycle for speed-strength sports. A is the block of concentrated strength loading, while B and C refer to the types of training identified in the diagram. (Siff & Verkhoshansky, 1999).

In cyclic sports of medium duration, the aerobic training covers the first half of the large mesocycle during which the GPP and concentrated strength loading take place (Fig 6.46).

At the beginning of the second half of the large mesocycle, when the LDTE is emerging markedly, the main emphasis is on speed work. After this, training is aimed at developing specialised endurance. In this respect, participation in competitions is one of the main ways of developing this endurance, where *competitions, of course, constitute the most specific form of special preparation in any sport.*

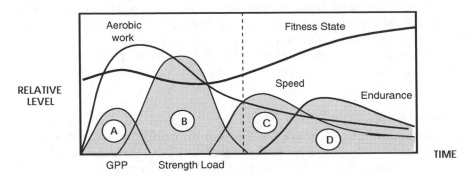

Figure 6.46 A model for constructing the training in cyclic sports requiring medium duration endurance. A is the block of concentrated strength loading, while B, C and D refer to the types of work indicated in the diagram. (Siff & Verkhoshansky, 1999).

6.14.5 Practical Principles of Programming

The programming of training over the annual cycle must first pay careful attention to the competition calendar and the adaptive characteristics of the body to intense muscular work. These factors may be in opposition, usually because of the competition calendar. For example, the dates of the main competitions may change radically, while the dates of traditional competitions remain the same. A worse situation arises if the competition season is extended and the length of the preparatory stages is shortened, which markedly complicates the programming and organisation of training. Under similar circumstances one should determine the optimal method by considering the following principles:

1. Organisation of training should provide favourable conditions for promoting functional adaptation of the body within the constraints of the competition calendar. The calendar should be co-ordinated with the periods and duration of the mesocycles. The contents of each of these stages is determined so as to enhance the current adaptation reserves (CAR) of the body.

2. It has already been mentioned that the optimal period for enhancing the current adaptation reserves is about 20 weeks for the most efficient loading of highly qualified athletes. However, the period of enhancing the current adaptation reserves can be increased or decreased over a small range, which requires an appropriate increase or decrease in the concentration of loading. It is important in this case not to exceed the optimal time limit, since excessive intensification of training can disrupt adaptation. Shorter mesocycles, which have a place, for example, in tri-cyclic periodisation (see Fig 6.42), should not shift achieving the objective of optimal enhancement of the current adaptation reserves (CAR) to the next stage.

3. To determine the boundaries of the mesocycles, one should be guided only by the dates of the main competitions. This rule should not be broken for any reason, including the desire to demonstrate impressive results at the beginning of the season.

4. There is some difference between the contents of the two mesocycles in the annual cycle. The loading of the preparatory phase is more specialised and intense during the second mesocycle than the first. Therefore, the first mesocycle should always be considered as the foundation for the second. The interests of intermediate competitions should not alter this objective.

When planning the annual cycle *one should be aware of the detrimental effect that competitive loading has on the athlete's state*, since it leads to serious exhaustion of nervous energy. Therefore, during the transition to the next mesocycle, it is necessary to include a recuperation period, the duration of which is determined individually, depending on the difficulty of the competitive stage.

6.15 A Sequence for Programming Annual Training

The science of programming training is a complex procedure involving numerous calculations. Its complexity, however, lies not so much in the quantity of calculations as in the insufficient basis for choosing and quantitatively determining the main operations. Therefore in practice, even experienced coaches need to make tentative computations which may have a low probability of producing a correct prognosis.

By taking into consideration the material of the preceding chapters, it is possible to perform the calculations when devising training programmes, so as to recommend a definite sequence and contribution of different training loads over time and provide an objective basis for making all calculations. So, when undertaking the task of programming training, it is useful to adhere to the following sequence of logical operations, where each calculation is made by taking into account the calculation made in the preceding operation (Verkhoshansky, 1985):

1. *Determination of progress in sporting results and their dates of achievement.* This is the primary objective of training: this refers to the prescription and sequencing of specific training loads of a particular intensity, volume and duration to achieve a predicted performance goal in a given competition. Here, a multi-faceted objective assessment of the athlete's potential and the competition calendar are the basis for making the calculation. One takes into consideration the progress of the athlete's preparation during the preceding training stages and those changes which are realistically feasible in the current year at his level of mastery. The calculations rely on a predictive model of the dynamics of the sport results relative to the competition calendar.

2. *Determination of the necessary changes in Special Physical Preparedness and Technical-Tactical Proficiency.* This is necessary for ensuring that the athlete achieves the desired performance goals in the given competitions. The calculations are based on an objective assessment of the athlete's special preparedness, analysis of the rate of improvement in functional capabilities in the preceding stages and identification of those capabilities which need to be enhanced. The calculation is expressed in the form of specific goals, relative to the functional indicators and the characteristics of technical proficiency which must be achieved in the important competitions. Subjective ratings of perceived effort (RPE) can be very useful in offering further guidance.

3. *Formulation of quantitative models of the dynamics of the fitness state in the annual cycle.* The competition calendar, the level of special physical preparedness and the dates of the main competition form the basis for this calculation. The calculation is reflected in the trends of the dynamics of the most important functional indicators so that these indicators peak in the main competitions.

4. *Selection of the composition of the training means and methods.* This stipulates the required increase in special physical preparedness and technical-tactical proficiency during all stages of training. The determination is made by assessing the training potential of the means and methods, as well as the desired increase in special physical preparedness.

5. *Calculation of the general volume of loading for all the training means.* This is necessary for meeting the objectives of the physical, technical-tactical and competition preparation of athletes. The accumulated effect of the loading in all preceding stages and the chosen forms of loading organisation of different primary emphasis, forms the basis for making this calculation.

6. *Division of the annual cycle into mesocycles.* This is determined by the structure and strategic objectives of the periodisation regime. The calculation is made by taking into account the competition calendar and the dates necessary for optimal increase of the body's current adaptation reserves.

7. *Calculation of the distribution of loading over the annual cycle.* This involves all of the means used to achieve the desired dynamics of the athlete's fitness state. The calculation is based on careful analysis of the preceding training stages, the general volume of loading in each stage, the principal models of training for the specific sport, and the major objectives of programming training. The calculation is expressed in terms of the quantitative dynamics of the loading imposed by the fundamental training means over the annual cycle.

8. *Organisation of training loads over the mesocycle.* The calculation is based on the principles of mesocycle construction, the characteristics of the LDTE of concentrated strength loading and the forms of the organisation of loading of different primary emphasis. The calculation is expressed in the form of a detailed training programme giving the specific distribution of loading during each of the microcycles which constitute the mesocycle. Provision should always be made available for introducing contingency changes in programmes, necessitated by unforeseen incidents such as injuries, changes in competitive timetables and personal disasters.

6.16 Managing the Training Process

Management offers control over the course of training and its prescription, based on a comparison of the actual dynamics of training with previous target standards. These previous target standards may include the sporting results and the indicators which reflect the changes in technical proficiency, as well as in the athlete's fitness state in response to training and competition loading. One corrects the course of training by changing the appropriate parameters of the loading. Thus, the management of training involves assessment and control of the athlete's fitness state, careful calculation of the loading executed and analysis of the interrelation between them. In doing so, it is necessary to apply the following guidelines (Verkhoshansky, 1985):

1. One should first select the most informative fitness characteristics in order to assess the special physical preparedness, technical proficiency and psychological state of the athlete. These characteristics can be obtained by employing special laboratory methods, control exercises (pedagogical tests) or functional sporting or standardised field tests.

2. Control over the course of training can only be effective if one regularly analyses the dynamics of the athlete's state. When doing this, (a) testing should be done regularly once or twice a month, independent of the periodisation and structure of the training stages, (b) the testing procedure should not be excessively demanding on the time and energy of the athlete, (c) the testing conditions must be kept constant to exclude the possibility of random factors affecting the results, and (d) the testing must have functional relevance.

3. Management requires a systematic comparison (over monthly periods) of the actual results and target goals of the training. If there is a discrepancy, it is necessary to carefully analyse the situation, determine the cause for such a discrepancy and revise the training programme.

One should consider yet another important aspect of managing training, namely *the keeping of meticulous training records*. This is very simple and it is surprising that many coaches have not taken it seriously enough until recently. This simplest part of management is a source of unique material which can make an invaluable contribution to extending the theories and practice of training, in particular, the problem of programming.

The coach's planning, calculation and documentation is extremely important for programming training. Unfortunately many coaches have developed a dismissive attitude towards detailed documentation of short and long term training programmes at the team and individual level, relying on their preference for intuition and standard traditional methods. However, documentation is not simply a supplementary responsibility that reflects the coach's efficiency, but an important attribute of professional management upon which the success of his athletes' preparation is largely dependent. It also offers a scientific, objective way of determining efficient training methods which lead to continuous progress and a decrease in overtraining and injury. It can enhance the practical skills, creativity, diagnostic ability and problem-solving capability of the coach, and enable him to cooperate with scientists in raising the methodology of special sports preparation to a new level of excellence.

The documentation records all of the parameters of training and should provide clear and accessible application of its material, especially the principal strategic features of training construction. The following basic forms of documentation for programming and controlling training can be recommended:

1. *A principal model of the annual training.* The model should clearly and concisely reflect the general strategy and the principal organisation of the training. Therefore, it should be constructed in diagrammatic form, for example, as in Figures 6.39-6.42. The principal model provides a good school for the coach's professional thinking and at the same time the graphic form of the model makes it easy for the coach to convey his ideas to pupils. The extent to which they understand his ideas will largely determine the success of the training. The recording of training loads and calculation of loading intensity, volume and distribution of loads in different intensity zones should follow the format discussed earlier (see 6.2.2).

2. *A quantitative model of the training scheme.* This is calculated for the individual or the group on the basis of the principal model and includes the computation of the dynamics of the most important indicators of special physical preparedness and technical preparedness relative to the competition calendar.

   It stipulates the general annual volume of loading for all of the training means and its distribution by months, with the aim of achieving the planned dynamics of special preparedness reflected by the model. The annual cycle of training known to be successful with qualified athletes can serve as a model of the necessary training structure.

3. *A programme for the mesocycle of preparation.* This is worked out on the basis of weekly cycles in the organisation of the loading. The chosen microcyclic distribution of means of different primary emphasis takes into account the objectives of the mesocycle and the individual characteristics of the athlete's preparation. These are the fundamental working documents which the coach uses to organise and control the training.

4. *The individualised long-term chart.* This describes the long-term dynamics (volume and intensity) of the training load executed with the fundamental means, as well as the corresponding changes in the functional indicators which reflect the athlete's fitness state and sporting results. The composition of the chart is an important condition for the control and management of training, and chiefly for the analysis of its effectiveness and for making recommendations for future planning.

It is important to record not only the quantitative indicators of athletic state, but also the athlete's own perceptions of how he feels daily in executing the prescribed training exercises, alongside observations of general state of health and motivation. Often, the onset of a cold, reduced appetite, mood changes or altered sleep patterns may be more informative than mathematical calculations in detecting overtraining timeously. Finally, the chart would always make provision for contingency training to cope with the unexpected or unplanned, such as soreness, injury or illness.

6.17 The Future of Programming Training

The necessity for programming is a result of the demands of modern sport, the concept of concentrated block loading having been made possible by the progress of science and competitive experience. However, this chapter takes only the first steps in this direction, but it is hoped that it offers useful practical guidelines and points specialists in the direction of further research.

Considering the relative novelty of the problem, it is natural that many of the questions will not have been answered. Those directions of scientific search in which one should seek the answers to these questions have been ascertained. With respect to this, the most important areas are the study of the characteristics of long-term and compensatory adaptation to intense exercise and observation of the principal trends in the dynamics of the athlete's state during prolonged training stages, as produced by different loading schemes (in terms of their contents, volume and organisation).

It is obvious that further research in these directions is impossible without the active participation of sport physiologists and biochemists. It is necessary for them to overcome the traditionally restricted descriptive approaches so as to appreciate the full complexity of the structure and contents of the training process and to understand their exact role in solving the problems arising from this. It is very important to point out that it is impossible to solve these problems by observing only physiological and biochemical mechanisms. It is impossible to separate, as is customary, the role of the motor processes from the mechanisms of energy production, and examine them in a general way outside their normal, integrated functioning under specific conditions of specialised training. The pitfalls of such a separation become apparent when one attempts to extract some practical recommendations from studies which change one variable at a time in an experiment of unrealistically short duration or limited complexity, using a sample of athletes of diverse levels of qualification.

Further elaboration of the problem of programming should be carried out by taking into account its general pedagogical principles derived from reliable research. In this respect it is important to point out that it is unacceptable to understand programming as the following of some instructions which prescribe a rigid order in the organisation of training. Furthermore, it is also senseless to view it as the creation of a precise algorithm, as is done in chess. Programming in sport is an art based on specific principles, which allows the coach creative initiative in making the final decisions.

In this book such principles have been expressed in the form of various models of training over the annual cycle. However, practical utilisation of these principles for programming requires elaboration of numerous other questions. The latter include the sequence of loading in the mesocycles and their composition in the microcycles, as well as rational ways of combining the contents of these microcycles into a system, taking into account the specific type of sport, the chosen loading, the period of training, the athlete's level of qualification and individual characteristics. It is the role of the coach to solve such problems.

STRENGTH TRAINING METHODS

The preceding chapters have extracted many of the principles, means and methods of strength training, but it cannot be claimed that the task of presenting an exhaustive holistic system is complete. Many further steps have to be taken to produce an integrated system of strength conditioning, guided by thorough research and examination of practical methods implemented by anyone for whom the quest for strength is important. As mentioned in Chapter 1, the sources of information on the art and science of strength training are the following:

- Weightlifting and Powerlifting
- Bodybuilding
- Supplementary resistance training
- Physical therapy
- Scientific research

The weight training gymnasium, whose origins lie in Grecian and pre-Grecian times, has provided a natural laboratory replete with subjects who have used weightlifting, powerlifting or bodybuilding to explore the boundaries of human muscle development for their specific purposes. It should not be surprising that this should have become a fertile setting for experientially discovering strength training methods. Weightlifters have become experts at developing explosive strength and skill, bodybuilders at producing massive hypertrophy and low body fat, and powerlifters at developing slow speed and maximal isometric strength.

Only in recent years, has science begun to investigate seriously the foundations, validity and scope of the vast amount of practical information gathered by several generations of adherents of the 'Iron Game'. Consequently, resistance training is rapidly losing stigmas such as 'slowing one down', 'making one muscle-bound', 'decreasing flexibility' and 'causing back injury'. Scientists entering the field of strength training have been surprised at the enormous body of knowledge accumulated by competitors in the strength sports and have been devoting their ingenuity to devise reproducible experiments to investigate all training methods for different subjects at different stages of fitness. Their research has also led them to add to this encyclopaedia of strength training techniques various methods taken from other sports requiring the display of different types of strength fitness, in particular, track-and-field. Thus, plyometrics, circuit training and cross training became recognised as valuable training methods.

Few coaches have realised that physiotherapy also offers many useful adjunct methods of musculoskeletal and neuromuscular training, such as electrostimulation, accelerated recuperation and PNF (proprioceptive neuromuscular facilitation). Because of the broad scope of training offered by PNF, this system is discussed in detail later in this chapter.

As has been stressed throughout this text, all strength training depends on two dominant factors (e.g. see Ch 1), namely structural conditioning and functional (central nervous and neuromuscular) conditioning. Thus, strength training may be categorised according to its major structural and functional aims relative to the importance of nervous system training methods (Fig 7.1). The numerous methods and techniques of training may then be added hierarchically below each of these major aims.

It is tempting to attempt to devise a single extensive flowchart to categorise and interrelate all of the better known methods of resistance training, but the extent of overlap between the different methods makes the final result logically tedious, unattractive and largely unusable. Instead, it is simpler to organise the different methods as a loosely interconnected array of columns and rows, showing only some of the more obvious relationships (Fig 7.2). The merit of this type of chart is that it enables one to see at a glance the variety of many of the methods which were discussed in previous chapters. Where necessary, any terminology and methods that did not appear explicitly in the book are described later, so as to furnish the reader with a compendium of methods for practical application.

In using the summary depicted in Figure 7.2, it is important to note that some of the training methods may be used to achieve several different aims by altering variables such as the load, number of repetitions and rest intervals. For example, *pyramiding* should not be regarded merely as a bodybuilding method, because it may also be used in the earlier preparatory stages to meet several general training aims such as increased muscle hypertrophy, strength and endurance, depending on the load and number of repetitions (which are inversely related). Therefore, pyramiding has been classified separately to show the different forms of pyramiding that are commonly used in the broad field of strength training.

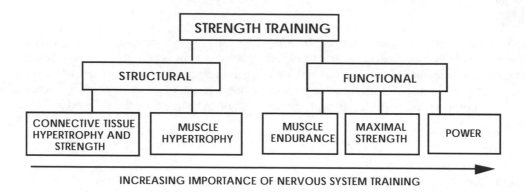

Figure 7.1 Broad classification of the major aims of strength training. The development of power refers to the qualities of strength-speed and speed-strength, as discussed throughout this text.

The method of *quasi-isometrics* occurs as a natural consequence of training with near-maximal loads, since it is impossible to move any heavy load at high speed without the use of ballistic techniques. However, there is a discrete method of quasi-isometrics (nowadays popularised in bodybuilding circles as the *superslow method*), which entails performing very slow controlled repetitions with even moderately heavy or lighter loads. In this case the athlete chooses to move the load slowly; with heavier weights he has no option but to move slowly.

Flexibility training has not been elaborated upon beyond its broad subdivision into static, active and other forms, since details of its development were discussed earlier in depth (3.5). It should also be noted that several of the other training methods with heavy resistance used over a full range of movement constitute very effective means of active stretching.

In organising any training programme, it should always be remembered that great emphasis should be placed on increasing the mass and strength of the connective tissues, such as the tendons, ligaments, cartilages and joint capsules, particularly during the early stages of training and transition phases to levels of higher competitive intensity (see 1.6.2). An essential part of the general preparatory phase of all training is also low intensity, prolonged cyclical activity to enhance cardiovascular and circulatory processes, as well as capillarisation in all the relevant muscle groups. This same type of activity can also play a useful role in restoration between intensive training sessions and phases.

7.1 Bodybuilding and Other Strength Training Methods

The selection of any resistance training method to achieve a desired training effect may be determined on the basis of competitive experience and research into the phenomena of strength, adaptation, specificity and supercompensation, which were discussed in great detail in the preceding chapters. The various resistance training methods are categorised according to the general scheme presented in Figure 7.2.

In doing so, it is important to appreciate that certain methods classified under one heading may sometimes also be used to produce effects falling under other headings. For instance, *cheating* and *restricted range repetitions*, although classified as supramaximal methods, may also be used submaximally or circamaximally. It the role of the coach to choose a given method according to the intended training goal and adapt it accordingly. In this regard, Table 1.1, which was based largely on the practical experience of generations of bodybuilders and weightlifters, may serve as an initial guide to be viewed in the light of the scheme depicted in Figure 7.1.

The choice between a focus on hypertrophy or nervous system training may be based on performance in tests of explosive strength and speed-strength (e.g. vertical jump), as well as on the magnitude of the strength deficit discussed early in Chapter 1. If this deficit at any stage is large, then it would be appropriate to concentrate more on weightlifting and reactive methods, whereas, if the deficit is small, submaximal bodybuilding methods should be relied upon.

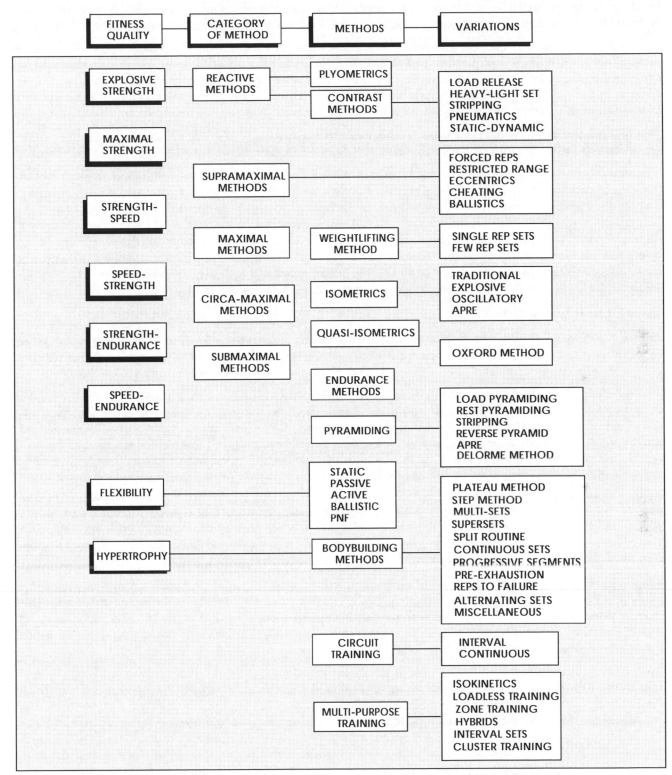

Figure 7.2 Extended categorisation of the different forms of strength training for different structural and functional purposes.

Maximal Methods

Weightlifting Method This method is characterised by single repetition explosive sets or low repetition sets (2-3 reps), in which each repetition is separated from the next by a short rest period (1-5 minutes, depending on how close the load is to a 1RM). Sometimes this method is referred to as the *interval set* method. This 1RM set with optimal recovery intervals between sets has been adopted by bodybuilders as the *rest-pause method*, which also involves doing sets of 1RM, but with rest periods of 10-20 seconds. This shorter rest is possible, since bodybuilding movements do not require the high levels of skill, speed and coordination of the Olympic lifts.

Maximal or circa-maximal concentrics This is a variation of the above method in which the concentric phase of a 1RM or near 1RM lift is completed, then the bar is allowed to drop to its starting position without being controlled by the muscles. In its weightlifting form, the athlete loads the bar with rubber bumper plates so that he can drop it from its final position to the platform so as to avoid executing the depleting eccentric lowering phase. In bodybuilding, a partner usually assists in the lowering (or eccentric) phase.

Maximal isometrics Maximal slow isometrics or explosive isometrics (see 4.2.4) are executed in single or few repetition sets lasting about 5 seconds with rest intervals of 2-3 minutes between sets.

Maximal eccentrics This method (see 4.2.5) involves taking a maximal eccentric weight (about 30-40% greater than one's maximum concentric lift) from racks or from a starting position in which the load is raised by a partner. The load is carefully controlled until the end position is reached, when the partner lifts it through the concentric phase again. Note that, although similar to the 'forced reps' method, the eccentric method (or 'negatives') does not require the athlete to produce any concentric contraction. Often the eccentric method is regarded as one of the 'supramaximal' methods and as such, carries an increased risk of injury. Eccentrics are associated with greater muscle soreness than most other methods and should not be used too frequently. Its dangers can be reduced by selecting the load carefully and avoiding sudden changes in movement velocity or trajectory.

Supramaximal Methods

Forced repetitions This method involves working to failure with a given load, then executing a few more repetitions with the aid of a training partner, who provides the minimal assistance necessary to enable the concentric phase to be completed successfully. The eccentric phase of the exercise is carried out without help.

Restricted range repetitions The athlete chooses a load which is heavier than the maximum that he can use for the complete cycle of the exercise, then he performs a few small range concentric-eccentric repetitions near his strongest region of action for that exercise. If these repetitions are performed at the end of a normal 5-8 repetition concentric-eccentric set to the point where the muscles begin to 'burn', this method is known as *burning reps* to the body-building fraternity. One may also execute concentric or eccentric restricted range movements with the aid of a partner (as with the forced repetition method).

In weightlifting or powerlifting, an exercise may be performed over a specific range with a load greater than one's capability for the full movement to rectify any deficit of strength in that region. Typical examples are pulling exercises around knee-to-lower thigh level and squats or bench presses in the range of one's 'sticking point'. Power racks or plinths are commonly to secure the weight in a given starting position. Restricted range exercises may also be done with maximal or submaximal loads, depending on one's training purpose.

Cheating This method involves the use of momentum, bouncing of the bar against the body, swaying the body, using accessory muscles or otherwise completing an exercise by deviating from its traditionally strict form. This may be done to complete any exercise with weights heavier than one's 1RM or at the end of a fairly heavy set which has taken one to the point of failure. There are recommended safe ways of cheating and these must be followed religiously if injury is to be avoided.

Ballistics This method is sometimes regarded as a form of cheating and involves lowering or dropping a weight rapidly to recruit the myotatic stretch reflex or exploit the stored elastic energy in the tendons and other connective tissues. Although this method is classified as supramaximal, the training load is not necessarily supramaximal; rather, it is the resulting muscle tension that reaches this level of intensity.

Circa-maximal Methods

These methods, which may involve all of the preceding methods, implicate training with loads that are close to one's 1RM (characteristically about 90-97.5% of 1RM). The main difference between maximal and circa-maximal methods is that the latter may be performed with several successive repetitions without a prolonged rest interval.

Submaximal Methods

Submaximal or repetition methods characteristically involve training with loads of about 60-80% of one's 1RM to the point of failure on the last set. The smaller loads enable the exercise to be performed with multiple repetitions, mainly for bodybuilding reasons such as hypertrophy or muscle definition.

A. Classical Bodybuilding Regime This is one of the best known elementary bodybuilding methods and involves 3 to 5 sets of 8-10 repetitions with the same load, allowing a rest interval of 2-5 minutes between sets. This may also be regarded as a particular case of the *plateau system* of training with an unchanging load. Another classical method involves increasing the load with each set so that the athlete is compelled to progressively decrease the number of repetitions from 10 in the first set to 4-5 repetitions in the last set. The rest interval increases as the load increases. This is a typical form of the *pyramid system* of training.

B. Extensive Bodybuilding Regime This high volume method involves 3-5 sets of 15-20 repetitions with a load of about 60-70%. The rest interval between sets is 2-3 minutes, increasing with increase in load from set to set.

C. Intensive Bodybuilding Regime This high intensity method involves 3-5 sets of 5-8 repetitions with a load of 80-90% (see Figs 1.8 and 1.9). The heavier loads mean that the rest interval between sets should be between 2-5 minutes, increasing with increase in load.

Each of the preceding regimes may use the following methods which have been defined earlier: forced repetitions, cheating, eccentrics (negatives), burning repetitions and ballistics. In addition, the following methods are popularly used:

Supersets A superset usually consists of two separate exercises in which the athlete performs set 1 of exercise 1, moves immediately to set 1 of exercise 2, then performs set 2 of exercise 1, set 2 of exercise 2 and so on until the chosen number of sets is completed. Since supersets are not intended to develop strength, the athlete allows little or no rest between sets. Sometimes supersets involve more than two exercises, in which case it is probably more appropriate to refer to the extended method as *multi-setting*. A well-known type of multi-set is the *giant set*, which comprises 4-6 different exercises performed in a mini-circuit.

Pre-exhaustion This involves performing a single-joint exercise which preferentially exhausts one of the muscle groups that will be used in the following multi-joint exercise. Not only does this work the one muscle group intensively, but it compels other muscles to act strongly as accessory muscles. For example, if supine dumbbell flyes are performed before a bench press, the pectoral and anterior deltoid muscles are pre-exhausted and the triceps are forced to become more vigorously involved.

Repetitions to Failure This method simply involves continuing the exercise until it is impossible to execute another repetition without assistance. It is often used for muscle endurance and definition training.

Split Routine This system involves dividing a routine into two distinct components, each of which trains a different body zone in successive workouts. For example, upper body exercises may be done on one day, followed by lower body exercises the next day. Another system may involve flexor and adductor training on one day, with extensor and abductor training on the next day. Sometimes, the advanced athlete may execute one part of the split early in the day and the other part later. A common weekly split routine prescribes split training on Monday-Tuesday, resting on Wednesday, more split training on Thursday-Friday, completed by a weekend of passive or active rest.

Plateau Method After a specific warmup with a light weight, the load remains constant for 3-4 sets (e.g. 50 x 10, 70 x 6, 70 x 6, 70 x 6). This method is commonly used during the early stages of training novices or for transitional active rest phases after weeks of heavy training.

Step Method The number of repetitions is kept fixed, while the load is increased after each set until the prescribed number of repetitions can no longer be maintained (e.g. 60 x 3, 70 x 3, 80 x 3, 85 x 3).

Stripping (Descending Set) Method Some bodybuilders also use the name 'Drop Sets' for this method. It involves working progressively with an increasing load and a decreasing number of repetitions in a pyramid fashion until a target load is reached with about 3-4 repetitions. A partner immediately removes 5-10 kg and the athlete exercises to failure. Another 5-10 kg is removed at this point and the athlete continues again to failure. This process is usually continued until the starting weight or less is reached. This method is commonly used for muscle endurance and definition training. If the rising pyramid allows the athlete to reach a 1RM or 2RM with no more than 6 repetitions for any set, then stripping offers a logical way of developing strength and muscle endurance, since the use of higher repetition sets is too fatiguing to enable one to reach a true 1RM.

Pyramid Method This method characteristically involves performing 4-5 sets of an exercise where the load is progressively increased and the number of repetitions decreased with each set. A typical sub-maximal example would be 10 x 70%.1RM, 8 x 80%.1RM, 6 x 85%.1RM, 4 x 90%.1RM, whereas a maximal strength example would be 6 x 85%.1RM, 4 x 90%.1RM, 2 x 97%.1RM, 1 x 100%.1RM (values derived from the equations associated with Fig 1.9). The rest interval between sets is 2-6 minutes, depending on the load used, the aim of the pyramid and the number of the set (the rest increases with load).

One may distinguish between three different types of pyramiding: *load pyramiding* (the method just described), *repetition pyramiding*, in which the number of repetitions with a fixed load is increased by one or two repetitions per set (e.g. from an initial 4 to a maximum of 10), and *rest pyramiding*, in which the interval between sets with a given load is progressively decreased. In the last case it is unusual to increase the load simultaneously; if done, the increments are kept small (2.5-5 kg). Other training methods which involve some form of pyramiding are the DeLorme Method (see 5.2.1) and APRE (see 5.2.2). Pyramiding is rarely used by serious athletes today; they find it more beneficial to progress rapidly to the main training load and performing higher repetition work on the way down from a maximum, if absolutely necessary.

Reverse Pyramid Method This method usually requires the athlete to pyramid to a final set with a particular number of repetitions, then to work down the pyramid in reverse order using the same number of repetitions for each load that was used previously in working upwards. It is very similar to the stripping method, but does not require the athlete to exercise to failure as the load decreases with each set.

Interval Training Methods As in track athletics, the primary aim of interval training is generally to develop strength-endurance by means of systematically alternating work and recovery phases. The duration of the rest (preferably active rest) periods is insufficient to permit full recovery, so that the athlete is forced to cope with increasing exhaustion and thereby develop muscular endurance. Because of increasing fatigue and the greater likelihood of injury under such conditions, exercises that require high levels of skill are not recommended. It should be noted that much weightlifting and powerlifting training relies on a specific form of interval resistance training, namely the use of single repetitions of near-maximal weights with a few seconds of rest between repetitions. Thus, one may distinguish between two broad categories of interval resistance training: one to increase strength or power and the other to increase endurance. With reference to the latter, there are two basic endurance interval weight training methods: extensive and intensive.

• *Extensive Interval Training* increases medium duration strength-endurance with loads of low to average intensity, as well as the capacity to recover after such activity. Since the training load is less than 40% of maximum, arterial blood flow is not restricted by muscle contraction and 'aerobic' energy processes predominate over 'anaerobic' processes. Training loads are between 30-40% of 1RM for 5-6 sets of 20-30 repetitions per set, with rest intervals of 1-2 minutes. The most appropriate exercises involve the larger muscle groups such as the quadriceps, glutei, pectorals and erector spinae; exercises such as bicep curls, calf raises and tricep push-downs play a minimal role in elevating the heart rate to the level recommended for aerobic conditioning, e.g. 75% of (220-Age). Specially designed circuit training programmes can meet the requirements for extensive interval training.

• *Intensive Interval Training* increases short-duration strength-endurance with medium to fairly high intensity loads and the capacity to recover after such activity. The higher training loads inhibit arterial blood flow and anaerobic energy processes predominate over aerobic processes. Training loads are 50-60% of 1RM for 3-6 sets, where each set is performed to failure and rest intervals last 10-90 seconds, depending on the exercises, load, the athlete's level of special fitness and duration of loading. The high loading intensity can readily increase heart rates to over 180 beats/min. Special circuits may be designed to offer this type of training, in which case the rest interval between successive circuits is 1-3 minutes.

Zone Training This refers to training a specific body zone in a particular workout session so that an entire body training regime using this method must be spread over several sessions or days. Split routines constitute one variation of this method.

Cluster Training This term is applied to another form of interval training that requires one to perform one or more repetitions with a 10-20 second interval between each repetition or cluster of repetitions in an extended set. Characteristically, the minimum load used is one's 5RM and 4-6 sets are performed. As is the case with general interval training, there are two forms of clustering: extensive and intensive. *Extensive clustering* involves 4-6 repetitions with one's 4-6RM, with 10 second rest intervals between each cluster. It may also be performed in a way which is similar to stripping: after each set, the load is decreased by 10-20% and a 10 second rest is taken before the next set. *Intensive clustering* involves 4-6 sets of only one repetition with 75-90% of 1RM, with about a 20 second rest between repetitions for 4-6 repetitions.

Continuous Tension Sets This term is applied to any set in which each repetition is done smoothly without ballistic bounce, cheating or significant pause at either end of the motion. Characteristically, the movements are executed fairly slowly without the joints locking completely at any stage of the exercise. Movements done in circular patterns such as cycling or arm ergometry produce continuous tension naturally and easily.

Progressive Segmental Training This method involves dividing the range of movement into 2-4 segments, then performing 3-7 repetitions in each successive segment. A popular form of this system in bodybuilding is known as *'Twenty-Ones'*, which consists of 7 repetitions done over three segments of a given exercise. Thus, in the case of bicep curls, the bar is lifted for 7 repetitions over the first third of the range, 7 repetitions over the middle third and 7 repetitions over the final third to the shoulders (or frequently, over the full range of movement).

Some weightlifters, such as the Russian midheavyweight, Rigert, used this method for training the pull in the clean and the snatch. For instance, in the case of the clean pull, the bar first was raised to just below the knees for 1-3 repetitions, next the bar was moved for 1-3 repetitions between this point and mid-thigh, and, finally, 1-3 repetitions were performed between mid-thigh and waist level with full shoulder shrug and extension onto the toes. Frequently, the set was completed with a full clean pull from the ground.

One bodybuilding variation is to exercise various segments of range in a different or random order or pattern every set or workout to minimise the possibility of early accommodation to a predictable regime, which can diminish the training effect. For want of a better term, this method might be referred to as *Random Segmental Training*.

Hybrid Training This method of complexing various movements in a given exercise refers to exercise in which each repetition consists of two or more separate movements between the starting and end points. The weightlifting clean-and-jerk, which combines a pull from the ground, with a front squat, followed by a thrust overhead, is probably the best known hybrid exercise. Not only does this lift consist of these discrete movements, but it also exercises an extensive variety of muscle groups, including the quadriceps, glutei, erector spinae, trapezii, hamstrings, deltoids, gastrocnemius and triceps. It is doubtful if any manoeuvre in any other sport rivals the clean-and-jerk or clean-and-push-press in recruiting maximal or near maximal contraction in so many muscle groups in such a short time (Table 3.12 gives the actual energy expenditure for the major lifts; the clean-and-jerk costs over 60kJ per maximal lift, higher than all other lifts). This is due to the fact that all hybrid exercises involves more joints of the body moving through a greater number of degrees of freedom. Their value in producing a more concentrated form of circuit training then becomes obvious. Instead of doing three separate exercises at three different stations, one can do all of them in a single repetition or at a single station.

The hybrid method refers not only to a single repetition consisting of several different movements, but also to the *hybrid set*, which comprises a different movement for each repetition of the set.

Examples of *hybrid repetitions* are:

- Barbell or DB curl + overhead standing press (normal or reverse grip)
- Back or front squat + press (or push press or jerk)
- Squat + good morning
- DB lateral raises (palms pronated) + upright row
- DB bench press + bent elbow pullovers (or flyes)

Examples of *hybrid sets* are:

- Reps 1-5: DB press; Reps 6-10: DB curl; Reps 11-15: Lateral raises
- Reps 1-5: narrow-grip bench press; Reps 6-10: wide-grip bench press
- Reps 1-5: squats; Reps 6-15: calf raises
- Reps 1-5: squats; Reps 6-10: overhead press or push press
- Reps 1-5: DB bench press; Reps 6-10: bent-elbow DB flyes; Reps 11-15: bent-elbow DB pullovers.

It is unnecessary to do the same number of repetitions for each movement in a hybrid set. For instance, one could perform the following set:

Reps 1-3: Power clean from the hang (3 reps); Reps 4-8: front squat (5 reps); Reps 9-10: push press (2 reps). According to the recording convention in 6.6.2, this routine may be written down as follows for a bar loaded to 80kg, for a set of 3 repetitions:

Power clean / front squat / push press : $\dfrac{80^3}{3+5+2}$

Numerous hybrid repetitions and sets may be devised by the inventive coach, as long as certain guidelines are followed to avoid injury for this demanding type of training. The load must be selected so that it can be performed without excessive strain in the weakest movement of the hybrid. The order of movements should always be arranged to permit their safe and controlled execution without causing exhaustion, impaired technique or overloading. A much larger selection of hybrid exercises commonly used in heavy strength training is provided in the following chapter (Ch 8.4).

Compensatory Acceleration Training (CAT) Discussed periodically in earlier chapters, this method refers to the process of deliberately trying to accelerate the bar throughout the concentric phase of the movement, instead of allowing the load alone to determine how one should move. According to Newton's Second Law (F = m.a), an increase in acceleration will increase muscle tension and enhance the training effect of any resistance exercise. Similarly, the training effect of an entire movement may also be enhanced by deliberately slowing the motion down during its eccentric phase, a process which may be termed Compensatory Deceleration Training. If one combines both of these deliberate control approaches, the resulting method may be called Compensatory Action Training. However, the original name of Compensatory Acceleration Training still may be retained, because acceleration in biomechanics may be either positive or negative (i.e. deceleration).

Other Methods Besides the methods described above, several other training variants were discussed elsewhere in detail, such as the DeLorme, McCloy and Oxford (5.2.1), dynamic APRE (5.2.2), isokinetics (4.2.6), and electrostimulation (4.2.1) methods.

Reactive Methods

Reactive methods are intended to develop power and explosive strength by imposing specific demands on nervous processes. One of these methods, namely *plyometrics*, has already been discussed at length earlier (5.2.4). This category is completed by adding another group of reactive methods, known as *Contrast Methods*:

Load release This method involves executing an exercise with an added load, then releasing the load suddenly during the lift, so that the contrast in stimulus received by the nervous system produces a rapid acceleration. For example, an athlete may execute a repetition of 'dips' or pullups as powerfully as possible with a load grasped between the legs, then release the load early during the next repetition and accelerate rapidly upwards for the remainder of the movement. The *stripping* method discussed earlier in this section, offers a non-explosive variation of this method. As mentioned earlier, the contrast method also refers to the sudden release of a parachute attached with a harness to an athlete running, swimming or cycling at high speed.

Pneumatics This method is much the same as the preceding contrast method. Instead of exercising with an added weight, one trains on a machine which offers resistance with compressed air. This system enables the air pressure to be quickly increased or decreased at any stage of a movement at the touch of a button, thereby enabling the athlete to decrease the resistance fairly rapidly, though not as rapidly as with the load release method. In the USA, the Keiser company makes a well-known range of these pneumatic machines.

Heavy-Light Set This method involves performing a low repetition heavy set, decreasing the load by about 20%, taking a rest of 10-20 seconds, then executing the lighter set as rapidly as possible for 3-5 repetitions. The nervous system remains briefly adapted to the heavy load if the rest interval is brief and the muscles are temporarily able to operate in this super-stimulated condition to produce a very powerful and rapid contraction with the lightened load.

Static-Dynamic Method This method exploits the fact that preliminary isometric tension using one or very few repetitions can increase the dynamic strength and explosive strength of a subsequent action, as a result of the after-effect phenomenon (see 3.3.1 and 3.4.2). The magnitude of the after-effect is influenced by many factors, including the duration of static loading, muscular fatigue and the interval between the static stimulus and the subsequent action.

Miscellaneous Methods

There are a host of different bodybuilding methods that offer interesting and innovative ways of training the body, predominantly for achieving greater muscle hypertrophy. These are not discussed at length here because they are of minimal significance for developing most of the specific functional types of strength fitness required in competitive sport. Only a brief summary of some of the better known bodybuilding methods is given to provide the coach with working definitions of methods that he may wish to apply in an hypertrophy phase for a given athlete. The intention of most of these methods is to offer a novel variation to shock the body or particular muscle group out of any prevailing state of habituation or stagnation and thereby encourage adaptation at a higher level of performance.

Strict Sets Probably the best known of all types of classical bodybuilding training is the strict set which refers to any set that is done according to precise form without the use of momentum, any deviation from the prescribed kinesiological pattern or any form of 'cheating'. It is advisable that all beginners learn first with strict sets to create the appropriate neuromuscular patterns of control before moving to other variations.

Muscle Priority Sets These are sets which are organised so that the most undeveloped muscle groups are exercised first in a workout to ensure that the athlete has sufficient energy and motivation to devote to developing the relevant muscles.

Major to Minor Muscle Sets This method entails exercising the muscles in a sequence that begins with the largest or most powerful muscles and progresses to the smaller or weaker muscles. Instructors often are taught that this is the most effective way to train and this is generally acceptable for the beginner in the general preparation phase, but it should not be stipulated as general principle for all training. There are many reasons to deviate from this order, such as to use pre-exhaustion training to develop stubborn muscles, to follow the muscle priority system given directly above, to facilitate recovery after heavy training of the same muscles in a previous workout, to accommodate two or more workouts on one day, and to obey principles of *functional priority* discussed earlier in this text (i.e. technical skills > speed-strength > strength-speed > strength > strength-endurance > general endurance).

Alternating Sets This involves alternating sets of exercises for different regions of the body to achieve specific training goals. There are several ways in which alternation is used: major-minor muscle (staggered) sets, upper-lower body sets and agonist-antagonist sets. *Staggered Sets* are supersets which alternate one set for major muscle groups with a set for minor muscles in an attempt to gainfully use the long rest intervals between each set of exercises for the major muscles. *Upper-Lower Body Sets*, sometimes inappropriately called peripheral heart action (PHA) sets, alternate a set for the upper body with one for the lower body. This switch to heavy activation of one body part tends to promote reflexive relaxation of another distant body part, a process first described by Setchinov in the early 1900s. Proponents of the PHA concept believe that this system avoids engorging one muscle part with blood and encourages the development of circulatory fitness. The fact is that all human resisted movement and not just PHA encourages peripheral circulation and PHA offers no superior cardio-circulatory benefits compared with other systems of resistance training. *Agonist-Antagonist Sets* exercise agonist muscles of one joint with the antagonistic muscles of the same joint (e.g. triceps followed by biceps), either in the form of supersets or as successive sets.

Tempo Changing Sets These sets involve changing the tempo (or pace) of an exercise during each set, so that either one repetition may be performed faster or slower than other repetitions, or the duration of the concentric, isometric and eccentric phases of a single repetition may be changed relative to one another during each repetition. This variation, like any other forms that stimulate the body in an unexpected way, may be of value in preventing habituation and stagnation (see Fig 1.32) after long periods of training.

Diminishing Sets This method entails trying to perform a very large number of repetitions (usually 100) in as few sets as possible with the same load, with a minimal rest period between sets, for example 30-25-20-15-10. The newcomer to this method may have to use as many as 10-12 sets, but the ultimate aim is to decrease the number of necessary sets rather than to increase the load. When one is capable of executing the 100 repetitions in 4-5 sets, then the load should be increased for the next workout.

Rep Pausing Sets This method entails taking a short rest break during the execution of a set to facilitate recovery, diminish the pain of effort or overcome any loss of motivation before completing the remaining repetitions.

Holding Sets This method involves holding the weight statically at a given point during or at the end of a movement to isometrically strengthen the muscles, the tendons and joint capsules, as well as improving overall balance in certain lifts above the head (e.g. the clean or press).

Cumulative Sets This method entails beginning with a set of one repetition and adding on one repetition to each set until a final set to failure is reached. Usually this method employs one's 10RM, with 10 second rest intervals between each set.

Peak Contraction Sets This method requires you to complete each repetition at the point of maximal muscle contraction (see Figs 2.8, 2.9) and not at the end of range when the force has already diminished significantly. Usually, one consciously attempts to increase muscle tension in that position by means of intense isometric or quasi-isometric contraction.

Methods for Overcoming Barriers

The inevitable reaching of a 'sticking point' in training is one of single most frustrating experiences in the life of any athlete. It may lead to loss of form, loss of interest, decrease in motivation, the unnecessary or premature reliance on anabolic substances, an endless search for plausible ergogenic aids, injury or even the end of one's sporting career. Therefore, it is useful to become aware of a repertoire of various strategies which may implemented to help one break through these performance barriers. Among some of the methods are the following:

1. Attempt to increase the number of repetitions with near maximal loads. Thus, for example, try to increase your 2RM to a 3RM or your 3RM to a 5RM

2. Decrease your higher repetition training and include more 1RM, 2RM or 3RM training

3. Use CAT (Compensatory Acceleration Training) methods with lighter loads

4. Increase loads by unfamiliar increments, since sticking points often relate to the numerical value of the load which one associates with one's current 1RM. Thus, of increasing to one's 1RM of 100kg via a succession of sets like 80 - 90 - 95 - 100kg, change the sequence to sets of 80 - 92.5 - 97.5 - 102.5kg.

5. Change your warm-up strategy. Instead of wasting energy on prolonged repetitions or sets, devise a less demanding warm-up which conserves energy for the heaviest lifts.

6. Increase the increment in loads used in successive sets, provided that warm-up has been adequate. Thus, instead of using successive sets of 60 - 70 - 80 - 90 - 100kg, change to a sequence such as 60 - 80 - 100kg, where you may perform some more repetitions with 60kg, if you feel that a longer warm-up suits you better. To compensate for any decrease in overall volume of loading, you may add a few heavier sets or plateau with another few sets at 100kg.

7. If you uses pyramids, use fewer repetition sets to reach your maximum, then do your repetition work during a reverse pyramid down from your maximum. This can be especially useful if you wish to concurrently work on strength and hypertrophy.

8. Add minimal increments near your attempts with your 1RM or reps to failure training. This requires the use of very light weights of 0.5 - 1.25kg, which may be bought from suppliers of competitive lifting equipment or specially made by engineering shops. When one adds these weights, you do not count the extra load; you simply train as if the load is the same as if these small increments were not there. Sometimes, you may even sneak these weights between the larger plates if you wish to help a colleague break through some largely psychological barrier.

9. Use any of the contrast training methods discussed earlier.

10. Change some aspects of your typical training session, such as the order or duration of various exercises.

11. Use supramaximal adaptation training (SAT) methods, which entail actions like taking a load which is significantly heavier than your 1RM off a rack and supporting it, executing 'lock-outs' at the end of range, or performing small end-of-range repetitions.

12. Alter or improve your technique in problematic exercises. Sometimes your sticking point is due to imperfect technique, so that a skilled coach, together with video analysis of your movements, can help you carry out the necessary changes. It is unwise to attempt any changes in technique close to any competitions, unless there is something seriously inefficient or unsafe in your existing technique.

13. Ensure that your rest periods between sets or repetitions are optimal. Rests which are either too short or too long both may disrupt your ability to perform optimally, so it is essential that you experiment or apply appropriate tests (e.g. heart rate, motor control) to determine rest intervals which best suit you. In competition, however, the rules or number of competitors may not allow you optimal rest between attempts, so that it is vital that you train with different rest intervals to learn to cope with such situations.

14. Take a short break from your regular training to overcome mental stagnation and facilitate restoration.

15. Use fewer exercises in your workout

16. Include more variation in your workout.

17. Use shorter, more frequent workouts

18. Subdivide your workouts into rational modules of a few exercises, then do two or more modules per day.

20. Use ballistic methods to move through a sticking point in an exercise.

21. Perform loaded isometric holds at crucial points

22. Include formal restoration in your training programme, if you do not already do so

23. Implement appropriate mental strategies by consulting qualified specialists

24. Take a short break from the problem exercise or event

25. Implement a basic periodisation programme or at least an portion of one, if you are not already following one.

26. Use assistance exercises to strengthen areas of weakness in the problem exercise

27. Use 'forced repetitions' with the aid of a training partner (details given earlier in Ch 7.1)

28. Use variable resistance methods such as free weights combined with elastics or chains.

Concluding Remarks

The above summary by no means exhausts the repertoire of methods and variations of resistance training that is used in resistance training, but it serves as a rapid reference for the major methods which are most frequently used in the training of high-level athletes. It intentionally does not address several other methods quoted or 'invented' by writers in popular bodybuilding magazines, simply because they differ only in name and a few minor details from existing methods and do not constitute any major new contribution to the field of strength training.

In applying any of the methods discussed in this section, it is essential that the detailed information concerning their mechanisms and use given in earlier chapters be consulted in conjunction with the above summaries. It should never be forgotten that no methods operate in isolation of one another; each method has immediate and delayed training effects which have significant effects on other methods that follow hours, days or even weeks later (e.g. see 3.3.1, 3.4, 5.3, 5.4 and all Ch 6).

The next section examines a physical conditioning system which is widely used in physiotherapy, but is rarely regarded as a means of training the normal athlete, except occasionally in the specific situation of improving flexibility. This system, known by the somewhat daunting name of Proprioceptive Neuromuscular Facilitation or, PNF for short, however, can offer a highly comprehensive strength training system that encompasses and augments many of the methods and techniques of resistance exercise.

7.2 PNF as a Training System

Strength training is often regarded as a discipline confined largely to the gymnasium or sports field. Unfortunately, this can obscure the fact that it can and does appear in other situations which have little direct connection with sport.

In particular, PNF *(Proprioceptive Neuromuscular Facilitation)* contains many useful techniques which can play an important role in the strength training of athletes. It is one of the aims of this section to show that PNF is a comprehensive conditioning system which includes not only many of the principles already covered in this book, but also adds insights which complement these principles.

PNF is invariably regarded by conditioning coaches as a special type of sophisticated stretching, alongside static, ballistic and passive stretching. PNF is far more than just another stretching technique; *it is actually an entire system of therapy* comprising a broad spectrum of different techniques and procedures for rehabilitating patients suffering from various musculoskeletal injuries or disabilities. Stretching constitutes but one of many aspects of the full repertoire of PNF methods, yet even those enlightened coaches who use PNF extol only its virtues as a stretching system.

PNF was developed by Herman Kabat from 1946-1951 on the basis of work by renowned physiologists including Sherrington, Hellebrand, McGraw, and Pavlov. It created a practical rehabilitative system for applying findings on the reflexes of the body, motor development of the infant and the neuromuscular responses of adults.

Essentially, PNF recognizes that *all physical conditioning depends primarily on neuromuscular processes* involving sensitive receptors (proprioceptors) in the muscles, tendons and joints which enable a person to stabilise and move the body and its parts in space and time. Appropriate recruitment of the various stretch reflexes of the body, therefore, forms a vital part of PNF conditioning.

7.2.1 Definition and Scope of PNF

Formally, PNF is defined as *a system for promoting the response of neuromuscular mechanisms by stimulating the proprioceptors.* Knott and Voss state quite simply that PNF techniques involve placing a demand where a response is required. Its relation to the well-known SAID (Specific Adaptation to Imposed Demands) principle then becomes clear.

Essentially, two types of PNF may be recognised: *classical PNF* and *modified PNF*. The former refers to the hands-on clinical approach described in the Knott and Voss text, while the latter refers to an approach which adapts certain PNF techniques and principles for application by hand or apparatus in physical conditioning.

In applying classical PNF, the physical therapist stabilises specific parts of the body with the hands or body, while the other hand is used to grip the extremity or relevant part of the limb of the patient to offer highly specific patterns of resistance. The physical therapist's hand presses in a predetermined direction and manner to force the patient to execute what is termed a *pattern*, that trajectory of the limb which most efficiently recruits the relevant muscles. These patterns are usually imposed so that the extremity of the patient's limb is compelled to follow a spiral or diagonal path which crosses the sagittal midline of the body. Depending on the nature and severity of the injury or disability, the therapist will encourage the patient to produce isometric or dynamic contractions for an appropriate period against the resistance of the hand.

PNF stipulates that the muscle contraction must be maximal throughout the current range of movement, thereby ensuring that summation occurs at all times. Summation refers to the adding together of individual muscle twitches to produce strong, cooperative muscle movements. It occurs by imposing exercise of high intensity or prolonged duration to increase either the number of motor units contracting simultaneously or their rate of firing (or both).

At times, the therapist will produce a strong involuntary contraction in a debilitated muscle by imposing a sharp jerk during extension of the joint, thereby eliciting the *myotatic stretch reflex* produced by the muscle spindles. This is particularly useful if the patient finds it difficult to initiate or sustain a muscle contraction. PNF recognizes that the myotatic stretch reflex actually consists of a short duration, powerful dynamic (*phasic)* stretch reflex and a longer duration, weaker static (*tonic)* stretch reflex (see Fig 3.33). Consequently, short and long duration stretching loads are imposed in PNF to achieve different muscular responses. At other times, resistance will be increased or prolonged so as to enhance activation of the *Golgi tendon reflex*, thereby tending to reduce the tension in a muscle and promote local relaxation, which is sometimes desirable in facilitating the execution of a certain pattern (see Fig 3.33).

PNF also relies on the phenomenon of *reciprocal inhibition* in which strong contraction of the agonist muscles causes reflex relaxation of the antagonist muscles to prevent the latter from being injured. Application of this technique can produce a significantly stronger contraction of the agonists.

In the clinical setting, PNF requires the therapist to make regular use of verbal and non-verbal signals, including contacts with the hands or highly specific spoken commands to direct, instruct and motivate the patient. Sometimes, PNF implements various supplementary methods to augment facilitation produced by other primary means. These include the use of vibration, massage, ice, heat, electrostimulation, ultrasound or stroking.

PNF and the Neuromuscular Reflexes

PNF makes extensive use of the different reflexes which serve to protect the body, stabilise and mobilise it for action under a wide variety of circumstances (see Fig 3.33). As we have already learned, plyometric methods recruit the myotatic stretch reflex to activate the muscles after a strong eccentric shock phase. There are many other reflex systems in the body which mediate action automatically to avoid the potentially dangerous and inefficient responses that would be caused by reliance on slower voluntary processes. A knowledge of these reflex mechanisms is vital to musculoskeletal conditioning, a fact which is stressed in PNF.

A tendency to focus on bodybuilding or general weight training techniques over-emphasizes the role of muscle contraction, which is really the end-product of the interaction of various voluntary and reflex neuromotor processes. PNF serves the valuable purpose of recognising neuromuscular mechanisms as the dominant feature of all physical movement, rehabilitation and training. Intensity, duration, speed, type and patterns of muscle activity are primarily a consequence of neuromuscular processes and the relevant reflexes of the body.

7.2.2 Relationship of PNF to Physical Conditioning

PNF may be seen to provide a highly systematic approach to improving directly all the S-factors of fitness and several of the other specialised fitness qualities analysed in Chapter 1 (see 1.14.3), except cardiovascular endurance and psychological fitness.

The discipline of PNF teaches therapists to apply repetitions of graded resistance, to incorporate phases of relaxation, to elicit reflexes to facilitate contraction and greater range of movement, to impose specific patterns of passive and active movement, to use supplementary procedures for enhancing performance and to generally stimulate all neuromuscular processes related to voluntary and involuntary movement. No training method could be required to offer much more than this repertoire to qualify as an all-round conditioning system.

7.2.3 The Fundamentals of PNF

PNF may be categorised in terms of five P-factors: *Principles*, *Procedures*, *Patterns*, *Positions* and *Postures*, with joint *Pivots* and *Pacing* (Timing) as important sub-categories. The methods comprising these factors were formulated from findings on neuromuscular development, such as the functional evolution of all movement from motor immaturity to motor maturity in the growing child or novice athlete in definite sequences progressing logically from:

- total to individuated
- proximal to distal, distal to proximal
- mobile to stabile
- gross to selective

- reflexive to deliberate
- overlapping to integrative
- incoordinate to coordinate

7.2.3.1 The Principles of PNF

The basic principles of PNF may be summarised as follows:

1. Use of spiral and diagonal movement patterns
2. Motion crossing the sagittal midline of the body
3. Recruitment of all movement components, especially:

   - flexion-extension
   - adduction-abduction
   - internal-external rotation

4. Exercising of related muscle groups
5. Judicious eliciting of reflexes
6. Movement free of pain, but not free of effort
7. Comfortable full-range movement
8. Application of maximal resistance throughout the range of non-ballistic movement
9. Use of maximal resistance to promote overflow (irradiation) of muscle activity from stronger to weaker patterns. In particular, use of *successive induction* or contraction of agonists directly before contraction of antagonists.
10. Use of multiple joint and muscle action
11. Commencement of motion in the strongest range
12. Use of static and dynamic conditions
13. Appropriate positioning of joints to optimise conditioning
14. Exercising of agonists and antagonists
15. Repeated contractions to facilitate motor learning, conditioning and adaptation
16. Selection of appropriate sensory cues (tactile, auditory, visual) to facilitate action
17. Emphasis on visuo-motor and audio-motor coordination
18. Use of distal to proximal sequences in neuromuscularly mature subjects

19. Use of stronger muscles to augment the weaker
20. Progression from primitive to complex actions
21. Planning of each phase to lay foundations for the next phase
22. All activities are integrated and goal directed
23. Use of adjunct techniques (cold, electrostimulation, massage, vibration, stroking).

Immediately it may be seen that employment of any of the above principles in training implies conscious or unconscious reliance on aspects of the PNF system.

7.2.3.2 Procedures of PNF

The procedures (or techniques) used in PNF include:

1. Use of specific manual contacts with the body to facilitate and guide movement
2. Application of maximal tolerated resistance
3. The use of oral commands and non-verbal cues to facilitate correct movement
4. Eliciting of maximal stretch reflex in the lengthened muscle range (Starling's Law)
5. Use of appropriate timing and sequencing of all actions
6. Application of traction or approximation (compression) to stimulate joint receptors
7. Inclusion of recuperative motion to reduce or avoid fatigue produced by resisted activity
8. Use of *Specific Activation Techniques* to develop full range of voluntary movement
9. The use of *Specific Relaxation Techniques*.

The **Specific Activation Techniques** (of 8 above) need to be elaborated upon, as follows:

• *Repeated Contractions (RC)*

Repetition of muscle contraction is necessary for motor learning and the development of strength, muscle endurance and flexibility. PNF uses precise sequences or patterns of isometric, concentric and eccentric contraction, sometimes augmented by eliciting various neuromuscular reflexes (i.e. methods which may be similar to some types of plyometrics).

• *Rhythmic Initiation (RI)*

This technique employs phases of voluntary relaxation, passive movement and repeated dynamic contractions of the major muscle groups involved in the agonistic pattern of movement. It can be valuable with subjects who struggle to initiate activity because of rigidity or spasticity.

• *Reversal of Antagonists (RA)*

This action occurs naturally in numerous activities such as walking, running and sawing wood. If the antagonists do not reverse competently in terms of strength, speed and coordination, motor efficiency is impaired. PNF uses three methods of reversal: slow reversal, slow-reversal-hold and rhythmic stabilisation.

Slow reversal (SR) involves dynamic contraction of the antagonist slowly followed by dynamic contraction of the agonist. *Slow reversal-hold* (SRH) employs dynamic contraction followed by isometric contraction of the antagonist, finally followed by the same contraction sequence for the agonist. *Rhythmic stabilisation* (RS) involves isometric contraction of the antagonist, followed by isometric contraction of the agonist, thereby producing co-contraction of the antagonists.

The **Specific Relaxation Techniques** (of 9 above) similarly need to be expanded upon, since they include the so-called PNF stretching techniques popularly used in athletic conditioning.

• *Contract-Relax (CR)*, which involves a dynamic contraction of the antagonist against maximal resistance, followed by a phase of relaxation. This technique is repeated several times beginning and continuing from a point where the limb concerned is moved to its limit of pain-free action. The practitioner resists the contraction as strongly as possible and then instructs the client to relax before decreasing the force and waiting for the relaxation to occur. The limb is moved passively to its new limit of extension and the process is continued gently for a few repetitions.

- *Hold-Relax* (HR) is similar to contract-relax except that isometric rather than dynamic contraction against maximal resistance is applied at the limit of the client's movement before relaxation is commanded.

- *Slow-Reversal-Hold-Relax* (SRHR) comprises four stages: dynamic contraction of the antagonists involved, isometric contraction of the antagonists, brief voluntary relaxation, and finally, dynamic contraction of the agonists. These stages are applied to the muscles in the specific pattern needed to relax the group of muscles concerned, using several repetitions to enhance functional flexibility.

7.2.3.3 Patterns of PNF

Probably the most neglected aspect of PNF by coaches is the employment of specific *patterns* of joint and limb movement to recruit and condition muscles in the most efficient or appropriate manner. Physiotherapists spend considerable time learning the intricacies of patterns to stabilise some parts of the body and to activate other parts using the procedures outlined above.

In conditioning the developing neuromuscular systems of the patient, the novice or the child, there is always an emphasis on progression from primitive to complex, gross to individuated, mobile to stabile, reflexive to deliberative, proximal to distal, and incoordinate to coordinate. Contrary to common belief, *the novice must be taught from a base of mobility to progress to stability*, just as an infant learns to stand by first moving, staggering and exploring the environment.

The movement patterns involve the application of all the above Principles of PNF, such as the use of spirals and diagonals, crossing of the body's midline, the judicious eliciting of reflexes, and emphasis of muscle actions by use of correct timing. Movement is promoted by the eyes following the extremities, or the extremities following the eyes.

Since all physical conditioning requires a constant interplay of *mobility* and *stability*, all patterns implicate some parts of the body in stabilising and other parts in mobilising. For instance, both static strength and static muscular endurance might have to be developed in the back muscles of an athlete, while three-dimensional dynamic strength, dynamic muscular endurance and dynamic flexibility might have to be developed in the upper leg. This type of conditioning cannot be applied by machines, although a pulley system may be used to produce the appropriate whole-body patterns of movement required. In other situations, the goal of training may be to prevent motion and to stimulate stability or maintain balance. Compensatory movements of additional muscle groups may be resisted or they may even be elicited by brief, sudden actions or deviations from optimal patterns.

The importance of these patterns cannot be overestimated, since they can enhance the effectiveness of any training session. They stimulate more thorough involvement and motor development than the less-than-optimal patterns imposed by the abundance of linear or cam machines on the market. No machines other than the traditional high-low pulley machines allow the user to produce PNF patterns.

Some devices such as pec-decks, back hyperextension machines, seated pressing machines, hack-squat machines and leg extension machines (to mention a few) cause such large deviations from recommended PNF patterns that they can impose excessive loading on certain joints and are suitable only for a small proportion of the training of highly conditioned athletes. Even then, machine training is often not functionally similar to the natural patterns of exercise movement upon which PNF is based, so that it requires a disproportionate number of machines to approximate the training offered by free weight and pulley training in three-dimensional space under conditions of *pacing* or *normal timing* (yet another PNF principle). Normal timing refers to the timing of the phases of a movement or series of movements which occur naturally in a uninjured person carrying out a given activity efficiently and safely.

PNF offers an enormous repertoire of patterns including those for sitting; sitting up; sitting up and rotating; standing; kneeling; crawling; raising the head; moving the arms from above to below and vice versa; raising and lowering the legs; moving the trunk in flexion, extension and rotation; and raising or lowering the body. There are distinctive patterns for actions with straightened limbs, flexed limbs and extended limbs (e.g., see Figs 7.3 to 7.8).

Since weight training is aimed at maximal muscle conditioning via the use of techniques experimented with by weightlifters, bodybuilders and powerlifters for many years on every conceivable type of apparatus, there is no better environment to apply modified PNF for improving overall conditioning. Brief examples of how PNF may be adapted for use in the gymnasium environment are given later, but space does not permit a full description to be given of how PNF techniques may be integrated into most resistance workouts. For further information, the videotapes on applied PNF training prepared by the NSCA may be consulted (Siff, 1989).

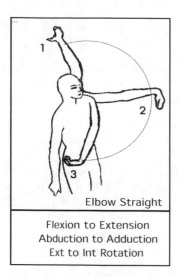
Elbow Straight
Flexion to Extension
Abduction to Adduction
Ext to Int Rotation

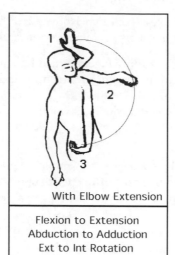
With Elbow Extension
Flexion to Extension
Abduction to Adduction
Ext to Int Rotation

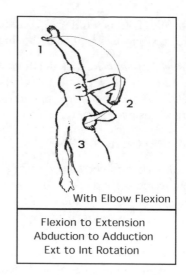
With Elbow Flexion
Flexion to Extension
Abduction to Adduction
Ext to Int Rotation

Figure 7.3 PNF Upper Extremity patterns from shoulder flexion to shoulder extension

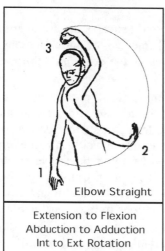
Elbow Straight
Extension to Flexion
Abduction to Adduction
Int to Ext Rotation

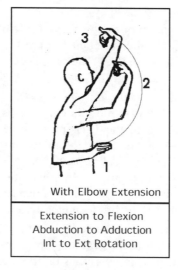
With Elbow Extension
Extension to Flexion
Abduction to Adduction
Int to Ext Rotation

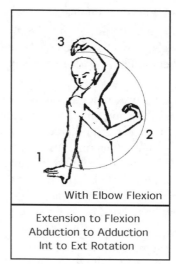
With Elbow Flexion
Extension to Flexion
Abduction to Adduction
Int to Ext Rotation

Figure 7.4 PNF Upper Extremity patterns from shoulder extension to shoulder flexion

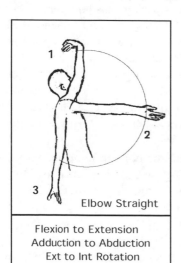
Elbow Straight
Flexion to Extension
Adduction to Abduction
Ext to Int Rotation

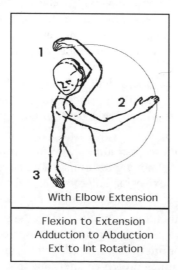
With Elbow Extension
Flexion to Extension
Adduction to Abduction
Ext to Int Rotation

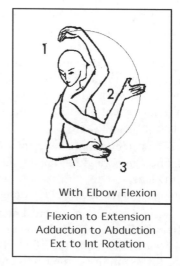
With Elbow Flexion
Flexion to Extension
Adduction to Abduction
Ext to Int Rotation

Figure 7.5 PNF Upper Extremity patterns from shoulder extension to shoulder flexion

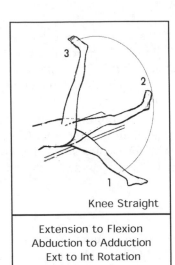

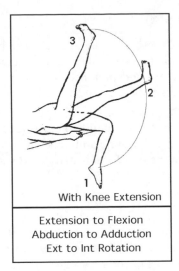

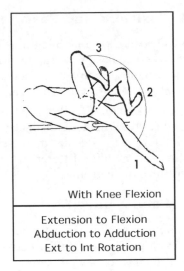

Knee Straight	With Knee Extension	With Knee Flexion
Extension to Flexion Abduction to Adduction Ext to Int Rotation	Extension to Flexion Abduction to Adduction Ext to Int Rotation	Extension to Flexion Abduction to Adduction Ext to Int Rotation

Figure 7.6 PNF Lower Extremity patterns from hip extension to hip flexion (legs start apart)

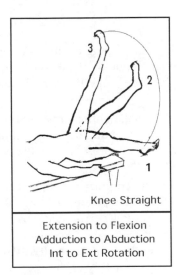

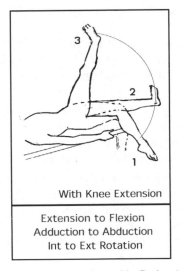

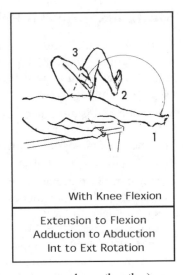

Knee Straight	With Knee Extension	With Knee Flexion
Extension to Flexion Adduction to Abduction Int to Ext Rotation	Extension to Flexion Adduction to Abduction Int to Ext Rotation	Extension to Flexion Adduction to Abduction Int to Ext Rotation

Figure 7.7 PNF Lower Extremity patterns from hip extension to hip flexion (one leg starts crossed over the other)

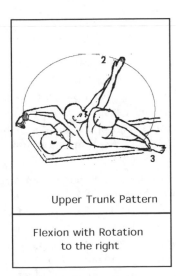

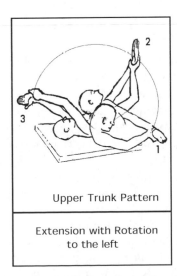

Upper Trunk Pattern	Upper Trunk Pattern
Flexion with Rotation to the right	Extension with Rotation to the left

Figure 7.8 PNF Trunk Rotation pattern. This pattern may be done in a supine or standing position and taken further into trunk and hip flexion to serve as a very effective exercise for all of the abdominal muscles. Resistance may be offered with a cable machine.

7.2.3.4 Positions and Postures of PNF

Positions and *postures* are an integral part of the use of PNF patterns. The body and its limbs have to be held in carefully prescribed postures, with the joints and limbs maintained in certain positions or moved from position to position to establish stability of some systems and mobility of others in order to enhance neuromuscular development and safety. All action can then take place around specific joints as *pivots*.

For instance, a dumbbell curl performed with the elbow dug firmly into the side will produce activation patterns and results which are distinctly different from dumbbell curls done with the elbow and shoulder free to flex, extend or rotate. Besides the possibility for cheating and trapezius involvement for the unrestrained elbow curl, another less familiar difference between the two curls is that downward traction can occur at the shoulder joint for the unrestrained curl.

7.2.3.5 Pacing in PNF

Normal timing or pacing refers to the timing of the phases of a movement or series of movements which occur naturally in an uninjured, healthy person carrying out a prescribed activity efficiently and safely. The optimal timing of each phase of any movement is vital for all neuromuscular conditioning, functional strength development and perfection of motor skill.

7.2.4 Modifications to PNF

Modified PNF refers to the adapting of classical PNF for use in the athletic conditioning setting or fitness class. Not only does it modify some PNF partner stretches for use by unassisted individuals, but it can also include application or adaptation of *any* of the PNF *Principles, Procedures, Patterns, Positions* and *Postures* in the normal conditioning environment.

Pulleys and dumbbells are especially suitable for application of the spiral and diagonal, midline-crossing PNF techniques. The standing full-range cable cross-over exercise with external-internal rotation of the shoulder joint furnishes just one example of an adapted PNF pattern. Barbell training provides fewer opportunities for the use of PNF training, while machines offer the fewest possibilities of all for use of modified PNF.

This does not imply that barbell and machine training should be avoided. On the contrary, it can be used effectively under special circumstances, sometimes to cause intentional deviations from PNF patterns to adapt the body to potentially harmful actions which may occur in real sporting situations. A major error in the use of machines is that they are invariably regarded as offering greater stability and safety for beginners than free weights. In fact, their design imposes body positions, postures and activation of pivots which usually differ considerably from those recommended by PNF and compromise the effectiveness and safety of the exercise. Thus, instructors must always 'spot' for the users of machines as well as free weights, just as the physiotherapist regularly uses manual contacts and verbal reinforcement

Pattern Deviations and Safety Factors

It should be remembered that the patterns of PNF were devised for rehabilitation, not elite sporting training, so that *it is not incorrect to employ patterns of movement which may deviate significantly from those stipulated in PNF*. The latter system generally stipulates execution of all patterns close to the body, a situation which occurs seldom in sport. There are times when forceful or rapid movements have to be executed with the distal extremities far from the relevant joints, thereby imposing large torque on these joints. If training always ensures that this degree of torque or force is avoided, then it will not prepare the athlete for the rigors of the sport and will increase susceptibility to overtraining and injury.

As in engineering, one must plan for a certain *safety factor* which allows the athlete to manage even larger forces than those which may be encountered in competition. For example, a safety factor of 1.2 means that a system can cope with a maximal loading of 0.2 or 20% greater than normally expected. The appropriate use of heavy supplementary resistance training ('cross training') can be especially valuable in this regard, provided that it does not alter the neuromuscular patterns needed in the given sport. It should never to forgotten that high levels of skill and reactive ability in sport are vital in ensuring that sporting action is efficient and safe. Far too many athletes (e.g. in football and rugby) believe that increase in strength and bodymass will automatically protect them from injury. If one executes a movement in an inefficient manner or reacts too slowly to produce adequate force, then even gigantic strength or structural bulk can be inadequate to prevent injury.

7.2.5 Functional Neuromuscular Conditioning

Although some members of the strength conditioning profession have used the term 'modified PNF' for many years, its appropriateness needs to be re-examined for several reasons. *Firstly*, it is sometimes desirable to deviate from strict PNF principles to achieve a specific goal. *Secondly*, there are other movement disciplines such as Feldenkrais, Alexander, yoga, Tai Chi and Laban which offer invaluable additional methods of conditioning. *Thirdly*, PNF might not only involve neuromuscular processes, since contractile activity in a muscle may be facilitated by local after-discharge of the same muscle. *Fourthly*, the PNF repertoire includes methods which may not be classified accurately as proprioceptive, such as cognitive, perceptual and other sensory mechanisms. *Finally*, the term Proprioceptive Neuromuscular Facilitation is too technically daunting for the average coach or athlete.

Therefore, the term *Functional Neuromuscular Conditioning (FNC)* might be more appropriate, since PNF and other movement disciplines all stress the importance of optimising the conditioning effect to produce functional fitness of the neuromuscular system. Because Wolff's Law states that function precedes structure, FNC may be seen to embrace all-round development of function and structure. In other words, FNC should be regarded as an entire conditioning system capable of developing any desired type of musculoskeletal fitness.

Lately, the term 'functional training' has been promoted as a unique and modern method of training. In fact, it is nothing much more than a synonym for 'action specific', 'activity specific' or 'sport specific' training. To be entirely accurate, 'functional training' should address not only the motor qualities, but also the metabolic requirements of a given activity, so, where we encounter the term 'functional training' it is more correctly a synonym for FNC. Finally, it is misleading to classify a single exercise as being "non-functional", since functional conditioning can comprise a combination of general and specific, 'functional' and 'non-functional' exercises. Indeed, this type of combined GPP and SPP methods forms the basis of all periodisation.

7.3 Combinations of Resistance Methods

It is well know that the output force or torque that any muscle can produce changes with joint angle, with the greatest force usually being possible after the joint has passed through the midpoint of the movement. This means that any given load will tend to underload certain muscles over some part of the movement range. Earlier, we discussed the method of CAT (Compensatory Acceleration Training) which enables the athlete to increase muscle tension by deliberate attempts to continue to move the load as fast as possible, but various machines such as isokinetic or variable resistance also have been used for years to offer resistance that better fits the strength curves of muscles or joints.

One of the most top Powerlifting coaches in the USA, Louie Simmons, has been successfully using chains and elastic bands attached to bars to offer variable resistance in major exercises such as the bench press, squat and deadlift, so that one can lift against a predetermined resistance range from beginning to end of a movement (Fig 7.9). The author has used various other combinations of free weight loads and machines such as isokinetic dynamometers to change the resistance pattern against which the athlete trains (see next section).

Figure 7.9 Mel Siff and Louie Simmons (right) at the Westside Gym in Ohio (Photo: Diane Black, 2000)

In all cases of variable resistance training, it is important to fully understand the emphasis of the resistance training being used, because frequent use of any inappropriate training method or resistance pattern can be detrimental to the performance of the actual sporting movements. Thus, if one needs to concentrate on power development, one has to be very careful to enhance Rate of Force Development and to train regularly with loads that do not exceed about 60-70 percent of one's maximum, if one's goal is maximal power development.

Scientific Analysis of Different Strength Training Combinations

The first combination to be investigated was a combination of free weight and isokinetic resistance, with the same group of subjects being analysed under separate inertial and isokinetic conditions, then finally under a combination of both types of resistance applied using a cable machine specially designed and constructed for this purpose by one of Siff's mechanical engineering students at the University of the Witwatersrand in South Africa (Fradd, 1995). The most interesting findings appear in Table 7.1 and the following selection of graphs (Figs 7.10-7.12).

Table 7.1 Summary of results obtained from analysis of elbow flexion movement under different resistance conditions (Velocity in m/sec, power in Watts and force in Newtons).

Resistance	Max Velocity	Mean Power	Peak Power	Mean Force	Peak Force
Isoinertial	1.49	151	306	184	219
Isokinetic	0.42	80	129	247	350
Combined	0.38	102	131	336	380

In interpreting this information, it is important to note that the shape of the curves varies with every individual, according to their motor characteristics, and, in the combined scenario, with the magnitude of the inertial load and the velocity of isokinetic resistance. The combined resistance may be made more auxotonic (free weight) if the added weight is large and more isokinetic if the added load is relatively small. It would be well to note that there may be significant variation among graphs produced by different individuals, because their force output characteristics depend to a large extent on their training history and sporting background.

1. Greatest mean and peak power is produced under free weight conditions, reaching a peak approximately midway through the movement (Fig 7.10)

2. Free weight force production is greatest during the earliest phases of joint movement (Fig 7.10)

3. Power production is considerably lower under isokinetic and combined conditions, but remains near its peak value for a considerable part of the range (Figs 7.11, 7.12)

4. Mean and peak force production is greatest during combined conditions, and may peak twice during the movement, most commonly near the beginning and the end of range

5. Isokinetic force plateaus about one-third through the range, but commonly increases near end of range.

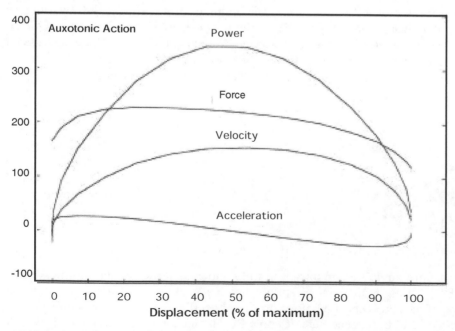

Figure 7.10 Resisted elbow flexion movement under free weight (auxotonic or isoinertial) conditions.

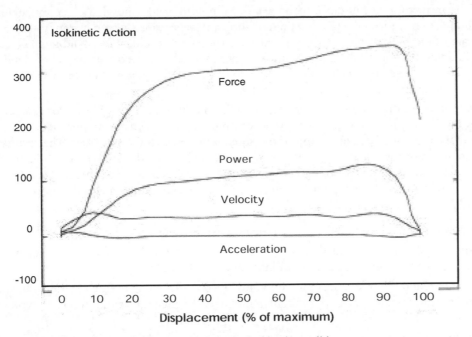

Figure 7.11 Resisted elbow flexion movement under isokinetic conditions

If we examine Figure 7.10, we will note that peak force is produced near the beginning of the movement and that peak power and peak velocity are both attained about halfway through the movement, when elbow angle is approximately 90 degrees. Approximately half the movement is spent in acceleration and half in deceleration. If this graph is compared with the graphs in Figures 7.11 and 7.12, it will be seen that the peak power generated under auxotonic (isoinertial) conditions is some three times greater than under isokinetic or combined auxotonic-isokinetic conditions. This will not always be the case, since the shape of the graph under combined conditions is determined by the resistance offered by the free weights and the isokinetic machine relative to one another.

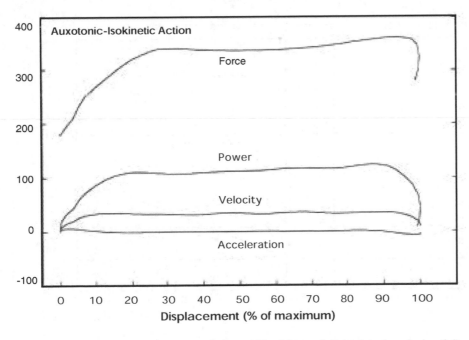

Figure 7.12 Resisted elbow flexion movement under combined free-weight (auxotonic or isoinertial) and isokinetic conditions

The next resistance hybrid to be examined was a combination of free weights and elastic band resistance, using a box squatting exercise in a power rack with strong elastic bands attached between the ends of the bar and the base of the rack. The length of the elastic bands was adjusted so that elastic resistance varied between set limits at the lowest and the highest positions of the movement. For those who wish to train with bands, they may be constructed at low cost out of thick gauge bungee cord formed into a continuous loop and secured with rope clamps. The exact tension in the cables may be measured by standing on a bathroom scale (or pair of scales) while holding the bar and stretched cable at the starting and end points of the movement. Another method is to secure a band at one end and measure its extension with a series of loads to enable you to draw a load vs extension graph. From this graph, you can then read off the extra force exerted by the cables for a given extension.

Thus, the powerlifters involved in this study experienced, in addition to the squat weight of 200kg, an added elastic resistance of 150kg at the lowest position while sitting down on the box with knees at approximately right angles and a greatest elastic resistance of 250kg at the top of the squat with knees fully extended. The results are expressed in the form of percentages of the squat weight used (Fig 7.13). This method allowed the powerlifters to train under special overload conditions intended to strengthen specific weaknesses in the movement characteristics produced under normal loaded conditions. The main differences between this combined method and free weight training were:

1. A greater mean and peak force were produced throughout the range of movement

2. The descent onto the box tended to be accelerated above the normal gravitational rate of 9.8m/sec squared, so that greater eccentric force had to be generated to control the downward motion

3. The stronger eccentric loading and the brief transition period involved while sitting before exploding upwards provided neuromuscular stimulation which approximates that usually encountered in popular plyometric training.

4. The force generated during the later stages increased, in strong contrast to the situation of normal squatting in which force production tends to decrease significantly.

As with the other combined method of free weights and isokinetics, it is important to note that there tend to be large individual variations and that the exact shape of the combined resistance curve depends on the magnitude of the weights load relative to the top and bottom resistance provided by the elastic bands.

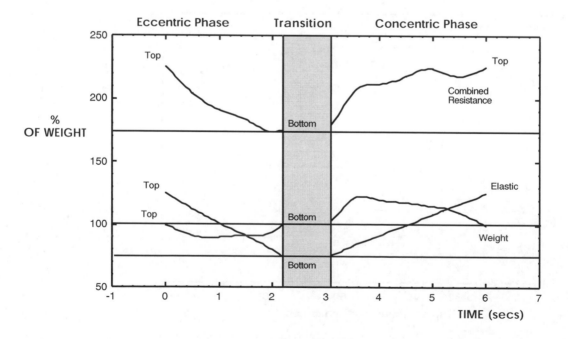

Figure 7.13 Resisted box squatting under combined free weights and elastically resisted conditions.

Although this research was carried out on box squatting, similar combinations of free weights and elastic bands may be used very effectively over a variety of different ranges of movement with other major exercises such as the deadlift, the clean, the bench press, good mornings and one arm deadlifts. These bands may also be attached between the fixed and moving parts of pulley and various other training machines, thereby offering combined free weights and band resistance for a wide variety of bodybuilding and general strength exercises.

Another hybrid training method involves the combined use of free weights and chains, a method that was also pioneered in the USA by Louie Simmons primarily for powerlifting purposes. In this case, heavy duty chains are attached at either end of the loaded barbell, so that, as the weight is lifted further off the floor, the more links of chain are raised and the more the resistance increases. The additional resistance offered by the chains may be varied by using different gauges of chain or different combinations of heavy and lighter gauge chains.

Accelerated Powermetrics

The use of elastic bands provides not only added resistance during the concentric phase of the movement, but it can also be allowed to accelerate the load during the eccentric phase, thereby providing involuntary or passive acceleration. We thus note that elastic bands and plyometric actions provide similar methods of enhancing muscle tension. In the case of plyometrics, the body or its limbs are subjected to greater force during the amortisation phase of the exercise by momentum acting on the body through the acceleration of gravity (e.g., during a drop jump) or the action of a propelled object, while in the case of band training, the greater force is provided by external elastic tension.

These methods of increasing force during the amortisation or eccentric phase of an exercise are actually involuntary or passive, since muscle action is not being intentionally used to impose greater force on the body. There is, however, also an active or voluntary form of imposing greater force on the body, which may be called *actively accelerated powermetrics*.

Let me now elaborate on how one can use *actively accelerated powermetrics* to do the bench press, squat, dip for the jerk, 'Romanian deadlift' (or mid range clean pull from the hang) and various other exercises in a way which can be even more forceful than the load dropping and catching methods discussed in Ch 4.2.3. This type of training may be done in two voluntary forms, namely *accelerated eccentric* and *accelerated ballistic* training, neither of which requires anyone or any special machine to drop the load onto your hands or feet such as the "plyometric bench" described in Figure 4.6. As noted above, together with the passive acceleration imposed during the eccentric phase of an exercise by elastic bands, these methods can extend the repertoire of "powermetric" training drills. In summary, then, here are the four main ways of using *accelerated powermetrics*:

1. Passively accelerated eccentrics: Here bands are used, but, instead of resisting the action of the stretched bands to decelerate the bar or keep it moving down at approximately constant speed during the eccentric phase, allow the elastic tension to accelerate the bar during this phase. Then, after a suitable range of movement, halt the movement as rapidly as you can.

2. Passively accelerated eccentrics: Here you rely on a partner to accelerate the bar during the eccentric phase by pushing downwards on it, like an inverse form of "forced reps". Instead of resisting the action throughout the amortisation phase, allow the bar to accelerate and then, after a suitable range of movement, halt the movement as rapidly as you can.

3. Actively accelerated eccentrics: Here you rely solely on your muscles. Instead of resisting the action of gravity to decelerate the bar or keep it moving down at approximately constant speed or allowing it to drop almost freely under gravitational acceleration during the eccentric phase, you deliberately pull the bar downwards as fast as you can and stop the downward motion before you reach the end of the movement. For safety reasons, do not allow the accelerated load to force you into your extreme end position of joint action. Unlike the form of accelerated eccentrics offered by elastic bands, the force added to gravitational force ceases if one stops voluntarily accelerating the bar.

4. Actively accelerated ballistics (or rebounds): Here you again rely solely on your muscles. Instead of lowering the bar slowly or allowing it to drop under gravitational acceleration, deliberately pull the bar downwards as fast as you can, stop the downward motion at a suitable point before the end of the movement and as rapidly as you can, try to accelerate the bar upwards into a powerful concentric movement.

Whatever you do, do not overestimate your capabilities, because all of these forms of *accelerated powermetrics* can be very demanding on the body. In general, you should start learning this movement with relatively light loads in the bench press or squat (say, about 40-50kg, depending on your strength and training experience) and use very few repetitions. Obviously the load used in exercises which involve smaller and weaker muscle groups should be considerably lower than that. Remember that this is really a type of 'supramaximal' force training and it can impose extremely large stresses on your soft tissues.

The important thing to remember is that this form of training, according to Newton's Second Law, focuses on force being increased by means of acceleration and not added mass. As you progress, recall that maximal power production, depending on the specific exercise, occurs with loads of between 50-70 percent of one's 1RM, so it is unnecessary ever to exceed this range of loading in these accelerated training methods (unless one uses them over a very small range of motion).

7.4 Muscle Training

It is sometimes necessary to know which groups of muscles are carrying out a moving or stabilising role when an exercise programme is being devised. This analysis requires a good working knowledge of functional anatomy, especially as many terms used to describe popular movements in bodybuilding often disguise the intricacy and subtleties of the joint actions. For instance, 'bicep curls' do not involve the brachial biceps only, but also the brachialis and brachialis to differing degrees, depending on hand position and speed of movement.

It should be remembered that the concept of *muscle isolation* training which is rife in bodybuilding is very misleading, as discussed in detail earlier (4.2.9). Muscle isolation incorrectly implies that only one specific muscle group is activated by a given exercise. Isolation may occur to a significant extent when the resistance to movement is small, but with increasing load, the relevant stabilisers of the body and joints, as well as assistant movers, come more strongly into play.

This why it is vital to remember that all human movement involves the intricate orchestration of concurrent and sequential contractions of movers and stabilisers. Each muscular symphony is different for a specific sporting action and a knowledge of functional anatomy allows us to identify the muscle groups in each movement and how they are involved in concentric, eccentric and isometric types of contraction. This section summarises some of the essential functional anatomy that was presented earlier in the form of *Movement Matrices* (see 3.7) to enable us to analyse joint actions in sport and to prescribe supplementary strengthening exercises on a kinesiologically logical basis.

Before any analysis of complex multi-articular movement is attempted, the last section at the end of Chapter 3 (entitled *Limitations of Anatomical Movement Analysis*) should be borne in mind. Here it was stressed that the classical methods of functional anatomy define a given muscle, for instance, as a flexor or extensor, on the basis of the torque that it produces around a single joint, but the nature of the body as a linked system of many joints means that muscles which do not span other joints can still produce acceleration about those joints.

Recently, largely as a consequence of individuals attempting to extrapolate to the general fitness world some of the muscle isolating methods used by physical therapists for injury rehabilitation, it has become fairly fashionable to encounter special programmes to train 'core stabilisation' with balancing tools such as wobble boards and physio balls, augmented by activation of the transversus abdominis (TA) to strengthen the trunk. All too often, it seems to be forgotten that stability of the core or trunk cannot be exhibited without the periphery of the body being firmly secured on a solid surface, unless, of course, the athlete has to use the core independently of the floor or any other apparatus, as in diving, trampolining and jumping. Well meaning instructions to activate TA during dynamic actions such as lifting and wrestling are highly inappropriate, because conscious intervention in any such movements can lead to "paralysis by analysis". Anyway, if the athlete is taught the optimal way to carry out any movement, the body naturally activates muscles in the most appropriate way for that given activity. After all, the body "knows only of movement, not muscles". Finally, no research has yet shown that isolationist training or ball/board balancing skills transpose to 'functional' sporting action, so that time spent on such pursuits usually can be better spent on more sport specific drills, unless the aim is to resolve some injury.

7.4.1 A Summary of Movements of the Joints

As before, this section also approaches kinesiology from the point of view of joint actions rather than by analysis of which specific muscle groups produce a given movement. To use this information, simply identify the joint action and then identify which muscles produce that action. For a graphical method of obtaining the same information, consult the Movement Matrices in Section 3.7.

Movements of the Spine

Extension: Bilateral action of the erector spinae and semispinalis. (Neck extension by bilateral action of splenius capitis, semispinalis capitis).

Flexion: Bilateral action of rectus abdominis and psoas. (Neck flexion by bilateral action of sternocleidomastoid and scaleni).

Lateral flexion: Unilateral action of the iliocostalis and longissimus components of erector spinae, the internal and external abdominal obliques, quadratus lumborum and psoas. (Neck tilting by unilateral action of sternocleidomastoid, scaleni, splenius capitis).

Rotation: The external abdominal obliques of one side acting in conjunction with the opposite internal oblique. (Neck rotation by muscle action including unilateral action of semispinalis and splenius cervicis).

Movements of the Knee Joint

Extension: Rectus femoris, vastus medialis, vastus lateralis, vastus intermedius.

Flexion: Mainly the hamstrings, assisted by sartorius, gracilis and gastrocnemius. Popliteus initiates flexion by unlocking the extended knee.

Medial rotation (of tibia relative to femur): Semimembranosus, semitendinosus, sartorius, gracilis, popliteus.

Lateral rotation (of tibia relative to femur): Biceps femoris.

Movements of the Hip Joint

Extension: Femoral biceps, semimembranosus, semitendinosus, hamstring portion of adductor magnus, gluteus maximus (when the action requires greater force).

Flexion: Iliopsoas, rectus femoris (particularly if the knee is extended), tensor fasciae latae, sartorius, adductor longus, adductor brevis, the adductor portion of adductor magnus, pectineus, the anterior fibres of gluteus medius and minimus.

Abduction: Gluteus medius and minimus, possibly weakly assisted by tensor fasciae latae, piriformis and obturator internus.

Adduction: Adductor magnus, longus and brevis, assisted by gracilis and pectineus, with possible weak assistance from quadratus femoris and obturator externus.

Medial rotation: Tensor fasciae latae, anterior fibres of gluteus medius and minimus.

Lateral rotation: Gluteus maximus, sartorius, iliopsoas, pectineus, the posterior fibres of gluteus medius and minimus, the lateral rotators (piriformis, quadratus femoris, obturator internus and externus, gemellus superior and inferior).

Movements of the Shoulder Joint

Extension: Latissimus dorsi, teres major and minor, posterior deltoid, infraspinatus and the long head of triceps.

Flexion: Across the chest - pectoralis major, anterior deltoid, coracobrachialis, biceps. Upwards in sagittal plane - posterior deltoid, upper trapezius (for scapular rotation).

Abduction: Deltoids, supraspinatus (for scapular rotation).

Adduction: Pectoralis major, teres major, latissimus dorsi, coracobrachialis, subscapularis, and the long head of triceps.

Lateral rotation: Teres minor, infraspinatus, posterior deltoid.

Medial rotation: Pectoralis major, anterior deltoid, teres major, subscapularis, latissimus dorsi.

Scapular Retraction: Trapezius, levator scapulae, rhomboid major and minor.

Scapular Protraction: Serratus anterior, pectoralis minor.

Shoulder Girdle Elevation: Levator scapulae, trapezius (upper fibres), rhomboid major and minor, serratus anterior(superior part).

Shoulder Girdle Depression: Trapezius (lower fibres) - and gravity.

Movements of the Elbow Joint

Extension: Triceps, anconeus.

Flexion: Brachialis, brachioradialis (particularly if the movement is rapid). Also biceps (if forearm is supinated) and pronator teres (if forearm is pronated).

Note: Apparent rotation of the elbow joint is actually rotation at the wrist - the radius and ulna twist about one another, so there is no rotation of the elbow joint as a whole.

Movements of the Ankle Joint

Plantarflexion: Gastrocnemius, soleus, tibialis posterior and flexor digitorum longus, weakly assisted by plantaris, peroneus longus and peroneus brevis.

Dorsiflexion: Tibialis anterior, peroneus tertius, extensor hallucis longus, and extensor digitorum longus.

Inversion: Flexor digitorum longus, flexor hallucis longus and tibialis anterior, assisted by extensor hallucis longus.

Eversion: Extensor digitorum longus, peroneus tertius, peroneus longus, peroneus brevis.

7.4.2 Examination of Some Joint Actions

The application of the Movement Matrices or the above summary enables us to appreciate how ill understood some popular exercises are. For instance, so-called 'calf raises' or 'heel raises' are commonly regarded as exercises to develop gastrocnemius and soleus. However, it should be noted that plantarflexion also involves action of *plantaris, flexor digitorum longus, flexor hallucis longus* and *tibialis posterior*. Moreover, inward rotation or inversion of the foot more strongly recruits the last three muscles named, so that heel raises with inversion tend to activate all of the plantarflexors more strongly. Popular emphasis on heel raising in invariably causes one to neglect the antagonistic action of the dorsiflexors such as tibialis anterior. The summary above reveals that it is important to dorsiflex with both inversion and eversion of the ankle if all dorsiflexors are to be exercised adequately.

It is important to distinguish between unilateral and bilateral actions of certain muscle groups, such as the *erector spinae*. Acting unilaterally, they serve to laterally extend the trunk, whereas acting bilaterally and symmetrically, they extend the trunk backwards without any lateral movement occurring. It should also be noted that lateral action of the long muscles of the back does not produce spinal rotation and that the only muscle of the back which is involved in spinal rotation is *multifidus*. The major initiators of trunk rotation are the internal and external obliques and the strengthening of these muscles, therefore, is vital for all sporting activities that require rotation of the trunk.

It should also be noted that *rectus abdominis*, although it might be considered an antagonist of the erector spinae, does not produce any lateral action of the trunk. Both groups of obliques acting bilaterally produce trunk flexion so as to augment action by rectus abdominis, so it is incorrect to state that trunk flexion is solely a result of contraction of rectus abdominis. It is also interesting to note that if situps are done with a lateral flexing of the trunk, the rectus abdominis are not significantly involved, but the *obliques* and *psoas* are strongly contracted.

7.5 Use of Strength Training Compendium

The classification and interrelation of the host of strength training means and methods is still at a stage similar to that of atomic physics earlier this century when no truly coherent scheme had been worked out to compartmentalise the rapidly growing list of sub-atomic particles. Relationships between different masses, charges, quantum numbers and spins of particles were intuitively suspected, but not theoretically formalised or experimentally confirmed.

Similarly, bodybuilding magazines and competitors in all aspects of the Iron Game identified a vast array of different training methods and techniques, while physiotherapists and other medical personnel separately developed their own scheme of physical conditioning, yet no overall grand scheme emerged to integrate the two approaches and their individual multitudes of training methods. Therefore, the author was invited to address the 1989 conference of the NSCA (National Strength and Conditioning Association) in the USA to show how therapeutic PNF could serve as a complete conditioning system for the uninjured athlete and how it relates to existing strength training methods (Siff, 1989). Until that time, PNF was generally regarded as a special type of stretching system by sports coaches who used it. However, it was not appreciated that PNF can act as a training system for all aspects of musculoskeletal conditioning in the competitive athlete, nor did many physiotherapists know that some of the bodybuilding and weightlifting methods could be valuable in the rehabilitation setting.

An overview of this presentation and workshop acted as the basis for Chapter 7.2 above, which should enable the coach to select consult the list of principles and apply those procedures that best meet the needs of the athlete in a given situation. For instance, instead of prescribing the use of the pec-deck for conditioning the pectoral and deltoid muscles of a baseball pitcher or javelin thrower, he would recommend the use of a pulley machine in a specific spiral-diagonal pattern (see 7.2.3.1) of cable-crossovers that cross the sagittal midline of the body. The movement would be performed over a comfortable full range, involve multiple joints besides just the shoulder and position the joints to optimise strengthening (i.e. principles of 7.2.3.1).

The effectiveness of many other training activities in sport may similarly be enhanced by involving other PNF methods, such as pre-stretch, exercising of agonists and antagonists, use of static and dynamic conditions, cheating to compel stronger muscles to help the weaker ones, optimal timing, use of full-range specific patterns of diagonal-spiral motions (details in Knott & Voss, 1977), application of maximal resistance throughout the non-ballistic movement range, and commencement of motion in the strongest range. Such PNF principles integrate very naturally into the extensive scheme of bodybuilding and weightlifting methods and thereby furnish an extremely comprehensive array of supplementary training variations which can be invaluable in all cross training programmes.

The neuromuscular emphasis of this integrated package of methods can be most helpful in enhancing the functional co-development of strength, flexibility, muscle endurance and speed in any particular movement. For instance, stretching exercises are often performed in a static manner separately from the main exercises, when their effectiveness would increase markedly if the latter were also to be used statically and dynamically over a full range with progressively increasing resistance incorporating relevant PNF procedures. Thus, the complementary nature of methods from the Iron Game and the field of rehabilitation may be seen to offer an impressive compendium of highly effective structural and functional training techniques. A thorough knowledge of these techniques is invaluable to the creative and dedicated coach.

7.6 Training for Hypertrophy?

There are numerous theories and beliefs about what the best formula is to follow for producing greatest muscle hypertrophy. One such concept is that every exercise must maintain a prolonged muscle tension time for at least 40 seconds or so if one wishes to produce maximal hypertrophy.

Some have commented that "All the big bodybuilders who I trained with did their reps pretty fast, which makes me seriously question the Time Under Tension theory, though I am sure there are exceptions, as there always are to each rule. However, it's not the biggest guys I see who are counting the seconds on the way up or down. Others have added that "People with extreme genetics who are using huge amounts of drugs will probably get big no matter what kind of weight training and rep speed they're doing. What's more important is finding out how much rep speed matters for a natural bodybuilder with average genetics."

Now, what we are all trying to identify here are the most important factors in stimulating muscle hypertrophy, or we should rather say, musculo-collagenous hypertrophy, since training affects the entire muscle complex, not just the muscles. Physical loading also stimulates bone hypertrophy, especially at the sites of maximal stress concentration, but that is of little consequence to the bodybuilder because bone size and definition are not seen by spectators, though this phenomenon may assist us later in answering some other questions about muscle growth. Any Hypertrophy Formula has to be based on many well-known observations on muscle physiology and mechanics. Some of these observations are:

1. The fundamental stimulus in all strength and tissue hypertrophy quite simply is physical loading.

2. The physical loading must not exceed the mechanical strength of the tissues involved.

3. Increase in strength and hypertrophy is not instantaneous, but occurs predominantly during a certain recovery period after loading

4. All tissues do not hypertrophy or strengthen at the same rate or to the same degree

5. Strength and hypertrophy increase is minimal unless a certain minimal threshold load is imposed

6. The minimal threshold is not fixed, but increases with level of adaptation, which ensures that rate of progress slows down or ceases

7. The concept of tension time per se is meaningless, since loading even for very prolonged periods may have no effects of strength and hypertrophy if the tension does not exceed this minimum threshold

8. The effects of tension on tissue depend not only on the magnitude or duration of the tension, but the way in which the tension is produced or maintained. For example, one can use high or low Rates of Tension Development, and one can increase tension by use of a large, slowly accelerated load or a smaller, rapidly accelerated load (in accordance with Newton II: Force = Mass x Acceleration)

9. Long periods of muscle 'time under tension' as imposed by cyclical activities such as endurance running, cycling and swimming are not known generally to produce significant increases in strength or hypertrophy.

10. Continued increase in strength and hypertrophy is a consequence of progressive incremental increase in loading (principle of progressive overload)

11. Changes in strength and hypertrophy are not linear or continuous. For example, a 10% increase in load does not necessarily produce a 10% increase in strength. Some changes may be delayed or marked at certain stages.

12. Muscles rarely are able to produce 100% of their maximum potential, due to a variety of reasons such as protective inhibition by certain reflexes.

13. Increase in strength and hypertrophy may or may not be associated with some form of fatigue

14. It is difficult to distinguish between the limitations imposed by short-term fatigue and those imposed by reflex inhibition of maximal force production

15. Fatigue is not a single discrete factor, but a multi-faceted process involving phenomena such as central and peripheral fatigue, slow and fast fatigue, and short-term and long-term fatigue.

16. Muscle tension is not constant during any movement, but varies between zero and a certain maximum as joint angles change

17. Muscle tension is not produced under the same conditions throughout any movement, but changes between concentric, eccentric and isometric modes of action

18. Muscles comprise smaller groups of fibres which exhibit different rates of fatigue, fatigue-resistance and ability to generate force (e.g. so-called slow and fast twitch fibres)

19. All muscle tension and patterns of muscle recruitment are a consequence of nervous activity, so that increase in strength and hypertrophy ultimately are the result of specific patterns of nervous excitation.

20. Increase in strength is not necessarily associated with increase in hypertrophy or vice versa

21. Strength and hypertrophy diminish if physical loading is not imposed regularly at certain intervals

22. Strength and hypertrophy increase may be stimulated by active muscle contraction, passive stretching, vibrational oscillation or external electrical stimulation.

There are many other observations which are relevant to our quest to find the ideal, individualised physique or strength building program, but these should suffice to show that a 'Time Under Tension' formula or any other highly prescriptive rule is oversimplistic in satisfying many of the above observations.

When someone stated that "People with extreme genetics who are using huge amounts of drugs will probably get big no matter what kind of weight training and rep speed they're doing", he is probably far closer to the truth than anyone who religiously propounds simplistic Tension Time theories. One has to remember that the marketability of a certain fitness figure or group, according to well-established marketing principles, depends on slogans and simply stated formulae.

The public usually feels far more comfortable with cerebrally undemanding mantras and 'fast food' solutions than with far more accurate, more complex methods. That is a major reason why many fitness figures write as they do and market their catch phrases simplistically as they do - society has been processed by the mass media to behave like that and they usually do not want to be forced to think too deeply or to have their convenient current beliefs questioned, because that entails a serious threat to their psychological safety. Humankind has always been like that and they receive what they have been processed or educated to want.

DESIGNING SPORT SPECIFIC STRENGTH PROGRAMMES

Preparation for sport comprises two distinct conditioning aspects: *training* and *practice*. These aspects are often confused, which frequently results in conditioning sessions being structured to provide both training and practice, a compromise which generally does not produce optimal results.

Training refers to the process of enhancing the physical and mental condition of the athlete, whereas *practice* refers to the process of perfecting the technical skills demanded by the particular sport. Traditionally, 'practice' in the West in many sports has included elements of 'fitness' training in the form of jogging around the field, push-ups, sit-ups and other military type activities before game practice. This, however, wastes a coach's expertise and time. Ideally, the role of a coach is to enhance game skills, with the fitness conditioning handled by specific conditioning coaches, as is rapidly becoming the case with the more popular sports in the USA.

In identifying the distinction between training and practice, one must remember that training for a specific sport may be either beneficial or detrimental to performance and that practice may suffer as a result of inappropriate conditioning. This is becoming increasingly likely, since 'cross training' has increased in popularity among fitness instructors with little experience in its use, which has led to scientifically dubious combinations of cycling, circuit training, jogging, swimming and so forth being imposed on athletes. Resurgence in the popularity of circuit training in commercial gymnasia is also exacerbating the problem. It is apparent that the principles of sport specific strength training need to become better known, particularly in the West.

Arduous fitness training regimes in the gymnasium or on the sports field may not necessarily result in superior competitive ability. Conversely, avoidance of supplementary training may prevent an athlete from fulfilling his or her potential. All supplementary activities and recuperation methods must be carefully selected, planned and sequenced to ensure that they contribute directly to enhancing sports performance. One even has to pose the question whether or not the time spent on a particular supplementary activity could not be better spent on sport specific practice.

8.1 Preliminary Considerations

Among the most important factors for introducing scientific sport specific training are :

1. Sports training must be a year-round and multi-year process. An off-season lay-off followed by less than one month of moderate pre-season training can be a major cause of low levels of overall fitness among athletes and an increased incidence of injuries. The early off-season is one period where popular cross training can be used successfully. Generally, the integration of supplementary or cross training becomes increasingly difficult as the season progresses and player fitness or proficiency improves.

2. *Specialist coaches* are required for the different components of sports conditioning. Very few single coaches are equipped to handle strategic skills, movement skills, physical conditioning, psychological preparation, biomechanical analysis, fitness assessment and rehabilitation routines. Just as there is a playing team, so there has to be an efficient coaching team comprising all the relevant experts.

3. *Scientific fitness training* has to be integrated into every athlete's programme. In particular, it is not possible to enhance adequately strength, hypertrophy, speed and flexibility without use of supplementary resistance training. This type of training is most efficiently achieved in an appropriately equipped gymnasium using logically selected exercises sequenced carefully in terms of intensity, volume, muscle group, patterns of movement and restoration intervals.

   Because few gymnasium staff have formal training in designing scientific supplementary conditioning routines, athletes should be provided with scientific programmes prepared by teams of experts and supervised by accredited sports conditioning coaches. Ideally, every major sports complex should have its own conditioning gymnasium to centralise all aspects of in-season and off-season preparation for players.

4. Periodic *scientific testing* of the various components of athlete fitness is necessary. Ideally, the season should begin with a *pre-test phase* of a few weeks followed by a fitness screening session to test strength, speed, reaction time, muscle endurance, flexibility, psychological preparedness and other factors vital to successful participation in serious skills practice.

5. Sports preparation sessions must be devoted largely to enhancing tactical and technical skills, rather than to improving *general physical fitness*. If fitness training is to be included in preparation sessions, then it must be done to improve the *specific fitness* qualities required in the actual sports event. This may take the form of practice games or contests, so that players can obtain realistic practice under simulated competitive conditions.

6. *Technological analysis* of movement and sporting skills must be performed regularly, because limitations to performance may lie in imperfect skills rather than deficiencies in physical or mental fitness. Periodic slow-motion video replay of player skills, accompanied by step-by-step analysis of recordings can provide valuable technical teaching. At a more detailed level, analysis by high speed video, force plate and electromyograph can yield invaluable information.

Ideally, athletes should acquire the necessary general fitness in their own time or preferably under the control of a specialist strength coach and not waste a technical coach's time in organising crash courses in physical conditioning. In devising any training programme, it is important to note that efficiency of play and prevention of injury depend on acquisition of high levels of neuromuscular skill in all types of movement likely to be encountered in the specific sport.

Review of Some Important Principles

The physical preparation of the athlete may be conveniently analysed if one notes the similarities between the production of motor output in sport and the production of a musical symphony by an orchestra. In both cases the output is a complex pattern and perfection of this pattern in both cases is the ultimate objective. The central nervous system acts as the conductor which controls the different systems that contribute to the final pattern, just as the human conductor controls the players in an orchestra to produce the required musical pattern. Just as there are many different instruments played by different musicians in an orchestra, so there are many muscles, tendons and other physical units which are controlled by different neural programmes in the human body. If the timing, intensities, duration and any other contributing factors are incorrect during any phase of the process in either case, the final result will be less than optimal.

The perfection of the output pattern depends on the ability to optimally use and integrate the contributions of every subsystem in space and time. This entails having a working understanding of all of the subsystems and practising their use until each individual system can be used efficiently on their own and then in harmony with many other systems. In the case of any orchestra, this requires the conductor to understand all the instruments and how their specific contributions can best be summated to produce the desired sound patterns.

In the case of sporting performance, it is important to understand the nature of the physical systems involved in producing skilled movement. This entails understanding how the nervous and neuromuscular systems interact to produce certain motor qualities that are necessary for successful performance in any given sport (Fig 8.1). This then enables one to train and practise in the most efficient manner.

Essentially, the training process simply involves compelling the body to adapt to a higher level of functioning via the imposition of appropriate physical and mental stresses. The existing levels of hormonal, neural and musculoskeletal integrity have to be raised at a rate which is optimal for the individual at a given stage in his/his career. This means that a given intensity, volume and density of loading has to be used to alter both the actual and perceived thresholds of performance, a process that relies on feedforward and feedback mechanisms, as well as voluntary and involuntary methods of intervention to achieve the desired results.

It is most relevant to note that excellence of performance is not simply a matter of strengthening the musculoskeletal system by altering the physical structure of all of its components and by increasing the ability of the neural system to orchestrate more powerful movements. In producing limit performance, the athlete is strongly influenced by the psychological perception of the load involved, not simply the actual load. If the load "feels" insurmountable or technically too demanding, despite the fact that the body is well-equipped to handle that given load, failure is highly likely. This is why the training process must teach the athlete to cope with both the perceived and actual load being undertaken.

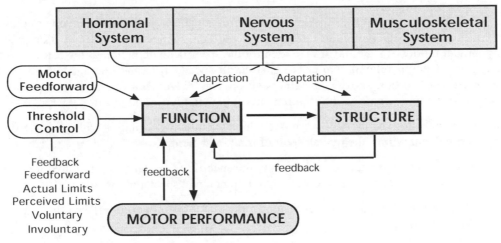

Figure 8.1 The Sports Training Process summarised in the form of a systems model. The arrow from Function to Structure is in bold to emphasize the well-known fact that function precedes structure.

The athlete really is operating in terms of a type of "virtual reality" in which *perceptions* of effort and *feedforward* images of the forthcoming effort strongly determine the final outcome of the sporting action. This is why the training process is one which not only improves the structural and functional capabilities of the body, but also shows the athlete how to manipulate "virtual realities" for all of the actions involved in given sport. This "virtual reality" training imparts to the athlete great skill in minimising the size of any detrimental differences between perceived and actual loading and technical skill. After all, the goal of all sporting performance is to make the existing task feel easier and easier so that the existing level of performance may be raised. So, if the training program is to be effective, it must make the training loads and skills "feel" progressively easier and this may be achieved by optimal implementation of principles such as that of fluctuating gradual overload (not simply progressive gradual overload) and SAID (Specific Adaptation to Imposed Demands).

Methods of Increasing Muscle Tension

The fundamental mechanical aspect of all resistance training is the imposition of optimal progressive increases in loading so that muscle tension may be increased, thereby stimulating the neuromuscular and hormonal systems to adapt to higher levels of stress. The following are some of the methods of increasing muscle tension which have been addressed in the preceding pages and which may be used in devising a training program:

1. Voluntary use of Compensatory Action to facilitate changes in movement characteristics
2. Use of suddenly terminated eccentric actions
3. Involuntary use of reflexive explosive rebound or plyometric actions
4. Voluntary use of prestretch to facilitate stronger muscle contraction
5. Use of free weights combined with elastic bands, chains or isokinetic loads
6. Application of electrical stimulation (ES)
7. Concurrent combination of ES and voluntary movements
8. Application of vibration to limbs
9. Cognitive/Mental techniques (such as visualisation and motivational strategies)

8.2 Needs Analysis and Sports Modelling

Conditioning programmes for most sports should involve several different, but related, types of analysis:

- Sport Analysis
- Event Analysis
- Match or Game Analysis
- Position Analysis
- Player Analysis
- Injury Analysis
- Movement Analysis (kinesiology and biomechanical analysis)
- Physiological and Anatomical Analysis (for the specific sport).

- *Sport Analysis* refers to the identifying the most important fitness qualities required for anyone to play a given sport successfully. It examines the particular fitness profile required for successful participation in that sport. It will use the pyramidal model of fitness (Ch 1) to identify the specific combination of the S-factors of fitness and the precise type of strength-related qualities (e.g. strength-speed, strength-endurance or static strength) which play dominant roles in that sport. Match, position and player analysis follow the same general approach, but detailed attention is paid to the requirements at match, player and position level.

- *Event Analysis* refers to analysing the particular event in which the athlete specialises within a given sport, e.g. the shotput as a specific event within the overall sport of track-and-field.

- *Match Analysis* (Game Analysis) in a team sport refers to the specific fitness qualities required for playing in a particular event at a particular venue under specific environmental and spectator conditions.

- *Position Analysis* refers to the specific qualities required for a player to operate efficiently and safely in a specific role or position in a team sport.

- *Player Analysis* refers to the particular balance of fitness factors which characterise a specific individual, whose build and other personal characteristics determine the appropriate type of fitness for that individual in a specific role or position. Testing will identify any strengths and weaknesses to enable the coach to devise a suitable training programme for that athlete.

- *Injury Analysis* investigates the most frequently occurring injuries, as well as the injuries sustained by specific players in certain positions in team sports.

- *Movement (Kinesiological) Analysis* examines the movement patterns, forces, velocities, and joint angles, and identifies the muscles and other parts of the body used to execute the specific joint and whole body actions produced by athletes. The patterns of movement rely on developing the appropriate balance between *stability* of certain parts of the body and *mobility* of other parts. This means that certain muscles may be required to produce high levels of static strength, while other muscles may be required to produce high levels of dynamic strength-speed or flexibility-speed.

    It is used to determine which are the safest and most efficient ways of producing every movement in the particular sport, as well as to identify how to condition the most important muscles and soft tissues in each player. It also identifies strengths and weaknesses in given skills and provides valuable instructional feedback to coaches and players.

- *Physiological and Anatomical Analysis* refers to determination of which energy system, types of muscle fibre, nutritional regime, oxygen consumption and other bodily processes are characteristic of the athlete. It also covers kinanthropometry, the study of the relative proportions of the body's components in contributing to sporting performance.

Selection of Training Needs

Once the above analyses have been carried out, it is possible to devise more scientific training and practice sessions for the given sport in general and for specific players. At this point one may draw up for each athlete a *Multifactorial Fitness Profile (MFP)* derived from the pyramidal model (Table 8.1). This entails marking off on a scale of 1 to 5 the relative levels of each fitness factor required for world-class performance in the sport, alongside the corresponding level displayed by the athlete, based upon scientific tests of these abilities.

    Testing should include measurement of any strength deficit so as to ascertain whether more attention needs to be devoted to hypertrophy or neuromuscular training (see Ch 1). If any fitness factor of the athlete displays a lower score than that required for top performance, it indicates that special training must be dedicated to enhancing that factor. Conversely, training devoted to developing a specific fitness factor must be curtailed if its score exceeds that required by the sport.

    Before a training programme is drawn up, it is important to recall that fitness is highly specific and context dependent. Thus, the exercises and their manner of execution in a fitness programme must be prescribed with a full awareness of the *specificity* of the following factors (see 1.3 also):

Table 8.1   MULTIFACTORIAL FITNESS PROFILE (MFP)

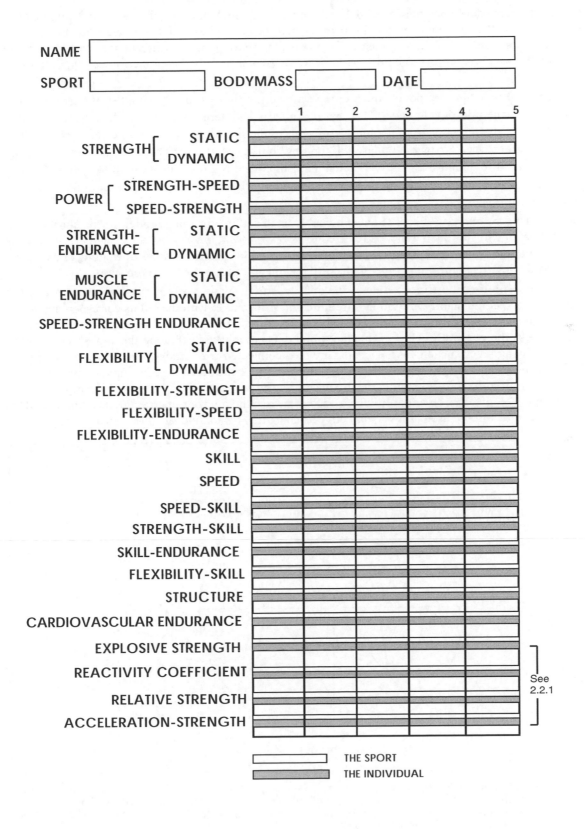

- Type of Muscle Contraction
- Movement Pattern
- Region of Movement
- Velocity of Movement
- Force of Contraction
- Muscle Fibre Recruitment
- Metabolism
- Biochemical Adaptation
- Flexibility

This means that exercises should be chosen not only on the basis of which muscles groups are to be trained but also on features such as the intensity of the load, the speed of each phase of the movement, the relative contributions of concentric, eccentric and isometric contraction, the sporting movement patterns, functional range of movement, and the relative periods to be devoted to cardiovascular, muscle endurance and strength training during each phase.

It is important that one does not devise the training scheme simply by drawing up a list of exercises for a given session or week (the microcycle level), but by planning a long-term sequence of training cycles (the macrocycle level). One should work from the long-term goals to the short-term goals. This entails drawing up a carefully periodised chart (see Ch 6) which phases all training so that specific performance goals are reached at given times in the annual (e.g. national and world championships) and multi-annual (e.g. the Olympic Games) plan. This approach also enables one to identify more accurately the specific qualities required by specific players in specific positions in the relevant sport.

The methods of *needs analysis* discussed above enable us to set up a training model for the sport and for specific players, a scientific approach which is referred to as *Sports Modelling* (see 6.12). This relies on the needs analysis and periodic testing to design short, intermediate and long term modules of training and practice which focus on producing the appropriate type of physical and mental fitness for the given sport.

Another way of depicting the fitness state of the athlete is to draw up a *Fitness Polygon* with all of the relevant qualities spaced equidistantly around the circumference of a circle, with the radius corresponding to the maximum value which each quality can have (Fig 8.2). Various laboratory, field or competitive tests are administered to assess the current level of each quality and dots are marked off along the appropriate radii to record approximately the level in each case. The dots are then connected with straight lines, thereby producing the athlete's fitness polygon. The corresponding polygon may also be drawn in to represent the relative values of all the qualities required for proficiency in the given sport. The athlete is then able to see clearly where his strengths and weaknesses lie, thereby enabling his coach to devise the appropriate training programme. This simple visual scheme may also be used as a very effective teaching tool for individual athletes, teams and coaches.

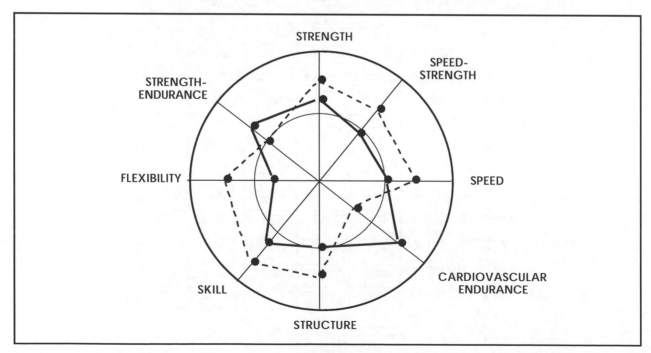

Figure 8.2 Fitness Polygon showing the relative levels of each fitness quality. The solid-outline polygon represents the current fitness state of the athlete, while the dashed-outline polygon represents the desired level of each quality for prowess in a given sport. The outermost circle is the maximum level of all qualities. The qualities shown are solely for illustrative purposes and do not refer to any specific sport. Structure refers to size, bodymass, proportions etc.

In the example provided, the athlete needs to improve strength, speed-strength, speed, skill, structure (e.g. by increasing lean bodymass and decreasing bodyfat) and flexibility, but has more than enough cardiovascular endurance and strength-endurance, so that he needs to spend less time on training these qualities. The same sort of fitness polygon may be constructed by placing the most relevant laboratory or field test items around the circumference of the diagram. So, instead of writing the various motor qualities around its periphery, we simply replace them with test items such as vertical jump, 40m sprint, triple jump, 3RM bench press and power clean.

The final preparation scheme for each team member may now be drawn up in a *training journal* which records the short-term and long-term quantitative goals and exercises, as well as the subjective, psychological and emotional goals and observations (as detailed in the periodisation material covered in Ch 6.2) . This journal may include graphical representations of overall fitness state, such as the Multifactorial Fitness Profile or the Fitness Polygon. Finally, all progress, recuperation regimens, and a list of soreness, injuries and other unplanned negative events are registered. The purpose of this journal is to enable the player to reach or maintain peak form throughout the season and especially for specific events. At a more detailed level, fitness training for a given sport may be considered in terms of the *general fitness factors* required by any participants in the game and the *specific fitness factors* required by individuals playing specific roles in specific positions or at specific times.

General Fitness Issues

It is vital to devise a programme in which training for one motor quality does not interact negatively with training for other fitness qualities. For instance, any unnecessary or prolonged emphasis on cardiovascular conditioning may decrease strength, hypertrophy and explosive power. In the individual workout, it is usually inappropriate to perform endurance activities before strength and speed training (Fig 1.7). While recovery from bursts of activity may be facilitated in part by the cardiovascular and circulatory mechanisms of the *long term energy system*, most activity in sports played on a field relies predominantly on the short and intermediate term non-oxidative energy systems. The *short term* (ATP-CP) system provides energy for explosive bursts of activity lasting for no longer than 2 or 3 seconds, while the *intermediate* energy system is mainly involved with furnishing fuel for fairly intense activity of up to about 45 seconds (see 1.13).

Having identified the type of running or energy system training which is necessary for fitness in the relevant sport, we may then turn our attention to the type of strength and speed training required. In doing so, it is helpful to examine which fitness factors need to be trained and the main muscle groups which need strengthening in the different players. The introduction to more explosive training, especially plyometric methods, should be done cautiously and progressively, following the guidelines offered earlier (5.2.4).

Injuries

General injury analysis identifies problem areas in a given sport and enables us to tailor the training programme to the needs of certain players. In addition to accidental injuries, there are *overtraining injuries*, comprising two classes (see 8.6): *overload injuries* (caused by too large a load at any instant) and *overuse injuries* (caused by very frequent application of a given load). These may occur in practice or in the gymnasium.

For example, the shins or back may be overloaded by a single forceful action, or they may gradually develop overuse injuries over a prolonged period of sub-maximal effort, as in distance running. In this case, overload injuries initiated by hard heel strike may be diminished by the use of suitable footwear, but correction of technical faults and impact conditioning should take place first. In the cross training setting, loads, training periods, volumes and rest periods must be carefully planned and synchronised with sports practices to avoid both classes of overtraining injury.

Training programmes must sometimes be devised to rehabilitate athletes after injury, a task which is usually left to the physical therapist, who often has little education in retraining an athlete for high level competition. Rehabilitation must follow the same stages of periodised training as normal training, using means that are detailed throughout this text. It is always vital to remember that *return to competitive preparedness is never complete until the athlete perceives the injury to be fully healed*, regardless of what any physical tests might indicate. A personal tale is highly relevant in this regard. One of my colleagues is a well-known physiotherapist for a national soccer team and his final test for any injured players is to have them stand on a high chair or table; he then requests them to jump to the floor, and, if he detects any trepidation or hesitation, he concludes that the overall rehabilitation is incomplete. This, of course, is indicative of what actually might happen in sport; all the clinical tests may show that the athlete is "back to normal", but the athlete's perception of his/her condition may be very different and that is what determines one's ability or willingness to exert oneself fully in any sport. In other words, one should always apply post-injury performance tests which examine not only the physiological and anatomical readiness for a return to competition, but also the psychological factors which may also affect one's preparedness.

Training to Avoid Injury

Avoidance of certain exercises which are regarded as potentially harmful may sometimes be unwise, because those very movements may occur periodically in the sport or during practice. This well-meaning approach can predispose athletes to injury since they will not have acquired the necessary involuntary motor skills to cope with higher risk actions. Therefore, it can be valuable to progressively introduce skills intended to prepare the athlete to minimise the chance of accidents and injury. Training of reactive ability can be extremely helpful in this regard, although too many athletes strengthen the body instead to achieve this end. It would be far better for them to improve speed of reaction, speed of movement, ability to anticipate impending dangers and to learn to manage dangerous events while they are happening. It is surprising how few rugby and American football players never learn how to fall from their colleagues in judo and wrestling, yet falling and violent bodily contact are integral parts of their games.

Training of the Soft Tissues

So far, only muscle training has been discussed. However, all movements, especially those executed at high speed, depend on the storage and release of elastic energy from the tendons. Moreover, passive stability, flexibility and protection of the joints depends on the integrity of the ligaments and other connective tissues around the joint. Since all muscle action and joint movement involves the nervous system, proper *neuromuscular training* based on recruitment of reflexes in specific patterns, is a vital component of all training and practice.

This implies that *physical training must prepare muscles, tendons, ligaments and other connective tissues, as well as the bones*, to meet the demands imposed by the given sport. Overemphasis on resistance training for purely bodybuilding reasons is inadvisable and unnecessary for the athlete, unless an analysis of strength deficit has revealed the need for increased hypertrophy during the general preparatory phase. Research has revealed that the development of the passive tissues of the body (such as tendons, ligaments and bones) depends on the intensity and duration of resistance imposed on the body, and that heavy or rapidly imposed loads can play a valuable role in developing all-round muscle and connective tissue integrity. The periodic use of low intensity, longer duration training can also play a useful role in improving capillarisation and recoverability of muscle tissue after strenuous exercise.

8.3 The Training Programme

The most efficient way of providing controlled resistance training is with weights and machines. Lest it be thought that adequacy of a training facility depends on expensive machines and circuits, it must be emphasized that all athletes require three-dimensional exercise which produces functional fitness for their sport. Most machines constrain the user to operate about a fixed axis of rotation in two dimensions, often over a partial range of motion and in patterns which can disrupt the natural patterns required in the given sport (see 4.2.7).

In fact, the spiral and diagonal patterns used by physiotherapists with PNF (proprioceptive neuromuscular facilitation) are particularly suitable for providing the three dimensional joint conditioning necessary in sport. Modified PNF principles, procedures and patterns may be devised to enable players to apply them in the gym with free barbells, dumbbells, pulley machines, partners and certain machines (see 7.2).

As discussed before (4.2.7), it usually requires a greater number of machines than free weights or pulley systems to provide the necessary and sufficient degree of three-dimensional muscle and other soft tissue fitness. The claims for greater safety with machines are not necessarily correct, since many machines (such as seated leg press, bench press machines, squatting machines and 'pec decks') are intrinsically less safe than their free weights equivalent, unless 'spotted' by an assistant and used over a limited range. All types of training pose certain risks, so that learning of correct technique is the best safeguard against injury. The importance of a well-qualified conditioning coach then becomes obvious. Machines and machine circuits may play a limited introductory role in the early off-season, to enable injured athletes to 'train around' an injury, or to periodically supplement free weight and pulley system training, but their exclusive use is not suitable as the main form of resistance training for the serious athlete.

Plyometric training has been covered earlier in some detail. If it is to be used effectively and safely, it is advisable to apply the guidelines appearing in Chapter 5.2.4.

Components of the Training Programme

Before prescribing any exercise programme, it is useful to apply the following checklist:

Is the given exercise and its method of execution:

- Necessary?
- Sufficient?
- Appropriate?
- Effective?
- Challenging? (or interesting, enjoyable?)
- Safe?

In addition, you must examine the following *P-factors of Exercise Prescription*:

- Purpose
- Person (Player or athlete)
- Practitioner (coach or instructor)
- Principles (of training means and methods)
- Procedures (for using specific methods and exercises)
- Period or Phase of training
- Place (and facilities)
- Position (of player or of joints)
- Pivots (joints involved).

Once you have applied these checklists carefully, you may set up an encyclopaedia of resistance exercises for possible use by all the players. These exercises should also include activities for warming up (pre-event preparation) and enhancing *functional or sport specific flexibility*, because static stretches on their own are inadequate for meeting the dynamic full range movements of the given sport. Superior sport specific flexibility and flexibility-strength is produced by full range dynamic movements executed in specific patterns against heavy resistance or using hold-relax or contract-relax methods borrowed from PNF (see Ch 7). You should now be ready to set up a training programme incorporating the following components that have been discussed in detail in preceding chapters.

The General Components

- Means
- Methods
- Exercises
- Techniques

The Specific Components

1. Conditioning Purpose (bodybuilding, weightlifting, supplementary training, etc.)
2. Type of Fitness (in terms of a fitness profile)
3. Body Zones
4. Muscle Groups
5. Type of Muscle Tension (static, dynamic, etc.)
6. Type of Movement (extension, flexion, adduction, etc.)
7. Type of Resistance Modality or Apparatus
8. The Specific Exercises
9. Exercise Method (maximum load, pyramids, supersets, forced reps, etc.)
10. Exercise Variables :
    - Speed of movement
    - Acceleration
    - Load
    - Repetitions per set

- Number of sets
- Series (groups of sets)
- Intensity of resistance (average load per workout)
- Volume of resistance (a measure of total work done per workout)
- Density of exercises (a measure of the number of exercises per unit time)
- Sequence of exercises
- Frequency of workouts
- Pattern of movement
- Range of movement
- Duration of movement, set or series
- Rest periods (between movements, sets and workouts)
- Duration of workouts
- Number of exercises per workout
- Variation of technique
- Warming-up and stretching activities
- Supplementary sports or manual labour

11. Organisation of the Training Programme
    - Training session
    - Training day
    - Restoration means and methods
    - Distributed/ concentrated loading
    - Microcycles
    - Mesocycles
    - Long mesocycles
    - Macrocycle
    - Long macrocycle

Statute of Fitness Limitations

An overall scheme that can be extremely useful in planning any training or rehabilitation programme is one which I call the *Statute of Fitness Limitations*. It is so named because it entails starting any client from an initial state which is limited in the following manner:

- Limited Intensity or Load
- Limited Duration (of a movement or set)
- Limited Volume (of the entire exercise or session)
- Limited Density
- Limited Acceleration (and deceleration)
- Limited Power
- Limited Rate of Force (or Acceleration) Development (RFD)
- Limited Velocity
- Limited Range
- Limited Complexity

Thus, one prescribes an exercise in which all of the above variables are limited initially, then, as the individual adapts, so you gradually decrease the limitations in a manner which optimally suits that person. The logical way to decrease these limitations is to apply two ratings which we covered in Chapter 6:

- Rating of Perceived Effort - RPE (by the person)
- Rating of Technique (by the coach)

If the decrease in limitation of any variable does not cause any deterioration in technique or an unnecessarily high RPE, then one can continue with at least that level of stress on the body.

We have already discussed the well-known *Principle of Gradual Progressive Overload*; the above scheme extends this principle beyond this simple framework and prescribes a type of "gradual overload" with respect to all of the above factors. Obviously, some variables will eventually become constant, because, for example, the range of movement (ROM) of any joint cannot be increased indefinitely, while the acceleration, power (mean and peak), complexity, and RFD depend upon each different exercise. Eventually, the main variables which can be progressively increased (or have limitations decreased) are the load, the duration and the volume, with increases in loading being necessary for power and strength increase and duration and volume being more appropriate for developing local and general endurance. At a more detailed level, increase in volume of complex practice may be necessary for enhancing motor skill.

The Minimax Principle and Training Economics

A great variety of programmes may be assembled to achieve specific training or rehabilitation objectives, so how are we to select the most appropriate for any given athlete, especially since so many people are now promoting adjunct training methods such as "core training", "stability training", "functional training" and "balance training"? Besides the obvious tailoring of a programme to suitably interest, challenge and match individual characteristics and needs, it is very helpful to borrow a concept from science and management, called the *Minimax Principle*, which is one of the cornerstones of sound economics. Essentially this means using the minimum effort to achieve the maximum results, preferably in the least time. In science, it is similar to the principles of least action, least path or least energy. Thus, it is vital that you carefully scrutinise every variation of a given training programme to ensure that you employ the one which best obeys the minimax principle, especially since time must be regarded as a precious commodity, not only in costly business ventures, but also in sports preparation. So, by all means use balancing balls, wobble boards and special supplementary drills if they enhance the economy of the training process; otherwise rely on using existing exercises which address several training needs at the same time.

List of Popular Resistance Exercises

A very abbreviated mini-encyclopaedia of popular resistance exercises follows, with some of the main (prime and assistant) mover muscles which they involve (Ch 8.4 gives an extensive list of largely Weightlifting and Powerlifting exercises). In some cases, the stabilising muscles which have not been identified are so strongly contracted that they are being efficiently conditioned at the same time as the prime movers. For example, heavy overhead presses, squats and tricep push downs can produce higher levels of tension in the abdominal muscles (trunk stabilisers) than sit-ups.

This categorisation of exercises according to the prime moving muscles recruited in a given resistance exercise has served the bodybuilding community very well for many decades, but a more logical, educational and thorough approach is to examine:

- which joints are being moved throughout the exercise
- which joints are being stabilised throughout the exercise

Once you have done this, you need to identify which type of joint action (such as flexion, adduction or medial rotation) is involved in each case. Then if you refer to the *Movement Matrix System* (see 3.7), you can read off from the tables provided the corresponding muscle groups which produce those joint actions. In this way, you may then deduce which muscle groups are responsible for all moving and stabilising actions in any given exercise.

Chest

Bench press (wide grip: pectoralis major, anterior deltoids, triceps)
Bench press (narrow grip: triceps, pectoralis major, anterior deltoids)
Incline bench (upper pectorals, deltoids, triceps)
Decline bench press (lower pectorals, deltoids, triceps)
Supine dumbbell flyes or pulley flyes (slow with bent elbows: pectorals, anterior deltoids)
Supine bent-arm pullovers (pectorals, lats, teres major)
Pec deck (pectoralis major, anterior deltoids)
Cable crossovers (pectorals, anterior deltoids, lats)

Legs

Front and back squats (quadriceps, gluteus, erector spinae, thigh adductors)
Leg extension machine or pulleys (quadriceps, leg adductors)
Leg press machine (quadriceps, gluteus maximus)

Leg curl machine or pulley (hamstrings)
Lunge (quadriceps, gluteus, calf muscles, hamstrings)
Deadlifts and 'good mornings' (hamstrings, lower back muscles)
Seated or standing pulley leg sweeps (inward: thigh adductors)
Seated or standing pulley leg sweeps (outward: thigh abductors)
Standing pulley leg sweeps (backward: gluteus)
Standing pulley leg sweeps (forwards: hip flexors)
Calf raises (standing: plantarflexors and calf muscles, especially gastrocnemius)
Calf raises (seated or bent knee: plantarflexors and calf muscles, especially soleus)
Donkey calf raises (gastrocnemius or soleus or both, depending on knee angle)

Back

Deadlifts; clean pulls (bent knees: spinal erectors, hamstrings, quadriceps)
'Hyperextensions' (slowly up and down: spinal erectors, gluteus)
Upright rowing (upper back and shoulders: trapezius, deltoids, elbow flexors)
Shoulder shrugs (upper back: trapezius, rhomboids)
Good mornings (small range, 'flat' back, bent knees: spinal erectors, hamstrings, glutei)
Lat machine pull-downs (upper back muscles: lats, teres major)
Bent-over rowing ('flat back', bent knees: lats, posterior deltoids, elbow flexors)
Curl-grip lat pull-downs (lats, biceps and other elbow flexors)
Seated pulley rowing (lats, teres minor, traps, deltoids, elbow flexors)

Shoulders

Lateral raises with dumbbells or pulleys (deltoids, traps, rhomboids)
Front raises (deltoids, trapezius)
Upright rowing (traps, deltoids, elbow flexors)
Shrugs (traps, rhomboids, levator scapulae)
Standing or seated press (deltoids, triceps)
Prone flyes or horizontal cable pull-backs (infraspinatus, traps, rhomboids)
Front arm raises (front and middle deltoids)
Dips (pecs, front deltoids, triceps, upper traps, serratus anterior)

Arms

Curls (barbell, dumbbell or pulley: biceps and other elbow flexors)
Curl-grip pull-ups (biceps and other elbow flexors, lats)
Tricep push-downs (with pulleys: triceps)
Tricep extensions (behind or alongside the head: triceps)
Narrow grip bench press (triceps, pectorals)
Tricep kick-backs (with dumbbells or pulleys: triceps)
Reverse grip curls (biceps and other elbow flexors, forearm muscles)
Half dumbbell or broomstick wrist twists (up, down, sideways, circle: wrist muscles)

Mid-section

Bent-knee sit-ups (feet free, back on mat: abdominals, obliques)
Bent-knee sit-ups (feet fixed: abdominals, obliques, hip flexors)
Bent knee sit-ups with twist (slow, with twist from beginning: abdominal muscles)
Side bends (with DB or pulleys: obliques, quadratus lumborum, spinal erectors)
Side sit-ups (obliques, quadratus lumborum, spinal erectors)
Seated or hanging leg pull-ins or pikes (lower abdominals, hip flexors)
Hanging leg-raises (hip flexors, abdominals, rectus femoris)
Supine leg-raises with posterior pelvic tilt and trunk curled partially up
Trunk curl-ups from the buttocks, hands holding grips to stabilise shoulders.

Extensive use of many muscles

Clean from ground onto front of shoulders
Power clean from ground onto shoulders

Cleans from the hang onto the shoulders
High pulls from the ground
Power snatches from the ground or the hang
Overhead push-presses or push-jerks
Clean-and-jerk or clean and push-press
Pulls from ground with a shrug and rise onto toes
Overhead squats with barbell held with a snatch grip
Overhead lunges with barbell held with a snatch grip
One arm snatches with dumbbells or kettlebells

This is neither a complete list of all possible exercises, nor a list of all the exercises that should be performed by the athlete. They simply act as a very abbreviated compendium of exercises from which a few may be chosen from each group to train the necessary muscles of a specific player. An indication of the way in which this short list of exercises can be expanded enormously is In prescribing any of these exercises in a training programme, it is important to recognise that they may be divided into three broad categories for most sports, as follows:

- *Competitive Exercises.* These are exercises that are actually performed in competition.

- *Special Physical Preparation exercises.* These exercises may be similar to the competitive movements or largely dissimilar exercises that may develop the specific motor qualities required in the sport.

- *General Physical Preparation exercises.* These exercises are usually different from the competition movements in type, pattern, mode of execution and speed, and are intended for general development to form a foundation for later stages of training.

The ability to place all exercises (and the different techniques of using them) into these categories enables one to avoid making any serious errors in selecting any of them to achieve a specific training purpose at a given stage of a periodisation scheme.

8.4 Classification of Exercises for Sports Training

8.4.1 Principles of Exercise Classification

In Russia, not only is all training broadly divided into general preparatory, special preparatory and competitive phases, but all exercises are classified similarly into different groups and subgroups for use in general physical education and in each specific sport. This global process of classification, which is still not systematised in the West, became widely applied throughout the USSR largely due to the exhortations of one of the founders of physical education theory in Russia, A Novikov (1949), who considered that exercises should be uniformly classified for all aspects of physical education, if their scientific and practical potential was not to be wasted. He stressed that exercise classification, the most important foundation for education and training, is one of the primary principles of the physical education system.

Matveyev (1977) noted that an assemblage of the means and methods of sport training constitutes a system of training exercises. The following revised excerpts from Chapter 2 of the complicated English translation of his book, *The Fundamentals of Sports Training* (1981), are relevant in this regard:

One of the essential distinctions to be made in classifying the exercises used in sport training is their similarity or difference compared with the specific movements characterising a given sport. According to this distinction, the exercises may be subdivided into *competition* and *preparatory* exercises, then into *special preparatory* and *general preparatory* exercises.

The competition exercises: These are the actual exercises used in sport competition and performed in the same way as during competition. The competition exercises of the given sport play an extremely important role in training, since, without them, it is impossible to fully equip the athlete with the specific requirements of the given sport, and stimulate the development of specific preparedness. The special preparatory exercises consist of elements of the competition actions and variations of them, as well as actions similar to them, in terms of the form and the character of the abilities displayed. Depending on the primary emphasis of the special preparatory exercises, one may recognise *preliminary exercises* (to help the athlete master the movement) and *developmental exercises* (to develop physical qualities). Both classes of exercise are introduced at the different stages of training in unequal proportions.

The general preparatory exercises. The exercises in this group are the fundamental, practical means to achieve the athlete's general preparation. In principle, they are much broader in scope and more varied than the other groups of exercises. The list of such exercises is theoretically unlimited, though practically their use is restricted by the time which can be taken without detriment from other means of training and by the availability of equipment. Two requirements are important for selection of the general preparatory exercises: Firstly, the athlete must have a comprehensive background of multi-faceted physical education. Secondly, the contents of the athlete's general preparation should reflect the specifics of the sport.

General preparatory exercises serve several functions:

   (a) to form, strengthen or restore motor skills which play an auxiliary, facilitatory role in sport perfecting

   (b) to teach abilities developed insufficiently by the given sport, increase the general work capacity or preserve it

   (c) to provide active rest, promote restoration after strenuous loading and counteract the monotony of training.

These functions define the role of the general preparatory exercises in the athlete's training programme.

His classification of competitive exercises further illustrates the meticulous attention to detail used in the Russian system of training and physical education (Table 8.2).

Table 8.2 Categorisation of Competitive Exercises in Different Types of Sport

Overall Grouping	Groups	Subgroups & Types of Exercises
Monostructural Exercises (relatively stable forms)	1. Speed and Strength Exercises	A. Jumps B. Throws (Shot, javelin, etc) C. Lifting weights D. Sprint
	2. Cyclic Endurance	A. High intensity endurance events B. Low and medium intensity endurance
Polystructural Exercises (variable forms)	1. Team Games	A. High intensity interval B. Prolonged relatively continuous
	2. Sporting Combat	A. Non physical contact (fencing etc) B. Physical Contact (boxing, wrestling etc)
Complexes of Exercises	1. Dual and Combined Events with a stable content	A. Homogeneous Two-event & Combined events (skating 4-events, Alpine 3-events etc) B. Non-homogeneous dual and combined events (decathlon, pentathlon, ski dual etc)
	2. Dual and Combined Events with a periodically renewed content	A. Aesthetic Sports (gymnastics, diving, skating, acrobatics etc)

8.4.2 Classification of Weightlifting Exercises

It is instructive to examine the approach used to categorise the way in which training exercises are classified in Olympic Weightlifting in Russia. A similar approach may then be applied in any other sport if this model is used as a guideline. The classification of weightlifting exercises follows the same principles employed extensively in other sports, namely (Medvedev, 1986):

- *Group 1* consists of the competition exercises (in weightlifting, the Snatch and Clean & Jerk)

- *Group 2* combines the Special Preparatory exercises, divided into several subgroups:

   - auxiliary Snatch exercises

   - auxiliary Clean & Jerk exercises

   - auxiliary exercises for the legs, back, (torso), arms and shoulder girdle

- *Group 3* consists of General Preparatory exercises, i.e. exercises for general physical training.

One has to consider two interrelated factors when examining the competition and special preparatory means. For instance, all of the exercises, depending on their coordination structure, method of training and amount of resistance, to a great or lesser extent develop the necessary physical qualities, and contribute (also to a greater or a less extent) to the perfecting of technical mastery. Therefore, it is appropriate to divide all of the exercises of the first and second groups into two independent parts.

Group 1 combines the competition and special preparatory (auxiliary) means. The overwhelming majority these exercises are in conformity with the technique of the classic Snatch and classic Clean & Jerk. Besides this, athletes lift heavy weights in these exercises, working at great power. So, this exercise group constitutes the fundamental group in weightlifting training.

The special preparatory (developmental) exercises are concentrated in Group 2. They are done with barbells, on training devices, with kettlebells and using other resistances. For the most part, developmental exercises have a local effect. They are executed with relatively light weights, and due to their diverse technique structure, the power developed from these exercises is relatively small. The aforementioned exercises in this group can be significantly different in technique from the competition exercises. The developmental exercises serve as additional means for preparing weightlifters. However, the function of these exercises is not limited to this role.

Additional exercises, executed with large amplitude in the joints have a positive effect on developing the tendons and ligaments. It is necessary to take into consideration that the mechanical strength of the tendons and ligaments increases comparatively slowly during training. The forced development of speed-strength can result in a discrepancy between the increase in the muscular speed-strength capacity and the strength of the tendons and ligaments, which can lead to injury. Therefore, it is necessary to devote time to strengthening the tendons and ligaments, which is accomplished by high volume work of lower intensity. It is desirable that the movements be executed through the maximum possible joint range and in all directions. Additional exercises meet these requirements.

So, in order to more objectively assess the training influence, the athlete is subjected to exercises from Group 1, their loading is counted as fundamental, while the loading in the Group 2 is considered additional. Finally, it is important that *fundamental and additional training loads should be calculated and analysed separately.*

Categorisation of Fundamental and Additional Exercises

The fundamental exercises are divided into 12 groups and the additional exercises into 4 groups.

Categorisation of the Fundamental Means

1. Classic Snatch.
2. Squat Snatch: from different starting positions, using different regimes of muscular work, etc.
3. Power Snatch: from different starting positions, using different regimes of muscular activity, etc.
4. Snatch Pull: with all of the variations listed in the preceding exercise.
5. Classic Clean and Jerk: the squat style clean and jerk.
6. Squat Clean: with all of the variations listed in exercise 2 (the squat snatch).
7. Jerk: from stands, from behind the head, push-jerk, half-jerk, jerk combinations, jerks with different regimes of muscular activity.
8. Power Clean: with all of the variations listed in exercise 3.
9. Clean Pull: with all of the variations listed in exercise 3.
10. Barbell Squats: on the shoulders, on the chest, with the barbell at arms length overhead, combinations, with different regimes of muscular activity, etc.
11. Good mornings - barbell on the shoulders, with the legs flexed, with a vertical jump, pulley good morning (clean and snatch grip)
12. Pressing: standing press, push-press from the chest and behind the head, push-press behind the head with a snatch grip bench press, combinations, etc.

Categorisation of Additional Means

13. Exercises for the Legs: lunges (barbell held between the legs, on the chest, on the shoulders), jumps with a barbell on the shoulders (barbell in the hands), leg press, etc.
14. Exercises for the Back (torso): good mornings, good mornings with the legs straight, good morning with other forms of resistance on the shoulders, hyperextensions, etc.
15. Exercises for the Arms and Shoulder Girdle: all types rowing, press behind head, snatch grip (standing, in a squat position), seated press, incline barbell press, etc.
16. The Snatch and Clean & Jerk Exercises with weights less than 60% .

General Preparatory Exercises in Weightlifting

This group of exercises has been drawn from the following sport disciplines:

1. Track and Field: Acceleration runs: 400 - 1000 meters, all types of jumping exercises, throwing the hammer, discus (different weights), shotput (different weights), tossing a kettlebell backwards (different weights), cross-country running 1-3 km.
2. Gymnastics
3. Acrobatics
4. Sport Games: volleyball, basketball, soccer
5. Mobility Games
6. Cycling
7. Rowing
8. Swimming
9. Winter Sports: skiing, skating
10. Hiking

Of the above-mentioned types of sports, the following are appropriate for juveniles: gymnastics, acrobatics, mobility games, skating, middle-distance running.

List of Exercises in Weightlifting Training

One hundred different weightlifting exercises were selected in drawing up the multi-year piece-meal programs. The weightlifting exercises are numbered according to Medvedev's system of classification and categorisation.

Fundamental Exercises

Snatch Exercises

Group 1

1. Classic Snatch from the floor (squat and split variations)

Group 2

2. Snatch, starting with bar below the knees (squat and split variations)
3. Snatch, starting with bar at knee level (squat and split variations)
4. Snatch, starting with bar above the knees (squat and split variations)
5. Snatch, legs straight, torso leaning forward (squat and split variations)
6. Snatch, from a standing erect starting position (squat and split variations)
7. Snatch, while standing on a block (squat and split variations)

Group 3

8. Power Snatch, from the floor
9. Power Snatch, starting with the barbell below the knees
10. Power Snatch, starting with the barbell at knee level
11. Power Snatch, starting with the barbell above the knees
12. Power Snatch, legs straight, torso leaning over
13. Power Snatch, standing on a block
14. Power Snatch, followed by overhead squat

Group 4

15. Snatch Pull, from the floor (with or without rise onto toes)
16. Snatch Pull, starting with barbell below the knees (from hang or plinths)
17. Snatch Pull, starting with barbell at knee level (from hang or plinths)
18. Snatch Pull, starting with barbell above the knees (from hang or plinths)
19. Snatch Pull, up to knee level
20. Snatch Pull, standing on a block (with or without rise onto toes)

21. Snatch Pull, up until the legs are straight, torso leaning forward
22. Snatch Pull slowly, followed by a fast pull
23. Snatch Pull to knees, followed by snatch pull overhead
24. Snatch Pull, slowly, followed by slow lowering of the barbell (also, Snatch pull-throughs from hips)
25. Snatch Pull, plus snatch pull from below the knees, plus snatch pull from above the knees
26. Snatch Pull with four, 3-second stops (at the instant of starting lift, at knees, above the knees, heels raised)
27. Snatch Pull with four stops, lower slowly, followed by fast snatch pull
28. Snatch Pull, followed by classic snatch.

The Clean and Jerk Exercises

Group 5

29. Classic Clean & Jerk, from the floor

Group 6

30. Clean & Jerk, starting with barbell below the knees
31. Clean & Jerk, starting with the barbell at knee level
32. Clean & Jerk, starting with the barbell above the knees

Group 7

33. Power Clean, from the floor.
34. Power Clean, starting with the barbell below the knees (from hang or plinths)
35. Power Clean, starting with the barbell at knee level (from hang or plinths)
36. Power Clean, starting with the barbell above the knees (from hang or plinths)
37. Power Clean, squat next, then jerk
38. Power Clean, push-jerk next, then overhead squat
39. Push-Jerk, after a power clean
40. Push-Jerk, barbell taken from stands
41. Push-Jerk, followed by jerk, barbell taken from stands
42. Push-Jerk, from behind the head, followed by overhead squat
43. Half-Jerk, followed by the jerk, barbell taken from stands
44. Jerk, barbell taken from stands
45. Jerk, from behind the head
46. Squat, followed by jerk behind the head
47. Front Squat, followed by jerk

Group 9

48. Clean Pull, from the floor
49. Clean Pull, starting with the barbell below the knees
50. Clean Pull, starting with the barbell at knee level
51. Clean Pull, starting with the barbell above the knees
52. Clean Pull, to knee level
53. Clean Pull, standing on a block
54. Clean Pull, until the legs are straight
55. Clean Pull, slow first pull, followed by a fast second pull
56. Clean Pull, normal upward pull, lowering the barbell slowly
57. Clean Pull, slowly up, plus lower slowly
58. Clean Pull, with four stops upwards
59. Clean Pull, with four stops, followed by fast full clean pull
60. Clean Pull, with a medium hand spacing
61. Clean Pull, to knee level, followed by full clean pull
62. Clean Pull, followed by squat clean

Squats

Group 10

63. Back Squat.

64. Front Squat
65. Back Squat, lowering slowly and rising quickly

Good Mornings

Group 11

66. Good Morning pull using a pulley, snatch grip
67. Good Morning, with the knees flexed
68. Good Morning, with the knees flexed, followed by vertical jump

Pressing

Group 12

69. Press, with a clean grip or slightly wider
70. Push-Press
71. Push Press, followed by overhead squat
72. Push Press, behind the head, followed by overhead squat (clean grip)
73. Push Press, behind the head, snatch hand spacing, plus overhead squat
74. Press into a squat snatch position, snatch or wide clean grip
75. Bench Press, clean grip

Exercises of Additional Loading

Group 13 : Exercises for the Legs

76. Back Squats, with heels raised (standing on the balls of the feet)
77. Leg Press, on leg press machine
78. Lunge, barbell on the shoulders
79. Lunge, barbell on the chest
80. Lunge, barbell held between the legs
81. Vertical Jump, starting with barbell below the knees, snatch grip
82. Depth Jump.

Group 14 : Exercises for the Back

83. Prone Back Extensions ('hyperextensions'), barbell behind the head
84. Good Morning, legs straight
85. Good Morning, seated on the floor
86. Good Morning, seated on a bench

Group 15 : Exercises for the Arms and Shoulder Girdle

87. Press behind the head, with a snatch grip
88. Press behind the head with a snatch grip, plus overhead squat
89. Press behind the head while in the squat position, snatch grip
90. Seated Press
91. Incline Barbell Press (different inclinations)
92. Snatch Stretch Exercise (a snatch from the floor without squatting under), with clean grip
93. Snatch Stretch Exercise (snatch from the floor without squatting under), with snatch grip
94. Snatch Stretch Exercise, with a clean hand spacing, followed by overhead squat
95. Snatch Stretch Exercise, starting with the barbell at knee level, with a clean grip
96. Snatch Stretch Exercise, with the barbell at knee level and using a thumbless grip
97. Snatch Stretch Exercise, starting with barbell above the knees, clean grip
98. Snatch Stretch Exercise, starting with barbell above the knees, snatch grip
99. Snatch Stretch Exercise, starting from thighs with knees and torso straight, clean grip
100. Snatch Stretch Exercise, starting from thighs with knees and torso straight, snatch grip

Examples of Powerlifting Exercises

Bench Press Variations

1. Bench Press, snatch grip with barbell (BB)

2. Bench Press, narrow grip
3. Bench Press, jerk grip
4. Bench Press, hands touching
5. Bench Press, starting at rest from chest (different grip spacings)
6. Bench Press, with bounce at bottom, very lightly touching chest
7. Bench Press, slow down, fast up
8. Bench Press, slow down, slow up
9. Bench Press, fast down, fast up
10. Bench Press, lower chest
11. Bench Press, mid chest
12. Bench Press, to clavicles
13. Bench Press, reverse grip (palms supinated)
14. Bench Press, thumbless grip
15. Bench Press, elbows close to body, arms rotated laterally (all variations)
16. Bench Press, elbows rotated away from body, arms rotated medially (all variations)
17. Bench Press, limited range between set points on power rack (BB, DB, machines)
18. Bench Press, isometric, pressing against bar fixed at selected point
19. Bench Press, driving up to stops on power rack, then pressing isometrically
20. Bench Press, forced reps with partner helping at sticking point
21. Bench Press, continuous reps without rest at top or bottom
22. Bench Press, replacing bar on rack between each repetition
23. Bench Press, eccentric only (raised by partner)
24. Bench Press, concentric only (lowered by partner)
25. Bench Press, feet on bench (all variations)
26. Bench Press, from different starting positions on plinths
27. Bench Press, load release at selected point
28. Bench Press, plyometric thrust at given point against light load
29. Bench Press, using conventional machine (using above variations)
30. Bench Press, using variable resistance machine
31. Bench Press, holding at different stages on way up or down or both
32. Bench Press with dumbbells (using all of the above variations)
33. Bench Press with DB, rotating DBs on the way up and down
34. Seated Bench (Chest) Press, using machine (all variations)
35. Bench Press, on decline bench (all variations)
36. Bench Press, on incline bench (all variations)
37. Bench Press, with firm sponge or board on chest
38. Bench Press with attached chains or elastic bands
39. Oscillating Bench Press, elbows slightly bent
40. Bench press held at given level, partner pushes down with oscillating thrusts

Squat Variations

1. Weightlifting Back Squat (full squat, bar high on shoulders, torso fairly erect)
2. Powerlifting Back Squat (half-squat, bar low on shoulders, feet wide, buttocks thrust back)
3. Front Squat (full range, part range)
4. Back Squat (WL or PWL), heels raised on plank
5. Back Squat (WL or PWL), toes raised on plank
6. Back Squat (WL or PWL), narrow foot spacing
7. Back Squat (WL or PWL), feet parallel
8. Back Squat (WL or PWL), feet rotated outwards
9. Back Squat (WL or PWL), slow down, fast up
10. Back Squat (WL or PWL), fast down, slow up
11. Back Squat (WL or PWL), continuous without stop at top or bottom
12. Back Squat (WL or PWL), replacing weight on racks between each repetition
13. Back Squat (WL or PWL), followed by thrust onto toes
14. Back Squat (WL or PWL), concentric only, lowered by partners

15. Back Squat (WL or PWL), eccentric only, raised by partners
16. Back Squat (WL or PWL), from different starting positions
17. Back Squat (WL or PWL), upward drive to push isometrically against stops on power rack
18. Back Squat (WL or PWL), limited range between two set levels on power rack
19. Back Squat (WL or PWL), forced resistance with partner helping through sticking point
20. Back Squat, bar held overhead with Snatch grip
21. Hip Thrust Squat, hips thrust forwards rapidly and driving onto toes at end of squat
22. Drop Squat, bar held with snatch grip, jerked overhead while dropping into squat
23. Squat, part-range on calf machine, driving into calf raises
24. Squat, standing on benches, weight hanging between legs, suspended from hips
25. Squats, balancing on balls of feet for entire move
26. Squats, standing on balance board, light to moderate load
27. One-legged Squats, with dumbbells
28. Squats, using machines (all variations)
29. Back Squat (WL or PWL), load removed or released at specific point
30. Box squats (different depths, resting or just touching)
31. Squats, with attached chains or elastic bands
32. Squats with back sliding along a smooth pole
33. Weightlifting Squat, push press load off shoulders at end of squat
34. Weightlifting Squat, push-jerk load off shoulders at end of squat
35. Squat, followed by thrust jump with dumbbells in both hands, drop DB before landing
36. Squat Landings, eccentric amortisation of knee flexion after dropping from a bench
37. Oscillating Squats, small range with slightly flexed knees (off racks, front or back)
38. Zercher Squats (barbell held in front of body in the crook of the arms)

Deadlift Variations

1. Deadlift, bent-knee (normal grip, reverse grip or alternate grip)
2. Deadlift, straight knee (all grips)
3. Deadlift, standing on bench or blocks (straight or bent knee)
4. Deadlift, partial range (from hang or rack)
5. Deadlift, so-called Romanian deadlift (pull from below knees position)
6. Deadlift, bent knee raise, straight knee lowering
7. Deadlift, different speeds over different ranges
8. Deadlift, with shrug
9. Deadlift, with calf raise
10. Deadlift, with calf raise and shrug
11. Deadlift, feet close, feet wide (Sumo style)
12. Deadlift, bounce off platform (using soft rubber plates or thick rubber blocks on surface)
13. Deadlift, with isometric stops at different levels
14. Deadlift, oscillating over small range (of whole movement)
15. Deadlift, using isokinetic dynamometer (e.g. 'MiniGym')
16. Deadlift, only concentric phase
17. Deadlift, only eccentric phase (lifted off thigh-height rack)
18. Deadlift, bar behind legs ('Hack Squat')
19. Deadlift, with attached chains or elastic bands
20. Deadlift, bar diagonally between legs ('Straddle Lift')
21. Deadlift, isometric hold at given level, off rack
22. Deadlift, standing on blocks
23. Zercher deadlift (bar held in crooks of arms)
24. Dumbbell deadlift (many of above variations)
25. Deadlift with thick diameter bar (or sleeve fitted over normal bar)

Examples of Hybrid Lifting Exercises

Note here that in this list the clean pull and deadlift, or press, push-press and jerk, or front and back squats may be interchanged in several cases to suit one's specific needs and applications. In some cases, one may also use dumbbells instead of barbells for some of the exercises. Some other hybrids appear in the preceding list of fundamental weightlifting exercises.

1. Clean pull (or deadlift) + shrug
2. Clean pull + calf raise
3. Clean pull + calf raise + shrug
4. Clean pull from hang + shrug
5. Clean pull from hang + calf raise + shrug
6. Clean pull up + Straight leg deadlift down
7. Clean pull to below knee + pull below knee to mid thigh + pull from ground
8. Clean pull from below knee + clean pull to shoulders
9. Clean pull from below knee + clean pull to shoulders + front squat
10. Clean pull + clean pull to shoulders + push press (or jerk) + front squat
11. Clean pull + clean pull to shoulders + front squat + push press (or jerk)
12. Pull from hang + front squat
13. Pull from hang + front squat + calf raise (squat thrust)
14. Pull from hang + front squat + push press (jerk)
15. Good morning (bent knees) + partial squat to straighten knees (squat thrust)
16. Good morning (bent knees) + partial squat (to straighten knees) + calf raise
17. Good morning + back squat
18. Squat + good morning (range depends on load)
19. Squat + push press behind neck
20. Front squat + push press (jerk)
21. Back squat (wide hand spacing) + push press behind neck into snatch position
22. Push press (wide hand spacing) + drop into overhead squat (bar in snatch position)
23. Front Squat + push press in front (jerk)
24. Back Squat + push press behind neck
25. Push press (jerk) off racks + squats
26. Power clean + front squat
27. Push press + jerk
28. Press + push press (jerk)
29. Dumbbell (DB) pulls + DB cleans to shoulders
30. DB power cleans + DB push press
31. DB power cleans + DB front squat
32. Split clean + lunge squat
33. Split snatch + overhead split squat
34. Power snatch + overhead squat
35. Snatch from hang + overhead squat (various hang levels)
36. Snatch from plinth (various levels) + overhead squat
37. Snatch pull throughs from hips + overhead squats
38. Oscillating Front Squat (knees slightly bent) + push press (jerk)
39. Power Clean + Oscillating Front Squat (knees slightly bent) + push press (jerk)
40. Bench press (BP) + partial range BP
41. Bench press (BP) + partial range BP + oscillating BP (elbows slightly bent)

8.5 Overtraining

Overtraining and exhaustion are both a consequence of imbalance between stress and adaptability of the body. Successful adaptation implicates supercompensatory (adaptive reconstructive) processes that lead to a higher functional level of the body, whereas unsuccessful adaptation depletes the current adaptation reserves (see 1.14). Any imbalance causes the body's homeostatic mechanisms to decrease stress or enforce short- or long-term rest to prevent further damage. Exhaustion is the systemic result of short-term imbalance, whereas overtraining is the result of imbalance accumulated over a prolonged period. Although Selye's General Adaptation Syndrome (1.14) is one of the useful models for understanding adaptation and overtraining, it must be appreciated that its use of the term 'energy' does not simply concern the supply of energy for metabolic processes. Energy exchanges in the body are involved with many other events such as tissue repair and nervous impulses. It follows that overtraining is closely related to an inadequate rate of recovery and adaptation of:

- the energy systems of the body (see 1.13)
- cell repair and growth mechanisms (see 1.11)
- hormonal systems (see 1.12 and 1.13.7)
- nervous processes (see 1.12).

The insidious road to overtraining is signposted, not always clearly, by residual fatigue or soreness, persistent minor injuries, loss of motivation, or lack of progress. The Two Factor Model of Training (1.15.3) emphasizes the central role played by fatigue in the overall preparedness process. It is vital that the existence of acute or chronic fatigue symptoms be recognised by the athlete and his coach, since the popular practice of forcing oneself through these negative phases can lead to acute or chronic injury.

There are two types of overtraining: general and local. *General overtraining* affects the whole body and results in stagnation of a decrease in performance, whereas *local overtraining* affects a specific body part. Note that the execution of excessively demanding exercise routines currently is also categorised into two classes: *overtraining* (chronic excessive training) and *overreaching (*acute excessive training), so that one needs to assess if the excessive training is of an acute or chronic nature.

Adaptation to physical, psychological or environmental stress depends on the inextricable links (Fig 8.3) between the central nervous system (the fast control system of the body) and the endocrine system (the slow control system). Any changes in the central nervous and endocrine systems can affect performance in the muscular system. The endocrine system in particular controls an intricate group of glands whose hormones are vital to all aspects of human life.

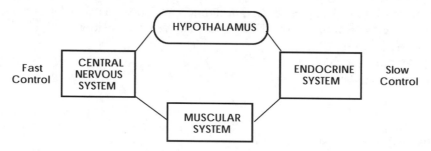

Figure 8.3 Some of the physiological control systems involved with motor processes.

For instance, the adrenal glands selectively prepare the skeletal muscle for physical activity in the face of stress. The hormone thyroxine, secreted by the thyroid gland, not only increases the rate at which cells burn their fuel (glucose), but it is involved in various anti-stress responses, including demands for extra energy. Human growth hormone (HGH), secreted by the pituitary gland in the brain, plays an essential role in general growth and in the elevation of blood glucose. Insulin, secreted by the pancreas, is concerned with the metabolism of glucose, and the sex hormones such as testosterone influence sexual behaviour and muscle growth in the male.

This central role played by certain hormones in the occurrence and management of stress implies that it is logical to associate general overtraining, a stress related phenomenon, with some disturbance of the endocrine system. Researchers sometimes identify at least two types of general overtraining on this basis (Israel, 1963), both of which are compared in Table 8.2:

(a) *A-overtraining* (Addisonic overtraining) named after Addison's disease, which is associated with diminished activity of the adrenal glands. This category of overtraining affects predominantly the parasympathetic pathways of the autonomic nervous system and is difficult to detect early, due to the absence of any dramatic symptoms. Suspicion that something is amiss may be aroused by the appearance of stagnation or deterioration of the athlete's performance.

(b) *B-overtraining* (Basedowic overtraining), named after Basedow's disease, which is associated with thyroid hyperactivity. This category of overtraining affects predominantly the sympathetic pathways of the autonomic nervous system and, as the classical type of overtraining with its abundance of symptoms, is easy to diagnose.

Overtraining has also been shown to be associated with electrocardiographic changes, in particular a smaller T wave, so that Table 8.3 could no doubt be extended to include such features.

The presence of local overtraining is relatively simple to recognise, since it is often accompanied by stiffness or soreness of a particular muscle group which does not subside with alternate days of rest. Moreover, the performance of that muscle group might be static or diminished and some of the symptoms of general overtraining, such as impaired coordination, might be present. In weight training, this situation may be revealed by outstanding performance in one supplementary exercise such as the squat, but diminished performance in another exercise such as the bench press.

Table 8.3 Symptomatic comparison of A and B types of overtraining

Variables	A-Overtraining	B-Overtraining
1. Blood pressure	diastolic increase to over 100mm Hg, during and after physical stress	slight increase
2. Coordination	impaired	impaired, with increased reaction time
3. Bodymass	normal	decrease
4. Endurance	slight increase in tiredness	tendency to tire easily
5. Sleep requirements	no increase	increase
6. Resting pulse	low	elevated
7. Body temperature	normal	slightly increased
8. Appetite	normal	reduced
9. Metabolism	normal	altered, with increased tendency to sweat; abnormally increased breathing rate under stress
10. General muscle soreness	little or none	mild to pronounced, with tendency to muscle stiffness and pain
11. General resistance	normal	tendency to headaches, colds, fever blisters; prolonged recuperation
12. Recovery time	normal or slightly increased	increased
13. Psychological changes	none, other than slight loss in motivation	nervousness, poor motivation, inner unease, eventual depression

In the case of strength training, overtraining injuries may be the result of too many repetitions or sets, regular training with near maximum loads, training the same muscle groups too frequently, inadequate recovery periods, insufficient rest or faulty execution of any movement.

In prescribing training to avoid overtraining, it is relevant to add another quotation by Selye: "The goal is certainly not to avoid stress - stress is a part of life. It is a natural by-product of all our activities .... But in order to express yourself fully, you must first find your optimum stress level and then use your adaptation energy at a rate and in a direction adjusted to the innate structure of your mind and body. It is not easy .... It takes much practice and almost constant self-analysis" (Selye,1956). This statement summarises what constitutes an effective training programme - a carefully designed sequence of physical and mental stresses in given conditioning workouts, with one's condition being constantly monitored and restoration being planned in a way and at a rate appropriate to one's current level of stress.

In terms of the *Two-Factor (Fitness-Fatigue) Model of Training* (1.16.3), it becomes clear that one has to monitor the negative effects of fatigue alongside the positive increases in fitness being elicited by short- and long-term training. This is one reason why great emphasis was placed earlier (Ch 6) on monitoring the effects of different means and loads on functional indicators and sporting results. In this context, it needs to be recalled that preparedness is the summated result of the opposing fitness and fatigue after-effects of training (1.16.3).

8.6 Restoration and Stress Management

Restoration is an integral part of overall training and practice, so that it must be applied with the short-term and long-term goals constantly in mind. A comprehensive training programme alternates different training techniques with situationally appropriate restorative means. Individualisation of approach is vital, as is variation, though not simply for the sake of it. Full restoration can sometimes be undesirable and that some Russian experts emphasize the importance of periodically training on a basis of *non-recovery* (Siff & Yessis, 1992). It should also be pointed out that *restoration* in training and competition is not synonymous with *rehabilitation*, which refers to the treatment of overtraining, illness or injury.

Immediate use of artificial means which facilitate restoration can weaken the natural ability of the body to restore itself and promote supercompensation. Massage is not enough, saunas are part of the picture, reflexology is limited; all individual modalities are insufficient to guarantee optimal restoration in modern sport. With prolonged use of any given means of restoration, the recuperative effect decreases, so that Russian experts usually recommend that the same restorative means should not be applied more than once or twice a week in the same form. They consider that, in applying local-effect procedures, it is advisable to have a single day's break after every two days of application. In particular, the body adapts more rapidly to local-effect restorative means than to general restorative means (Siff & Yessis, 1992).

Restoration is based upon the awareness that three fairly discrete phases of the normal recovery process may be distinguished (Zalessky, 1979):

- *On-going recovery*, which takes place during the activity itself
- *Rapid recovery*, which occurs immediately after exercise, leading to removal of metabolic by-products and replenishment of depleted energy resources
- *Delayed recovery*, which surpasses the initial level if training loads are not excessive

Popular sports and bodybuilding magazines in the West often quote that the Russian and Eastern European athletes may train as often as five times a day. Scores of 'Soviet' training programmes are quoted, Western athletes frequently follow them religiously, yet they pay scant attention to the contents and structure of the phases between training exercises and sessions. Here, the trend appears to be constant action, but the importance of goal-directed episodes of *inaction*, known and formalised by Indian and Chinese sages for thousands of years, does not seem to be appreciated.

All meditation and hypnosis became labelled as potentially dangerous by those who failed to understand its nature. Much of the innovative scientific analysis of these so-called Eastern disciplines was carried out by Western researchers, but somehow their methods were rarely applied in sport, partly because of the stigma still attached to it by traditionalists. These techniques were annexed very effectively by the Russians, even though they have been known since the earliest past to primitive people in all countries of the world. Until recently, science regarded the ancient arts as worthless superstition and it happened that adaptations of these methods by Western New Age practitioners or Alternative Therapists often reduced them to a mockery.

Certainly, many of these techniques may work because they are placebos, because the user believes in them. Yet, this is a very good reason not to dismiss them. If the mind can be focused by an apparently illogical or foolish concept to perform unusual feats of performance or healing, then it is vital that we uncover the underlying physiological principles which make the *placebo effect* (or 'faith factor') so powerful. Placebos can produce positive and negative effects; it is up to science to sift the useful from the harmful.

The placebo effect can also confound the validity of many restoration techniques, which work not because of any special merits, but because the practitioner persuades the user of its value. Thus, you will find that one therapist will swear that aromatherapy with a certain fragrance will help, while another may claim the opposite. Another will extol the virtue of deep transverse friction for adhesions, whereas yet another will have equal success with therapeutic touch. Virtually every claim by one massage therapist will be countered by another 'expert'.

The therapeutic world is replete with claims and counter-claims about the efficacy of specific remedies, largely because physical and mental healing are inextricably linked. Often, one cannot separate the therapy from the therapist, since *the therapy often succeeds because of the rapport between therapist and client*. This is precisely what makes scientific research so difficult - great care has to be taken to choose experimental and control groups and to exclude as far as possible all confounding factors such as the placebo effect and human interaction. Nevertheless in sports restoration, this knowledge is of great importance: *The rapport between you and the athlete is central to the success of the therapy*. In short, the belief of the athlete in you and your therapy (and sometimes an outside force, depending on the athlete's belief system) is an integral part of successful restoration.

In integrating research and practice as part of a highly successful training system, the Russians usually recognise three classes of restoration (Siff & Yessis, 1992):

- *Pedagogical (coaching) restoration*, which employs carefully periodised programmes to optimise the balance between training stresses and natural recuperative processes. Appropriate combinational training, known in the West as 'cross training', as well as active rest fall into this category. Low intensity cyclical, rhythmical, circulatory or cardiovascular activities can also be very useful for promoting recovery after demanding strength training sessions. The organisation of training into microcycles, mesocycles and macrocycles, with a preparatory period divided into General and Special Physical Preparation is done specifically to promote supercompensation via suitable phasing of loading and restoration regimes (see Ch 6). The use of other intermediate phases such as stabilisation and transition form part of this scheme.

- *Medico-biological restoration*, which covers a broad spectrum of therapeutic measures offered by medical and allied practitioners. Sometimes, this category is subdivided into physiotherapeutic and pharmacological measures, and includes massage, acupressure and technological therapy. Some workers subdivide physical measures into natural means (e.g. massage, showers, heat, sunlight and training outdoors) and additional means (such as electrostimulation, electrosleep, diathermy, acupuncture, baro-chambers, laser therapy and ultrasound). Similarly, pharmacological means may be subdivided into natural and synthetic means.

- *Psychological restoration*, which involves management of the mental state. Techniques include hypnosis, self-hypnosis, auto-suggestion, autogenics, visualisation, progressive relaxation, guided imagery, music therapy and learning techniques. Some of these techniques rely on the use of electronic apparatus such as biofeedback machines, music therapy, electrodermal devices and computer games.

The Russian restoration system recognises the *specificity of each technique or sequence of techniques* for a particular sport, phase of training, individual athlete, time of the day, type of stress and type of fitness. It applies different techniques before, during, shortly after and a long time after training and competitions. Meticulous records are kept reflecting the athlete's daily variation in physical and psychological state, a process which implies close cooperation between athletes, coaches and therapists. Often, the athlete is encouraged to shed dependence on the therapist and to learn *self-restoration* procedures (Siff & Yessis, 1992).

It is not unusual for top Russian athletes to receive over an hour of restoration every day, with regular alternation of individualised methods and periodic training superimposed on a state of non-restoration. As emphasized earlier, a clear distinction is drawn between *restoration* and *rehabilitation*. Restoration is an integral part of the overall training programme, planned to fit in at the most effective and appropriate stages of training. Rehabilitation refers to therapy to restore an injured athlete to full functional capability. Very often the need for rehabilitation is the consequence of inadequate restoration, especially imperfect pedagogical restoration, i.e. a training schedule which produces overtraining. Although accidents can happen which are largely outside the control of the athlete, the essence of training is to maximise performance and minimise injuries, pain and soreness.

In addition to these categories of formal restoration, it is essential to encourage natural recovery relating to family, living conditions, lifestyle, nutrition, leisure activities, beneficial socialisation, team atmosphere, work conditions, spiritual needs and coaching team interaction. After all, problems which lie outside the training setting can easily predominate over training problems in determining the success of the athlete in competition.

Stress and Restorative Measures

Table 8.4 below identifies some of the symptoms of overtraining stress.

Table 8.4 Functions affected by physiological and psychological stress

• Heart rate	• Sleep patterns	• Reaction time
• Blood pressure	• Body temperature	• Posture
• Muscular tension	• Concentration and alertness	• Pupil size (of the eye)
• Muscle irritability	• Digestion, gastric acidity	• General irritability, mood, stability
• Pain threshold	• Endocrine secretion	• Tissue repair and growth
• Brain rhythms	• Immune response	• Secretion of endogenous opiates
• Breathing patterns	• Fine motor control	

These symptoms reflect an extensive array of changes which take place in the body in response to excessive stress. In general, stress produces acute (short-term) and chronic (long-term) effects on variables including those listed in Table 8.4. There are many standard tests for and ways of observing most of the indicators of stress below; the thorough preparation of the athlete demands that they be applied regularly and appropriate restoration interventions be used.

Application of Restoration Measures

The application of restoration or stress management techniques, like any other therapies, must be done so by understanding the following features of therapeutic prescription:

• Indications	• Dosage	• Symptoms of misuse
• Contraindications	• Directions for use	• Treatment of misuse
• Effects	• Special precautions	• Dependence on therapy
• Side-effects		

In managing stress, be it be produced by sport or any other daily events, it is important to analyse the effect of the following on the sufferer:

• Perception of the stress and its effects	• Intensity or quality of stress
• Attitude towards the stress	• Volume or quantity of stress
• Sensory input associated with the stress	• Density or concentration of stresses
• Motor activity and its effect on the stress	• Duration of stress
• Response of the body and mind to the stress	• Onset of the stress
• Hierarchies of stresses acting at any instant	• Causes of the stress

Once the above guidelines have been followed, it is useful to examine carefully the following factors before undertaking any form of therapy:

• Procedures (types of therapy)	• Place
• Purpose of Therapy	• Period
• Person	• Position
• Practitioner	• Pain/Pleasure

Then, ask the following questions: Is it -

• Appropriate
• Effective
• Sufficient
• Safe
• Enjoyable ?

Once you have applied this checklist, you may now select the appropriate restoration means and methods for a given person at a given time. It is important to appreciate the distinction between means and methods of restoration, because these concepts are often confused or interchangeably used. The *means* refers to the broad general type of restoration measure (e.g. massage), whereas the *method* refers to that specific technique chosen (e.g. kneading massage) which falls within that means. In other words, each *means* comprises many different *methods*, each with its own techniques and variations of techniques.

Restoration Means

As discussed earlier, the following broad categories of restoration means may be recognised:

- Pedagogical/coaching
- Biological/medical
- Psychological

The pedagogical/coaching/training methodology and periodisation principles which underlie all successful sports preparation are outside the scope of this text. The reader who is seriously involved with the entire training process, however, should familiarise himself thoroughly with Russian books covering those topics in detail because they complement the material given here. The main restorative means (other than pedagogical) fall into the following categories:

- Physical means
- Medical means
- Psychological means

These categories may be subdivided further as shown in Table 8.5, although this categorisation should not be regarded as definitive or exclusive. For instance, physiotherapeutic means could also be recognised, but this discipline could be regarded as one of the medical means. It also embraces active means, physical means and others, so that it and other professional specialisations have not been labelled as single restricted means. Even more detailed categories of each means may be offered, as summarised in the sections which follow.

Some of the major physical means of restoration are listed in Table 8.6, while the main means of psychological restoration appear in Table 8.7. After careful selection to suit the individual and situation, they may be offered by a therapist or self-administered by the athlete, after they have been learned from an experienced therapist or coach.

Table 8.5 Categories of different restorative means in sport and exercise.

Physical Means	Medical Means	Psychological Means
Passive	Pharmacological	Therapist-administered
Active	Psychiatric	Self-administered
Combined	Surgical	Combined
	Nutritional	
	Combined	

Before using any of the above means, or any other means of restoration itemised in this section, it is vital to consider the background and attitudes of the athlete, because these factors can have a profound effect on the efficacy of any regime. Since we are dealing with the human mind, we can never focus entirely on physical issues alone, because powerful, emotional or unrecognised subconscious mental states, like the placebo phenomenon, can hinder or help the restoration or the training process.

Table 8.6 Passive and active physical means of restoration (active means mainly in the last column)

Classical massage	Electronic technology	Physical activity
PNF (Neuromuscular means)	Laser therapy	Recreational sport
Myofascial trigger point massage	Passive machines	Manual labour
Acupressure/ shiatsu	Vibromassagers	Dance
Hydrotherapy	Barotherapy (pressure)	Play
Stretching techniques	Balneo-therapy (baths)	Postural realignment
Flotation	Reflexology	Breathing regimens
Aromatherapy	Aromatherapy	Progressive relaxation
Therapeutic Touch	PNF (Neuromuscular means)	Tai Chi
Electronic technology	Self-massage (active/passive)	Yoga
	Stretching	

Table 8.7 Psychological Means of Restoration

Psychotherapy	Music/sound therapy
Hypnosis	Singing/chanting
Autogenic training	Meditation
Operant conditioning	Religion
Visualisation/ Guided imagery	Biofeedback training
Sensory deprivation/modification	Neurolinguistic programming
Screaming/shouting	Laughter/tears

The popularity of massage deems that further details of its different methods be given.

Massage Methods

Table 8.8 The major methods of massage

Effleurage - long, smooth stroking	Pressing - sustained or oscillatory
Frottage - rubbing	Slapping
Petrissage - kneading	Hacking
Friction - deep kneading	Lifting, pulling
Tapotement - percussion	Clapping, cupping
Vibration - trembling, shaking	Deep transverse friction
Nerve stroking - light stroking	Therapeutic Touch
Rolling, wringing, jostling	Cryokinetics
Squeezing	Barotherapy
Drilling	Electrostimulation

In applying massage, there are numerous other variables which have to be considered, such as those detailed in Table 8.9.

Massage Variables

The massaging point of contact is of particular relevance. One may massage with many parts of the body, including the hand, knuckle, elbow, feet or heels. The hands and fingers may also be used in a large variety of ways: the main contacts here include the palms, finger tips, phalangeal knuckles, hand knuckles, gripping with both hands, knife-edge of hand, pads of fingers, thumb, pad of thumb, scissors between thumb and fingers, and fist. Although the feet or parts of the feet are commonly used in the East, they are not frequently used in the West, particularly because of patient perception and our concept of professionalism.

Table 8.9 The main variables in the application of massage

Means	Duration
Methods	Tempo
Apparatus	Environment
Hand or other massaging contact	Psychological state
Depth	Direction
Frequency	Rest intervals
Pressure	Therapist: personal features
Lubricant	Client: personal features
Positioning	Variation
Sequence	Ethics, privacy, respect

The mode of movement is also extremely varied: massage may be executed using one or both hands or many of the above techniques in a linear fashion, circularly, in spirals concentrically or eccentrically, transversally or longitudinally relative to the muscles, pulsating into and out of the muscles, just touching the surface, vibrating, holding, squeezing, twisting, pinching, lifting and pressing. Massage may be applied as a means of restoration or rehabilitation. In sports preparation, its main roles, as described by many Russian experts, are:

- *Warming*
- *Loosening*
- *Pre-start relaxation*
- *Pre-start stimulation*

446

- *Mobilisation*
- *Restoration during and after workouts or competitions*

It should always be remembered that massage, like any other form of therapy, can pose certain risks. In particular, you should take careful note of contra-indications listed in Table 8.10.

Table 8.10 Contraindications for massage

Broken or bleeding tissue	Arthritis with inflammation
Inflamed, bruised, swollen tissue	Stomach area during pregnancy
Strains, sprains, tissue rupture	Stomach area during nausea, vomiting, diarrhoea, gastric upset
Varicose veins	Haemorrhaged tissue
Painful, hypersensitive regions	Jaundice
Phlebitis (inflammation of veins)	Thigh, hip, chest, gluteal massage during menstruation
Thrombosis (clots)	Dermatitis, urticaria or any skin irritation or allergy
Swellings, lumps, moles, warts	Contagious Conditions
Fractures	Malignant Tissue

The above list refers specifically to massage which makes definite contact with the body, and does not necessarily preclude the use of non-contact techniques such as *Therapeutic Touch* (Krieger, 1979). In addition, this list refers only to physical contra-indications; there are also several good psychological or ethical reasons why massage might be contraindicated for a particular client at a given time. Alternative therapies, then, should obviously be considered.

Lest disproportionate reliance be placed upon massage as the sole or main means of restoration, the reader must be reminded of a recurrent theme throughout this book, namely that overuse of any technique leads to eventual ineffectiveness. Several experts stress the existence of a *complementarity effect* produced by the integrated use of several restorative means and methods carefully introduced at specific stages of a training programme. The reader would be well advised to remember this principle, to experiment with variations, to keep records and to devise recipes which consistently yield successful results. Client feeling and appreciation are not enough; in sports restoration, the basic indicators are improved performance and fewer injuries.

All restoration should be offered in accordance with a highly professional *Code of Conduct* which ensures that the client receives therapy which undoubtedly enhances his or her quality of life and takes account of human factors and needs such as privacy, confidentiality, hygiene, honesty, integrity, dignity, respect and politeness.

The practitioner should, at all times, be aware of any personal limitations and be professional enough to call on the assistance of someone else who may be more qualified in certain fields. This will never lower one's status or integrity; on the contrary, it will enhance one's overall professionalism and credibility.

Further Fundamentals of Sports Recovery

The acceleration of recovery following strenuous training and competitive loads has been a major concern of Russian training research for many years. Work done to date has convinced scientists and coaches that systematic use of recovery methods makes it possible to significantly and sometimes rapidly increase the volume and intensity of training while simultaneously decreasing the incidence of musculoskeletal injuries. Talyshev (1977) stresses that two sides to the problem of recovery of full work capacity must be distinguished:

- Situations in which it is necessary to achieve immediate, most complete recovery (e.g. during competition)
- Recovery methods used during the course of daily training in order to increase its work capacity.

Russian research showed that the deeper the fatigue one experiences during a workout, the greater the after-effects, and the more intense is the flow of recovery processes (which, usually 'supercompensate' beyond the initial level, provided that training loads are carefully prescribed). This represents the process whereby fitness increases.

However, if certain recovery methods are employed after a workout, then the positive after-effects (or training effect) stimulated by the workout tend to be negated and the overall training effect can be significantly diminished. Thus, the unskilled use of recovery methods can markedly increase the amount of training work and yet not provide a corresponding training effect. Therefore, the combining of workout methods with recovery methods at different stages of training becomes a serious scientific and practical problem, especially since it is very difficult to evaluate the effectiveness of specific recovery method. From a practical point of view, it is more advisable to test the effectiveness of a specific recovery method by using test loads that approximate most closely the natural training conditions, by using loads in sports exercises that are typically encountered in a given sport (Talyshev, 1977).

It may also be inappropriate to routinely apply restoration on a frequent basis, since increase in work capacity can be stimulated by using workouts which are specially calculated to produce incomplete restoration. This may be achieved by prescribing some individual sessions which are especially demanding for some body zones or processes or the use of several sessions per day for a limited period. Some authorities recommend that, during periods immediately preceding competitions, especially in the strength and power sports, it is often advisable to conduct intense workouts with minimal use of restoration, unless there are very clear indications that this may be necessary (Kopysov, 1980). However, for all *incomplete restoration* workouts, some general rules apply (Zalessky, 1980):

- The athlete should be completely healthy and in good functional state
- Incomplete restoration should not last for more than 2-3 days
- After such workout phases, all means should be used to facilitate full restoration
- Medical guidance or assistance should always be available during such phases.

With respect to the amount and characteristics of any training load, it should be noted that changes in the immune response (as reflected by the presence of colds and other apparently minor sicknesses) which accompany conditions of prolonged stressful loading, indicate the end of the general adaptation syndrome during the period of physical exhaustion, and the immediate need to decrease the loading and increase the amount of general restoration. This change in immune response is not necessarily directly associated with the physical loads, but may also relate strongly to increase in emotional stress, due, for instance, to the impending competitions or any other events involving large changes of psychological state. Timeous intervention is essential whenever the slightest hints of such disruptions in immune status become apparent.

Similar recommendations for timely use of appropriate restoration apply to training which does not necessarily place great demands on qualities such as strength and endurance. In particular, careful attention has to be paid to changes in motor control or movement skill, since all sporting action relies fundamentally on muscle action controlled by the nervous system. This is why mention was made earlier (Ch 6.2) of the monitoring value of the coach making regular ratings of the technical perfection of the athlete's execution of important movements or activities. Quantitative measurement of individual indicators of motor proficiency, such as balancing tests, reaction time, movement speed in prescribed actions, coordination, and eye-hand, eye-foot and eye-object skills, can also furnish useful data to assess if there are any significant disruptions in motor control.

For those athletes who have the services of scientific institutes, the functional state of the neuromuscular system (NMS) may be assessed by methods such as monitoring of the quasi-stationary electrical potential of the brain, quantitative muscle palpation (using probes such as the myotonometer devised by Siff) and measurement of skin conductance or impedance at acupuncture points (Shishkin, 1989). Makarova & Stupnitsky (1983) discovered that local muscle contraction (LMC) reflected by tonometry displays a clear topography and often coincides with the acupuncture points. They also found that changes in these indicators and their distribution over the body depend on the specifics of muscle activity and on the level of the athlete's preparation, with the existence of pronounced LMC coinciding with a poorer functional state of the NMS. In this case, there is also increased muscle tonus, decreased strength, an increase in time for muscle relaxation and impaired rheographic indicators (which reflect the return viscoelastic flow of muscle on being dented by a standard probe), all of which point to a diminished work capacity.

Makarova & Stupnitsky (1983), in studying such indicators over year long training programmes, noted that a characteristic change in the skin impedance whenever there is significant disruption in the athlete's adaptation to physical and psychological loading, so they used this information, sometimes assisted by other standard physiological tests (such as heart rate, blood pressure, flicker fusion rate in vision and reaction time), to modify the training programme and prescribe appropriate restoration.

In doing this, athletes were placed into one of four different groups, depending on these indicators and their self perception of their functional state at any given time (Fig 8.3). Athletes with no disruptions in self-feeling, work capacity or NMS were placed in Group I, whereas those with definite complaints and muscle disturbances formed Group III. Athletes with minor local disturbances (Group II) fell between Groups I and III, while Group IV contained athletes with acute illnesses (colds etc.).

This diagnostic process was repeated once per weekly microcycle, and the results obtained enabled restorative or rehabilitative means appropriate to each group to be prescribed by specialists (Fig 8.4). The main restorative efforts were carried out with athletes in Groups II-IV, with minimal application to those in Group I. The main means used with Group II were point-reflexive and local reflexive procedures focusing on the problematic body zones and functional changes, accompanied by a small amount of general restoration. Conversely, in Group IV, general restoration means predominated over lesser used local reflexive methods, with the entire rehabilitative process (which might include medication and other medical means) being carried out under medical supervision.

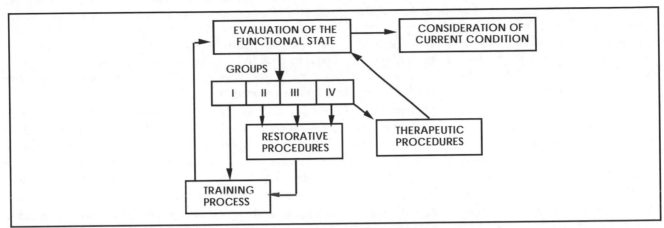

Figure 8.4 Organisation of the systems of restoration for athletes (Makarova & Stupnitsky, 1983)

The question of exactly when to apply recovery methods during training is also of great importance - are these most appropriate immediately after a workout or after a certain delay? The highest intensity and rate of recovery is observed immediately upon cessation of exercise, after which it diminishes gradually (Talyshev, 1977). Logically, *it is more advisable to accelerate recovery processes when their natural rate is slowing down.* However, it is impossible to determine this moment without special research methods, and applying these during daily training process is impractical.

Therefore, Talyshev (1977) conducted research on a large group of highly qualified athletes who followed a standardised training programme. Following a workout, the athletes took a sauna in combination with hydrotherapy - in one case directly after the workout; in the other cases, 3, 6, and 9 hours later, accompanied by a large battery of physiological tests.

In all cases, work capacity dropped sharply immediately after the workout, and if baths and hydrotherapy were not used, noticeable recovery commenced on the following day. These methods applied immediately upon completion of the workout led to a marked increase in work capacity immediately following the therapy and 3 hours later. However, this increase slowed down, and work capacity did not recover and even fell below its initial level on the following day.

The use of baths and hydrotherapy 3 hours after the workout led to a pronounced increase in work capacity 6 hours after the therapy (9 hours after the workout). Work capacity returned to its initial level on the following day. With the use of this therapy regime 6 hours, and especially 9 hours, after the completion of the workout session, work capacity not only recovered on the following day, but there was significant increase (supercompensation).

Generalising from this research, Talyshev (1977) concluded that work capacity and its magnitude depend strongly on the time at which the restorative methods are applied. When an immediate effect is necessary, namely when the greatest work capacity recovery after a short span of time is needed (e.g. between morning and afternoon workouts), it is advisable to employ restorative methods immediately after workouts or morning starts. If, however, a high work capacity is required on the following day, then it is better to employ recovery methods 6-9 hours after the workout or competition. If the workout or competition ends late in the evening, it is preferable to start recovery procedures in the morning, shortly after awakening.

Related work has shown that it is best to employ full-body recovery methods (e.g. sauna, hydrotherapy, general massage) after large volume of general training work. In contrast, local methods (e.g. pressure methods, local manual or vibrational massage, local heating) are preferable following the execution of work which strongly stresses specific muscle groups. However, this recommendation is still fairly general and the question remains as to how does the dosage of a specific recovery method relates to the severity of the training load.

Complexes and Periodisation in Restoration

The tendency to apply restorative means and methods largely at random, depending on one's preferences and training, should be avoided, since different processes or body components (nervous, muscular, ligamentous, metabolic, psychological, cardiovascular etc.) fatigue, recover and adapt at different rates and to different degrees, depending on the nature of the loading and the athlete. The value of combining, complexing and periodising training loads according to individualised programmes has achieved a high degree of acceptance, but the value of a similar approach in restoration often tends to be ignored. Of course, the nature of many of the restorative methods, especially the manual forms, means that it is not possible to quantitatively compute volumes and intensities, as is generally the case with training loading. That is why one more frequently refers to the use of restorative complexes or of periodised training programmes which incorporate restorative procedures.

The preceding section summarised a small proportion of extensive Russian research which has revealed the influence of the timing of specific general and local restorative methods on restoration and rehabilitation using many different manual, technological, ergogenic and psychological methods. There we noted that inappropriate timing can delay or even reverse recovery after training, yet many well-meaning therapists quite casually employ massage, spinal manipulation, electrostimulation, hydrotherapy and other common methods simply because the athlete feels 'tired', sore, stressed or unmotivated.

A more thorough exposition of the entire topic of using restorative complexes and periodised programmes which optimally combine stress and restorative loading is covered elsewhere (Siff & Yessis, 1992), so a typical example of such an approach will just be given here.

The Soviet track cycling team, for a period of 5 years, successfully used this type of programme of restoration, (Goletz & Osadchy, 1986) divided into three basic groups of means, namely:

- Group 1 (Basic means) for rapidly eliminating the fatigue following a training session
- Group 2 (On-going means) for restoring the individual components of athletic preparedness to elevate the work capacity of these components during subsequent training sessions
- Group 3 (Operative means) for stimulating work capacity directly before or during a workout or competition.

In the yearly training cycle, the system of using specific groups of restorative means was closely linked to the objectives of the individual stages of training. Because the same restorative means diminish their effectiveness when they are used over prolonged periods, the restorative means were alternated, regarding both content and volume, depending on the stage of the annual cycle.

During the general base-building stage of training, only *basic* type restorative means were applied, since this stage of training is marked by concentrated, high-volume workloads requiring an increased energy expenditure and deep adaptation of the athlete's entire body. At the end of the microcycle, before a rest day, the restoration involved a hydro session or a short, gentle swimming session, combined with restorative massage, warm baths using various essences (e.g. pine, eucalyptus, sea salt), and a hot-cold contrast bath or shower.

As the training programme progressed, *basic* and *ongoing* means were used in accordance with the training plans of a specific microcycle, and the cyclists underwent general restorative massage, localised manual massage, restorative baths with various essences (pine, eucalyptus, sea salt), showers (hot, warm, contrast), and light therapy (ultraviolet and infrared). At the end of the microcycle, hydro procedures were used in combination with physiotherapeutic measures, such as electrotherapy, electromagnetic fields, ultrasound and barometric techniques.

Then, as the competitive season commenced with the usual winter indoor competitions involving a series of national and international competitions, there was an increased role for non-relaxing *operative* means of preliminary stimulation of work capacity, such as the following:

(a) *For the sprint and heat groups:* brisk pre-start massage of the primary working leg muscles (using stroking, rubbing, kneading, shaking) for 8-12 minutes; massage of the segmental areas of the back and torso for 3-5 minutes; tonic-type friction with heating embrocations.

(b) *For the pace groups:* hydromassage in a hot pine bath for 3-5 minutes, needle or cold shower for 8-13 minutes, light kneading and tonic-type rubbing of the primary working leg muscles with heating embrocations or a contrast shower for 3-5 mins, brisk pre-start massage of the leg muscles (using stroking, rubbing, kneading, percussion) for 8-12 minutes, non-relaxing massage of the segmental and portal zones for 3-5 minutes, rubbing with a heating embrocation.

After training over competitive distances, the cyclists were exposed to a wide array of restorative means in the form of groups of whole-body and localised manual massage procedures with restorative balsams, restorative baths with various essences, high pressure hydromassages performed in these baths, showers (needle, pulsating, circular, rain, contrast), light radiation (ultraviolet and infrared), and ionised air. Following any competition an active and passive hydrobathing procedure was applied in combination with a group of physiotherapeutic restoration means.

During the second specialised base-building stage of training, the restoration involved *basic* and *on-going* means, with the procedures being the same as during the first specialised base-building stage of training. During the later special preparation stage, athletes participated in a large number of road races and the restorative means were planned with this fact in mind. During all stages, the training programme was designed to serve the dual purpose of pedagogical restoration, namely the use of careful periodisation to increase the functional level of fitness components (such as strength, strength-endurance and speed), as well as to facilitate 'over-recovery' or supercompensation. Special local muscle relaxing and range of movement activities formed an integral component of all training sessions to minimise drops in training effectiveness due to negative acute after-effects of any exercises.

Before outdoor track competitions (15-20 minutes before), brisk preliminary massage was performed for 8-10 minutes with heating embrocations on the major working muscles, the lumbar area, and segments of the torso and arms. After actual competitions the athletes took a warm pine or sea bath for 10-15 minutes, a warm rain-type shower and restorative massage for 30 minutes with restorative balsams or tonic-type friction embrocations.

The stage of early competitions is characterised by lower volume, more intense specialised loads geared mainly toward improving speed and speed endurance, stimulating supercompensatory reactions, restoring energy reserves, and increasing the level of special work capacity. Therefore, the restorative means applied here were similar to those used during the preceding winter competitive stage.

The most concentrated period of use of physical means to increase work capacity is the stage of immediate pre-competitive preparation, which has as its goal to lay the foundation for achieving the highest level of preparedness for the season's major competitions (World Championships and Olympic Games).

In accordance with the structure of the training load, the team was exposed to the entire arsenal of restorative means, organised into groups of procedures necessary to bring about an optimal functional state in the athlete, including some of the well-known psychological methods of progressive relaxation, self-hypnosis, guided imagery and autogenics. The content of the restorative means during one of the training phases, namely the pre-competitive stage, is illustrated by the example of a 'shock' microcycle of training for top-class cyclists for the a major national competition (Table 8.11).

Table 8.11 The structure of a training microcycle of the stage of immediate competitive preparation with complex combinations of training loads and restorative measures

Days of the Microcycle

Time	Variables	Day 1	Day 2	Day 3	Day 4	Day 5	Day 6	Day 7
AM AM AM AM	Type load/ Magnitude/ Restorative measures	Aerobic/ Medium/ Warm salt bath	Aerobic/ Medium Localised hand massage	Aerobic/ Light contrast rain-type shower, segmental massage	Aerobic/ Light Sauna, local hand massage	Aerobic/ Medium Localised hand massage	Aerobic/ Medium Warm salt bath	Aerobic/ Medium Contrast rain-type shower, segmental massage
PM PM PM PM	Type load/ Magnitude Restorative measures	Anaerobic/ Medium Warm pine bath, local hand massage with restorative balsams	Speed/ Heavy Indifferent equivalent bath, hydro-massage, warm rain shower	Anaerobic/ Heavy, Hot pine bath, Charcot shower (stream), local massage of the working muscles w/restorative balsams		Complex/ Heavy Warm pine bath, hydro-massage, warm rain-type shower	Complex/ Medium Warm equivalent bath, hot stream shower, local massage of working muscles	Complex/ Heavy Sauna, whole-body restora-tive massage, contrast procedures

451

Research into Restoration Methods

This is sometimes a tendency to dismiss the effects of many restorative means as placebo or psychological in origin. However, there has been a large amount of Russian research into the physiological effects of restoration, some of which is summarised here to correct this misconception.

For example, research into the effects of massage, in particular that massage indeed causes effects which are not simply placebo or circulatory in nature (Birukov & Pelsahov, 1979). They found different effects of massage on the central and peripheral systems, as well as differences in the effects produced by each different type of massage (Fig 8.5). In particular, the following findings are most noteworthy:

1. Massage does not have an identical effect on the central and peripheral systems of the body. The condition of the peripheral systems changes in the same direction, while the functional state of the brain changes over a much wider range, depending on the initial levels existing before the massage.

2. Individual massage methods change the condition of the separate subsystems of the body in different ways. The influence of individual massage techniques depends largely on the initial functional condition before the application of massage. It is important to understand these differences before one casually applies a standard or popular group of massage techniques.

3. Massage generally has a favourable influence on all subsystems of the body, optimising their state by increasing or decreasing the level of activation of the cortex and sub-cortical systems of the brain. It also changes the relationship between them in the overall process of central nervous regulation.

4. When using massage as a method of restructuring and restoring, it is necessary to differentiate the approach by taking into consideration the initial level of excitation. As discussed before, measures of factors such as simple reaction time, skin impedance, dynamometry and tonometry can be used as indicators of this state.

Research into the circulatory effects of massage by the injection of radioactive Xenon markers into the blood has shown that sports massage dilates the peripheral blood vessels, speeds up venous and muscle blood flow, and causes a small, but significant, increase in the oxygen saturation of arterial blood (Dubrovsky, 1982). Concurrent myotonometer measurements revealed a decrease in muscle tone, leading Dubrovsky to conclude that decrease in muscle tone caused by enhanced blood flow. The latter finding also emphasizes that mild active restoration offers some definite advantages over strictly passive methods on their own.

Marked differences have been noted between the effects of manual versus machine massage. For example, mechanical vibromassage (35-100 Hz) causes an acute decrease in blood circulation, associated with the vasoconstrictive effect of vibration (Burovykh et al, 1976). Moreover, the increase in muscle blood supply after manual massage is due primarily to dilation of the lumen of the small arterial vessels, rather than the popularly believed concept of venous drainage. This same research showed that increase in blood flow also relates to the tissue warming effects of some forms of massage, as well as showing a decrease in muscle temperature (0.5-1.0 deg C) due to vibromassage, indicating that the vibromassage-elicited decrease in blood flow may be a result of vasoconstriction.

These findings imply that deep manual massage is more effective for enhancing blood flow and relaxation than higher frequency vibromassage, which should be used for the reflexogenic application of stimulating the neuromuscular system. However, if one has access to a vibromassager whose frequency of vibration may be changed, lower frequencies (10-15 Hz) can be used to promote general restoration, blood flow, muscle relaxation and decreased arterial pressure, provided that care is taken not to apply it over nervous plexuses or prominent bony areas. Other findings emerging from this and related work are:

- Massage of the proximal, larger muscles before the distal muscles, if blood circulation is to be maximally encouraged.

- Deeper massage techniques (such as kneading and squeezing) should be used preferentially if one wishes to stimulate blood flow and muscle metabolism

- Percussive massage methods (such as chopping, tapping and slapping) stimulate the nervous system, raise venous pressure and diminish blood microcirculation, so they should not be used for relaxation or general restoration

- Reflexive massage (e.g. acupressure point, trigger point) techniques often produce a more marked and quicker recovery after training sessions, so that it may be unnecessary to rely solely on more conventional means, especially if restoration of the central nervous system is desired (Peshkov, 1981)

- Microcurrent application (Ch 4.2) applied either locally or across the central nervous system can exert a marked influence on different aspects of physiological and psychological stress. Local microstimulation or electrical acupressure point stimulation can accelerate recovery and tissue repair, while central microstimulation (or, central electroanalgesia) across the skull and spinal column can be extremely helpful in resolving nervous stresses, including sleep disturbances, impaired motor control, increased blood pressure, resting pulse rate and exercise-related electrocardiographic disturbances (Shidlovsky et al, 1979).

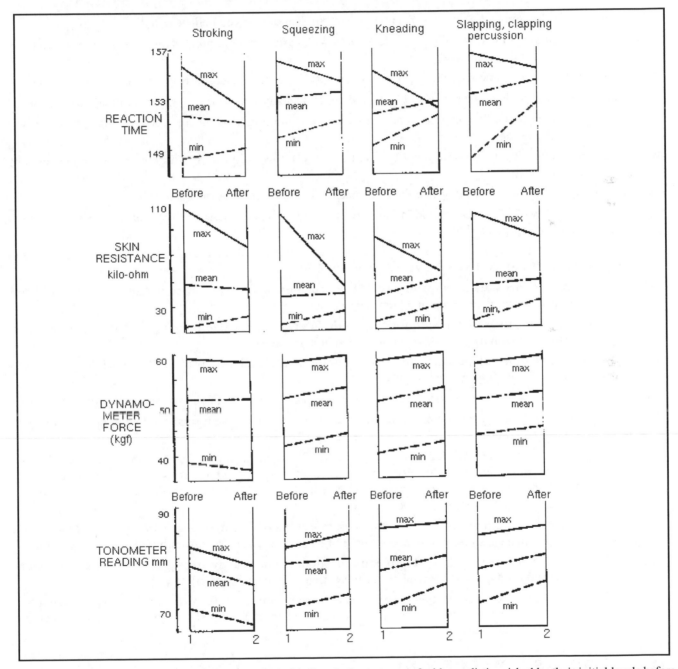

Figure 8.5 Dynamics of the psychological-physiological indices in three groups of athletes, distinguished by their initial levels before and after massage--2. I -- Reaction times over 24 hours; II -- Skin resistance in kohm; III --Dynamometer in kg force; IV -- Tonometry reading in mm. Solid top line--Maximum indices before massage; Middle line--Mean indices; Dashed lowest line--Minimal indices before massage.

Sports Science and Stress Management

Much earlier in this book we learned that all training is a form of stressing the body in an optimal manner to enable the body to adapt to the high levels of stress of competitive sport. Many of these sports training principles and adaptation theory are very useful in helping one cope with physical and mental stress both in and away from the competitive arena or training venue. *Superadaptation* (supercompensation) or *innoculation* against specific stresses is possible by exposing yourself to properly structured doses of manageable stress. Russian methods of training Olympic champions may be used by all of us to enhance our quality of life. Very significantly, stress avoidance can make you more vulnerable to future stresses. The following list of methods that have been assembled largely from previous chapters of this text offer some useful insights into the management of stress.

1. Virtually any technique will work, irrespective of scientific validity, if you believe in it.

2. A technique that is obtained at high cost in terms of effort, cash or commitment is more likely to work than one that is obtained at little or no cost.

3. A technique that is taught or acquired in an exciting, emotional or challenging way is more likely to be successful.

4. A technique that appeals to the basic beliefs, prejudices and background of the user is more likely to succeed.

5. No technique is universally superior to another: a given technique is better for a given individual in a given situation at a given time.

6. Stress is not static, but a dynamic physiological and psychological process which needs to be managed by dynamic techniques.

7. In managing stress you must not ignore the influence of your subconscious or superconscious.

8. To improve quality of life, each individual must optimise, though not necessarily avoid or diminish stress in any given situation at any given time.

9. The concept of stress optimisation is not always accurate: high performance may occur with altered states of consciousness when stress levels are very high or very low.

10. Regular exposure to a stressor may produce either adaptation or sensitisation, so that the same level of stress may not produce the same response at a later stage.

11. Initial response to stress may result not only in flight or fight, but also freezing, or temporary mental or physical paralysis, which may be the most damaging effect of stress.

12. The existence of supercompensatory processes implies that planned exposure to manageable stresses may enable one to cope with higher levels of stress.

13. An understanding of movement (kinaesthetic and motor) processes is invaluable to the management of stress.

14. Stress produces physiological and psychological reactions, so that it may be managed by use of physiological or psychological techniques.

15. Our perception or interpretation of stress or pain may be more powerful than the stress, pain or stimulus itself. Therefore, alteration of our perceptions and thoughts may manage the stress effectively. In particular, we should understand that our perception or assessment of the attractiveness or repulsiveness of the stressor can alter our belief that the stressor can be managed.

16. The mind may be viewed to handle information in four ways (Carl Jung): *sensation, intuition, thinking* and *feeling*, so we can manage stress in any one or more of these ways to suit the given individual and situation.

17. The left-right or vertical-lateral models of brain functioning limit our awareness that several major regions, besides the left and right cortical hemispheres, can be used to manage stress effectively.

18. Evidence from the great philosophers and sages of the world indicates that we may not be simply independent living systems: we may have access to a vast seldom-tapped source of energy via specific altered states of consciousness.

8.7 The Use of Testing

The role of appropriate testing has been mentioned throughout this text, based on a clear understanding of the differences between laboratory tests of work capacity and the functional or field tests of fitness and preparedness (see 1.4). It has been stated that the most specific test of all is performance in the actual sporting event. All other tests have varying degrees of correlation with performance or selected actions in the given sport.

It is relevant to summarise what my Canadian colleague, Dr Duncan Mc Dougall, has to say about the value of suitable, well-planned tests (Mc Dougall et al, 1982):

1. They identify individual strengths and weaknesses and provide data for determining the baseline for training programmes.
2. They provide feedback on the effectiveness of training programmes.
3. They provide information on the athlete's state of health
4. They provide an educational process which teaches the athlete to understand more competently his/her body and the demands of the sport.

It is equally important to heed his remarks on the scope and limitations of testing , which so often tend to be ignored by sports scientists whose main role appears to be research publications rather than practical application of the data:

"Laboratory testing is not a magical tool for predicting future gold medallists. It has severe limitations for identifying potential talent in that scientists still do not know how to determine 'genetic limits' and therefore cannot predict potential to improve. For example, the use of muscle biopsies to estimate muscle fiber types and thus predict endurance or power performance is highly questionable....

The complete performance of any athlete is a composite of many different factors of which physiological function is only one. It is therefore unwise to attempt to predict performance from any single physiological test or battery of physiological tests - especially in sports where technical, tactical, and psychological components may relegate physiology to a lesser role. Similarly, in the selection of athletes for competition or for teams, physiological tests should only augment information which is available on actual performances or field observations".

In addition, McDougall identifies 7 characteristics of an effective testing programme (McDougall et al, 1982):

1. The variables which are tested must be directly relevant to the given sport
2. The tests must be valid (test what it claims to), reliable and reproducible
3. The testing procedures must be as sport specific as possible
4. The testing situation must be rigidly controlled
5. Testing must be repeated at regular, appropriate intervals
6. The tests must respect the athlete's human rights (including ethics, confidentiality and risks)
7. The results must be interpreted in understandable language directly to the athlete and coach.

It is not the intention of this section to reiterate what has already been written by several authorities in the field of testing. Instead, the reader is encouraged to consult texts such as that of McDougall and his colleagues for further details of the more popular types of sports testing (Mc Dougall et al, 1982). We simply wish to provide information which is not readily available.

The Vertical Jump Test

This well-known test may be applied in several different ways. Invariably it requires the subject to leap from a standing position with a preliminary dip and touch a measuring device sideways with one's dominant hand. Recalling the specificity of training, it is important to note that the results of this test correlate best with conditions which are most similar to that of the test. Therefore, it is useful to repeat the test with the non-dominant hand or in the frontal plane with the athlete using both hands to reach for the target. Moreover, there are several different initial conditions for executing this test:

1. Starting statically from an optimum knee flexed position using no arm swing
2. Starting statically from an optimum knee flexed position using arm swing
3. Starting statically from sitting on a low seat using (a) no arm swing, or (b) arm swing
4. Starting dynamically with an optimal knee dip using no arm swing
5. Starting dynamically with an optimal knee dip using arm swing.

The major difference between the first two methods is that jumping without arm-swing is intended to focus primarily on the role played by extension of the lower extremity and trunk, without the picture being confounded by the use of arm momentum. The major difference between the static and dynamic starts is that the absence of an initial sharp dip allows one to focus more on starting strength and the role played by the contractile (actin-myosin) component of the muscle complex, instead of the more plyometric rebound action encouraged by the use of the dip. This can sometimes assist one in ascertaining whether the athlete needs more strength (or functional hypertrophy) training or more rebound, nervous system training.

It can also be helpful to perform the static tests from different initial knee angles to obtain a profile of individual jumping characteristics. For example, if the maximum vertical jump is attained for a fairly large knee angle, which is generally associated with a slower overall jumping time from start to finish of the action, then it is obvious that the athlete needs to concentrate on modifying his range and speed of maximal strength production.

Table 8.12 provides guidelines concerning the depth of loaded knee dips. This reveals that the dip characteristically is deeper for heavier loads or persons and that in all cases the pause during the dip should not last longer than 0.25 second. Herein lies the benefit of performing push jerks or jerks off racks with different weights as a form of supplementary plyometric training. After all, plyometric training is of little value if it fails to enhance adequately explosive strength or power over the range required in a given activity. The use of drills which do not correlate strongly with the functional needs of a given sport constitute one of the most common errors in popular plyometric training.

Table 8.12 Parameters of the Jerk Phase of the Olympic Clean-and-Jerk (Vorobyev, 1978)

Weight of Bar (kg)	Duration of dip (secs)	Depth of Dip (cm)	Duration of Pause in Dip (secs)	Duration of Jerk (secs)
120 -140	0.15 - 0.20	5 - 8	0.00 - 0.15	0.15 - 0.20
160 - 180	0.20 - 0.30	8 - 10	0.00 - 0.20	0.20 - 0.25
200 - 220	0.40 - 0.50	10 - 15	0.00 - 0.25	0.25 - 0.35

In the context of the above research, it is important to note that measurements were performed with the use of an Olympic weightlifting bar, so that the values of the parameters during the pause and jerk phase will be different for other training bars. It has been found that *optimal interaction between bar and lifter occurs when the frequency of oscillation of the bar is twice that of the lifter's movement* (Vorobyev, 1978).

Guidelines concerning the vertical jump height for different levels of competitive weightlifter may be obtained from Table 8.13. The individual results for some of the subjects is noteworthy. Former high jump world record holder, Valery Brumel, had a best vertical jump of 102 cm, while the Superheavyweight champion weightlifter, Zhabotinski, could reach a maximum of 91cm, despite his enormous bodymass (over 140kg). In other words, these competitors displayed exceptional absolute vertical jumps, as well as excellent relative vertical jumps (height per unit bodymass) and leg power.

Table 8.13 Mean dynamic start Vertical Jump for Olympic Weightlifters from all divisions (Vorobyev, 1978)

Class of Lifter	Vertical Jump (cm)
Novice	57.3
Class III	58.1
Class II	65.3
Class I	67.8
Master of Sport	72.3
Elite	85.5

Muscle Strength Ratios

Some testing examines the strength of certain paired 'agonist-antagonist' muscle groups relative to one another in attempts to identify apparent muscle imbalances, the most commonly quoted being the 60:40 ratio of knee extension to knee flexion strength (i.e. extensors 1.5 times stronger than flexors). The limitations associated with this type of measurement have been discussed earlier (Section 4.2.6.2). It just remains to add that these ratios not only vary with joint angle, joint velocity and type of movement, but also with muscle group and the type of athlete. For instance, the relative isometric strength (per 1kg bodymass) of the larger extensor muscles in Olympic weightlifters is 11.51 ± 1.78, and for the major flexors it is 4.02 ± 0.69 (Vorobyev, 1978). In general, their major extensors are on average 2.86 times stronger than their major flexors, a figure which is very different

SUPERTRAINING

from the isokinetic value of 1.5 cited by sports physiotherapists for the average person (whatever this entity might be).

Among the best Russian weightlifters the relative maximum strength of extensors to flexors is as follows: arms 1.6:1, trunk 4.3:1, thighs 4.3:1, and lower leg 5.4:1. The application of these findings on their own to sport or rehabilitation is incomplete and must be accompanied by the profile of strength produced at important joint angles in every given sport, in accordance with the principle of dynamic correspondence, especially the accentuated region of force production (Section 4.3).

Work Capacity and Functional Pressure Tests

Various tests were discussed earlier (Chapter 6.2.2) under the heading "Training Intensity, Heart Rate and Other Tests" to introduce tests which can be helpful in assessing physical work capacity in strength athletes and this information should be regarded as an extension of that earlier material.

One of the other methods used by Russian coaches is the cardiac function Shtanga Functional Pressure test to ascertain if the athlete is overtraining (described by Vyurberg, 1953). Because it involves breath holding and rapid expulsion of air, this test is regarded as being particularly suitable for athletes like Olympic weightlifters and wrestlers, whose sports require them to strain against heavy resistance. This test requires the athlete to breath in relaxed fashion for a few minutes, then inhaling maximally and holding the breath for 15-20 seconds before stopping the nose and exhaling as forcibly as possible for 2 seconds. This action is accompanied by a sharp rise in intrathoracic pressure and diminished flow of blood to the heart.

Blood pressure is measured before the test (BP1), immediately afterwards (BP2), and after 2 minutes of relaxed breathing (BP3), since the purpose of this test is to analyse changes in blood pressure (BP). Systolic blood pressure increases significantly during the recuperation stage after the disturbance in cardiac activity by the test. If the contractile processes of the myocardium are normal, as in the well-prepared athlete who is not exhibiting chronic fatigue, the blood pressure decreases briefly by 5-10mm Hg.

Research conducted by Ulchenko (1982) among elite weightlifters during their specific preparation stage for competition applied this test in the following manner:

Test 1: BP1, BP2 and BP3 measured before training

Test 2: The same three BP measures were taken during the most intense training loading

This work produced the following interpretations of the findings

1. BP decrease after Test 1 or no change after Test 2. This is regarded as an excellent reaction.
2. BP increase of up to 5mm Hg immediately after Test 2 and recovery of normal BP after 2 minutes rest. This is considered to be a good reaction.
3. BP increase of up to 7mm Hg after Test 2 and 5 minutes recovery time. This is regarded as satisfactory.
4. BP increase of 10mm Hg or more after Test 2 and prolonged elevation of BP afterwards. This is regarded as an unsatisfactory response and is associated with an overtraining state.

The individual results for one of the weightlifters involved in this study is very instructional. This athlete reported feeling fit and strong and his RPE (Rating of Perceived Effort) was low during non-maximal loads (with exercises including clean pulls and back squats), but the Shtanga Test revealed that the actual functional state of the lifter was below par. The results for his analysis were:

Test 1: BP1 was 130/70, BP2 was 140/75 and BP3 was 135/70. The 10mm increase in BP after the pressure test was regarded as unsatisfactory.

Test 2: BP1 was 140/66, BP2 was 160/70 and BP3 was 142/70. The 20mm increase in BP after the pressure test significantly exceeded the initial value and this also indicated an unsatisfactory response.

Interestingly, this lifter and several others whose pressure tests were deemed to be unacceptable did not improve their results in the competition which followed these tests and their coaches were advised to modify their training programmes until the pressure tests indicated a better functional state.

Ulchenko remarked that, contrary to what some coaches believe, diligent observation of cardiovascular function may certainly be relevant to the Olympic weightlifter and other strength athletes. He considered that this is especially important, since the type of loading encountered in these sports involves straining, breath-holding and high nervous tension which, in the presence of even small disturbances in functioning of the cardiovascular system, can aggravate the situation. He, therefore, strongly advised the regular application of this pressure test to identify the existence of any latent changes which may be taking place in the athlete's work capacity. He stated that the underlying cause of this diminished functional state is certainly due to weakening of the heart's contractile ability and that it would be useful to apply the pressure test as an almost daily routine to ensure that the training regime is not causing overtraining.

It is noteworthy that subjective assessments by the athlete (including RPE) did not accurately reveal his functional state, which emphasizes the importance of administering both objective and subjective tests (see Ch 6.2.2), especially if one wishes to ensure the appropriateness of a given periodisation scheme for any athlete.

8.8 Injury and Safety in Strength Training

The design of any exercise programme would be incomplete without serious attention being paid to all aspects of safety in training, including safety of the means and methods of training, the individual exercises, the combination of exercises, the intensity, the volume of exercise, the timing of training loads, and the recovery periods (between repetitions, sets and sessions). An otherwise carefully-devised training programme is of little value if it causes injury to the athlete.

Injuries may be caused by accident or overtraining. The former often depends on factors which lie outside the direct control of the athlete and concern dangers arising unexpectedly in the environment or through the actions of other competitors. Nevertheless, thorough physical preparation, astute situation analysis, training of reactive ability, efficient ongoing interpretation of feedback from cues provided by other players or the environment, and good anticipation can prove invaluable in minimising the risks posed by accident or unexpected events in sport.

At the very outset, let us reiterate what has been said before: *There is no such thing as a dangerous exercise .... There is only a dangerous way of doing any exercise.* Is this a valid general rule? While it is very often true, we also have to note that:

* Injury is often a cumulative process
* The most recent exercise or activity can be the final trigger
* Injuries may be the result of "too much, too soon" of a safe thing (overtraining)
* Injuries may be caused by inadequate pre-exercise preparation ("warm-up")
* Accidents happen
* Cause and effect are not linearly related
* Individual responses to exercise are different
* Injuries are context or situation dependent

This leads us to state some *fundamental principles of the injury process*:

* Injuries are not necessarily determinate, predictable and preventable
* Causes of acute traumatic injury are more readily identifiable
* Causes of insidious injury are much more hypothetical
* Injury can be minimised, but not entirely prevented
* Injury and Adaptation are both the result of stress. No stress - no progress - no injury !
* There is no sharp zone of distinction between safety and danger, balance and imbalance.

The common belief of "the more training the better" or "no gain without pain" has persisted since ancient times, largely as a result of the notion that increasing levels of success demand more work and pain. This often unfortunate principle sometimes continues to be imposed on misguided athletes either by themselves or by uninformed coaches, since they maintain that the optimum training load is the maximum training load a person can endure without injury.

The more enlightened coaches have modified this archaic system in a more sensible direction. They consider that 'the more training the better' principle is still sound provided that a person commences training at low intensity and continually increases intensity and duration within individual limits of endurance and the time available. Their new package includes stretching exercises, as they believe that lack of suppleness is the major non-traumatic cause of injuries. They, together with several medical experts, assert that there is no clinical condition identifiable as overtraining and that the term 'overtraining injury' more precisely should be applied to damage caused by lack of suppleness, faulty technique, inappropriate footwear and so on.

As we shall learn in more detail later, *overtraining* classically is categorised as follows: *overload* (too large a load at any given instant - "too heavy") and *overuse* (too large a quantity of work or exercise - "too much")

The fact remains that the equivalent of overtraining and overtraining injuries is well known in physics and engineering, under much the same categories as those just described - damage resulting either from too great a load at any given instant or too great an amount of work being imposed upon a given system. Very large forces due to the imposition of either large masses or large accelerations can lead to rapid failure of any mechanical system (remembering that large force may be the result of large mass or large acceleration or both, according to Newton's 2nd Law: Force = Mass x Acceleration).

The frequent application of moderate forces or the occasional application of large, impulsive forces can cause metal fatigue, structural failure or general deterioration of some or many of the components of a system. This is the reason why all cars, machines and structures require regular inspection and maintenance. The human body, however, performs a great deal, but not all, of its own repair (most of it during periods of what we call passive or active "rest", "restoration" or "recuperation"). Small injuries are accompanied by the usual internal bleeding and the formation of scar tissue, which eventually restores most or all of the original functioning of the damaged part. Larger injuries often require surgical intervention, but whatever the extent of the injury, it is clear that structural weakening or failure of an engineering system has its parallel in the human body, whether it be called 'overtraining injury', 'overuse injury' or something else.

It would then possibly appear as if overtraining is the sole cause of non-accidental training injuries, whereas undertraining is safe and merely leads to lack of progress. This is only partly true. Consistent undertraining, which never familiarizes the athlete with high stress levels or the so-called 'pain-barrier', may expose him to risk during the excitement of a competition. Moreover, undertraining accompanied by faulty technique, drug usage, inadequate sleep, poor nutrition or the use of unsuitable equipment can also lead to injury.

It is. also misleading to categorically classify specific movements as dangerous. Many manoeuvres which necessitate a high degree of skill or courage should undoubtedly be labelled as intrinsically dangerous for the average person, but not for the expert performer. There are safe and dangerous ways of executing virtually every human movement, including sitting, standing and walking. Moreover, all exercise imposes a certain type and degree of stress on specific parts of the body. Hence, if one considers the type of stress and the integrity of the body structure involved, a useful categorization of exercise emerges (Fig 8.6).

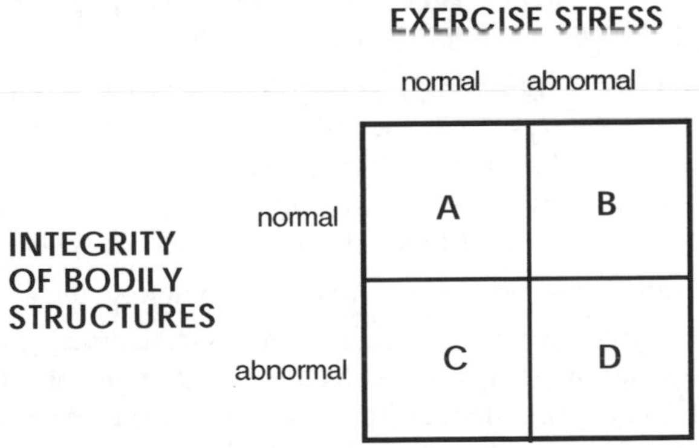

EXERCISE STRESS

	normal	abnormal
normal	A	B
abnormal	C	D

INTEGRITY OF BODILY STRUCTURES

Figure 8.6 Classification of exercises in terms of levels of stress (Siff, 1984)

For want of more descriptive terms, the terms 'normal and 'abnormal' have been used. 'Normality' is always a relative expression and here it applies at a specific time to the individual, whose structure imposes a certain range of efficient, injury-free operation. 'Abnormal' stress in this context refers generally to loading of excessive duration, magnitude or inappropriate movement pattern, where 'excessive' refers to loading that is at or beyond certain limits of the athlete's current level of structural or functional adaptation. A structure of 'abnormal' integrity is one which is unprepared, injured, diseased, genetically unsound, fatigued, or generally impaired in structure or function at a given time (Siff, 1984).

Safety of exercise can be considerably enhanced if one ensures that activity very rarely falls outside category A, except to permit astute application of the principle of gradual progressive overload (Fig 8.6). This entails a thorough familiarity with general principles of kinesiology and the specific capabilities of the individual at any given time.

This section focuses largely on category B exercise (abnormal stress on normal structures) encountered in non-contact sports, mainly because this is the most frequently underestimated type of unsafe exercise.

Overtraining is entirely controllable by the athlete and may be avoided if he/she recognises that it may be produced in two ways:

- *Overuse* - the imposition of excessive loading in terms of duration or volume
- *Overload* - the imposition of an excessively heavy load or intensity of exercise.

Both types of overtraining can be avoided if the athlete remembers to plan, record and monitor the volume (repetitions, sets and rest periods in resistance training; duration and distance in running and other cyclic activities) and intensity (maximum weight used; time or speed in running, etc.).   Remember that we noted in the previous section the modern distinction being made between acute 'over-exercise' (*overreaching*) and chronic 'over-exercise' (*overtraining*).

Biomechanical Models of the Injury Process

The different proneness to injury by individuals is not always appreciated by athletes and their coaches, largely because genetic or structural susceptibility to damage is not easy to measure. Injury proneness depends on a variety of factors including inherent muscle, tendon and ligament strength and mechanical stiffness (not the same as the "stiffness" relating to limitation in range of movement); the ratio of 'functional' force/torque production between so-called 'agonistic' and 'antagonistic' muscles; limb leverages; and previous injury.

The fundamental principle of animal motion is that *all activity is the result of balance between stability and mobility* in the body, with safety relying heavily on how efficiently this dynamic balance is controlled in all sporting movements. All sporting performance and training involve the learning and perfection of processes which produce the appropriate and effective interaction of mechanisms which stabilise and those which mobilise the joints from instant to instant during a given activity.   As discussed in the next section, certain muscles act in a phasic role as prime movers or assistant movers, while others act in a tonic or postural role as stabilisers. Sometimes the roles of the muscles will interchange during certain activities and stabilisers will become movers and vice versa. The balance between stability and mobility depends on the neuromuscular integration of factors such as strength, endurance and range of movement, as well as the mechanical properties of the tissues involved (in particular, mechanical stiffness and damping ratio). This process is summarised graphically in Figure 3.

Neuromuscular processes, including the various reflexes of the body, orchestrate the overall interplay between stability and mobility to produce motor skill. Range of movement and stiffness are intimately related to flexibility, where the 'stiffness' referred to here is the mechanical stiffness of the tissues comprising the muscle complex (the spring constant k in the Hooke's Law equation relating force F to extension x: $F = k.x$) and not 'joint stiffness' which is a popular synonym for inflexibility or limited range of movement. Stiffness also determines the ability of the deformable tissues to store elastic energy ($EE = \frac{1}{2} k.x^2$). Damping efficiency, the ability to absorb and dissipate shock or vibration, plays a major role in the storage and utilisation of elastic energy, as well as the prevention of injury during activities involving rapid acceleration and deceleration. Although only strength is illustrated in the figure, the term includes all the different types of strength, while endurance refers to both muscular endurance and cardiovascular endurance, factors which relate directly to the onset of fatigue during stabilisation or mobilisation.

The relationship between stability and mobility forms a vital part of physiotherapeutic PNF (proprioceptive neuromuscular facilitation), whose means and methods of physical conditioning may be extended to offer an extensive system of strength training (Fig 8.7).

The role of mechanical stiffness of the soft tissues in overtraining injuries may be appreciated by examining the behaviour of two ideal springs of different stiffness stretching as a result of absorbing the same amount of energy (Fig 8.8).

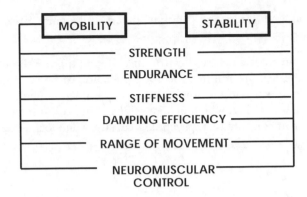

Figure 8.7 The interrelation between stability and mobility in human activity (see Ch 1).

The stiffer spring A, in absorbing the energy E, is forced to its elastic limit at a, whereas the less stiff spring B extends further to C, but reaches nowhere near its elastic limit at b. It is possible, too, that certain individuals may have similar tissue stiffness but higher elastic limits. Again, the result will be a superior ability to absorb energy as imposed for instance .on the soft tissues of the knee by running, jumping or squatting (Siff 1982a, b). This analysis is particularly relevant to an understanding of tendon injuries, since much of the muscle activity in running is associated with tensioning of the tendons to store energy, a process which involves little length change in the muscle fibres themselves (Alexander et al, 1967).

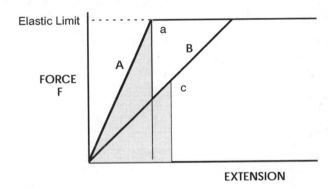

Figure 8.8 Force-extension behaviour of two ideal springs of different stiffness absorbing the same amount of energy E. The elastic limit is the same for both springs. The shaded area up to a is the same as the shaded area up to c and represents the energy absorbed, E (Siff 1982a, b)

Instead of referring solely to "overtraining injuries" it might be more valuable to talk of "exercise imbalance injuries". Such a term would embrace any form of unbalanced training, be it excessive, drug assisted or technically faulty.

The occurrence of "exercise imbalance injuries" may then be described scientifically on the basis of a qualitative topological model, called Catastrophe Theory by its inventor, Prof Rene Thom (Woodcock & Davis, 1980). Theories which consider overtraining to be a gradual, continuous change from health to injury do not adequately describe the abrupt appearance of some overtraining injuries.

Catastrophe theory uses abstract multi-dimensional surfaces to describe such changes of state. It provides a behaviour surface, something like a buckled carpet, whose characteristics (such as its shape) are determined by one or more control dimensions. In the case of joint or general body stability the behaviour surface describes the state of health of the joint or body. The nature of this behaviour surface may be regarded as depending on the following four control factors:

Structural Predisposition to Injury: This depends on heredity, structural changes caused by previous exercise, earlier injuries, ageing and so on.

Technique Stress: This is stress caused by faulty technique, posture and equipment, including footwear.

Physical Stress: This concerns the exercise load and frequency, current illness, adequacy of sleep, and environmental conditions (such as temperature and altitude).

Psychological Stress: There are several different types of catastrophe structure, depending on the number of behaviour and control dimensions. In the case under discussion there is one dimension of behaviour (state of health) and the four control dimensions given above, so that the appropriate system would be a "butterfly catastrophe". To depict this requires a 5 - dimensional drawing, which is impossible. However, if the four control dimensions are reduced to two by keeping two of them constant (e.g. psychological stress and technique stress), a useful version of the "butterfly" surface may be sketched (Fig 8.9).

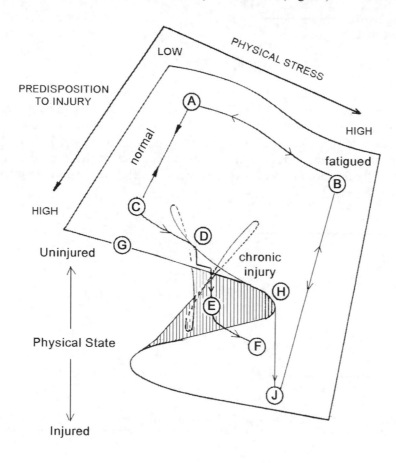

Figure 8.9 Butterfly Catastrophe Model of the Injury Process (Siff 1982a, b)

Consider someone with a predisposition to injury. This athlete's state before commencing exercise will be represented by point A. As the level of physical stress increases, so will the body progress towards a state of exhaustion at B. The natural tendency then will be to relax slightly to a more comfortable level back along path AB towards the initial state A, then to produce re-exertion and repeat the process back and forth within the limits of individual endurance.

A person with a very high predisposition to injury may begin exercising in a state G and without suffering undue stress may reach the threshold H. Any small increase in training load, however, may precipitate him without significant physical warning into the injured state at J. This is vital to remember, since damage may be occurring constantly and insidiously without producing pain signals. Often pain occurs when it is too late to take evasive action. This is especially true of the cumulative damage caused by years of executing very stressful exercises in terms of either intensity, volume or both.

The extent and location of the butterfly fold depends on the individual and may be influenced, for example, by appropriate supplementary training, medical treatment or ergogenic aids (drugs or supplements).

Consider now the individual who may begin a sporting career in a state C. Under moderate stress this athlete may progress to the critical point D and become trapped for prolonged periods in a region of the butterfly fold in

462

a state of chronic injury which rest or medical attention may rectify, but only as long as the stressful activity which caused the injury is discontinued.

The person with very low predisposition to injury is not necessarily immune to overtraining or exercise imbalance injury. For instance, he may ignore the usual symptoms of exhaustion while approaching state B and progress towards an injured state such as F. This type of individual, characterized by intense motivation, may even shift the body's initial state from A towards C or increase the extent of the fold by training in a state of residual stress caused by inadequate rest.

Different combinations of any two control dimensions may be selected as the variables instead of "predisposition to injury" and "physical stress". In this way the athlete and coach can appreciate the importance of the four control dimensions (given earlier) in planning a training routine to minimize occurrence of exercise imbalance or overtraining injuries. The athlete should rely on objective and subjective tests to identify personal characteristic paths of operation on the behaviour surface and avoid exercising or competing too close to the catastrophe fold (Siff 1982a, b).

General Biomechanical Causes of Injury

The general biomechanical causes of injury may be summarised as follows:

1. The force or stress component (force per unit area of tissue) on some part of the body is excessive in a particular direction (this may be caused by very large mass or very large acceleration)
2. The torque or moment about a certain pivot or joint is excessive
3. Momentum is too great to be adequately utilised or dissipated
4. The work load or energy involved over a given period is excessive
5. The power generated by the muscles is excessive at a particular instant
6. The strain (change in relative length, $\Delta L/L$) in any tissues is excessive
7. The mechanical properties of any given tissues are inadequate to handle the loading
8. The Rate of Force Development (RFD) is excessive at a particular instant
9. Frictional forces are too large (mat burns or jerkiness) or too small (slipping)

These general categories may be expanded to identify some more specific causes of injury:

- Inappropriate warming up (pre-activity preparation) or stretching
- Inappropriate or inefficient patterns of movement
- Unsafe use of momentum to execute a movement
- Excessive range of movement for a particular joint
- Inappropriate phases of muscular tension or relaxation
- Use of inappropriate soft tissues for a particular action
- Magnitude of acceleration or deceleration is too great
- Imposition of an excessive load on any part of the body
- Use of inappropriate sequences of exercises
- Excessive exertion during exhaustion, distress, illness or injury
- Use of inadequate rest, recovery time or methods of recuperation
- Use of inappropriate or faulty equipment
- Excessive impact forces on body parts making contact with an object or surface
- Inappropriate or inefficient breathing patterns
- Excessive duration of any activity.
- Inability to effectively interpret and use proprioceptive and other sensory feedback
- Inability to effectively visualize, predict or use feedforward
- Inefficient use of breathing or breath-holding patterns

With particular reference to injuries produced by inefficient patterns of movement, one must appreciate that deviations from normal patterns may be caused by:

- Pain, soreness, stiffness or discomfort
- Muscle weakness or imbalance between muscle groups

- Any limitation in the range of joint range of movement in any direction
- Uncoordinated movement
- Musculoskeletal changes
- Fatigue
- Changes in surface, footwear, equipment or environment
- Neural changes
- Visual or balance changes
- Emotional disturbance.

It is necessary to dispel the belief that all injuries are accompanied by pain. In many cases, such as disintegration of cartilages and hyperflexion damage to the spine, the onset of pain may occur only once the injury has become extensive or serious. Microruptures of soft tissue or similar minor injuries may be unheralded by pain signals until they have accumulated over a sufficiently long period to incapacitate the athlete. Overtraining or regular impact (e.g. caused by running on hard surfaces or by blows to the head in contact sports) are associated with this insidious type of injury process. Individual perception of pain differs markedly among individuals or under different emotional or fatigue states, so that it is unreliable to use the perception of pain to assess the safety of any exercise.

However, it should be noted that the perception of pain by the central nervous system (CNS) can reorganise the motor control system to minimise the pain, which can result in reflex inhibition of the muscles to exert maximal strength and thereby lead to muscle weakness (Stokes & Young, 1984). In fact, even if the injury is not accompanied by pain, this can also occur. This is very common with even relatively insubstantial injuries of the knee such as patellar tendinitis, peripatellar pain syndrome or chondromalacia patellae, which significantly reduce the ability of the quadriceps to produce powerful contraction. It is possible that the pain caused by muscle swelling or delayed onset muscle soreness (DOMS) may also provoke the CNS into responding with alternative motor programs which distribute force production over a larger number of muscle fibres and diminish the efficiency and magnitude of strength output (Stauber, 1989). The importance of dealing with even minor pain, soreness or injury then becomes obvious.

In the light of current paranoia about the dangers of certain exercises, it is vital to appreciate that the *lack of safety in exercise is not simply a consequence of so-called dangerous exercises, but also one of unsafe execution of any exercise*. Exercise safety must always be viewed in the context of the overall training session or programme for each specific individual. While certain exercises may be intrinsically less safe for the relative novice to training, they may pose minimal risks for the same person after several months of training. Conversely, the least demanding and simplest of exercises may cause serious injury to an elite athlete who is careless, unmotivated or overtrained.

For beginners it is undoubtedly preferable to err on the side of conservatism. In doing so, one should remember that religious avoidance of certain exercises can lead to an overall imbalance between muscle groups or in motor coordination and increase the likelihood of injury during the sports event. Furthermore, the avoidance of exercising a muscle group in a particular way never enhances safety; it simply weakens those muscles relative to the exercise pattern which is avoided.

Injury Prevention by Imperfection Training

The occurrence of injury is partly related to the philosophy of injury prevention. Currently, the emphasis is placed almost exclusively on prevention by means of avoidance of so-called 'dangerous' exercises and excessive volumes or intensities of loading. Unfortunately, this approach is limited in that it tends to neglect the vital aspect of preparation to cope with less than optimal training and competitive situations. *All-round sports training must include the capability of coping with unexpected and sub-optimal conditions.* In certain sports where accidents or unexpected situations often occur, such as the martial arts, parachuting and motor racing, participants are taught how to cope with events that can have serious consequences. This type of preparation needs to be adopted far more extensively in all sports so that the athlete is able to anticipate threatening situations, react much more rapidly to unexpected circumstances, take action to avoid or minimise injury, and cope with sub-optimal conditions by practising with imperfectly executed movements.

These strategies are rarely invoked, but they should be a standard item in the training repertoire of every athlete. After all, it is rarely possible to produce perfection of movement every time or to balance one's training loads very precisely, so it is logical to programme the nervous system and brain to respond with effective contingency actions whenever imperfections of movement or accidents occur. For instance, it is not unusual to witness Russian weightlifters holding a snatch overhead in the low squat position and shifting in different directions to move the bar into unstable positions which they are then compelled to control by astute postural adjustments.

In general, exercise safety is largely a consequence of skill development (neuromuscular efficiency) and may be enhanced by imposing activities which progress carefully with respect to factors such as complexity, intensity, volume, speed, range of movement, duration, variety, level of fatigue and mental state.

8.9 Safety and Training Apparel

8.9.1 Lifting, Belts and Breathing

The weightlifting belt has persisted in its existing form ever since Olympic Weightlifting emerged as a sport. Those who use it claim that it definitely supports the back; those who do not, state categorically that their backs are strong enough not to rely on external support. Many lifters believe that a belt is necessary for the clean-and-jerk alone, even though in the snatch their backs are being called upon to support more than three-quarters of the weight lifted in the jerk. Some authorities regard the benefits of the belt to be mainly psychological.

Who is correct? What is the truth behind use of the lifting belt? To answer these questions, it is necessary to analyse the physiology and biomechanics of the trunk during lifting, as well as the traditional design of the present belt.

Some lifters assert that the belt helps keeps the flat. This claim is definitely not accurate, because we all see lifters rounding their backs even when they are wearing thick, wide belts. Strong muscles and not strong belts keep your back flat. Relaxation of your back muscles causes you to impose much greater stress on the ligaments and intervertebral discs of your back. No amount of belt support is going to solve this problem.

In one sense, however, a belt can assist you in keeping your back flat - not by lending support, but rather by creating an awareness of the direction of curvature of your lower back. In this respect, you are relying on what may be called your sixth sense, the sense called proprioception by physiologists. This is the sense that gives you information about the position of the body and its parts; tension in the muscles, tendons and other soft tissues; pressure on the skin; and physical balance. When you are wearing a belt, its pressure exerted on the skin and muscles below it tells you a lot about the tension in the muscles, the pressure in your abdomen and the straightness of your back. For this reason alone, it is probably a good idea to wear a belt during occasional maximal attempts, although it is not a good idea to rely entirely on a belt without learning how to position your back correctly and tense the right muscles at the right time. Belts per se do not weaken the trunk musculature; it is only if one persists in relying on a tightly worn belt for long periods that this possibility may occur.

What about the contention that a belt will support your back? A belt actually plays a relatively minor role in directly supporting any load that you may hold overhead, other than limiting the tendency to hyperextend the lumbar spine during the lifting. Your muscles do this job by keeping your skeleton in the correct supportive posture and the downward force is exerted through the joints (including ligaments, cartilages and discs) to the platform. The air in your lungs plays a vital role in this process.

Many medical and other authorities state that one should never hold the breath when training with weights. This well-meaning, but misinformed, advice can lead to serious injury. While it is advisable during many exercises to inhale before the effort and exhale with the effort, without holding the breath, it is important to hold the breath briefly while raising any load in the standing position. As discussed earlier (3.4.9), this is essential because the breath-holding (or Valsalva) manoeuvre increases the pressure in your abdomen and supports your lower spine. Without breath-holding, far greater pressure is exerted on vulnerable structures of the lumbar spine, in particular the intervertebral discs and ligaments. Prolonged breath-holding (of more than a few seconds) causes dramatic increase in blood-pressure, followed by sudden drop in this pressure after exhalation, so it is definitely not advisable for anyone, particularly older folk and those with cardiovascular disease.

What has all this to do with the lifting belt? Without a belt, the pressure within the abdomen stimulates activity in certain of the stomach muscles to act as an internal restraint for the pressure. The belt can assist these muscles by acting as an external restraint for the abdominal pressure. In other words, the belt supports the stomach more than the back. Nevertheless, by supporting the trunk while the breath is being held, it indirectly supports the back.

It must be added that it is not simply a matter of arbitrary breath-holding, since the degree to which this takes place relates closely to the type of work being done. In the case of speed-strength sports, it has been found that *greatest production of force occurs when the lungs are filled to about 75 percent of their maximum capacity* for the short interval when muscle tension is highest (Vorobyev, 1978).

A word has to be said about the role of the abdominal muscles in lifting. Contrary to common belief, the abdominal muscles (rectus abdominis) do not contract to any significant degree during lifting or pushing. Studies of the electrical activity of the stomach show that it is deeper muscles of the stomach (the internal and external obliques) which are much more active during lifting. The apparent hardening of the 'abdominals' on straining is usually caused by passive bulging of these muscles and their sheaths. The one time when the abdominals contract powerfully in the standing position occurs during explosive expulsion of air from the lungs or during backward extension of the torso. This implies that abdominal exercises should be augmented by side-bending, heavy lifting or twisting activities to strengthen all the different muscle groups that contribute to stomach and torso stability.

These facts now enable us to redesign the belt for improved efficiency. Like the powerlifting belt, the front portion of the modified weightlifting belt should be wider to distribute the abdominal pressure more effectively, but not so wide as to cause discomfort or impede movement of the abdominal and hip regions. At the same time, the buckle should be shifted to the side to allow you to pull the bar close to the body without occurrence of the fairly common problem of striking the belt in front.

8.9.2 Shoes and Safety

Shoe manufacturers would have athletes believe that the primary solution to most athletic injuries is the wearing of expensive footwear. Ailments such as shin splints, iliotibial band syndrome and peripatellar pain are attributed variously to excessive shock loading of the limbs, pronation or supination.

Research, however, reveals that fewer injuries occur among those who wear thin soled shoes and that current athletic footwear may even be injurious (Robbins et al, 1988). The paradoxical observation of a much lower incidence of running injuries reported in barefoot populations implies that modern running shoes may produce injuries that normally would not occur without their use (Robbins & Hanna, 1987). Furthermore, running shoes seem to be associated with fewer injuries in fitness classes than so-called 'aerobics shoes'. Nigg (1986) reports that, on firm shock absorbing mats, the difference in heel strike force is minimal between bare feet, thick-soled shoes and thin-soled shoes. Nigg also points out that the use of any shoe usually increases the tendency of the foot to pronate, particularly if the impact forces are smaller.

Moreover, several studies have shown that there is no correlation between the amount of shoe cushioning and impact absorption by footwear during locomotion (Robbins et al, 1988; Clarke et al, 1982). Similarly, epidemiological studies have failed to provide evidence that expensive modern athletic footwear enhances protection from injury to the lower extremities (Caspersen et al, 1984; Powell et al, 1986). Thus, it would appear that safety of the lower extremity is not simply a consequence of suitable footwear, but of learning how to move the body efficiently while wearing a specific type of shoe.

Shoe Design

Clearly, the science of athletic shoe design is far from being exact. For instance, the current focus is on foot pronation. Other possible causes of injury such as toe, ankle, knee and hip movement in three dimensions are largely neglected. Moreover, footwear design is based almost exclusively on theoretical models which postulate that shock loading and the inability of the human anatomy to adapt to this loading are the primary causes of running injuries. This becomes evident from the claims of manufacturers that their specific shoes correct excessive pronation, control the rear-foot, offer superior arch support or absorb shock effectively. These shoes do not modify the impact forces during locomotion, a fact which casts severe doubt on the cushioning philosophy that forms the foundation of all current shoe design.

Studies by Robbins et al (1988) have shown that the sole of the bare foot exhibits a powerful plantar surface protective response which diminishes plantar loading on ground contact, thereby reducing the risk of damage from overloading during locomotion. Their work also revealed that this response was not apparent among subjects who always wear shoes, especially the highly shock-absorbing shoes generally worn by runners. They concluded this protective response prevents injury by decreasing system rigidity, thereby diminishing the peak force during foot impact. The lack of the protective response among shoe wearers apparently is due to diminished plantar sensory feedback, possibly combined with mechanical interference with arch deflection by shoe laces, heel counters and arch supports (Robbins et al, 1988). It would seem that sufficient regular locomotor activity without footwear should be done daily to maintain the sensitivity of the plantar protective reflex and that less emphasis should be concentrated on designing passive shock-absorbing or pronation-modifying shoes.

Little work has been done on relating lower limb injury to anthropometric factors such as bodymass, height or limb length, or other factors including level of qualification, movement intensity, muscle fibre distribution, patterns of EMG activity, feedback processes or bone density. No research has examined aerobics or 'cross training' shoes with this degree of thoroughness, nor has it carried out entirely satisfactory three-dimensional studies of all physical factors influencing the efficiency of whole body movement from initiation to termination of a locomotor action, in particular with respect to the optimal design of any shoe.

Irrespective of how well designed shoes are, they must be used correctly in different movements. In doing so the user must be aware that shoes always reduce the proprioceptive and tactile sensitivity to the surface on which they are being used.

Another reflex is also worthy of attention. Forces exerted on the shoe are delayed in being transmitted through its shock absorbing sole en route to the foot. The reflex positive supporting reaction (see 3.5.3), which normally operates highly efficiently in bare feet to produce strong reflex extension of the legs and stabilisation of the body, is delayed in facilitating rapid cybernetic control and correction of unsafe movements when shoes are worn. In particular, the locus of application of pressure to the surface of the sole of the foot determines the position to which the limb will extend (Guyton, 1984), so that inappropriate geometry of the shoe can significantly alter the pattern of recruitment of the muscles of the lower extremities.

In contrast, the use of bare feet on firm, very high density chip-foam mats in the average fitness class preserves proprioceptive efficiency, lowers the centre of gravity of the body and, unlike shoes, does not increase the lever arm length from the point of heel contact to the ankle joint, thereby reducing the moments of force about all joints of the lower limb.

Shoes in the Weights Facility

It is interesting to examine the role of shoes in the weight training gymnasium. In particular, running shoes or any shock-absorbing shoes suitable for the aerobics class are potentially unsafe in the gymnasium. For instance, compression of any part of the sole during squats, cleans, deadlifts, standing presses, good mornings, snatches, pulls and other standing exercises can cause general instability and consequent injury. Moreover, inappropriate height of the heel can shift the centre of gravity of the body forward, thereby increasing stress on the knee joint and altering the optimal patterns of movement for safe, maximal lifts from the ground. These are all major reasons why powerlifters often wear thin heelless shoes much like ballet pumps.

Even firm soled shoes may be dangerous for use in Olympic Weightlifting unless they allow a certain degree of controlled foot sliding necessary for correcting minor trajectory errors of the bar, especially during the jerk.

The underlying message is the same. Comfortable shoes should be used which are appropriate for the individual and the sport. These should then be used safely and correctly, if necessary by studying slow motion replays of the action involved.

8.10 Safety and Machine Training

Most circuit training in the professional gymnasium environment is based on the use of specific machines. Therefore, it is essential that the instructor becomes aware of machine features which are rarely pointed out by manufacturers. It is commonly believed that gymnasium machines are intrinsically safer than free weights and require far less skill in using them. This fallacy is one reason why injuries are still regularly sustained by those who rely solely on machines for training. Machines, like free weights, are special devices for offering mechanical resistance to users intent on improving muscular performance or size, and as such, must be operated correctly to ensure safety and effectiveness. The ability to use machines properly depends on an adequate knowledge of the merits, deficiencies and the principles underlying the design of each machine.

One also needs to know the similarities and differences between a machine exercise and the equivalent free weights exercise, with particular attention being paid to which muscles act as prime movers and stabilisers at all stages of the exercise, as well as which tendons and ligaments are significantly stressed. The following list has been compiled to introduce the fundamentals of safe training on machines:

- *Seated vertical pressing machines* often force you to round the lower back, lean forward from the hip and hyperextend the lumbar spine, so that you should be aware of these problems and counteract them. Moreover, you should remember that seated pressing or lifting exercises impose larger stresses on the lumbar spine than their standing equivalents (as much as 90% more, Chaffin & Andersson, 1984), so that they should not be regarded as basic exercises for novices.

- *Seated vertical pressing machines* often have foot rests situated in a position which makes it difficult for you to stabilise your hips and lower back. You should either keep your feet firmly on the ground or ensure that you are steady and controlled throughout the movement. Furthermore, seated pressing produces greater lumbar spinal stress than standing presses with barbells or dumbbells, especially if you use a very full range of movement which causes the pelvis to tuck under you and rounds the lumbar spine.

- *Seated leg press machines* are notorious for providing backrests which do not match the natural curvatures of the spine, thereby promoting lumbar flexion when you exert maximum force with your legs. You must concentrate on maintaining your normal neutral lumbar curvature and avoid using a range of knee flexion that results in pelvic rotation and marked flexion of the lumbar spine. Never allow the weight to return so rapidly that the momentum forces the lumbar spine to round.

- *Lying inclined or vertical leg press* machines usually allow you to bend your knees until the upper thighs touch the abdomen and cause forced lumbar flexion: one must resist this tendency, carefully limit the range of knee flexion and perform the movement slowly.

- *Prone leg curl machines* which have a flat or slightly rounded lying surface frequently can force the lumbar spine into hyperextension. You should place a roll of firm sponge rubber or towelling under your hip joint and concentrate on keeping the buttocks from thrusting upwards. A sudden jerk with the knees fully extended can damage the muscles crossing the knee joint, especially popliteus.

- *Hack squat machines* can impose excessive shearing force on the knee and are a poor, unsafe substitute for the free standing squat: if you use them, you should ensure that a partner helps you start with your knees extended and that you control the movement carefully at all times.

- Virtually *all bench press machines* compel you to start from your weakest biomechanical position with the bar at chest level. Moreover, they do not permit you to begin with a pre-stretch in the lowest position: a partner should help you raise the bar so that you can begin from the extended elbow position.

- *'Pec decks'* usually compel you to start from a weak biomechanical position in which your shoulder joint tends to rotate externally: a partner should pull the grips forward so that you can start with your arms together in front of your chest. While you are moving, resist excessive external rotation of the shoulder joint and any tendency for momentum to force your shoulders beyond their maximum normal range of movement.

- *Calf-raise machines* often force the lumbar spine to flex, particularly with heavy loads. You should always maintain your normal neutral lumbar curvature and avoid trying to jerk the load too rapidly upwards.

- *Seated back extension machines* in which you lean forwards, then push the padded resistance arm backwards often compel you to start with a flexed lumbar spine and end with loaded hyperextension. You should use only a small range of forward and backward movement, and never begin from a position of pronounced forward leaning. This exercise can impose a greater compressive and transverse loading on lower spinal structures than an equivalent deadlift, since the seated position does not allow the hip and knee joints any freedom to modify the magnitude or direction of loading on the lower back.

- *Seated spinal twist machines* often allow you to flex the lumbar spine while you are rotating, as well as imposing excessive torsional loading on spinal ligaments: you must always maintain a strictly upright posture and severely limit range and speed of rotation. Standing spinal or hip twisting machines can place excessive torsional loading on the knee and lower spine and are little more than useless for 'trimming the waist'.

- Many *abdominal machines* provide supports which allow you to grip with the backs of the heels, calves or thighs, thereby negating the value of knee flexion and enabling you to rely more strongly on your iliopsoas (hip flexor) muscles. If your intention is to involve the hip flexor muscles less, you should perform the exercise slowly and avoid any tendency to grip in this way. Remember, of course, that the abdominal and hip flexor muscles are meant to function in an integrated fashion, so there is nothing intrinsically 'wrong' about doing abdominal exercises which also recruit the iliopsoas group; what may be most risky is the inappropriate timing of the involvement of the different muscles in any trunk exercises.

- All *sit-up boards* with grips for the ankles or feet compel the hip flexor muscles to become involved from the earliest stages of the sit-up and increase spinal stress, unless one deliberately executes the curl-up phase of the trunk before hip flexion is attempted. If used for a specific training purpose, the average person generally should execute this type of sit-up as a very slow upward and downward curl-up. One of the most negative aspects of doing large volumes of these types of sit-up is their tendency to decrease the range of movement of the hip joint, thereby adversely affecting running, walking, jumping, jerking and kicking efficiency, and increasing lumbar spinal stress. If you do limited range sit-ups, afterwards you should always stretch the iliopsoas muscles under resistive loading to maintain mobility of the hip and lower spinal joints. Long, deep lunges with the trunk upright can be very helpful in this regard.

- *Standing leg raise machines* which require you to raise your legs while resting your elbows on arm rests and pressing your back against a backrest do not necessarily decrease the tendency for lumbar spinal hyperextension to occur. To ensure that this does not happen, you should shift forward so that the back does not touch the backrest and execute the movement as a crunching form of a gymnastics "pike" (with rear end being hoisted upwards) slowly from beginning to end.

- *Standing hip adduction/abduction machines* which require you to stand and push or pull the straightened leg against a loaded lever arm can permit excessive simultaneous spinal rotation or flexion/extension to occur. This type of complex spinal action can be harmful to the lumbar spine and should be controlled very carefully in the gym training environment.

- *'Smith' vertical press machines* which constrain the bar to slide upward on vertical poles often impose a larger load on the spine, shoulders and wrists than standing presses with free weights. You should avoid using heavy loads, high speeds of movement or momentum to keep the bar moving.

- *Prone leg curl machines*, even those with an inclined surface which flexes the hips, often cause you to hyperextend the lumbar spine under compressive loading. You should be aware of this possibility and stabilise your hips accordingly or rather use a standing leg curl or pulley machine.

- Many *seated bent-arm pullover machines* force the lumbar spine into marked hyperextension if used jerkily or over an excessive range: you should avoid this tendency, particularly by restricting your range of movement to suit your body's natural limits.

- Most *hyperextension machines* increase the stress on the hamstrings and soft tissues of the knee, particularly the popliteal muscle and the joint capsule. Frequently, they do not permit you to change the height of the foot restraint or the distance between the hips and the ankles, so that the knee tends to be hyperextended and the advisable movement trajectory for the spine cannot be followed. To avoid damage to the structures of the knee or spine, you should not accelerate or decelerate rapidly. In addition, return to the upright posture after inversion can produce postural hypotension and consequent fainting, so you should keep your head low, stand up gently and move the legs after completing the exercise. Individuals with abnormally low or high blood pressure should avoid the use of such devices.

- Note that *any machine which requires you to sit* prevents you from using your hip, knee and ankle joints to absorb shock or redistribute loading. The posture of stable neutral pelvic tilt becomes far more difficult to maintain throughout the exercise, spinal hyperextension or hyperflexion occurs more easily and spinal stress becomes much more likely.

- Machines are commonly used in *circuits* which compel you to race against timing devices, thereby making it far more likely that you will not take the time to correctly stabilise your body, use correct technique or avoid reliance on momentum. Only competitive athletes have to train to compete against the clock; the average gym client is there to enhance fitness or shape and should reject unnecessary intimidation by a clock or instructor. Interval Circuit Training (ICT) with carefully controlled, slower use of heavier loads and rest periods between stations tends to be safer than hastily executed, lower intensity Continuous Circuit Training (CCT).

- Machines which are not well designed, maintained or lubricated can impose unnecessarily large loads or unpredictable patterns of resistance on the body: you should report any such machines to the gym supervisor and avoid using them until they are in good working order.

- Numerous machines compel you to start the exercise with limbs and joints in a biomechanically weak or vulnerable position (e.g. seated bench press, seated leg press, bench press machine and Smith machine). If this is the case, always ask a partner to help you begin in a safer position and to 'spot' you during the movement.

- It is important to know that, if a machine prevents any joint from moving, then there will usually be an increase in stress on adjacent joints. For instance, the seated leg extension machine tends to immobilise the hip joint, so that greater stress falls on the nearby knee joint. Similarly spinal stress generally increases for all machines which compel you to push against a load in a seated position. Besides changing to equivalent free weights exercises, you could carefully control the speed and transition accelerations throughout such exercises.

The above list is by no means complete, but it should suffice to increase your awareness that machines are not inherently safer than free weights and that all types of resistance training require learning of the appropriate technical skills for efficiency and safety. The instructor should be acutely aware of this fact and should never assume that a client does not need to be closely supervised at all times, even when using machines. He should always appreciate that *continuous observation and spotting are just as important for machines as for free weights* exercises if the safety claims of machine manufacturers are to be realised in practice.

8.11 Protection by the Muscles

Exercise texts often state that resistance training is valuable because stronger muscles protect the joints from injury. Electromyographic studies of many common activities show that this is a faulty belief, especially as protective reflexes do not operate or do not operate effectively during many movements involving forced flexion near the end range of movement of the joints.

Muscles can protect only if they are adequately contracted in the appropriate pattern to control the imposed load. Yet, many texts on training for contact sports such as rugby and American football still argue that large, strong muscles prevent spinal injuries, in particular. A relaxed massive and powerful muscle is almost as useless as a relaxed small muscle in protecting a joint. When the muscles are relaxed, the ligaments associated with the joint have to prevent displacement, rupture or dislocation.

Protection by the muscles is a function of the various extensor reflexes and the characteristics of the eccentric strength of the relevant muscles. It depends on many factors including starting strength, how rapidly the muscles are recruited to contract (the quality of reactive ability discussed in Section 5.3.3), the efficiency of coordinated action by appropriate muscle groups, the strength of the eccentric contraction, eccentric endurance, isometric strength and strength endurance after movement ceases, strength-flexibility, the elasticity of the muscle complex and the strength of the connective tissues involved.

The protective process also depends on the initial state of the major stabilisers and movers involved when the threatening load is imposed on the body. This load may be imposed on a part supported by isometric, concentric or eccentric movement, or even on a part completely at rest. In other words, depending on initial conditions at the moment of loading, adequacy of protection will be determined by isometric strength and endurance, and concentric or eccentric strength, strength-speed and strength-endurance, as well as by overflow or compensatory muscle activity to furnish supplementary support for the major stabilisers and movers.

General strength training on its own is inadequate to guarantee improved muscular protection for the body. The large range of processes implicated in musculoskeletal protection emphasizes the importance of special strength training in the properly-sequenced, multi-faceted manner discussed earlier in this book.

Basmajian (1978) reports that *ligaments play a much greater part in supporting loads than is generally believed, unless conscious effort is made to recruit the relevant muscles.* In most situations where traction is exerted across a joint, muscles appear to play only a secondary role to ligaments. Thus, deadlifts, toe-touches and 'aerobic' activities involving flexion and rotation of the spine may rely more on the spinal ligaments than the erector spinae in stabilising the spine. Training to increase ligament hypertrophy and strength thus would appear to be just as important as muscle strengthening.

Moreover, what is often termed 'muscle fatigue' in many strenuous exercises involving loading of the limbs is frequently not due to fatigue of muscle. This 'fatigue' probably arises from the painful feeling of tension in the capsule and ligaments of the joint, not from overworked muscles. In fact, the muscles may not even be significantly contracting. It appears, too, as if the fatigue of back, legs and feet experienced during standing is not a muscular phenomenon (Basmajian, 1978).

Basmajian also questions the validity of 'ligamento-muscular protective reflexes', since reflex muscle activity often fails to occur when a limb is loaded. Apparently a great deal still has to be learned about the mechanics of neuromuscular action.

8.12 Towards the Future

The scientific foundation of special strength training is gradually beginning to emerge. However, there are still many unanswered questions. Therefore, the authors appreciate the possible displeasure of the reader who anticipated finding the precise answer to this question in this book: for all this complicated analysis, how does one develop sport specific strength? However, it is hoped that the reader appreciates the complexities of this question and the futility of attempts to give an exact prescription in each case, based on the vast diversity of variations which determine the training method for each individual. The design of special strength training programmes still depends on conducting a symphony of intuition, practical experience and scientific research. Reliance on any one of these factors in isolation of the others does not enable us to formulate definitive programmes for specific strength training in all sports.

Non-Physical Factors

At the same time, the central role played by non-physical factors must never be forgotten. Autogenic training, visualisation, hypnosis, biofeedback, motivational techniques and other psychological methods have formed an integral part of Russian and Eastern European training for many years. Although some of these methods have been mentioned in passing throughout this text, it would benefit the reader to consult specialised books in these fields, such as the extensive survey by Murphy and White (1978) of altered states associated with outstanding performances in different sports. A better understanding of mental processes will make one appreciate that even the most meticulous prescription of all the training means and methods in this book will not guarantee success unless the mind enables the body to utilise its full potential during training, restoration and competition.

For instance, it has repeatedly been shown that one's attitude during training or competition has a profound effect on physical performance, this being a complicating factor when one attempts to compare the research done on different subjects by different scientists under different conditions. Highly motivated subjects will usually produce superior performances, especially in the presence of spectators. The increase in aggression by anabolic steroids is also regarded as one of the reasons why these drugs can improve performance. *Visualisation techniques which require the athlete to fervently concentrate on accelerating the training load can increase power and speed of movement.* Other research in which athletes performed loadless weightlifting movements with a broomstick while imagining effort against maximal loads revealed improvements in strength and skill (Kovalik, 1978). More widespread use of this type of highly motivated, mood-linked, goal-specific visualisation (or 'imagineering') will, no doubt, become recognised as a vital part of modern training.

The absence of this state during all exercises is a major reason why the average client in the fitness facility does not improve to the same extent as his elite athletic peer. Book-reading, mirror gazing, social chatting, listening to pop music, TV-watching and admiring the opposite sex in the training setting are all activities that disrupt the mind-set necessary for producing optimal results and are important factors to consider if one chooses to exercise in the average fitness centre.

With reference to the role of psychological factors in determining sporting excellence, it must be stressed that this does not imply invoking the vague notions of mind-body power which are helping to market hundreds of self-development courses of dubious validity. The fact that many of these courses are successful, however outrageous and unscientific their methodologies may be, has a great deal to do with the placebo effect (or faith factor). In other words, certain methods of mental or physical training or healing work, despite the actual methods themselves: they succeed largely because the user is persuaded to believe strongly in them. Investigation of the placebo effect and the influence of the mind on health, disease and recovery has led to the establishment of disciplines such as psychopharmacology and psychoneuroimmunology to sort out the sense from the nonsense. This concept is not original, for it was said thousands of years ago: "As you think, so shall you be"; all that has been done today has been to analyse it in acceptable scientific terms. As research probes the past more thoroughly and manages to wed emergent theories with findings, so some of the ancient wisdom will be vindicated and applied, while the remainder will be discarded.

The paradigms acceptable to the scientific communities in which the research is done, however, always has a profound effect on the approval, funding and applications of the research. Consequently, the West with its long-term adherence to the linear, binary, positive-negative Aristotelian thinking model has preferred to ignore much of the research done by workers in the less accredited realms of what is called parapsychology. In Russia and Eastern Europe, this field has formed part of mainstream psychology, which has tended to integrate neuropsychology and physiological psychology far more into its overall research than the West. Western sports psychology has applied questionnaires, profiles of behavioural states, motivational strategies, passive visualisation and a few relaxation techniques, while Russian scientists have applied similar methods, but often in far more integrated form by use of special instruments devised in medicine and engineering.

Thus, indicators such as training level, state of preparedness, response to stress, memorising skills, dominant character traits, thinking skills, alertness, mood, aggressiveness, motor ability and reactiveness have been monitored by measurements of electrodermal impedance (for stress), quasi-stationary and very low frequency electrical fields of the central nervous system (Siff, 1977), phase and impedance electrocardiography, seismotonography (for muscle tension), motor tremor, eye-blink, reaction time and low-inertia grip-strength.

When the author visited the psychodiagnostic laboratory in the sports psychology section of the Institute for Physical Education Research in 1991, he inquired if work by Russian neuroscientists such as Aladjalova (on infraslow and DC brain potentials) had been applied in sports training (e.g. Aladjalova, 1964). Pleased that a Westerner was very familiar with their colleague's unusual work, the scientists there responded by spending a considerable amount of time explaining and demonstrating their methods to him. In doing so, they considered it reprehensible that the West had not used the extensive and original work of their own scientists such as Becker, who had manipulated DC potentials across the brain to induce anaesthesia, hypnosis and analgesia, as well as to facilitate wound healing and tissue regeneration elsewhere in the body (Siff, 1977). An obvious lesson here is that the success of any national sports programme depends on integrating expertise drawn from traditional and non-traditional sources into the educational, training and research effort.

These scientists regarded the following as other limiting factors in Western sports development: the dominance of cardiovascular physiology and orthopaedics in sports medicine, the almost complete absence of formal methods of restoration, the lack of adequate biomechanics training in physical education, a general unfamiliarity with Russian and Eastern research and training, the decreasing standard of general education, the lack of individual discipline and national pride, and the low level of coaching ability (in Russia many of the coaches are more academically qualified than teachers).

In more recent years, the Western use of fMRI (functional MRI) scanning of the brain and other parts of the body during some human movements has started to fill some of the gaps between 'Western' and 'Eastern' schools of sports science. However, in both of these settings, little work has been done to examine the possible relationship between the electrical activity of the brain (EEG) and the electrical activity of the muscles (EMG) in a wide number of motor activities. It will be interesting to see if any research in this field will lead to a greater understanding of the neurophysiological aspects of human performance.

Although biofeedback has been well researched and clinically applied in Western medicine, it has been routinely used to a far greater extent in Russia and Eastern Europe for teaching the athlete control over several physiological and psychological variables. In addition, microelectric currents often have been used for recuperation, while computers have been widely applied for teaching motor skills, analysing performance, examining coach-player and player-player interactions; and medical interventions are broadly applied in numerous fields. Certain overseas companies, notably some in Austria, have donated mobile psychodiagnostic laboratories to Russian sports institutions, in return for which Russia has provided collaborative research and training.

Lessons from Modern Physics

The potentially enormous contribution waiting to be applied to exercise science by innovative research and theory from modern physics should not be neglected any longer. Many problems existing in exercise physiology research are the result of applying linear, all-or-none, simple cause-effect, isolationist methods to biological and psychological systems of exceptional, interconnected complexity. For instance, the schism between 'aerobic' and strength training is a direct consequence of the highly polarised preoccupation of exercise physiologists with cardiovascular activity. The attention paid in this book to individuality, diversity, asymmetry, delayed effects, conjugate sequences and interactivity of processes is intended to minimise reliance on classical determinism. Further progress will undoubtedly be stimulated by borrowing non-linear methods from catastrophe theory, chaos theory and fuzzy logic systems to explain sudden beneficial or harmful changes of state in adaptation space (e.g. supercompensation, muscle injury or heart attacks), as discussed elsewhere (Siff, 1981, 1982).

Changes of State

Concepts that can cloud the nature of fitness are those of stability, equilibrium, balance and homeostasis, because they create the misleading impression of a fixed level or point above and below which the organism is in mortal danger, operating inefficiently or heading towards breakdown. This is yet another manifestation of binary-logic Aristotelian thinking that tends to exclude the possibilities for shifting levels of balance or operation, as is the case with all biological functions. Yet, physiological science refers religiously to measures such as specific lactate thresholds, normal blood pH (acidity), normal blood pressure, exercise heart rate, the alpha brain rhythm (8-13Hz) and normal blood sugar level. The fact is that there is considerable variation in all of these measures and in the individual manner of variation from person to person and situation to situation.

In this respect it is important to recall that several types of balance or stability are recognised: stable, unstable, metastable and multistable equilibrium. In fact, long-term stability is a rarity since the body is always correcting physiological processes so that they constantly overshoot and undershoot certain marks, which themselves are drifting back and forth about an imaginary mean level. Nevertheless, we use the term *stable* to refer to the maintenance of a certain state for a prolonged period, which is returned to after anything disturbs the initial stability. *Unstable* simply refers to the lack of maintenance of any state for a sustained period; any disturbance causes the system to shift to another uncontrolled state. *Metastability* refers to a state which persists until a disturbance happens to move it to another state of stability. *Multistability* refers to a system that can exhibit stability in not one, but a variety of different states.

Thus, in theorising about balance in physiological processes, adaptation and fitness, it is important always to consider the possibility that there may be more than one type of stability during and after training and that changes in state from an expected norm may not necessarily be undesirable or dangerous. We should also not be surprised by sudden changes of state and not the wave-like transitions that have been discussed in detail earlier in this text. Most athletes are familiar with inexplicable rapid loss of form or exceptional leaps in performance that occur a few times in a lifetime (such as the long jump records of Bob Beamon and Mike Powell). A better understanding of these spike-like transients in the fitness state may be furnished by the application of chaos and catastrophe theory, the aim being to produce training conditions to make such events more likely.

The work on *non-equilibrium systems* by 1977 Nobel prize-winner, Ilya Prigogine, may be of particular value in this regard. He showed that non-equilibrium may be a source of impending order (Prigogine & Stengers, 1984). All systems comprise subsystems in a continual state of fluctuation in which one or more fluctuations can totally disrupt the existing organisation and produce an unpredictable leap to 'chaos' or to a more differentiated, higher level of organisation (known as a dissipative structure, because it requires more energy to sustain this state). One of the most controversial aspects of this concept (which accompanied the foundation of the discipline known as NLD - *nonlinear dynamics*) is that Prigogine maintains that order can occur spontaneously or by chance through a process of self-organisation. Investigation into how specific patterns of training or mental states can promote the conditions for enhanced self-organisation may then be of profit in the quest to produce sporting excellence.

Fuzzy Fitness

However modern and exciting the world of modern exercise science may appear to be, it still tends to be dominated by a type of thinking which was revered and promulgated by the ancient Grecians, especially Aristotle and Plato. This thinking model is based on the concept that everything may be polarised into categories of light or dark, all or none, positive or negative, odd or even, on or off, strong or weak, right or wrong, good or evil, white or black, left or right, up or down, hot or cold and so forth. Everything belongs either to one category (set) or to another, but not to both concurrently.

In the world of fitness training, we find a host of these polarities, such as aerobic vs anaerobic training, cardiovascular vs strength training, fit vs unfit, slow twitch vs fast twitch muscles, static vs dynamic, mobilisers vs stabilisers, and physical vs mental. The action potential propagated by the nerves is caused by neurons being 'on' rather than 'off', with sub-threshold, non-propagated potential fluctuations generally being ignored.

Cardiovascular training is regarded as purely a cardiovascular, heart-lung process which involves no anaerobic metabolism. Flexibility is best developed by static, slow stretches. Muscle hypertrophy is best developed by 8-12 repetitions of resistance training, strength by 3-5 repetitions, power by 1-3 repetitions. One specific contraindicated exercise causes a specific injury. Aerobic training occurs below the lactate turnpoint or threshold, whereas anaerobic training occurs above this zone. In periodisation there is one type of training for the preparatory phase and another for the competitive phase. Either-or thinking generally defines the territory in each case. Events, training and research invariably take place between well defined numerical limits; there is little acknowledgment of vagueness or fuzziness.

During the 1920s, Polish logician Lukasiewicz devised a system of multi-valued logic in which propositions can assume any fractional values between 0 and 1. In 1937, Max Black wrote an article entitled 'Vagueness: An Exercise in Logical Analysis' in the journal *Philosophy of Science*, in which he applied multi-valued logic to sets of objects and drew the first multi-valued (fuzzy) set curves. The scientific world took scant note of these early works until 1965 when Lotfi Zadeh at the University of California, Berkeley, published the paper 'Fuzzy Sets' in the journal *Information and Control*, in which he applied Lukasiewicz's logic to every element in a set.

However, it took until the mid-1970s for fuzzy logic to be practically applied. This was done by Ebrahim Mamdani of Queen Mary College in London when he designed a fuzzy controller for a steam engine. Since then, the Japanese in particular have applied fuzzy logic to control hundreds of electronics products, household appliances and transportation networks in what has become a multi-billion dollar industry.

In brief, fuzzy logic is a logical system based on the recognition that *everything is a matter of degree*. For example, close scrutiny of research reveals that no muscular activity is 100% aerobic or anaerobic. At any instant, the activity comprises a percentage of each. Fuzzy logic, as discussed earlier is a system that allows us to do deal with the shades of gray and vagueness that typify many aspects of life.

In exercise physiology, it will caution us not to rigidly apply concepts such as 'lactate threshold' or any other threshold or turning 'point', for that matter, since this clearly implies that up to some level there is minimal lactate and a fraction above that level, there is suddenly abundant lactate. In many physiological situations, the identification of changes of state occurring at quantitatively precise levels disguises the fact that changes take place over a range which displays a relatively steep or relatively gradual slope. Thus, an athlete competing in a distance event judges his pace by tuning into how hard or easy a given pace is. If the pace is 'too demanding', he decides to 'slow down a bit', and vice versa if the pace is 'too easy'. He never operates in terms of absolute measures, precise calculations and percentage increases to ensure that his pulse rate is exactly 145 beats per minute. In many walks of life, we control processes in terms of how they feel to us, ranging from putting on the appropriate pressure on the brake pedal to stop a car timeously to throwing a ball accurately in baseball.

Scientists can perform fairly accurate analysis under laboratory conditions, but the athlete cannot produces a performance by stipulating exact values to everything he does. A powerlifter competing in the squat event has to judge when the depth of the squat is legally low enough to be passed, a feat which he achieves by purely subjective feeling based on experience. It is clear that the athlete constantly uses vague concepts such as 'too fast', 'too low' or 'that feels good' to produce competitive excellence. No biomechanical or physiological analysis has yet succeeded in measuring all the variables involved in producing world records and teaching them to any athlete to improve further. In other words, sporting performance is far more typical of fuzzy, vague logic than it is of precise mathematical formulae.

The essence of fuzzy logic is to enable us to use apparently vague or inexact descriptions of processes to improve on the existing performance of systems which inappropriately use unwarranted precision in their controlling systems.

An example of how fuzzy logic may be used to explain the relationship between the duration (or intensity) of activity at any moment to the contributions of the three main energy processes in the body (see 1.14) is illustrated in Figure 8.10.

This model emphasizes that optimal efficiency for any given duration (or intensity) of exercise depends on the concurrent different contributions of the short, intermediate and long-term energy systems. This enables us to think less in terms of one activity being aerobic and another anaerobic, and to plan training so that the dynamic balance between the three energy mechanisms is shifted in the most appropriate direction for any given sport.

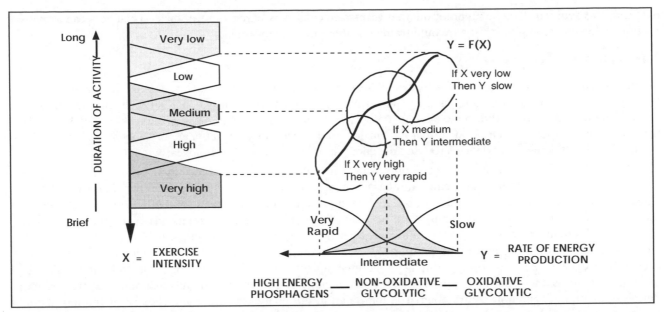

Figure 8.10 The application of fuzzy logic to understanding the dependence of the intensity (or duration) of any exercise on the three major metabolic processes. The method uses rules that relate fuzzy sets of rates of energy production such as 'very rapid' to fuzzy sets of exercise duration such as 'very short'. The relationship between the X and Y sets produces a chain of fuzzy patches, which can approximate a performance curve $Y = F(X)$.

Application of New Methods

In extolling the merits of using innovative ideas, applying the findings of new research and using modern technology in training, it is important to issue a few words of caution. With the popularisation of such methods, there is always the possibility that commercialisation, individual short-term successes and media attention will result in athletes implementing them without sufficient circumspection. For instance, the West is becoming far more aware of the value of massage, *Biologically Active Substances* (BAS), adaptogens (natural substances used to facilitate adaptation to stress), foods as drugs, electrical stimulation and pressure point therapy in training, especially as fitness professionals have begun to recognise their commercial potential.

In applying these methods, it is vital to remember that all these modalities of recovery and stimulation should not be applied in isolation, but integrated correctly into the overall training programme. There is always an interaction between all of the effects produced on the body by beneficial and detrimental stressors, which is the reason why great emphasis was laid on training after-effects, partial effects and cumulative effects (Ch 6).

Coaches in Russia are taught that regular reliance on any means to improve performance and to accelerate adaptation may be unwise because the system accommodates to them and they tend to lose their effectiveness. Basic massage may appear to be quite innocuous, especially as it 'feels so good' after exercise, but its constant use in much the same manner can diminish its benefits or even inhibit performance. Consequently, Russian coaches recommend *partial restoration* and *limited zone massage*, at the same time communicating regularly with the massage specialists who work with their athletes. These specialists can usually manually detect in the soft tissues of athletes that may be of great relevance in the early diagnosis of overtraining or unbalanced training.

An important implication of this is that it is essential for all personnel working with an athlete in any way whatsoever to keep in regular contact to ensure that all training programmes are properly monitored and modified, if necessary. It is interesting to note that all Russian coaches and physical education coaches spend 700-900 hours over several semesters learning and practising sports massage, which identifies yet another area in which Western sports training needs attention.

Russian coaches have already remarked on the indiscriminate use of nutritional ergogenic aids promoted widely by Western drug companies since drug testing became more rigorous. They consider that ingestion of most amino acid supplements, trace minerals and carbohydrate drinks is largely unwarranted and useless, especially since almost none of these supplements has been integrated into a carefully periodised training programme. They stress that the use of any *Biologically Active Substance* must be properly selected on the basis of a clear understanding of chrononutrition so that negative interactions and detrimental effects of prolonged usage can be avoided. They also point out that adaptation caused by chronic use of these substances can actually produce a lower training effect than would training without these supplements.

Innovations in Testing

While considerable testing in the West relies on the use of expensive devices such as isokinetic dynamometers, force plates, high speed video and gas analysers, Russian scientists frequently construct their own apparatus or create field tests that are useful to the average coach away from the laboratory setting. Moreover, they tend to be used more under sporting conditions rather than mainly in the laboratory on stationary ergometers and treadmills, often relying on telemetering devices to relay the information to a receiving station nearby.

For instance, invasive testing of metabolic changes is replaced or supplemented by use of *seismotonography*, a system which uses mechanical means to measure muscle tension (stiffness) and damping ratio (Siff, 1986). These measures can be very informative, because changes in muscle tone during and after training can give an indication of whether the training is sufficient or excessive, if different restoration means are optimally effective and if the athlete has recovered enough to resume training. This method, together with other auxiliary methods such as electromyography and plethysmography (to measure blood flow), is especially applied to assess the presence of excessive hypertrophy, which can diminish muscle metabolism, drainage of metabolites, balanced growth of tendons and other connective tissue, work capacity and relative strength. Estimation of the strength deficit of contractile and non-contractile tissue forms part of this analysis to ascertain whether the training should focus on promoting hypertrophic or nervous changes in the body (see Ch 1).

As we noted earlier, innovative measuring of heart and breathing rate before, during and after exercise, after rapid changes in posture, before and after breath holding is also included among the many simple tests that scientists use in Russia, as are specific balance tests with and without the eyes closed.

Similar tests formed the basis for biomechanics Research and Design projects for the author's senior mechanical engineering students at the University of the Witwatersrand, South Africa, and some of them were successfully used with different athletes, illustrating that low cost improvisation can be implemented easily in any sports training schemes, even in so-called Third World countries.

Kinaesthetic Manipulation and Education

Traditionally the human has five senses, with the so-called 'sixth sense' identified as some vague psychic ability. Actually we do have six senses: the *kinaesthetic sense* or the sense of being aware of where the body and its components are in space in time. To do this, it relies on the proprioceptors in the muscles, connective tissues and joints to integrate information from these areas with the senses of balance and touch, as well as with subtle control mechanisms involving breathing. Any contact with external objects such sporting apparatus, an opponent, clothing and shoes, can, via their effect on the kinaesthetic sense, profoundly influence performance.

This happens unconsciously during all sporting activity both to enhance and to inhibit performance. For instance, forward flexion of the neck during a squat, clean or deadlift can cause a reflex relaxation of the spine, disrupt the optimal lifting pattern and endanger the lifter. As discussed earlier (8.8), shoes can alter the proprioceptive sensitivity of the foot and various control reflexes of the lower extremities, thereby distorting gait and other movement patterns. The correct use of the weightlifting belt in proprioceptive lifting training or enhancing trunk stability, sometimes in conjunction with strain measuring devices, was also discussed earlier (Ch 8.8).

In the therapy situation, physical therapists are taught the importance of manual contacts between therapist and patient during the application of PNF (7.2). They are also shown how to stroke the surface of the skin, vibrate the joints and exert pressure on various myofascial trigger points to treat musculoskeletal stress, pain and other problems. For thousands of years pressure application, massage techniques, postural manipulation and other methods of kinaesthetic manipulation have been applied in the Far East. These techniques were studied and applied in Russia and Eastern Europe to form part of the overall methodology for producing sporting prowess.

There it was found that touch, massage, visual cueing, the sketching of movements and other kinaesthetic awareness activities were not only useful in therapy, but also to enhance coaching skills and athletic performance. Thus, massage specialists used their hands to palpate the muscles and other soft tissues to identify patterns of tension and development in the bodies of their athletes, while scientists applied myotensometry, electromyography and body zone impedance measurement to do the same at a quantitative level. The results were communicated to coaches to enable them to touch, stroke or strongly press the appropriate areas of their athletes to relax, stimulate, delay fatigue or guide them during training. The coach learned how to touch or hold parts of the body to facilitate learning of movements, improve 'visualisation' (mental mapping) of movement patterns and characteristics, and to increase strength of specific stabilisers or mobilisers. For example, touching of the back, head and buttocks was used to teach novices the starting and pulling positions in the Olympic lifts, as well as many manoeuvres in gymnastics, dance, track-and-field and swimming.

Descriptions of these techniques have appeared for many decades in the Russian publications such as *Legkaya Atletika* (Light Athletics), *Tyezhelaya Atletika* (Weightlifting) and *Teoriya i Praktika Fizischeskoi Kultury* (Theory and Practice of Physical Culture). They also formed part of the basic philosophy of physical training taught to all Russian physical education students, as discussed in Section 1.2 of this text.

Techniques of pressing neurolymphatic points, nervous plexuses, motor regions and acupressure points, as well as slapping, tissue lifting and percussive techniques on the passive and actively moving body were demonstrated and taught to the author and his students between 1992-1994 by a member of the Bulgarian national weightlifting team, who informed him that all coaches and physical education students in his country had to spend three semesters of their undergraduate programmes mastering techniques of restoration and massage. The same cautionary recommendation to avoid overusing the same kinaesthetic strategies was stressed to ensure that athletes do not habituate to the same mode of learning, recovery or control.

The production and control of muscular force is one of the primary tasks in all sport, a process which relies on kinaesthetic awareness of what is happening within the musculoskeletal system in response to events in the sporting environment. The athlete has to process some sensations reaching the body from outside and other sensations being produced inside the body. The conscious and subconscious ability to compute and apply just the correct amount of force at every instant of movement results in the exceptional feats of modern sport, particularly those events which require precision and reproducibility of motor perfection. The great importance of understanding the role played by perception of physiological and psychological stress should never be underestimated or neglected, since the "virtual reality" taking place within the athlete's mind can be the deciding factor between success and failure, between sporting excellence and sporting mediocrity.

Farfel et al (1975) set out to ascertain the type of information upon which this motor control is based by examining the ability of weightlifters to estimate the forces which they exert during different lifts and different stages of various lifts (Sokolov, 1982). After studying a group of elite Russian weightlifters (Masters of Sport Class), they concluded that the ability of even world class weightlifters to estimate the force (relative to their experience of what a 1RM load feels like) they are exerting at different stages of the Olympic lifts under static and explosive conditions is very poor. Measurements made on special pulling dynamometers showed that errors of as much as 100% were common. It was concluded that this weakness in being able to accurately control force is the result of inappropriate training methods and that the lifters needed to systematically perfect their 'muscle sense', both by developing an acute inner feel for kinaesthetic processes and by using biofeedback information from specialised dynamometers to enable them to quantitatively imprint this awareness.

Awareness and use of the kinaesthetic awareness procedures mentioned in this section can serve as an invaluable adjunct to coaching and training. Acquisition of the necessary skills is no longer as remote as it used to be, especially since the drastic changes in the formely communist countries of Eastern Europe and the Soviet Union have resulted in many very competent experts in sport emigrating to the West in search of employment.

Advances in Methods of Coaching

Sometimes the current focus on physiological and biomechanical measurement in sports science makes one lose sight of the importance of improving our methods of motor learning. An understanding of how to programme the human biocomputer effectively by sensory and motor activity is vital to the growth of performance, especially in the light of discoveries that structure and function in the central nervous system is not as rigidly determined as hitherto thought (Ch 1: under 'Neural Changes with Training').

Sometimes, apparently logical methods of learning are not necessarily found to be the most effective. For instance, Russian researchers have discovered that teaching a new movement in its natural sequential order from start to finish is not necessarily as effective as *teaching the action in the reverse order* (Vorobyev, 1978). They found that learning of the Olympic weightlifting snatch from the final drop phase backwards to the starting pull is 40 percent more effective than the conventional order of learning. They also examined the effect of breaking sporting movements down into basic components and having athletes learn each element separately before attempting the whole movement. This method of *component learning* also proved to be superior to the conventional method of natural sequence learning.

In the preceding section, the value of improving kinaesthetic awareness in enhancing sporting prowess was also raised. When this is considered along with other advances in training such as reverse order learning, cognitive plyometrics, periodisation guided by ratings of perceived effort, biofeedback learning, and conjugate sequence loading, it becomes apparent that technology must always be accompanied by progress in coaching methodology and pedagogy. Methods derived from teaching intellectual subjects (such as suggestology and autogenics) can also prove to be valuable in accelerating and perfecting the learning of sporting skills (Ostrander & Schröder, 1979, 1994; Hutchison, 1986). In this context, it should be noted that technology changes the external environment of the athlete, whereas coaching methods (sometimes via the use of technology) change the athlete.

Concluding Remarks

The basic theme of the book consisted not so much of the attempt to answer the question of how to develop strength in each specific case as it was to show what one needs to know in order to do this. Creative application and refinement in specific situations of those principles and ideas already identified will rapidly lead to success. At any rate, this is more beneficial than to unquestioningly follow traditional recipes whose value is not enduring.

It is necessary to mention another task which confronted the author, namely to emphasize the unresolved problems in strength training science and to identify the paths along which the reader's personal interests and enthusiasm might be directed. Such problems are still numerous and the resolution of even the least of them brings us closer to the time when we will be able to present a definitive scientific and practically effective system of special strength training for athletes.

REFERENCES
AND BIBLIOGRAPHY

Abbate F, Sargeant A, Verdijk P, de Haan A., Effect of high-frequency initial pulses and post-tetanic potentiation on power output of skeletal muscle *J of Appl Physiology* 88: 1, 35-40, Jan 2000

Abernethy PJ, Jurimae J, Logan P, Taylor A & Thayer R (1994) Acute and chronic response of skeletal muscle to resistance training *Sports Med* 17(1): 22-38.

Abbott BC & Aubert X (1952) The force exerted by active striated muscle during and after change of length *J Physiol (London)* 117: 77-86

Adams GR, Hather B, Baldwin K & Dudley G (1993) Skeletal muscle myosin heavy chain composition and resistance training. *J Appl Physiol* Feb;74(2): 911-5

Alabin V & Yushkevitch T (1978) Talent selection in the sprint *Legkaya Atletika* 5: 15

Aladjalova N (1964) Slow electrical processes in the brain *Progress in Brain Research* Vol 7, Elsevier

Alexander, R et al, eds (1967) *Mechanics and Energetics of Animal Locomotion* p 67

Alon G (1985) High voltage stimulation: effects of electrode size on basic excitatory responses *Physical Therapy* 65: 890-895

Alway SE, Grumbt W, Gonyea WJ & Stray-Gundersen J (1989) Contrasts in muscle and myofibers of elite male and female bodybuilders *J Appl Physiol* 67(1): 24-31

Andersen JL & Aagaard P (2000) Myosin heavy chain IIX overshoot in human skeletal muscle *Muscle Nerve* Jul; 23(7): 1095-104

Andersen JL, Schjerling P & Saltin B (2000) Muscle, Genes and Athletic Performance *Sci American* Sept, 283(3): 48-55

Andriacchi TP, Andersson GB, Ortengren R & Mikosz RP (1984) A study of factors influencing muscle activity about the knee joint. *J Orthop Res* 1(3): 266-75

Andrews J G (1982) On the relationship between resultant joint torques and muscular activity *Med Sci Sports Exerc* 14: 361-367

Andrews J G (1985) A general method for determining the functional role of a muscle *J Biomech Eng* 107: 348-353

Andrews J G (1987) The functional role of the hamstrings and quadriceps during cycling: Lombard's paradox revisited *J Biomech* 20: 565-575

Antonio J & Gonyea W (1993) Skeletal muscle fiber hyperplasia *Med Sci Sports Exerc* Dec; 25(12): 1333-45

Antonio J & Gonyea W (1994) Muscle fiber splitting in stretch-enlarged avian muscle *Med Sci Sports Exerc* 26(8): 973-977,

Bachouchi N & Morel J (1989) Behaviour of crossbridges in stretched or compressed muscle fibres *J Theor Biol* 141(2): 143-57

Bacou F., Rouanet P., Barjot C, Janmot C, Vigneron P & d'Albis A (1996) Expression of myosin isoforms in denervated, cross-reinnervated and electrically stimulated rabbit muscles *Eur J Biochem* 236: 539-547.

Bagni MA, Cecchi G & Schoenberg M (1988) A model of force production that explains the lag between crossbridge attachment and force after electrical stimulation of striated muscle fibers *Biophys J* 54(6):1105-14

Banister EW (1979) The perception of effort: an inductive approach. *Eur J Appl Physiol* 41(2):141-50

Banister EW & Calvert TW (1980) Planning for future performance: implications for long term training. *Can J Appl Sport Sci* Sep;5(3):170-6

Banister EW & Cameron BJ (1990) Exercise-induced hyperammonemia: peripheral and central effects. *Int J Sports Med* May 11 Suppl 2:S129-42

Banister EW, Morton R & Fitz-Clarke J (1992) Dose/response effects of exercise modeled from training: physical and biochemical measures. *Ann Physiol Anthropol* 11(3):345-56

Baratta RV, Solomonow M, Best R, Zembo M & D'Ambrosia R (1995) Force-velocity relations of nine load-moving skeletal muscles *Med Biol Eng Comput* Jul; 33(4): 537-44

Barjot C, Rouanet P, Vigneron P, Janmot C, d'Albis A & Bacou F (1998) Transformation of slow-or fast-twitch rabbit muscles after cross-reinnervation or low frequency stimulation does not alter the in vitro properties of their satellite cells. *J of Muscle Research and Cell Motility* 19: 25-32.

Basmajian J (1978) *Muscles Alive* Williams & Wilkins Co, Baltimore

Beaulieu J (1986) *Stretching for All Sports* Athletic Press : 36-57

Berger R (1962) Comparison between resistance load and strength improvement *Res Quart* 33: 637

Berger R (1965) Comparison of the effect of various weight training loads on strength *Res Quart* 36: 141

Berger R (1970) Relationship between dynamic strength and dynamic endurance *Res Quart* 41: 115-6

Berger R (1982) *Applied Exercise Physiology* Lea & Febiger, Philadelphia

Bigland-Ritchie B & Woods J (1984) Changes in muscle contractile properties and neural control during human muscular fatigue *Muscle & Nerve* 7:691-9

Binder-Macleod S A (1995) Variable-frequency stimulation patterns for the optimization of force during muscle fatigue. Muscle wisdom and the catch-like property. *Adv Exp Med Biol* 384: 227-40

Blokhin I & Monastirskii A (1985) Physiological and methodological aspects of optimising the breathing and movement phases in the snatch and clean-and-jerk in weightlifters *Teoriya i Fizischeskoi Kultury* 11: 22-4

Bondarchuk A et al (1984) Adaptation *Legkoatletikicheckie Metanya* Russia 1: 78-81

Booth F & Gould E (1975) Effects of training and disuse on connective tissue *Exerc & Sports Sciences Rev* 3: 84-112

Bosco C (1982) Physiological considerations of strength and explosive power and jumping drills (plyometric exercise) *Proceedings of Conference '82: Planning for Elite Performance, Canadian Track & Field Assoc* Ottawa 1-5 Aug 1982: 27-37

Bosco C, Komi P, Thihanyi J, Kekete G & Apor P (1982) Mechanical power test and fibre composition of human leg extensor muscles *Eur J of Appl Physiol*

Bosco C & Komi (1979a) Potentiation of mechanical behaviour of the human skeletal muscle through prestretching *Acta Physiol Scand* 106: 467-472

Bosco C & Komi (1979b) Mechanical characteristics and fiber composition of human leg extensor muscle *Eur J of Appl Physiol* 41: 275-284

Bosco C, Tihanyi J, Komi P, Fekete G & Apor P (1982) Store and recoil of elastic energy in slow and fast types of human skeletal muscles. *Acta Physiol Scand* 116: 343-349

Bosco C, Cardinale M, Colli R, Tihanyi J, von Duvillard S & Viru A (1998) The influence of whole body vibration on jumping ability. *Biology of Sport*, 15(3):1-8

Brenner B (1991) Rapid dissociation and reassociation of actomyosin cross-bridges during force generation: a newly observed facet of cross-bridge action in muscle *Proc Natl Acad Sci (USA)* 88(23):10490-4

Brenner B (1993) Dynamic actin interaction of cross-bridges during force generation: implications for cross-bridge action in muscle *Adv Exp Med Biol* 332: 531-543

Brenner B & Eisenberg E (1987) The mechanism of muscle contraction: Biochemical, mechanical, and structural approaches to elucidate cross-bridge action in muscle *Basic Res Cardiol* 82, Suppl 2:3-16

Brooks G & Fahey T (1984) *Exercise Physiology: Human Bioenergetics and its Applications* John Wiley & Sons, New York

Brooks V (1983) Motor control: How posture and movements are controlled *Physical Therapy* 63 (5): 664-673

Brown G.L.and von Euler U The after effects of a tetanus on mammalian muscle *J.Physiol* 93: 39-60, 1938

Bullough P, Goodfellow J & O'Connor J (1973) The relationship between degenerative changes and load-bearing in the human hip *J Bone Joint Surg (Br)* 55(4): 746-758

Burke RE, Radomin R, Zajac F Catch property in single mammalian motor units *Science* 168: 122-124, 1970

Burke RE (1981) Motor Units: anatomy, physiology and functional organisation In: JM Brookhart & VB Mountcastle (eds) *Handbook of Physiology. The Nervous System. Motor Control.* American Physiol Soc 2(1), 1: 345-422

Burovykh A, Samtsova A & Manuilov I (1976) The effects of sports massage techniques on muscular blood circulation *Teoriya i Fizischeskoi Kultury* 2: 21-24

Busso T, Hakkinen K, Pakarinen A, Carasso C, Lacour J, Komi P & Kauhanen H (1990) A systems model of training responses and its relationship to hormonal responses in elite weightlifters. *Eur J Appl Physiol* 61(1-2): 48-54

Busso T, Candau R & Lacour J (1994) Fatigue and fitness modelled from the effects of training on performance *Eur J Appl Physiol* 69(1): 50-4.

Caiozzo V, Barnes W, Prietto C & McMaster W (1981) The effect of isometric precontractions on the slow velocity-high force region of the in-vivo force-velocity relationship *Med & Sci in Sports & Ex* 13: 128

Caiozzo V, Laird T, Chow K, Prietto C & McMaster W (1982) The use of precontractions to enhance the in-vivo force-velocity relationship *Med & Science in Sports & Ex* 14: 162

Caiozzo V, Herrick R & Baldwin K (1991) The influence of hyperthyroidism on the maximal shortening velocity and myosin isoform distribution in slow and fast skeletal muscle *Am J Physiol* 261: C285-295

Caiozzo V, Swoap J, Tao M, Menzel D, & Baldwin K (1993) Single fiber analyses of type IIA myosin heavy chain myosin isoform expression by altered mechanical activity *Am J Physiol* 265: C842-C850

Caiozzo V & Haddad F (1996) Thyroid hormone: Modulation of muscle structure, function, and adaptive responses to mechanical loading *Exerc Sport Sci Revs* 24: 321-361

Caspersen C, Powell K, Koplan P et al (1984) The incidence of injuries and hazards in recreational and fitness runners *Med Sci Sports Exerc* 16: 113

Cavagna G (1977) Storage and utilization of elastic energy in skeletal muscle *Exer & Sport Sciences Rev* 4: 89-129

Chadwick DJ & Ackrill K (1996) Ciba Foundation Symposium: Circadian clocks and their adjustment *Progress in Brain Research*, Vol 111 Hypothalamic integration of circadian rhythms

Chaffin D & Andersson G (1984) *Occupational Biomechanics* John Wiley & Sons : 302-308

Chapman A & Caldwell G (1985) The use of muscle strength in inertial loading. In Winter D, Norman D, Wells R et al (Eds) *Biomechanics IX-A* Human Kinetics Publ : 44-49

Chernyak A, Karomov E & Butchinov Y (1979) Distribution of load volume and intensity throughout the year *Tyazhelaya Atletika* : 15-17

Chu D (1992) *Jumping into Plyometrics* Leisure Press, Champaign, Illinois

Clarke T, Frederick E & Cooper L (1982) The effects of shoe cushioning upon selected force and temporal patterns in running *Med Sci Sports Exerc* 14: 144

Clarke RS, Hellon R & Lind A (1958) The duration of sustained contractions of the human forearm at different muscle temperatures *J Physiol* 143: 454-473

Cooper K H (1968) *Aerobics* Bantam Books

Coyle E, Feiring D et al (1981) Specificity of power improvements through slow and fast isokinetic training. *J Appl Physiol: Respir, Environ & Exerc Physiol* 51: 1437-1442

Davies C, Dooley P, McDonagh M & White M (1985) Adaptation of mechanical properties of muscle to high force training in man. *J Physiol* 365: 277-284

DeLorme T & Watkins A (eds) (1951) *Progressive Resistance Exercise* Appleton-Century-Crofts, N York

DeLorme T (1945) Restoration of muscle power by heavy resistance exercise *J Bone Joint Surg* 27: 645-667

DeLuca C (1985) Control properties of motor units. *J Exp Biol* 115: 125-136

DeVries H (1961) Prevention of muscular stress after exercise. *Research Quart* 32: 177-185

DeVries H (1966) *Physiology of Exercise for Physical Education and Athletics* Wm C Brown : 87-112

DeVries H (1974) *Physiology of Exercise* Wm C Brown, Dubuque, Iowa

Diachikov V (1964) The perfection of athletes' physical preparation In Ozolin N (op cit)

Dons B, Bollerup K, Bonde-Petersen F & Hancke S (1979) The effect of weight-lifting exercise related to muscle fibre composition and muscle cross-sectional area in humans. *Eur J App Physiol* 40: 95-106

Dubrovsky V (1982) Changes in muscle and venous blood flow after massage *Teoriya i Praktika Fizescheskoi Kultury* 4: 56-57

Duchateau J & Hainaut K (1984) Training effects on muscle fatigue in man *Europ J App Physiol* 53: 248-252

Dursenev L & Raevsky L (1978) Strength training of jumpers *Teoriya i Praktika Fizescheskoi Kultury* 10: 62

Dvorkin LS (1988) *The Young Weightlifter* USSR - also available in English translation of Dvorkin LS (1992) *Weightlifting and Age: Scientific & Pedagogical Fundamentals of a Multi-Year System of Training Junior Weightlifters* Sportivny Press, Livonia

Edstrom L & Grimby L (1986) Effect of exercise on the motor unit. *Muscle & Nerve* 9:104-126

Edwards R (1981) Human muscle function and fatigue. In Porter R & Whelan J (eds) *Human Muscle Fatigue: Physiological Mechanisms.* Pitman Medical : 1-18

Eisenberg B, Brown J & Salmons S (1984) Restoration of fast muscle characteristics following cessation of chronic stimulation: the ultrastructure of slow-to-fast transformation *Cell Tissue Res* 238: 221-230

Elliott D (1967) The biomechanical properties of tendon in relation to muscular strength *Ann Phys Med* 9: 1

Ennion S, Sant'ana Pereira J, Sargeant A, Young A, & Goldspink G (1995) Characterization of human skeletal muscle fibres according to the myosin heavy chains they express. *J Muscle Res Cell Motil* Feb;16(1): 35-43

Enoka R (1988) Muscle strength and its development: New perspectives. *Sports Medicine* 6: 146-168

Enoka RM (1996) Commentary-Neural and neuromuscular aspects of muscle fatigue *Muscle & Nerve* Suppl 4: S31-S32.

Ericson L (1992) *Lisa Ericson's Seated Aerobic Workout.* Video available from Sports Training Inc, PO Box 460429, Escondido, California 92046, USA

Evarts E (1973) Brain mechanisms in movement . *Scientific Amer* July 73 : 96

Evarts E (1979) Brain mechanisms of movement. *Scientific Amer* July 79: 146

Fahey T & Brown C (1973) Effects of an anabolic steroid on the strength, body composition and endurance of college males when accompanied by a weight training program. *Med & Science in Sports* 5: 272-276

Finer JT, Mehta A & Spudich J (1995) Characterization of single actin-myosin interactions *Biophys J* 68(4 Suppl):291S-297S

Fitz-Clarke JR, Morton RH & Banister EW (1991) Optimizing athletic performance by influence curves. *J Appl Physiol* Sep; 71(3): 1151-8

Fogel L (1963) *Biotechnology: Concepts and Applications* Prentice-Hall : 228

Ford LE, Huxley AF & Simmons R (1985) Tension transients during steady shortening of frog muscle fibres *J Physiol (Lond)* 361:131-50

Fox E & Mathews D (1974) *Interval Training* WB Saunders, Philadelphia

Fox E & Mathews D (1981) *The Physiological Basis of Physical Education and Athletics.* Saunders College Publ, Philadelphia

Frankel V & Nordin M (1980) *Basic Biomechanics of the Skeletal System* Lea & Febiger : 87-110

Friden J, Seger J, Sjostrom M & Ekblom B (1983b) Adaptive response in human skeletal muscle subjected to prolonged eccentric training. *Int J Sports Med* 4(3): 177-183

Friden J, Sjostrom M & Ekblom B (1983a) Myofibrillar damage following intense eccentric exercise in man. *Int J Sports Med* 4(3): 170-176

Fry AC, Kraemer W, van Boreselen F et al (1994a) Catecholamine responses to short-term, high intensity resistance exercise overtraining *J Apply Physiol* 77(2): 941-946

Fry AC, Kraemer W, Stone M, et al (1994b) Acute endocrine responses to over-reaching before and after 1 year of weightlifting training *Can J Appl Physiol* 19(4): 400-410

Fung Y (1981) *Biomechanics: Mechanical Properties of Living Tissue* Springer-Verlag : 302

Gao Jia-Hong, Parsons L, Bower J Jinhu Xiong, Jinqi Li, & Fox ((1996) Cerebellum Implicated in Sensory Acquisition and Discrimination Rather Than Motor Control *Science* Apr 26, Vol 272

Gandevia SC (1998) Neural control in human muscle fatigue: changes in muscle afferents, motoneurones and motor cortical drive *Acta Physiol Scand* 162(3):275-83

Garland SJ, Griffin L & Ivanova T (1997) Motor unit discharge rate is not associated with muscle relaxation time in sustained submaximal contractions in humans. *Neurosci Lett* Dec 12; 239 (1):25-8

Garrett W (1986) Basic science of musculotendinous injuries. In Nicholas J & Hershman E (eds) *The Lower Extremity and Spine in Sports Medicine* CV Mosby Co, St Louis : 42-58

Geeves MA (1991) The influence of pressure on actin and myosin interactions in solution and in single muscle fibres *J Cell Sci* Suppl, 14: 31-35

Gekakis N, Saez L, Delahaye-Brown AM, Myers MP, Sehgal A, Young M & Weitz C (1995) Isolation of timeless by PER protein interaction: defective interaction between timeless protein and long-period mutant PERL *Science* Nov 3; 270(5237): 811-5

Gibbs WW (1998) News and Analysis: Dogma Overturned *Scientifc American* : 19-20

Gold HK, Spann JF & Braunwald E (1970) Effect of alterations in the thyroid state on the intrinsic contractile properties of isolated ray skeletal muscle *J Clin Invest* 49: 849-854

Goldberg A, Etlinger J , Goldspink D & Jablecki C (1975) Mechanism of work-induced hypertrophy of skeletal muscle. *Med & Science in Sports & Exer* 7: 185-198

Goldspink D F (1980) Physiological factors influencing protein turnover and muscle growth in mammals. In Goldspink D (ed) *Development and specialization of skeletal muscle.* Soc for Exptal Biol Seminar Series 7, Cambridge, Cambridge Univ Press : 67-89

Goldspink G (1978) Muscle energetics and animal locomotion: In Alexander R McN (ed) *Mechanics and Energetics of Animal Locomotion* : 57-81

Goldspink G (1992) The brains behind the brawn. *New Scientist* 1 Aug 92: 28-33

Goletz V & Osadchy V (1986) The complex use of restorative meas in different satges of training *Velosipedniy Sport* 1:23-26

Gollnick P & Saltin B (1982) Significance of skeletal muscle oxidative enzyme enhancement with endurance training. *Clin Physiol* 2: 1-12

Gonyea W (1980) Role of exercise in inducing increases in skeletal muscle fiber number *J Appl Physiol: Respirat Environ Exer Physiol* 48: 421-426

Gordon E (1967) Anatomical and biochemical adaptation of muscle to different exercises *JAMA* 201: 755-9

Grange RW, Vandenboom R, Houston M Physiological significance of myosin phosphorylation in skeletal muscle. *Can J Appl Physiol* 18: 229-242, 1993

Green H (1988) Neuromuscular aspects of fatigue. *Science Periodical on Res & Technol in Sport (SPORTS)* Coaching Assoc of Canada. 8(3): 1-16

Green P (1967) Problems of organization of motor systems. In Rosen & Snell (eds) *Progress in Theoretical Biology* Vol 2 : 79

Greene P & McMahon T (1979) Reflex stiffness of man's anti-gravity muscles during kneebends while carrying extra weights. *J Biomechs* 12: 881-891

Grotmol S, Totland G & Kryvi H (1988) A general, computer-based method for the study of the spatial distribution of muscle fiber types in skeletal muscle *Anat Embryol* 177: 421-426.

Guyton A (1984) *Textbook of Medical Physiology* WB Saunders Co, Philad 6th ed

Hagbarth KE & Macefield VG (1995) The fusimotor system. Its role in fatigue *Adv Exp Med Biol* 384:259-70

Haggmark T, Jansson E & Svane B (1978) Cross-sectional area of the thigh muscle in man measured by computed tomography. *Scand J Clin Lab Invest* 38: 355-360

Häkkinen K (1985) Factors influencing trainability of muscular strength during short term and prolonged training. *National Strength & Conditioning (NSCA) Journal* 7(2) : 32-36

Häkkinen K, Kauhanen H & Komi P (1985) Comparison of neuromuscular performance capacities between weightlifters, powerlifters and bodybuilders *International Olympic Lifter*, USA 7: 24-26

Häkkinen K (1989) Neuromuscular and hormonal adaptations during strength and power training *J Sports Med* 29: 9-26

Häkkinen K & Komi P (1986) Training-induced changes in neuromusculat performance under voluntary and reflex conditions *Eur J Appl Physiol* 55: 147

Häkkinen K & Pakarinen A (1993a) Acute hormonal responses to two different fatiguing heavy-resistance protocols in male athletes *J Appl Physiol* 74(2): 882-887

Häkkinen K & Pakarinen A (1993b) Serum hormones and strength development during strength training in middle-aged and elderly males and females *Acta Phsiol Scand* 150: 1-9

Hall S (1985) The Brain branches out *Science 85* June 1985

Hamalainen N & Pette D (1995) Patterns of myosin isoforms in mammalian skeletal muscle fibres. *Microsc Res Tech* Apr 1; 30(5): 381-9

Hanes DP & Schall JD (1996) Neural Control of Voluntary Movement Initiation *Science* October 18; 274: 427-430

Harbin G, Durst L & Harbin D (1989) Evaluation of oculomotor response in relationship to sports performance *Med Sci in Sports & Exercise* 21 (3) : 258-262

Harre D (ed) (1971) *Trainingslehre*. Sportverlag, Berlin

Hather BM, Tesch PA, Buchanan P & Dudley GA (1991) Influence of eccentric actions on skeletal muscle adaptations to resistance training. *Acta Physiol Scand* Oct;143(2): 177-85

Herzog W, Guimaraes A, Anton M & Carter-Erdman K (1991) Moment-length relations of rectus femoris muscles of speed skaters/cyclists and runners. Med Sci Sports Exerc Nov; 23 (11):1289-96

Herzog W (1996) Force-sharing among synergistic muscles: Theoretical Considerations and Experimental Approaches *Exer Sport Sci Revs* 24: 173-203

Hetrick G & Wilmore J (1979) Androgen levels and muscle hypertrophy during an eight-week training program for men/women. *Med Sci Sports* 11: 102

Hettinger T & Muller E (1966) *Muskelleistung and Muskeltraining*. Arbeitsphysiologie 15: 111-126

Hettinger T (1966) *Isometric muscle training*. Georg Thieme Verlag, Stuttgard

Hettinger T W (1961) *The Physiology of Strength*

Hikida R, Staron R et al (1983) Muscle fiber necrosis associated with marathon runners *J of Neurolog Sciences* 59: 185-203

Hill A V (1953) The mechanics of active muscle. *Proc Roy Soc Lond (Biol)* 141: 104-117

Hirose K, Franzini-Armstrong C, Goldman Y & Murray J (1994) Structural changes in muscle crossbridges accompanying force generation. *J Cell Biol* Nov;127(3): 763-78

Hislop H & Perrine J (1967) The isokinetic concept of exercise. *Phys Ther* 47: 114-7

Holland G (1968) The physiology of flexibility: A review of the literature *Kinesiology Review* : 49-62

Hortobágyi T, Houmard J, Fraser D, Dudek R, Jean Lambert & Tracy J (1998) Normal forces and myofibrillar disruption after repeated eccentric exercise *J of Physiology* Feb; (84) 2: 492-498

Hortobagyi T, Dempsey L, Fraser D, Zheng D, Hamilton G, Lambert J & Dohm L (2000) Changes in muscle strength, muscle fibre size and myofibrillar gene expression after immobilization and retraining in humans. *J Physiol* Apr 1;524 Pt 1:293-304.

Horwill F (1992) Periodization - Plausible or Piffle? *Modern Athlete & Coach*, Adelaide, 30 (1): 11-13.

Horwill F (1995) It's results that count. *Track Technique* Los Altos (Cal.) 130: 4142-4143, 4165.

Houmard JA (1991) Impact of reduced training on performance in endurance athletes. *Sports Med* Dec;12(6): 380-93

Howard J & Enoka R (1987) Enhancement of maximum force by contralateral-limb stimulation *J of Biomechs* 20:908

Hutchison M (1986) *MegaBrain: New Tools and Techniques for Brain Growth and Mind Expansion* Ballantine Books

Huxley A F (1974) Muscular Contraction *J Physiol* 243: 1-44

Iashvili A (1982) Active and passive flexibility in athletes specializing in different sports *Teoriya i Praktika Fizischeskoi Kultury* (translated by M Yessis) 7: 51-52

Ikai M & Fukunaga T (1968) Calculation of muscle strength per unit cross-sectional area of human muscle by means of ultrasonic measurement *Int Z Angew Physiol* 26: 26-32

Israel S (1963) Das Akute Entlastungssyndrom *Theorie und Praxis der Korperkultur* 12

Israel S (1972) *The acute syndrome of detraining* GDR National Olympic Comm, Berlin 2: 30-35

Janmey P, Hvidt S, Oster G, Lamb J, Stossel T & Hartwig J (1990) Effect of ATP on actin filament stiffness *Nature* 347(6288): 95-99

Johns R & Wright V (1962)   Relative importance of various tissues in joint stiffness *J of App Physiol* 17: 824-828

Johnson B, Adamczyk J, Tennoe K & Stromme S (1976) A comparison of concentric and eccentric muscle training. *Med Sci Sports* 8: 35-38

Jones LA (1995) The senses of effort and force during fatiguing contractions *Adv Exp Med Biol* 384: 305-13

Jurimae J, Abernethy P, Quigley B, Blake K & McEniery M (1997) Differences in muscle contractile characteristics among bodybuilders, endurance trainers and control subjects *Eur J Appl Physiol* 75: 357-362

Kabat H (1958) *Proprioceptive facilitation in therapeutic exercises.* In Licht M (ed) *Therapeutic Exercises* Waverley Press, Baltimore

Kanehisa H & Miyashita M (1983a) Effect of isometric and isokinetic muscle training on static strength and dynamic power *Eur J Appl Physiol* 52: 104-106

Kanehisa H & Miyashita M (1983b) Specificity of velocity in strength training *Eur J of App Physiol* 52: 104

Kaneko M, Komi P & Aura O (1984) Mechanical efficiency of concentric and eccentric exercises performed with medium to fast contraction rates. *Scand J Sport Sci* 6(1): 15-20

Karba R, Stefanovska A & Dordevic S (1990) Human skeletal muscle: phasic type of electrical stimulation increases its contractile speed *Ann Biomed Eng* 18(5):479-90 & 18(6):711

Karpman VL, Orel V, Stepanova S, Belina O & Sinyakov A (1882)   A Test for determining the Physical Preparedness of Weightlifters *Weightlifting Yearbook 1982* Fizkultura I Sport, Moscow:

Keith L (1977) Exercise: Some new options   *Sports Illustrated* 7 March 77 :27

Kempson G (1975) Mechanical properties of articular cartilage and their relationship to matrix degradation with age *Ann Rheum Dis* 34, Suppl 2: 111-113

Kennedy J, Hawkins R, Willis R & Sanylchuk K (1976) Tension studies of human knee ligaments: yield point, ultimate failure and disruption of the cruciate and tibial collateral ligaments. *J Bone & Joint Surg* 58A: 350

Kenyon, GT (1997) A model of long-term memory storage in the cerebellar cortex: A possible role for plasticity at parallel fiber synapses onto stellate/basket interneurons. *Proc Natl Acad Sci USA.* 94: 14200-14205

Kernell D & Monster A (1982) Time course and properties of late adaptation in spinal motoneurons of the cat. *Exp Brain Res* 46: 191-196

Kernell, D. (1998). Muscle Regionalization. *Can J Appl Physiol* 23(1):1-22.

Klein DC, Moore RY & Reppert R (1991) *Suprachiasmatic Nucleus: The Mind's Clock*

Knapik J, Wright J, Mawdsley R & Braun J (1983) Isometric, isotonic and isokinetic torque variations in four muscle groups through a range of joint motion. *J Amer Phys Ther Assoc* 63: 938-947

Knight K (1979) Knee rehabilitation by the daily adjustable progressive resistive exercise technique. *Amer J Sports Med* 7 (6) : 336-337

Knight K (1986) Understanding sports rehabilitation: learn the DAPRE technique *Fitness Management*, USA   May/June & July/Aug 1986

Knott M & Voss D (1977)   *Proprioceptive Neuromuscular Facilitation* Balliere, Tindall & Cassell

Koh TJ & Herzog W (1998) Eccentric training does not increase sarcomere number in rabbit dorsiflexor muscles. *J of Biomechs* 31, 499-501.

Komulainen J, Kalliokoski R, Koskinen S, Drost M, Kuipers H & Hesselink M (2000) Controlled lengthening or shortening contraction-induced damage is followed by fiber hypertrophy in rat skeletal muscle. *Int J Sports Med* Feb; 21(2): 107-12

Komi P & Buskirk E (1972) Effect of eccentric and concentric muscle conditioning on tension and electrical activity of human muscle. *Ergonomics* 15: 417-434

Komi P (1973a) Measurement of force-velocity relationship in human muscle under concentric and eccentric contractions. *Med Sport: Biomechanics III* 8: 224-229

Komi P (1973b) Relationship between muscle tension, EMG and velocity of contraction under concentric and eccentric work In J Desmedt (ed) *New Developments in Electromyography and Clinical Neurophysiology* Karger, Basle 1: 596-606

Komi P (1984) Physiological and biomechanical correlates of muscle function *Exerc & Sports Sciences Rev* 14: 81-121

Konstantinov O (1979) Training programme for high level javelin throwers *Legkaya Atletika* 12: 8-11

Kopysov V (1978) Vibration massage in the pre-competition conditioning of weightlifters *Tyazhelaya Atletika*, 52-53

Kopysov V (1980) Recovery in the training of Weightlifters *Teoriya i Praktika Fizischeskoi Kultury* 8: 18-19

Kovalik A (1978) Prevention of overstress to the skeletal-joint system of weightlifters *Teoriya i Praktika Fizischeskoi Kultury* 4: 36-39

Kovanen V, Suominen H & Heikkinen E (1984) Mechanical properties of fast and slow skeletal muscle with special reference to collagen and endurance training. *J Biomechs* 17(10): 725-735

Kraemer & Koziris (1992) Muscle strength training: techniques and considerations *Phys Ther Prac* 2(1): 56-68\

Kraemer & Koziris (1994) Olympic weightlifting and powerlifting In D Lamb, H Knuttgen & R Murray (eds) *Physiology and Nutrition for Competitive Sport* pp1-54

Kugelberg E & Lindegren B (1979) Transmission and contraction fatigue of rat motor units in relation to succinate dehydrogenase activity of motor unit fibres. *J Physiol* 288: 285-300

Kusnetsov V & Fiskalov I (1985) Correlations between speed and strength in cyclic locomotion *Teoriya i Praktika Fizischeskoi Kultury* 8:6

Kusnetsov V (1975) *Strength Preparation: Theoretical Foundations of muscle strength development. (German)* Sportverlag, Berlin

Lamb D (1984) *The Physiology of Exercise* MacMillan, New York

Larsson L & Tesch PA (1986) Motor unit fibre density in extremely hypertrophied skeletal muscles in man. *Eur J Appl Physiol* 55: 130-136, 1986.

Lebedev, M.A. & Peliakov A V (1991). Analysis of the interference electromyogram of human soleus muscle after exposure to vibration. *Neirofiziologia* 23 (1): 57-65 (article in Russian, summary in English)

Levin A & Wyman J (1927) The viscous elastic properties of muscle *Proc Royal Soc (B)* London 101: 218-243

Lindh M (1979) Increase of muscle strength from isometric quadriceps exercise at different knee angles. *Scand J of Rehab Med* 11: 33-36

Lindstedt SL, McGlothlin T, Percy E & Pifer J (1998) Task-specific design of skeletal muscle: balancing muscle structural composition *Comp Biochem Physiol B Biochem Mol Biol* 120 (1):35-40

Lomo T, Westgaard R & Dahl H (1974) Contractile properties of musle: control by pattern of muscle activity in the rat *Proc Roy Soc Med (B)* 187: 99-103

Lotze M, Montoya P, Erb M, Hülsmann E, Flor H, Uwe Klosec U, Birbaumer N & Grodd W (1999) Activation of Cortical and Cerebellar Motor Areas during Executed and Imagined Hand Movements: An fMRI Study *J of Cognitive Neuroscience* 1999;11:491-501

Luo Y, Cooke R & Pate E (1994) Effect of series elasticity on delay in development of tension relative to stiffness during muscle activation *Am J Physiol* 267(6 Pt 1): C 1598-1606

Lynn, R & Morgan DL (1994) Decline running produces more sarcomeres in rat vastus intermedius muscle fibers than does incline running. *J of Appl Physiol* 77, 1439-1444

MacDougall J D, Sale D, Elder G & Sutton J (1982) Muscle ultrastructural characteristics of elite powerlifters and bodybuilders. *Eur J Appl Physiol* 48: 117-126

MacDougall J, Wenger H & Green H (1982) *Physiological Testing of the Elite Athlete* Canadian Assoc of Sport Sciences

Magnusson SP, Aagard P, Simonsen E & Bojsen-Moller F (1998) A biomechanical evaluation of cyclic and static stretch in human skeletal muscle. *Int J Sports Med* Jul; 19(5): 310-6

Maier N (1963) *Problem-solving Discussions and Conferences: Leadership Methods and Skills* McGraw-Hill

Makharova T & Stupnitsky Y (1983) The functional state of the neuromuscular system in restoration *Teoriya I Praktika Fizischeskoi Kultury* 12: 39-40

Mansour J M & Pereira J M (1987) Quantitative functional anatomy of the lower limb with application to human gait *J Biomech* 20: 51-58

Masamitsu Ito, Kawakami Y, Ichinose Y, Fukashiro S & Fukunaga T (1998) Non-isometric behavior of fascicles during isometric contractions of a human muscle *J of Physiol* Oct; (85)4: 1230-1235

Maton B (1981) Human motor unit activity during the onset of muscle fatigue in submaximal isometric and isotonic contraction *Europ J Appl Physiol* 46: 271-281

Matthews P (1973) The advances of the last decade of animal experimentation upon muscle spindles In Desmedt J (ed) *New Developments in Electromyography and Clinical Neurophysiology* Karger, Basel 3: 95-125

Matveyev L (1977) *Fundamentals of Sports Training* Fizkultura i Sport Publ, Moscow (Russian)

Matveyev L (1981) *Fundamentals of Sports Training* Progress Publ , Moscow (English)

Maximenko G (1979) Physical qualities and results in middle-distance running *Legkaya Atletika* 5: 15

McCloy C (1948) *Endurance.* The Physical Educator 5: 9-23

McDonagh M & Davies C (1984) Adaptive response of mammalian muscle to exercise with high loads *Eur J Appl Physiol* 52: 139-155

MacDougall JD, Sale DG, Alway SE & Sutton J (1984) Muscle fiber number in biceps brachii in bodybuilders and control subjects *J Appl Physiol* 57: 1399-1403

Mardsen CD, Meadows J, Merton P Isolated single motor units in human muscle and their rate of discharge during maximal voluntary effort *J Physiol* 217: 12-13, 1971

McArdle WD, Katch FI & Katch VL *Exercise Physiology* (1991) Lea & Febiger 3rd Ed . 136

Medical Chronicle (1978) South Africa May 78: 9

Medvedev A N (1986) *A System of Multi-Year Training in Weightlifting* Fizkultura i Sport, Moscow

Mijailovich SM, Fredberg J & Butler J (1996) On the theory of muscle contraction: filament extensibility and the development of isometric force and stiffness *Biophys J* 71(3):1475-84

Miller R, Mirka A & Maxfield M (1981) Rate of tension development in isometric contractions of a human hand *Exp Neurol* 73: 267-285

Minegawa Y et al (1978) Cited in Bosco (1982): 29

Minns R, Soden P & Jackson D (1973) The role of the fibrous components and ground substance in the mechanical properties of biological tissues *J Biomechs* 6: 153-165

Moffroid M & Whipple R (1970) Specificity of speed of exercise *Physical Therapy* 50: 1693-1699

Monod H & Scherrer J (1967) Capacité de travail statique d'une groupe msusculaire synergique chez l'homme *C R Soc Biol* 151: 1358-1369

Montagni S & Cardinale M (1996) *Beach Handball* Federazione Italiana Giuoco Handball pp 113-126

Moore-Ede MC, Campbell S & Reiter R (1992) *Electromagnetic Fields and Circadian Rhythmicity*

Moore RY & Eichler V (1972) Loss of a circadian adrenal corticosterone rhythm following suprachiasmatic lesions in the rat. *Brain Res* Jul 13; 42(1): 201-6.

Morimoto S (1986) Effect of length change in muscle fibers on conduction velocity in human motor units *Jpn J Physiol* 36(4):773-82

Mujika I, Busso T, Lacoste L, Barale F, Geyssant A & Chatard J (1996) Modeled responses to training and taper in competitive swimmers. *Med Sci Sports Exerc* Feb;28(2):251-8

Murphy M & White R (1978) *The Psychic Side of Sports* Adison-Wesley

Myers MP, Wager-Smith K, Wesley C, Young M & Sehgal A (1995) Positional cloning and sequence analysis of the Drosophila clock gene, timeless *Science* Nov 3; 270(5237): 805-8.

Nachemson A & Evans J (1968) Some mechanical properties of the third lumbar interlaminar ligament (ligamentum flavum) *J Biomechs* 1: 211

Nagai K (1992) Central Regulation of Energy Metabolism with special reference to Circadian Rhythm

Nicol C, Avela J & Komi P (1997) Effects of repeated exhaustive stretch-shortening cycle exercise (SSC) on short latency reflex responses *Med Sci iSports Exerc* 29(5): Supplement: 1125

Nigg B (1986) Ed: *Biomechanics of Running Shoes* Human Kinetics Publ

Nikituk B & Samoilov N (1990) The adaptive mechanisms of muscle fibres to exercise and possibilities for controlling them *Teoriya i Praktika Fizischeskoi Kultury* 5: 11-14

Novik G, Saxonov A & Saxonov N (1980) Heart Rate - an indicator of a Weightlifter's special work capacity *Tyazhelaya Atletika* 9: 43-44

Noyes F (1977) Functional properties of knee ligaments and alterations induced by immobilization: a correlative biomechanical and histological study in primates *Clin Orthop & Rel Res* 123: 210-242

Nurmekivi A (1987) Running: adapt the method to the athlete *Legyaka Atletika* 10: 8

Nygaard E & Nielsen E (1978) Skeletal muscle fiber capillarisation with extreme endurance training in man. In Eriksson B, Furberg B (Eds). *Swimming Medicine IV* (vol. 6, pp. 282-293). University Park Press, Baltimore

O'Leary DD, Hope K, Sale G Post-tetanic potentiation of human dorsiflexors *J of Appl Physiology* 83(6): 2131-2138, 1997

O'Shea J (1966) Development of strength and muscle hypertrophy through selected weight programs *Res Quart* 37: 95-107

Osternig L R (1986) Isokinetic dynamometry: Implications for muscle testing and rehabilitation *Exer & Sport Sci Rev* 14:45-80

Ostrander S & Schroeder L (1981) *Superlearning* Sphere Books

Ostrander S & Schroeder L (1994) *Superlearning 2000* Souvenir Press

Ozolin N (1971) *Athlete's training system for competition (Russian)* Fizkultura i Sport Publ, Moscow

Palmer BM & Moore RL Myosin light chain phosphorylation and tension potentiation in mouse skeletal muscle. *Am J Physiol* 257 C1012-C1019, 1989

Paschall H B (1954*) Development of Strength* Vigour Press, London

Pate E & Cooke R (1986) A model for the interaction of muscle cross-bridges with ligands which compete with ATP *J Theor Biol* 118(2): 215-30

Pavlov I (1927) *Conditioned Reflexes* Oxford Univ Press, London

Peters TJ & Waterman RH (1983) *In Search of Excellence* Warner Books, New York

Piazzesi G, Linari M & Lombardi V (1993) Kinetics of regeneration of cross-bridge power stroke in shortening muscle *Adv Exp Med Biol* 332:691-701

Perrine J & Edgerton V (1978) Muscle force-velocity and power-velocity relationships under isokinetic loading *Med & Science in Sports* 10: 159-166

Peshkov V (1981) The effect of restorative point massage on the functional state of gymnasts *Teoriya i Praktika Fizescheskoi Kultury* 12: 35

Petrofsky JS & Hendershot D (1984) The interrelationship between blood pressure, intramuscular pressure and isometric endurance in fast and slow twitch skeletal muscle in the cat. *Eur J Appl Physiol* 53: 106-111

Petrofsky JS & Phillips C (1986) The physiology of static exercise *Exerc Sport Sci Revs* 14: 1-44

Pette D & Vrbova G (1985) Neural control of phenotypic expression in mammalian muscle fibres *Muscle & Nerve* 8: 676-689

Pipes TV(1994) Strength training and fiber types *Scholastic Coach* March, 63: 67-70.

Platonov V (1988) The principles of biochemical adaptation in the sports training process *Adaptatsia v Sport* Russia 32-45

Pope M, Johnson R, Brown P & Tishe C (1978) The role of the musculature in injuries to the medial collateral ligament *Proc of the 6th New England Bioeng Conf* : 175-178

Powell K, Kohl H, Caspersen C & Blair S (1986) An epidemiological perspective on the causes of running injuries *Phys Sports Medicine* 14: 100-114

Prigogine I & Stengers I (1984) *Order out of Chaos* Flamingo

Radcliffe J & Farantinos R (1985) *Plyometrics: Explosive Power* Human Kinetics Publ

Raitsin L (1974) The effectiveness of isometric and electrostimulated training on muscle strength at different joint angles. *Yessis Review of Soviet Phys Ed & Sports* 11: 35-39

Rapoport M, van Reekum R & Mayberg, H. (2000) The Role of the Cerebellum in Cognition and Behavior: A Selective Review. *J Neuropsychiarty Clin Neurosci* 12: 193-198

Rasch P (1979) *Weight Training*. Wm C Brown, Dubuque, Iowa

Ratov IP & Kryazhev V (1986) The endurance problem and prospects for new approaches to solving it *Teoriya i Praktika Fizischeskoi Kultury* 4:5-9 (transl in *Soviet Sports Review* 1990, 25(2) : 56)

Redfern PH & Lemmer B (1997) *Handbook of Experimental Pharmacology: Physiology and Pharmacology of Biological Rhythms*

Reding, Serge (1971) Personal Communication

Robbins S & Hanna A (1987) Running related injury prevention through barefoot adaptations *Med Sci Sports Exerc* 19: 148-156

Robbins S, Hanna A & Gouw G (1988) Overload protection: avoidance response to heavy plantar surface loading *Med Sci Sports Exerc* 20(1) : 85-92

Rodgers K & Berger R (1974) Motor unit involvement and tension showing maximum voluntary concentric, eccentric and isometric contractions of the elbow flexors. *Med & Sci Sports* 6. 253-259

Rohmert W (1968) Right-left comparison of isometric arm muscle training with different training regimes for eight year old children (German) *Int Zangew Physiol* 26: 363

Roman R (1986) *Trenirovka Tyazheloatleta (Training of the Weightlifter)* Fizkultura i Sport Moscow

Rosentzweig J & Hinson M (1972) Comparison of isometric, isotonic and isokinetic exercise by electromyograph. *Arch Phys Med & Rehab* 53: 249-250

Rosenzweig M (1984) Experience, Memory and the Brain *American Psychologist* April 1984

Roy RR, Baldwin KM & Edgerton VR (1991) The Plasticity of Skeletal Muscle: Effects of Neuromuscular Activity *Exer Sport Sci Revs* 19: 269-312

Russ DW & Binder-Macleod S (1999) Variable-frequency trains offset low-frequency fatigue in human skeletal muscle *Muscle Nerve* Jul; 22(7):874-82

Sale D & MacDougall J D (1981) Specificity in Strength Training: A review for the coach and athlete. *SPORTS* Coaching Ass of Canada : 1-7

Sale D, McComas A, MacDougall J & Upton A (1982) Neuromuscular adaptation in human thenar muscles following strength training and immobilization. *J Appl Physiol: Respirat, Environ & Exercise Physiol* 53: 419-424

Saltin B & Rowell L (1980) Functional adaptations in physical activity and inactivity. *Federation Proc* 39: 1506-1513

Saltin B & Gollnick P (1983) Skeletal muscle adaptability: significance for metabolism and performance In: LD Peachey (ed) *Handbook of Physiology. Section 10. Skeletal Muscle* American Physiol Soc pp 555-631

Sapega A, Quedenfeld T, Moyer R & Butler R (1981) Biophysical factors in range-of-motion exercise *Physician & Sports Medicine* : 1140-1145

Schantz P, Randall Fox E, Norgen P & Tyden A (1981) The relationship between mean muscle fiber area and the muscle cross-sectional area of the thigh in subjects with large differences in thigh girth. *Acta Physiol Scand* 113: 537-539,

Schiaffino S & Reggiani C (1994) Myosin isoforms in mammalian skeletal muscle. *J Appl Physiol* Aug; 77(2): 493-501

Schneidman M (1979) *The Soviet Road to Olympus*

Schutt CE & Lindberg U (1993) A new perspective on muscle contraction *FEBS Lett* Jun 28;325(1-2):59-62

Schutz R et al (1984) Mechanoreceptors in human cruciate ligaments *J of Bone & Jt Surg* 64A, 7: 171

Secher N (1975) Isometric rowing strength of experienced and inexperienced oarsmen. *Med & Science in Sports* 7: 280-283

Seedhom B & Wright V (1988) Is repetitive loading a cause of osteoarthritis? *J Orthop Rheum* 1: 79-87

Seedhom B & Swann A (1985) Biomechanics of the osteoarthritic knee *Pendragon Papers No 1, Proc of Workshop* at Duke of Cornwall Dept of Rheum, Royal Cornwall Hosp, Truro, Cornwall Oct 1985

Seedhom B, Takeda T, Tsubuku M & Wright V (1977) Mechanical factors and patello-femoral osteoarthritis *Ann Rheum Dis* 38: 307-316

Sehgal A, Rothenfluh-Hilfiker A, Hunter-Ensor M, Chen Y, Myers MP, Young M (1995) Rhythmic expression of timeless: a basis for promoting circadian cycles in period gene autoregulation. *Science* Nov 3; 270(5237): 808-10.

Selye H (1956) *The Stress of Life* McGrawHill

Shepley B, MacDougall JD, Cipriano N, Sutton J, Tarnopolsky M & Coates G (1992) Physiological effects of tapering in highly trained athletes. *J Appl Physiol* Feb; 72(2): 706-11

Shidlovsky A, Kastrubin E & Grigoriev & (1979) The use of central electroanalgesia to strengthen the adaptive processes *Teoriya i Praktika Fizescheskoi Kultury* 10: 19-21

Shishkin L (1989) Answers provided by Computer *Sport in the USSR* 4(313) : 16

Sidorenko NP & Podlubnaia Z (1995) The possible restructuring of myosin bridges on the thick filament surface, caused by muscle activation *Biofizika* 40(3): 603-6

Siff M C (1977) *Modelling of electroencephalographic phenomena.* Unpublished MSc dissertation, Univ of Witwatersrand, S Africa

Siff M C (1981) A ballistic method for analysing knee stability *International Symposium on Sports Medicine* Wingate Inst, Israel 5-7 July

Siff M C (1982a) Physiological and Biophysical Analysis of Overtraining and Overtraining Injuries Proc of *19th Congr of SA Assoc for Sports Science, Phys Ed & Recr*, Pretoria, 6-8 Oct 1982

Siff M C (1982b) Application of Catastrophe Theory in analysing joint stability *Annual Congress of SA Physiological Society*, Bloemfontein, South Africa 13-15 Oct

Siff M C (1984) *Physiological Dangers of Exercise* SAASSPER Publications, S African Assoc for Sports Science, Physical Education & Recreation. ISBN 0 620 07504

Siff M C (1986) *Ballistic Analysis of Human Knee Stability* Unpublished PhD thesis, University of Witwatersrand, S Africa

Siff M C (1987) The science of flexibility and stretching. *Proc of 1987 SA Physio Congr*

Siff M C (1988) Biomathematical relationship between strength and bodymass. *S African J for Res in Sport, Phys Ed & Recr* 11(1) : 81-92

Siff M C (1989) *Strength-Flexibility Development through PNF* NSCA conference June 1989 : Videotapes distributed by NSCA, Lincoln, Nebraska. Also published as Siff M C (1991) Modified PNF as a system of physical conditioning *NSCA Journal* (13) 4 :73-77

Siff M C (1990) Applications of electrostimulation in physical conditioning: a review. *J of Appl Sports Science Res* 4 (1) : 20-26

Siff M C (1990) ed., *Professional Communication* Lex Patria S Africa Ch 8 p152 and Ch 2 (Management Theory)

Siff MC & Verkhoshansky YV (1999) *Supertraining* Supertraining International, Denver, 4th ed

Siff MC & Yessis M (1992) eds. *Sports Restoration and Massage* School of Mech Eng, University of Witwatersrand, S Africa

Siff M C (1998) *Facts and Fallacies of Fitness* School of Mechanical Eng, University of Witwatersrand, S Africa

Smerdu V, Karsch-Mizrachi I, Campione M, Leinwand L & Schiaffino S (1994) Type IIx myosin heavy chain transcripts are expressed in type IIb fibers of human skeletal muscle. *Am J Physiol* Dec; 267(6 Pt 1):C1723-8

Smith K & Smith M (1962) *Perception and Motion: An analysis of space-structured behaviour* Saunders Co, Philadelphia 7: 125-147

Smith L & Whitley L (1965) Influence of strengthening exercise on speed of limb movement. *Arch of Phys Med & Rehab* 46: 772-777

Smith L & Whitley L (1966) Influence of three different training programs on strength and speed of a limb movement. *Res Quart* 37: 132-142

Smith L (1964) Influence of strength training on pre-tensed and free-arm speed. *Res Quart* 35: 554-561

Soechting J & Roberts W (1975) Transfer characteristics between EMG activity and muscle tension under isometric conditions in man *J Physiol*, Paris 70: 779-793

Sokolov L (1982) Some Questions concerning the Perfection of Weightlifting Technique *1982 Weightlifting Yearbook* Fizkultura i Sport   Moscow

Spiridonova L & Kuznetsova M (1986) Restorative massage in the training of cross-country skiers *Teoriya i Praktika Fizescheskoi Kultury* 2: 50-52

Staron RS & Hikida RS (1992) Histochemical, biochemical and ultrastructural analyses of single human muscle fibers with special reference to the C fiber population *J Histochem Cytochem* 40: 563-568

Staron RS & & Johnson P Myosin polymorphism and differential expression in adult human skeletal muscle *Comp Biochem Physiol* 106B (3): 463-475

Staron R (1997) Human skeletal muscle fiber types:delineation, development, distribution *Can J Appl Physiol* 22(4): 307-327

Stauber WT (1989) Eccentric action of muscles: Physiology, Injury and Adaptation *Exerc Sport Sci Revs* 17: 157-186

Steinhaus A (1955) Strength from Morpugo to Muller - A half century of research *J of Assoc for Phys & Mental Rehab* 9: 147-150

Stepanaova S, Sinyakov A & Belina O (1983) Body composition and physical work capacity of the strongest weightlifters in the USSR *Tyazhelaya Atletika* 1: 29-31

Stephan FK & Zucker I (1972) Circadian rhythms in drinking behavior and locomotor activity of rats are eliminated by hypothalamic lesions. *Proc Natl Acad Sci* USA. Jun; 69(6): 1583-6.

Stephens D & Reid J (1988) Biomechanics of hamstring strains in sprinting events *Canadian J of Sport Sciences* 13(3): 78

Stokes M & Young A (1984) The contribution of reflex inhibition to arthrogenous muscle weakness *Clin Sci* 67: 7-14

Sutarno CG & McGill SM (1995) Isovelocity investigation of the lengthening behaviour of the erector spinae muscles. *Eur J Appl Physiol* 70(2):146-53

Suzuki S & Hutton R (1976)   Postcontractile motorneuron discharge produced by muscle afferent activation   *Medicine & Science in Sports* 8(4) : 258 - 264

Swanepoel M (1998) Joint Loading Personal communication

Tabachnik B (1979) How to find a sprinter *Legkaya Atletika* 3: 12-14

Talyshev F (1977) Recovery *Legkaya Atletika* 6:25

Tamaki T, Uchiyama S & Nakano S (1992) A weight-lifting exercise model for inducing hypertrophy in the hindlimb muscles of rats *Med Sci Sports Exerc* 24(8): 881-886

Tellier RD (1978) *Operations Management* Harper & Row

Terjung R (1979) Endocrine response to exercise. *Exer & Sport Sciences Revs* : 153-180

Tesch P & Larsson L (1982) Muscle hypertrophy in bodybuilders *Eur J Appl Physiol* 49: 301-306

Tesch PA, Komi PV, Jacobs I, Karlsson J (1983) Influence of lactate accumulation of EMG frequency spectrum during repeated concentric contractions *Acta Physiol Scand* 119: 61-67.

Tesch PA (1988). Skeletal muscle adaptation consequent to long-term heavy resistance exercise *Med Sci Sports Exerc* 20(5) Suppl. S132-S134.

Thepault-Mathieu C et al (1988) Myoelectrical and mechanical changes linked to length specificity during isometric training *J of Appl Physiol* 64 (4): 1500-5

Thihanyi J, Apor P & Fekete G (1982) Force-velocity-power characteristics and fibre composition in human knee extensor muscles *Eur J of Appl Physiol* 48: 331-343

Thistle H, Hislop H, Moffroid M et al (1967) Isokinetic contraction: a new concept of resistive exercise *Arch of Physical Medicine & Rehabilitation* 49: 279-282

Thomas V (1970) *Science and Sport* Little, Brown & Co, Boston : 145-150

Thomas N & Thornhill R (1996) Stretch activation and nonlinear elasticity of muscle cross-bridges *Biophys J* 70(6): 2807-18

Thomson DB & Chapman AE (1988) The mechanical response of active human muscle during and after stretch *Eur J Appl Physiol* 57(6): 691-697

Thorstensson A, Hulten B, von Dobeln W & Karlsson J (1976) Effect of strength training on enzyme activities and fibre characteristics in human skeletal muscle. *Acta Physiol Scandinavica* 96: 392-398

Tipton C, James S, Mergner W & Tcheng T (1970) Influence of exercise on strength of medial collateral knee ligaments of dogs. *Am J of Physiol* 218: 894-902

Tipton C, Matthes R & Sandage D (1974) In situ measurements of junction strength and ligament orientation in rats. *J Appl Physiol* 37: 758-761

Tipton C, Matthes R, Maynard J & Carey R (1975) The influence of physical activity on ligaments and tendons *Med & Science in Sports* 7: 165-175

Tipton C, Schild R & Tomanek R (1967) Influence of physical activity on the strength of knee ligaments in rats. *Amer J of Physiol* 212: 783-787

Tschiene P (1990) Der aktuelle Stand der Theorie des Trainings *Leistungssport* 3: 5-9.

Tschiene P (1991) Die Prioritat des biologischen Aspekts in der Theorie des Trainings *Leistungssport* 6: 5-11.

Tsuda Y, Yasutake H, Ishijima A & Yanagida T (1996) Torsional rigidity of single actin filaments and actin-actin bond breaking force under torsion measured directly by in vitro micromanipulation. *Proc Natl Acad Sci USA* 93(23):12937-42

Tumanyan G & Dzhanyan S (1980) Strength exercises as a means of improving active flexibility of wrestlers *Teoriya i Praktika Fizischeskoi Kultury* 10: 10-11

Ulchenko UF (1982) Assessing the Work Capacity of Weightlifters with Shtanga's Functional Pressure Test *Weightlifting Yearbook 1982* Fizkultura i Sport Moscow

Vandervoort A, Sale D & Moroz J (1984) Comparison of motor unit activation during unilateral and bilateral leg extension. *J Appl Physiol: Respir, Environ & Exerc Physiol* 56: 46-51

Vandervoort AA, Quinlan J & McComas AJ Twitch potentiation after voluntary contraction. *Exp Neurol* 81: 141-152, 1983

Verkhoshansky YV (1977) *Osnovi Spetsialnoi Silovoi Podgotovki i Sporte (Fundamentals of Special Strength Training in Sport)* Fizkultura i Sport Publishers, Moscow

Verkhoshansky YV (1978) Special Strength Training *Legkaya Atletika* 1:6

Verkhoshansky YV (1985) *Programming and Organisation of Training.* Fizkultura i Sport Publ, Moscow

Verkhoshansky YV (1996) Quickness and velocity in sports movements *IAAF Quarterly: New Studies in Athletics* 11(2-3): 29-37

VerhoshanskyYV (1997) The Path to a Scientific Theory and Methodology Of Sports Training *Teoriya i Praktika Fizischeskoi Kultury* 29/10/97.

Vigneron P, Dainat J & Bacou F (1989) Properties of skeletal muscle fibers. II. Hormonal influences *Reprod Nutr Dev* 29(1): 27-53

Viidik A (1973) Functional properties of collagenous tissues *Int Rev of Connective Tissue Res* 6: 127-215

Viitasalo J & Komi P (1978) Force-time characteristics and fibre composition in human leg extensor muscles *Eur J of Appl Physiol* 40: 7-15

Viitasalo J, Häkkinen K & Komi P (1982) Isometric and dynamic force production and muscle fibre composition in man *J of Human Movement Study*

Volkov V, Milner G & Nosov G (1975) The after-effects of training loads. *1975 Soviet Weightlifting Yearbook* Fizkultura i Sport Publ, Moscow

Von der Mark K (1981) Localization of collagen types in tissues *Int Rev of Connective Tissue Res* 9: 265-305

Vorobyev A (1978) *A Textbook on Weightlifting* International Weightlifting Federation, Budapest

Webster D (1976) *The Iron Game* John Geddes Printers Scotland

Weiss D (1976) Help prevent arm injuries with stretching exercises *Athletic Journal* Dec 76, 57: 50-54

Wiener N (1948) *Cybernetics: or, Control and Communication in the Animal and the Machine*

Williams M (1983) *Ergogenic Aids in Sport* Human Kinetics Publ

Williams JH, Ward CW, Spangenburg E & Nelson RM (1998) Functional aspects of skeletal muscle contractile apparatus and sarcoplasmic reticulum after fatigue *J of Physiol* Aug; (85) 2: 619-626

Wilson G, Elliot B & Wood G (1990) The use of elastic energy in sport *Sports Coach* 13(3): 8-10

Wilson G, Elliot B & Wood G (1991) The effect on performance of imposing a delay during a stretch-shorten cycle movement *Med Sci Sports Exerc* 23(3): 364-370

Woo S, Gomez M, Amiel D et al (1981) The effects of exercise on the biomechanical and biochemical properties of swine digital flexor tendons. *J Biomech Eng* 103: 51-56

Woodcock, A & Davis, M (1980) *Catastrophe Theory*, Penguin Books

Yamada S, Buffinger N, Dimario J & Strohman R (1989) Fibroblast growth factor is stored in fiber extracellular matrix and plays a role in regulating muscle hypertrophy *Med Sci Sports Exerc* 21(5): S173-S180

Yamada A & Takahashi K (1992) Sudden increase in speed of an actin filament moving on myosin cross-bridges of "mismatched" polarity observed when its leading end begins to interact with cross-bridges of 'matched' polarity *J Biochem (Tokyo)* 111(5): 676-80

Yessis M (1987) *Secrets of Soviet Sports Fitness and Training*   Arbor House

Young R, Ismail A, Brandley A & Corrigan D (1976) Effect of prolonged exercise on serum testosterone levels in adult men. *Brit J Sports Med* 10: 230-235

Yushkevich T (1989) Lower extremity strength asymmetry in sprinters *Teoriya i Praktika Fizischeskoi* Kultury 3: 27-29

Zajac F E & Gordon M F (1989) Determining muscle's force and action in multi-articular movement *Exerc Sport Sci Revs* 17: 187-230

Zalessky M (1979) Pedagogical, physiological and psychological means of restoration *Legkaya Atletika* 7: 20-22

Zalessky M (1980) Restoration for Runners and Walkers *Legkaya Atletika* 3: 10-13

Zalessky M & Burkhanov A (1981) Muscle condition and work capacity in track and field athletes *Legkaya Atletika* 1: 1-7

Zanon S (1989) Plyometrics: Past and Present *New Studies in Athletics* 4(1): 7-17

Zarkadas PC, Carter JB & Banister EW (1995) Modelling the effect of taper on performance, maximal oxygen uptake, and the anaerobic threshold in endurance triathletes. *Adv Exp Med Biol* 393:179-86

Zatsiorsky V (1968) *The Athlete's Physical Abilities*. Fizkultura i Sport Publishers, Moscow

Zatsiorsky V (1980) The development of endurance. In Matveyev L & Novikov A (eds) *Theory and Methodology of Physical Education* Fizkultura i Sport Publ, Moscow

Zatsiorsky V (1995) *Science and Practice of Strength Training* Human Kinetics

Zheljazkov T (1998) About Some Permanent Factors in Present Sports Training *Teoriya i Praktika Fizischeskoi Kultury* 11-12

Zinovieff A (1959) Heavy resistance exercise: the Oxford Technique *Brit J of Physical Med* 14: 129

Note:

- All the references for Ch 4.2 on electrostimulation are cited in Siff (1990). Many more are available at the following website, especially on microcurrent stimulation:

  http://www.sportsci.com/SPORTSCI/JANUARY/archives2.html

- Any other references which do not appear in the above list are cited in the two textbooks by Verkhoshansky (1977, 1985). Most of these are in Russian and, therefore, are not repeated here.

INDEX